THE MACMILLAN
AND SILK CUT
YACHTSMAN'S
HANDBOOK

THE
MACMILLAN
AND
SILK CUT
YACHTSMAN'S
HANDBOOK

Editors:
Commander R.L. Hewitt LVO RN MIMechE, MRINA, FRIN
Rear Admiral I.J. Lees-Spalding CB

Consultant Editors
K.E. Best
P.W. Boyd
B. D'Oliveira OBE, FRIN
T. Jeffery
Dr D.M. Justins MB, BS, FRCA
M.W. Richey MBE, Hon MRIN
J. Teale
E. Whelan
Dr B.D. Yallop PhD, BSc, ARCS, FRAS

MACMILLAN

First published 1984 by Macmillan London Limited
This edition published 1995 by Macmillan Reference Books
a division of Macmillan Publishers Limited
25 Eccleston Place, London SW1W 9NF
and Basingstoke

Associated companies throughout the world

ISBN 0–333–64564–2

Copyright © Macmillan London Limited 1984; Macmillan Press Limited 1990, 1992;
Pan Macmillan 1993; Macmillan Reference Books 1995

10 9 8 7 6 5 4 3 2 1

A CIP catalogue record for this book is available from the British Library

Important Note
Whilst every care has been taken in compiling the information contained in this
book, the Publishers, Editors and Sponsors accept no responsibility for any errors or
omissions, or for any accidents or mishaps which may arise from its use.

Correspondence
Letters on editorial matters should be addressed to:
  The Editors, *The Macmillan & Silk Cut Yachtsman's Handbook*
  Macmillan Reference Books
  25 Eccleston Place, London SW1W 9NF

Enquiries about despatch, invoicing or commercial matters should be addressed to:
  Customer Services Department
  Macmillan Press Limited
  Houndmills, Basingstoke, Hampshire RS21 2XS

Photoset by Parker Typesetting Service, Leicester

Printed and bound in Malaysia

Macmillan Consultant Editor: Klaus Boehm

Designed by Dick Vine

Artwork by Geoff Adams, Peter Barry, Chris Evans, Hilary Evans,
Bernard Fallon, Ray Harvey MRINA BSc CEng, Dick Vine, E.N. Wilson

Contents

The Macmillan & Silk Cut Yachtsman's Handbook

Although *The Macmillan & Silk Cut Yachtsman's Handbook*, which is not republished each year, is primarily intended as a companion volume to *The Macmillan & Silk Cut Nautical Almanac* (revised and reprinted annually), the book contains a very great deal of information on all aspects of owning, operating, maintaining and enjoying a modern yacht, and can be used independently of the *Almanac* if so desired.

However, Chapters 2–9 of this *Yachtsman's Handbook* and the *Almanac* deal with related subjects. Standing information and instructional details are included in this *Handbook*, while data that is subject to regular or occasional change will be published each year in the *Almanac*. Any important changes to the material in this *Handbook* which occur between reprintings will be notified in the Supplements to the *Almanac*. Taken in combination therefore, these two books provide the most comprehensive and economical set of references available to yachtsmen on navigation and other matters concerned with running a yacht.

This new edition of the *Handbook* has been revised and updated and is based on the Third Edition (1993), which included a great deal of additional information and two new chapters – one on multihulls and one on matters to be considered when first starting to race a yacht. Other additional material included:

- Revised chart symbols, in full colour
- Spanish vocabulary
- Expanded colour section on flags and burgees
- Quick reference flag etiquette
- New European Standards for lifejackets etc
- Quick-stop man overboard drill
- Safety check list
- Revision of First Aid at sea
- Emergency watermakers
- Being taken in tow
- Global Maritime Distress and Safety System
- Yeoman plotter
- Tidal streams in rivers
- Computer programs for tidal prediction
- Relation between Ordnance and Chart Datum
- CAD for yachts
- Resonators for antifouling
- Apparent wind, and how a boat sails
- Alternative power sources
- 'Smart' regulators for battery charging
- Diesel engine fault finding chart
- Expanded coverage of boat handling
- Etiquette afloat
- More legal advice

Who wrote it

To write this *Handbook*, Macmillan and Silk Cut have retained a team of editors and consultant editors who combine excellent knowledge of their various subjects with a wealth of practical experience of yachts and boats of all kinds.

The editors

Dick Hewitt has sailed since the age of seven. During 32 years in the Navy he took up ocean racing, helmed the Dragon *Bluebottle* in 1953/54 for HM The Queen and The Duke of Edinburgh with some distinction, regularly navigated the 12-metre yachts *Flica II* and *Sovereign* during the early 1960s, and competed in three Admiral's Cup series. But he says the yachting he enjoyed most was two years in HM Yacht *Britannia*, during which she went through the Panama Canal five times and Suez once.

As captain of the Navy sailing team he won races in boats as different as National Fireflies and Seaview Mermaids. He now enjoys racing a National Squib, based at Hamble.

He has served on the RYA Council, and on various committees, and has written a number of publications for the RYA which, in April 1980, honoured him with an award for his special services to yachting.

He was editor of the magazine *Motor Boat and Yachting* from 1972 to 1979, when he left to start work on the preparation of *The Macmillan & Silk Cut Nautical Almanac* which first appeared for 1981. He is a member of the Royal Yacht Squadron, Royal London Yacht Club, Royal Ocean Racing Club, Royal Southern Yacht Club, Royal Naval Sailing Association, Hamble River Sailing Club, Island Sailing Club, and the Cruising Association.

Tim Lees-Spalding joined the Navy from Blundells in 1938, aged 18. His early sailing experiences were from Teignmouth in South Devon, but later included sailing on the River Nile — where the helmsman stepped out of the boat onto a rock which swam away, proving to be a crocodile.

His sailing adventures in the Navy extended from the West Indies to the South China Sea, and he was once arrested by Tito's men for straying too close to Brioni in the Adriatic. Overland his journeys have included a trip home from Japan via Siberia, the Daily Express London–Sydney Marathon Car Rally, and taking a Land Rover across the Sahara Desert and through the jungles of the Congo.

For some years he was Administrator of the London International Film School. He is a member of the Royal Naval Sailing Association and the Flag Institute. He was co-editor of *The Macmillan & Silk Cut Nautical Almanac* from 1981 to 1991.

Other contributors

Keith Best (meteorological consultant) has been messing about in boats since school days. Most of his working life has been with the Meteorological Office performing a variety of tasks at numerous locations in Great Britain and abroad. He is probably best known as a presenter of weather forecasts on television and radio. Before taking early retirement he was one of the senior forecasters at the London Weather Centre where an important part of his work was forecasting for the extremely weather sensitive offshore oil industry. He continues to lead a very active life working with the weather as a freelance consultant and writer.

Patrick Boyd, while working for the journal *Yachting Monthly*, wrote a book called *Catamarans in Close-Up* in 1972. This was about fitting out an Iroquois shell, cruising in the finished catamaran and subsequently doing Boat Tests on multihulls for *Yachting Monthly*. In 1972 he joined Camper & Nicholsons' Yacht Agency, and started up their London office. There he gained experience of yacht broking, organising charters in the Mediterranean and Caribbean, and started the C & N Multihull Division which he subsequently bought in 1982 and continues to run under his own name from his farmhouse in Surrey. He is a past President of the Association of Brokers and Yacht Agents and of the Yacht Brokers, Designers and Surveyors Association. He runs courses for yacht brokers and is a Holdings Board member of the British Marine Industries Federation.

Basil D'Oliveira (navigational aids) is a retired Wing Commander who subsequently worked in the Civil Aviation Authority, and is now co-editor of *The Macmillan & Silk Cut Nautical Almanac*. His specialised interest is in electronic navigation aids, a subject which he has covered in various yachting journals. His sailing activities have included cruising in the Pacific, New Zealand and the Caribbean, as well as Mediterranean and home waters. He was part-owner for five years of a Nicholson 35, in which he made two cruises to the Mediterranean. His main contribution to the *Handbook* are advice on radio navigation aids, and the sections which deal with the use of calculators and computers for coastal navigation, tidal prediction etc.

Timothy Jeffery began his sailing in Strangford Lough, Northern Ireland, in 1970 and qualified as a Royal Yachting Association Senior Instructor. He was Features Editor of the leading journal *Yachting World*, and is now yachting correspondent for *The Daily Telegraph*. He has sailed and raced in many parts of the world including the Caribbean, United States of America, the Red Sea, New Zealand and a host of European countries. He has competed in the Southern Ocean Racing Conference, Fastnet Race and One Top Cup, besides covering numerous other events. He is also the author of *Practical Sailing: The Modern Cruising Yacht*.

Douglas Justins, who contributed the section on first aid afloat, is an anaesthetist at a London hospital, who sailed the Sydney–Dover leg of the *Financial Times* Clipper Race, is a regular crew in RORC races and competitor in the Three Peaks Race.

Michael Richey was for many years the Director of the Royal Institute of Navigation which, in 1979, as an exceptional measure, conferred on him its gold medal in recognition of his outstanding contribution to the Institute's objects of advancing the science and practice of navigation and of promoting knowledge in navigation and its associated sciences. He was Secretary General and later President of the International Association of Institutes of Navigation. He has navigated in many ocean races, on both sides of the Atlantic, over the last 35 years. He has also crossed the Atlantic alone several times and undertaken other long voyages in his junk-rigged Folkboat *Jester*. In 1986 he received the Royal Cruising Club's Medal for Seamanship.

John Teale has been an independent yacht and commerical craft designer for the past 25 years or so. Before that he was in the design or drawing offices of such concerns as John I. Thornycroft, Brooke Marine, Watercraft and the RNLI and also worked for the east coast yacht designer, J. Francis Jones. For two spells he was on the editorial staff of the magazine *Motor Boat and Yachting*, once under Dick Hewitt.

He has lived and worked in South Africa, Sweden and Ireland but now resides in Somerleyton, Suffolk where he also bases his boat. This is the 24th craft he has owned and of these he actually built 13 (the biggest being 26ft (7.9m) in length). Most of his work is now in steel with a fair sprinkling of timber plus the occasional aluminium alloy vessel.

Edmund Whelan is the General Services Manager of the Royal Yachting Association. A barrister at law, he is responsible for co-ordinating all the legal and parliamentary activities of the RYA, and provides legal advice and guidance to the Association's personal members and affiliated clubs. His sailing career has encompassed just about everything from Cadets to Class 1 ocean racers. He is an active member of the Bar Yacht Club and the Junior Offshore Group, cruising and racing a Sigma 38 in the Solent.

Bernard Yallop is Head of HM Nautical Almanac Office and is in charge of the production of *The Astronomical Almanac, The Nautical Almanac, The Air Almanac, The Star Alamanac for Land Surveyors, Astronomical Phenomena* and *Sight Reduction Tables for Air Navigation, AP 3270*. Since 1974 he has been interested in the application of calculators and personal computers to sight reduction. He started by solving the problem of producing simple algorithms for calculating the positions of the navigational bodies. Some of his neat calculator ephemerides appear in Chapter 5. His methods and formulae using short-term algorithms are published every five years in the booklet *Compact Data for Astronomy and Navigation*. In 1989 he introduced a new section on sight reduction by direct computation in *The Nautical Almanac*.

Chapter 1

Introduction

Contents

1.1 About this Handbook

1.1.1 Introduction

When *The Macmillan & Silk Cut Nautical Almanac* was first published in 1981, many users suggested that it could with benefit be divided into two books - an almanac with all the navigational data which is subject to annual change, and a permanent handbook giving more lasting information. This was what was done when *The Macmillan & Silk Cut Yachtsman's Handbook* was first published in 1984. A new edition appeared in 1988.

The opportunity has now been taken to revise and expand the *Handbook* still further with this new edition, which includes even more subjects of a permanent nature that are concerned with owning and using a boat. It is intended to be used as a reference book alongside *The Macmillan & Silk Cut Nautical Almanac,* which will continue to be published each year with the navigational information which changes completely (such as tide tables and the ephemeris) or which is liable to alter and must be kept up to date.

Chapters 2-9 of the *Handbook* and the *Almanac* deal with related subjects, and these chapters are cross-referenced where this is helpful to the user.

Chapters 10-21 of this *Handbook* relate to using and looking after a boat. So, supplemented by the *Almanac* for navigational details liable to change, the *Handbook* provides the yachtsman or yachtswoman with the information needed to own, operate and care for a boat in a sensible and responsible manner.

The term 'yachtsman' in the title and in the text refers equally to those of the opposite sex who go afloat in craft of any type.

1

The aim throughout has been to present information at least to the standard and depth of knowledge that would be expected of a candidate for the Royal Yachting Association/Department of Transport Yachtmaster (Offshore) Certificate.

1.1.2 Who wrote it

In general this *Handbook* was originally compiled by the same team as had been responsible for the earlier editions of *The Macmillan & Silk Cut Nautical Almanac,* with some additions. John Teale wrote Chapters 10, 12 and 14, while Basil D'Oliveira advised on the use of electronic calculators and navigational aids. Michael Richey and Keith Best were largely responsible for Chapters 5 and 7, and Dr Douglas Justins for First Aid afloat in Chapter 8.

For the second (1988) edition Edmund Whelan explained the legal aspects of boat owning, and Timothy Jeffery added a new chapter on the important subject of a sailor's wardrobe.

In this new edition Basil D'Oliveira, Michael Richey, Keith Best and Douglas Justins have all substantially revised their respective chapters. Patrick Boyd has contributed a chapter on multihulls, there is a new chapter on the elements of yacht racing, and Dr Bernard Yallop has written the section on calculators or micro-processors for astro-navigation. The rest of the text throughout the book has been revised and brought up to date.

Most of the contributors are practical and experienced yachtsmen, who have owned boats. Between them they combine expert knowledge on all aspects of using and running a yacht.

1.1.3 How to use it

The subject matter of the following chapters is related in the *Handbook* and the *Almanac:*

Chapter 2	General Information
3	Coastal Navigation
4	Radio Navigational Aids
5	Astro-Navigation
6	Communications
7	Weather
8	Safety
9	Tides

For ease of reference, each chapter is divided into numbered sections, prefaced by the number of the chapter. Thus the sections in Chapter 7 (for example) are numbered 7.1, 7.2, 7.3 and so on. Within each section, the key paragraphs are numbered, as for example 7.3.1, 7.3.2, 7.3.3 and so on. Diagrams carry the chapter number, followed by a consecutive number in brackets. There is a comprehensive index at the back of the *Handbook*.

1.1.4 Acknowledgments

The Editors wish to record their thanks to the many individuals and official bodies who have assisted by providing essential information and much advice in the preparation of this *Handbook*. They include the Hydrographic Office of the Ministry of Defence, HM Stationery Office, HM Customs & Excise, the Met. Office, HM Coastguard, BT, the Department of Trade, the Radiocommunications Agency, the Royal Yachting Association, the Royal National Lifeboat Institution, the British Marine Industries Federation, the International Maritime Organisation, Inmarsat, and Lloyd's Register of Shipping.

The following illustrations are derived from Crown Copyright diagrams in Admiralty Publications, with the kind permission of the Controller of Her Majesty's Stationery Office:

Fig. 3(14), Fig. 5(10), Fig. 6(3), Fig. 6(4), Fig. 6(6), Fig. 7(24), Fig. 9(6), Fig. 9(7), Fig. 9(9), Fig. 9(12), Fig. 9(18) and Fig. 9(19).

Figs. 9(23), 9(24) and 9(25) are published by permission of the Marine Information and Advisory Service, of the Institute of Oceanographic Sciences.

Extracts from the *International Code of Signals,* 1969 and from *Weather Services for Shipping* are published with the permission of the Controller of HM Stationery Office. *International Regulations for Preventing Collisions at Sea, 1972* are reproduced by permission of the International Maritime Organisation.

Technical information on ropes has kindly been supplied by Bridon Fibres and Plastics Limited, the makers of Marina yacht ropes. The illustrations of bends, hitches and splices are taken from their *Marina Manual of Yacht Ropes,* available at most chandlers.

The colour cloud scenes are published with acknowledgment to R. K. Pilsbury/BP Educational Service. The photographs are by R. K. Pilsbury ISO, FRPS, FRMetS.

Acknowledgment is made to the RYA Seamanship Foundation for assistance with illustrating the IALA buoyage system, to *Yachting World* for their help in illustrating navigation lights, and to The Flag Institute for advice on national maritime flags.

1.2 Getting Afloat

1.2.1 Responsibilities of yachtsmen

Being in charge of any boat at sea, even as mate of the watch while the skipper snatches a couple of hours' sleep, places serious responsibility on the individual concerned. For the skipper that responsibility is total, since he is solely accountable for the safety of the yacht and her crew - even while he is asleep.

Apart from being able to handle the boat under sail and/or power in all conditions (which may include winds of gale force), the skipper must be completely familiar with every aspect of the boat and her equipment, and be able to cope with whatever emergencies may arise – such as fire, man overboard, engine failure or dismasting. He needs to understand the rule of the road and be able to interpret it in a seamanlike way. He must be competent to navigate safely from place to place and be able to read the weather. Very importantly, the skipper has a duty to select and train his crew so that they can play their full part in managing the boat and so that they are neither a danger to themselves or to others on board.

All these requirements, and many others, are described in the pages which follow. They are based on considerable theoretical knowledge and practical experience, without which it would be rash for any skipper to put to sea. One of the attractions of yachting is the freedom which it offers - the sense of getting away from all the restrictions which seem to govern life ashore. But as well as being a pleasure, going to sea is something of an adventure, and it does involve complying with certain regulations, safeguarding the welfare of your crew, and even taking responsibility for the lives of people in other vessels or manning the rescue services.

In Britain we are lucky that the authorities have so far been anxious to place the minimum restraints on the use of small pleasure craft, although the Department of Transport has introduced regulations that enforce safety standards on all yachts and power craft used for commercial purposes. Yachts over 13.7m (45ft) in overall length are required by law to carry certain safety equipment, but there are no such legal requirements for smaller craft. Nor are there (as yet) compulsory standards of competence for those who skipper or handle yachts. Such regulations would be difficult and expensive to enforce, but they do exist in other countries and it should not be imagined that our authorities would be deterred from imposing tedious rules and expensive licences if the situation should so require. The best safeguard against such an eventuality is that all who go afloat for pleasure should have sufficient knowledge and practical experience to be able to cope with any problem that can reasonably be foreseen, and that their boats should be built, equipped and maintained to a proper standard.

It is however quite possible that safety regulations and standards of competence may be forced on British yachtsmen by European legislation, which has already introduced common standards for items of safety equipment such as lifejackets.

1.2.2 Training schemes

There is no requirement in the UK for anyone to hold a certificate of competence to use a yacht, of less than 80 GRT, for sport or recreation. This freedom from regulation imposes a duty of self-sufficiency on all yachtsmen; it is up to them to make sure that they have the knowledge, skill and experience to handle their boat safely.

Since the late 1960s the Royal Yachting Association (see 2.7.1) has operated a range of voluntary training schemes which encompass windsurfing, dinghy sailing, powerboating and cruising under power and sail. The schemes aim to ensure that appropriate training is available to everyone who wants to learn to sail or use a powerboat, or who wants to improve their boathandling, seamanship and navigation.

The RYA training schemes are operated by a range of more than a thousand recognised teaching establishments, which include clubs, local authority sailing centres, night schools and commercial sailing schools. To gain recognition they must show that they have suitable boats for teaching which are sound and well equipped, qualified instructors and adequate shoreside teaching facilities. A list of the schools and the courses they offer is available from the RYA at RYA House, Romsey Road, Eastleigh, Hants SO50 9YA.

The RYA believes that its voluntary system of training is a more effective way of keeping the risks inherent in yachting down to an acceptable level than a system of compulsory 'driving licences' could possibly be. By its very nature, a compulsory system would have to be confined to a test of the lowest acceptable level of proficiency. The voluntary scheme, on the other hand, can encourage much higher standards.

1.2.3 Dinghy and keelboat courses

Most successful racing helmsmen started sailing in dinghies and anyone who wants to learn to sail, whatever their eventual boat-owning ambitions may be, would be well advised to start with a dinghy sailing course. They must, however, be prepared to get wet. Dinghies are unballasted, they depend on the weight of the crew to keep them upright and at some stage a capsize is almost inevitable. An integral part of learning to sail dinghies is learning to right a capsized boat, which entails a short swim.

The RYA has separate dinghy training schemes for juniors and adults. The differences between the two are not so much in what is learnt as in the way that it is learnt. Details of the schemes are set out in Fig. 1(1) and Fig. 1(2).

Traditionally, dinghy sailing was taught in boats such as Wayfarers, in which the instructor sailed with his students. While this system is still used and is very effective, it is now just as common for students to go straight into single-handed dinghies such as Optimists, Toppers or Lasers, with the instructor working from a powerboat accompanying up to six dinghies. The speed of learning is generally faster, with each student spending much more time at the tiller; the satisfaction of achievement is much enhanced.

For those with no aspirations to live on board a boat but who want to learn in something larger and more stable than a dinghy the RYA keelboat scheme provides appropriate courses. It is broadly similar to the adult dinghy sailing scheme but excludes capsize recovery and places more emphasis on handling larger heavier boats.

	Level 1 Start Sailing	Level 2 Basic Skills	Level 3 Improving Techniques	Level 4 Racing Techniques	Level 5 Advanced Skills
Rigging	Wind awareness, rigging a single-hander or training dinghy.	Rigging a training dinghy or dayboat, reefing ashore, parts of the boat and sails.	As Level 2 (using all the boat's equipment)	Rigging a racing dinghy as appropriate, rig tuning controls.	Rigging any type of dinghy or dayboat, including spinnaker/ trapeze.
Ropework	Figure of eight, round turn and two half-hitches.	Bowline.	Fisherman's bend, splicing/sealing whipping. Sheetbend, clove hitch, rolling hitch		
Launching/ Recovery	Wind awareness, use of trolley, launching, leaving the shore, coming ashore.	Storage ashore, paddling, rowing.	Leaving/return-ing to beach, jetty or mooring. Windward/ leeward shores. Use of anchor.		As Level 3. Sailing backwards.
Sailing techniques and manoeuvres	Wind awareness, reaching, stopping, tacking, getting out of irons, sailing upwind and downwind.	The five essentials. Man overboard recovery.	Anchoring, heaving to, reefing afloat, towing/being towed.	Advanced tacking/gybing, sailing to windward, mark rounding.	As Level 3, using all boat's equipment to best advantage, rudderless sailing, sailing without a centreboard, sailing in a tight circle.
Capsize recovery	Stay with boat.	Righting – scoop, righting a single-hander.	Righting an inverted dinghy.		As Level 3 plus full bailing.
Racing	Clubs and classes.	The course, starting procedure.	Mark rounding.	Starting techniques, rules, tactics.	
Sailing theory and background	Basic rules: port/starboard, windward boat, overtaking boat.	Points of sailing, no go zone, basic aerodynamic theory, buoyage, sea/inland advice.	Sea terms, resuscitation and First Aid, IRPCS.	Handicap v. Class racing. Club racing, sailing instructions, insurance.	Navigation for dinghies and day boats, construction and repair.
Meteorology	Onshore/offshore winds.	Sources of forecasts, when to reef.	Simple met. and interpretation of forecasts.	Local weather patterns, strategy.	Detailed interpretation, planning for day's journey.
Clothing/equip- ment	Clothing, personal buoyancy.	Boat buoyancy, safety equipment.			Requirements for day's journey/dinghy cruising.

Fig. 1(1) RYA National Dinghy Certificate Scheme.

1.2.4 Powerboat courses

The RYA powerboat training scheme provides courses in handling the many different types of small powerboat, concentrating particularly on the faster planing boats.

The first two levels of course cover the basics of seamanship, boathandling and safety. Higher levels of course are available for various powerboat activities such as water skiing, diving and sailing club rescue. These courses are operated in

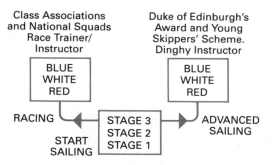

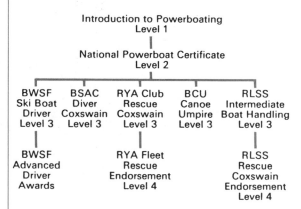

conjunction with the appropriate governing bodies of other water sports. Fig. 1(3) shows the range of courses that are available.

Fig. 1(2) RYA Young Sailors Scheme 1993. The aim is to provide a clear progression of training within the sport for all young people, in three sections. Start Sailing courses provide the essential practical techniques and background knowledge for the competent sailor. After that, participants can continue in either racing or non-competitive sailing, although many will wish to acquire the techniques in both disciplines. The three levels of Racing courses provide the skills needed for club, class and national events, while Advanced Sailing courses provide the seamanship skills and background knowledge required for independent leisure sailing.

Fig. 1(3) Structure of National Powerboating Courses.

Course	Suggested minimum pre-course experience	Assumed knowledge	Course content	Ability after course	Minimum duration
Competent Crew practical	None	None	Basic seamanship and helmsmanship.	Useful crew member.	5 days
Day Skipper shorebased*	Some practical experience desirable.	None	Basic seamanship and introduction to navigation and meteorology.		
Day Skipper practical (yacht)†	5 days, 100 miles, 4 night hours.	Basic navigation and sailing ability.	Basic pilotage, boat handling, seamanship and navigation.	Skipper a small yacht in familiar waters by day.	5 days
Watch Leader practical (sail training)	5 days, 100 miles, 4 night hours.	Basic navigation and sailing ability.	Navigation, seamanship and watch organisation.	Take charge of a watch on a sail training vessel.	5 days
Coastal Skipper Yachtmaster Offshore shorebased*		Navigation to Day Skipper shorebased standard.	Offshore and coastal navigation and pilotage, meteorology.		
Coastal Skipper practical†	15 days (2 days as skipper). 300 miles, 8 night hours.	Navigation to Coastal Skipper shorebased standard. Sailing to Day Skipper practical standard.	Skippering techniques for coastal and offshore passages.	Skipper, a yacht on coastal passages by day and night.	5 days
Yachtmaster Ocean shorebased	Coastal and offshore sailing.	Navigation to Coastal Skipper and Yachtmaster Offshore shorebased standard.	Astro-navigation, ocean meteorology and passage planning.		

* Syllabus is the same for sailing and motor cruising yachtsmen.
† Can be taken in tidal or non-tidal waters.

Fig. 1(4) RYA National Cruising Scheme – Training Courses (Sail).

Course	Suggested minimum pre-course experience	Assumed knowledge	Course content	Ability after course	Duration
Introduction to Motor Cruising	None	None	Boating safety and basic seamanship.	Useful crew member in motor cruiser.	
Helmsman's course	Some practical experience desirable.	Introduction to motor cruising course.	Boating safety, helmsmanship, boat handling. Introduction to engine maintenance.	Competent to handle motor cruiser of specific type in sheltered waters.	2 days
Day Skipper shorebased*	Some practical experience desirable.	None	Basic seamanship and introduction to navigation and meteorology.		
Day Skipper practical (yacht)†	2 days	Basic navigation and helmsmanship.	Pilotage, boat handling, seamanship and navigation.	Skipper a motor cruiser in familiar waters by day.	4 days
Coastal Skipper/ Yachtmaster Offshore shorebased*		Navigation to Day Skipper shorebased standard.	Offshore and coastal navigation and pilotage, meteorology.		
Coastal Skipper practical†	15 days (2 days as skipper), 300 miles, 8 night hours.	Navigation to Coastal Skipper shorebased standard. Boat handling to Day Skipper practical standard.	Skippering techniques for coastal and offshore passages.	Skipper a motor cruiser on coastal passages by day and night.	5 days
Yachtmaster Ocean shorebased	Coastal and offshore passages.	Navigation to Coastal Skipper and Yachtmaster Offshore shorebased standard.	Astro-navigation, ocean meteorology and passage planning.		

* Syllabus is the same for sailing and motor cruising yachtsmen.
† Can be taken in tidal or non-tidal waters.

Fig. 1(5) RYA National Cruising Scheme – Motor Cruising Courses.

1.2.5 Yachtmaster training scheme (Power and Sail)

Unlike the other RYA training schemes the courses for cruising yachtsmen are aimed at preparing participants for exams for certificates of competence, at Coastal Skipper, Yachtmaster Offshore and Yachtmaster Ocean level.

These training schemes consist of three complementary elements.

(1) *Shorebased courses*. These are generally taken as night school courses, over the two winter terms, although they are also available by correspondence or as full-time courses of about one week. They concentrate on navigation and meteorology.

(2) *Practical courses*. These are five-day courses, offered by recognised sailing schools around the coast and by a limited number of schools based overseas.

(3) *Practical experience*. While it is possible to teach the full syllabus for Yachtmaster Offshore in two winters of night school courses and three five-day practical courses, it is impossible to become a competent yacht skipper without spending a considerable amount of time putting the lessons learnt in the classroom and the sailing school into practice in a range of different locations and under different weather conditions at sea. Hence every practical course syllabus specifies a minimum recommended level of pre-course experience and every candidate must have a specified amount of experience to be eligible to take an exam for a Coastal Skipper or Yachtmaster certificate of competence. Details of the courses which make up the Yachtmaster training scheme are shown in Fig. 1(4) and Fig. 1(5).

The syllabuses for the Coastal Skipper, Yachtmaster Offshore and Yachtmaster Ocean exams are set by the Yachtmaster Qualification Panel. The chairman and two members of the panel are appointed by the RYA and other members are appointed by the Marine Directorate of the Department of Transport, the Department of Education, the Association of Sea Training Organisations and the Service sailing associations.

Coastal Skipper and Yachtmaster Offshore exams are carried out, as far as possible, as practical tests. The candidate must provide the boat in which to take the exam and many find that the most effective way to do this is to take the exam in a boat belonging to a sailing school at the end of a course.

Yachtmaster Ocean exams are oral, with questions based on the candidate's qualifying ocean passage and the exam includes an assessment of the results of the candidate's astro-navigation carried out at sea.

Details of the pre-exam requirements and the form of examination are shown in Fig. 1(6).

Although there is no requirement to hold a certificate of competence to skipper a British yacht of less than 80 GRT, yachts over this size are subject to the provisions of the Merchant Shipping (Certification of Deck Officers) Regulations. Holders of Yachtmaster certificates are exempted from these regulations (for passages appropriate to their level of Yachtmaster Certificate) in yachts up to 200 GRT, provided that they are not used for commercial purposes.

A Yachtmaster certificate may also be used as a qualification to skipper a yacht of up to 24 metres in length, used for commercial purposes, subject to some additional provisions which do not apply to the amateur sailor. The certificate holder must pass a medical exam, have attended a survival course and revalidate his qualification five-yearly by showing that he has recent sea experience and continues to be medically fit.

1.2.6 Association of Sea Training Organisations

The Association of Sea Training Organisations (ASTO) comprises those organisations (such as the Sail Training Association and the Ocean Youth Club) which operate sea training vessels or encourage sea training. By different methods they all aim to provide an opportunity for young people to go to sea in a sailing vessel, thereby not only experiencing a unique adventure but also developing their initiative, sense of responsibility, discipline and team work.

A bursary scheme can help defray the cost of a cruise for those who cannot afford it. Some of the vessels have vacancies for adults and many of them welcome suitably experienced yachtsmen who can help take charge. From time to time ASTO vessels take part in the Tall Ship races together with sail training vessels from other countries.

Details can be obtained from the Association of Sail Training Organisations, c/o Royal Yachting Association, RYA House, Romsey Road, Eastleigh, Hants SO50 9YA.

There are many organisations which help individuals to get afloat. In many instances they provide boats and equipment, either for a charge or after paying a small subscription. The British Marine Industries Federation (BMIF) provides a free leaflet on boating information for young people; for a copy ring Schools Afloat on (01483) 429792.

Grade of examination	Minimum seatime (within 10 years of exam)	Form of examination	Certificate required before examination
RYA/DTp Coastal Skipper	30 days, 2 days as skipper, 800 miles, 12 night hours.*	Practical	Restricted (VHF only) Radio Operator's Certificate
RYA/DTp Yachtmaster Offshore	50 days, 5 days as skipper, 5 passages over 60M, including 2 overnight and 2 as skipper.	Practical	Restricted (VHF only) Radio Operator's Certificate, First Aid Certificate
RYA/DTp Yachtmaster Ocean	Ocean passage as skipper or mate of watch.	Oral and assessment of sights taken at sea. (Written exam in lieu of shore-based course completion certificate.)	RYA/DTp Yachtmaster Offshore Certificate and Yachtmaster Ocean shorebased course completion certificate.

* For holders of the Coastal Skipper Practical Course Completion Certificate the seatime requirement is reduced to: 20 days, 2 days as skipper, 400 miles, 12 night hours.

Fig. 1(6) Examinations – RYA/DTp Certificates of Competence.
To apply for certificates of competence obtain an application form from the RYA or any of the examination centres listed at the end of the G15 Log Book. Examination dates are arranged by these centres to suit the mutual convenience of candidates and examiners. For the practical exam for Coastal Skipper and Yachtmaster Offshore candidates must provide a cruising yacht, normally not less than 24ft LOA, in sound, seaworthy condition and equipped to the standard set out in RYA booklet C8, *Cruising Yacht Safety*. The yacht must be equipped with a full and up-to-date set of charts and navigational publications and be efficiently crewed, as the examiner will not take part in the management of the yacht during the exam.

1.3 How to buy a boat

1.3.1 Choosing a boat

There are so many boats of different types and sizes on the market, plus of course a large number of second-hand boats at any time, that the choice can be quite bewildering even for the relatively experienced yachtsman. Do not hesitate to seek advice on this important step. A bad decision here may, in every sense of the word, prove to be a disaster, which at best may put you and your family off boats for ever. In order to arrive at the right solution you need to ask yourself a lot of questions, and it is important that the answers are well-considered and truthful.

First, why do you want a boat at all? In this context you need to decide where the boat is to be kept, how often she is to be used, where she is going to operate, and who is likely to be on board. Will the boat take the place of holiday trips, or only be used for occasional weekends during the summer?

If you can satisfy yourself, and perhaps your wife, that a boat is justified, exactly how much money can you afford for the project? Remember that, quite apart from the first cost, to run and maintain a boat of any size is going to incur the expenditure of several hundred pounds a year for items such as insurance, moorings, fuel, maintenance and repairs. If he has sufficient time available a handyman may be able to save money on the last two items, but the others are inescapable. An allowance should also be made for depreciation in the value of the boat year by year, and for the capital locked up in her. If money has to be borrowed for the purchase (see 1.3.8) the cost of servicing the loan must be considered. When buying a new boat remember that quite a large sum will be needed for vital equipment which is not included in the price - navigational items, safety equipment, a tender, galley gear and other domestic items are likely to fall into this category. This is one possible reason for buying a second-hand boat, where most of such items will probably be included. Taking all these figures into account gives some idea of the cost, and hence the size, of boat that can be afforded.

Then it is time to return to such questions as where the boat is to be kept. Will she be on a mooring, and how sheltered will it be? Will she need to dry out-either when on the mooring or in her intended cruising area? Remember that the smallest cruising boats (but only the smallest) can be kept ashore on a trailer, and towed to different locations. Is it intended to sail locally, or to undertake coastal cruises, or perhaps sail further offshore? What sort of crew will normally be available, and how strong are they in physique and in experience? Is the boat to be sail or power, or a combination of the two?

By now a general idea of the type and size of boat should be developing, and it will be time to start considering which of the many cruising boats available might fit the specification. Study the appropriate magazines to see what is on offer, and visit one of the major boat shows.

It is, however, necessary to consider some more detailed requirements which might include hull form and material, accommodation layout, rig, type of engine and deck plan. Unless you are an experienced yachtsman it may be advisable to seek advice on some of these points, although mention is made of them in the chapters which follow.

Before starting to search in earnest, draw up a detailed specification, based on the answers to the questions above, and decide on the priority of the various items. Make sure that the requirements are not mutually exclusive, or your hunt will be a waste of time and money. Travel is expensive, so try to cover boats in your locality before journeying to the other end of the country.

You may discover that your dream boat does not exist in production form, and there may be good reasons for this. But if you wish to persist the only solution would be to have a boat specifically designed and built for your purpose – an expensive undertaking in all probability, but one likely to produce the best answer for unusual requirements.

Another possible approach is to take a stock hull (a large variety of glassfibre mouldings are readily available, for example) and have it completed to your own specifications. If you have the necessary skills and plenty of spare time, you may be able to undertake some of this work yourself, with a consequent saving in cost.

There are two ways that an individual owner may be able to afford a more expensive boat-part ownership and time sharing. The former is well established, even if it does provide practical difficulties. It is essential that partners have a common approach to how the boat is operated and maintained, and problems are likely to arise when one wishes to sell his share. Time sharing is relatively new, and one wonders how it (and the boats concerned) will stand the test of time.

If you find it difficult to justify owning a boat because of the limited use she might have, do not overlook the possibility of chartering which is described in 1.7.

1.3.2 Buying a boat – general

New boats are sold either by their builders or by distributors acting as agents of the builder or, in the case of yachts built overseas, by importers acting as principals rather than as agents. The larger firms advertise prominently, and exhibit their products at the major boat shows, but there are many smaller yards which produce good boats and have lower overheads. In boat building, big is not necessarily beautiful. Second-hand boats are sold either privately by the owner (sometimes in a boat auction), or through a yacht broker.

It is helpful to have some understanding of modern consumer legislation, which is described in *The Yachtsman's Lawyer* edited by Edmund Whelan and published by the RYA (G9).

Standard forms of agreement for buying boats are jointly sponsored by the British Marine Industries Federation (see 2.7.3) and the Royal Yachting Association (see 2.7.1). In order to try to eliminate any problems it is always advisable to use one of these agreements since they define the rights and liabilities of the seller and the buyer at all stages of the contract, and particularly in the event of something going wrong - such as the builder going into receivership before delivery of the yacht. The relevant agreements are entitled *Agreement for the Construction of a New Craft* and *Agreement for the Sale of a Stock Boat*. The Royal Yachting Association also publishes detailed advice in their booklet *Buying a New Yacht*. If the builder or agent offers another form of agreement, it should be carefully compared with the standard form agreements before any commitment is made.

Where a boat is being sold by an agent on behalf of a UK builder, it will be worthwhile obtaining an undertaking from the builder that he will honour any contractual obligations either before or after delivery of the boat in the event of the agent going out of business. Any such undertaking should be secured before any commitment is made.

The private purchaser of a boat (or any boat owner who enters into transactions with chandlers, sailmakers, riggers, engineers or any supplier of goods) has substantial consumer protection under the Sale of Goods Act 1979. This Act which re-enacts and codifies earlier legislation runs to sixty-four sections, but the consumer's general concern will be limited to Section 12 (legal right of the seller to sell goods), Section 13 (goods to correspond with the seller's description or sample) and Section 14 (goods to be fit for the purpose for which they are required and to be of merchantable quality).

Section 12 provides that the seller must have the right to sell the goods. If he is not the owner, or if a third party (e.g. a finance company) has an interest in the goods, the Act will impose a condition to protect the buyer whether or not the seller knew his title was defective (unless the parties have made a specific agreement to the contrary). In such a case the buyer may repudiate the contract and claim a full refund of the purchase price in addition to damages for any resulting loss.

Section 13 provides that goods sold by description must comply in all material particulars with that description, failing which the buyer may reject the goods or claim damages. This would be relevant where the agreed specification of a standard yacht was changed between the order and delivery without the agreement of the buyer. Even if a yacht was capable of modification so as to comply, unless the difference in specification was minimal, the buyer would be entitled to rejection or damages.

If the buyer decides that he wishes to exercise his option to reject, this must be exercised promptly; a delay of even a few weeks can be fatal to the right to reject, although of course he can still claim damages.

Section 14, which applies only to goods sold in the course of a business, imposes a general condition that goods must be of merchantable quality, and a specific condition that they must be fit for the purpose for which they are purchased. Goods must be as fit 'for the purpose for which goods of that kind are commonly bought as is reasonable to expect having regard to any description applied to them, the price (if relevant) and all the other relevant circumstances'. Although one or two minor defects may not render goods of unmerchantable quality, a series of minor defects which taken together amount to a shoddy finish would entitle the buyer to reject.

Section 14 also provides that where goods are sold in the course of a business and the buyer makes known to the seller, expressly or impliedly, the purpose for which the goods are required, there is an implied condition that the goods will be reasonably fit for that purpose. This provision only applies where the buyer relied on the seller's skill and judgement in advising him on his requirements. The seller is not deemed to promise that the goods are absolutely suitable, rather that they are reasonably fit for the purpose. A boat may be reasonably fit for the purpose even though she is known to require repairs or modifications to be absolutely suitable for that purpose; on the other hand even a minor defect making her unfit will entitle the buyer to reject, provided his rejection is made as soon as possible after delivery of the boat. For example, the National Rivers Authority, British Waterways Board, and the Broads Authority impose a set of precise construction and equipment standards on new craft coming onto their navigations. If the builder or dealer had been told that the boat was required to comply with those standards, and she failed to pass the scrutiny of an authority's licensing inspector, the buyer may be entitled to reject the boat (or claim damages) unless the defects were really trivial.

In dealing with Sale of Goods Act cases it is important to pursue your rights quickly, as a court may decide that a delay implies acceptance of the goods with all their faults, or you may be deemed to have had enough use of the goods to endanger your rights to receive damages. Also it is important to pursue any complaint against the seller rather than the manufacturer or builder, since the seller is the one with the obligation under the Sale of Goods Act to remedy matters. You only need concern yourself with any additional warranty provided by the manufacturer if the seller is unable to meet his contractual obligations.

Be warned that if you buy a boat (or even an item of equipment) direct from an overseas supplier, you are unlikely to have any claim under English law if some problem should arise.

1.3.3 Buying a new boat

A standard form of agreement for the construction of new craft is obtainable from the British Marine Industries Federation or from the Royal Yachting Association. In a boat which is being built to order instalment payments should be agreed, typically as follows: 10 per cent on signing the agreement; 30 per cent on the hull being available at the builders; 40 per cent on the completion of interior joinery work, installation of the engine, or stepping of the mast; 20 per cent on completion of the acceptance trial to the satisfaction of the customer.

An important feature of the standard form agreement is the provision for the property (i.e. the right of ownership) in the yacht, her raw materials and other component parts and equipment to pass to the buyer as soon as they have been allocated to the job by the builder, subject only to the builder's lien in respect of incomplete stage payments. This provision gives valuable protection in the event of the builder going into liquidation as the yacht herself will not be an asset of the company. The purchaser should ensure that valuable items such as engines, sails, spars etc. received by the yard prior to completion of the yacht are clearly identified as being appropriated to his contract. Some form of insurance needs to be arranged for such items.

It should be noted that where VAT is payable it forms part of the price, and the figures written into the contract should include VAT at the rate applicable at the date of the agreement. The form also sets out the expected dates for an acceptance trial, and for delivery. It may also include an Agreed Damages Clause, as a time-penalty against late delivery.

For stock production boats the above system of stage payments is usually modified to provide for a deposit of (say) 10 per cent on order, and the balance on delivery.

A purchaser should insist on a proper sea trial for any boat, whether she is new or second-hand. Ideally such a trial should demonstrate not only that the boat is in working order but she and all the equipment therein perform in accordance with the designed specification. This takes a lot of time, though, and can only be achieved with expensive instrumentation. So yacht owners have to be content with a purely functional trial. This, however, should demonstrate all aspects of the boat and her equipment. It should, for example, be shown that the engine runs satisfactorily for a reasonable time, without overheating and without undue noise or vibration, and that it propels the boat at the designed speed while operating within its designed rpm. Ahead and astern operation of the gearbox should be demonstrated. Engine instrumentation should be checked, together with any alarms that may be fitted (for example to indicate high circulating water temperature). Similar trials should be conducted for all other items of equipment - anchor windlass, steering gear, navigational instruments, autopilot, bilge pumps, refrigerator, galley stove, lighting system etc.

The purchaser may refuse to accept the boat until any faults exposed by the acceptance trial have been rectified. When this has been done the buyer must sign the acceptance form and make the final payment, whereupon ownership of the boat is transferred to the purchaser – who should arrange insurance cover from that moment (see 1.3.9).

Should any fault subsequently develop with the boat, the buyer still has redress as described above. Any such dispute may be argued in the courts, but the British Marine Industries Federation also sponsor a scheme of arbitration for settling disagreements between yards and their customers. This is certainly speedier and less formal than court proceedings, but it is more suitable for deciding questions of fact such as the value and standard of work done, rather than questions of law such as rights and liabilities arising out of a contract. Both parties must be agreeable to this procedure, and this may be written into the original contract. Notes on arbitration are available on application to the BMIF, Meadlake Place, Thorpe Lea Road, Egham, Surrey TW20 8HE.

The possible bankruptcy of a boat builder has always been of concern to clients, but the problem has been somewhat reduced by the inclusion of a special clause in the agreement referred to above, which establishes that material or equipment obtained by the builder specifically for a certain contract becomes the property of the purchaser of the boat on settlement of the first instalment payment. The purchaser should ensure that valuable items, such as an engine, received by the yard are clearly identified as being appropriated for his yacht.

1.3.4 Buying a second-hand boat

Second-hand boats are mostly sold through yacht brokers, or are advertised and sold privately. A few are sold at marine auctions, where it should be noted that a boat is sold as she lies, so that it is very important to find out all about her before bidding.

Unless the equipment, specification or condition of the yacht has been specifically misrepresented by the seller or his agent, a buyer is unlikely to have legal redress against a private individual who sells him a boat which proves to be unsatisfactory. There is only automatic protection for the purchaser in this respect if he buys the boat from somebody who is selling her in connection with his trade or business. So, although there may be good bargains to be had, buying a second-hand boat can be chancy for an inexperienced yachtsman unless he is prepared to seek professional advice. Use the services of a qualified surveyor – see 1.3.7.

It is important to investigate the question of title. With a registered yacht contact the Registry of Shipping and Seamen (see 1.5.1) who can confirm the present owner(s) and whether the boat is subject to a marine mortgage. Otherwise check whatever documents are available (e.g. Builder's Certificate and subsequent contracts or bills of sale). Note that Small Ships Registration (see 1.5.2) does not give clear proof of ownership.

Since an increasing number of finance houses are now offering customers unregistered mortgages, this is becoming a particular risk for subsequent buyers. Unfortunately there is no means (short of enquiring from each and every finance house in the marine market) whether an unregistered mortgage is outstanding, if the seller chooses to conceal the fact. In recent years a number of innocent private buyers have had their boats repossessed by finance houses where the sellers had failed to settle an outstanding mortgage on receipt of the purchase money.

When buying direct from an individual it is most advisable to have a written agreement, which should cover the following points. The intending purchaser, having paid a deposit of 10 per cent of the agreed price, is free to arrange a survey of the boat at his own expense within a period of 14 days. On completion of the survey the purchaser may withdraw from the agreement, in which case he must restore the boat to her original condition before his deposit is refunded. If the purchaser wishes to proceed, any defects found on survey must be discussed between the two parties, so that the seller either agrees to make them good or to reduce the price accordingly, taking into consideration the age and value of the boat. If agreement cannot be reached, the contract is void. The agreement should include statements to the effect that the boat is being sold free of all encumbrances or lien (i.e. that nobody else has any claim on the boat). There may be an outstanding marine mortgage (which will only be obvious if registered) or personal loan attached to the boat; or a boat yard, chandler, marina or salvage claimant may have a continuing lien. A declaration should also be obtained that there are no known defects other than those which have been shown to the purchaser.

If a yacht is registered under Part I of the Merchant Shipping Act, 1993, certain additional formalities have to be completed. These involve a bill of sale and a declaration of eligibility, which have to be forwarded with the Certificate of Registry and the appropriate fee to the Registry of Shipping and Seamen. For a yacht on the Small Ships Register, registration is automatically terminated on change of ownership, and the certificate should be surrendered by the previous owner. The new owner must make a fresh application. More information about registration appears in 1.5.1 and 1.5.2.

If you are buying a boat with a trailer and you have doubts about the latter's condition or legality (see 16.2), it is advisable to consult one of the motoring organisations.

1.3.5 Yacht brokers

Yacht brokers provide an important service for buying and selling boats. Those who belong to the Association of Brokers and Yacht Agents, or to the Yacht Brokers, Designers and Surveyors Association or to The Yacht Harbour Association operate under a *Code of Practice for the Sale of Used Boats*, obtainable from the British Marine Industries Federation (see 2.7.3). They use a standard form of agreement, which sets out the following terms. The agreed purchase price is stated, and 10 per cent of this is paid on signing the agreement, allowing the purchaser to have the yacht hauled out and surveyed at his own expense. This survey should normally be completed within 14 days, although this period may be extended by agreement. Within a stated time of completion of the survey, if any material defects or deficiencies have been found, the purchaser may either reject the yacht (giving notice of the defects or deficiencies discovered), or ask the seller either to make good such shortcomings or to reduce the price accordingly.

If the sale proceeds, the agreement states the yacht is considered to have been accepted by the purchaser and the balance of the agreed price to be due if:
(1) A period of 14 days elapses, and no survey has been made, or
(2) after an agreed time after the survey the purchaser has not acted, or
(3) the seller remedies any specified defects to the satisfaction of the surveyor, or
(4) an agreed reduction in price is made.

The form also includes other provisions concerning the obligations of the two parties, default by the purchaser, the transfer of risk, and arbitration procedure in the event of any dispute.

If you are buying a boat of any size, or if you are not experienced in such matters, it is most advisable to deal through a yacht broker. He can advise on the suitability of a boat for your particular purpose, and can track down those which are likely to suit your requirements. He can help with the arrangements for slipping and survey (very useful if you happen to live elsewhere), with insurance (see 1.3.9), and with a mortgage, if required (see 1.3.8). He can check details such as the inventory of the boat, and ensure that documentation is properly completed so that title is fully transferred. Further information can be obtained from the Yacht Brokers, Designers and Surveyors Association (YBDSA), Wheel House, Petersfield Road, Whitehill, Bordon, Hants GU35 9BU. Tel: (01420) 473862. Fax: (01420) 488328.

The YBDSA is the professional body for individual yacht brokers (as opposed to brokerage companies). To become a member an individual must have a record of continuous trading for a number of years, to have an established reputation, and prove that he or she has the necessary experience. An application must be proposed and seconded by members to whom he or she is known professionally, and names are circulated to the membership for approval. The procedure is common to the election of designer and surveyor members (see 1.3.7), except that they must also submit samples of their work for scrutiny.

It should be explained that if the seller is a private individual (not selling the boat in the course of trade or business), and if that fact is known to the buyer, there is no question of warranty on the sale of a second-hand yacht, because the purchaser is quite at liberty to inspect the craft and to satisfy himself as to her condition - either in person or by employing a surveyor. It must be emphasised that a surveyor should always be used, except perhaps in the case of a very small and cheap boat where the buyer has enough experience to detect any serious faults. The work of surveyors is discussed in 1.3.7. On the matter of defects, a broker is legally liable to divulge known defects to a purchaser when acting in a sale.

The services of a yacht broker naturally cost money, and the fees are paid by the seller of the boat, as an agreed commission based on the selling price. For guidance the normal rates are as follows (plus VAT). For vessels in the United Kingdom: 8 per cent of the selling price (on inland waters: 10 per cent). Where there is an overseas component in the deal (vessel, owner or buyer): 10 per cent of the selling price.

Buying and selling yachts can be a complicated business, particularly when the boat, the seller and the buyer are well separated geographically. It often involves two brokers, and the provision of access etc by the yard or yacht harbour where the boat is lying. Consequently the Code of Practice referred to above makes provision for a fair split of the total commission between those concerned. (Further notes on the work of yacht brokers in the sale of yachts appear in 1.4.3.)

1.3.6 Part-exchange of yachts

In recent years the practice of trading in a second-hand yacht against the purchase of a new one has greatly increased, and several yacht builders and distributors now offer this facility. Some firms only accept their own make of boat in such transactions, while others will take any boat that is in sufficiently good condition for re-sale, but may limit the value of the second-hand boat compared to the cost of the new one. Some builders and dealers operate their own brokerage firms to dispose of boats taken in part-exchange, while others sell them through normal brokerage channels.

Inevitably the price offered for part-exchange is less than could be obtained by private sale or through a yacht broker, and sometimes it is well below that figure. But to offset this there are certain advantages - no commission to be paid, none of the costs such as advertising that are incurred in a private sale, plus the benefit of being able to make an immediate transaction which may enable advantage to be taken of a special discount on the price of the new boat.

It should, however, be emphasised that there are no general rules which govern such transactions, along the lines of those operated by the Association of Brokers and Yacht Agents for brokerage sales, so anybody buying a boat on part-exchange should look into the deal very carefully.

1.3.7 Surveyors

As already stated in 1.3.4, it is foolish to buy a second-hand boat without recourse to a proper survey, with the boat out of the water. To get a proper survey you need a proper surveyor, and it is a sad fact that a small minority of surveyors lack the knowledge and experience required. It is best to employ a person who is a member of the Yacht Brokers, Designers and Surveyors Association (YBDSA), and who has professional qualifications. The YBDSA will provide details of their surveyors in your area, on application to their office at Wheel House, Petersfield Road, Whitehill, Bordon Hampshire, GU35 9BU. Tel: (01420) 473862. Fax: (01420) 488328.

The purpose of a full survey is to determine the condition of the entire yacht-hull, rig, machinery, gear and all the equipment which pertains to her operation. A competent surveyor should report on every aspect of the boat's structure, depending on the materials concerned. He should comment on whether the condition of the various items is attributable to fair wear and tear, or whether other factors such as poor design, inferior materials, bad workmanship or lack of maintenance are involved. His examination should include all items such as fastenings, chain plates, shafting, steering gear and rudder fittings. It may be that the engine itself will need to be dealt with as a separate item, although the surveyor should certainly be able to assess the general installation.

It is a good idea to have a preliminary inspection of the yacht with the surveyor. He should then be able to judge, from his experience, which parts of the boat may require more careful scrutiny or where expensive dismantling may perhaps be avoided. Then give the surveyor his instructions in writing, as this forms the contract with him. Apart from condition surveys, as described above, surveyors also assess accident damage for insurance purposes, or undertake the supervision of repairs or modifications.

1.3.8 Marine finance

Many people buying boats need at least some measure of financial help and borrowing money is expensive at the best of times, so it pays to shop around and get the best rates and the most favourable repayment terms. It is also necessary to consider whether registration is needed, whether a survey will be required (and to what extent), what security may be asked for, and what the effect of future changes of interest rate will be. Tax relief on interest charges is not allowable unless your inspector can be convinced that the boat is your sole or principal residence.

Small boats and marine equipment can be financed by personal loans which are available from various institutions including banks and the major finance houses. Some marine traders offer similar facilities which, although possibly more expensive, may provide protection against sub-standard goods.

Larger and more expensive craft can be purchased on a marine mortgage, where the required loan is secured against a mortgage on the boat. The precise details vary. The cost of the loan (i.e. the interest to be charged) may be added to the sum financed at the outset, and the total then repaid in equal instalments. But nowadays it is more common for institutions to offer contracts where the interest varies with the money market, usually related to the Finance House Base Rate. This can be done either by altering the amount of the instalments from time to time, or by keeping the instalments the same and altering the number of payments (i.e. the time over which repayment is made). Normally the borrower is expected to put down 20 per cent of the purchase price, but sometimes more. The repayment period is typically five years, with a maximum term of ten years for some special schemes.

Only a statutory mortgage provides the necessary legal security for a sea-going vessel, and this requires the yacht to be registered (see 1.5.1). An increasing number of Finance Houses now provide loans against a non-statutory mortgage (not applicable under Scottish law) for which registration is not required. This is certainly an attractive option for a buyer, as it avoids the need for expensive registration under the 1993 Merchant Shipping Act, but as referred to above (1.3.4) the practice can give rise to abuses and to a subsequent purchaser having no knowledge of the mortgage.

A survey is not normally required for a new boat, but is needed for a second-hand one. The yacht must be insured against all normal risks, as described in 1.3.9.

Marine mortgages can be arranged to provide for stage payments for a boat under construction, and also to finance major refits or improvements.

1.3.9 Yacht insurance
Any owner should insure his boat for her full value, which will not necessarily be the purchase price. Since marine insurance is a contract for an agreed value rather than the market value of the vessel, it is open to the owner to agree any sum he wishes with the insurer. Any appreciable discrepancy between price paid and proposed

insured value should however be explained to the insurer as, in the event of a claim, he may repudiate on the grounds of mis-disclosure of material facts. Nothing is ever certain at sea, and however careful a skipper may be there is always a risk that a boat can become a total loss or be seriously damaged. Yacht policies are normally based on the standard Lloyd's marine policy, modified by what are called the Institute Yacht Clauses, but some underwriters have worded their own policies: these may be easier to understand, but are not necessarily better in other respects. In any case it is important to read the proposal form very carefully, and to fill in the answers to the various questions accurately and truthfully - or the insurers may subsequently be entitled to deny liability in the event of a claim.

The policy normally covers the boat for a certain period in commission each year. Should it be required to extend this period, be sure to inform the company beforehand. Similarly cover is arranged for a certain cruising area (as for example, in order of risk, non-tidal waters of the United Kingdom, coastal cruising within a certain radius of the home port, or full sea-going cruising within what are described as home trade limits between Brest and the Elbe). Make certain that the declared limits are kept, or make special arrangements when necessary. European inland waters, for example, are not normally included.

The policy contains numerous warranties, either implied or expressed. These can be identified by reading the various clauses carefully, and they usually include the following important points:

(1) In the case of any loss or damage occurring it is the duty of the owner to take all steps necessary to minimise further loss, and the underwriters will contribute to any charges properly incurred by the owner in taking such steps.

(2) Insurance does not cover charter or hire of the boat, unless this is specially arranged.

(3) In the event of any incident which may give rise to a claim, prompt notice must be given to the underwriters. Tenders may be required for repairs to be undertaken.

(4) A reduction may be made to a claim for fair wear and tear in respect of items such as outboard motors, sails and running rigging.

(5) Items of equipment are only covered for theft where forcible entry or removal can be shown. Outboards must be securely locked to the boat. Tenders must be clearly marked with the name of the parent vessel. No claim is allowable for dropping an outboard overboard.

(6) No claim is allowable for sails which are blown out, unless due to damage to spars or caused by the yacht being stranded or in collision. The exclusion applies equally to sails stowed on self-furling gear which are liable to unfurl and flog when the yacht is

left unattended. Also excluded is damage to sails while racing, unless caused by the boat being stranded, sunk, on fire or in collision. Racing risks may however be covered as a separate item with extra premium.

(7) Damage to or loss of engine or other mechanical or electrical items is only covered if caused by the yacht being flooded, sunk, stranded, burned or in collision; or while being moved to or from the yacht; or by theft of the entire boat; or by theft following forcible entry; or by fire in a store ashore; or by malicious acts.

(8) Personal effects are not covered, unless specially arranged.

(9) Boats with a speed of 17 knots or more are subject to 'Speedboat Clauses' which specify certain conditions and require additional premiums.

(10) Clauses dealing with Third Party Liability deserve special attention. Cover for at least £500,000 is recommended. Normally cover includes somebody using the boat with the consent of the owner, but this should be confirmed. Note that if a young person (say) took the boat away without permission, liability would not be accepted.

(11) As for motor insurance, if the insured bears the first £50 (say) of any claim, a small reduction in premium may be agreed.

(12) When trailing by road, a boat may be covered for accidental loss or damage, but the policy excludes all third party liabilities or offences against the current road traffic legislation.

(13) In the event of no claim being made under the policy, a no-claim bonus will be granted by most insurers. This is typically a premium reduction of 5 per cent after one year, $7\frac{1}{2}$ per cent after two years, 10 per cent after three years and 15 per cent after four years.

(14) In the case of yachts over 15 years old, most underwriters will require a recent survey on first insurance, followed by periodic surveys thereafter.

The standard contract of marine insurance is a complex document giving rise to a number of grounds upon which an underwriter may endeavour to repudiate a claim. The following grounds of repudiation are frequently referred to by underwriters but will not, in fact, entitle them to repudiate:

(1) That the loss or damage was due to the owner's negligence. Section 6 of the Marine Insurance Act 1906 specifically provides that the underwriter is liable for any loss proximately caused by a peril insured against even though the loss would not have happened but for the misconduct or negligence of the master or crew.

(2) That the yacht was not maintained in a seaworthy condition. The Lloyd's standard form policy in fact contains no warranty that the yacht should be 'seaworthy'. If that were

the case, then no loss or damage caused by stress of weather would ever be recoverable, and policies with a specific warranty of seaworthiness should be avoided. The underwriter is however entitled to repudiate; claim where the design or condition of the yacht was such as to render the loss or damage inevitable in the normal course of navigation or use of the yacht. If the damage was 'fortuitous' it is recoverable, if 'inevitable' it is not. The Marine Insurance Act 1906 specifically excludes wear and tear.

(3) That the yacht was being sailed single-handed at the time of the loss. Here again there is no duty on the owner to ensure that the yacht is fully manned (unless the policy contains a specific warranty to this effect), although a failure to disclose on the proposal form that the yacht is habitually to be sailed single or short-handed may be held as failure to disclose material facts and may be grounds for repudiation.

In marine insurance matters it is important to have some understanding of the limitation of liability, which was introduced to protect the owner of a vessel from the negligence of the vessel's master or crew (but not from his own negligence). Limitation of liability has to be obtained by a limiting decree from the courts, which can be expensive, and it overrides the normal insurance policy by restricting the amount of damages payable depending on the registered tonnage of the vessel limiting liability. A higher limit is set for personal injury than for damage to property.

If, for example, two boats collide and the owner of the boat which is at fault limits liability, the innocent owner may not recover the full cost of whatever repairs are needed. This is one very good reason for a boat to be fully insured, whatever the experience and competence of the skipper and crew, rather than to be covered only for third party risks.

Where an innocent owner's insurers assume liability for part of a claim (because the guilty owner's insurers limit liability), the innocent owner stands to lose his no-claim bonus, although some insurers recognise the injustice of this.

Due to the expense of obtaining a limiting decree, the parties often agree that the owner claiming limited liability shall pay rather more than the strict legal limit (but less than the limit plus the cost of the decree). Hence the innocent owner, or his insurers, can recover rather more than the limit imposed by the tonnage rule.

Marine insurance is a specialised business. Either deal with a broker who is experienced in yacht insurance or write off to a number of established companies who advertise in the yachting press, and ask for their proposal forms. When these are received it will be apparent that some companies give wider cover than others. Complete those forms which seem the most satisfactory for your purpose, and then compare the quotations. It should be recognised, however, that firms with the lowest premiums are not necessarily the best when it comes to settling claims. Useful information is given in RYA books *The Yachtsman's Lawyer* and *Around the Red Tape* which cover problems which may be met by clubs as well as by individual yachtsmen. Also see *Marine Law for Boat Owners* by Edmund Whelan.

1.4 Selling a boat

1.4.1 General points on selling

At this stage of the book it may seem premature to consider selling, but most yachtsmen change their boat at least once-generally because they wish to trade up to something larger - and so it is appropriate to discuss it at this point, while dealing with the transfer of ownership in general terms. There are basically two ways of selling a boat - privately or through a yacht broker. There is a third method, by means of a boat auction, but this is comparatively rare and follows a similar procedure to any other kind of auction sale.

It is vital to decide the right price for the boat. This implies a good knowledge of the market and is where a yacht broker can advise. It is also important to present the boat in the best possible condition - clean and tidy, and with all outstanding defects attended to as far as possible.

1.4.2 Selling privately

On the face of it, selling a boat privately should give the maximum return. This, however, assumes that the owner can correctly judge what the asking price should be. This ought to be the most that can be obtained within whatever time limit is set for the sale, but few yachtsmen can have sufficient insight to the second-hand market unless they have a boat which is of a type that is numerically large and is regularly traded.

Most probably some advertising costs will be incurred, and these can soon build up at 75p or more per word for classified advertisements in most yachting journals. To include a small photograph of the boat is likely to cost about £50 a time. When drafting an advertisement it is perfectly fair to emphasise the particular merits of the boat, but important not to misrepresent her condition. In order to answer enquiries (which may conveniently be arranged at a price through a box number), it is useful to have a printed sheet which gives full particulars of the boat, where she is lying, and arrangements for inspection. One or two good photographs should be included. There needs to be an accurate inventory of equipment to be sold with the boat.

The seller will have to attend at the boat whenever potential buyers wish to inspect her. Apart from travelling costs, this can involve a good deal of waiting around - particularly for those who never show up. It can also be expected that some viewers will arrive without the slightest intention of buying the boat.

Be sure that the boat is scrupulously clean, inside and out, and that all repairs have been made good before she is put on the market. If there are known defects or important examinations outstanding it is best to declare them honestly, rather than to have them exposed subsequently.

Naturally it creates a better impression if the boat can be inspected conveniently and in good surroundings, rather than in a mud berth a couple of miles from the nearest road.

Once an individual shows real interest in buying the boat, it is likely that negotiations will start on the price. It is necessary to be prepared for this, and to decide the lowest figure to accept. Much will depend on how long the boat has been on the market, what other offers have been received and the urgency of the sale.

When a price has been agreed the sale can proceed in the way described in 1.3.4. As stated there, it is most advisable to have a written agreement. It is most important to make sure that the entire payment has been received before the boat is surrendered.

If the boat is registered you will need to complete a bill of sale (ROS20). The new owner will have to complete a declaration of eligibility and forward it with the Certificate of British Registry, the bill of sale and the required fee to the Registry of Shipping and Seamen (see 1.5.1).

Wray Castle, Ship Radio Licensing (see 6.6.2) must be advised of the transfer of the boat to new ownership. If the local Coastguard hold details of the boat, advise them so that they withdraw your CG66. Inform your insurance company by telephone that the boat has changed hands. Return any permit you may hold for a special ensign (see 6.8.2) to the club concerned, and make sure that such ensign is not transferred with the boat.

1.4.3 Selling through a yacht broker

Although it costs money, selling through a yacht broker eliminates most of the work and problems that are involved with a private sale, and because a broker has access to a wide market it may enable a higher price to be obtained or a quicker sale to be achieved. It is advisable to instruct a broker who is a member of the Yacht Brokers, Designers and Surveyors Association, or whose firm is affiliated to the Association of Brokers and Yacht Agents. These two associations, together with the Yacht Harbour Association, operate under a *Code of Practice for the Sale of Used Boats*. This is fundamentally a trade agreement, but it ensures good business standards and is of benefit to clients because of the protection it affords.

When instructing a broker to sell a boat, the owner will be asked to complete a form which requires full particulars of the boat and of her material condition. It is important that the statements are accurate. At the same time it should be agreed with the broker whether or not he is to be the sole agent (see below) and whether the owner may at the same time try to obtain a private sale (not very popular with brokers). Arrangements should also be made with the broker about viewers inspecting the boat, to ensure that they are accompanied by a responsible person.

A broker acts as a go-between for buyers and sellers of yachts all over the world. If a broker is appointed as sole agent he will pass full details of the boat to other selected brokers, who will receive half of the eventual commission if they produce a sale. Central listing facilities, as offered by Foreshore Computing Ltd., Warsash, Hants, allow the interchange of information about boats for sale between all participating brokerage firms, so that the net is spread as wide as possible.

Very importantly, a broker is able to advise on the correct price at which a boat should be offered - a price that is likely to attract some response, but which will be fair to the seller. It is in the interest of the broker to obtain the best figure possible, because his commission is based on the selling price (see I.3.5).

Any advertising material produced by the broker must be accurate because, being in business, he is liable under the Trade Descriptions Act. He will advertise the boat in whichever journal(s) he considers most appropriate, and will handle all enquiries and inspections. When a potential buyer appears the broker will prepare a Sale Agreement on a standard form of contract. If the sale proceeds after survey, he can advise the owner regarding any defects that may have been found, in order to negotiate a fair price. The general procedure is outlined in 1.3.4. Finally the broker prepares the bill of sale, and ensures that title is not transferred until the purchase money has been received.

1.5 Documentation of yachts

1.5.1 Registering British ships

The law covering registration of British ships is the Merchant Shipping (Registration etc.) Act 1993 and the Merchant Shipping (Registration of Ships) Regulations 1993, available from HMSO. The requirements are summarised below. For an informative booklet, copies of Registry forms and advice on registration write to the Registry of Shipping and Seamen (RSS), PO Box 165, Cardiff, CF4 5FU. Or telephone the RSS Helpline on 01891 615353.

The Register is in four Parts:
Part I for merchant ships and pleasure vessels;
Part II for fishing vessels;
Part III for Small Ships;

Part IV for bareboat charter ships.

Part III registration is done by the DVLA at Swansea, see 1.5.2. Otherwise registration is handled by RSS.

Apply for registration well in advance, since it can take time. Make sure that the necessary documentation is properly completed and accompanied by the correct fee. Details are available from RSS and cheques are payable to 'Department of Transport'.

Applications should be made by post to RSS with the following completed forms: application to register a British ship and declaration of eligibility. For a new ship (yacht) you must provide the builder's certificate; if you are not named on the certificate you will need other papers such as bills of sale or receipts, which link you to the ship. For an older ship, or one which has been registered before, you need to provide either a previous bill or bills of sale showing the ownership of the ship for at least five years previously, or if the ship has been registered with full registration at any time within the last five years, a bill or bills of sale evidencing all transfers of ownership during the period since last registered. Note that RSS will not accept copies of documents.

Every ship must be surveyed before it can be registered. This must be done by an approved classification society. For ships less than 13.7m (45ft) in length contact: Lloyd's Register of Shipping (Yacht & Small Craft Department); the Royal Yachting Association; the Yacht Brokers, Designers and Surveyors Association; or one of the classification societies below.

For ships more than 13.7m (45ft) in length, contact: American Bureau of Shipping, Bureau Veritas, Det Norske Veritas, Germanischer Lloyd, or Lloyd's Register of Shipping.

For the purpose of registration, ships (other than Small Ships) are divided into 64 shares. You may be registered as the owner of all or any of the shares. Any share may be owned by up to five people or companies as joint owners. Joint owners must act together in selling or mortgaging a vessel.

You will be asked to choose a name that is different from any other ship on the Register. The Registry may refuse a name which might cause confusion in an emergency or which could be regarded as offensive. So have more than one name in mind. If your chosen name is available it will only be reserved for you for three months. Permission must be obtained to change the name of a registered ship.

When completing the application form you will be asked to choose a port with which you want your ship to be associated. The ports of choice available for Part I register include most of the main harbours in England, Scotland, Wales and Northern Ireland. A list is available from RSS.

A certificate of registry lasts for five years. If ownership changes during that period a new five year certificate will be issued.

Registered owners or mortgagees must write to

the Registry if their name or address changes. There is no fee for this.

It is not compulsory to register a ship or yacht but you must do so if: you intend to leave UK waters (this requirement can be satisfied by the Small Ships Register); or if the vessel is more than 24m (79ft) and you want to wear the Red Ensign; or if you want to register a mortgage on the vessel.

The following persons may register a vessel on Part I of the Register:
(1) British citizens
(2) Persons who are nationals of a European Economic Area country (the EEA) other than the United Kingdom and who are 'established' in the UK. To be 'established' a person must make an economic contribution to the UK, e.g. have a job or business. As at 21 March 1994 the EEA countries are: Austria, Belgium, Denmark, Eire, Finland, France, Germany, Greece, Holland, Iceland, Italy, Luxembourg, Norway, Portugal, Spain, Sweden and the UK (including Gibraltar but excluding the Channel Islands and the Isle of Man).
(3) British Dependent Territories citizens
(4) British overseas citizens
(5) Persons who under the British Nationality Act 1981 are British subjects
(6) Persons who under the Hong Kong (British Nationality) Order are British Nationals Overseas
(7) Bodies corporate incorporated in one of the EEA countries
(8) Bodies corporate incorporated in any relevant overseas possession and having their principal place of business in the UK or any such possession
(9) European Economic Interest Groupings (for further information contact the Registry).

These individuals, companies, local authorities and groups eligible to register a vessel are called 'qualified persons'. At least 33 of the shares in the vessel must be owned by qualified persons to be eligible for registration.

When none of the qualified owners are resident in the UK a representative person must be appointed. He may be either an individual resident in the UK, or a company incorporated in one of the EEA countries with a place of business in the UK.

If the vessel is owned by more than one qualified person (and no representative person has been appointed), one of the qualified owners who lives in the UK must be appointed as the managing owner. All correspondence will be sent to that person unless another person, such as an agent, is so nominated.

When the Registry is satisfied that all documents are correct it will issue an official number which has to be carved into the ship. This number never changes and will stay with the vessel at all times. The Registry issues a 'carving and marking note' (C&M) showing the official

number and other details to be marked on the vessel. For pleasure vessels less than 24m in length the owner may sign the C&M note. Otherwise it must be certified by a surveyor.

When the carving note is returned and the fees have been paid the ship is formally registered and a certificate of registry is issued containing details of the ship and her owners. The certificate establishes the ship's nationality and tonnage. It does not prove ownership or show mortgages.

For details of registering a bareboat charter craft under Part IV of the Register, apply to RSS.

On the death of a joint owner (or joint mortgagee) his interest passes to the surviving joint owners (or mortgagees). Write to the Registry enclosing the certificate of registry and one of the following: death certificate, burial/cremation certificate, grant of probate, or letters of administration. These need to be an original or a copy certified by a court or solicitor.

On the death of a sole owner (or mortgagee) interest passes to the executors or administrators named on the proof of death. Inform the Registry and surrender the certificate of registry. New owners must apply promptly for the transmission to be registered, or registration may be cancelled.

If you sell a registered ship or shares to qualified owners you must complete a bill of sale (available from the Registry). Hand over the bill of sale to the buyer. You must also write and tell the Registry who the buyer is and send them your certificate of registry.

If you buy a registered vessel the procedure is to obtain a bill of sale and to register the transfer by completing a declaration of eligibility on the form available from the Registry, forwarding both with the appropriate fee. You must apply within 30 days or registration may be cancelled and you will be faced with the more expensive business of applying for registration.

However when buying a registered boat it is wise to see if the seller has registered his ownership by inspecting the Register either personally or by a transcript, on payment of a fee. Then it can be seen if there is an outstanding mortgage on the boat but be aware that there is no means of reserving title, and in theory a vessel could be mortgaged the very next day. It is however now possible to record a 'Mortgage Intent', valid for 30 days but renewable. This registers the mortgage's priority, and details are available from RSS.

When the boat is already registered and therefore named, it is easier to transfer registration on change of ownership if the name remains with the vessel. This should be part of the deal, but sometimes the seller wishes to retain the name for his next boat. Then another name has to be given either before or after the change of ownership. Either way costs money and may take time to complete.

Where a purchaser finds that a yacht is registered in the name of a previous owner who cannot be traced, or who has not completed a bill of sale correctly, or who has some reason to refuse to sign a bill of sale, there is nothing the new owner can do to force him to sign a bill of sale, nor has the Registrar any discretion to shortcut the formalities on transfer (as he has on original registration). It will therefore be necessary to instruct a solicitor experienced in marine registration problems to prepare an application to the High Court for a direction to the Registrar to amend the record. This can be an expensive and time consuming business, and intending buyers of yachts on the Part I register can avoid these problems by ensuring that the documents are all in order before parting with their money.

To register a mortgage, the mortgagee (the person or company lending you the money) must complete a mortgage deed (available from the Registry) which you must sign and forward with the appropriate fee. It will then be registered and returned to the mortgagee.

A mortgage remains on the Register until the Registry are told that it has been discharged, even if the vessel is sold to another person or the loan repaid. The discharge section on the back of the deed must be completed by the lender and the deed sent to the Registry who will register the discharge and return the endorsed deed. There is no charge for this service.

1.5.2 Small Ships Register (Part III of the Register of British Ships)

The Merchant Shipping Act 1983 set up a Small Ships Register for vessels less than 24m (79ft) in length. Instead of being measured under the tonnage regulations of the 1894 Act, such vessels are measured by overall length.

In March 1994 the Small Ships Register was closed and all ships registered on it were transferred to Part III of the Register of British Ships. Part XI of the Merchant Shipping (Registration of Ships) Regulations 1993 sets out the requirements for registering a Small Ship. A Small Ship may be registered if it is wholly owned by individuals resident in the UK who are British citizens, EU citizens who are established in the UK in accordance with Article 52 of the European Treaty, or Commonwealth citizens. Other UK resident foreign nationals are not eligible.

Registration, which costs £10, is normally for a period of five years. Application should be made on form SSR1, available at many clubs and other centres, to the Register of British Ships Part III (Small Ships Register), Driver and Vehicle Licensing Agency (DVLA), Swansea, SA99 1BX. Tel: 01792 783355. Part III of the Register is open to all craft, irrespective of any commercial use to which it is put, except that ships owned by companies, fishing vessels and submersibles are not eligible and must continue to register on Part I. Not all foreign authorities will accept a Part III certificate in respect of pleasure vessels in commercial use.

The Part III procedure satisfies requirements for privileged ensigns and for embarking duty free stores, but it provides no facility for establishing title (ownership) or for recording marine mortgages. For a yacht which cruises extensively it is better to have full registration as in 1.5.1.

1.5.3 International Certificate for Pleasure Navigation

With the introduction of the Small Ships (Part III) Register (see 1.5.2) this certificate now has no relevance in respect of yachts owned by United Kingdom or Commonwealth citizens who are resident in the United Kingdom. However, it is still available to foreign citizens resident in the United Kingdom unable to register a yacht on their own national register.

1.5.4 International Certificate of Competence

Unless a skipper or owner has an appropriate RYA Certificate for a boat which he is taking abroad (i.e. Sportsboat, Motor Cruising, Day Skipper or the RYA/DTp Coastal Skipper or Yachtmaster Offshore), it may be necessary in some countries to produce a certificate of competence. This is now only issued by the RYA to persons passing a test at an RYA-recognised teaching establishment, or holding the relevant certificate, or with professional or services seagoing qualification.

Any club with an appropriately qualified instructor can be recognised for testing. The Certificate now carries a photograph and is valid for three years.

Existing (HOCC) certificates remain valid and will be transferable when they expire. The fee for a certificate for non-members of the RYA is £20.00, and they remain free to members.

1.5.5 Lloyd's Register of Shipping

Lloyd's Register (LR) provides a range of certification services for designers and builders of small craft, confirming that specific design and construction requirements have been verified by LR's surveyors.

Certification procedure involves the inspection and acceptance of the builder's workshops and facilities, and of his quality control documentation and procedures; approval of material and equipment for craft built under LR survey; the examination of drawings for hull, propulsion and auxiliary machinery and associated systems; and survey during construction by periodical visits to monitor quality control and make direct inspections.

Yachts built under such supervision can be classed ✠ 100A1. The Maltese cross shows that the boat was built under survey; the 100A implies that the best materials were used and that the workmanship conformed to good practice. The ultimate digit 1 indicates that the yacht carries adequate anchors, cables and warps. To keep in

Boat details

Owner's name .... Address ....

....Tel. No ....

Name................................... Official No ....Port of Registry ....

Displacement .... Thames tonnage .... Register tonnage ....

LOA .... LWL .... Beam .... Draught ....

Sail area .... (actual) .... (measured) Mast height above WL ....

Sail No. .... Rating .... Date of issue .... TMF.............

Designer....................................... Builder .... When built ....

Classification .... Date and place of last survey ....

Insurance company................................... Policy No. .... Renewal date ....

Engine make/type/serial No. (s) ....

H.P. .... at .... rpm.   Fuel cons. .... at .... rpm

Fuel capacity .... Fresh water .... Lub. oil type/grade ....

Gearbox .... Lub. oil type .... Capacities ....

Propeller diam. .... Pitch ....

Battery capacity .... Date new.......................................

Radio call sign .... Ship Licence No. .... Renewal due ....

Compass last swung................... Liferaft serviced .... Serial No. ....

Flares renewed .... Other safety equipment checked ....

Serial Nos.

Outboard .... Radio ....

....

Boat last slipped .... Antifouling used .... Coats..

Anchor cable markings ....

CG Form 66 held by .... Shore contact ....

Tel. Nos.

Harbour Master .... Boatyard .... Sailmaker ....

Yacht Club .... Customs .... Coastguard ....

Weather ....

....

Other information

....

class a yacht must be subject to regular inspection by LR surveyors.

Other services offered by LR include the following:

(1) Fibre Reinforced Plastics (FRP) Hull Moulding Note - issued when the moulding of hull or deck components has been completed under survey, and documented to the satisfaction of the LR surveyor.

(2) Hull Construction Certificate (HCC)-issued to a builder when hull, deck and other components contributing to structural and watertight integrity have been completed under survey and documented to the satisfaction of the LR surveyor.

(3) Machinery Installation Certificate (MIC) issued to a builder when main and auxiliary machinery, and associated systems, have been installed and tested under LR survey, and when trials have been satisfactorily completed.

(4) Lloyd's Register Building Certificate (LRBC) issued from LR's Headquarters in London when the attending surveyor's reports on hull and machinery surveys for HCC and MIC, plus successful trials, have been examined and verified.

Lloyd's also undertakes condition surveys of yachts which have been moulded or built in accordance with LR Rules and under supervision for owners or purchasers.

For further information contact Yacht and Small Craft Services, Lloyd's Register of Shipping, 71 Fenchurch Street, London EC3M 4BS. Tel: 0171-709 9I66. Fax: 0171-488 4796.

1.6 Looking after a boat

1.6.1 An organised approach

Having once taken the important step of buying a boat, a whole lot of new problems arise about how to look after her. Proper maintenance of a boat is important for two reasons. First, unless she is kept in good order even a new boat will soon tend to become unreliable in various respects, and a boat which is not reliable is unseaworthy and a possible danger. Second, unless a boat is well maintained she will start to depreciate in value much more quickly than one which is well looked after. Repairs of any kind are expensive, so it is much more sensible to try to forestall any failures.

In the chapters which follow, advice is given on various aspects of running and looking after a boat, but it is important for any owner to get himself well organised from the outset, so no excuse is offered for introducing the subject now.

Organisation is perhaps the key word, because the successful operation of a modern yacht does require administrative ability, a methodical approach towards her material preparation, and systematic maintenance. A boat is a substantial capital investment, and one which can deteriorate all too quickly unless properly serviced and maintained. A systematic approach to all this work is essential, particularly where the owner does not live near the boat and is therefore unable to carry out routine upkeep during the week. Come the weekend and such chores as inspecting the rigging aloft are liable to be neglected in the rush to cast off the mooring and get away to sea.

In general a well organised boat - where the gear is reliable, and everything functions as it should - is also a much happier affair for her owner and her crew than one where things are left to chance. She is also likely to be much safer.

So why not get organised? For a start an owner should find it useful to complete the page of Boat Details provided, so that a record is kept of at least some of the more important facts that should be known. For a particularly comprehensive record of a boat and her equipment, reference is suggested to *Ready for sea* (International Log Book).

Perhaps some yachtsmen may consider that any such form of documentation is making rather a business of what is essentially a sporting activity. But experience has shown that a systematic approach to all the work and routine checks which are required to get a boat into good order and to keep her in that state is well worth the initial effort which is involved. Even in a fairly simple yacht there are a number of things which have to be memorised unless they are put down on paper and some of us are not always too good at remembering details in the heat of the moment.

In an age when an increasing number of boats are berthed in marinas, and often spend a substantial proportion of their lives secured alongside, it is hoped that this *Handbook* will encourage owners and skippers to make worthwhile cruises to other ports and harbours. Boats are for going places, and the satisfaction of successfully completing a well planned passage and of arriving in some strange harbour - yet fully aware of the possible dangers it presents as well as the facilities which it offers - must be experienced to be believed.

Many people find the joys of cruising infectious and for a lucky few it becomes a way of life. But most of us lack either the time or the money, if not both, to be able to make long and adventurous passages across the oceans. However, any coastal cruise can be something of a challenge, and there is plenty to be learned especially if you are new to the game- so please read on.

1.7 Chartering

1.7.1 Chartering – general

While discussing yacht ownership, it is natural to consider chartering, which has become big business in recent years. On one side of the coin a yachtsman can help to pay some of his running costs or the instalments on his marine mortgage by chartering his boat. On the other side, chartering allows a person who does not own a boat, for whatever reason, to get afloat and enjoy a holiday not necessarily in home waters but perhaps in more reliably sunny climes. In either case it is important to have a proper written agreement (or charter party) which covers every conceivable eventuality.

Under the Merchant Shipping (Vessels in Commercial Use for Sport or Pleasure) Regulations 1993 all vessels proceeding more than 15 miles from the point of departure or more than 3 miles from land on a commercial basis must either comply with the Load Line Regulations or, if under 24m in length, claim exemption by complying with one of the two Codes of Practice below.

These are the Safety of Small Commercial Sailing Vessels – a Code of Practice. ISBN 0-11-551184-9. And the Safety of Small Commercial Motor Vessels – a Code of Practice. ISBN 0-11-551185-7. Both are available at £2.40 from HMSO or the RYA.

They cover nearly all the matters related to the safety of a yacht including construction, stability, machinery, equipment and manning. These were developed by the DOT in consultation with a working group representing the interested parties.

With reference to chartering it is necessary to understand certain terms:

Bareboat charter. This means that the yacht is supplied, but no crew or skipper. Bareboat charters are usually applicable to yachts up to about 12m (40ft). The owner or the charter company will need some evidence as to the competence of the charterer, or they may insist on providing a skipper (at extra cost) for the first few days until they are satisfied that the boat is in good hands. Less experienced charterers should either arrange for a skipper in advance, or consider one of the growing number of flotilla cruises which are now available (see 1.7.6).

Crewed charter. This implies that the yacht is supplied complete with skipper and crew, the number of which depends on the size and luxury of the yacht concerned. A crewed charter yacht of, say, 15m (50ft) might be crewed by a husband and wife team who live on board. Larger yachts come with larger crews (and possibly a larger bill for feeding them).

Headboat. A headboat is a yacht or similar craft which carries a number of passengers, not necessarily of the same party, at so much a head more like a floating hotel or a miniature cruise ship.

1.7.2 An owner chartering his boat

If sensibly managed, a yachtsman can recover at least some of the expense of running his yacht by chartering her (bareboat) for a few weeks each year. Should he have the time available, perhaps as a retired person, he can of course alternatively offer skippered charters. For the sort of person who uses his boat very regularly, and possibly

keeps her in commission throughout the year, chartering is not such an attractive proposition as for the yachtsman who finds it difficult to make full use of his boat.

The main problem for the private owner with bareboat chartering is to find responsible people who will take good care of his yacht, and commercially he is in direct competition with charter companies and their fleets of boats. At best it must be anticipated that there will be much more wear and tear on the boat and her gear (so increasing maintenance costs), and some charterers may not leave the boat as clean and tidy as the owner might wish. If the yacht is based at her normal home port it may perhaps be possible for the owner to advertise and book the charters, to meet the charterers when they arrive and show them the boat, to check over the boat and her inventory on completion of the charter, and then to clean and service the boat before the next party arrives. But this is quite a tall order, and it is more than likely that somebody else will have to do some of these tasks. If time is short between charters there may well be problems with spares that are suddenly needed, since the private owner cannot afford the sort of spares back-up that is expected in a well-run charter company. If the yacht is based abroad, say in the Mediterranean, it will definitely be necessary to employ a reliable agent to look after the boat, so this will syphon off some of the profit.

It is essential to have a proper form of agreement (charter party) covering such items as the date, time and place for taking over and handing back the boat; booking deposit; balance of the charter money (payable before the charter starts); arrangements for cancellation; a security deposit for loss or damage (returnable on completion of the charter); any insurance excess which the charterer may have to bear; cruising limits, where applicable; payment for items such as fuel, harbour dues, food, laundry etc; what penalty may be imposed for late return of the boat; and, should a crew be carried, who pays for their food.

Before chartering your boat-even to a friend for the weekend - it is essential to inform your insurance company.

Under Section 94 of the Public Health Act 1907 local authorities in England and Wales have power to grant licences for pleasure boats to be let for hire to the public or to be used for carrying passengers for hire. Under these powers a vessel let on charter can be controlled by her local authority in matters of equipment, insurance, competence of skipper, and even permissible cruising limits in specified weather conditions. These powers arise when a vessel is 'let for hire' or 'carries passengers for hire'. The hire contract, under general legal principles, is made at the place where notification of acceptance of the offer to hire occurs (and in the case of contracts by letter, where the letter of acceptance is posted). If the actual hire agreement is made outside the local licensing authority area, then even if the vessel is used within its area, no 'letting' arises within its jurisdiction.

1.7.3 Bareboat chartering

Many people nowadays find it preferable to charter a yacht for two or three weeks rather than face the continuing responsibility of looking after a boat for 12 months a year. Because so many British harbours have become increasingly congested and unattractive, and since air fares are now cheaper in real terms, those who charter are often sensibly inclined to do so in areas like the Mediterranean or Caribbean, where the weather is more reliable. One of the attractions of chartering is the ability to explore different places. There are however quite a few charter boats available around the British Isles, with some of them in nicer areas such as the west coast of Scotland.

Whatever company or private owner you charter from, be sure to have the sort of written agreement described in 1.7.2. Find out as much as possible about the firm or the individual concerned, preferably from people who have had first-hand experience of the boats or boat. Check carefully what equipment is provided - you should be sent a comprehensive list. Pay particular regard to navigational items and to safety equipment. What is the age of the boat, and is she the best type for your purpose? Does the accommodation really match your requirements? Look closely at insurance to see what excess is included, and check the third party cover, which should be for at least £500,000. What sort of service is provided in the event of some problem developing with the boat during the charter period (probably none, if you are chartering from a private individual). If the boat becomes unusable, what refund will be offered?

1.7.4 Bareboat chartering in Britain

Chartering in home waters is naturally cheaper, because travel costs are much reduced. Also, if required, it is feasible to change the composition of the crew during the charter. Several of the more responsible British charter firms belong to the Yacht Charter Association, which demands certain minimum standards for equipment, spares and service from its member companies. Details can be obtained from the Secretary, Yacht Charter Association, 60 Silverdale, New Milton, Hants BH25 7DE. Tel: New Milton (01425) 619004. Fax: (01425) 610967. The YCA publishes a *Guide to Charter* with information on the rights of both charterer and operator, advice on setting up a charter business, and a summary of the Department of Transport's suggested requirements for a Code of Practice to cover charter yachts.

For a wide range of other charter opportunities see the advertisement pages of current yachting journals.

1.7.5 Bareboat chartering abroad

Opportunities are steadily increasing for people who want to charter boats in other parts of the world. There are established operations in the Mediterranean and in the Caribbean, where the British Virgin Islands are popular and well provided with responsible charter operators. Other areas include the Bahamas and the Great Barrier Reef in Australia.

In most cases the yachts are fitted with radiotelephones, allowing them to keep in touch with base, and invaluable should any problem arise with the boat. The company is likely to have a fast motor boat, which can reach any yacht which has trouble with gear or engine (for example) in a matter of a few hours. With the larger companies the spares back-up is usually very impressive, with makes and types of equipment rationalised amongst their fleet, which may number 50 boats.

Similar considerations apply in respect of choosing the boat and company as in 1.7.3. If going to the Caribbean (say), travel becomes a major factor-certainly in cost. Any responsible charter company, or their agent in this country, will not only advise on route and timings but do the necessary booking. Get in early, so as to take full advantage of whatever cheap fares are available. Also remember that when taking travelling into account, a three week holiday is more economical per week than a fortnight's holiday, particularly since a few charter companies make reductions for the third week of a charter.

Most companies will arrange for provisioning the boat in advance, to a scale agreed by the charterers. It is often wise to take advantage of such a scheme, since there may be no convenient shops on arrival. 'Split provisioning' provides enough food if three or four main meals are taken ashore each week.

The inventory is normally very comprehensive and the firm should provide a detailed list. Although items such as snorkel gear are included binoculars are usually not provided. It may be advisable to take your own pilot guide to the area concerned. The firm will almost certainly give a 'chart briefing' ashore, in which will be described the better anchorages and shore facilities, where to get items such as ice, and any areas which are 'off limits'. In some localities sailing is forbidden after dark, due to the absence of shore lights and the danger of reefs.

1.7.6 Flotilla sailing

Flotilla sailing gives a good opportunity for less experienced sailors to start cruising, with advice from the flotilla 'leader' always readily available. Probably the boats are fitted with VHF radiotelephones, so that help is readily on call.

Most flotilla operations are in relatively small yachts, sleeping four or six persons, and often ideal for a family holiday. The leader knows the area - the best anchorages, the more attractive harbours, and the places ashore where food and drink are good and cheap. He can also help, where necessary, with matters such as Customs formalities.

It is likely that such a holiday will be offered as a complete 'package', including air travel and transfers. Greece is the most popular area, but in recent years there has been increasing charter activity in Turkey. The several firms which specialise in this operation advertise regularly in the yachting press.

1.7.7 Larger charter yachts

A fully-crewed charter yacht can provide an unequalled holiday, and at a cost per person which compares quite favourably with a cruise in a luxury passenger ship. But in a charter yacht you have complete freedom about the itinerary and about every aspect of life on board. And of course there's that added bonus-you choose your fellow passengers!

The range of yachts available is enormous from 12m (40ft) sailing yachts with perhaps a skipper and cook/stewardess, to 60m (200ft) motor yachts which can accommodate 20 guests and as many crew.

Certain standard terms are used in describing charter rates:

Western Mediterranean Terms include the hire of the yacht with her crew, and insurance of the yacht. Operating expenses such as food and fuel are borne by the charterer.

Greek Terms include the hire of the yacht and crew, and insurance of the yacht, and also the crews' food, fuel for five hours cruising per day, harbour dues, water and ship's laundry.

Caribbean Terms include hire and insurance of the yacht, the crews' salaries and food, all maintenance, fuel, laundry, harbour dues and three meals per day for the charterer's guests.

Operating expenses such as fuel and food for the crew vary considerably, depending on the area, while the charterer's food bill also depends on the sort of cuisine expected. Charter agents will give advice on these sorts of expenses, and also whether quoted charter rates may be subject to local taxes.

Chapter 2

General Information

Contents

2.1 Rule of the Road

Any skipper should have a sound working knowledge of the 'Collision Regulations', as they are often called, so that at sea or in a busy harbour he can apply them almost instinctively. It is also necessary to be able to recognize the lights, shapes and other signals which are prescribed for different types of vessels under various conditions.

The 1972 regulations, which came into force in 1977, are printed below, and include various amendments which came into force on 1 June 1983 and on 19 November 1989. Also included are diagrams and explanatory notes which do not form part of the official regulations.

The angular measure of $22\frac{1}{2}°$ (as for example in Rule 13(b) or Rule 22(a) etc) derives from the original use of 'points' in this context. There being 32 points in $360°$, two points equal $22\frac{1}{2}°$.

International Regulations for Preventing Collisions at Sea, 1972

Published by the International Maritime Organization (IMO) and reprinted with permission.

Part A – General

Rule 1 *Application*

(a) These Rules shall apply to all vessels upon the high seas and in all waters connected therewith navigable by seagoing vessels.

(b) Nothing in these Rules shall interfere with the operations of special rules made by an appropriate authority for roadsteads, harbours, rivers, lakes or inland waterways connected with the high seas and navigable by seagoing vessels. Such special rules shall conform as closely as possible to these Rules.

(c) Nothing in these Rules shall interfere with the operation of any special rules made by the Government of any State with respect to additional station or signal lights, shapes or whistle signals for ships of war and vessels proceeding under convoy, or with respect to additional station or signal lights or shapes for fishing vessels engaged in fishing as a fleet. These additional station or signal lights, shapes or whistle signals, shall, so far as possible, be such that they cannot be mistaken for any light, shape or signal authorized elsewhere under these Rules.

(d) Traffic separation schemes may be adopted by the Organization for the purpose of these Rules.

(e) Whenever the Government concerned shall have determined that a vessel of special construction or purpose cannot comply fully with the provisions of any of these Rules with respect to the number, position, range or arc of visibility of lights or shapes, as well as to the disposition and characteristics of sound-signalling appliances, such vessel shall comply with such other provisions in regard to the number, position, range or arc of visibility of lights or shapes, as well as to the disposition and characteristics of sound-signalling appliances, as her Government shall have determined to be the closest possible compliance with these Rules in respect of that vessel.

Notes

1. Rule l(a) – Harbour and similar authorities may make special rules for their own waters, but they should conform as closely as possible to these Rules.

2. Rule l(c) – Details of such lights and signals are shown in the Annual Summary of Admiralty Notices to Mariners.

3. Rule l(d) – See Rule 10.

4. Rule l(e) – Submarines, for example carry their steaming lights low down, and in other warships the disposition of the masts brings the steaming lights closer together than would otherwise be required, which can make it difficult to judge their aspect.

Rule 2 *Responsibility*

(a) Nothing in these Rules shall exonerate any vessel, or the owner, master or crew thereof, from the consequences of any neglect to comply with these Rules or of the neglect of any precaution which may be required by the ordinary practice of seamen, or by the special circumstances of the case.

(b) In construing and complying with these Rules due regard shall be had to all dangers of navigation and collision and to any special circumstances, including the limitations of the vessels involved, which may make a departure from these Rules necessary to avoid immediate danger.

Notes

1. What Rule 2 implies is that rules alone are not enough – it is the seamanlike actions (taking into consideration all the relevant factors) of those who have to interpret and apply them that avoid collisions.

2. The Rules do not give any vessel 'right of way' over another completely regardless of special circumstances which may apply; factors to consider might be the presence of other vessels under way or at anchor, shallow water, poor visibility, traffic separation schemes, fishing fleets etc – or the handling characteristics of the vessels concerned in the prevailing conditions.

3. Rule 2(b) specifically states that a departure from these Rules may be necessary in certain circumstances, and that to avoid immediate danger a vessel is not merely justified in doing this, but is expected to do so.

Rule 3 *General Definitions*

For the purpose of these Rules, except where the context otherwise requires:

(a) The word 'vessel' includes every description of water craft, including non-displacement craft and seaplanes, used or capable of being used as a means of transportation on water.

(b) The term 'power-driven vessel' means any vessel propelled by machinery.

(c) The term 'sailing vessel' means any vessel under sail provided that propelling machinery, if fitted, is not being used.

(d) The term 'vessel engaged in fishing' means any vessel fishing with nets, lines, trawls, or other fishing apparatus which restrict manoeuvrability, but does not include a vessel fishing with trolling lines or other fishing apparatus which do not restrict manoeuvrability.

(e) The word 'seaplane' includes any aircraft designed to manoeuvre on the water.

(f) The term 'vessel not under command' means a vessel which through some exceptional circumstances is unable to manoeuvre as required by these Rules and is therefore unable to keep out of the way of another vessel.

(g) The term 'vessel restricted in her ability to manoeuvre' means a vessel which from the nature of her work is restricted in her ability to manoeuvre as required by these Rules and is therefore unable to keep out of the way of another vessel. The term 'vessels restricted in their ability to manoeuvre' shall include but not be limited to:

   (i) a vessel engaged in laying, servicing or picking up a navigation mark, submarine cable or pipeline;

   (ii) a vessel engaged in dredging, surveying or underwater operations;

   (iii) a vessel engaged in replenishment or transferring persons, provisions or cargo while underway;

   (iv) a vessel engaged in the launching or recovery of aircraft;

   (v) a vessel engaged in mineclearance operations;

   (vi) a vessel engaged in a towing operation such as severely restricts the towing vessel and her tow in their ability to deviate from their course.

(h) The term 'vessel constrained by her draught' means a power-driven vessel which because of her draught in relation to the available depth and width of navigable water is severely restricted in her ability to deviate from the course she is following.

(i) The word 'underway' means that a vessel is not at anchor, or made fast to the shore, or aground.

(j) The words 'length' and 'breadth' of a vessel mean her length overall and greatest breadth.

(k) Vessels shall be deemed to be in sight of one another only when one can be observed visually from the other.

(l) The term 'restricted visibility' means any condition in which visibility is restricted by fog, mist, falling snow, heavy rainstorms, sandstorms or any other similar causes.

Part B – Steering and Sailing Rules

SECTION I – CONDUCT OF VESSELS IN ANY CONDITION OF VISIBILITY

Rule 4 *Application*
Rules in this Section apply in any condition of visibility.

Rule 5 *Look-out*
Every vessel shall at all times maintain a proper look-out by sight and hearing as well as by all available means appropriate in the prevailing circumstances and conditions so as to make a full appraisal of the situation and of the risk of collision.

Notes
1. A most important rule for all seamen, including yachtsmen. In sailing yachts, particular care is needed to cover arcs which may be blinded by sails or by the heel of the boat. In yachts with a wheelhouse certain arcs may be wooded by the boat's structure.
2. During darkness care must be taken to preserve night vision, by having only dim and well screened lights for the compass and the chart-table – and throughout the accommodation.
3. A look-out must use his ears as well as his eyes, particularly in restricted visibility, when one crew member should if possible be stationed forward.

Rule 6 *Safe Speed*
Every vessel shall at all times proceed at a safe speed so that she can take proper and effective action to avoid collision and be stopped within a distance appropriate to the prevailing circumstances and conditions.

In determining a safe speed the following factors shall be among those taken into account:
(a) By all vessels:
   (i) the state of visibility;
   (ii) the traffic density including concentrations of fishing vessels or any other vessels;
   (iii) the manoeuvrability of the vessel with special reference to stopping distance and turning ability in the prevailing conditions;
   (iv) at night the presence of background light such as from shore lights or from back scatter of her own lights;
   (v) the state of wind, sea and current, and the proximity of navigational hazards;
   (vi) the draught in relation to the available depth of water.
(b) Additionally, by vessels with operational radar;
   (i) the characteristics, efficiency and limitations of the radar equipment;
   (ii) any constraints imposed by the radar range scale in use;
   (iii) the effect on radar detection of the sea state, weather and other sources of interference;

(iv) the possibility that small vessels, ice and other floating objects may not be detected by radar at an adequate range;

(v) the number, location and movement of vessels detected by radar;

(vi) the more exact assessment of the visibility that may be possible when radar is used to determine the range of vessels or other objects in the vicinity.

Notes

1. Large ships going fast cannot stop quickly. The faster two vessels are approaching each other, the less time there is for either to appreciate the situation and take the necessary action to avoid a collision – and the greater the impact should such action fail.

2. For motor yachts the same considerations apply as for larger ships, particularly of course at night or in bad visibility. So far as sailing yachts are concerned, sheer speed is not so much a problem as the way the boat is sailed. For example a boat under spinnaker and with her main boom guyed forward sacrifices considerable manoeuvrability in the quest for greater speed; even if she is only doing eight knots through the water, such action would contravene Rule 6 in poor visibility, or amongst a lot of other vessels.

3. Radar is not infallible. Experience is needed to adjust the set correctly for the prevailing conditions, and to interpret what is seen on the screen.

Rule 7 *Risk of Collision*

(a) Every vessel shall use all available means appropriate to the prevailing circumstances and conditions to determine if risk of collision exists. If there is any doubt such risk shall be deemed to exist.

(b) Proper use shall be made of radar equipment if fitted and operational, including long-range scanning to obtain early warning of risk of collision and radar plotting or equivalent systematic observation of detected objects.

(c) Assumptions shall not be made on the basis of scanty information, especially scanty radar information.

(d) In determining if risk of collision exists the following considerations shall be among those taken into account:

    (i) such risk shall be deemed to exist if the compass bearing of an approaching vessel does not appreciably change;

    (ii) such risk may sometimes exist even when an appreciable bearing change is evident, particularly when approaching a very large vessel or a tow or when approaching a vessel at close range.

Notes

1. So far as yachts are concerned the invariable rule should be to take a compass bearing, and record it, of any approaching or crossing vessel; then take a series of bearings at suitable intervals. Unless the actual bearing (not the relative bearing) changes appreciably, there is risk of collision.

2. Particular care should be taken in respect of Rule 7(d)(ii). Taking bearings of the bow of a supertanker might show that a yacht would miss that end, but she might hit the other.

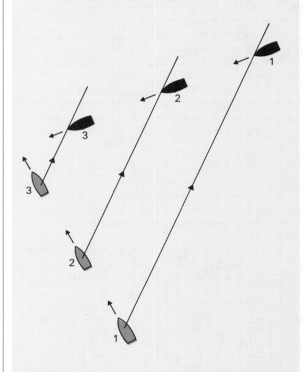

Fig. 2(1) Rule 7. The bearing of Black from Blue (and of Blue from Black) is steady. Blue should have taken action long before position 2 by altering course to starboard by at least 45°, to pass under Black's stern.

Rule 8 *Action to Avoid Collision*

(a) Any action taken to avoid collision shall, if the circumstances of the case admit, be positive, made in ample time and with due regard to the observance of good seamanship.

(b) Any alteration of course and/or speed to avoid collision shall, if the circumstances of the case admit, be large enough to be readily apparent to another vessel observing visually or by radar; a succession of small alterations of course and/or speed should be avoided.

(c) If there is sufficient sea room, alteration of course alone may be the most effective action to avoid a close-quarters situation provided that it is made in good time, is substantial and does not result in another close-quarters situation.

(d) Action taken to avoid collision with another vessel shall be such as to result in passing at a safe distance. The effectiveness of the action shall be carefully checked until the other vessel is finally past and clear.

(e) If necessary to avoid collision or allow more time to assess the situation, a vessel shall slacken her speed or take all way off by stopping or reversing her means of propulsion.

(f)   (i) A vessel which, by any of these Rules, is required not to impede the passage or safe passage of another vessel shall, when required by the circumstances of the case, take early action to allow sufficient sea room for the safe passage of the other vessel.

    (ii) A vessel required not to impede the passage or safe passage of another vessel is not relieved of this obligation if approaching the other vessel so as to involve risk of collision and shall, when taking action, have full regard to the action which may be required by the Rules of this part.

    (iii) A vessel the passage of which is not to be impeded remains fully obliged to comply with the Rules of this part when the two vessels are approaching one another so as to involve risk of collision.

Notes

1. This Rule emphasises the importance of taking early and positive action to avoid collision, and of watching the situation until the other vessel is well clear. Large and distinct alterations of course and/or speed are much more evident to the other skipper than a succession of small ones. This is particularly so at night when, by altering course to show a different light, a vessel can make her intentions completely clear.

2. While keeping clear of one vessel it is important to keep a good watch on others in the vicinity.

3. If necessary slow down, stop, or even go astern. Apart from minimising the effect of any collision, this gives more time to assess the situation. Such action can seldom be wrong when in poor visibility another vessel is detected forward of the beam.

4. Rule 8(f) takes account of three phases of a developing situation. It is important for small vessels navigating in traffic separation schemes to be aware of their obligation not to impede vessels following traffic lanes, and of the subtle change to the concept of steam giving way to sail. See also 2.2.19.

Rule 9 *Narrow Channels*

(a) A vessel proceeding along the course of a narrow channel or fairway shall keep as near to the outer limit of the channel or fairway which lies on her starboard side as is safe and practicable.

(b) A vessel of less than 20 metres in length or a sailing vessel shall not impede the passage of a vessel which can safely navigate only within a narrow channel or fairway.

(c) A vessel engaged in fishing shall not impede the passage of any other vessel navigating within a narrow channel or fairway.

(d) A vessel shall not cross a narrow channel or fairway if such crossing impedes the passage of a vessel which can safely navigate only within such channel or fairway. The latter vessel may use the sound signal prescribed in Rule 34(d) if in doubt as to the intention of the crossing vessel.

(e)   (i) In a narrow channel or fairway when overtaking can take place only if the vessel to be overtaken has to take action to permit safe passing, the vessel intending to overtake shall indicate her intention by sounding the appropriate signal prescribed in Rule 34(c)(i). The vessel to be overtaken shall, if in agreement, sound the appropriate signal prescribed in Rule 34(c)(ii) and take steps to permit safe passing. If in doubt she may sound the signals prescribed in Rule 34(d).

    (ii) This Rule does not relieve the overtaking vessel of her obligation under Rule 13.

(f) A vessel nearing a bend or an area of a narrow channel or fairway where other vessels may be obscured by an intervening obstruction shall navigate with particular alertness and caution and shall sound the appropriate signal prescribed in Rule 34(e).

(g) Any vessel shall, if the circumstances of the case admit, avoid anchoring in a narrow channel.

Notes

1. A 'narrow channel' is not defined, and depends upon the relative sizes of the vessels and the waters concerned.

2. Sailing yachts are required to keep to the starboard side of a fairway, as far as practicable, just as much as power-driven vessels, and are equally bound by Rules 9(b) and 9(d).

3. All yachts must avoid impeding a vessel which can safely navigate only within a narrow channel or fairway, which means that they should keep sufficiently clear so that risk of collision does not develop.

Rule 10 *Traffic Separation Schemes*

(a) This Rule applies to traffic separation schemes adopted by the Organization and does not relieve any vessel of her obligation under any other Rule.

(b) A vessel using a traffic separation scheme shall:

(i) proceed in the appropriate traffic lane in the general direction of traffic flow for that lane;

(ii) so far as practicable keep clear of a traffic separation line or separation zone;

(iii) normally join or leave a traffic lane at the termination of the lane, but when joining or leaving from either side shall do so at as small an angle to the general direction of traffic flow as practicable.

(c) A vessel shall so far as practicable avoid crossing traffic lanes, but if obliged to do so shall cross on a heading as nearly as practicable at right angles to the general direction of traffic flow.

(d) (i) A vessel shall not use an inshore traffic zone when she can safely use the appropriate traffic lane within the adjacent traffic separation scheme. However, vessels of less than 20 metres in length, sailing vessels and vessels engaged in fishing may use the inshore traffic zone.

(ii) Notwithstanding sub-paragraph (d) (i) a vessel may use an inshore traffic zone when en route to or from a port, offshore installation or structure, pilot station or any other place situated within the traffic zone, or to avoid immediate danger.

(e) A vessel other than a crossing vessel or a vessel joining or leaving a lane shall not normally enter a separation zone or cross a separation line except:

(i) in cases of emergency to avoid immediate danger;

(ii) to engage in fishing within a separation zone.

(f) A vessel navigating in areas near the terminations of traffic separation schemes shall do so with particular caution.

(g) A vessel shall so far as practicable avoid anchoring in a traffic separation scheme or in areas near its terminations.

(h) A vessel not using a traffic separation scheme shall avoid it by as wide a margin as is practicable.

(i) A vessel engaged in fishing shall not impede the passage of any vessel following a traffic lane.

(j) A vessel of less than 20 metres in length or a sailing vessel shall not impede the safe passage of a power-driven vessel following a traffic lane.

(k) A vessel restricted in her ability to manoeuvre when engaged in an operation for the maintenance of safety of navigation in a traffic separation scheme is exempted from complying with this Rule to the extent necessary to carry out the operation.

(l) A vessel restricted in her ability to manoeuvre when engaged in an operation for the laying, servicing or picking up of a submarine cable, within a traffic separation scheme, is exempted from complying with this Rule to the extent necessary to carry out the operation.

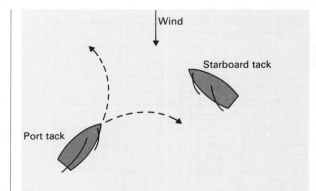

Fig. 2(2) Rule 12(a)(i). When two sailing boats are on opposite tacks the one on port tack (on the left above) must keep clear.

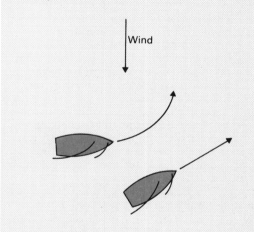

Fig. 2(3) Rule 12(a)(ii). When two sailing boats are on the same tack, the windward one (on the left above) must keep clear.

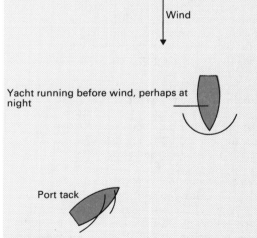

Fig. 2(4) Rule 12(a)(iii). If a port tack sailing yacht cannot decide whether an approaching vessel under sail to windward is on port or starboard tack, she shall keep clear.

Note
Comments on Traffic Separation Schemes and the interpretation of Rule 10 are given in Section 2.2.19.

SECTION II – CONDUCT OF VESSELS IN SIGHT OF ONE ANOTHER

Rule 11 *Application*
Rules in this Section apply to vessels in sight of one another.

Rule 12 *Sailing Vessels*
(a) When two sailing vessels are approaching one another, so as to involve risk of collision, one of them shall keep out of the way of the other as follows:
   (i) when each has the wind on a different side, the vessel which has the wind on the port side shall keep out of the way of the other;
   (ii) when both have the wind on the same side, the vessel which is to windward shall keep out of the way of the vessel which is to leeward;
   (iii) if a vessel with the wind on the port side sees a vessel to windward and cannot determine with certainty whether the other vessel has the wind on the port or on the starboard side, she shall keep out of the way of the other.
(b) For purposes of this Rule the windward side shall be deemed to be the side opposite to that on which the mainsail is carried or, in the case of a square-rigged vessel, the side opposite to that on which the largest fore-and-aft sail is carried.

Notes
1. The implications of this rule are shown in Figs. 2(2), 2(3) and 2(4). Rules 8, 13, 16 and 17(a), (b) and (d) also refer. Rule 12 does not apply if either of the two vessels under sail is also motoring.
2. One sailing vessel overtaking another – from a direction more than $22\frac{1}{2}°$ abaft the beam – must keep clear, regardless of the wind direction, under Rule 13 which overrides all other Rules in Part B, Sections I and II.
3. Rule 12(a)(iii) applies particularly at night.

Rule 13 *Overtaking*
(a) Notwithstanding anything contained in the Rules of Part B, Sections I and II any vessel overtaking any other shall keep out of the way of the vessel being overtaken.
(b) A vessel shall be deemed to be overtaking when coming up with another vessel from a direction more than $22\frac{1}{2}°$ abaft her beam, that is, in such a position with reference to the vessel she is overtaking, that at night she would be able to see only the sternlight of that vessel but neither of her sidelights.

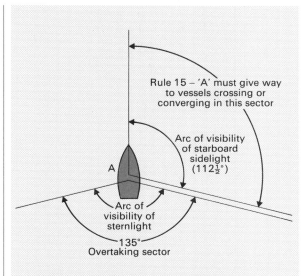

Fig. 2(5) Rule 13. Any vessel coming up with and overtaking A in this sector (ie when her sternlight is visible but neither of her sidelights) must keep out of her way.

(c) When a vessel is in any doubt as to whether she is overtaking another, she shall assume that this is the case and act accordingly.
(d) Any subsequent alteration of the bearing between the two vessels shall not make the overtaking vessel a crossing vessel within the meaning of these Rules or relieve her of the duty of keeping clear of the overtaken vessel until she is finally past and clear.

Notes
1. Although the overtaking vessel always has the obligation to keep clear, the one overtaken also has a duty not to hamper her.
2. Before altering course always look astern to make sure another vessel is not coming up on either quarter.

Rule 14 *Head-on Situation*
(a) When two power-driven vessels are meeting on reciprocal or nearly reciprocal courses so as to involve risk of collision each shall alter her course to starboard so that each shall pass on the port side of the other.
(b) Such a situation shall be deemed to exist when a vessel sees the other ahead or nearly ahead and by night she could see the masthead lights of the other in a line or nearly in a line and/or both sidelights and by day she observes the corresponding aspect of the other vessel.
(c) When a vessel is in any doubt as to whether such a situation exists she shall assume that it does exist and act accordingly.

Notes

1. This Rule applies only to power-driven vessels, and places equal responsibility on two vessels meeting on nearly reciprocal courses, both to alter course to starboard. See Fig. 2(6).

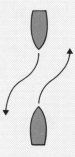

Fig. 2(6) Rule 14. When two power-driven vessels are approaching on reciprocal or nearly reciprocal courses, each shall alter to starboard so that they pass port to port.

2. A substantial alteration may be required, accompanied by the appropriate sound signal, see Rule 34.
3. This Rule is summed up by the adage 'Green to green, red to red – perfect safety, go ahead'.

Rule 15 *Crossing Situation*

When two power-driven vessels are crossing so as to involve risk of collision, the vessel which has the other on her own starboard side shall keep out of the way and shall, if the circumstances of the case admit, avoid crossing ahead of the other vessel.

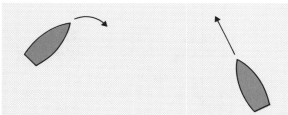

Fig. 2(7) Rule 15. When two power-driven vessels are crossing so as to involve risk of collision, the one which has the other on her starboard side shall keep clear, and should if possible avoid crossing ahead of the other.

Notes

1. 'If to starboard red appear, 'tis your duty to keep clear'. This applies even if the vessel which has the other on her starboard side is underway but stopped, unless she is not under command.
2. Normally the correct action for the giving-way vessel is to alter course to starboard. Very exceptionally (if for example there is shallow water to starboard) an alteration to port may be justified – in which case a substantial alteration may be needed to avoid crossing ahead of the other vessel.

3. Rule 15 does not apply if one of the vessels is in the categories described in Rule 18(a)(i), (ii) or (iii).

Rule 16 *Action by Give-way Vessel*

Every vessel which is directed to keep out of the way of another vessel shall, so far as possible, take early and substantial action to keep well clear.

Rule 17 *Action by Stand-on Vessel*

(a)　(i)　Where one of two vessels is to keep out of the way the other shall keep her course and speed.

　　(ii)　The latter vessel may however take action to avoid collision by her manoeuvre alone, as soon as it becomes apparent to her that the vessel required to keep out of the way is not taking appropriate action in compliance with these Rules.

(b) When, from any cause, the vessel required to keep her course and speed finds herself so close that collision cannot be avoided by the action of the give-way vessel alone, she shall take such action as will best aid to avoid collision.

(c) A power-driven vessel which takes action in a crossing situation in accordance with sub-paragraph (a)(ii) of this Rule to avoid collision with another power-driven vessel shall, if the circumstances of the case admit, not alter course to port for a vessel on her own port side.

(d) This Rule does not relieve the give-way vessel of her obligation to keep out of the way.

Notes

1. The stand-on vessel is only required to hold her course and speed under Rule 17(a)(i) in a two-vessel situation, and not at long range before risk of collision develops -this is the opportunity for a yacht to avoid confronting a larger vessel, particularly since a yacht will usually see a large ship before the ship sees her.
2. Once risk of collision develops, the stand-on vessel is required to hold her course and speed. But when it becomes apparent that the other is not taking action she may take avoiding action herself. This must not conflict with possible belated action by the give-way vessel, and hence in accordance with Rule 17(c) she should normally alter course substantially to starboard.
3. In the case of a manoeuvrable yacht the best action may often be to turn completely away from an oncoming ship.
4. Rule 17(b) makes it compulsory for the stand-on vessel to take the best possible avoiding action in the circumstances.

Rule 18 *Responsibilities between Vessels*

Except where Rules 9, 10 and 13 otherwise require:

(a) A power-driven vessel underway shall keep out of the way of:
   (i) a vessel not under command;
   (ii) a vessel restricted in her ability to manoeuvre;
   (iii) a vessel engaged in fishing;
   (iv) a sailing vessel.
(b) A sailing vessel underway shall keep out of the way of:
   (i) a vessel not under command;
   (ii) a vessel restricted in her ability to manoeuvre;
   (iii) a vessel engaged in fishing.
(c) A vessel engaged in fishing when underway shall so far as possible, keep out of the way of:
   (i) a vessel not under command;
   (ii) a vessel restricted in her ability to manoeuvre.
(d) (i) Any vessel other than a vessel not under command or a vessel restricted in her ability to manoeuvre shall, if the circumstances of the case admit, avoid impeding the safe passage of a vessel constrained by her draught, exhibiting the signals in Rule 28.
   (ii) A vessel constrained by her draught shall navigate with particular caution having full regard to her special condition.
(e) A seaplane on the water shall, in general, keep well clear of all vessels and avoid impeding their navigation. In circumstances, however, where risk of collision exists, she shall comply with the Rules of this Part.

Notes
1. Rule 18 may not apply in narrow channels or traffic schemes, and does not apply in overtaking situations.
2. Although a power-driven vessel is required to keep clear of sailing vessels, sailing yachts which are possibly making frequent alterations of course should keep clear of larger ships.
3. In the event of a power-driven vessel failing to take early action to keep out of the way, a sailing yacht can usually avoid collision by conforming with Rule 17(a)(ii).
4. A sailing yacht is required to keep clear of a power-driven vessel under the provisions of Rules 9(b), 10(j), 13 and 18(b), and she is also required to avoid impeding a vessel constrained by her draught.

SECTION III – CONDUCT OF VESSELS IN RESTRICTED VISIBILITY

Rule 19 *Conduct of Vessels in Restricted Visibility*
(a) This Rule applies to vessels not in sight of one another when navigating in or near an area of restricted visibility.

(b) Every vessel shall proceed at a safe speed adapted to the prevailing circumstances and conditions of restricted visibility. A power-driven vessel shall have her engines ready for immediate manoeuvre.
(c) Every vessel shall have due regard to the prevailing circumstances and conditions of restricted visibility when complying with the Rules of Section 1 of this Part.
(d) A vessel which detects by radar alone the presence of another vessel shall determine if a close-quarters situation is developing and/or risk of collision exists. If so, she shall take avoiding action in ample time, provided that when such action consists of an alteration of course, so far as possible the following shall be avoided:
   (i) an alteration of course to port for a vessel forward of the beam, other than for a vessel being overtaken;
   (ii) an alteration of course towards a vessel abeam or abaft the beam.
(e) Except where it has been determined that a risk of collision does not exist, every vessel which hears apparently forward of her beam the fog signal of another vessel, or which cannot avoid a close-quarters situation with another vessel forward of her beam, shall reduce her speed to the minimum at which she can be kept on her course. She shall if necessary take all her way off and in any event navigate with extreme caution until danger of collision is over.

Notes
1. When vessels can see each other they are subject to the Rules in Section II.
2. Safe speed is covered by Rule 6, and look-outs in Rule 5. Other safety factors for a yacht are an efficient radar reflector (properly mounted in the 'catch rain' position); keeping clear of shipping lanes and narrow channels (preferably keeping in water which is too shallow for larger ships); and being ready for immediate and drastic alterations of course – by not setting sails like spinnakers. In really thick fog the best action is to anchor in relatively shallow water, and comply with Rule 35(g) or (i).

Part C – Lights and shapes

Rule 20 *Application*
(a) Rules in this Part shall be complied with in all weathers.
(b) The Rules concerning lights shall be complied with from sunset to sunrise, and during such times no other lights shall be exhibited, except such lights as cannot be mistaken for the lights specified in these Rules or do not impair their visibility or distinctive character, or interfere with the keeping of a proper look-out.

(c) The lights prescribed by these Rules shall, if carried, also be exhibited from sunrise to sunset in restricted visibility and may be exhibited in all other circumstances when it is deemed necessary.

(d) The rules concerning shapes shall be complied with by day.

(e) The lights and shapes specified in these Rules shall comply with the provisions of Annex I to these Regulations.

Rule 21 *Definitions*

(a) 'Masthead light' means a white light placed over the fore and aft centreline of the vessel showing an unbroken light over an arc of the horizon of 225° and so fixed as to show the light from right ahead to $22\frac{1}{2}$° abaft the beam on either side of the vessel.

(b) 'Sidelights' means a green light on the starboard side and a red light on the port side each showing an unbroken light over an arc of the horizon of $112\frac{1}{2}$° and so fixed as to show the light from right ahead to $22\frac{1}{2}$° abaft the beam on its respective side. In a vessel of less than 20 metres in length the sidelights may be combined in one lantern carried on the fore and aft centreline of the vessel.

(c) 'Sternlight' means a white light placed as nearly as practicable at the stern showing an unbroken light over an arc of the horizon of 135° and so fixed as to show the light $67\frac{1}{2}$° from right aft on each side of the vessel.

(d) 'Towing light' means a yellow light having the same characteristics as the 'sternlight' defined in paragraph (c) of this Rule.

(e) 'All-round light' means a light showing an unbroken light over an arc of the horizon of 360°.

(f) 'Flashing light' means a light flashing at regular intervals at a frequency of 120 flashes or more per minute.

Notes

1. Although in Rule 21(a) the term masthead light is used, the light does not necessarily have to be on a mast. It should however be above and clear of all other lights and obstructions.
2. With respect to Rule 21(c), a power-driven vessel of less than 12 metres may, under rule 23(c) as revised, have her sternlight combined with the masthead light to form an all-round white light with improved visibility astern.

Rule 22 *Visibility of Lights*

The lights prescribed in these Rules shall have an intensity as specified in Section 8 of Annex I to these Regulations so as to be visible at the following minimum ranges:

(a) In vessels of 50 metres or more in length:
- a masthead light, 6 miles;
- a sidelight, 3 miles;
- a sternlight, 3 miles;
- a towing light, 3 miles;
- a white, red, green or yellow all-round light, 3 miles;

(b) In vessels of 12 metres or more in length but less than 50 metres in length:
- a masthead light, 5 miles; except that where the length of the vessel is less than 20 metres, 3 miles;
- a sidelight, 2 miles;
- a sternlight, 2 miles;
- a towing light, 2 miles;
- a white, red, green or yellow all-round light, 2 miles;

(c) In vessels of less than 12 metres in length:
- a masthead light, 2 miles;
- a sidelight, 1 mile;
- a sternlight, 2 miles;
- a towing light, 2 miles;
- a white, red, green or yellow all-round light, 2 miles.

(d) In inconspicuous, partly submerged vessels or objects being towed: - a white all-round light, 3 miles.

Rule 23 *Power-driven Vessels Underway*

(a) A power-driven vessel underway shall exhibit:
  (i) a masthead light forward;
  (ii) a second masthead light abaft of and higher than the forward one; except that a vessel of less than 50 metres in length shall not be obliged to exhibit such light but may do so;
  (iii) sidelights;
  (iv) a sternlight.

(b) An air-cushion vessel when operating in the non-displacement mode shall, in addition to the lights prescribed in paragraph (a) of this Rule, exhibit an all-round flashing yellow light.

(c)   (i) A power-driven vessel of less than 12 metres in length may in lieu of the lights prescribed in paragraph (a) of this Rule exhibit an all-round white light and sidelights;
  (ii) a power-driven vessel of less than 7 metres in length whose maximum speed does not exceed 7 knots may in lieu of the lights prescribed in paragraph (a) of this Rule exhibit an all-round white light and shall, if practicable, also exhibit sidelights;
  (iii) the masthead light or all-round white light on a power-driven vessel of less than 12 metres in length may be displaced from the fore and aft centreline of the vessel if centreline fitting is not practicable, provided that the sidelights are combined in one lantern which shall be carried on the fore and aft centreline of the vessel or located as nearly as

practicable in the same fore and aft line as the masthead light or the all-round white light.

Notes

1. The specifications for lights in Annex I are much more precise than used to be the case.
2. The lights to be displayed by various classes of vessels are illustrated on pages 55-58.
3. Under Rule 23(c) – as revised from 1 June 1983 – a yacht of less than 12 metres under power may show sidelights (or a combined lantern) and a single all-round white light (which combines the previous requirement for a separate masthead light and sternlight). The white light must be at least 1 metre above the sidelights (or combined lantern).

Rule 24 *Towing and Pushing*

(a) A power-driven vessel when towing shall exhibit:
  (i) instead of the light prescribed in Rule 23(a)(i) or (a)(ii), two masthead lights in a vertical line. When the length of the tow, measuring from the stern of the towing vessel to the after end of the tow exceeds 200 metres, three such lights in a vertical line;
  (ii) sidelights;
  (iii) a sternlight;
  (iv) a towing light in a vertical line above the sternlight;
  (v) when the length of the tow exceeds 200 metres, a diamond shape where it can best be seen.

(b) When a pushing vessel and a vessel being pushed ahead are rigidly connected in a composite unit they shall be regarded as a power-driven vessel and exhibit the lights prescribed in Rule 23.

(c) A power-driven vessel when pushing ahead or towing alongside, except in the case of a composite unit, shall exhibit:
  (i) instead of the light prescribed in Rule 23(a)(i) or (a)(ii), two masthead lights in a vertical line;
  (ii) sidelights;
  (iii) a sternlight.

(d) A power-driven vessel to which paragraphs (a) or (c) of this Rule apply shall also comply with Rule 23(a)(ii).

(e) A vessel or object being towed, other than those mentioned in paragraph (g) of this Rule, shall exhibit:
  (i) sidelights;
  (ii) a sternlight;
  (iii) when the length of the tow exceeds 200 metres, a diamond shape where it can best be seen.

(f) Provided that any number of vessels being towed alongside or pushed in a group shall be lighted as one vessel:
  (i) a vessel being pushed ahead, not being part of a composite unit, shall exhibit at the forward end, sidelights;
  (ii) a vessel being towed alongside shall exhibit a sternlight and at the forward end, sidelights.

(g) An inconspicuous, partly submerged vessel or object, or combination of such vessels or objects being towed, shall exhibit:
  (i) if it is less than 25 metres in breadth, one all-round white light at or near the forward end and one at or near the after end except that dracones need not exhibit a light at or near the forward end;
  (ii) if it is 25 metres or more in breadth, two additional all-round white lights at or near the extremities of its breadth;
  (iii) if it exceeds 100 metres in length, additional all-round white lights between the lights prescribed in sub-paragraphs (i) and (ii) so that the distance between the lights shall not exceed 100 metres;
  (iv) a diamond shape at or near the aftermost extremity of the last vessel or object being towed and if the length of the tow exceeds 200 metres an additional diamond shape where it can best be seen and located as far forward as is practicable.

(h) Where from any sufficient cause it is impracticable for a vessel or object being towed to exhibit the lights or shapes prescribed in paragraph (e) or (g) of this Rule, all possible measures shall be taken to light the vessel or object towed or at least to indicate the presence of such vessel or object.

(i) Where from any sufficient cause it is impracticable for a vessel not normally engaged in towing operations to display the lights prescribed in paragraph (a) or (c) of this Rule, such vessel shall not be required to exhibit those lights when engaged in towing another vessel in distress or otherwise in need of assistance. All possible measures shall be taken to indicate the nature of the relationship between the towing vessel and the vessel being towed as authorized by Rule 36, in particular by illuminating the towline.

Rule 25 *Sailing Vessels Underway and Vessels under Oars*

(a) A sailing vessel underway shall exhibit:
  (i) sidelights;
  (ii) a sternlight.

(b) In a sailing vessel of less than 20 metres in length the lights prescribed in paragraph (a) of this Rule may be combined in one lantern carried at or near the top of the mast where it can best be seen.

(c) A sailing vessel underway may, in addition to the lights prescribed in paragraph (a) of this Rule, exhibit at or near the top of the mast, where they can best be seen, two all-round lights in a vertical line, the upper being red and the lower green, but these lights shall not be exhibited in conjunction with the combined lantern permitted by paragraph (b) of this Rule.

(d) (i) A sailing vessel of less than 7 metres in length shall, if practicable, exhibit the lights prescribed in paragraph (a) or (b) of this Rule, but if she does not, she shall have ready at hand an electric torch or lighted lantern showing a white light which shall be exhibited in sufficient time to prevent collision.

(ii) A vessel under oars may exhibit the lights prescribed in this Rule for sailing vessels, but if she does not, she shall have ready at hand an electric torch or lighted lantern showing a white light which shall be exhibited in sufficient time to prevent collision.

(e) A vessel proceeding under sail when also being propelled by machinery shall exhibit forward where it can best be seen a conical shape, apex downwards.

Rule 26 *Fishing Vessels*

(a) A vessel engaged in fishing, whether underway or at anchor, shall exhibit only the lights and shapes prescribed in this Rule.

(b) A vessel when engaged in trawling, by which is meant the dragging through the water of a dredge net or other apparatus used as a fishing appliance, shall exhibit:

(i) two all-round lights in a vertical line, the upper being green and the lower white, or a shape consisting of two cones with their apexes together in a vertical line one above the other; a vessel of less than 20 metres in length may instead of this shape exhibit a basket;

(ii) a masthead light abaft of and higher than the all-round green light; a vessel of less than 50 metres in length shall not be obliged to exhibit such a light but may do so;

(iii) when making way through the water, in addition to the lights prescribed in this paragraph, sidelights and a sternlight.

(c) A vessel engaged in fishing, other than trawling, shall exhibit:

(i) two all-round lights in a vertical line, the upper being red and the lower white, or a shape consisting of two cones with apexes together in a vertical line one above the other; a vessel of less than 20 metres in length may instead of this shape exhibit a basket;

(ii) when there is outlying gear extending more than 150 metres horizontally from the vessel, an all-round white light or a cone apex upwards in the direction of the gear;

(iii) when making way through the water, in addition to the lights prescribed in this paragraph, sidelights and a sternlight.

(d) A vessel engaged in fishing in close proximity to other vessels engaged in fishing may exhibit the additional signals described in Annex II to these Regulations.

(e) A vessel when not engaged in fishing shall not exhibit the lights or shapes prescribed in this Rule, but only those prescribed for a vessel of her length.

Rule 27 *Vessels not Under Command or Restricted in their Ability to Manoeuvre*

(a) A vessel not under command shall exhibit:

(i) two all-round red lights in a vertical line where they can best be seen;

(ii) two balls or similar shapes in a vertical line where they can best be seen;

(iii) when making way through the water, in addition to the lights prescribed in this paragraph, sidelights and a sternlight.

(b) A vessel restricted in her ability to manoeuvre, except a vessel engaged in mineclearance operations, shall exhibit:

(i) three all-round lights in a vertical line where they can best be seen. The highest and lowest of these lights shall be red and the middle light shall be white;

(ii) three shapes in a vertical line where they can best be seen. The highest and lowest of these shapes shall be balls and the middle one a diamond;

(iii) when making way through the water, a masthead light or lights, sidelights and a sternlight, in addition to the lights prescribed in sub-paragraph (i);

(iv) when at anchor, in addition to the lights or shapes prescribed in sub-paragraphs (i) and (ii), the light, lights or shape prescribed in Rule 30.

(c) A power-driven vessel engaged in a towing operation such as severely restricts the towing vessel and her tow in their ability to deviate from their course shall, in addition to the lights or shapes prescribed in Rule 24(a), exhibit the lights or shapes prescribed in sub-paragraphs (b)(i) and (ii) of this Rule.

(d) A vessel engaged in dredging or underwater operations, when restricted in her ability to manoeuvre, shall exhibit the lights and shapes prescribed in sub-paragraphs (b)(i), (ii) and (iii) of this Rule and shall, in addition, when an obstruction exists, exhibit:
  (i) two all-round red lights or two balls in a vertical line to indicate the side on which the obstruction exists;
  (ii) two all-round green lights or two diamonds in a vertical line to indicate the side on which another vessel may pass;
  (iii) when at anchor, the lights or shapes prescribed in this paragraph instead of the lights or shape prescribed in Rule 30.

(e) Whenever the size of a vessel engaged in diving operations makes it impracticable to exhibit all lights and shapes prescribed in paragraph (d) of this Rule, the following shall be exhibited:
  (i) three all-round lights in a vertical line where they can best be seen. The highest and lowest of these lights shall be red and the middle light shall be white;
  (ii) a rigid replica of the International Code flag 'A' not less than 1 metre in height. Measures shall be taken to ensure its all-round visibility.

(f) A vessel engaged in mineclearance operations shall in addition to the lights prescribed for a power-driven vessel in Rule 23 or to the lights or shape prescribed for a vessel at anchor in Rule 30 as appropriate, exhibit three all-round green lights or three balls. One of these lights or shapes shall be exhibited near the foremast head and one at each end of the foreyard. These lights or shapes indicate that it is dangerous for another vessel to approach within 1000 metres of the mineclearance vessel.

(g) Vessels of less than 12 metres in length, except those engaged in diving operations, shall not be required to exhibit the lights and shapes prescribed in this Rule.

(h) The signals prescribed in this Rule are not signals of vessels in distress and requiring assistance. Such signals are contained in Annex IV to these Regulations.

Rule 28 *Vessels Constrained by their Draught*

A vessel constrained by her draught may, in addition to the lights prescribed for power-driven vessels in Rule 23, exhibit where they can best be seen three all-round red lights in a vertical line, or a cylinder.

Rule 29 *Pilot Vessels*

(a) A vessel engaged on pilotage duty shall exhibit:
  (i) at or near the masthead, two all-round lights in a vertical line, the upper being white and the lower red;
  (ii) when underway, in addition, sidelights and a sternlight;
  (iii) when at anchor, in addition to the lights prescribed in sub-paragraph (i), the light, lights or shape prescribed in Rule 30 for vessels at anchor.

(b) A pilot vessel when not engaged on pilotage duty shall exhibit the lights or shapes prescribed for a similar vessel of her length.

Rule 30 *Anchored Vessels and Vessels Aground*

(a) A vessel at anchor shall exhibit where it can best be seen:
  (i) in the fore part, an all-round white light or one ball;
  (ii) at or near the stern and at a lower level than the light prescribed in sub-paragraph (i), an all-round white light.

(b) A vessel of less than 50 metres in length may exhibit an all-round white light where it can best be seen instead of the lights prescribed in paragraph (a) of this Rule.

(c) A vessel at anchor may, and a vessel of 100 metres and more in length shall, also use the available working or equivalent lights to illuminate her decks.

(d) A vessel aground shall exhibit the lights prescribed in paragraph (a) or (b) of this Rule and in addition, where they can best be seen:
  (i) two all-round red lights in a vertical line;
  (ii) three balls in a vertical line.

(e) A vessel of less than 7 metres in length, when at anchor not in or near a narrow channel, fairway or anchorage, or where other vessels normally navigate, shall not be required to exhibit the lights or shape prescribed in paragraphs (a) and (b) of this Rule.

(f) A vessel of less than 12 metres in length, when aground, shall not be required to exhibit the lights or shapes prescribed in sub-paragraphs (d)(i) and (ii) of this Rule.

Note

As written this Rule places obligations on the great majority of yachtsmen to display anchor balls or anchor lights, the only exception (in certain circumstances) being for a boat of less than 7 metres in length (Rule 30(e)).

Rule 31 *Seaplanes*

Where it is impracticable for a seaplane to exhibit lights and shapes of the characteristics or in the positions prescribed in the Rules of this Part she shall exhibit lights and shapes as closely similar in characteristics and position as is possible.

Part D – Sound and light signals

Rule 32 *Definitions*
(a) The word 'whistle' means any sound signalling appliance capable of producing the prescribed blasts and which complies with the specifications in Annex III to these Regulations.
(b) The term 'short blast' means a blast of about one second's duration.
(c) The term 'prolonged blast' means a blast of from four to six second's duration.

Rule 33 *Equipment for Sound Signals*
(a) A vessel of 12 metres or more in length shall be provided with a whistle and a bell and a vessel of 100 metres or more in length shall, in addition, be provided with a gong, the tone and sound of which cannot be confused with that of the bell. The whistle, bell and gong shall comply with the specifications in Annex III to these Regulations. The bell or gong or both may be replaced by other equipment having the same respective sound characteristics, provided that manual sounding of the prescribed signals shall always be possible.
(b) A vessel of less than 12 metres in length shall not be obliged to carry the sound signalling appliances prescribed in paragraph (a) of this Rule but if she does not, she shall be provided with some other means of making an efficient sound signal.

Notes
1. Rule 33(b) permits vessels less than 12 metres in length to carry alternative sound signals, but they must be efficient.
2. The effectiveness of a sound signal should be judged against its audibility from the bridge of a large ship, with conflicting noise from other sources. Some sound signals carried in yachts do not measure up to this standard.

Rule 34 *Manoeuvring and Warning Signals*
(a) When vessels are in sight of one another, a power-driven vessel underway, when manoeuvring as authorized or required by these Rules, shall indicate that manoeuvre by the following signals on her whistle:
   – one short blast to mean 'I am altering my course to starboard';
   – two short blasts to mean 'I am altering my course to port';
   – three short blasts to mean 'I am operating astern propulsion'.

(b) Any vessel may supplement the whistle signals prescribed in paragraph (a) of this Rule by light signals, repeated as appropriate, whilst the manoeuvre is being carried out:
   (i) these light signals shall have the following significance:
   – one flash to mean 'I am altering my course to starboard';
   – two flashes to mean 'I am altering my course to port';
   – three flashes to mean 'I am operating astern propulsion'.
   (ii) the duration of each flash shall be about one second, the interval between flashes shall be about one second, and the interval between successive signals shall be not less than ten seconds;
   (iii) the light used for this signal shall, if fitted, be an all-round white light, visible at a minimum range of 5 miles, and shall comply with the provision of Annex I to these Regulations.
(c) When in sight of one another in a narrow channel or fairway:
   (i) a vessel intending to overtake another shall in compliance with Rule 9(e)(i) indicate her intention by the following signals on her whistle:
   – two prolonged blasts followed by one short blast to mean 'I intend to overtake you on your starboard side';
   – two prolonged blasts followed by two short blasts to mean 'I intend to overtake you on your port side';
   (ii) the vessel about to be overtaken when acting in accordance with Rule 9(e)(i) shall indicate her agreement by the following signal on her whistle:
   – one prolonged, one short, one prolonged and one short blast, in that order.
(d) When vessels in sight of one another are approaching each other and from any cause either vessel fails to understand the intentions or actions of the other, or is in doubt whether sufficient action is being taken by the other to avoid collision, the vessel in doubt shall immediately indicate such doubt by giving at least five short and rapid blasts on the whistle. Such signal may be supplemented by a light signal of at least five short and rapid flashes.
(e) A vessel nearing a bend or an area of a channel or fairway where other vessels may be obscured by an intervening obstruction shall sound one prolonged blast. Such signal shall be answered with a prolonged blast by any approaching vessel that may be within hearing around the bend or behind the intervening obstruction.
(f) If whistles are fitted on a vessel at a distance apart of more than 100 metres, one whistle only shall be used for giving manoeuvring and warning signals.

Note

1. Under Rule 34(a), three short blasts means 'I am operating astern propulsion', but this does not necessarily mean that the vessel is going astern – particularly with a large ship which may take some time to lose her way, even with the engines running astern.

Rule 35 *Sound Signals in Restricted Visibility*

In or near an area of restricted visibility, whether by day or night, the signals prescribed in this Rule shall be used as follows:

(a) A power-driven vessel making way through the water shall sound at intervals of not more than 2 minutes one prolonged blast.

(b) A power-driven vessel underway but stopped and making no way through the water shall sound at intervals of not more than 2 minutes two prolonged blasts in succession with an interval of about 2 seconds between them.

(c) A vessel not under command, a vessel restricted in her ability to manoeuvre, a vessel constrained by her draught, a sailing vessel, a vessel engaged in fishing and a vessel engaged in towing or pushing another vessel shall, instead of the signals prescribed in paragraphs (a) or (b) of this Rule, sound at intervals of not more than 2 minutes three blasts in succession, namely one prolonged followed by two short blasts.

(d) A vessel engaged in fishing, when at anchor, and a vessel restricted in her ability to manoeuvre when carrying out her work at anchor, shall instead of the signals prescribed in paragraph (g) of this Rule sound the signal prescribed in paragraph (c) of this Rule.

(e) A vessel towed or if more than one vessel is towed the last vessel of the tow, if manned, shall at intervals of not more than 2 minutes sound four blasts in succession, namely one prolonged followed by three short blasts. When practicable, this signal shall be made immediately after the signal made by the towing vessel.

(f) When a pushing vessel and a vessel being pushed ahead are rigidly connected in a composite unit they shall be regarded as a power-driven vessel and shall give the signals prescribed in paragraphs (a) or (b) of this Rule.

(g) A vessel at anchor shall at intervals of not more than one minute ring the bell rapidly for about 5 seconds. In a vessel of 100 metres or more in length the bell shall be sounded in the forepart of the vessel and immediately after the ringing of the bell the gong shall be sounded rapidly for about 5 seconds in the after part of the vessel. A vessel at anchor may in addition sound three blasts in succession, namely one short, one prolonged and one short blast, to give warning of her position and of the possibility of collision to an approaching vessel.

(h) A vessel aground shall give the bell signal and if required the gong signal prescribed in paragraph (g) of this Rule and shall, in addition, give three separate and distinct strokes of the bell immediately before and after the rapid ringing of the bell. A vessel aground may in addition sound an appropriate whistle signal.

   (i) A vessel of less than 12 metres in length shall not be obliged to give the above-mentioned signals but, if she does not, shall make some other efficient sound signal at intervals of not more than 2 minutes.

   (ii) A pilot vessel when engaged on pilotage duty may in addition to the signals prescribed in paragraphs (a), (b) or (g) of this Rule sound an identity signal consisting of four short blasts.

Notes

1. A sailing vessel underway sounds one prolonged blast, followed by two short ('D').
2. Sound signals are made when a vessel is near (not necessarily in) an area of restricted visibility.
3. The maximum interval between all whistle or foghorn signals is two minutes; they should be sounded more frequently if other craft are near.

Rule 36 *Signals to Attract Attention*

If necessary to attract the attention of another vessel any vessel may make light or sound signals that cannot be mistaken for any signal authorized elsewhere in these Rules, or may direct the beam of her searchlight in the direction of the danger, in such a way as not to embarrass any vessel. Any light to attract the attention of another vessel shall be such that it cannot be mistaken for any aid to navigation. For the purpose of this Rule the use of high intensity intermittent or revolving lights, such as strobe lights, shall be avoided.

Notes

1. Although a powerful torch shone on the sails, or in the general direction of an approaching vessel, may call attention to a yacht's presence, the most effective means is by a white hand flare.
2. Do not use any signal which may be mistaken for one elsewhere in the Rules, particularly distress signals. (See Rule 37 and Annex IV).
3. Strobe lights, which can be confused with a North cardinal buoy, must not be used.

Rule 37 *Distress Signals*

When a vessel is in distress and requires assistance she shall use or exhibit the signals described in Annex IV to these Regulations.

Part E – Exemptions

Rule 38 *Exemptions (summary only)*

Most of the original exemptions granted for implementing changes to lights etc are now time expired. Only the following are still valid.

Any vessel (or class of vessels) provided that she complies with the requirements of the International Regulations for Preventing Collisions at Sea, 1960, the keel of which is laid or which is at a corresponding stage of construction before the entry into force of these Regulations may be exempted from compliance therewith as follows:

(c) The repositioning of lights as a result of conversion from Imperial to metric units and rounding off measurement figures, permanent exemption.

(d)   (i) The repositioning of masthead lights on vessels of less than 150 metres in length, resulting from the prescriptions of Section 3(a) of Annex I to these Regulations, permanent exemption.

  (h) The repositioning of all-round lights resulting from the prescription of Section 9(b) of Annex I to these Regulations, permanent exemption.

> *Notes*
> 1. As explained above, the majority of exemptions were for periods of four or nine years from the entry into force of these Regulations on 15 July 1977, and have thus expired.
> 2. (c), (d) (i) and (h) above are still valid.

Annex I

POSITIONING AND TECHNICAL DETAILS OF LIGHTS AND SHAPES

1. Definition

The term 'height above the hull' means height above the uppermost continuous deck. This height shall be measured from the position vertically beneath the location of the light.

2. Vertical positioning and spacing of lights

(a) On a power-driven vessel of 20 metres or more in length the masthead lights shall be placed as follows:

  (i) the forward masthead light, or if only one masthead light is carried, then that light, at a height above the hull of not less than 6 metres and, if the breadth of the vessel exceeds 6 metres, then at a height above the hull not less than such breadth, so however that the light need not be placed at a greater height above the hull than 12 metres;

  (ii) when two masthead lights are carried the after one shall be at least 4.5 metres vertically higher than the forward one.

(b) The vertical separation of masthead lights of power-driven vessels shall be such that in all normal conditions of trim the after light will be seen over and separate from the forward light at a distance of 1000 metres from the stem when viewed from sea level.

(c) The masthead light of a power-driven vessel of 12 metres but less than 20 metres in length shall be placed at a height above the gunwale of not less than 2.5 metres.

(d) A power-driven vessel of less than 12 metres in length may carry the uppermost light at a height of less than 2.5 metres above the gunwhale. When however a masthead light is carried in addition to sidelights and a sternlight or the all-round light prescribed in Rule 23(c) (i) is carried in addition to sidelights, then such masthead light or all-round light shall be carried at least 1 metre higher than the sidelights.

(e) One of the two or three masthead lights prescribed for a power-driven vessel when engaged in towing or pushing another vessel shall be placed in the same position as either the forward masthead light or the after masthead light; provided that, if carried on the aftermast, the lowest after masthead light shall be at least 4.5 metres vertically higher than the forward masthead light.

(f)   (i) The masthead light or lights prescribed in Rule 23(a) shall be so placed as to be above and clear of all other lights and obstructions except as described in sub-paragraph (ii).

  (ii) When it is impracticable to carry the all-round lights prescribed by Rule 27(b)(i) or Rule 28 below the masthead lights, they may be carried above the after masthead light(s) or vertically in between the forward masthead light(s) and after masthead light(s), provided that in the latter case the requirement of Section 3(c) of this Annex shall be complied with.

(g) The sidelights of a power-driven vessel shall be placed at a height above the hull not greater than three-quarters of that of the forward masthead light. They shall not be so low as to be interfered with by deck lights.

(h) The sidelights, if in a combined lantern and carried on a power-driven vessel of less than 20 metres in length, shall be placed not less than 1 metre below the masthead light.

(i) When the Rules prescribe two or three lights to be carried in a vertical line, they shall be spaced as follows:
  (i) on a vessel of 20 metres in length or more such lights shall be spaced not less than 2 metres apart, and the lowest of these lights shall, except where a towing light is required, be placed at a height of not less than 4 metres above the hull;
  (ii) on a vessel of less than 20 metres in length such lights shall be spaced not less than 1 metre apart and the lowest of these lights shall, except where a towing light is required, be placed at a height of not less than 2 metres above the gunwhale.
  (iii) when three lights are carried they shall be equally spaced.
(j) The lower of the two all-round lights prescribed for a vessel when engaged in fishing shall be at a height above the sidelights not less than twice the distance between the two vertical lights.
(k) The forward anchor light prescribed in Rule 30(a)(i), when two are carried, shall not be less than 4.5 metres above the after one. On a vessel of 50 metres or more in length this forward anchor light shall be placed at a height of not less than 6 metres above the hull.

3. Horizontal positioning and spacing of lights

(a) When two masthead lights are prescribed for a power-driven vessel, the horizontal distance between them shall not be less than one half of the length of the vessel but need not be more than 100 metres. The forward light shall be placed not more than one quarter of the length of the vessel from the stem.
(b) On a power-driven vessel of 20 metres or more in length the sidelights shall not be placed in front of the forward masthead lights. They shall be placed at or near the side of the vessel.
(c) When the lights prescribed in Rule 27(b)(i) or Rule 28 are placed vertically between the forward masthead light(s) and the after masthead light(s) these all-round lights shall be placed at a horizontal distance of not less than 2 metres from the fore and aft centreline of the vessel in the athwartship direction.

4. Details of location of direction-indicating lights for fishing vessels, dredgers and vessels engaged in underwater operations

(a) The light indicating the direction of the outlying gear from a vessel engaged in fishing as prescribed in Rule 26(c)(ii) shall be placed at a horizontal distance of not less than 2 metres and not more than 6 metres away from the two all-round red and white lights. This light shall be placed not higher than the all-round white light prescribed in Rule 26(c)(i) and not lower than the sidelights.

(b) The lights and shapes on a vessel engaged in dredging or underwater operations to indicate the obstructed side and/or the side on which it is safe to pass, as prescribed in Rule 27(d)(i) and (ii), shall be placed at the maximum practical horizontal distance, but in no case less than 2 metres from the lights or shapes prescribed in Rule 27(b)(i) and (ii). In no case shall the upper of these lights or shapes be at a greater height than the lower of the three lights or shapes prescribed in Rule 27(b)(i) and (ii).

5. Screens for sidelights

The sidelights of vessels of 20 metres or more in length shall be fitted with inboard screens painted matt black, and meeting the requirements of Section 9 of this Annex. On vessels of less than 20 metres in length, the sidelights, if necessary to meet the requirements of Section 9 of this Annex, shall be fitted with inboard matt black screens. With a combined lantern, using a single vertical filament and a very narrow division between the green and red sections, external screens need not be fitted.

6. Shapes

(a) Shapes shall be black and of the following sizes:
  (i) a ball shall have a diameter of not less than 0.6 metre;
  (ii) a cone shall have a base diameter of not less than 0.6 metre and a height equal to its diameter;
  (iii) a cylinder shall have a diameter of at least 0.6 metre and a height of twice its diameter;
  (iv) a diamond shape shall consist of two cones as defined in (ii) above having a common base.
(b) The vertical distance between shapes shall be at least 1.5 metres.
(c) In a vessel of less than 20 metres in length shapes of lesser dimensions but commensurate with the size of the vessel may be used and the distance apart may be correspondingly reduced.

7. Colour specification of lights

The chromaticity of all navigation lights shall conform to the following standards, which lie within the boundaries of the area of the diagram specified for each colour by the International Commission on Illumination (CIE). The boundaries of the area for each colour are given by indicating the corner co-ordinates, which are as follows:
  (i) *White*
     x   0.525 0.525 0.452 0.310 0.310 0.443
     y   0.382 0.440 0.440 0.348 0.283 0.382
  (ii) *Green*
     x   0.028 0.009 0.300 0.203
     y   0.385 0.723 0.511 0.356

(iii) *Red*

| x | 0.680 | 0.660 | 0.735 | 0.721 |
| y | 0.320 | 0.320 | 0.265 | 0.259 |

(iv) *Yellow*

| x | 0.612 | 0.618 | 0.575 | 0.575 |
| y | 0.382 | 0.382 | 0.425 | 0.406 |

8. Intensity of lights

(a) The minimum luminous intensity of lights shall be calculated by using the formula:

$$I = 3.43 \times 10^6 \times T \times D^2 \times K^{-D}$$

where I is luminous intensity in candelas under service conditions,

T is threshold factor 2×10^{-7} lux,

D is range of visibility (luminous range) of the light in nautical miles,

K is atmospheric transmissivity.

For prescribed lights the value of K shall be 0.8, corresponding to a meteorological visibility of approximately 13 nautical miles.

(a) A selection of figures derived from the formula is given in the following table:

Range of visibility (luminous range) of light in nautical miles	Luminous intensity of light in candelas for K = 0.8
D	I
1	0.9
2	4.3
3	12
4	27
5	52
6	94

Note: The maximum luminous intensity of navigation lights should be limited to avoid undue glare. This shall not be achieved by a variable control of the luminous intensity.

9. Horizontal sectors

(a) (i) In the forward direction, sidelights fitted on the vessel shall show the minimum required intensities. The intensities shall decrease to reach practical cut-off between 1° and 3° outside the prescribed sectors.

(ii) For sternlights and masthead lights and at $22\frac{1}{2}°$ abaft the beam for sidelights, the minimum required intensities shall be maintained over the arc of the horizon up to 5° within the limits of the sectors prescribed in Rule 21. From 5° within the prescribed sectors the intensity may decrease by 50 per cent up to the prescribed limits; it shall decrease steadily to reach practical cut-off at not more than 5° outside the prescribed sectors.

(b) All-round lights shall be so located as not to be obscured by masts, topmasts or structures within angular sectors of more than 6°, except anchor lights prescribed in Rule 30, which need not be placed at an impracticable height above the hull.

10. Vertical sectors

(a) The vertical sectors of electric lights as fitted, with the exception of lights on sailing vessels underway, shall ensure that:

(i) at least the required minimum intensity is maintained at all angles from 5° above to 5° below the horizontal;

(ii) at least 60 per cent of the required minimum intensity is maintained from $7\frac{1}{2}°$ above to $7\frac{1}{2}°$ below the horizontal.

(b) In the case of sailing vessels underway the vertical sectors of electric lights as fitted shall ensure that:

(i) at least the required minimum intensity is maintained at all angles from 5° above to 5° below the horizontal;

(ii) at least 50 per cent of the required minimum intensity is maintained from 25° above to 25° below the horizontal.

(c) In the case of lights other than electric these specifications shall be met as closely as possible.

11. Intensity of non-electric lights

Non-electric lights shall so far as practicable comply with the minimum intensities, as specified in the Table given in Section 8 of this Annex.

12. Manoeuvring light

Notwithstanding the provisions of paragraph 2(f) of this Annex the manoeuvring light described in Rule 34(b) shall be placed in the same fore and aft vertical plane as the masthead light or lights and, where practicable, at a minimum height of 2 metres vertically above the forward masthead light, provided that it shall be carried not less than 2 metres vertically above or below the after masthead light. On a vessel where only one masthead light is carried the manoeuvring light, if fitted, shall be carried where it can best be seen, not less than 2 metres vertically apart from the masthead light.

13. Approval

The construction of lights and shapes and the installation of lights on board the vessel shall be to the satisfaction of the appropriate authority of the State whose flag the vessel is entitled to fly.

Annex II

ADDITIONAL SIGNALS FOR FISHING VESSELS FISHING IN CLOSE PROXIMITY

1. General

The lights mentioned herein shall, if exhibited in pursuance of Rule 26(d), be placed where they can best be seen. They shall be at least 0.9 metre apart but at a lower level than lights prescribed in Rule 26(b)(i) and (c)(i). The lights shall be visible all round the horizon at a distance of at least 1 mile but at a lesser distance than the lights prescribed by these Rules for fishing vessels.

2. Signals for trawlers

(a) Vessels when engaged in trawling, whether using demersal or pelagic gear, may exhibit:
   - (i) when shooting their nets:
     two white lights in a vertical line;
   - (ii) when hauling their nets:
     one white light over one red light in a vertical line;
   - (iii) when the net has come fast upon an obstruction:
     two red lights in a vertical line.

(b) Each vessel engaged in pair trawling may exhibit:
   - (i) by night, a searchlight directed forward and in the direction of the other vessel of the pair;
   - (ii) when shooting or hauling their nets or when their nets have come fast upon an obstruction, the lights prescribed in 2(a) above.

3. Signals for purse seiners

Vessels engaged in fishing with purse seine gear may exhibit two yellow lights in a vertical line. These lights shall flash alternately every second and with equal light and occultation duration. These lights may be exhibited only when the vessel is hampered by its fishing gear.

Annex III

TECHNICAL DETAILS OF SOUND SIGNAL APPLIANCES

1. Whistles

(a) *Frequencies and range of audibility*
The fundamental frequency of the signal shall lie within the range 70-700Hz.

The range of audibility of the signal from a whistle shall be determined by those frequencies, which may include the fundamental and/or one or more higher frequencies, which lie within the range 180-700Hz ($\pm$ 1 per cent) and which provide the sound pressure levels specified in paragraph l(c) below.

(b) *Limits of fundamental frequencies*
To ensure a wide variety of whistle characteristics, the fundamental frequency of a whistle shall be between the following limits:
   - (i) 70-200Hz, for a vessel 200 metres or more in length;
   - (ii) 130-350Hz, for a vessel 75 metres but less than 200 metres in length
   - (iii) 250-700Hz, for a vessel less than 75 metres in length.

(c) *Sound signal intensity and range of audibility*
A whistle fitted in a vessel shall provide, in the direction of maximum intensity of the whistle and at a distance of 1 metre from it, a sound pressure level in at least one 1/3rd-octave band within the range of frequencies 180–700Hz ($\pm$ 1 per cent) of not less than the appropriate figure given in the table below.

Length of vessel in metres	$\frac{1}{3}$rd-octave band level at 1 metre in dB referred to 2×10^{-5} N/m^2	Audibility range in nautical miles
200 or more	143	2
75 but less than 200	138	1.5
20 but less than 75	130	1
Less than 20	120	0.5

The range of audibility in the table above is for information and is approximately the range at which a whistle may be heard on its forward axis with 90 per cent probability in conditions of still air on board a vessel having average background noise level at the listening posts (taken to be 68dB in the octave band centred on 250Hz and 63dB in the octave band centred on 500Hz).

In practice the range at which a whistle may be heard is extremely variable and depends critically on weather conditions; the values given can be regarded as typical but under conditions of strong wind or high ambient noise level at the listening post the range may be much reduced.

(d) *Directional properties*
The sound pressure level of a directional whistle shall be not more than 4dB below the prescribed sound pressure level on the axis at any direction in the horizontal plane within $\pm 45°$ of the axis. The sound pressure level at any other direction in the horizontal plane shall be not more than 10dB below the prescribed sound pressure level on the axis, so that the range in any direction will be at least half the range on the forward axis. The sound pressure level shall be measured in that 1/3rd-octave band which determines the audibility range.

(e) *Positioning of whistles*
When a directional whistle is to be used as the only whistle on a vessel, it shall be installed with its maximum intensity directed straight ahead.

A whistle shall be placed as high as practicable on a vessel, in order to reduce interception of the emitted sound by obstructions and also to minimise hearing damage risk to personnel. The sound pressure level of the vessel's own signal at listening posts shall not exceed 110dB (A) and so far as practicable should not exceed 100dB (A).

(f) *Fitting of more than one whistle*
If whistles are fitted at a distance apart of more

than 100 metres, it shall be so arranged that they are not sounded simultaneously.

(g) *Combined whistle systems*

If due to the presence of obstructions the sound field of a single whistle or of one of the whistles referred to in paragraph l(f) above is likely to have a zone of greatly reduced signal level, it is recommended that a combined whistle system be fitted so as to overcome this reduction. For the purposes of the Rules a combined whistle system is to be regarded as a single whistle. The whistles of a combined system shall be located at a distance apart of not more than 100 metres and arranged to be sounded simultaneously. The frequency of any one whistle shall differ from those of the others by at least 10Hz.

2. Bell or gong

(a) *Intensity of signal*

A bell or gong, or other device having similar sound characteristics shall produce a sound pressure level of not less than 110dB at a distance of 1 metre from it.

(b) *Construction*

Bells and gongs shall be made of corrosion-resistant material and designed to give a clear tone. The diameter of the mouth of the bell shall be not less than 300mm for vessels of 20 metres or more in length, and shall be not less than 200mm for vessels of 12 metres or more but of less than 20 metres in length. Where practicable, a power-driven bell striker is recommended to ensure constant force but manual operation shall be possible. The mass of the striker shall be not less than 3 per cent of the mass of the bell.

3. Approval

The construction of sound signal appliances, their performance and their installation on board the vessel shall be to the satisfaction of the appropriate authority of the State whose flag the vessel is entitled to fly.

Annex IV

DISTRESS SIGNALS

1. The following signals, used or exhibited either together or separately, indicate distress and need of assistance:
   (a) a gun or other explosive signal fired at intervals of about a minute;
   (b) a continuous sounding with any fog-signalling apparatus;
   (c) rockets or shells, throwing red stars fired one at a time at short intervals;
   (d) a signal made by radiotelegraphy or by any other signalling method consisting of the group · · · — — — · · · (SOS) in the Morse code;
   (e) a signal sent by radiotelephony consisting of the spoken word 'Mayday';
   (f) the International Code Signal of distress indicated by N.C.;
   (g) a signal consisting of a square flag having above or below it a ball or anything resembling a ball;
   (h) flames on the vessel (as from a burning tar barrel, oil barrel, etc);
   (i) a rocket parachute flare or a hand flare showing a red light;
   (j) a smoke signal giving off orange-coloured smoke;
   (k) slowly and repeatedly raising and lowering arms outstretched to each side;
   (l) the radiotelegraph alarm signal;
   (m) the radiotelephone alarm signal;
   (n) signals transmitted by emergency position-indicating radio beacons;
   (o) approved signals transmitted by radiocommunication systems;
   (p) the digital selective calling distress signal.
2. The use or exhibition of any of the foregoing signals except for the purpose of indicating distress and need of assistance and the use of other signals which may be confused with any of the above signals is prohibited.
3. Attention is drawn to the relevant sections of the International Code of Signals, the Merchant Ship Search and Rescue Manual and the following signals:
   (a) a piece of orange-coloured canvas with either a black square and circle or other appropriate symbol (for identification from the air);
   (b) a dye marker.

Notes
1. A distress signal must only be made when a vessel is in serious and immediate danger, and help is urgently required.
2. Of those listed above, the following are the ones more suited to yachts and small craft, and their use is more fully described under 'Safety' in 8.3.10, (b), (d), (e), (f), (g), (i), (j) and (k)
3. With reference to 1.(l) above, the radiotelegraph alarm signal is a series of twelve four-second dashes with intervals of one second.
4. With reference to 1.(m) above, the radiotelephone alarm signal is two audio tones transmitted alternately at a frequency of 2200Hz and 1300Hz for a duration of 30 seconds to one minute.
5. With reference to 1.(n) above, the signal is either as in 4. above, or a series of single tones at a frequency of 1300Hz.
6. With reference to 1.(p) above, DSC Distress Alerts are sent on VHF Ch 70, on MF on 2187.5kHz, and on selected HF frequencies. They can also be sent via satellite with either absolute priority in general communications channels or on exclusive distress/safety channels.

2.2 Limits and Dangers

Although we talk about the 'freedom of the sea', yachtsmen should recognise that limits and restrictions are imposed by international agreements or by national decrees. These brief notes do not give full legal coverage of these matters: subjects such as international waters and fishing limits are complicated and liable to international dispute.

2.2.1 Territorial waters

Countries may exercise sovereignty over the territorial sea along their coasts, but the width varies as does the method of measurement. In

Country	Territorial waters	Fishing jurisdiction
Algeria[1]	12	50
Albania, Cyprus, Israel, Italy[1], Monaco, Netherlands Antilles, Tunisia[1], Turkey, Yugoslavia[1]	12	12
Anguilla, Bahamas, British Virgin Islands, Denmark[1], Montserrat Pitcairn	3	200
Finland	4	12
Antigua/Barbuda, Argentina[1], Australia[1], Bangladesh, Barbados, Belgium, Bermuda, Brazil, Brunei, Bulgaria, Burma[1], Cambodia[1], Canada[1], Cape Verde Islands, Cayman, Chile[1], Colombia[1], Costa Rica, Cuba[1], Dominica, Egypt[1], Equatorial Guinea, Estonia, Falkland Islands[1], Fiji, France[1], Gabon, Gambia, Germany[1], Georgia, Ghana, Grenada, Guatemala, Guinea[1], Guyana, Haiti, Honduras, Iceland[1], India, Indonesia, Irish Republic[1], Jamaica, Japan, Kenya, Korea (North), Latvia, Lithuania, Madagascar[1], Malaysia[1], Mauritius[1], Mexico[1], Mozambique[1], Namibia, Netherlands[1], New Zealand Oman[1], Pakistan, Papua New Guinea, Philippines, Poland, Portugal[1], Romania[1], Russia[1], St Helena, St Kitts/Nevis, St Lucia, St Vincent & Grenadines, Senegal[1], Seychelles, Solomon Islands, South Africa, Sri Lanka, Sweden[1], Taiwan, Thailand, Tonga, Turks & Caicos, United Kingdom[1], USA, Venezuela[1] Vietnam[1], Western Samoa, Yemen, Zaire	12	200
Greece	6	6
Dominican Republic[1]	6	200
Libya	12	20
Malta	12	25
Norway	4	200
Angola	20	200
Benin, Congo, Ecuador[1], El Salvador, Liberia, Nicaragua, Panama, Peru, Sierra Leone, Somalia, Uruguay	200	200

Note: [1]Uses straight baseline systems along either all or part of the coast.

Fig. 2(8) The breadth of sea. in nautical miles, claimed for territorial waters and for fishing jurisdiction.

general (as in the United Kingdom) the baseline is the low water line along the coasts of the mainland and islands. Deep bays may be closed by a line up to 24 miles (38km) in length across the entrance, or at a point where the bay narrows to that distance. Coasts which are deeply indented or with a fringe of islands, such as the west coast of Scotland, may have a system of straight baselines.

Waters on the landward side of these baselines are internal waters, over which the country concerned has sovereignty. In the territorial sea foreign vessels have the right of innocent passage but must obey laws and regulations of the state concerned. Innocent passage does not allow anchoring except where necessary for ordinary navigation or due to force majeure or distress.

The table in Fig. 2(8) shows the breadth of sea claimed by various countries as territorial waters and as fishing limits (see below).

2.2.2 Fishing limits

Most states control fishing for 200 miles (322km) from the baselines referred to in 2.2.1. The UK (like other European countries) exercises fisheries jurisdiction to 200 miles (322km) from territorial sea baselines, or to a median line with other countries where that line is less than 200 miles (322km). The UK claims exclusive fishing rights for six miles, with jurisdiction over a further six-mile zone in which other countries with established traditional rights may fish.

2.2.3 Fishing vessels

Yachtsmen should remember that, whether under sail or power, a yacht must keep clear of a vessel trawling or fishing. Such vessels should show the shapes or lights as in Rule 26 of the Collision Regulations (see 2.1). Fishing boats are often very insistent as to their rights and it is best to give them a wide berth.

Particular concentrations of fishing vessels round the coasts of Britain are likely to be met as outlined below. Keep a good look-out, and remember that drift nets may extend a mile or more – usually to windward of the fishing boat.

(1) England – South Coast. Single and pair trawlers may be met between the Scillies and Start Point, generally within 19km (12 miles) of the coast from September to March. Hand-line boats fish in this area throughout the year. Pots and nets are placed in areas all along the south coast, sometimes 24km (15 miles) offshore. Oyster dredgers operate in the Western Solent.

(2) England – East Coast. Fixed fishing gear is often met up to 19km (12 miles) offshore, from north Norfolk to the Scottish border.

(3) England – North-east Coast. Concentrations of vessels fishing for sprats may be met from October to March, up to 120km (75 miles) offshore between 53° 00′ N and 55° 30′ N. Small fishing boats with salmon drift nets may be concentrated from April to August up to 10km (6 miles) offshore between Whitby and Holy Island.

(4) England – North-west Coast. Concentrations of fishing boats, mostly single and pair trawlers, may be met during August and September within 19km (12 miles) of land between Chicken Rock and Douglas. Concentrations of trawlers may be met up to 40km (25 miles) west of Morecambe light-buoy in April/May and from mid-August to October.

(5) Scotland. Concentrations of vessels fishing for mackerel and herring may be met June-December in the Minches and Firth of Clyde, and outside the Hebrides.

2.2.4 Surveying ships

While surveying, these display the signals prescribed in Rule 27(b) of the Collision Regulations, and may also show International Code group 'IR' ('I am engaged in submarine survey work. Keep clear of me and go slow'). During this work a survey ship may proceed across shipping lanes, and may tow gear up to 300m (900ft) astern.

Vessels undertake seismic surveys while exploring for oil or gas; they may tow a detector cable up to 3.2km (2 miles) astern and initiate harmless explosions.

2.2.5 Measured distances

Around the coast are measured distances, shown on charts and in Sailing Directions, where vessels run speed trials and calibrate logs, etc. Such vessels fly the International Code flags 'SM', and should be given a wide berth – including the turning area each end of the run.

2.2.6 Hovercraft

Hovercraft are mostly met in coastal waters. Since they can be blown sideways by the wind, their aspect may not indicate their true direction of travel. At night or in poor visibility they show a quick-flashing yellow light. Their noise may make sound signals inaudible.

2.2.7 Dracones

Dracones are flexible oil barges, which float very low in the water and are difficult to see. By day the towing vessel shows a black diamond shape, and the dracone (or last dracone, if more than one) tows a float with a similar shape. By night the towing vessel shows the lights prescribed by the Collision Regulations, and may illuminate the tow by searchlight. The dracone (or last dracone) tows a float with a white all-round light.

2.2.8 Incinerator vessels

Vessels burning chemical waste may be met in areas designated on charts and in Sailing Directions. These vessels have limited manoeuvrability, and show the signals prescribed in Rule 27(b) of the Collision Regulations. Avoid the noxious fumes by passing to windward.

2.2.9 Navigational aids

Take care when passing navigational buoys, Lanbys, light-vessels, etc. Larger ships are asked to be vigilant due to the damage they can cause to such aids, possibly with serious consequences for other vessels. In the case of yachts, however, it is more likely to be the yacht which will be damaged by any collision. Nevertheless, any contact should be reported at once (e.g. via HM Coastguard or the nearest coast radio station) in case damage has been done to the navigational aid. It is an offence to make fast to any navigational aid.

2.2.10 Warships on exercises

Yachtsmen should realise the possible danger in approaching a formation of warships, or other vessels in convoy, too closely. Warships operating aircraft may have to steer as dictated by the wind, when they will show the lights or shapes as in Rule 27(b) of the Collision Regulations. Aircraft carriers may have masthead lights displaced to one side of the vessel, normally to starboard, while their sidelights may be each side of the hull or each side of the island. At night they may use red or white night deck lighting. Due to their configuration, some other warships cannot comply fully with the requirements for navigation lights.

Warships replenishing at sea are connected to auxiliary vessels by jackstays and hoses, and are restricted in manoeuvrability and speed. They display the appropriate signals in Rule 27(b), and other vessels must keep well clear.

2.2.11 Practice and exercise areas

Areas for firing or bombing exercises, and for other defence exercises, occur round the United Kingdom, and in many other parts of the world. Those in Home Waters are shown on six small scale Admiralty charts of the PEXA series. In general, details of these areas are not shown on charts or in navigational publications, except for such range beacons, lights or buoys which may help navigation. Practice areas are marked by yellow buoys with two red stripes intersecting at the top, and the letters 'DZ' in black on the sides.

An annual *Notice to Mariners* describes the sorts of practices carried out. Warning signals, if given, are usually red flags by day, and fixed or flashing red lights by night. Range authorities are responsible for ensuring that the area is clear, and that there is no danger to vessels in the vicinity (see 19.1.2). If a yacht finds herself in an area where practices or exercises are in progress she should, if possible, maintain her course and speed; but if she is not able to do this for navigational reasons, she should clear the area as quickly as possible.

Information on the activities in the following exercise areas can be obtained from the authorities indicated below:

Plymouth Exercise Areas – Devonport Operations Room, Plymouth. Tel: (01752) 563777, ext 2182/3.
Portland Exercise Areas – Portland Operations Room, Portland. Tel: (01305) 820311, ext 2357/8/9 or VHF Ch 14.

Portsmouth Exercise Areas — MRSC Solent Coastguard, Lee-on-Solent. Tel: (01705) 552100 or VHF Ch 16; 08.

Scotland and Northern Ireland Exercise Areas — The Office of the Flag Officer Scotland and Northern Ireland, Maritime Headquarters, Pitreavie, Dunfermline. Tel: (01383) 412161, ext 389.

Clyde Exercise Areas — Faslane Operations Room, Helensburgh. Tel: (01436) 4321, ext 6100.

Warnings of submarine (SUBFACTS) and gunnery exercises (GUNFACTS) are broadcast by local Coastguard and Coast Radio Stations. For details see *The Macmillan & Silk Cut Nautical Almanac*.

2.2.12 Submarines

Submarines may be encountered anywhere at sea, not just in designated Submarine Exercise Areas. The masthead lights and sidelights of submarines are placed well forward, and low above the water; similarly the stern light, which may be obscured by spray or wash. Some submarines carry an additional yellow quick-flashing light above the after masthead light.

International Code group 'NE2' flown by a surface ship indicates that submarines are in the vicinity. A submarine below periscope depth occasionally streams red and yellow or red and white floats on the surface astern of her. The following pyrotechnics and smoke signals may be used by submerged submarines:

Smoke	*Signifies*
White smoke candle (with or without flame or dye). Yellow smoke candles. Green flares launched about 60m (200ft) into the air, burning for about 5 secs.	Indicates position in response to request from ship or aircraft.
Red flares (characteristics as for green flares above). If submarine does not surface within five minutes, assume she is in distress and sunk.	Keep clear, am carrying out emergency surfacing procedure. Do not stop propellers. Clear the area. Stand by to help.
Two white or yellow smoke candles released singly about 3 minutes apart.	Keep clear, am preparing to surface. Do not stop propellers. Clear the immediate vicinity.

A submarine unable to surface will show her position by:
(1) Releasing an indicator buoy (with a whip aerial) on the end of a long line, which must not be broken. See below.
(2) Firing candles with white flame and white smoke, or just yellow smoke. Some may have a dye marker and a message carrier.

(3) Pumping out fuel, lubricating oil.
(4) Blowing out air.

A submarine indicator buoy is semi-spherical in shape, 76cm in diameter and 90cm deep. It has vertical strips of reflective tape alternately red and white, and carries a three-digit serial number under the words 'Forward' or 'Aft', and the words 'Finder inform Navy, Coastguard or Police. Do not secure to or touch'. A light flashes every two seconds for about 72 hours. An automatic distress signal is transmitted on 8364kHz and 243MHz for about 72 hours. It is attached to the submarine by a 1000m length of braid line.

A submarine indicator buoy should not be confused with a sonobuoy, dropped by aircraft to detect submarines. A British sonobuoy is a thinner and longer cylinder, and although it has a whip aerial it does not have a light or the marking described above.

2.2.13 Mine countermeasures – exercises

Minelaying and mine countermeasures exercises are normally confined to certain areas, published in *Notices to Mariners* each year. Harmless practice mines which lie on the bottom and eject red, green or white flares may be used.

The lights shown by mineclearance vessels are in Rule 27(f) of the Collision Regulations. Minehunters show the lights prescribed for a vessel restricted in her ability to manoeuvre, and usually work with small craft from which divers may be operating, or may be controlling a wire guided submersible. Boats with divers exhibit Flag 'A' of the International Code. The mine hunter shows Flag 'A' by day when divers are operating, or signals the letter 'A' by flashing light at night if approached by other vessels. Yachts should keep well clear of such operations, which may extend 1000m (3300ft) from the minehunter.

Minesweeping and minehunting operations require the laying of small buoys, usually fitted with a radar reflector, which may have numeral or alphabetical flags attached. At night such buoys are illuminated with green, white or red flashing lights, which are visible for about 1.6km (1 mile).

2.2.14 Minefields

Most of the minefields laid during World War II have been swept, but in a few areas mines can still be a hazard – as may uncharted wrecks or shoals therein which have not been surveyed. Any drifting mine that is seen is likely to be a lost exercise mine, but it should be reported. Do not try to recover it or take it in tow.

2.2.15 Wrecks

Under the Protection of Wrecks Act, 1973, some wrecks are protected due to their historical or archaeological significance. It is prohibited to anchor in these areas, or to dive, or to tamper with any part of the wreck. Certain dangerous wrecks are also designated prohibited areas under the same Act. These sites are shown on charts and in

Sailing Directions, and are listed in a *Notice to Mariners,* published annually.

2.2.16 Offshore oil and gas fields

Where preliminary surveys show the possibility of oil or gas in commercial quantities, a drilling rig is used to drill test wells. These rigs are large structures, marked by lights and fog signals, and there may be lighters and other support vessels moored nearby, with mooring wires extending a mile from the rig itself. These rigs are moved from place to place and hence their positions are not charted, although they may be promulgated in *Temporary Notices to Mariners* or broadcast in Navigational Warnings from coast radio stations. Three main types of drilling rig are used:

(1) Jack-up rigs are towed into position, the steel legs are lowered to the sea bed, and the drilling platform is then jacked-up above sea level. They are used in shallower waters.
(2) Semi-submersible rigs float on submerged caissons, and some are self-propelled. They are used in depths up to about 300m (1000ft).
(3) Drillships are used in deeper waters, where mooring is impossible, and are kept precisely in position by electronic station-keeping gear which actuates a number of propellers round the vessels. By these means drillships can be used in depths of 2500m (8000ft) or more.

Several exploration wells may be drilled to establish the extent of a field. Those wells not required are sealed, while others are capped with pipes etc, projecting above the sea bed, and are marked on charts as 'Well' or 'Wellhead'.

When oil or gas is to be extracted from a field, a production platform is installed. These massive structures are shown on charts and in Sailing Directions, and are marked by lights and usually by fog signals. They may have mooring points for tankers, or mooring buoys and other dangers a mile or more away.

Permanent platforms are marked by lights flashing Morse 'U' every 15 seconds, while fog signals sound Morse 'U' every 30 seconds. Corners of the platform not marked by the main light are marked by red lights flashing Morse 'U'.

Under international law, safety zones of up to 500m (1690ft) are established round drilling rigs, production platforms and single point moorings (SPM). Yachts must not enter these zones except to save life, or on account of stress of weather or if in distress.

2.2.17 Submarine cables

Cables, sometimes carrying high voltage, are laid in coastal waters and are shown on charts. Damage to such cables can be very costly, and yachts should avoid anchoring near them. If a yacht fouls a cable, every effort should be made to clear it by normal means, but great care must be taken not to damage the cable. If necessary the anchor warp or chain should be buoyed and slipped, but in no circumstances should the cable be cut or damaged.

2.2.18 Overhead power cables

In various estuaries and rivers high-voltage overhead cables present a serious danger to craft passing underneath. Depending on the voltage concerned, a safety margin of at least 4m (13ft) should be allowed for the possible discharge of electric current to the mast of a yacht.

The elevation of cables (and similar obstructions) is shown on charts as the height above Mean High Water Springs (MHWS). Spurious radar echoes can be received, and can easily be misinterpreted, when passing under power cables.

2.2.19 Traffic separation schemes

Under Rule 10 of the *International Regulations for Preventing Collisions at Sea (1972),* it is a legal requirement to observe traffic separation schemes which have been adopted by the International Maritime Organization (IMO).

Separation schemes are essential for the safety of larger ships, and while they may at times be inconvenient for yachtsmen they must be accepted as another element of passage planning, and should be avoided where possible.

Separation schemes are marked on Admiralty charts but are liable to detailed amendment and should be kept up to date from *Notices to Mariners.* Those schemes currently in force around the British Isles are summarised in *The Macmillan & Silk Cut Nautical Almanac.*

Rule 10 is stated in full in 2.1 (International Regulations for Preventing Collisions at Sea). It should be clearly understood that the whole of Rule 10 is applicable to yachts.

Contrary to the impression gained by some people, traffic separation schemes and Rule 10 do not modify the Collision Regulations when two vessels meet or converge. If for example a vessel is proceeding under power down a traffic lane, and another vessel which is crossing that lane appears on a collision course on her starboard bow, then the vessel in the lane is obliged to keep clear – just as if she had been in mid-ocean. The crossing vessel, however, if less than 20m (65ft) in length or a sailing vessel, would in this case have infringed

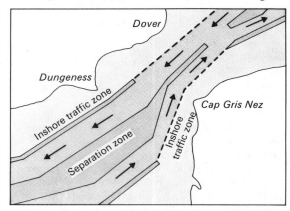

Fig. 2(9) Traffic separation scheme – Dover Strait.

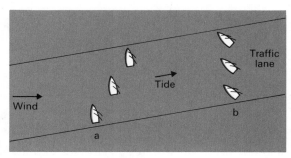

Fig. 2(10) When crossing a traffic lane, and considering the effects of wind and tide, (a) is the correct course – steering at right angles to the traffic lane, crossing as quickly as possible, and presenting a clear aspect to other lane users.

Rule 10(j). The term 'shall not impede' is explained in Rule 8(f) as taking early action to give sufficient sea room for the safe passage of the other vessel (by navigating so as to avoid the risk of collision). If however a situation develops so as to involve risk of collision, then the relevant Rules must be complied with.

Rule 8(f) is in three parts, and takes account of three phases of a developing situation. Phase 1 (para (i)) tells the vessel that is required 'not to impede' the safe passage of another vessel to take early action to allow sufficient sea room for the other vessel. Phase 2 (para (ii)) deals with the situation when risk of collision is involved, and states that the vessel required 'not to impede' still has this obligation even though she may be the stand-on vessel under other Rules, but that in taking action account must be taken of possible manoeuvres by the other vessel. The final phase (para (iii)) is reached when action or the lack of it under Phase 1 or 2 leads to a collision risk situation which requires the action of both vessels; here the Rules state that the vessel 'not to be impeded' must comply fully with the Rules.

A sailing yacht beating to windward must keep to the correct lane, so that she is proceeding 'in the general direction of traffic flow'. Even so she must not 'impede' the safe passage of a power-driven vessel following the lane. She must certainly not beat to windward in the wrong lane – against the traffic flow.

If there is much traffic it would be more prudent to motor to windward along the correct lane, rather than tack backwards and forwards with the risk of impeding some vessel. Alternatively it may be better still to use the inshore traffic zone, to which there is no objection provided that the yacht keeps well clear of the boundary of the adjacent lane.

Should it be necessary to cross a traffic lane, do so heading at as near right angles as possible regardless of tidal stream – thereby reducing the time crossing to the minimum and also presenting a clear aspect to lane users – who again must not be impeded. In a sailing yacht, if the wind falls light and speed drops much below three knots, the engine should be used if one is fitted.

It is accepted that, due to leeway and/or tidal stream, when maintaining a *heading* at right angles to the traffic flow a yacht's *track* (as seen for example on a shore radar set) may not be at right angles to the traffic flow, but no official action will result from any identification made if it is evident that the yacht made every effort to steer the required course.

In order to comply with traffic separation schemes, accurate navigation is important, so that a yacht knows exactly where she is in relation to traffic lanes etc.

Note that 'YG' in the *International Code* means 'You appear not to be complying with the traffic separation scheme'. There are heavy financial penalties for breaking the rules.

2.3 HM Customs

2.3.1 General information

From 1 January 1993 the European Union (EU) became a single market. EU yachtsmen can now enjoy unhindered movement for themselves and their boats within the EU, provided that all due taxes have been paid in some country within the Community. This has resulted in significant relaxations to the previous United Kingdom (UK) Customs procedures for yachts arriving directly from or departing for other EU countries.

There are similar relaxations in other EU countries, but varying in detail. There are also some changes to HM Customs procedures for yachts arriving from or departing for non-EU countries, although the general principles remain much as before. The regulations for the temporary importation (TI) of boats into EU countries have also been changed.

Details of the alterations in HM Customs procedures are given in new Customs Notice 8B. Copies of this and further advice can be obtained from Customs and Excise Offices (but not VAT offices) or from HM Customs and Excise, CD4B, First Floor West, New King's Beam House, 22 Upper Ground, London SE1 9PJ. Tel: 0171-865 4748.

The laws covered by Notice 8B are:
(1) the Pleasure Craft (Arrival and Report) Regulations, 1990, made under 35(4) and 42(1) of the Customs and Excise Management Act 1979 as amended, and
(2) the Commissioners' Directions made under sections 35(1) and 64(2) of that Act.

Notice 8B is not the law, but an interpretation of what the law says. It replaced Notices 8 and 8A, now cancelled. Yachtsmen who intend to take their boats foreign are advised to obtain a copy and to study it. 'Foreign' is defined as all countries outside the UK, including their territorial waters. The Channel Islands and the Republic of Ireland count as foreign, but not the Isle of Man.

Countries of the European Union are: Austria, Belgium, Denmark, Germany, Greece, Finland, France, the Irish Republic, Italy, Luxembourg, the Netherlands, Portugal, Spain (but not the Canary Islands), Sweden, the United Kingdom (but not the Channel Islands).

Even if you are only cruising to or from EU countries, Customs officers may ask where you are going or where you have arrived from; and they still have the right to board your boat to check for drugs, firearms, animals that may carry rabies, and for other prohibited or restricted goods (see 2.3.5).

Common offences against UK Customs law are:
(1) Failure to clear outwards, including late submission of forms (where clearance is required).
(2) Failure to fly flag 'Q' within territorial waters on arrival (where required).
(3) Failure to report correctly.

All the above could result in prosecution and a fine.

The following offences are dealt with more seriously:
(1) Failure to declare excess goods.
(2) Failure to declare prohibited or restricted goods.

Carrying prohibited drugs or firearms and not declaring them will certainly result in prosecution, loss of the vessel and all her equipment.

2.3.2 Departure from the United Kingdom

If you are proceeding only to other EU states, you do not need to tell HM Customs that you are leaving, unless asked. But if going directly to a country outside the EU (this includes the Channel Islands) you must follow this procedure:
(1) Obtain Form C1331, available at HM Customs offices, most yacht clubs and marinas. A separate form is required for each voyage to or from a non-EU country. For telephone numbers of UK Customs offices see Chapter 10 of the *Macmillan & Silk Cut Nautical Almanac*.
(2) Complete sections (i) and (ii) on part 1 of Form C1331.
(3) Before departure from UK deliver part 1 at the place of departure by handing it to a Customs officer, putting it in a Customs box, or taking it to the local Customs office.
(4) Retain part 2 onboard as evidence of your notification of departure.
(5) If you have on board anybody who does not have the right to live in the UK, you must inform the Immigration officer (normally the Customs officer) before you sail. This is not necessary if you are only going to the Channel Islands, Republic of Ireland or Isle of Man.

The form must be delivered as in (3) above before you expect to leave the UK. Failure to carry out the above procedure may result in prosecution and a fine.

Departure from the UK may be delayed up to 48 hours from the time stated on part 1 of Form C1331. After this a fresh copy of the form must be completed.

If the voyage is abandoned after part 1 of Form C1331 has been delivered, notify the departure office accordingly. Mark part 2 of the form 'Voyage Abandoned' and deliver it to the same office.

You may be able to ship duty-free stores if you are proceeding to a port south of Brest or north of the north bank of the Eider. You cannot take stores to the Republic of Ireland or to the Channel Islands. Application must be made in advance. Details of how to ship stores or to re-ship previously landed surplus duty-free stores can be obtained from Customs offices.

If you are shipping stores under bond, or on which you are claiming repayment of customs charges, they must be placed on board under Customs seal, and must not be used in UK waters without paying duty.

If you carry goods other than reasonable quantities of personal belongings and stores, your boat is no longer a pleasure craft and becomes a commercial vessel – see Customs notice 69.

2.3.3 Arrival from outside the EU

A yacht arriving directly from outside the EU must fly flag 'Q' on reaching the 12 mile limit of UK territorial waters. It must be clearly visible and suitably illuminated at night, and must not be lowered until all Customs formalities are complete. Failure may result in prosecution. On arrival contact a Customs officer, who will tell you what to do. You will need to complete sections (i) and (iii) on part 1 of Form C1331, which the Customs officer will provide if necessary. Retain the other part as your record. You may not land goods or persons, or transfer them to another vessel until a Customs officer says so.

You are required to declare:
(1) Any animals or birds on board (see 2.3.6).
(2) Any prohibited or restricted goods (see 2.3.5).
(3) Any duty-free ship's stores.
(4) Any goods that are to be left in the UK.
(5) Any tobacco goods, alcoholic drinks, perfumes and toilet waters in excess of current duty-free tourist allowances (see below).

Most goods are liable to VAT and some are also subject to duties, levies and import licensing controls. If anybody on board fails to declare such goods they may be confiscated and that person may have to pay a heavy fine.

For yachts returning via the Channel Islands, if it can be shown that goods were obtained duty and tax paid in another EU country, and provided they are for personal use, no further duty is payable.

Goods in excess of the published allowances may be:
(1) Released on payment of duty, or
(2) Placed under seal on board the vessel until they leave the UK, or

(3) Handed to the Customs officer for custody until either arrangements are made to re-export them, or duty is paid.

If goods are smuggled the boat may be seized and the person(s) concerned may have to pay a heavy fine or go to prison.

Any person who is not an EU national must have permission from the Immigration officer (normally the Customs officer) to enter the country if they arrive from outside:

(1) the UK
(2) the Isle of Man
(3) the Republic of Ireland, or
(4) the Channel Islands.

It is the skipper's responsibility to make sure that this is complied with. If anybody on board requires immigration clearance the appropriate Immigration Form must be completed.

Duty-free allowances

The current (1994) Customs allowances for goods obtained anywhere outside the EU are as follows:
Cigarettes: 200, or Cigarillos: 100, or Cigars: 50, or Tobacco: 250g.
Still table wine: 2 litres
Spirits, strong liqueurs over 22% volume: 1 litre, or Fortified or sparkling wine, other liqueurs: 2 litres, or Additional still table wine: 2 litres
Perfume: 60cc/ml
Toilet water: 250cc/ml
All other goods including gifts and souvenirs: £136 worth

Note that anybody under the age of 17 is not entitled to tobacco or drinks allowances.

VAT on boats

Vessels under 12m in length arriving in the EU are liable to Customs duty. All vessels designed or adapted for recreation or pleasure use are liable to VAT.

However, these charges are not payable if temporary importation (TI) is granted. See 2.3.7. The vessel must only be used by the owner or another visitor to the EU who is so authorised, and she must not be lent, hired or sold in the EU.

Relief is also given for an owner moving home to the UK. For further details see Customs Notice 8B.

2.3.4 Arrival from another EU country

When arriving in UK waters direct from another EU country (note that this does not include the Channel Islands), there is no need to hoist flag 'Q'. In the normal course of events there may be no need to report to HM Customs, but you must do so if any of the following apply:

(1) If there are any animals or birds on board. The licensing requirements are the same as for a boat arriving from outside the EU. See 2.3.6.
(2) If you have any prohibited or restricted goods on board. See 2.3.5.
(3) If you have any non-EU nationals on board.

Provided they are for your own personal use, there is no further tax to pay on goods which you have obtained in the European Union. Personal use includes gifts, but if you are receiving any payment in return for buying alcohol and tobacco the transaction is dutiable and must be declared accordingly. EU law sets out the guide levels as below, and if you bring in more than the amounts shown you must be able to establish that the goods are for your own personal use:

Cigarettes: 800. Cigarillos: 400. Cigars: 200. Smoking tobacco: 1kg. Spirits: 10 litres. Intermediate products, such as port and sherry: 20 litres. Wine: 90 litres (of which not more than 60 litres may be sparkling). Beer: 110 litres.

For other goods from EU duty free shops the allowance is £71.

HM Customs will continue to check for drugs, firearms, animals and other prohibited goods being brought into the country, and the penalties for infringement remain severe.

2.3.5 Prohibited or restricted goods

Wherever you arrive from you must declare any prohibited or restricted goods. Prohibited goods are completely banned. Restricted goods may only be imported under certain conditions, e.g. possession of a licence. Customs Notice 9 gives details of these, but they include the following:

(1) Controlled drugs such as heroin, morphine, opium, cocaine, cannabis, amphetamines (including benzedrine), and lysergide (LSD).
(2) Firearms of all types including gas pistols, stun guns and electric shock batons, ammunition and explosives, including fireworks.
(3) Indecent or obscene videos, films, books, magazines and other articles.
(4) Animals and birds whether alive or dead (stuffed), and items derived from rare species, including fur skins, ivory and reptile skin products. See also 2.3.6.
(5) Radio transmitters (walkie talkies, CB radios etc) not approved for use in the UK.
(6) Counterfeit goods.
(7) Flick knives and other offensive weapons, including some martial arts weapons.
(8) Meat and poultry, and their derivatives which are not fully cooked.
(9) Plants, parts of plants and plant produce, including trees and shrubs, potatoes and certain other vegetables, fruit bulbs and seeds.

2.3.6 Animals and birds

Animals and birds (including domestic pets) are subject to strict control. You must tell the Customs at the port of arrival, and have a 'British import licence (rabies)', issued in advance by the Ministry of Agriculture, Fisheries and Food or by the Scottish Office of Agriculture and Fisheries, to allow the import of any animal or bird at certain designated ports before they enter quarantine. Animals or birds brought to the UK without a licence must be kept enclosed, below deck, and not allowed to come into contact with any other animals. Contravention may result in a heavy fine and imprisonment.

2.3.7 VAT and the Single Market

From 1 January 1993 an EU resident has been able to move a yacht on which VAT has been paid between EU countries without restriction. But because Customs authorities in different states are still establishing the VAT status of yachts moored therein, it is necessary to carry proof that tax has been paid.

If the original VAT receipt for the boat is not held, it is possible, after providing evidence of a boat's tax paid status, to obtain a Form C88 (EU Single Administrative Document, or SAD) from HM Customs. Such evidence could comprise the boat's Part 1 registration documents, insurance policy, builder's certificate, records of surveys or repairs, berthing records, or correspondence with previous owners etc. EU Customs officials may require proof that the boat is the one referred to on the SAD, which can be supported by including hull numbers, work's number etc. or other physical identification when applying for the SAD.

HM Customs have indicated that they will consider to be VAT paid, any UK owned vessel for which it can be demonstrated that she was built before 31 December 1984 and was in EU waters at midnight on 31 December 1992.

From 1 January 1993, any EU national purchasing a new boat for use in EU waters is required to pay VAT on the purchase price as follows:
(1) For boats up to 7.5m in length: VAT is payable in the country of origin – where the boat is purchased.
(2) For boats longer than 7.5m: VAT is payable in the country of destination or use, and the owner is required to account for VAT in that country. It should be noted that VAT rates vary from country to country, with a minimum standard rate of 15%. Note however that some EU states are more likely to agree modest valuations than in the UK.

An EU national purchasing a boat in the EU, but planning to keep her permanently outside the EU, can still buy the boat as a VAT free export, as for example under the UK Sailaway Boat Scheme.

A boat will always be liable to VAT (and possibly to Customs duty) if she is purchased by an EU resident outside the EU and imported into the EU – even if VAT has already been paid on the boat, or is she was first used before 1 January 1985, or if the tax due is 'insignificant'. This is a different situation to the re-importation by an EU resident of a boat which that person owned when she was last exported from the EU, when relief can be claimed if the facts can be proved.

From the foregoing it is very necessary to carry onboard the following when visiting other EU states: preferably a VAT receipt or SAD (above); or failing that evidence of the boat's location on 31 December 1992, evidence of age if built before 31 December 1984, plus bill of sale where relevant, and registration certificate.

Care needs to be taken with the purchase of a boat which is under temporary importation (TI), where the rules may be interpreted differently in different EU states.

The Channel Islands, not being within the EU, are subject to changed conditions. Individual Channel Islands residents are allowed TI into the EU, including the UK, under the same rules as apply to other non-EU nationals, described below.

Useful information is given in *Pleasure Craft and the Single Market* (Yacht Leaflet 1993), available from HM Customs and Excise.

Temporary importation (TI)

EU residents are no longer able to keep VAT-free boats under temporary importation (TI) in other EU countries. A visitor to the EU does not have to pay customs charges on a boat provided:
(1) He normally (i.e. at least for 185 days in any 12 months) lives outside the EU.
(2) The boat is exported when he next leaves the EU, or when it has been in the EU for a total of six months in any 12 month period, whichever comes first. The period of TI cannot be extended by moving the boat to another EU member state.
(3) The boat is used only by the owner or another visitor to the EU authorised by the owner.
(4) The boat is not lent, hired or sold in the EU.
(5) The boat, if registered, is registered outside the EU (or in the Channel Islands).
(6) The owner (normally as shown by the registration document) is a person or company established outside the EU (or in the Channel Islands).

Let HM Customs know if the boat cannot be exported when the owner leaves the EU, or if it is wished to keep the boat in the EU for more than six months. Infringement of these regulations may result in confiscation of the vessel. Spares and accessories may be imported free of duty and VAT by arrangement with HM Customs.

2.3.8 Liaison with HM Customs

Yachtmen are encouraged to work with HM Customs in their efforts to combat the drug trade. It is not suggested that owners and crews should act as law enforcement officers, but they may on occasion be able to help with information about drug smuggling and other serious customs offences. All information received by HM Customs will be treated in strict confidence.

Be aware of suspicious activities and notify HM Customs as quickly as possible about:
(1) Suspicious vessels.
(2) Crews acting in an unusual manner.
(3) Unusual activities in remote places.
(4) Small boats approaching larger vessels or fishing vessels.
(5) Suspect packages on the beach, at sea, or in port areas.

Contact can be made ashore by dialling 0800 59 5000 Customs Freefone Drugs, or by contacting the local Customs Office (whether at home or abroad). At sea it is bet to record details and report to Customs on arrival. It may be unwise to use radio communication because it is not secure.

An owner should take all practical steps to make his vessel secure, particularly when unattended or abroad, so that items cannot be put aboard without his knowledge. HM Customs launches and staff on patrol duty will investigate suspicious activities or circumstances in and around moored vessels, and where practicable they will correct minor problems for the owner or report to the appropriate authority. This work can be minimised if owners act responsibly, and follow the required procedures for arrival and departure.

2.3.9 Light dues

Yachts of 20 tons and over are liable to an annual payment for light dues (see 2.7.4). Customs officers may check that such payment has been made when visiting a vessel. The tonnage limit is determined by register tonnage for a registered vessel, or by Thames measurement if unregistered. Details of the current charges can be obtained from local Customs offices.

2.4 Regulations in European Countries

2.4.1 General

Before cruising to any foreign country it is necessary to be aware of the various formalities required, which are likely to include the items listed below. Brief notes on countries in Europe are given below. More detailed information can be obtained from the RYA booklet C1 and C2 (*Planning a Foreign Cruise* Vols 1 and 2) or from the London tourist office of the country concerned.

On 1 January 1993 fiscal frontiers and border controls between EU member states came to an end, together with the temporary importation of boats from one EU country to another. A boat owned by an EU resident can now be moved freely within the EU provided VAT has been paid. It is no longer possible for an EU resident to buy a boat and keep her anywhere in the EU without paying tax, either at the point of sale or in the country of destination depending on circumstances. Zero-rated sales to non-EU countries are not affected.

As stated in 2.3.7, boats owned by non-EU residents may be temporarily imported into the EU tax free for six months, which may be extended for laying up or for repairs.

There are of course various other matters, as listed below, which have to be taken into account when cruising abroad. In the event of problems in a foreign country help can be received from the nearest British Consul, but the assistance he can give is limited. Where necessary he can issue an emergency passport, advise on the transfer of funds, help in the event of death or accident, advise on organisations which can trace missing persons, or assist with repatriation to the UK.

(1) It is essential to conform to British Customs requirements, as stated in 2.3.

(2) The yacht must carry a registration document – either a Certificate of Registry under Part I of the Merchant Shipping Act (see 1.5.1), or under Part III (Small Ships Register) as described in 1.5.2.

(3) The yacht should in any case be insured, but some countries insist on third party cover. It may be necessary to extend the normal cruising limits.

(4) Increasingly, European countries are requiring certificates of competence – either for all boats (as in Portugal, Spain and Greece), or for larger and faster craft, and/or for inland waterways. It is therefore becoming ever more advisable for yachtsmen to obtain the appropriate RYA Yachtmaster certificates as described in 1.2.5, if they intend to cruise European waters. In the meantime a visiting owner, or skipper should at least hold an International Certificate of Competence (see 1.5.5).

(5) Take passports for all the crew, plus any visas or special vaccination certificates that may be needed. It is necessary to comply with health and immigration regulations – reporting any infectious disease, for example. Consideration should be given to health insurance. Reciprocal National Health cover is given in EU countries by EU Form E111.

(6) Customs formalities vary in different countries, and it is the skipper's responsibility to find out what they are and to conform. In most countries outside the EU it is obligatory to fly Flag 'Q' on arrival, particularly if carrying more dutiable stores than the normal 'tourist' allowance, and if in doubt this is the safest procedure. Possibly the customs officer will visit the yacht, but more probably the skipper will need to go to the Customs office on arrival, and produce documents such as the certificate of registry and the passports of the crew. It is useful to carry duplicated lists showing the names of the persons on board and their passport numbers.

In general terms all EU countries have relaxed their Customs procedures for yachts moving within the EU in a similar way to the changes in HM Customs requirements previously mentioned in 2.3.1. But for other countries, in the absence of specific information to the contrary it is necessary to report on arrival, and always if there are any exceptional goods or stores to be declared. Changes in procedures can be expected for countries joining the EU.

Further information should be available from the authorities stated for individual countries.

In some countries it is a requirement to clear Customs outwards, on final departure.

(7) A British-owned yacht should wear the Red Ensign (or a special ensign, if eligible – see 6.8.2, although blue ensigns are liable to be misunderstood) in foreign waters, and also a courtesy ensign for the country concerned. Flag 'Q' must be carried in order to comply with Customs formalities.

(8) Many countries have strict rules about foreign yachts being used for any form of commercial activity, such as charter without special permission.

(9) It is necessary to conform to any local regulations concerning radiotelephone transmissions in foreign harbours. The Ship Radio Licence must be on board, together with the operator's Certificate of Competence.

(10) All countries now have regulations about putting any form of waste over the side, and require gash to be deposited only in special dumps ashore. See 19.6.1 and 19.6.3.

(11) It is necessary to consider matters such as galley fuel, since Continental gas cylinders are different from those generally used in Britain, see 14.1.13.

2.4.2 Belgium

Telephone code from UK: 00 32. Craft from non-EU countries must fly flag 'Q' at port of entry. The yacht may be boarded by Customs officers and/or Immigration officers. Seagoing craft must have basic safety equipment, and have their name and home port marked on the stern. There are special formalities for yachts staying more than two months. No restrictions on crew changes. On inland waters boats are required to fly the 'drapeau de navigation', a red flag with a white rectangular centre. The motor sailing cone is enforced. RYA Coastal Skipper Certificate required for navigating the Schelde estuary.

Belgian Tourist Office, Premier House, 2 Gayton Road, Harrow, Middlesex HA1 2XU. Tel: 0181-861 3300. Fax: 0181-427 6760.

2.4.3 Denmark

Telephone code from UK: 00 45. Yachts from an EU or Scandinavian country not carrying stores in excess of normal allowances need not report to Customs on arrival, but others must do so. Excess dutiable stores must be declared, and will be put under seal. No restrictions on crew changes. Danish authorities insist on one lifejacket per crew member.

Danish Tourist Board, Sceptre House, 169-173 Regent Street, London W1R 8PY. Tel: 0171-734 2637. Fax: 0171-494 2170.

2.4.4 Finland

Telephone code from UK: 00 358. There is strict control over routes to harbours for Customs and passport control (call on VHF Ch 74), for which the main harbours are: Mariehamn, Kemi, Oulu, Vaasa, Naantali, Turku, Hanko, Helsinki and Hamina. Many areas are prohibited to foreign yachts. Government vessels may stop and search yachts ('L' in International Code), and actively enforce various regulations. Any excess alcohol or tobacco over the normal 'tourist' allowance must be declared on entry. Wines and spirits can only be bought from state liquor stores.

Finnish Tourist Board UK Office, 66 Haymarket, London SW1Y 4RF. Tel: 0171-839 4048. Fax: 0171-321 0696.

2.4.5 France

Telephone code from UK: 00 33. British yachts must be registered, either under Part I or on Small Ships Register. No Certificate of Competence needed (unless required in the country of origin), but charterers of French motor boats under 15m must have a certificate – the International Certificate of Competence is accepted together with a copy of the Code Européen de Voies de la Navigation Intérieur (CEVNI). More stringent rules apply to vessels over 15m. British yachts may now be lent or chartered without restriction provided any income is declared to French revenue and the boat has been 'acquired or imported in accordance with general conditions of taxation in the domestic market of a Member State'.

It is not necessary to fly flag 'Q', or to clear Customs on entry, if the purpose of the visit is legitimate and no goods are carried which should be declared, and no notifiable illness onboard.

French Tourist Office, 178 Piccadilly, London W1V 0AL. Tel: 0171-499 6911.

2.4.6 Germany

Telephone code from UK: 00 49. It is not necessary to fly flag 'Q' if coming from an EU or Scandinavian country. Clear (if necessary) Customs at Borkum, Norderney, Norddeich, Wilhelmshaven, Kiel, Travemunde, Bremerhaven or Cuxhaven (not Helgoland). If only intending to transit Kiel Canal (for which special rules apply, obtainable at locks) it is not necessary to clear Customs, but fly Third Substitute. A Certificate of Competence is required for the inland waterways and the Rhine Police Regulations must be carried on the Rhine. The motor sailing cone is strongly enforced in German waters. No restrictions on crew changes.

German National Tourist Office, Nightingale House, 65 Curzon Street, London W1. Tel: 0171-495 3990.

Lights for Motor Yachts

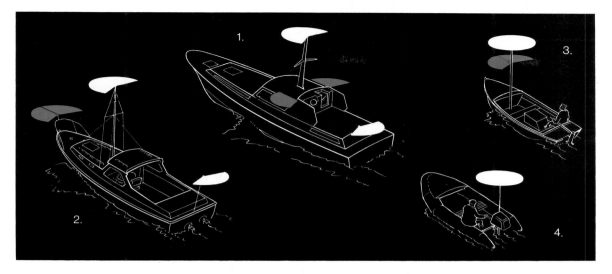

Requirements depend on the length of the boat. The white masthead light shows over an arc $112\frac{1}{2}°$ on either bow; sidelights (red to port, green to starboard) each show from ahead to $22\frac{1}{2}°$ abaft the beam; the white sternlight shows $67\frac{1}{2}°$ either side.

1. 12–20 metres overall. A combined lantern may be used for sidelights in boats under 20m, but individual sidelights are preferable. Visibility: masthead light – 3 miles; sidelights and sternlight – 2 miles.

2. Under 12 metres overall. Masthead light must be at least one metre above sidelights (or combined lantern, as shown). Visibility: masthead light and sternlight (which may be combined in one all-round light) – 2 miles; sidelights – 1 mile

3 and 4. Boats under 7m overall length, and with a maximum speed of 7 knots, need only carry a white all round light visible for two miles. If practicable they should also carry sidelights.

Lights for Sailing Yachts

Vessels under sail (only) carry sidelights and sternlight, but no white masthead light. In boats under 20m the sidelights and sternlight may be combined in one lantern at the masthead, with the red and green sidelights

visible 2 miles, and the white sternlight 2 miles. An all-round red light over an all-round green light may also be shown at or near the masthead, but not in conjunction with the combined tricolour lantern described above.

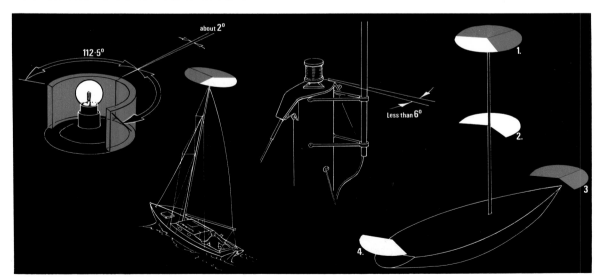

For yachts under 12m, sidelights must be visible 1 mile. To show over the correct arcs a combined lantern must be well engineered. A 25 watt bulb should be fitted to allow for voltage drop in the wiring. A combined lantern must not be shrouded by any other fitting over an arc of more than 6°

Four separate lanterns meet all requirements for a sailing yacht under 12m. Lantern 1 is used under sail, with minimum battery drain, and lanterns 3 and 4 together provide a stand-by should 1 fail. Lanterns 2, 3 and 4 together are shown when under power. 1, 2 and 4 can be combined in a dual-switched lantern at the masthead.

A power-driven vessel over 50m must carry a second masthead light aft, and higher than the forward one.

If under 50m, a vessel under power need show only one masthead light. If under 12m, the masthead light may be combined with sternlight.

A sailing boat, when motoring (even with sails set), is a power-driven vessel and must conform accordingly.

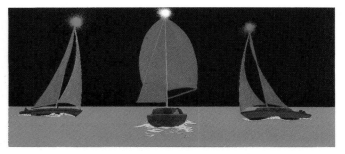

Sidelights of sailing yachts, when mounted low down as on the pulpit, may be obscured in a seaway.

The optional arrangement of a combined masthead lantern for sailing boat under 20m gives better visibility, as well as conserving the battery.

A small boat under oars need only show a white light, in time to prevent collision.

A tug and her tow. The tug shows a yellow towing light above her sternlight, and also shows a second masthead light forward. If the length of tow exceeds 200m the tug shows three masthead lights forward, arranged vertically, and both tug and tow show a diamond shape by day.

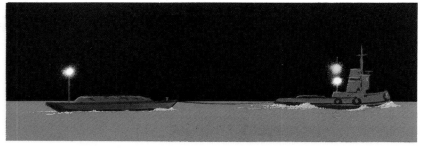

The tug (left) and tow from ahead. From this aspect the second masthead light of the tug could be confused with the aft masthead light of a ship more than 50m in length.

A vessel trawling, which should be given a wide berth. By day all vessels engaged in fishing show two cones, arranged vertically, point to point: or, if less than 20m, they exhibit a basket.

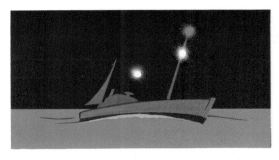

A vessel fishing (not trawling) and not making way (or she would show sidelights and sternlight). Gear extending more than 150m is shown by the all-round white light in that direction.

Fishing vessels often work together in a fleet, and it is best to take substantial avoiding action accordingly.

Vessels engaged in pair trawling may exhibit a searchlight directed forward and in the direction of the other vessel of the pair.

A vessel with restricted ability to manoeuvre. Masthead light and sidelights indicate she is making way through the water.

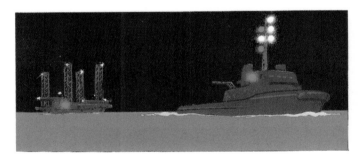

A tug (right) and tow, with restricted ability to manoeuvre. The three masthead lights of the tug indicate that the tow is more than 200m.

A dredger shows two vertical red lights (balls by day) on her foul side, and two vertical green lights (diamonds by day) on her clear side.

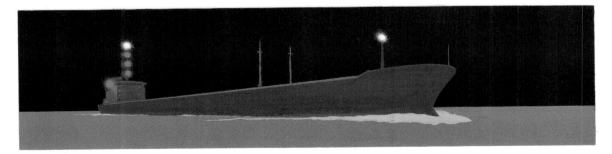

A vessel constrained by her draught shows three red lights vertically (or by day a cylinder) where best seen.

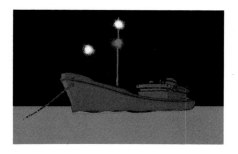

A vessel engaged in pilotage duties, at anchor.

Vessels over 100m in length are required to show their deck lights when at anchor, and these may obscure other lights which are less bright.

Great care is often needed to differentiate between navigation lights of nearby vessels and lights ashore.

A vessel not under command shows two balls (or by night, two red lights) in a vertical line.

By day a vessel aground shows three balls in a vertical line, by night she shows her normal anchor light(s) plus two red lights vertically.

A minesweeper, with gear streamed, shows (in addition to the lights for a power-driven vessel) three green lights, or by day three balls, one at the foremast head and one at each yardarm.

Small vessels engaged in diving operations are required to exhibit a rigid replica of International Code flag 'A', not less than 1 metre in height. Such craft should be given a wide berth.

IALA Buoyage (Region A)

Lateral marks

Used generally to mark the sides of well defined navigable channels.

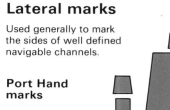

Port Hand marks

Light:
Colour – red
Rhythm – any

Navigable channel

Direction of buoyage

Starboard Hand marks

Light:
Colour – green
Rhythm – any

Cardinal marks

Used to indicate the direction from the mark in which the best navigable water lies, or to draw attention to a bend, junction or fork in a channel, or to mark the end of a shoal.

Lights: Always white

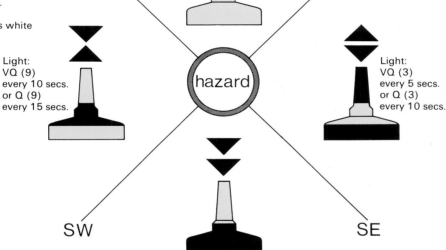

NW

NE

Light: VQ or Q

Light:
VQ (9)
every 10 secs.
or Q (9)
every 15 secs.

hazard

Light:
VQ (3)
every 5 secs.
or Q (3)
every 10 secs.

SW

SE

Light: VQ (6) + LFl every 10 secs. or Q (6) + LFl every 15 secs.

Other marks

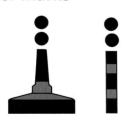

Isolated danger marks

Use: To mark a small isolated danger with navigable water all round.
Light: Colour – white
Rhythm – group flashing (2)

Safe water marks

Use: Mid-channel or landfall
Light: Colour – white
Rhythm – Isophase, occulting,
1 long flash every 10 seconds, or
Morse A.

Special marks

Shape: Not conflicting with lateral or safe water marks
Light: Colour — yellow
Rhythm – different from other white lights used on buoys.

Coastal Navigation - Admiralty Metric Chart Symbols See also Chapter 3 (3.2.7)

A selection of the more common symbols from Admiralty Publication 5011

Reproduced by kind permission of H.M. Stationery Office and the Hydrographer of the Navy

THE COASTLINE	ARTIFICIAL FEATURES	RADIO AND RADAR
Coastline, surveyed	Sea wall	Non-directional radiobeacon — RC
Coast imperfectly known or shoreline unsurveyed	Breakwater	Directional radiobeacon — RD, RD 269°30'
Steep coast, Cliffs	Groyne (always dry) / Groyne (intertidal)	Rotating pattern radiobeacon — RW
Sandy shore		Radio direction-finding station — RG
Low Water Line	Patent slip	Radio/TV mast, Radio/TV tower
Foreshore, Mud	Lock	Dish aerial
Foreshore, Sand	Hulk	Coast radio station providing QTG service — R
Foreshore, Boulders, Stones, Gravel and Shingle	Steps, Landing stairs	Coast radar station — Ra
Foreshore, Rock	Overhead cable, Telephone line, Telegraph line with vertical clearance	Radar transponder beacon — Racon
Foreshore, Sand and Mud	Discharge pipe, water, sewer, outfall	Radar reflector (not usually charted on IALA System buoys)
Limiting danger line	Fixed bridge with vertical clearance	Radar-conspicuous feature
Breakers along a shore	Opening bridge with vertical clearance / Ferry	Aeronautical radiobeacon — Aero RC
Half-tide channel (on intertidal ground)	Training wall	Floating marks with Racons

Coastal Navigation - Admiralty Metric Chart Symbols See also Chapter 3 (3.2.7)

A selection of the more common symbols from Admiralty Publication 5011

Reproduced by kind permission of H.M. Stationery Office and the Hydrographer of the Navy

DANGERS	DANGERS	LIMITS

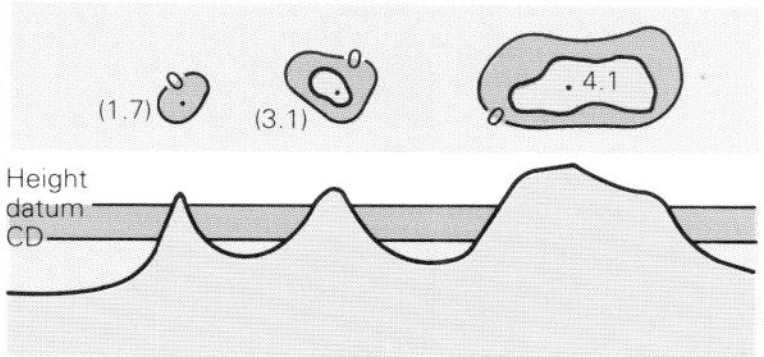

DANGERS (column 1)

(1.7)   (3.1)   · 4.1

Height datum CD

Rock which does not cover, height above High Water

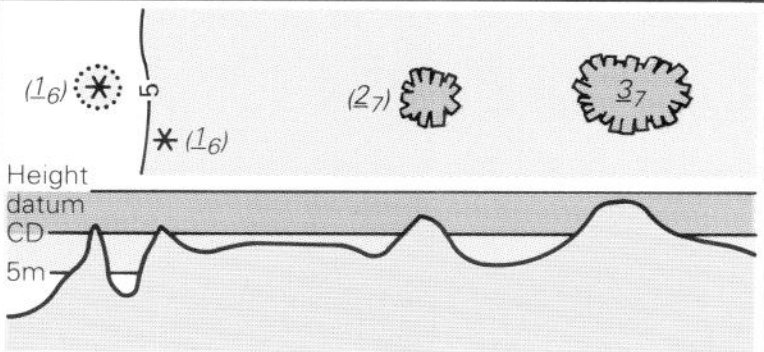

(1₆)   ✳ (1₆)   (2₇)   3₇

Height datum CD 5m

Rock which covers and uncovers, height above Chart Datum

✳

Rock awash at the level of Chart Datum

⊕ R   +   ⊕   + +

A rock or rock ledge over which the exact depth is unknown but which is considered to be dangerous to surface navigation

10₇ R   16₅ R

Shoal sounding on isolated rock

35 R

Submerged rock not dangerous to surface navigation

6₄ Wk   11₂ Wk

Wreck which has been swept by wire to the depth shown

Wk

Large scale charts

Wreck showing any part of hull or superstructure at the level of Chart Datum

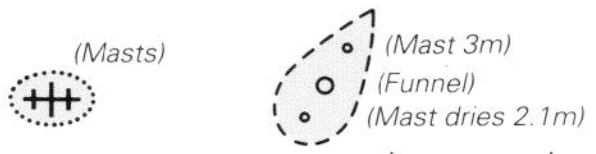

(Masts)   (Mast 3m) (Funnel) (Mast dries 2.1m)

Large scale charts

Wreck of which the mast(s) only are visible

⊞   ⊞

Wrecks, depths unknown. On left considered dangerous to surface navigation, and on right not considered dangerous

DANGERS (column 2)

7₃ Wk   20 Wk

Wreck over which the depth has been obtained by sounding, but not by wire sweep

20 Wk

Wreck over which the exact depth is unknown, but which is considered to have a safe clearance at the depth shown

Foul   Foul   Foul
#

The remains of a wreck, or other foul area no longer dangerous to surface navigation, but to be avoided by vessels anchoring, trawling, etc.

4₆ Obstn   16₈ Obstn

Obstruction, depth known

4₆ Obstn   16₈ Obstn

Obstruction which has been swept by wire to the depth shown

Overfalls, tide rips, races

Eddies

Kelp

19
5₈
18   Br

Breakers

(2₄)   2₄

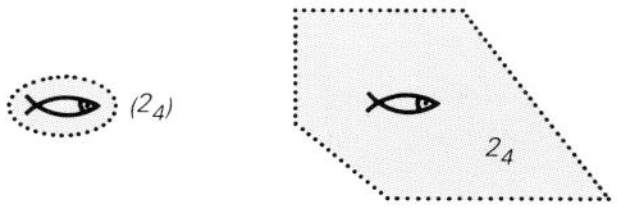

Fish haven, depth known

LIMITS (column 3)

2 Bns ≠ 270°30'

Leading line (the firm line is the track to be followed)

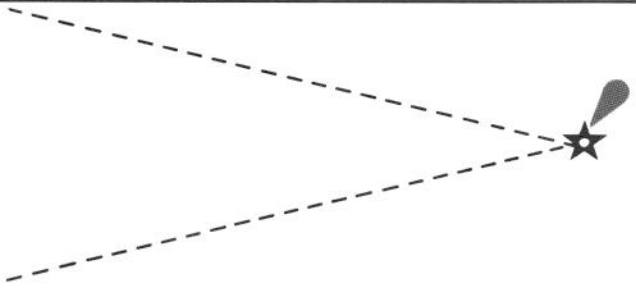

★

Limit of sector

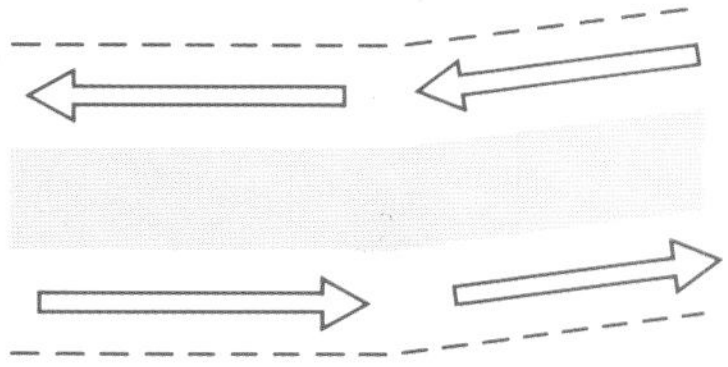

Traffic separation scheme: one-way traffic lanes (separated by zone)

∿∿∿∿∿

Submarine cable (telegraph & telephone)

∿∿∿∿∿

Submarine cable (power)

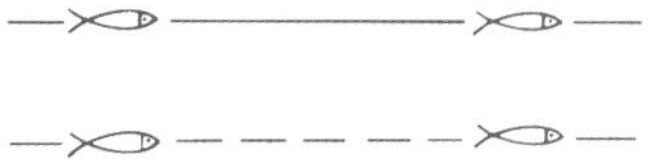

Limits of national fishing zones

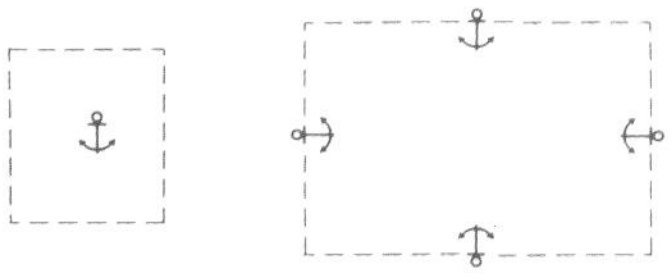

⚓   ⚓

Anchorage area in general. Type of anchorage may be specified, e.g. by number or name, DW (deep water), tanker, 24h (for periods up to 24 hours), small craft etc.

Anchoring prohibited

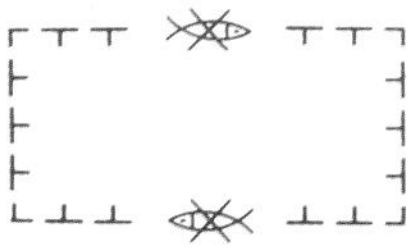

Fishing prohibited

International Port Traffic Signals

No	Lights		Main message
1	⬤⬤⬤	Flashing	Serious emergency – all vessels to stop or divert according to instructions
2	⬤⬤⬤		Vessels shall not proceed (*Note*: Some ports may use an exemption signal, as in 2a below)
3	⬤⬤⬤	Fixed or Slow Occulting	Vessels may proceed. One way traffic
4	⬤⬤◯		Vessels may proceed. Two way traffic
5	⬤◯⬤		A vessel may proceed only when she has received specific orders to do so (*Note*: Some ports may use an exemption signal, as in 5a below)
	Exemption signals and messages		
2a	◯⬤ ⬤⬤	Fixed or Slow Occulting	Vessels shall not proceed, except that vessels which navigate outside the main channel need not comply with the main message
5a	◯⬤ ◯⬤		A vessel may proceed only when she has received specific orders to do so, except that vessels which navigate outside the main channel need not comply with the main message
	Auxiliary signals and messages		
	White and/or yellow lights, displayed to the right of the main lights		Local meanings, as promulgated in local port orders

This new system is gradually being introduced, but its general adoption is likely to take many years.

Notes on use:

(1) The main movement message given by a port traffic signal shall always comprise three lights, disposed vertically. No additional light shall be added to the column carrying the main message. (The fact that the main message always consists of three vertical lights allows the mariner to recognise it as a traffic signal, and not lights of navigational significance). The signals may also be used to control traffic at locks and bridges.

(2) Red lights indicate 'Do not proceed'.

(3) Green lights indicate 'Proceed, subject to the conditions stipulated'.
    (For examples, see opposite).
  Note that, to avoid confusion, red and green lights are never displayed together.

(4) A single yellow light, displayed to the left of the column carrying main messages Nos 2 or 5, at the level of the upper light, may be used to indicate that 'Vessels which can safely navigate outside the main channel need not comply with the main message'. This signal is of obvious significance to yachtsmen.

(5) Signals which are auxiliary to the main message may be devised by local authorities. Such auxiliary signals should employ only white and/or yellow lights, and should be displayed to the right of the column carrying the main message. Ports with complex entrances and much traffic may need many auxiliary signals, which will have to be documented; but smaller harbours with less traffic may only need one or two of the basic signals, such as 'Vessels shall not proceed' and 'Vessels may proceed, two way traffic'.
  Some signals may be omni-directional – exhibited to all vessels simultaneously: others must be directional, and be shown either to vessels entering or to vessels leaving harbour.
  Signal No 5 is based on the assumption that some other means of communication such as VHF radio, signal lamp, loud hailer, or auxiliary signal will be used to inform a vessel that she may specifically proceed.
  The 'Serious Emergency' signal must be flashing, at least 60 flashes per minute. All other signals must be either fixed or slow occulting (the latter useful when background glare is a problem). A mixture of fixed and occulting lights must not be used.

2.4.7 Greece

Telephone code from UK: 00 30. On arrival fly flag 'Q' and enter at one of the 50 or so recognised ports of entry where there are customs, immigration and health authorities. The requirement to obtain a Transit Log has been discontinued except for fuel. Registration is required and the skipper must have an International Certificate of Competence, or the equivalent. It is necessary to wear a Greek courtesy ensign. Proof of VAT payment should be carried. If transiting Corinth Canal it is advisable to have proof of net tonnage (e.g. Part I Registry).

National Tourist Organisation of Greece, 4 Conduit Street, London, W1R 0DJ. Tel: 0171-499 9758.

2.4.8 Irish Republic

Telephone code from UK: 00 353. Yachts from non-EU countries (whether or not with dutiable stores) must fly flag 'Q' by day or show a red light over a white light by night, and report to local Customs (or Civic Guard, where no Customs officer is stationed). Further details from the Revenue Commissioners, Dublin Castle, Dublin 2. No passports are required by UK citizens.

Bord Failte Eireann (Irish Tourist Board), Ireland House, 150 New Bond Street, London W1Y 0AQ. Tel: 0171-493 3201. Fax: 0171-493 9065.

2.4.9 Italy

Telephone code from UK: 00 39. On arrival it is necessary to obtain a *Constituto* (yacht passport and carnet) from the Port Office. This requires production of ship's papers, passports of the crew together with a nominal list of the crew giving date and place of birth, passport number and nationality. Also required is a certificate of insurance with an Italian translation, and showing that the insurance company has reciprocal arrangements for third party liabilities with an Italian company.

The *Constituto* is valid for 12 months and has to be shown at subsequent ports, and surrendered on final departure. A *tassa di stazionamento* (sojourn tax) has to be pre-paid by visiting yachts; this is on a daily rate, and is reduced if pre-paid for two, four or twelve months. The tax is based on tonnage.

Foreign yachts must not be chartered. Crew changes should be recorded on the *Constituto*.

Italian State Tourist Office, 1 Princes Street, London W1R 8AY. Tel: 0171-408 1254. Fax: 0171-493 6695.

2.4.10 Netherlands

Telephone code from UK: 00 31. Ports of entry are Breskens, Terneuzen, Vlissingen, Schiedam, Rotterdam, Ijmuiden, Den Helder, West Terschelling, Harlingen, Lauwersoog and Delfzijl. In summer only: Roompotsluis, Oudeschild and Vlieland. On arrival non-EU yachts report to Customs with documentation and passports to obtain a *Verklaring* (entry certificate), which must be retained for inspection at other places. Fly flag 'Q' if dutiable goods are carried.

Yachts must carry and obey the *Binnenvaart Politie Reglement* (collision regulations etc), and also (where applicable) the special regulations which apply to the Rivers Rhine, Lek and Waal. For boats over 15m, or capable of more than 10 knots, a Certificate of Competence recognised by Dutch authorities is required. For the Schelde, IJsselmeer or Waddensee this must be the RYA Coastal Skipper Certificate.

Handheld VHF radios must be correctly licensed, and yachts with VHF radios must keep watch on the required VTS frequencies.

Yachts with Very pistols require a firearms certificate, and must be declared on entry. No restrictions on crew changes, but the boat must not be chartered while in Dutch waters.

Netherlands Tourist Office, 25–28 Buckingham Gate, London SW1E 6LD. Tel: 0171-630 0451. Fax: 0171-828 7941.

2.4.11 Norway

Telephone code from UK: 00 47. On arrival report to the customs (Toll) at one of the larger harbours such as Stromstad, Tonsberg, Oslo, Kristiansand, Mandal, Stavanger, Bergen or Alesund. The yacht must be registered, and must not be used for commercial purposes. The Norwegian flag should be flown as courtesy ensign. Excess liquor and tobacco is likely to be heavily taxed. In Norway wines and spirits are only available from state liquor shops, and it is an offence to sell or give liquor to a local. It is important to clear Customs outwards on departure. There are no restrictions on crew changes.

Norwegian Tourist Board, Charles House 5–11 Lower Regent Street, London SW1Y 4LR. Tel: 0171-839 6255. Fax: 0171-839 6014.

2.4.12 Portugal

Telephone code from UK: 00 351. Yachts from non-EU countries report to Customs and Immigration offices with documentation of the yacht and passports of the crew. Vessels must be registered and it is useful to have a nominal list of the crew. No restrictions on crew changes.

Portuguese National Tourist Office, 22–25A Sackvill Street, London W1X 1DE. Tel: 0171-494 1441. Fax: 0171-494 1868.

2.4.13 **Spain**

Telephone code from UK: 00 34. Entry should be made at a larger harbour and arrival reported to the Customs office where a Customs Permit (*Permiso Aduanero*) will be issued for the boat's stay in Spain. This permit is renewable and can be shown at subsequent ports of call, and must be stamped on final departure. It is valid for six months in each calendar year for residents of EU countries. The yacht must be registered and the skipper must have an International Certificate of Competence or the equivalent. There are no restrictions on crew changes provided an individual's passport is suitably stamped.

  Spanish National Tourist Office, 57–58 St James's Street, London SW1A 1LD. Tel: 0171-499 0901. Fax: 0171-629 4257.

2.4.14 **Sweden**

Telephone code from UK: 00 46. Entry must be made through one of the main harbours which have Customs and passport control. The Swedish Tourist Board provides an informative leaflet *Customs Regulations for Leisure Craft*, which gives full details on procedures. On leaving it is necessary to go through passport control, but not Customs unless carrying stores or goods which must be declared. Alcohol and tobacco in excess of the normal tourist allowance may be sealed up on board, or even put ashore. The yacht must not be chartered or lent while in Swedish waters. There are strict import restrictions on various items, including live animals. There are some prohibited (military) areas.

  Swedish Travel and Tourism Council, 73 Welbeck Street, London W1M 8AM. Tel: 0171-935 9784. Fax: 0171-935 5853.

2.4.15 **Turkey**

Telephone code from UK: 00 90. Enter only at a designated port of entry. Fly flag 'Q' and a courtesy ensign. On arrival, if not visited, the skipper should take the ship's papers, crew list and passports of crew to the harbour office where a Transit Log will be issued. The skipper should have a Certificate of Competency. There are complex rules about crew changes and non-family crew members. For details see RYA *Planning a Foreign Cruise*, Vol 2.

  Turkish Tourist Office, 170–173 Piccadilly, London W1V 9DD. Tel: 0171-734 8681. Fax: 0171-491 0773.

2.5 **Units and conversions**

2.5.1 **British units of weights and measures**

Lengths

12 inches	=	1 foot
3 feet	=	1 yard
6 feet	=	1 fathom
1 shackle	=	15 fathoms
1 cable	=	1/10 nautical mile (approx 200 yards)
1 nautical mile	=	approx 6080 feet
1 statute mile	=	1760 yards (5280 feet)

Weights (avoirdupois)

16 drams	=	1 ounce
16 ounces	=	1 pound
14 pounds	=	1 stone
28 pounds	=	1 quarter
4 quarters	=	1 hundredweight
20 hundredweights	=	1 ton (2240 lb)

Volume

4 gills	=	1 pint
2 pints	=	1 quart
4 quarts	=	1 gallon
2 gallons	=	1 peck
4 pecks	=	1 bushel
8 bushels	=	1 quarter
5 quarters	=	1 load
36 bushels	=	1 caldron

Area

144 sq in	=	1 sq ft
9 sq ft	=	1 sq yd
$30\frac{1}{4}$ sq yd	=	1 sq pole
40 sq poles	=	1 rood
4 roods	=	1 acre (4840 sq yd)
640 acres	=	1 sq mile

Weight and volume of water

One Imperial gallon	=	277.274 cu in, or 0.16 cu ft, or 10lb, or 4.546 litres
One US gallon	=	231 cu in, or 0.133 cu ft, or 8.33lb, or 0.83 Imp gallons, or 3.8 litres
One cu ft of water	=	6.232 Imp gallons, or 28.375 litres, or 0.284 cu metres, or 62.39lb
One cu ft of salt water weighs		64lb (or 1/35th ton)

Pressures

A column of water 1ft high	=	Pressure of 0.434lb/sq in
A column of water 1m high	=	Pressure of 1.43lb/sq in
A column of water 2.31ft high	=	Pressure of 1lb/sq in

At 30in mercury (34ft water) atmospheric
  pressure is 1 atmosphere (14.7lb/sq in)
Pressure in   = 0.068 × pressure in lb/sq in
  atmospheres

2.5.2. Système International (SI units)

The SI version of the metric system is based on
seven units denoting physical quantities. They are:

Quantity	Unit	Symbol
Length	metre	m
Mass	kilogram	kg
Time	second	s
Electric current	ampere	A
Thermodynamic temperature	kelvin	K
Luminous intensity	candela	cd
Amount of substance	mole	mol

(only used in physical chemistry)

Note that the kilogram, unit of mass, is the only
one with a multiple prefix.
1 kilogram = 1000 grams. Prefixes denoting

different sizes of this mass unit are attached to the
'gram', e.g. milligram = 1/1000 gram.

There are 15 derived units formed from base
and/or supplementary units. They are:

Quantity	Name of SI derived unit	Symbol
Force	newton	N
Energy	joule	J
Frequency	hertz	Hz
Pressure and stress	pascal	Pa
Power	watt	W
Quantity of electricity	coulomb	C
Electric potential	volt	V
Electrical capacitance	farad	F
Electrical resistance	ohm	Ω
Electrical conductance	siemens	S
Magnetic flux	weber	Wb
Flux density	tesla	T
Inductance	henry	H
Luminous flux	lumen	lm
Illuminance	lux	lx

Prefixes

The following prefixes are used to designate multiples:

			Prefix	Symbol
One thousand million	1 000 000 000	10^9	giga	G
One million	1 000 000	10^6	mega	M
One thousand	1 000	10^3	kilo	k
One hundred	100	10^2	hecto	h
Ten	10	10^1	deca	da
One tenth	0.1	10^{-1}	deci	d
One hundredth	0.01	10^{-2}	centi	c
One thousandth	0.001	10^{-3}	milli	m
One millionth	0.000 001	10^{-6}	micro	μ
One thousand millionth	0.000 000 001	10^{-9}	nano	n
One million millionth	0.000 000 000 001	10^{-12}	pico	p

2.5.3 Conversion factors and tables

To convert	Multiply by	To convert	Multiply by
Areas			
sq in to sq mm	645.16	sq mm to sq in	0.00155
sq in to sq cm	6.4516	sq cm to sq in	0.155
sq ft to sq m	0.0929	sq m to sq ft	10.76
sq yd to sq m	0.8361	sq m to sq yd	1.196
acres to sq m	4046.86	sq m to acres	0.000247
acres to sq yd	4840.0	sq yd to acres	0.0002
Consumption			
lb/hp/hr to gram/hp/hr	447.4	gram/hp/hr to lb/hp/hr	0.0022
Distances			
in to mm	25.40	mm to in	0.0394
in to cm	2.54	cm to in	0.394
ft to m	0.3048	m to ft	3.2808
yd to m	0.914	m to yd	1.094
fathoms to m	1.8288	m to fathoms	0.5468
statute miles to km	1.609	km to statute miles	0.6215
naut miles to statute	1.1515	statute miles to naut	0.8684
naut miles to m	1852	m to naut miles	0.00054

To convert	Multiply by	To convert	Multiply by
Force			
lbf to N	4.4482	N to lbf	0.2248
kgf to N	9.8066	N to kgf	0.101972
Mass			
oz to grams	28.35	grams to oz	0.0353
lb to kg	0.4536	kg to lb	2.205
ton to tonnes (1000kg)	1.016	tonnes to tons (2240lbs)	0.9842
tons to short (US) tons	1.12	short (US) tons to tons	0.893
Powers			
horsepower to kW	0.7457	kW to hp	1.341
hp to metric hp	1.014	metric hp to hp	0.9862
metric hp to kW	0.735	kW to metric hp	1.359
Pressures			
lb/sq in to kg/sq cm	0.0703	kg/sq cm to lb/sq in	14.22
lb/sq ft to kg/sq m	4.88	kg/sq m to lb/sq ft	0.205
lb/sq in to ft of water	2.31	ft of water to lb/sq in	0.433
lb/sq in to atmospheres	0.0680	atmospheres to lb/sq in	14.7
Speeds			
ft/sec to m/sec	0.3048	m/sec to ft/sec	3.281
ft/sec to knots	0.592	knots to ft/sec	1.689
ft/sec to miles/hr	0.682	miles/hr to ft/sec	1.467
ft/sec to m/sec	0.0051	m/sec to ft/min	196.8
knots to miles/hr	1.1515	miles/hr to knots	0.868
miles/hr to km/hr	1.6093	km/hr to miles/hr	0.6214
knots to km/hr	1.8520	km/hr to knots	0.5400
Torque			
lbf ft to Nm	1.3558	Nm to lbf ft	0.7376
kgf m to Nm	9.8066	Nm to kgf m	0.1020
lbf ft to kgf m	0.1383	kgf m to lbf ft	7.2330
Volumes			
cu in to cu cm	16.387	cu cm to cu in	0.061
cu ft to cu m	0.0283	cu m to cu ft	35.31
cu ft to galls	6.25	galls to cu ft	0.16
cu ft to litres	28.33	litres to cu ft	0.035
pints to litres	0.568	litres to pints	1.76
galls to litres	4.546	litres to galls	0.22
Imp galls to US galls	1.2	US galls to Imp galls	0.833
US barrels to cu m	0.16	cu m to US barrels	6.29

Feet to metres, metres to feet

Explanation: The central columns of figures in bold type can be referred in either direction. To the left to convert metres into feet, or to the right to convert feet into metres. For example, five lines down: 5 feet = 1.52 metres, and 5 metres = 16.40 feet.

Feet		Metres	Feet		Metres	Feet		Metres	Feet		Metres
3.28	**1**	0.30	45.93	**14**	4.27	88.58	**27**	8.23	131.23	**40**	12.19
6.56	**2**	0.61	49.21	**15**	4.57	91.86	**28**	8.53	134.51	**41**	12.50
9.84	**3**	0.91	52.49	**16**	4.88	95.14	**29**	8.84	137.80	**42**	12.80
13.12	**4**	1.22	55.77	**17**	5.18	98.43	**30**	9.14	141.08	**43**	13.11
16.40	**5**	1.52	59.06	**18**	5.49	101.71	**31**	9.45	144.36	**44**	13.41
19.69	**6**	1.83	62.34	**19**	5.79	104.99	**32**	9.75	147.64	**45**	13.72
22.97	**7**	2.13	65.62	**20**	6.10	108.27	**33**	10.06	150.92	**46**	14.02
26.25	**8**	2.44	68.90	**21**	6.40	111.55	**34**	10.36	154.20	**47**	14.33
29.53	**9**	2.74	72.18	**22**	6.71	114.83	**35**	10.67	157.48	**48**	14.63
32.81	**10**	3.05	75.46	**23**	7.01	118.11	**36**	10.97	160.76	**49**	14.94
36.09	**11**	3.55	78.74	**24**	7.32	121.39	**37**	11.28	164.04	**50**	15.24
39.37	**12**	3.66	82.02	**25**	7.62	124.67	**38**	11.58			
42.65	**13**	3.96	85.30	**26**	7.92	127.95	**39**	11.89			

Inches to millimetres

inches	0	1/16	1/8	3/16	1/4	5/16	3/8	7/16	1/2	9/16	5/8	11/16	3/4	13/16	7/8	15/16
0		1.6	3.2	4.8	6.4	7.9	9.5	11.1	12.7	14.3	15.9	17.5	19.1	20.6	22.2	23.8
1	25.4	27.0	28.6	30.2	31.7	33.3	34.9	36.5	38.1	39.7	41.2	42.9	44.4	46.0	47.6	49.2
2	50.8	52.4	54.0	55.6	57.1	58.7	60.3	61.9	63.5	65.1	66.7	68.3	69.8	71.4	73.0	74.6
3	76.2	77.8	79.4	81.0	82.5	84.1	85.7	87.3	88.9	90.5	92.1	93.6	95.2	96.8	98.4	100.0
4	101.6	103.2	104.8	106.4	108.0	109.5	111.1	112.7	114.3	115.9	117.5	119.1	120.7	122.2	123.8	125.4
5	127.0	128.6	130.2	131.8	133.4	134.9	136.5	138.1	139.7	141.3	142.9	144.5	146.1	147.6	149.2	150.8
6	152.4	154.0	155.6	157.2	158.8	160.3	161.9	163.5	165.1	166.7	168.3	169.9	171.5	173.0	174.6	176.2
7	177.8	179.4	181.0	182.6	184.2	185.7	187.3	188.9	190.5	192.1	193.7	195.3	196.9	198.4	200.0	201.6
8	203.2	204.8	206.4	208.0	209.6	211.1	212.7	214.3	215.9	217.5	219.1	220.7	222.3	223.8	225.4	227.0
9	228.6	230.2	231.8	233.4	235.0	236.5	238.1	239.7	241.3	242.9	244.5	246.1	247.7	249.2	250.8	252.4
10	254.0	255.6	257.2	258.8	260.4	261.9	263.5	265.1	266.7	268.3	269.9	271.5	273.1	274.6	276.2	277.8
11	279.4	281.0	282.6	284.2	285.7	287.3	288.9	290.5	292.1	293.7	295.3	296.9	298.4	300.0	301.6	303.2
12	304.8															

Feet and inches to millimetres

inches	0	1	2	3	4	5	6	7	8	9	10	11
feet												
1	305	330	356	381	406	432	457	483	508	533	559	584
2	610	635	660	686	711	737	762	787	813	838	864	889
3	914	940	965	991	1016	1041	1067	1092	1118	1143	1168	1194
4	1219	1245	1270	1295	1321	1346	1372	1397	1422	1448	1473	1499
5	1524	1549	1575	1600	1626	1651	1676	1702	1727	1753	1778	1803
6	1829	1854	1880	1905	1930	1956	1981	2007	2032	2057	2083	2108
7	2134	2159	2184	2210	2235	2261	2286	2311	2337	2362	2388	2413
8	2438	2464	2490	2515	2540	2565	2591	2616	2642	2667	2692	2718
9	2743	2769	2794	2819	2845	2870	2896	2921	2946	2972	2997	3023
10	3048	3073	3100	3124	3150	3175	3200	3226	3251	3277	3302	3327

Fathoms and feet to metres

The following table is useful for converting feet (or fathoms and feet) into metres, or vice versa:

Feet		6	12	18	24	30	36	42	48	54	60
Fathoms		1	2	3	4	5	6	7	8	9	10
Feet		1.8	3.6	5.5	7.3	9.1	10.9	12.8	14.6	16.4	18.3
1	0.3	2.1	3.9	5.8	7.6	9.4	11.3	13.1	14.9	16.7	18.6
2	0.6	2.4	4.2	6.1	7.9	9.7	11.6	13.4	15.2	17.0	18.9
3	0.9	2.7	4.5	6.4	8.2	10.0	11.9	13.7	15.5	17.3	19.2
4	1.2	3.0	4.9	6.7	8.5	10.3	12.2	14.0	15.8	17.7	19.5
5	1.5	3.3	5.2	7.0	8.8	10.6	12.5	14.3	16.1	18.0	19.8

Metres to nautical miles (m/n miles)
(1m = 0.0005399 n miles)

m	0	100	200	300	400	500	600	700	800	900
0	0	0.054	0.108	0.162	0.216	0.270	0.324	0.378	0.432	0.486
1000	0.540	0.594	0.648	0.729	0.756	0.810	0.864	0.918	0.972	1.026
2000	1.080	1.134	1.188	1.242	1.296	1.350	1.404	1.458	1.512	1.566
3000	1.620	1.674	1.728	1.782	1.836	1.890	1.944	1.998	2.052	2.106
4000	2.160	2.214	2.268	2.322	2.376	2.430	2.484	2.538	2.592	2.646
5000	2.700	2.754	2.808	2.862	2.916	2.970	3.024	3.078	3.132	3.168
6000	3.240	3.294	3.348	3.402	3.456	3.510	3.564	3.618	3.672	3.726
7000	3.780	3.834	3.888	3.942	3.996	4.050	4.104	4.158	4.212	4.266
8000	4.320	4.374	4.428	4.482	4.536	4.590	4.644	4.698	4.752	4.805
9000	4.859	4.913	4.967	5.021	5.075	5.129	5.183	5.237	5.291	5.345

Nautical miles to metres (n miles/m)
(1 n mile = 1852 m)

nm	0.0	0.1	0.2	0.3	0.4	0.5	0.6	0.7	0.8	0.9
0	0	185.2	370.4	555.6	740.8	926.0	1111.2	1296.4	1481.6	1666.8
1	1852.0	2037.2	2222.4	2407.6	2592.8	2778.0	2963.2	3148.4	3333.6	3518.8
2	3704.0	3889.2	4074.4	4259.6	4444.8	4630.0	4815.2	5000.4	5185.6	5370.8
3	5556.0	5741.2	5926.4	6111.6	6296.8	6482.0	6667.2	6852.4	7037.6	7222.8
4	7408.0	7593.2	7778.4	7963.6	8148.8	8334.0	8519.2	8704.4	8889.6	9074.8
5	9260.0	9445.2	9630.4	9815.6	10008.0	10186.0	10371.0	10556.0	10742.0	10927.0
6	11112.0	11297.0	11482.0	11668.0	11853.0	12038.0	12223.0	12408.0	12594.0	12779.0
7	12964.0	13149.0	13334.0	13520.0	13705.0	13890.0	14075.0	14260.0	14446.0	14631.0
8	14816.0	15001.0	15186.0	15372.0	15557.0	15742.0	15927.0	16112.0	16298.0	16483.0
9	16668.0	16853.0	17038.0	17224.0	17409.0	17594.0	17779.0	17964.0	18150.0	18335.0

Temperature – Fahrenheit to Celsius (Centigrade)

°F	°C	°F	°C	°F	°C
212	100	100	37.7	45	7.2
200	93.3	95	35.0	40	4.4
190	87.7	90	32.2	35	1.7
180	82.2	85	29.4	32	0.0
170	76.6	80	26.7	30	−1.1
160	71.1	75	23.9	25	−3.9
150	65.5	70	21.1	20	−6.7
140	60.0	65	18.3	15	−9.4
130	54.4	60	15.6	10	−12.2
120	48.8	55	12.8	5	−15.0
110	43.3	50	10.0	0	−17.7

Note: A more complete conversion scale is shown under Weather, Fig. 7(22).

To convert degrees Centigrade to Fahrenheit, multiply by 1.8 and add 32.
Example: $10°C \times 1.8 = 18 + 32 = 50°F$

To convert Fahrenheit to Centigrade, subtract 32 and divide by 1.8.

2.6 Glossaries

2.6.1 Glossary of nautical terms

It is hardly surprising that those who go to sea have built up their own vocabulary of nautical terms, because many of the things which are expressed in nautical language have no equivalent ashore. In a boat it is often necessary to give precise instructions quickly, so communication can be very important. It is therefore essential for a sailor to understand and use at least certain of the more common terms. Here is a selection.

Aback A sail is aback when trimmed so that the wind is on the forward side of it
Abaft Behind; further aft than
Abeam On the beam; at right angles to the fore-and-aft line of the vessel
Aboard In or on the vessel; on board
About (to go) To change tack
A-Bracket Fitting shaped as an inverted A supporting the end of the propeller shaft
Adrift Loose; broken away; late
Afloat Waterborne
Aft Towards the stern
Ahead In front of; the direction of the bows

Amidships Midway between bow and stern, of the rudder or helm when it is centred (fore-and-aft)

Astern Behind; the direction of the stern

Athwart Across

Avast Stop (e.g. 'Avast heaving' – stop heaving)

Awash Level with the surface of the water

Aweigh When the anchor has broken out of sea bed

Back Of the wind – when it changes direction anti-clockwise. To back a sail is to haul it to windward, so that the wind fills it on the other side

Backstay A stay holding mast from after side

Bailer A small receptacle for removing water from a boat (bailing)

Ballast Weight placed low down in a vessel to improve stability

Bar A shallow area (shoal) across the mouth of a harbour or river

Batten down To secure hatches, openings etc before proceeding to sea

Battens Flexible strips of wood or plastic slipped into pockets in the leech of a sail to retain its shape

Beacon A mark to assist navigation

Beam The width of a boat; the timber on which deck is laid

Bearing The direction of one object from another, usually referring to the compass

Bear away To steer the boat away from the direction of the wind

Bear off To push away (e.g. the jetty or another boat)

Beating Sailing to windward, by tacking with the wind first on one side and then on the other

Beaufort scale A numerical measure of wind strength

Becket A loop or eye

Before Towards the bow

Belay To secure a rope, or make it fast (colloquially, to countermand an order)

Bend A form of knot

Berth Space for sleeping, or for a vessel to dock

Bight The middle of a rope (not the ends)

Bilge The curve of the underwater part of a boat, nearest the keel

Binnacle The casing that holds a compass

Bitts A pair of vertical posts for securing mooring lines or anchor warps

Bitter end Inboard end of anchor cable

Block A plastic, metal or wooden shell holding one or more sheaves through which ropes are led

Bluff Steep-to, perpendicular

Boathook A stout stave with a hook at one end, used for bringing a boat alongside or for picking up a buoy

Bollard A vertical post on ship or shore, for securing mooring lines

Bolt rope A rope sewn to the luff or foot of a sail

Boom A spar used to extend the foot of a sail

Boom vang A rope used to hold a boom forward and downward

Bosun's chair A seat which can be attached to a halyard for sending a man aloft

Boot-topping Painted areas along the waterline

Bowline A knot that forms a fixed loop

Bow The front end of a vessel

Bowse To tighten (e.g. a rope or lashing)

Bowsprit Spar projecting forward from the stem

Bring up To come to anchor

Broach To swing broadside on to the sea

Bulkheads Vertical partitions or divisions within a vessel

Bulwarks Solid rails around the deck edge

Bunk A bed

Buoy A float used as a navigational mark, or to take a mooring line

Burgee A triangular flag denoting membership of a club, flown at the masthead

By the head A vessel trimmed bow down

By the lee When running downwind, if the wind blows from side on which the boom is lying, possibly causing a gybe

By the stern A vessel trimmed stern down

Cable Anchor chain; or, as a measure of distance, $\frac{1}{10}$ of a nautical mile, i.e. about 200 yards

Cardinal mark Indicating navigable water on the named side of the mark

Careen To heel a vessel over to work on her bottom

Carry away To break or part

Carry way To continue to move through the water

Carvel A method of construction which gives a smooth finish, with planks edge to edge

Cast off To let go

Catamaran A vessel with two parallel hulls, joined by beams

Caulk To make a watertight joint in seams between planks

Cavitation Vibration and loss of power, caused by aeration of propeller working surfaces

Centre of buoyancy Centre of the immersed volume of a vessel

Centreboard A plate which can be lowered from a housing in the bottom of the hull, to increase lateral resistance (i.e. reduce leeway)

Chain plates Strong points on the hull each side of the mast, for attachment of shrouds

Chart Datum The level to which soundings and drying heights on a chart are related

Check (of a rope) To ease out slowly; slowly to stop a vessel's movement

Chine The angle between the bottom and topsides in some designs of craft

Claw off Sailing close to the wind, to get off a lee shore

Cleat A fitting with projecting horns, for securing a rope

Clevis pin A small cylindrical pin, used in standing rigging

Clew The lower, aft corner of a sail, where the foot meets the leech

Clinker Method of wooden construction, where the edge of one plank overlaps the one below it

Close-hauled Sailing as close to the wind as possible

Clutter Unwanted reflections (e.g. from waves or rain) on a radar screen

Coachroof A raised structure to improve headroom below deck

Companion Ladder or stairway

Compass Navigational instrument which indicates a northerly point

Con To give orders to the helmsman

Contour A line on the chart joining points of equal elevation or equal depth

Counter The overhanging portion of the stern

Course The direction in which a boat is heading

Cradle Supporting frame for a boat out of the water

Cringle A loop, usually consisting of a metal eye roped to a sail

Crown (of an anchor) Where the arms join the shank

Crutch Metal fitting that drops into gunwale of a boat to take an oar

Davits Cranes for hoisting boats and tenders

Dead reckoning Calculating position from course steered and distance run

Deck The floor of a vessel

Deck head Underside of the deck

Deviation Compass error caused by magnetism of the vessel

Dip To lower and re-hoist the ensign as a salute

Displacement The weight of a vessel (equal to the weight of water she displaces)

Dog watches The two-hour watches from 1600-1800 and 1800-2000

Downhaul A rope pulling downwards, usually on the tack of a sail

Down helm An order to the helmsman to put the tiller 'down', i.e. away from the wind

Dowse To extinguish a light or lower a sail; also to spray with water

Draught The depth of a vessel beneath the water, to the lowest part of the hull

Drogue A form of sea anchor; used for boats, liferafts and lifebuoys

Ebb The falling tide

Echo sounder Electronic instrument to measure the depth of water

Ensign A vessel's national flag. The British maritime flags are the red, white or blue ensigns (never the Union Flag)

Fairlead An opening or fitting for leading a (mooring) rope

Fairway A navigable channel

Fathom A measurement of depth, equals six feet

Fender Used to prevent damage to the ship's side when lying alongside another vessel or a jetty

Fend off To push off

Fetch To reach a desired destination: the distance which the wind has blown over open water

Fiddle A lip around horizontal surfaces to stop objects falling/sliding off

Fix A position found from accurate bearings, or observations of heavenly bodies

Flare Outward spread of the topsides near the bow of a boat; pyrotechnic signal used to call attention

Flashing Flashing navigation light, with period of light less than period of darkness

Flood The rising tide

Foot The bottom edge of a sail

Fore-and-aft The boat's major, or longitudinal axis

Foreguy Rope leading forward from boom end, to hold boom forward

Forestay Stay which runs from stem to mast

Foretriangle Triangle formed by forestay, mast and deck

Forward Towards the bow

Foul Opposite of 'clear', e.g. 'foul anchor', foul bottom'

Fractional rig A rig where the forestay does not extend to the masthead (i.e. not a masthead rig)

Frap To bind together

Freeboard The height of the deck above the waterline

Freshen A strengthening of the wind

Furl To lower and gather in a sail

Gaff Spar at head of a fore-and-aft sail (not Bermuda rig)

Gale Wind of force 8 or 9 on the Beaufort scale (37-47 knots)

Galley The kitchen

Gimbals Two pivoted concentric rings that hold items such as compass or lamps level at sea

Go about To tack, and bring the wind on the other side of the sails

Gooseneck Fitting which holds the boom to the mast

Goosewinged Running before the wind, with the foresail set on one side and the mainsail on the other

Ground tackle Anchor gear

Gunwale The upper edge along the side of a boat

Guy A rope used to control a derrick or spar. In a sailing yacht usually refers to the spinnaker guy, which adjusts the trim of the spinnaker pole

Gybe Altering from one tack to the other by putting the boat's stern through the wind (as distinct from tacking)

Halyard Rope for hoisting a sail or flag

Handsomely Gently, or slowly

Hank Fitting for attaching the luff of a sail to a stay

Hard A place for beaching boats

Hard a-port, hard a-starboard Helm order to use maximum helm in the required direction

Hatchway A deck opening with a cover (hatch)

Haul To pull, or to change bearing

Hawse pipe Through which the anchor cable runs in larger vessels

Hawser A heavy rope for mooring or towing

Head The top corner of a sail

Header A wind shift which brings the wind further ahead

Heading The direction in which a boat is pointing

Heads Marine lavatory

Headsail A sail set forward of the mast

Head sea A sea from ahead

Heave-To To stop, or reduce speed, with vessel head to wind

Heaving line A light line with a weighted end for establishing contact with another vessel or shore

Heel The inclination of a vessel

Helm The tiller or wheel

Hitch To make a rope fast to an object (not another rope)

Holding ground The type of bottom for the anchor

Holiday Area left unpainted by mistake

Hourglass A spinnaker twisted in the middle, so that the wind fills the top and bottom parts

House Flag A rectangular, personal flag of owner

Hull The structure of a boat, to deck level

Inboard Towards the middle of a vessel

Inshore Towards the shore

Irons A sailing boat is in irons when stationary, head to wind, unable to pay off on either tack

Isophase A navigation light which flashes with equal periods of light and darkness

Jib Triangular sail, set forward of the mast

Jury Makeshift

Kedge A light or secondary anchor

Keel The lower fore-and-aft structure of a vessel

Kicking strap Tackle used to hold down boom, and reduce twist in sail

King spoke The spoke of steering wheel upright when rudder is centred

Knot One nautical mile per hour (speed)

Landfall First sight of land, approaching from seaward

Lashing Securing with rope

Lateral mark Navigation buoy marking port or starboard side of a well defined channel

Latitude Angular measurement of position north or south of equator

Launch To slip into the water

Lay The twist in the strands of a rope; or to go (e.g. along a course)

Lazy Extra or spare

Lead line Marked line with a lead weight, for measuring depth of water

Leading marks/lights Marks or lights which when brought into line indicate channel or best water

Leech The trailing (aft) edge of a sail

Lee helm The tendency of a boat to fall off the wind, due to improper balance

Leeward The side of a boat further from the wind (opposite to 'windward')

Leeshore Shore on to which the wind is blowing

Leeway The sideways movement of a boat, blown by the wind (to leeward)

Lifeline Line rigged to stop crew going overboard

Lift A wind shift allowing a boat to point higher (opposite to 'header'). Also a rope which supports a spar (e.g. spinnaker pole)

List Angle of heel

Log Instrument for measuring distance run through the water

Log book Record of vessel's movements, positions, etc

Longitude Angular measurement east or west of Greenwich meridian

Loom The inboard end of an oar; (of a light) reflection in the sky

Lubber's line Fixed mark on compass bowl, showing ship's head

Luff The leading edge of a sail. *To luff* – to sail closer to the wind

Mainsail Sail set on aft side of the main (principal) mast. Usually the largest working sail, and referred to as the main

Mainsheet Rope and tackle controlling mainsail

Make To reach port; (of tides) when range is increasing

Make fast To secure a rope to an object

Make water To leak

Man To provide the crew for certain functions, e.g. man the pumps

Marline spike Pointed steel tool, used for splicing

Marry To bring two ropes together

Meridian A north-south line through any point

Messenger A light line, used for example to make preliminary contact between two vessels prior to hauling over a larger hawser, e.g. for towing

Midships Helm order to centre the rudder

Miss stays To fail to tack through the wind

Mizzen The aft mast in a yawl or ketch

Moor To anchor with two anchors, or secure alongside

Neaps When the tide does not rise or fall very much

Nothing to port (or starboard) Not to steer any further to port (or starboard)

Null When a direction finding radio receiver gives the weakest signal from a station, indicating its bearing

Occulting A navigation light, with the period of light greater than the period of darkness

Off the wind Not close-hauled

Offing Distance to seaward

Overboard Over the side (into the water)

Overhaul (of a tackle) To draw the blocks apart

Painter The rope secured to the bows of a dinghy or tender, by which it is secured or towed

Pay off To allow the ship's head to swing away from the direction of the wind

Pay out To ease out a chain or rope

Pitch poled When a boat is rotated, stern over bow, in a very large sea

Pooped When a vessel is overtaken by a sea which breaks over the stern (poop)

Port (side) The left-hand side of a vessel looking forward

Port tack When a sailing vessel has the wind blowing from her port side, and her main boom is to starboard

Quarter Midway between the beam and right aft

Race A local area of disturbed water

Racon A beacon which responds to a radar set's transmission, and shows up on the display

Radar Electronic instrument that shows the positions of other objects (ships, shore, buoys etc)

Radiobeacon A radio transmitter of known frequency, position and signal, from which a navigator with a suitable receiver can obtain a position line

Range (of cable), to flake down lengths of cable on deck, before anchoring; (of tide) the difference in height between successive high and low waters

Reach A point of sailing with the wind roughly on the beam

Reef To reduce the area of a sail; a ridge of rocks

Reeve To pass the end of a rope through a block etc

Rhumb line A course which cuts all meridians at the same angle (a straight line on a Mercator's chart)

Riding light Anchor light

Rigging Ropes which support the masts, or control the sails

Rowlock A gap in the gunwale, into which an oar fits for rowing; also by common usage refers to a metal crutch, swivelling in the gunwale, for same purpose

Rubbing strake A piece of wood (usually) secured along the hull, that takes the wear alongside a jetty

Rudder Vertical plate, hinged on forward side, for steering

Run To sail before the wind: distance covered at sea

Samson post Post for securing anchor or tow line

Scantlings The dimensions of a vessel's timbers (constructional details)

Scuppers Holes in bulwarks to allow water to drain from deck

Scuttles Round openings in vessel's side

Seacock A valve on a pipe connected to the sea

Sheer The rising line of a vessel's side, towards bow and stern; to move a vessel relative to her anchor (e.g. by applying helm in a tideway)

Sheet Rope used to control a sail's angle to the wind

Ship To take on board

Shoal Shallow area of water

Shrouds Athwartships or lateral supports to mast

Skeg A fin extending aft of keel, and possibly supporting the rudder

Slack water When the tidal stream is stationary

Slip Slope for launching boats; to let something go

Sloop The most common rig for a sailing boat with one headsail and mainsail

Snatch block A block which can be hinged open to take the bight of a rope

Snub To check a line from running out round a winch cleat etc

Sound To ascertain the depth

Spinnaker A triangular, full-bellied sail set when reaching or running before the wind

Spreaders Struts each side of the mast, giving a wider angle for the support of the shrouds (also called crosstrees)

Spring Mooring rope led from forward aft, or from aft forward

Spring tide When the range of the tide is greatest (opposite of 'neaps')

Stanchion Vertical support for lifelines running round deck edge

Standing part The fixed (not running) part of a rope

Starboard The right-hand side of a vessel looking forward

Starboard tack When a sailing vessel has the wind blowing from her starboard side, and her main boom is to port

Stay Fore and aft support for mast

Steady Order to helmsman to maintain the course he is steering

Steerage way When a vessel is moving fast enough through the water to respond (answer) to her helm

Stem The foremost part of the hull

Stiff Not easily heeled over

Stop To secure a furled sail; to make up a spinnaker with cotton or elastic bands, so that it can be broken out (spread) after hoisting

Surge To allow a rope to be eased out under control round a winch or bollard

Swage A metal terminal pressed on to a wire rope

Swing (compass) Procedure for finding compass deviation

Tabernacle Deck fitting for the bottom of a mast that can be lowered

Tabling Reinforcement sewn to edge of a sail

Tack The forward lower corner of a sail, to work a boat to windward by sailing alternately on port/ starboard tacks

Tackle Ropes and blocks, to give increased hauling power

Take a turn To pass a rope around an object such as a cleat

Tang Fitting on mast for attachment of shroud or stay

Telltale Wool, yard or ribbon as wind indicator

Thwart Seat running across (athwart) an open boat

Tidal stream The horizontal movement of the sea, caused by the tide

Tide The periodic rise and fall in the level of the sea, caused by the action of the moon and sun

Tiller Bar connected to the rudder for operating same

Toggle Metal fittings in riggings, to allow free movement while retaining tension

Topping lift Lift (rope) rigged to end of main boom or spinnaker pole, to support it
Topsides Surfaces on the hull above water
Track A channel mounted to deck or spar, which takes a traveller (e.g. sail slide)
Transom The flat stern of some designs of vessel
Transducer A sensor (e.g. for depth or water speed) for passing data to a navigational instrument
Trick A period at the wheel
Trim To alter the set of sails; the fore-and-aft attitude of a boat in the water
Turn up To make a rope fast

Under way When a vessel is not anchored or secured to the land or shore in any way
Up and down When the anchor cable is vertical

Veer To pay out anchor cable; (of the wind) when it changes direction clockwise

Wake Disturbed water astern of a vessel as she moves ahead
Warp Rope used for mooring or anchoring, or moving a vessel
Wash The waves caused by a vessel's progress through the water
Watches Periods of duty for members of the crew
Weather (or windward) The side of a vessel nearer the wind (opposite to 'leeward')
Weather helm The tendency of a boat to come up into the wind, due to improper balance
Weigh To raise the anchor
Wetted surface The area of the boat under water
Wind rode When a vessel is lying to the wind (rather than the tide)

Yard A spar on a mast for spreading a sail
Yaw To steer an unsteady course

2.6.2 Five-language vocabulary

English	French	German	Dutch	Spanish
Types of boat				
Cruiser	Bateau de croisière	Kreuzeryacht	Toerjacht	Yate crucero
Cutter	Cotre	Kutter	Kotter	Cuter
Dinghy	Canot, dinghy	Dingi, Beiboot	Bijboot	Chinchorro
Ferry	Bac, ferry	Fähre	Veerboot	Pasaje
Fishing boat	Bateau de pêche	Fischereifahrzeug	Vissersboot	Pesquero
Ketch	Ketch	Ketsch	Kits	Queche
Launch	Vedette	Barkasse	Barkas	Lancha
Lifeboat	Bateau de sauvetage	Rettungsboot	Reddingboot	Bote salvavidas
Merchant vessel	Navire de commerce	Handelsschiff	Koopvaardijschip	Buque
Motor cruiser	Croiseur à moteur	Motorkreuzer	Motorkruiser	Motora
Motor sailer	Bateau mixte	Motorsegler	Motorzeiljacht	Moto-velero
Ocean racer	Bateau de course-croisière	Hochseerenyacht	Zeewedstrijdjacht	Yate de regatas oceánica
Pilot boat	Bateau pilote	Lotsenversetzboot	Loodskotter	Bote del práctico
Schooner	Goélette	Schoner	Schoener	Goleta
Sloop	Sloop	Slup	Sloep	Balandra
Tanker	Bateau citerne	Tanker, Tankschiff	Tanker, tankschip	Buque cisterna
Tug	Remorqueur	Schlepper	Sleepboot	Remolcador
Yacht	Yacht	Yacht	Jacht	Yate
Yawl	Yawl	Yawl	Yawl	Balandro de baticulo
Rigging Sails				
Backstay	Pataras	Achterstag, Backstag	Achterstag	Popparrás
Batten pocket	Étui ou gaine de latte	Lattenasche	Zeillatzak	Bolsa del sable
Boom	Bôme	Baum	Giek	Botavara
Bowsprit	Beaupré	Bugspriet	Boegspriet	Baupré
Chain plate	Cadène	Rüsteisen, Püttings	Putting	Cadenote
Clew	Point d'écoute	Schothorn	Schoothoorn	Puño de escota
Crosstrees	Barres de flèche	Saling	Dwarszaling	Crucetas
Foot	Bordure	Unterliek	Voetlijk	Pujamen
Forestay	Étai avant	Vorstag, Fockstag	Voorstag, fokkestag	Estay de proa
Genoa	Génois	Genua	Genua	Génova
Halyard	Drisse	Fall	Val	Driza
Head	Point de drisse	Kopf	Top	Puño

English	French	German	Dutch	Spanish
Jib	Foc	Fock	Fok	Foque
Leech	Chute	Achterliek	Achterlijk	Baluma
Luff	Envergure	Vorliek	Voorlijk	Gratil
Mainsail	Grand'voile	Grossegel	Grootzeil	Vela mayor
Mast	Mât	Mast	Mast	Palo
Mizzen	Artimon	Besan	Bezaan	Mesana
Mizzen staysail	Voile d'étai d'artimon	Besanstagsegel	Bezaanstagzeil	Entrepalos
Reef point	Garcette	Refföse	Knuttel	Tomadores de rizo
Shackle	Manille	Schäkel	Sluiting	Grillete
Sheet	Écoute	Schot	Schoot	Escota
Shroud	Hauban	Want	Want	Obenque
Spinnaker	Spinnaker	Spinnaker	Spinnaker	Espinaquer
Staysail	Trinquette	Stagsegel	Fok	Vela de estay
Tack	Point d'amure	Hals	Hals	Puño de amura

Materials etc.

English	French	German	Dutch	Spanish
Aluminium alloy	Aluminium	Aluminium	Aluminium	Aluminio
Bolt	Boulon	Bolzen	Bout	Perno
Bronze	Bronze	Bronze	Brons	Bronce
Glass fibre	Fibre de verre	Glasharz	Fiberglas	Fibra de vidrio
Gunmetal	Bronze de canon	Rotguss	Geshutsbrons	Brone de canon
Lead	Plomb	Blei	Lood	Plomo
Marine plywood	Bois contre plaqué marin	Schiffsbausperrholz	Scheepstriplex	Contrachapado
Nut	Écrou	Schraubenmutter	Moer	Tuerca
Nylon	Nylon	Nylon	Nylon	Nilón
Rivet	Rivet	Niet	Klinknagel	Remache
Screw	Vis	Schraube	Schroef	Tornillo
Stainless steel	Acier inoxydable	Rostfreier Stahl	Roestvrij staal	Acero inoxidable
Steel	Acier	Stahl	Staal	Acero
Terylene	Tergal	Polyester, Dacron	Dacron	Dacron
Washer	Rondelle	Unterlegscheibe	Ring	Arandela
Weld	Souder	Schweissen	Lassen	Soldar
Wood	Bois	Holz	Hout	Madera

Parts of a boat

English	French	German	Dutch	Spanish
Bilges	Cale	Bilge	Kim	Sentina
Bulkhead	Cloison	Schott	Schot	Mamparo
Cabin	Cabine	Kajüte	Kajuit	Camarote
Cockpit	Cockpit	Plicht, Cockpit	Kuip	Bañera
Deck	Pont	Deck	Dek	Cubierta
Fo'c'sle	Poste avant	Vorschiff	Vooronder	Castillo de proa
Galley	Cuisine	Kombüse	Kombuis	Cocina
Gunwale	Plat-bord	Dollbord	Dolboord	Regala
Hatch	Écoutille	Luk	Luik	Escotilla
Keel	Quille	Kiel	Kiel	Quilla
Lifeline	Filière	Rettungsleine, Reling	Zeereling	Pasamano
Pulpit	Balcon avant	Bugkanzel	Preekstoel	Púlpito
Rudder	Gouvernail	Ruder	Roer	Timón
Stanchion	Chandelier	Stütze	Steun	Candelero
Steering wheel	Roue de gouvernail	Steuerrad	Stuurrad	Rueda de timón
Stem	Étrave	Vorsteven	Voorsteven	Roda
Stern	Poupe	Heck	Achtersteven	Popa
Tiller	Barre	Pinne	Helmstok	Cana
Wheelhouse	Timonerie	Ruderhaus	Stuurhuis	Timonera

Engine etc

English	French	German	Dutch	Spanish
Alternator	Alternateur	Wechselstrom-generator	Wisselstroom-dynamo	Alternador

English	French	German	Dutch	Spanish
Atomiser, injector	Injecteur	Einspritzdüse	Inspuiter	Inyector
Battery	Batterie	Batterie	Accu	Bateria
Clutch	Embrayage	Kupplung	Koppeling	Embrague
Diesel fuel pump	Pompe d'injection	Einspritzpumpe	Brandstofinspuitpomp	Bomba de inyección
Distilled water	Eau distillée	Destilliertes Wasser	Gedistilleerd water	Agua destilada
Drive belt	Courroie de transmission	Treibriemen	Drijfriem	Correa
Fuel filter	Filtre à combustible	Treibstoffilter	Brandstoffilter	Filtro de combustible
Fresh water	Eau douce, potable	Trinkwasser	Drinkwater	Agua potable
Gearbox	Boîte de vitesse	Getreibe	Versnellingsbak	Caja de cambios
Generator	Dynamo	Lichtmaschine	Dynamo	Generado
Grease	Graisse	Fett	Vet	Grasa
Hose	Tuyau	Schlauch	Slang	Tubo
Hydraulic fluid	Liquide hydraulique	Hydraulisches Öl	Hydraulischeolie	Aceite hidráulico
Ignition coil	Bobine d'allumage	Zündspule	Onsteking-bobine	Bobina
Oil	Huile	Schmieröl	Olie	Aceite
Propeller	Hélice	Schraube	Schroef	Helice
Starter motor	Démarreur	Anlasser	Startmotor	Motor de arranque
Water pump	Pompe à eau	Wasserpumpe	Waterpomp	Bomba de agua

Navigation

English	French	German	Dutch	Spanish
Abeam	Par le travers	Querab	Dwars	Por el través
Ahead	En avant	Voraus	Voorwaarts	Avante
Anchorage	Mouillage	Ankerplatz	Ankerplaats	Fondeadero
Astern	En arrière	Rückwärts, achtern	Achteruit	Atrás
Bay	Baie	Bucht	Baai	Bahía
Beacon	Balise	Bake	Baken	Baliza
Binoculars	Jumelles	Fernglas	Kijker	Prismáticos
Buoy	Bouée	Tonne, Boje	Ton, boei	Boya
Channel	Chenal	Fahrwasser	Vaarwater	Canal
Chart	Carte marine	Seekarte	Zeekaart	Carta nautica
Compass	Compas	Kompass	Kompas	Compás
Course	Cap, route	Kurs	Koers	Rumbo
Degree	Degré	Grad	Graad	Grado
Depth	Profondeur	Tiefe	Diepte	Fondo
Deviation	Déviation	Deviation, Ablenkung	Deviatie	Desvío
Dividers	Pointes sèches	Kartenzirkel	Passer	Compas de puntas
East	Est	Ost	Oost	Este
Echo sounder	Écho sondeur	Echolot	Echolood	Sondar acustica
Estuary	Estuaire	Flussmündung	Mond	Estuario
Hand bearing compass	Compas de relèvement	Handpeilkompass	Handpeilkompas	Aguja de marcar
Headland	Promontoire	Vorgebirge	Voorgebergte	Punta
Island	Île	Insel	Eiland	Isla
Latitude	Latitude	Breite	Breedte	Latitud
Leading line	Alignement	Leitlinie	Geleidelijn	Enfilación
Longitude	Longitude	Länge	Lengte	Longitud
Mud	Vase	Schlick, Schlamm	Modder	Fango
North	Nord	Nord	Noord	Norte
Overfalls	Remous	Stromkabbelung	Stroomrafeling	Escarceos
Parallel rulers	Règles parallèles	Parallellineal	Parallellineaal	Paralelas
Patent log	Loch enregistreur	Patentlog	Patent log	Corredera de patente
Port	Bâbord	Backbord	Bakboord	Babor
Radio direction finder	Radiogoniomètre	Funkpeiler	Radio peiltoestel	Radio goniometro
Radio receiver	Poste récepteur	Rundfunkempfänger	Radio-ontvangtoestel	Receptor de radio

English	French	German	Dutch	Spanish
Reef	Récif	Riff	Rif	Arrecife
Rocks	Rochers	Klippen, Felsen	Rotsen	Piedras
Shoal	Haut fond	Untiefe	Droogte	Bajo
South	Sud	Süd	Zuid	Sud
Starboard	Tribord	Steuerbord	Stuurbord	Estribor
Variation	Déclinaison	Missweisung	Variatie	Variación
West	Ouest	West	West	Oeste

Tides

English	French	German	Dutch	Spanish
Chart datum	Zéro des cartes	Kartennull	Reductievlak:kaart-peil	Bajamar escorada
Depth	Profondeur	Tiefe	Diepte	Fondo
Ebb	Marée descendante	Ebbe	Eb	Vaciante
Flood	Marée montante	Flut	Vloed	Entrante
High water	Pleine mer	Hochwasser (HW)	Hoogwater (HW)	Pleamar
Low water	Basse mer	Niedrigwasser (NW)	Laagwater (LW)	Bajamar
Neap (tides)	Morte eau	Nipptide	Doodtij	Aguas muertas
Range	Amplitude	Tidenhub	Verval	Repunte
Rate	Vitesse	Geschwindigkeit	Snelheid	Velocidad
Set	Porter	Setzen	Zetten	Dirección
Spring (tides)	Vive eau, grande marée	Springtide	Springtij	Marea viva
Tidal stream	Courant	Gezeitenstrom	Getijstroom	Corriente

Numbers etc

English	French	German	Dutch	Spanish
One	un	eins	een	Uno
Two	deux	zwei	twee	Dos
Three	trois	drei	drie	Tres
Four	quatre	vier	vier	Cuatro
Five	cinq	fünf	vijf	Cinco
Six	six	sechs	zes	Seis
Seven	sept	sieben	zeven	Siete
Eight	huit	acht	acht	Ocho
Nine	neuf	neun	negen	Nueve
Ten	dix	zehn	tien	Diez
Six hours	Six heures	Sechs Stunden, -Uhr	Zes uren	Seis horas
Twelve hours	Douze heures	Zwölf Stunden	Twaalf uren	Doce horas
Eighteen hours	Dix-huit heures	Achtzehn Stunden	Achttien uren	Diez y ocho horas
Twenty-four hours	Vingt-quatre heures	Vier und zwanzig Stunden	Vier en twintig uren	Veinticuatro horas
Thirty-six hours	Trente-six heures	Sechs und dreissig Stunden	Zes en dertig uren	Treinta y seis horas
Forty-eight hours	Quarante-huit heures	Acht und vierzig Stunden	Acht en veertig uren	Cuarenta y ocho horas
Today	Aujourd'hui	Heute	Vandaag	Hoy
Tomorrow	Demain	Morgen	Morgen	Mañana

Radio

English	French	German	Dutch	Spanish
Call sign	Indicatif	Rufzeichen	Roepsein	Señal de llamada
Frequency	Fréquence	Frequenz	Frequentie	Frecuencia
Operating time	Heures d'émission	Sendezeit	Seintijd	Hora de servicio
Radio beacon	Radiophare	Funkfeuer	Radiobaken	Radiofaro
Radio station	Station d'émission	Rundfunksender	Radioomroepstation	Estación de radiodifusión
Radio telephone	Radio téléphone	Sprechfunk–Gerät	Radiotelefoon	Radio teléfono

Note: A five-language vocabulary of weather terms is given in Chapter 7 (Weather).

2.7 Yachting and marine organisations

2.7.1 Royal Yachting Association (RYA)

Although it started in 1875 as the body responsible for those involved in the 'gentlemanly' pursuit of yacht racing, the Royal Yachting Association has grown, like the increasingly popular sport it represents, into a national body which supports all forms of pleasure boating from sail and motor cruising to windsurfing, dinghy sailing and powerboat racing.

Its training courses from Junior Level 1 to Yachtmaster Offshore are respected and imitated the world over. Its racing division governs all forms of competitive sailing in Britain, from the ever-popular club activities right through to the British Olympic Sailing Team. But the RYA's activities do not stop at its extensive training and racing departments. With a gross turnover of £3.37 million per year and a staff of 70 people, the RYA is a sizeable organisation looking after every aspect of recreational boating activity from lobbying Parliament to protecting the UK yachtsman's interests in Brussels.

Empowered by its 70,000 personal members, 1500 affiliated clubs and classes and 1000 recognised sea schools, the RYA's job has never been more important for those who enjoy cruising and racing than it is today. As the RYA's President, the Princess Royal, commented in a recent speech: 'It is a strong and active membership that strengthens our voice not just in the UK but in Europe and elsewhere.' The freedom that yachtsmen now take for granted is coming under increasing pressure from outside bodies. Whether it is talk of compulsory licensing and registration or the European Commission proposing unnecessarily stringent rules and regulations in the construction and equipment of boats, the RYA always makes sure that the voice of the user is strongly represented.

The Association keeps a close eye on parliamentary bills, harbour revision orders, by-laws, planning applications and a mass of legislation which might affect the yachtsman. Whether it is a threat from a developer attempting to close down a local sailing club or a foreshore landowner trying to put mooring rents up by an exorbitant amount – the RYA with its large membership and breadth of previous experience has a better chance of making the yachtsman's case heard and represented than an individual club or member.

Reacting to recent concern from a large number of its members over the subject of rising berth fees, the RYA has set up a Marina Berth Holders' Initiative. The response has been very encouraging, with boat owners from all around the UK (not just the crowded South Coast) contacting the RYA's special coordinator with an interest in setting up a marina berth holders' association. These associations create a much-needed channel of communication between the marina owner and the user, not just in discussions over price, but also for such matters as facilities, boat security and special rallies.

The RYA is also a pervasive publisher, producing a wide range of reasonably priced and instructive booklets and videos giving detailed advice on subjects as varied as buying a new yacht, foreign cruising documentation or advanced windsurfing techniques such as 'cheese rolls' or 'forward loops'. Full RYA personal members can obtain a selection of these booklets free of charge as well as other individual benefits such as reduced insurance, free sail numbers, a special charge-free RYA Visa card, a regular quarterly magazine *RYA News* in addition to the option of being able to draw on the pool of legal, training or racing expertise at RYA House.

Further details of RYA membership, training courses (see 1.2.2-1.2.5) or activities can be obtained from the Royal Yachting Association, RYA House, Romsey Road, Eastleigh, Hants SO50 9YA. Tel: (01703) 627400. Fax: (01703) 629924.

2.7.2 RYA Seamanship Foundation

The Seamanship Foundation was established in 1973. It is registered under the Charities Act 1960 and its object is to encourage the practice of seamanship. It encourages and assists with training yachtsmen by producing a range of instructional aids, from sophisticated audio visual programmes to simple posters. The Foundation also provides lectures and demonstrations on the use of distress flares, liferafts, firefighting and other safety equipment.

The Foundation gives opportunity for sail training to those otherwise unable to afford it, either by providing boats or by subsidising training courses. Some one hundred boats and dinghies have been bought for use by youth clubs, Scouts and schools.

The Foundation is particularly involved in organising courses and providing boats or equipment to enable the disabled to learn to sail and afterwards participate on equal terms with the able-bodied. Every year the Foundation organises courses on cruising yachts for visually handicapped people, and in addition encourages and assists sailing clubs to run their own courses.

In 1994 the Foundation decided to concentrate on sailing for those with special needs, and handed over the Young Skippers Scheme to Southampton Institute of Higher Education. It now undertakes national responsibility for everyone with special needs for boating, and acts as secretariat for the National Disabled Sailing Committee.

The Foundation is supported entirely by subscriptions and donations from the public, and its ability to assist the deprived and handicapped depends directly on the support received. All enquiries should be addressed to: The Director,

RYA Seamanship Foundation, RYA House, Romsey Road, Eastleigh, Hants SO50 9YA.

2.7.3 British Marine Industries Federation (BMIF)

The BMIF is the trade federation of the boating industry in this country. It was originally formed in 1913, and has changed its name more than once over the years, but its office is now at Meadlake Place, Thorpe Lea Road, Egham, Surrey TW20 8HE. Tel: (01784) 473377. Fax: (01784) 439678.

There are 12 federated associations of boat building employers divided into regional areas. Group associations include the Association of Brokers and Yacht Agents, the Marine Trades Association, and the Marine Engine and Equipment Manufacturers Association, together with yacht charterers, sailing schools, moorings and marina operators, manufacturers and wholesalers of marine equipment, and pleasure craft operators.

In all the Federation represents about 1300 members engaged in the small craft industry – boat building and repairing, engine manufacturing, sail making, retailing marine equipment of all kinds, yacht agents, the supply of gear and services, in fact every aspect of the boating trade.

Through National Boat Shows Ltd the BMIF organises the London and Southampton International Boat Shows; it also sponsors other regional boat shows and organises stands at overseas exhibitions and trade missions to selected countries.

In 1992 the BMIF commissioned a comprehensive and independent environmental review of the marine industry – the first scientific assessment of the impact of boating on the environment.

In 20 other countries there are equivalents of the BMIF who collectively make up the International Council of Marine Industry Associations (ICOMIA).

2.7.4 Trinity House

The Corporation of Trinity House has three main functions: (a) it is the Lighthouse Authority for England and Wales, the Channel Islands and Gibraltar; (b) it is a Deep Sea Pilotage Authority; (c) it is a Charitable Organisation for the relief of mariners and their dependants. Each function is self-supporting .

A Charter of 1514 gave Trinity House powers to regulate pilotage. By the 17th century the activities of the Corporation included erecting beacons, laying buoys and granting certificates to pilots.

Trinity House is controlled by a Board of ten members with long experience in either the Merchant or Royal Navies, assisted by administrative, engineering and technical staff. It maintains 82 lighthouses, 13 light vessels or floats on station and nearly 550 buoys, two thirds of which are lit. It also inspects many marks which are maintained by local and Harbour Authorities.

Trinity House is responsible for dealing with wrecks around the coasts of England and Wales.

Trinity House together with the Northern Lighthouse Board and the Commissioners of Irish Lights (see below) manage the Decca Navigator chains in the British Isles.

Much development work has been done on new forms of lights, fog signals and beacons – often automatically operated. On the international scene Trinity House plays an important role in the International Association of Lighthouse Authorities (IALA).

Under the Pilotage Act 1987, responsibility for district pilotage was transferred to harbour authorities on 1 October 1988. From that date, after 474 years of distinguished history, Trinity House ceased to exist as a district pilotage authority.

Trinity House pioneered the scheme, now generally adopted elsewhere, of replacing cruising pilot cutters with fast shore-based launches for the transfer of pilots to and from ships.

The Trinity House Users Consultative Committee was originally established in 1975 so that yachtsmen and fishermen (for example) should be able to state their opinions and requirements regarding navigation and safety at sea. It includes representatives of the Royal Yachting Association, Department of Trade, the General Council of British Shipping, the Fisheries Organisation Society, and the National Federation of Sea Anglers.

The Royal Yachting Association coordinates requests from yachtsmen for alterations or additions to aids to navigation, and correspondence on such matters should be addressed to the Cruising Secretary, Royal Yachting Association, RYA House, Romsey Road, Eastleigh, Hants SO50 9YA.

Trinity House, Tower Hill, London EC3N 4DH. Tel: 0171-480 6601. Fax: 0171-480 7662.

In Scotland and Ireland, lights are maintained by the Northern Lighthouse Board and the Commissioners of Irish Lights respectively. Their addresses are as follows:

Northern Lighthouse Board, 84 George Street, Edinburgh EH2 3DA.

Commissioners of Irish Lights, 16 Lower Pembroke Street, Box 73, Dublin 2.

These two authorities, together with Trinity House, comprise the General Lighthouse Authorities.

Light dues

All expenses relating to lighthouses, buoys and beacons maintained by the General Lighthouse Authorities are met out of a self-supporting fund known as the General Lighthouse Fund. This fund is maintained by Light Dues, the collection and accounting for which are centralised and controlled from Trinity House. Light Dues are payable for each voyage in respect of ships arriving at or departing from ports in the United

Kingdom or the Republic of Ireland; but tugs, fishing vessels and yachts are liable to a periodic payment. However, among the list of exemptions are ships of less than 20 tons, so it follows that yachts in this category do not pay Light Dues.

The Institute of Chartered Shipbrokers acts as agents to collect Light Dues, which are remitted to the Department of Transport who manage the General Lighthouse Fund. Charges are normally reviewed annually by the Secretary of State for Transport, by a percentage increase or decrease on the basic scale, to maintain the level of the Fund. In 1991/92 the liability of ships to Light Dues was one voyage per month, with a maximum of seven liable voyages during the year. To give an example, larger ships liable to payments for each voyage were charged 35 pence per ton in that year.

2.7.5 Some useful addresses

Amateur Yacht Research Society, Pen Gally House, Wilcove, Torpoint, Cornwall PL11 2PG. Tel: (01752) 812003.

Association of Brokers and Yacht Agents, Wheel House, Petersfield Road, Whitehill, Bordon, Hants GU35 7BU. Tel: (01420) 473862. Fax: (01420) 488328.

British Level Rating Association, Secretary, 18/19 Bath Road, Cowes, Isle of Wight. Tel: Cowes (01983) 293303.

British Marine Industries Federation, Meadlake Place, Thorpe Lea Road, Egham, Surrey TW20 8HE. Tel: (01784) 473377. Fax: (01784) 439678.

British Sub-Aqua Club, Telford's Quay, Ellesmere Port, Cheshire L65 4FY. Tel: 0151-357 1951. Fax: 0151-357 1250.

British Waterways, Willow Grange, Church Road, Watford, Herts WD1 3QA. Tel: (01923) 226422. Fax: (01923) 226081.

Clyde Cruising Club, The Pentagon Centre, Suite 408, 36 Washington Street, Glasgow G3 8AZ. Tel: 0141 221 2774.

Cowes Combined Clubs, Secretary, 18/19 Bath Road, Cowes, Isle of Wight. Tel: Cowes (01983) 295744. Fax: (01983) 295329.

Cruising Association, CA House, 1 Northey Street, Limehouse Basin, London E14 8BT. Tel: 0171 537 2828. Fax: 0171 537 2266.

Driver and Vehicle Licensing Agency (DVLA), Swansea SA99 1BX. (01792) 783355.

HM Coastguard, Department of Transport, Spring Place, 105 Commercial Road, Southampton, SO1 0ZD. Tel: 01703 329486. Fax: 01703 329351.

HM Customs and Excise, Customs Directorate, 1st Floor West, New King's Beam House, 22 Upper Ground, London SE1 9PJ. Tel: 0171-865 4742.

International Maritime Organization, 4 Albert Embankment, London SE1 7SR. Tel: 0171-735 7611. Fax: 0171 587 3210.

Inland Waterways Association, 114 Regent's Park Road, London NW1 8UQ. Tel: 0171-586 2556. Fax: 0171-722 7213.

Inmarsat, 99 City Road, London EC1Y 1AX. Tel: 0171 728 1000. Fax: 0171 728 1044.

International Yacht Racing Union, 27 Broadwall, Waterloo, London SE1 9PL. Tel: 0171-928 6611. Fax: 0171-401 8304.

Junior Offshore Group, 43 Parklands Avenue, Cowes, Isle of Wight PO31 7NH. Tel: (01983) 290279. Fax: (01983) 292962.

Little Ship Club, Bell Wharf Lane, London EC4R 3TB. Tel: 0171-236 7729. Fax: 0171-236 9100.

Lloyd's Register of Shipping, Yacht and Small Craft Services, 71 Fenchurch Street, London EC3M 4BS. Tel: 0171-709 9166.

Marine Safety Agency, Spring Place, 105 Commercial Road, Southampton, SO1 0ZD. Tel: 01703 329160.

Maritime Trust, 2 Greenwich Church Street, London SE10 9BG. Tel: 0181 858 2698.

Meteorological Office (Marine Branch), Met O (OM), Scott Building, Eastern Road, Bracknell, Berks RG12 2PW. Tel: (01344) 420242. Fax: (01344) 855921.

Radiocommunications Agency, Ship Radio Licensing Section, Room 613, Waterloo Bridge House, Waterloo Road, London SE1 8UA. Tel: 0171-215 2047. Fax: 0171-620 2793.

Royal Cruising Club, at the Royal Thames Yacht Club (see below).

Royal Institute of Navigation, 1 Kensington Gore, London SW7 2AT. Tel: 0171-589 5021. Fax: 0171-823 8671.

Royal National Lifeboat Institution, West Quay Road, Poole, Dorset BH15 1HZ. Tel: Poole (01202) 671133. Fax: (01202) 670128.

Royal Naval Sailing Association, c/o Royal Naval Club, Pembroke Road, Portsmouth, Hants PO1 2NT. Tel: Portsmouth (01705) 823524. Fax: (01705) 870654.

Royal Ocean Racing Club, 20 St James's Place, London SW1A 1NN. Tel: 0171-493 2248. Fax: 0171-493 5252.

Royal Ocean Racing Club, Rating Office, Seahorse Building, Bath Road, Lymington, Hants SO41 9SE. Tel: (01590) 677030. Fax: (01590) 679478.

Royal Thames Yacht Club, 60 Knightsbridge, London SW1X 7FF. Tel: 0171-235 2121. Fax: 0171-245 9470.

Royal Yachting Association, RYA House, Romsey Road, Eastleigh, Hants SO50 9YA Tel: Eastleigh (01703) 627400. Fax: (01703) 629924.

Solent Cruising and Racing Association, 18–19 Bath Road, Cowes, Isle of Wight. Tel: Cowes (01983) 295744. Fax: (01983) 295329.

Sports Council, 70 Brompton Road, London SW3 1HE. Tel: 0171-589 3411.

Trinity House (Corporation of), Trinity House, Tower Hill, London EC3N 4DH. Tel: 0171-480 6601. Fax: 0171-480 7662.

United Kingdom Offshore Boating Association, 1 Carbis Close, Port Solent, Portsmouth PO6 4YW. Tel: (01705) 219949. Fax: (01705) 219969.

Yacht Brokers, Designers and Surveyors Association, Wheel House, Petersfield Road, Whitehill, Bordon, Hants GU35 7BU. Tel: (01420) 473862. Fax: (01420) 488328.

Chapter 3

Coastal Navigation

Contents

3.1 Terms and definitions

3.1.1 Latitude and longitude

The positions of vessels or objects on a nautical chart are referred to by their latitude and longitude. The latitude of a point is its angular distance north or south of the equator, measured from 0–90°N or S. The longitude is its angular distance east or west of the prime (Greenwich) meridian, measured from 0–180°E or W.

In angular measurement there are 360 degrees in a circle, and 60 minutes of arc to a degree. For greater accuracy there are 60 seconds to a minute, but latitude and longitude are more often shown in degrees, minutes and tenths of a minute – e.g. latitude 51°07'.6N. The scales are given along the border of an ordinary chart – latitude up and down each side, and longitude along the top and bottom.

Fig. 3(1) illustrates how the latitude and longitude of point A are referred to the equator

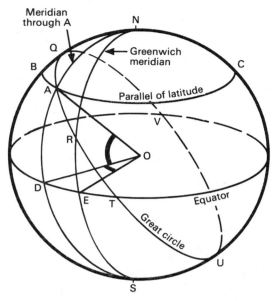

Fig. 3(1) Parallels of latitude, meridians and great circles.

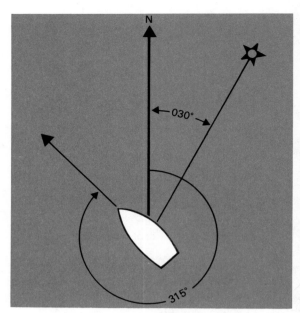

Fig. 3(2) A true bearing and a true course, related to true north.

and the Greenwich meridian respectively. Angle AOD is the latitude (north of the equator) and angle DOE is the longitude (west of Greenwich). BAC is the parallel of latitude through A, and NADS is the meridian through A.

3.1.2 Great circles
A great circle is the intersection of the surface of a sphere with a plane passing through its centre. The earth may be treated as a sphere, and in Fig. 3(1) it will be evident that all meridians are great circles (also passing through the poles). The equator is the only parallel of latitude which is a great circle. The circle indicated in the diagram by QARTUV is also a great circle.

The shortest distance between any two points on the surface of the earth lies along the great circle through them. Over long distances great circle sailing is sometimes used, either by means of special (gnomonic) charts, or by computing the courses and distances by formula, tables or calculator. See 3.3.16.

3.1.3 Courses and bearings
In order to proceed from place to place the navigator must have an indication of direction. Also if he knows the directions (bearings) of certain fixed objects marked on the chart he can establish his position. Courses and bearings are most simply measured in relation to true north, as given by the meridian passing through the place concerned – a line pointing straight up towards the top of a Mercator chart.

Courses and bearings are measured clockwise from north, and are always expressed in three figures. A true bearing of 090° is due east for example, and 180° is due south. In Fig. 3(2) the lighthouse bears 030° from the yacht, which is steering 315° (north west).

Course – rhumb line
The true course of a boat is the angle between true north and the direction in which she is heading, measured clockwise. As she sails along on a steady course she cuts all the meridians at the same angle. Such a line is called a rhumb line. If drawn on a globe it will normally appear as a spiral towards one of the poles, but as we will see (3.2.1) it is conveniently represented on a Mercator's chart by a straight line.

So a yacht, steering a steady course from one place to another, proceeds along a rhumb line. This is not quite the same as the line she would follow for the shortest distance between the two places, which would be the great circle joining them, but for practical navigation over comparatively short distances the difference is insignificant.

3.1.4 Standard navigational terms
Experienced skippers and navigators may well wish to preserve the terms which they have used to describe various features in navigation and chartwork. But certain standard terms as listed below are now used in shorebased courses. In any boat where more than one individual is involved in navigation, it is important to establish precisely the meanings of some terms in order to avoid confusion.

Track – the path followed or to be followed between one position and another. This path may be that over the ground (ground track) or through the water (water track).

*Track angle** – the direction of a track.

Track made good – the mean ground track actually achieved over a given period.

---

* The word *angle* will be omitted in normal use unless there is a possibility of confusion.

Heading – the horizontal direction of the ship's head at a given moment. (This term does not necessarily require movement of the vessel.)

Course (Co) – the intended heading.

Course to steer – the course related to the compass used by the helmsman.

Set – the direction towards which a current and/or tidal stream flows.

Drift – the distance covered in a given time due solely to the movement of a current and/or tidal stream.

*Drift angle** – the angular difference between the ground track and the water track.

Leeway – the effect of wind moving a vessel bodily to leeward.

*Leeway angle** – the angular difference between the water track and the ship's heading.

Dead reckoning – the process of maintaining or predicting an approximate record of progress by projecting course and distance from a known position.

DR position (DR) – (1) the general term for a position obtained by dead reckoning; (2) specifically a position obtained using true course and distance run, the latter derived from the log or engine revolutions as considered more appropriate.

Estimated position (EP) – a best possible approximation of a present or future position. It is based on course and distance since the last known position with an estimation made for leeway, set and drift, or by extrapolation from earlier fixes.

3.1.5 Variation

In yachts and boats, courses and bearings are actually measured by a magnetic compass, which tries to point to the magnetic north, and not true north, which is different. The angular amount by which magnetic north is displaced from true north is called the variation. If variation is west, the magnetic north is to the west of true north; if variation is east it is to the east.

Variation alters from place to place on the earth's surface and, to a lesser extent, with the passage of time. Currently around the British Isles it ranges from about 4°W in the Dover Strait to about 10°W in the west of Scotland. The variation in a certain area is shown on the chart, e.g. 'Variation 8°46′W (1975) decreasing about 5′ annually' or on modern charts more briefly as '8°46′W 1984 (9′E)'.

To correct a magnetic bearing or course to a true one, subtract westerly variation or add easterly. When converting from true to magnetic the opposite applies – add westerly variation or subtract easterly. Since in home waters variation is westerly, we will only consider this in the examples below. When in doubt it is helpful to draw a little diagram, like the ones shown.

In Fig. 3(3) a magnetic bearing of 081°(M) with a variation of 8°W results in a true bearing of 073°.

In Fig. 3(4) a true course of 030° and a variation of 7°W gives a magnetic course of 037°.

In order to distinguish this from a true course it is written 037°(M).

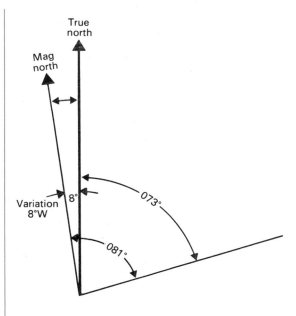

Fig. 3(3)

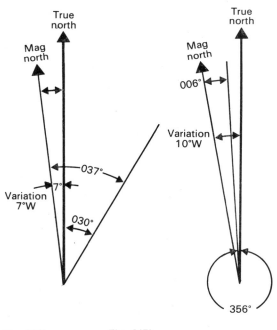

Fig. 3(4)   **Fig. 3(5)**

Figs 3(3)–3(5) The relation between true and magnetic courses and bearings, by applying westerly variation.

In Fig. 3(5) a true course of 356° with a variation of 10°W gives a magnetic course of 356 + 10 = 366° or 006°(M).

In certain isolated places there exist areas of Local Magnetic Anomaly. These are indicated on Admiralty charts by a wavy line, with figures such as ± 15° in the centre – indicating that within the enclosed area the magnetic variation may deviate from the normal by the value shown.

3.1.6 Deviation

Deviation, caused by the local magnetic field of the boat around the compass, deflects the compass needle away from magnetic north to which it would otherwise point. So this must be allowed for in addition to variation. If the compass is deflected to the west of magnetic north, deviation is west: if it is deflected to the east of magnetic north, deviation is east.

Unlike variation, deviation alters with the direction in which the boat is heading. It may be westerly when the boat is pointing one way, and easterly when it is pointing another.

Deviation can be very significant in steel boats, or in any boat where the compass is placed too close to a magnetic mass such as the engine or iron ballast keel. Temporary deviation of the compass

can be caused by inadvertently placing any magnetic object, such as a beer can, too close to it. In sailing boats which spend long periods on one tack or the other heeling error can also be a problem – see section 3.1.10.

In most boats deviation can largely be eliminated by a skilful compass adjuster, who places small corrector magnets near the compass so that they cancel out the local magnetic field. When the adjustment is complete, and as much of the deviation as possible has been removed, the boat is finally 'swung' on various headings (usually every 15°) to find out what deviation still remains, and a deviation card is drawn up as shown in Fig. 3(6). The procedures for checking, adjusting and swinging the compass are described in sections 3.1.7 to 3.1.11 below.

Deviation is applied in just the same way as variation. A useful mnemonic is the word CADET, meaning 'Compass to True, Add East'. The two end letters stand for 'Compass to True', and the three centre ones tell you to 'ADd East'. That is, when converting from compass to true add easterly variation or deviation (and subtract westerly).

Variation and deviation are added together to give the total compass error to be applied on any occasion. For example, if variation is 7°W and the deviation on the course being steered is 3°E, the total compass error is 4°W. In this instance a compass course of 168° – which is written in the form 168°(C)- would be a true course of 164°.

The conventional magnetic compass is being challenged by electronic fluxgate instruments with no moving parts to wear. As well as serving as a steering compass these can also serve as a heading sensor for various electronic devices – autopilot, Decca, Loran, GPS or plotter. A fluxgate compass is even available which can continuously measure the deviation of the yacht and compensate accordingly to an accuracy of ±0.5 degrees. Perhaps the days of the professional compass adjuster are numbered.

3.1.7 Compass checks

Every opportunity should be taken to check the accuracy of the steering compass. A quick comparison can always be made with a hand bearing compass, held on the fore and aft line well away from any metal object. This should show up any serious deviation on a particular course.

A more accurate method is to take a bearing of a known transit (two objects in line) and compare it with the bearing from the chart, remembering to allow for variation – where the bearing of a transit is shown on the chart (e.g. 'Lights in line') it is the true bearing from seaward. It is good practice to check the compass against all available transits, for example leading marks when entering or leaving harbour.

The sun, or any other heavenly body, can be used in conjunction with navigational tables which give the azimuth angle (Z) at the time and place

DEVIATION CARD Steering compass

Yacht _____

Date _____

Magnetic course	Deviation	Compass course
000	2W	002
015	2W	017
030	3W	033
045	3W	048
060	4W	064
075	3W	078
090	3W	093
105	3W	108
120	2W	122
135	1W	136
150	1W	151
165	1W	166
180	0	180
195	0	195
210	0	210
225	0	225
240	1E	239
255	2E	253
270	2E	268
285	3E	282
300	2E	298
315	1E	314
330	0	330
345	1W	346
360	2W	002

Fig. 3(6) Typical deviation card, showing actual magnetic course being steered compared to compass course.

TABLE 3(1) True bearing of sun at sunrise and sunset.													
	DECLINATION												
LAT	0°	1°	2°	3°	4°	5°	6°	7°	8°	9°	10°	11°	LAT
	°	°	°	°	°	°	°	°	°	°	°	°	
30°	90	88.8	87.7	86.5	85.4	84.2	83.1	81.9	80.7	79.6	78.4	77.3	30°
31°	90	88.8	87.7	86.5	85.3	84.2	83.0	81.9	80.6	79.5	78.3	77.1	31°
32°	90	88.8	87.6	86.5	85.3	84.1	82.9	81.7	80.5	79.4	78.2	77.0	32°
33°	90	88.8	87.6	86.4	85.2	84.0	82.8	81.6	80.4	79.2	78.0	76.8	33°
34°	90	88.8	87.6	86.4	85.2	84.0	82.7	81.5	80.3	79.1	77.9	76.7	34°
			87.5	86.3	85.1					79.0	77.8	76.5	

Fig. 3(7) Extract from Table 3(1) in *The Macmillan & Silk Cut Nautical Almanac.*

concerned. The azimuth angle is the true bearing of a heavenly body, measured (in the northern hemisphere) eastward or westward from true north. From the azimuth angle is derived the azimuth (Zn), which is the true bearing of the heavenly body in 360° nomenclature, measured from true north.

The relationship between Z and Zn depends upon the Local Hour Angle (LHA) of the heavenly body, which is the angle measured westwards at the pole between the observer's meridian and the meridian of the heavenly body. In northern latitudes if LHA is greater than 180°, Zn = Z. If LHA is less than 180°, Zn = 360° − Z.

In order to achieve sufficient accuracy for checking a compass an azimuth mirror is needed, and the altitude of the heavenly body should not be more than about 35°.

3.1.8 Bearing of sun, rising or setting
At sea the compass may conveniently be checked against the azimuth of the sun when rising or setting – the only astronomical observation which needs no instrument. It is only necessary to know the approximate latitude of the boat, and the declination of the sun or other heavenly body, in order to enter Table 3(1) of *The Macmillan & Silk Cut Nautical Almanac* – a portion of which is reproduced above – and extract the required figure.

For example, in latitude 33° and with declination 9°, the tabulated figure is 79.2 (say 79°) which must be applied as follows.

The tabulated figure obtained is the true bearing – measured from north if the declination is north, or from south if the declination is south; towards the east if rising, or towards the west if setting. The following examples show how to derive the true bearing in different circumstances.

DR Lat	Declin- ation	Sun	Tabulated bearing	True bearing
33°	9°N	Rising	79°	N79°E or 079°
33°	9°N	Setting	79°	N79°W or 281°
33°	9°S	Rising	79°	S79°E or 101°
33°	9°S	Setting	79°	S79°W or 259°

Having obtained the true bearing from the table, it is then necessary to apply the local magnetic variation and compare the resulting figure with the bearing from the compass in order to determine the deviation on the course being steered.

Due to refraction, which is about 34' when observing bodies on the horizon, the bearing of the sun should be taken when its lower limb is a little over half a diameter above the horizon.

Very few yachts' compasses are fitted with azimuth rings, and steering compasses are often wooded over large sectors so that it is impossible to take bearings with them. This difficulty can be overcome by steering the boat directly towards, or away from, the rising or setting sun, and lining it up with the mast, forestay etc. Or it may be possible to line up the sun directly on the beam, using some athwartships part of the boat's structure. In all cases it is important to remember that the deviation determined only applies to the course being steered at the time of the observation.

3.1.9 Compass adjusting
The steering (or master) compass is the key navigational instrument in any yacht, and its accuracy is most important. No compass should be relied on unless it has at least been checked by

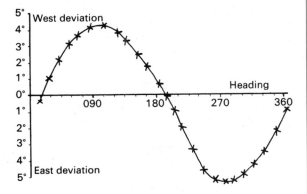

Fig. 3(8) Deviation curve, determined by swinging the compass.

'swinging', to determine the deviation on various headings. The procedure is outlined below.

If a compass swing shows that the deviation is not more than a degree or two on any heading, no further action is required. But very often larger deviations will be disclosed on certain courses, and when these are plotted against their respective headings a curve such as is shown in Fig. 3(8) will be found.

This deviation curve is the sum of five different coefficients, called A, B, C, D and E. Of these A and E can normally be neglected in small vessels, and no means are provided to correct for them. The causes of coefficient D are items such as steel decks, not usually present in yachts, so that normally the yachtsman is only concerned with coefficients B and C.

Coefficient B causes deviations on east-west headings, and coefficient C causes deviations on north-south headings. Luckily the effects of both B and C can be greatly reduced or eliminated by placing suitable magnets near the compass, so as to counteract the local distortion of the earth's magnetic field.

Unlike poles of magnets attract each other, while like poles repel each other. For compass adjusting a north-seeking pole (such as the north end of a compass needle) is marked as a red pole, and a south-seeking pole is marked as a blue pole. Hence the north magnetic pole is a blue pole. and the south magnetic pole is a red pole.

Coefficient B, which causes the trouble on east-west courses, can be corrected by using fore and aft magnets which fairly obviously have no effect on the direction of the compass needle when the boat is heading north or south (because they only strengthen or weaken the earth's magnetic field). If the magnet is placed red (north) end forward, it corrects easterly deviation on easterly courses and westerly deviation on westerly courses. Conversely, if the magnet is placed blue (south) end forward, it corrects westerly deviation on easterly courses and easterly deviation on westerly courses.

Similarly, coefficient C, which gives rise to deviation on north-south courses, can be corrected by adding athwartships magnets – which have no effect on the compass when the boat is heading east or west. A magnet with its red (north) end to starboard corrects easterly deviation on northerly headings, and corrects westerly deviation on southerly headings. A magnet with its blue (south) end to starboard corrects westerly deviation on northerly headings, and corrects easterly deviation on southerly headings.

The effect of either fore and aft or athwartships magnets can be increased or reduced by varying the strength of the magnet or its distance from the compass card. Older compasses had wooden corrector boxes, drilled with holes into which small magnets could be inserted. Modern compasses have built-in correctors, which can be adjusted by a screw action.

3.1.10 Heeling error

There is, however, another source of compass error which should be attended to first, and that is heeling error. Vertical magnetic forces do not affect the compass when the boat is upright, but can cause heeling error when she is inclined. This is more important in sailing boats, but even in a motor boat heeling error can make the compass unstable when the vessel rolls. Heeling error can only be removed when there is suitable provision for placing vertical magnets underneath the compass. The adjustment is carried out using an instrument called a dip needle, which is a horizontal magnet balanced on a knife edge. This is set up ashore, away from any magnetic influence, so that it is levelled with the north end pointing north (south in the southern hemisphere) by adjusting a balance weight. The dip needle is then put exactly in the position occupied by the compass, with the boat on an east/west heading and the needle pointing north. If it does not lie horizontally it can be adjusted by vertical correctors – red end up if the north end is dipped down, blue end up if the north end is raised.

Correction for heeling error must be done before any other corrections are made. By the same token, if any alteration is made to the vertical magnets used for heeling error correction, it is important to carry out a compass swing to check the deviation on all courses.

3.1.11 Compass swinging

The compass should be swung on specific occasions, or whenever there is reasonable doubt about its accuracy. Many yachts are not swung often enough, since with the passage of time the compensating magnets lose their magnetism. It should be done when the boat is new (or when a new compass is fitted), at the start of each season, if additional equipment (including electrical items) is fitted anywhere near the compass, and on any major change in latitude – say more than 10°.

A compass can be swung by taking bearings, from a known position, of an object about five miles or more away, using a pelorus or bearing plate. This consists of an azimuth ring graduated from 0°-360°, with a sighting arm for viewing the distant object. The pelorus is lined up with its zero mark in the fore and aft line of the boat, so that the relative bearing of the object can be read for various headings, and compared with the bearing from the chart. The principle is illustrated in Fig. 3(9) and in the accompanying table.

If a pelorus is not available it is possible to use a sextant, held horizontally, to take the bearings. First it is necessary to place two reference marks, accurately located on the centreline of the boat say with one on the aft side of the mast and the other at the aft end of the coachroof, and the observer near the stern.

Professional compass adjusters may use the sun rather than a distant terrestrial object, working from prepared azimuth tables. Unless conditions are very smooth, it is necessary for a yacht to be moored between three or four points, so that she can be warped round and held steady while the bearings are taken. Alternatively she can be kept under way, in the immediate vicinity of a buoy or beacon whose position is known. It is important however that the boat should not be close to large magnetic objects, and also to ensure that there are no tools or spare corrector magnets anywhere near the compass.

The procedure is then briefly as follows. With the boat heading due east, fore and aft magnets are placed so as to remove the deviation. The

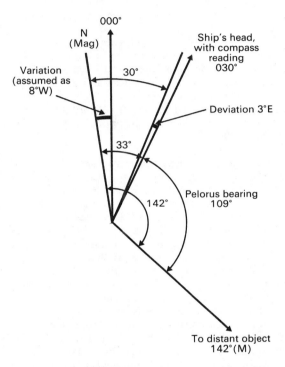

Fig. 3(9) The principle of compass swinging. How the relative bearing of a distant object, related to the known bearing from a certain position, gives the deviation on a particular heading, in this case 030°.

Ship's head (compass)	Pelorus bearing	Bearing of object by compass	Known bearing (Mag)	Deviation
000	140	140	142	2°E
030	109	139	142	3°E
060	081	141	142	1°E
090	052	142	142	0
120	023	143	142	1°W
etc				

procedure is then repeated with the boat heading due north, using athwartships magnets. The effect of these magnets is then examined with the boat heading due west and due south. If there is no appreciable deviation (say, less than 2°) no further correction is necessary, but if there is then remove half of it by placing the appropriate magnets. Then check again on east and north headings.

Having completed the adjustment so that the deviation on the four cardinal points is minimal,

and hopefully only 1° or so in each case, the boat is then swung through 360° to measure the remaining deviation at steps of, say, 30° and these are the readings which form the deviation card.

Remember to impress upon all on board the importance of keeping magnetic objects well away from the compass at all times. Things like camera light meters, metal spectacle cases and beer cans can have a considerable influence on even the best adjusted compass.

3.1.12 Hand bearing compass

A good hand bearing compass is essential for coastal navigation, and at sea for taking bearings of an approaching vessel to see whether the latter is on a collision course. It can also be used for a quick check of the yacht's steering compass, and in emergency it can be taken aboard the liferaft or tender.

Such a compass needs to be accurate, with a scale that is easy to read, and sufficiently damped for the card to settle quickly. Illumination must be provided for use at night, and this is now almost universally achieved with Betalights.

The traditional type of Sestrel (arm's length) compass is an excellent instrument, with which very accurate bearings can be taken, but it is relatively bulky and the prism somewhat vulnerable to damage. In emergency this type of hand bearer can be used as a steering compass. Other designs, such as the well-known Mini compass from Offshore Instruments, are more compact, and by using modern optical systems the compass can be held close to the eye, to eliminate parallax, with both the object and the figures on the card readily visible. Other makes include Silva, Plastimo, Ritchie and Suunto, and such compasses can be hung on a lanyard round the neck, and stuffed inside one's oilskin jacket, so that they are always available when required – a great advantage.

Working on a different principle is the Autohelm fluxgate personal compass which can take and store up to nine bearings at the touch of a button. Pressing another button brings the bearing up on a LCD display. There is also a stopwatch facility to time the interval between bearings, or the period of a flashing light.

For general daytime use it is difficult to fault the Offshore Binox – a pair of binoculars which includes a compass (plus a rangefinder recticule if required). The optical qualities of the Binox are excellent, and the compass is extremely deadbeat. It is light and compact, but expensive. Somewhat cheaper is the Francis Barker monocular version.

3.1.13 Relative bearings

Relative bearings are sometimes used at sea to indicate the direction of an object or another vessel in relation to the fore and aft line of one's own boat. Relative bearings to port are designated 'Red', and those to starboard 'Green', each being numbered from 000° (dead ahead) to 180° (dead astern). So a relative bearing of 'Green 080' indicates a direction 10° ahead of the starboard beam. 'Red 135' indicates a bearing on the port quarter.

The general concept of bearings relative to the ship's head is also used in connection with some types of radio direction finding equipment, described in Chapter 4.

3.1.14 Distances

Distances at sea are almost as important as directions. They are measured in nautical miles, often abbreviated to n mile or M, which are longer than statute or land miles. The nautical mile is the length of a minute of latitude at the place concerned, and because the earth is not a perfect sphere it varies slightly in length from 1843m (6046ft) at the equator to 1862m (6108ft) at the poles. However this is not a problem because the Mercator chart has a built-in scale of distances in the form of the latitude scale, which is marked down the margin either side.

Fig. 3(10) shows how a distance between two points on the chart is transferred to the latitude scale with dividers, in order to determine how far they are apart in nautical miles.

Instruments such as logs and radar sets which measure distances are calibrated on a mean figure of 1852m (6076ft), now universally adopted as the International Nautical Mile.

A cable is one-tenth of a nautical mile, or for practical purposes 183m (200yd). This unit is often met in sailing directions, and may be abbreviated to ca.

3.1.15 Speed

Speed at sea is measured in knots. A knot (sometimes abbreviated to kn or kt) is one nautical mile per hour, equivalent to 1.15 statute miles per hour.

Logs, which are the instruments used for measuring distance at sea, record in nautical miles, although some also measure speed – see 3.1.16.

Tables which relate time, speed and distance, and which can be used for computing speed from time over a measured (nautical) mile are given as Tables 3(5) and 3(6) in *The Macmillan & Silk Cut Nautical Almanac*.

3.1.16 Logs and speedometers

Except for a racing yacht the speed of a vessel through the water is of secondary importance to the distance actually run which, together with course steered, is the basis of dead reckoning (see 3.3.4). So some form of log is essential for any seagoing boat which is to make coastal cruises.

For simplicity, accuracy and reliability there is a great deal to be said for the traditional Walker Excelsior log, consisting of a rotator at the end of a long line connected to the instrument on the stern of the boat. The simplicity is obvious, the accuracy is due to the fact that the rotator is operating well astern of the hull, and reliability is ensured because, apart from routine cleaning and lubrication, maintenance is minimal. Furthermore, the whole can be stowed away in its box when not needed. It is, however, wise to carry a spare line and rotator.

When streaming a log, first hook it onto the indicator and then (retaining the rotator inboard) stream the bight of the line before letting the rotator go. Otherwise the rotator will twist the line into knots while it is being streamed. Similarly, when recovering it, unhook the end of the line from the indicator and pay it out astern as the

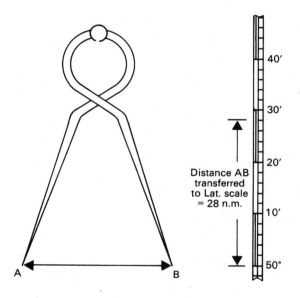

Fig. 3(10) Showing how dividers are used to transfer a certain distance AB on the chart to the latitude scale for measurement.

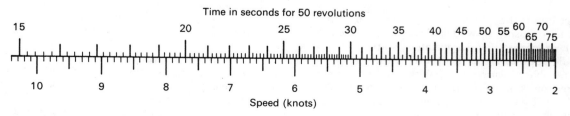

Fig. 3(11) Speed table for Walker's Excelsior IV Log (1166 revolutions per nautical mile).

rotator is taken in – allowing the line to untwist as it is eventually pulled inboard from the rotator end.

The Excelsior log makes 1166 revolutions per nautical mile, and it is easy to convert revolutions per minute (or the time to make 50 revolutions, for example) into the boat's speed. This can be done using the scale given in Fig. 3(11).

Modern technology has produced several other types of log – more expensive and not necessarily any more accurate, but more convenient to use. Some have a small impeller or paddlewheel mounted outside the hull; the rotating part incorporates a small magnet so that the magnetic impulse is passed to a unit inside the boat, which can count the number of pulses and hence record distance run and speed.

Some logs operate without any moving parts, so avoiding the problems of fouling by weed etc. An electro-magnetic log works on the principle that if a conductor moves in a magnetic field an electric current is induced in it, and the faster the movement the greater the current. The magnetic field is produced by an electromagnet inside the hull fitting, and the potential difference is sensed by two electrodes mounted flush with the outside of the hull.

Doppler logs measure the apparent shift in frequency between a transmitted signal and the signal reflected back from the water or (in shallower depths) from the bottom. When picking up the bottom signal the log measures distance and speed over the ground, rather than through the water. Others work on the speed of sound.

If it is to be relied on, any log should be calibrated by running the boat over a measured distance. The procedure is described in 3.3.15.

Most electronic logs incorporate some form of adjustment for calibration, and few have theoretical operating errors of less than $\pm 1\frac{1}{2}$ per cent. In practice the error is likely to be greater than this and may vary with speed. So log readings must be used with caution when (for example) approaching dangers in poor visibility.

3.1.17 Depths

The depth of water is always of concern to yachtsmen, and since modern echo sounders are reliable and cheap they are a most useful aid to navigation. But to gain full benefit from them it is necessary to understand exactly what they measure.

Further information and definitions of terms used in connection with the tides are given in Chapter 9.

Once a yachtsman is aware of the significance of the soundings marked on a chart and how the height of the tide is expressed above chart datum, the echo sounder (or lead line) becomes a useful navigation aid, apart from telling him when he is about to run aground.

It is best if the echo sounder is adjusted to give the actual distance of the sea bed below sea level,

and this should be checked with a lead line from time to time. Then, knowing the height of the tide at any moment (from tide tables) and the reading of the echo sounder, it is possible to calculate what depth should be shown on the chart.

Similarly the echo sounder can be used, perhaps in poor visibility, for 'contour navigation' following a certain depth contour, maybe along the edge (but just clear) of the main shipping channel.

When anchoring it is important to know the height of the tide at that time so that, in conjunction with the depth of water shown by the echo sounder (or lead line), it is possible to calculate what will be the greatest and least depths of water at that place. The greatest depth will dictate how much scope should be given to the anchor cable, while the least depth will of course govern whether or not the boat will be safely afloat at low water.

3.1.18 Echo sounders

An echo sounder is the most useful item of electronic equipment for a boat of any type, and there is a large range of models available. Properly used as described above, an echo sounder is a navigational aid – not just a means of preventing involuntary grounding.

All echo sounders work on a similar principle, although there are different ways of presenting the information. An electronic pulse, usually at 150 or 200kHz, is transmitted downwards from the transducer, fitted in the bottom of the boat. The signal received back from the sea bottom is amplified and then made into a readable display. For small boats the most common is the flashing display with a rotating arm, at the end of which there is a light source. The light flashes at zero when the pulse is emitted, and it flashes again when the amplified signal is received back. For practical purposes the speed of sound in water is constant at about 1490m/sec (4900ft/sec), although it is slightly affected by differences in temperature and salinity. Since the arm rotates at a constant speed, the time taken for the pulse to go to the bottom and back is represented by the angular displacement between the two flashes.

The receiver will also record echoes that are returned from intermediate objects, between the transducer and the sea bed – fish, weed etc. Also, with experience, the echo from a hard bottom, such as rock, can be distinguished from soft mud.

Other types of display incorporate either a needle on a dial (i.e. a meter display) or a digital readout. Either may include a special microprocessor which tries to sort out the extraneous signals from fish etc which otherwise may cause the display to fluctuate wildly.

Most modern echo sounders are sufficiently powerful to allow the transducer to be installed inside a glassfibre hull. Apart from eliminating the need for a hole through the bottom, this also solves any problem of fouling on the face of the transducer. It does however reduce the sensitivity at maximum depths.

Some echo sounders have shallow-water alarms which can be useful, particularly if cruising short handed. In addition, some models have a deep-water alarm, or anchor watch features.

The most versatile type of echo sounder has a visual record display whereby the flash (similar to that of a rotating flashing display) marks a moving sheet of paper and thus provides a recorded picture of the echoes from the sea bed and from the water above it. Some such sounders combine this graphical display with a flashing light display which can be used in isolation (to save paper).

Yet another method of presentation is by cathode ray tube – and in colour so that different types of echoes (surface contamination, plankton layers, shoals of fish, and type of bottom) can be readily distinguished. Naturally, such sophisticated equipment is expensive and its use is normally confined to fish finding and similar uses.

3.1.19 Lead line
Even when a yacht is fitted with an echo sounder it is desirable to carry a hand lead and line. Apart from being required in the event of any failure of the electronic instrument, it is also useful on occasions at anchor, to tell whether the anchor is dragging.

Traditionally, lead lines have been marked in fathoms, as follows. (One fathom is six feet.)

2 fathoms – Two strips of leather
3 fathoms – Three strips of leather
5 fathoms – A piece of white duck
7 fathoms – A piece of red bunting
10 fathoms – A piece of leather with a hole in it
13 fathoms – A piece of blue serge
15 fathoms – A piece of white duck
17 fathoms – A piece of red bunting
20 fathoms – Two knots.

With the change to metric units it is now more convenient for a lead line to be calibrated in metres, and the following markings are appropriate:

2 metres – Two strips of leather
3 metres – Three strips of leather
5 metres – A piece of white duck
7 metres – A piece of red bunting
10 metres – A piece of leather with a hole in it
13 metres – A piece of blue serge
15 metres – A piece of white duck
17 metres – A piece of red bunting
20 metres – Two knots

A 20 metre or 10 fathom lead line is more than adequate for most yachting purposes, particularly when mainly used as a stand-by for the echo sounder. Depending on the boat's normal cruising waters, a line of 10 metres should suffice.

3.1.20 Tidal streams
Almost as important to yachtsmen as the depth of water caused by the rise and fall of the tide are tidal streams – the horizontal movement of water, usually changing direction every six hours or so. Explanations of tidal streams are given in Chapter 9(9.9). Details of tidal streams around the coasts of Britain and Western Europe are given in *The Macmillan & Silk Cut Nautical Almanac.*

3.1.21 Meteorological conditions
Tidal heights are computed and predicted for average meteorological conditions, and can be quite seriously affected by unusual weather and, to a lesser extent, by changes in barometric pressure. Details are given in Chapter 9(9.7).

3.2 Charts

3.2.1 Mercator's projection
An adequate chart of an area is the first requirement for any form of navigation. Without it the sailor has no idea of the relative positions or distances of one feature from another, or of what goes on beneath the surface of the sea.

A chart, like a map, must be a compromise because it has to represent the curved shape of the globe on a flat piece of paper. Details of the coastline, for example, have to be distorted somewhat to get them on a flat surface.

Most charts are drawn on Mercator's projection with the meridians shown as equally spaced parallel lines running up and down the chart whereas in reality they converge towards the poles. The parallels of latitude, which in reality are equally spaced, are drawn on the chart further and further apart towards the poles.

Thus on a Mercator's chart land masses are greatly distorted in high latitudes, but this is not important around the British Isles.

A Mercator's chart has the following characteristics:
(1) A rhumb line, which cuts all the meridians at the same angle, is a straight line on the chart.
(2) The scale of distance is given by the latitude scale – at the latitude concerned.
(3) Angles on the earth's surface are equal to corresponding angles on the chart.
(4) Meridians are parallel straight lines, equally spaced, and the scale of longitude is constant for all latitudes.
(5) A great circle, which is the shortest distance between two points, appears as a curve. This is not a serious disadvantage unless long passages are contemplated.

3.2.2 Gnomonic charts
Some charts are based on a gnomonic (pronounced nom-on-ic) projection. Apart from harbour plans this projection is also used for polar charts and for great circle sailing. A gnomonic chart is a projection of the earth's surface from the centre on to a tangent plane, so that all great circles appear

as straight lines. Large scale gnomonic charts, as used for harbour plans, are used in just the same way as a Mercator's chart.

3.2.3 Scale

The amount of detail shown on a chart depends upon its scale. Large scale charts (typically 1:50,000) are used for harbours and approaches, while small scale charts (1:1,000,000 for example) may be used for coastlines. The scale is the relationship between a distance shown on the chart and the actual distance on land or sea: i.e. 1:50,000 means that one foot on the chart represents 50,000ft on land/sea. So large scale charts cover small areas and have small numbers in their scale, while small scales charts cover big areas and have big numbers.

The scale is shown near the title to the chart. It is most important to use the largest scale chart available, particularly for inshore pilotage, because a lot of inshore details are deliberately omitted from small scale charts.

A good idea of the scale of a chart can be obtained by looking at the latitude scale, remembering that one minute is one nautical mile. It will be noticed that on Admiralty charts the design of the latitude scale varies with the scale of the chart. Care is needed in reading latitude and longitude scales. Read off the correct number of degrees first (taking the lower of the two figures on either side of the position), and then the number of minutes.

3.2.4 Chart corrections

It is a false economy to carry too few charts, or charts which are out of date. Admiralty charts show the date of publication and also the date of the last correction at the bottom.

Corrections to charts and to other navigational publications from the Hydrographic Department (such as the *Admiralty List of Lights and Fog Signals* and the *Admiralty List of Radio Signals*) are issued in the weekly *Admiralty Notices to Mariners*, which can be obtained from chart agents or are available for consultation at Mercantile Marine Offices and Customs Offices.

A Small Craft Edition of Admiralty Notices to Mariners is published periodically for those who navigate small craft in the waters round the British Isles. It summarises the corrections which are of direct interest to yachtsmen.

3.2.5 Yachtsman's charts

Commercial charts are available which are specifically intended for use in small craft. They either have comparatively small sheets or they can be folded like a map, making them handy to use in a small space. Stanford's charts for example cover the principal coastal areas of the country, and the more important yachting harbours. They also give pilotage notes and other information useful to yachtsmen. They are available from chandlers or from the publishers: Stanford Charts,

PO Box 2747, Tollesbury, Maldon, Essex, CM9 8XE.

Imray, Laurie, Norie and Wilson (Imray's) produce three series of charts for yachtsmen. Their 'Y' series cover harbours or short lengths of coast, while the 'C' series are smaller scale for coastal cruising. The 'BB' series are even smaller scale, but are suitable for passage making. They are available from yacht suppliers or from the publishers at Wych House, The Broadway, St Ives, Huntingdon, Cambridgeshire.

The Admiralty introduced a new range of charts for small craft in 1992. These are selected standard Admiralty charts modified to meet the special needs of yachtsmen. They fold to a size of 215mm x 355mm (slightly bigger than A4), which is convenient enough for stowage. On the reverse is supplementary information derived from Admiralty publications such as radio services, safety information, weather and navigation warnings and tidal stream details. A total of 89 Small Craft Editions are on sale (1994) at £8.00 each. They are available from many chandlers and bookshops as well as from Admiralty Chart Agents. For further information contact the Hydrographic Office, Taunton, Somerset TA1 2DN. Tel: (01823) 337900 Ext 3706.

3.2.6 Admiralty charts

The full *Catalogue of Admiralty Charts and other Hydrographic Publications* (NP 131) lists some 6000 charts — sufficient to take a boat to almost every part of the world — as well as many other Admiralty publications. It also lists the location of Admiralty chart agents, which is repeated in *Admiralty Notice to Mariners* No. 2 each year.

A limited edition of the chart catalogue (NP 109) covering the British Isles and north-west Europe is published in January each year.

When ordered, charts should be referred to by their number as well as their title.

Apart from purely navigational charts the Hydrographic Department issues a variety of other charts and diagrams, of which the following may be of interest to yachtsmen:

(1) Latticed charts for electronic navigation systems such as Decca, Loran, Omega and Consol.
(2) Astronomical charts — azimuth diagrams and star charts, for navigational purposes.
(3) Routeing charts for ocean passages. The data includes routes and distances between ports, ocean currents, wind roses, ice limits, air and sea temperature, barometric pressure, and the incidence of fog and gales.
(4) Ships' boats' charts. Issued as a survival kit for ships' boats but useful for a liferaft on ocean passages.
(5) Instructional charts — cheap, uncorrected charts for navigational classes.
(6) Plotting charts.
(7) Uncorrected fathom charts of certain Scottish lochs and Irish loughs.

3.2.7 Admiralty charts symbols and abbreviations

To make proper use of a chart it is essential to know at least the more common symbols and abbreviations which are used in order to make the best use of the space available. They are described in detail in Admiralty Chart 5011, which is in booklet form (re-issued in 1991).

The information below refers to metric charts except where otherwise stated. There are still a number of older charts in use; in general the symbols and abbreviations on these are fairly similar but there is one notable exception as already stated, depths on metric charts are given in metres whereas on older charts they are shown either as fathoms and feet or (for inshore charts) as feet. Always check which units apply.

An obvious function of a chart is to show the outlines of the coast and of off-lying islands. On metric Admiralty charts these features are made distinct by the land being tinted buff, and drying areas (between high water and low water) being tinted green. Depths below 5 metres are tinted blue, and the 10 metre depth contour has a ribbon of blue tint. Features such as lights, radio aids, traffic separation schemes, prohibited anchorages, submarine cables, explosive dumping areas, submarine exercise areas, pipelines etc are shown in magenta.

Depths on metric charts are shown as metres (and tenths of metres in shallower waters). Drying heights (above chart datum) are also in metres and tenths of metres, and are underlined. Clearances below bridges etc are given at MHWS by a figure in metres. Heights of lights, hills etc are in metres above MHWS. On older (fathom) charts drying heights and elevations of lights etc are shown in feet.

Rocks are marked with crosses, like a plus sign. A dot in each corner shows that the rock is awash at chart datum; a plain cross or one surrounded by a circle of dots indicate a dangerous underwater rock. Rocky pinnacles may be marked with a drying height.

A wreck may be shown by the abbreviation Wk or by a symbol which is a horizontal line crossed by three vertical lines, the centre one being slightly longer. If surrounded by a ring of dots it may be dangerous. These and other more common symbols are shown on pages 60-61. Abbreviations on Admiralty metric charts are shown in Fig. 3(12). A range of certain pictorial symbols, introduced in 1983, is illustrated in Fig. 3(13).

3.2.8 Lights

Lights from lighthouses, light vessels and buoys which are lit are indicated on a chart by a magenta coloured flare. Alongside is written the characteristic of the light. The abbreviations and nomenclature were changed in 1979 by international agreement, and apply to both fathoms and metric charts. The new ones are now in general use, and are shown in Fig. 3(14) in the second column. The third column shows the older form (but only where there is a difference).

Lighthouses sometimes show a different coloured light in a certain sector or sectors to indicate either offlying dangers or the channel. Coastal lighthouses often do not shine inland, and their arcs of visibility and colour of light (if other than white) are given on the chart. The bearings shown are true from seaward, measured clockwise from 000° to 359°.

The elevation of a light is its height above high water (normally the level of Mean High Water Springs) and is now almost universally expressed in metres. Elevations will however be found in feet on older charts.

Leading lights consist of two or more lights which are aligned in order to form a leading line to be followed. Lights described as 'Lts in line' mark limits of areas, alignments of cables etc, and do not mark a direction to be followed.

A direction light shows over a narrow sector, indicating a direction to be followed. The sector may be flanked by sectors of reduced visibility or of a different colour.

In a description of a light structure, horizontal divisions of colour are termed bands, and vertical divisions are termed stripes.

Fog detector lights are fitted at or near certain light structures. Their purpose is to detect fog, to switch on fog signals and/or to transmit range of visibility to a data centre. Various types are in use: some are visible over a narrow arc, some show a powerful bluish flash, and some sweep back and forth and may be mistaken for signals.

3.2.9 Ranges of lights

The range of a light can be quoted in three ways:

(1) Luminous range is the maximum distance that a light can be seen, as determined by the intensity of the light and the meteorological visibility prevailing at the time. It takes no account of the elevation of the light, or of the observer's height of eye, or of the curvature of the earth. Meteorological visibility is the greatest distance at which a black object of suitable size can be seen against the horizon sky – or for night observations, could be seen if the general illumination were raised to the normal daylight level.

(2) Nominal range is the luminous range when the meteorological visibility is ten nautical miles. Because of their great intensity, many lights will be sighted at distances greater than the estimated meteorological visibility. The ranges of lights as published in *The Macmillan & Silk Cut Nautical Almanac* are nominal ranges.

(3) Geographical range is the maximum distance at which a light can theoretically reach an observer, as limited only by the curvature of the earth and the refraction of the atmosphere, and by the elevation of the light and the height of eye of the observer.

Coastal Features

Anch.	Anchorage
Appr.	Approaches
B.	Bay
C.	Cape
Chan.	Channel
Cr.	Creek
Ent.	Entrance
Est.	Estuary
G.	Gulf
Hn.	Haven
Hr.	Harbour
I.	Island
It	Islet
L.	Loch, Lough, Lake
Lndg.	Landing place
Mt.	Mountain, Mount
Mth.	Mouth
P.	Port
Pass.	Passage
Pt.	Point
Prom.	Promontory
R.	River
Rds.	Roads, Roadstead
Rk.	Rock
Sd.	Sound
Str.	Strait

Units

cm	Centimetre(s)
dm	Decimetre(s)
ft	Foot, Feet
Ht	Height
km	Kilometres
kn	Knots
Lat	Latitude
Long	Longitude
m	Metre(s)
M	Sea Mile(s)
mm	Millimetres
No	Number

Adjectives etc

abt	About
Aero	Aeronautical
Anct	Ancient
approx	Approximate
conspic	Conspicuous
dest	Destroyed
discont	Discontinued
dist	Distant
exper	Experimental
explos	Explosive
Gt, Grt	Great
Hr	Higher
(illum)	Illuminated
Lit	Little
LL	List of Lights
Lr	Lower
Mid	Middle
NM	Notice to Mariners

(P)	Preliminary
(priv)	Private
prohib	Prohibited
proj	Projected
prom	Prominent
S., St	Saint
SD	Sailing Directions
subm	Submerged
(T)	Temporary

Buildings etc

Ave	Avenue
Baty	Battery
Bldg	Building
Cas	Castle
Cath	Cathedral
Cemy	Cemetery
CG	Coastguard
Ch	Church, Chapel
Chy	Chimney
Col	Column
Cup	Cupola
Fm	Farm
FS	Flagstaff
Ft	Fort
Ho	House
Hosp	Hospital
LB	Lifeboat
Mon	Monument, Memorial
NB	Notice Board
Obsy	Observatory
Off	Office
PO	Post Office
Ru	Ruin
Sch	School
Sem	Semaphore
Sig	Signal
SS	Signal Station
St	Street
Sta	Station
Tel	Telephone
Tr	Tower
Va	Villa

Dangers

Bk.	Bank
cov.	Covers
dr	Dries
ED	Existence doubtful
Le	Ledge
Obstn	Obstruction
PA	Position approximate
PD	Position doubtful
pos	Position
Rep	Reported
Rf.	Reef
Sh.	Shoal
uncov.	Uncovers
unexam	Unexamined

Quality of the Bottom

Bo	Boulders
bk	Broken
c	Coarse
Ck	Chalk
Cy	Clay
f	Fine
G	Gravel
ga	Glacial
Gd	Ground
h	Hard
l	Large
M	Mud
Ml	Marl
Ms	Mussels
Oy	Oysters
Oz	Ooze
P	Pebbles
Qz	Quartz
R	Rock
S	Sand
Sh	Shells
sf	Stiff
sm	Small
Sn	Shingle
so	Soft
St	Stones
sy	Sticky
Wd	Weed

Tides and Currents

CD	Chart Datum
Dir	Direction
HAT	Highest Astronomical Tide
HW/LW	High Water/Low Water
kn	Knots
LAT	Lowest Astronomical Tide
MHW	Mean High Water
MHWN	Mean High Water Neaps
MHWS	Mean High Water Springs
MLW	Mean Low Water
MLWN	Mean Low Water Neaps
MLWS	Mean Low Water Springs
MSL	Mean Sea Level
MTL	Mean Tide Level
OD	Ordnance Datum
Sp/Np	Spring Tides/Neap Tides
Vel	Velocity

Compass

annly	Annually
Mag	Magnetic
Var	Variation

Fig. 3(12) Abbreviations used on Admiralty metric charts.

Ports and harbours

Anchor berth, numbered or lettered

Custom House

Crane

Fishing harbour

Quarantine, or Health Officer's Office

Quarantine anchorage

Harbour Master's Office

Anchorage for deep draught vessels

Areas and limits

Restricted area

Entry prohibited

Prohibited area

Anchoring prohibited

Fishing prohibited

Historic Wk

Historic wreck

Buildings

(30)

Height of a structure

Tower, in general

Castle, fort

Windmotor

Airfield

Chimney

Post Office

Water tower

or **Hosp**

Hospital

Oil tank, tank, gasholder

or **Mon**

Monument

Flare stack (on land)

Miscellaneous

Lifeboat

or **FS**

Flagstaff

SS

Signal station

Notice board

Beacon, in general

Cairn

2kn

Flood stream

3kn

Ebb stream

Current

B

Position for tidal stream data

!

Precautionary Area

Additional symbols of interest to yachtsmen

Slipway for small craft

Yacht marina

Restaurant

Visitors' mooring

Visitors' berth

Water tap

Fuel

Public landing

Public house or inn

Camping site

Caravan site

Public car park

Parking for boats/trailers

Toilets

Public telephone

Yacht or Sailing Club

Launderette

Nature reserve

Fig. 3(13) Pictorial symbols on Admiralty charts.

CLASS OF LIGHT		International abbreviations	Older form (where different)	Illustration Period shown ⊢——⊣
Fixed *(steady light)*		F		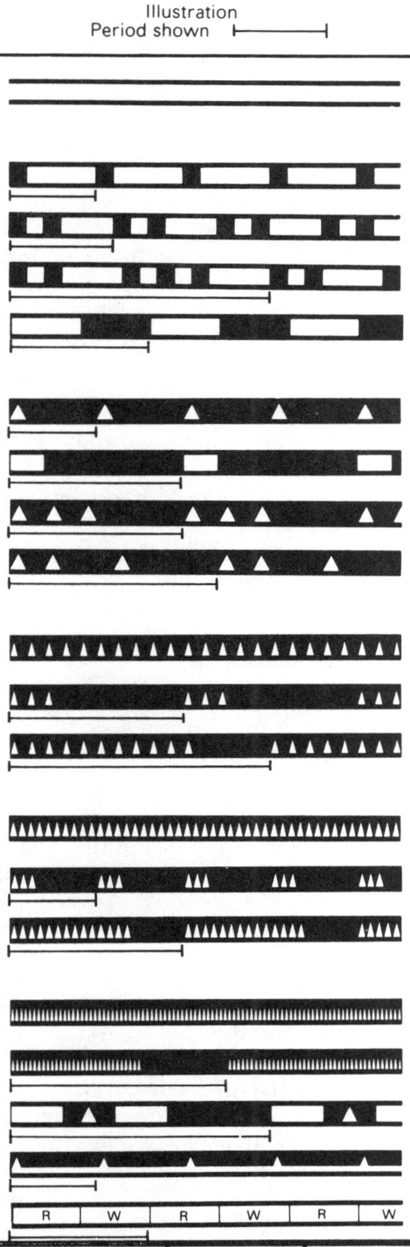
Occulting *(total duration of light more than dark)*				
Single-occulting		Oc	Occ	
Group-occulting	*e.g.*	Oc(2)	GpOcc(2)	
Composite group-occulting	*e.g.*	Oc(2+3)	GpOcc(2+3)	
Isophase *(light and dark equal)*		Iso		
Flashing *(total duration of light less than dark)*				
Single-flashing		Fl		
Long-flashing (flash 2s or longer)		LFl		
Group-flashing	*e.g.*	Fl(3)	GpFl(3)	
Composite group-flashing	*e.g.*	Fl(2+1)	GpFl(2+1)	
Quick *(50 to 79—usually either 50 or 60—flashes per minute)*				
Continuous quick		Q	QkFl	
Group quick	*e.g.*	Q(3)	QkFl(3)	
Interrupted quick		IQ	IntQkFl	
Very Quick *(80 to 159—usually either 100 or 120—flashes per minute)*				
Continuous very quick		VQ	VQkFl	
Group very quick	*e.g.*	VQ(3)	VQkFl(3)	
Interrupted very quick		IVQ	IntVQkFl	
Ultra Quick *(160 or more—usually 240 to 300—flashes per minute)*				
Continuous ultra quick		UQ		
Interrupted ultra quick		IUQ		
Morse Code	*e.g.*	Mo(K)		
Fixed and Flashing		FFl		
Alternating	*e.g.*	Al.WR	Alt.WR	

COLOUR	International abbreviations	Older form (where different)	RANGE in sea miles	International abbreviations	Older form
White	W *(may be omitted)*		*Single range* *e.g.*	15M	
Red	R				
Green	G		*2 ranges* *e.g.*	14/12M	14,12M
Yellow	Y				
Orange	Y	Or	*3 or more ranges* *e.g.*	22-18M	22,20,18M
Blue	Bu	Bl			
Violet	Vi				
ELEVATION is given in metres **(m)** or feet **(ft)**			**PERIOD** in seconds *e.g.*	5s	5sec

Reproduced by kind permission of H.M. Stationery Office and the Hydrographer of the Navy

Fig. 3(14) Light characters (Fathoms and Metric Charts).

On charts the range shown for a light is now the nominal range for countries where this range has been adopted (which includes all north-west Europe), or luminous range.

For Admiralty charts, until 1972 the geographical range of a light (for an observer's height of eye of 5m or 15ft) was shown, unless the luminous range of the light was less than the geographical range when the luminous range was inserted.

Distance from a light cannot be estimated from its apparent brightness. In thick weather the range of a light depends upon its intensity, and a weak light can easily be obscured at distances well below its tabulated range. Lights placed at a high elevation may be obscured by cloud. Glare from background light (e.g. a town) can greatly reduce the range at which a light is visible.

Abnormal refraction may allow a light to be seen further, and the loom of a light can often be detected well beyond its geographical range.

The distance at which a light dips (or rises) over the horizon, combined with a bearing of it, can give a useful fix, as explained in 3.3.13.

3.2.10 Light-vessels

Light-vessels are shown on the chart by a self-evident symbol and the letters 'Lt V'. Apart from their characteristic light, they show a white riding light forward. During fog or low visibility a light-vessel rings her bell rapidly between her normal fog signal when a vessel approaches.

If a light-vessel is out of position she does not show her normal light or make her normal fog signal. In these circumstances she may show by day two large black balls, one forward and one aft, and the International Code group 'LO'; or by night, a fixed red light at bow and stern, and red and white flares shown simultaneously every 15 minutes or on the approach of traffic.

3.2.11 Oil and gas platforms

Offshore oil and gas platforms are shown on the chart by a small square with a dot in the centre. They are marked by a light Mo(U) 15s 15M, and with lights Mo(U) R 15s 3M at each corner not marked by the light above. They sound a fog signal, Horn Mo(U) 30s.

3.2.12 Fog signals

Various fog signals are emitted by lighthouses, light-vessels and some navigational buoys, and the abbreviations used for them are indicated in brackets below. Sound is very unpredictable in fog, and signals may be heard at varying distances. Under sail it may help to heave-to when trying to pick up a fog signal; under power, the engine should be stopped for the same purpose.

The following are the main types of fog signals:

(1) Diaphone (Dia). Operated by compressed air, producing a powerful, low-pitched sound often ending with a grunt. Now rarely encountered.

(2) Horn (Horn). Uses compressed air or electricity to vibrate a diaphragm. Some produce sound of different pitch.

(3) Reed (Reed). Operated by compressed air, producing a weak high-pitched sound.

(4) Siren (Siren) Operated by compressed air. Various types produce sounds of different intensities.

(5) Nautophone (Nauto). Electronically operated, producing a high note, from a vibrated diaphragm.

(6) Tyfon (Tyfon). Produces a medium note, like a ship's siren.

(7) Gun (Gun). This type of fog signal is obsolescent. The sound may be accompanied by a bright flash.

(8) Explosive (Explos). Produces reports like the sound of a gun. Now very rarely encountered.

(9) Bell, Gong and Whistle (Bell, Gong, Whis). May be operated by hand, by machinery, or by wave motion.

Fog signals in Morse code have the letters 'Mo' shown, followed by the letter or letters of the signal.

3.3 Chartwork

3.3.1 Courses

Headings and courses may be expressed as True, Magnetic or Compass – which are notated as (T), (M) or (C) respectively. The same applies to bearings. The symbol (T) is usually omitted, as for example in *Admiralty Sailing Directions* and in most yachtsman's pilot guides which state in the explanatory notes that all courses and bearings are true.

Attention is called to the standard navigational terms which are stated in 3.1.4.

The course to steer (or the course ordered) is different from the ground track from one point to another, when it is necessary to make allowance for set and drift due to a current and/or tidal

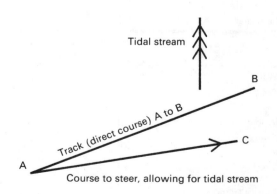

Fig. 3(15) The course to steer in order to get from place to place is often different from the direct course in order to allow for tidal stream and/or leeway.

stream. For example, in Fig. 3(15) the intended track of the boat is from A to B. Because the tidal stream is setting north, as indicated by the arrow in the diagram, it is necessary for the navigator to lay off a course in a direction such as AC, in order to achieve the required track AB. How the course AC is determined is explained in 3.3.3.

It is often important for the navigator to know the mean heading which the helmsman has actually achieved over a certain period (usually every half-hour). This may not be the same as the course to steer, or course ordered, because the helmsman will not always be able to maintain this for a variety of reasons.

Leeway is the angle between a boat's heading and the actual direction she is moving through the water (water track). The amount of leeway a boat will make depends upon various factors – her hull design, the amount of windage of sails and/or hull, the strength and direction of the wind relative to the boat, and her speed through the water. About five degrees may be a typical figure for the average cruising yacht when beating to windward. There is less leeway on a reach, and of course no sideways movement of the boat in the water when she is running dead before the wind.

Yachtsmen should be aware of the possible existence of surface drift which (distinct from tidal stream or ocean current) is caused by the wind blowing in a certain direction for any length of time, and which may persist for a while after the wind has changed direction.

3.3.2 Instruments and equipment

In order to perform the basic tasks of navigation it is necessary to have a reasonable chart table on which to work, and suitable instruments. A flat, smooth surface is needed on which to spread a chart. If space is very limited some form of portable board will suffice, but it is difficult to do justice to the job at sea unless one can work on a fixed surface. Good illumination is important, but the light must be screened so that it does not worry the helmsman. Over the chart table there should be a small shelf or bookcase for publications such as sailing directions. A list of these covering the waters round the British Isles and Europe is given in 15.6.5.

Some form of log is essential, for entering navigational records, and these requirements are discussed in 15.6.1.

Most navigators also like to have a notebook in which they can calculate such things as compass courses, tidal heights etc, where the information is accessible should it be needed later. This little book may also be used for planning a passage, and for noting down all sorts of information extracted from various sources.

A handy stowage is needed for the different instruments – plenty of soft pencils (2B), a good soft rubber, a pair of dividers, and a parallel ruler or some form of protractor for measuring and transferring courses and bearings on the chart.

Parallel rulers come in two types – the roller variety which is really more suitable for larger vessels, and the hinged type with two parallel strips of perspex connected by metal arms each end. Many yachtsmen however prefer one of the various protractors which are available, such as the Hurst plotter or a Douglas protractor, which are very much easier to use than parallel rulers in a small boat.

Types of plotters

The Hurst plotter has a square perspex grid (which can be aligned with a convenient meridian or parallel of latitude) as a base, a circular perspex disc graduated from 0 to 360° and adjustable for variation, and a rotating arm which can be aligned with the required course or bearing against the plotter's own compass rose. This device is simple and quick to use, and makes the conversion of bearings and courses from true to magnetic and vice versa unnecessary.

Another version is the Breton plotter which consists of a clear rectangle of plastic which has a rotating protractor with grid squares on it built into the centre. The grid is lined up with a convenient parallel of latitude or meridian of longitude on the chart, and the edge of the main body of the plotter is aligned with the required course or bearing, and read off against the central protractor which includes a scale where variation can be set.

A Douglas protractor is a perspex square, graduated round the edge from 0 to 360° in both directions, and with a small hole in the centre. The surface of the square is engraved with a grid, parallel to the sides, similar to the Hurst plotter. To establish the course from A to B the centre hole is placed over the line AB, the square is lined up with the nearest meridian or parallel of latitude with the north point at the top, and the course is then read off the edge of the square on the outer (clockwise) set of figures. A similar procedure is followed to determine the direction or bearing of an object.

Some navigators like to use navigational set squares, which are isosceles, right-angled triangles in perspex, graduated in degrees from the centre of the hypotenuse – from 0 to 180° on the outer scale, and from 180 to 360° on the inner. If for example the chimney in Fig. 3(16) bears 290°, one set square is aligned with the centre of its hypotenuse and its 290° mark on the nearest meridian, and then slid along the other square (or any suitable straight edge) until the hypotenuse cuts the chimney. The line of bearing is then drawn along the hypotenuse.

A completely different approach is provided by the Nautrack plotter, which takes some getting used to but which in fact has several attractions once the technique is mastered. The chart in use is slipped inside a clear plastic case, to which a special bearing plotter (called the Parallel Plate) will readily adhere. This is basically a plastic semi-

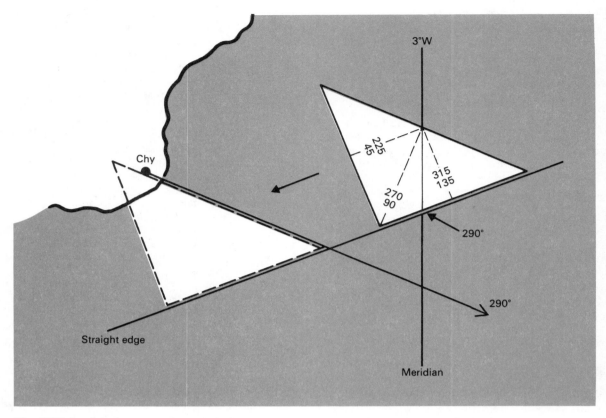

Fig. 3(16) Parallel rulers are not easy to manipulate in small boats, and some form of protractor is more convenient. Alternatively navigational set squares, as illustrated, provide a simple and cheap solution.

circle with a central 0-360° scale which rotates on top of a circular Variation Plate. The chart is protected and such few lines as need to be drawn can be done with a water soluble pen if plotting in the dry or with a Chinagraph pencil in an exposed position.

In addition there are two bearing arms, each with a Variation Plate on which is pivoted an arm 370mm (14½in) in length with a graduated 0–360° scale. The bearing arm is centred over any object on which a bearing is taken, and is pressed on to the chart cover. When two such bearings are taken the intersection of the arms provides the fix, without any line being drawn.

The Parallel Plate and a bearing arm can be used to solve relative velocity problems, for which purpose they are graduated to represent speeds or distances.

The chart cover can be rolled up for stowage, but not folded. It must be kept clean and free from dust. Grease or dirt can be washed off with warm water and a mild detergent.

Yeoman plotter

Increasingly yachtsmen are relying on electronic position fixing systems first Decca and Loran, then Transit, and now GPS which are all described in Chapter 4. But a latitude and longitude display on whatever 'navigator' is used still needs to be transferred to the chart in order that the position can be related to other features such as navigational dangers.

This can be done electronically by an Electronic Chart and Display Information System (ECDIS), but although the equipment available is improving all the time it remains expensive, bulky for the average yacht if it is to show much detail, and also power-consuming. The correction of chart data is also a problem. So for some time to come most yachtsmen will continue to use the conventional paper chart – a legal requirement in yachts over 12 metres – which provides all the detail needed, to a good standard of accuracy, and is simple to correct when required.

The Yeoman plotter is an electronic device which provides the essential link between whatever type of 'navigator' is used and the chart on the chart table. It dispenses with dividers, parallel rulers or mechanical plotting aids. It consists of a digitised mat or electronic grid on top of which the paper chart to be used is clipped and located. It can be used with any Mercator chart or harbour plan, and will accept an Admiralty chart folded in half. The electronic grid under the chart allows the Yeoman plotter (or puck) on the chart surface to convert any chosen position into latitude and longitude. Conversely, given latitude and longitude by (say) Decca or GPS, the Yeoman will guide you to that position on the chart by means of four illuminated red arrows pointing 90° apart. When the red lights go out, the puck is in the designated position.

When a chart is to be used for the first time it must be referenced. Three convenient positions – at the intersections of meridians and parallels of latitude – are entered as latitude and longitude into the Yeoman memory, which can accommodate references for 100 charts. Each chart is numbered by the user from 00 to 99. With these positions entered into the memory the plotting hole in the puck lens is placed over each reference point in turn, and the 'enter' key pressed. Thereafter, whenever that chart is clipped to the mat, it is only necessary to enter the chart number for the plotter to be ready for use.

Other items

A good pair of dividers, preferably of the crossover type which can be operated in one hand, are essential for chartwork, and a pencil compass can be useful for some problems.

Any cruising yacht needs at least one pair of efficient binoculars. A good arrangement is to have one pair for the skipper/navigator, and a spare pair for general ship's use. The correct choice is important. Prismatic binoculars are described by two sets of figures, thus 7x50. The first figure or figures refer to the magnification, 10 for example meaning that an object viewed will appear ten times larger and ten times nearer than if viewed with the naked eye. The second set of figures is the diameter of the objective lens (furthest from the eye) in mm, and this determines the amount of light admitted.

Another important dimension which is not immediately apparent but which can be quickly derived is the diameter of the exit pupil – the lens nearest the eye. This is determined by dividing the diameter of the objective pupil by the magnification. Hence for a 7x35 binocular the diameter of the exit pupil is 5mm. A large exit pupil passes more light to the eye and gives a brighter image. About 7mm is a desirable figure. This is particularly important in poor light, and is assisted by special coatings on the lenses and prisms of good quality binoculars.

For marine use it is unwise to buy binoculars with a magnification of more than 7 or 8, since at sea it is impossible to hold them sufficiently steady to get a good image. Exceptionally 9 x or 10 x can be used in large yachts which provide a steady platform. For general use 7x50 is recommended. In a yacht binoculars need to be sturdy and waterproof. Those which have individual focusing for each eyepiece are more resistant to water than those with central focusing. Some kind of rubber coating helps to protect binoculars from the knocks which they are bound to receive in the cockpit of a yacht.

Other items of navigational equipment which are needed are listed below:

(1) Steering compass, adjusted and swung, with up to date deviation card. (See sections 3.1.6 to 3.1.11). The compass must be properly sited for the helmsman, and illuminated at night.
(2) Hand bearing compass, for taking bearings of shore objects, lights, or other vessels for collision avoidance. (See section 3.1.12).
(3) Distance reading log, to record distance through the water. (See section 3.1.16).
(4) Echo sounder, or lead line. (See section 3.1.18).
(5) Reliable clock or watch. An alarm clock can be useful to catch the tide or to hear the shipping forecast.
(6) Radio receiver. The very minimum requirement is to be able to hear the shipping forecasts on 198kHz(1515m). (See section 6.5).
(7) Stop watch. For identifying the characteristics of lights.
(8) Sailing directions or pilotage guides for appropriate cruising areas (see 15.6.5).
(9) Barometer, or barograph.
(10) Chart magnifier.
(11) *The Macmillan & Silk Cut Nautical Almanac.*

Electronic charts

Today's microprocessor technology helps to process a vast amount of data received from navigation and instrument sensors which can then be displayed on a suitable visual display unit (VDU) in full colour. Such units are known as video plotters and it is incorrect to call them electronic charts. The received data is converted into a pictorial electronic plot showing current position, tracking, course to new waypoints, or other data, which is then shown against a digitised chart background, a grid, or another type of information overlay.

Several different developments are simultaneously taking place in the electronic plotting/charting field, each of which is different in concept. These include:
(1) Stand-alone colour video plotters which receive all data from other sensors.
(2) Colour video plotters which incorporate built-in GPS, Loran or Decca receivers.
(3) Integrated radar/plotters which provide overlay plotting information on a radar screen.
(4) Electronic Charts (EC) which may be facsimile reproductions of standard nautical charts, or computer generated charts.
(5) Electronic Chart Display and Information System (ECDIS).

Most video plotters available on the yacht market today take their information from a variety of different sources, assimilate the data received, and then present the information pictorially by showing the yacht's position in relation to a grid which can either be latitude and longitude, or a digitised basic outline of the coast. The simple outline charts used are first digitised and then stored in a cartridge, often called a chart pod.

Zoom and panning functions allow users to vary the chart scale from a quick overview of the complete chart, or to zoom in to a specific area for much greater detail.

Additional types of information such as bottom contours, buoys, lights, traffic routes, or wrecks etc. can be superimposed on the basic chart according to the degree of information and sophistication required. The small high-resolution screen, usually about 200mm (8in) in size, will show where the boat has been and where she is going, together with the current position obtained from the navigation sensor. Most video plotters will store at least 20 waypoints, and a number of event markers, and also display any tabulated data in a separate window on the screen.

A relatively new development is the integrated radar plotter which allows users to display plotting information normally seen on a video plotter on the radar screen. The idea behind this type of development is to provide for navigation while at the same time seeing where the boat is going on radar.

The first stage of development between the current crop of video plotters and the evolution of the full electronic chart display and information systems is the development of a suitable electronic chart and the necessity to have a standardised international electronic chart database in order to produce ECs. The EC is not just a paper chart in video form but something completely new and different while still possessing many chart-like features. Work on the development of a suitable electronic chart database is a vast undertaking for the various international Hydrographic Offices because of the magnitude of the task involved and resources available. The lack of internationally agreed specifications, coupled with deficiencies in many existing chart databases covering major areas of the world, do not make the transition to the full EC an easy process.

Another interesting development with much to commend it because of its familiarity with existing charts, is the storage of facsimile reproductions of present nautical charts on compact disc. In spite of its lower cost and simplicity, CD development has not yet had any impact in Europe because of more restrictive copyright limitations. A number of programmes for charting and plotting also exist for use on Macintosh, Atari or IBM type computers.

ECDIS is not yet available for the yacht market. Such equipment is still very much in the design and experimental stage even for big ships and is unlikely to appear until towards the end of the decade. When the specification for ECDIS has been finally agreed and standardised, the resulting equipment can be expected to amalgamate the present nautical paper chart in digitised electronic form, with position information from GPS or other position fixing sensors, together with inputs from on-board sensors such as course, speed or radar, and then present the combined information in a clear and self-evident form on high-resolution colour graphic and alphanumerical displays. In the longer term, ECDIS will undoubtedly improve the general safety of navigation by giving, in one combined display, a bird's eye view of the yacht in relation to other ships, channels, or navigational dangers in a fully automated way.

3.3.3 Chartwork

There are three basic procedures for working on the chart. First it is necessary to establish what should be the (compass) course to steer to get the boat from A to B, making due allowance for tidal streams and other factors, and ensuring that there are no hidden dangers along the route. For various reasons (e.g. wind direction) it may not be possible to steer the required course in practice, so secondly it is necessary to keep a running plot of the boat's position in order to monitor progress. Thirdly, opportunity should be taken to fix the boat's position at regular intervals by one of the methods which will be described.

Assuming that it is required to sail from point A to point B, first study the route on the chart and make quite certain that it does not pass over or near to shallow water, obstructions, prohibited areas, tide rips, or other hazards. Place the parallel ruler along the line AB, transfer it to the compass rose, and read off the true course. Suppose this is 073°. If variation is (say) 8°W this gives a magnetic course of 081°(M). Refer to the deviation card as in Fig. 3(6), and see what the deviation is on this heading. If it is for example 3°W then the compass course from A to B is 084°(C).

It is however more than likely that it will be necessary to make some allowance for tidal stream. In the example in Fig. 3(17) assume that the tidal stream is setting north at 2 knots, and that the boat's speed is 5 knots. From A construct AC pointing in the direction in which the tide is running (north), and two convenient units in length. From C, using a pair of compasses or dividers measure a length equal to five units (boat's speed) so that it meets AB at D. Draw AE parallel to CD. This is the course to steer (or course ordered). The boat starts from A, steering a course in the direction AE, but the tide carries it steadily north so that the ground track of the boat is along the line ADB.

The above assumes that the rate of the tidal stream remains constant at two knots, and that the speed of the boat is steady at five knots. On an actual passage either or both of these figures may change – the tidal stream may even reverse direction. In this case the passage must be divided up into a suitable number of parts, and the necessary course to steer calculated for each part, if it is desired to follow the track AB.

3.3.4 Plotting – Dead Reckoning (DR)

Referring to Fig. 3(18) if on sailing from point A the log reading is zero, after two hours on a course of (say) 080° it is possible to plot a rough position on the chart. If the log reading is ten miles, then

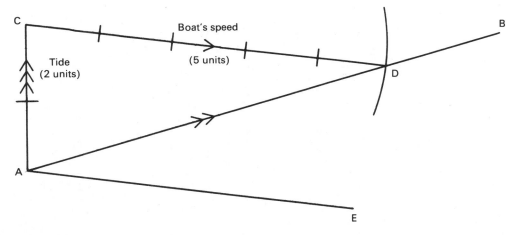

Fig. 3(17) How to determine the course to steer to allow for tidal stream.

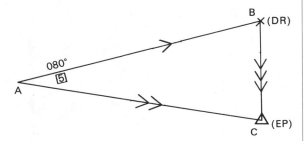

Fig. 3(18) Plotting – Dead Reckoning, indicated by a cross, and Estimated Position indicated by a triangle. By convention course has a single arrow, tidal stream three arrows, and the resultant track two arrows.

assuming that the course of 080° has been maintained and neglecting any other effects of wind or tide, the boat will have moved to B. B is called the Dead Reckoning position, or DR for short, and it is marked on the chart with a cross and the time alongside it.

Estimated Position (EP)
Still referring to Fig. 3(18), if while the boat is sailing from A to B the tidal stream is setting due south at a steady two knots, it will carry the boat four miles south during the two hours. The effect of the tidal stream is shown by the tidal vector BC in the diagram, and the boat will end up at C and not at B. C is called the Estimated Position (or EP) and is marked by a small triangle with a spot in the middle, and the time alongside.

The Estimated Position may be further refined by making an allowance for leeway (see 3.3.1).

3.3.5 Position fixing
Periodically (how often depends upon circumstances) it is necessary to check the boat's position, or take a fix. This is done by establishing two or more position lines; where they cross gives the position of the boat at the time of the observations. At times however even a single reliable position line can be very useful, as for

example to establish whether the boat is on her required track.

The most positive way of getting a position line is by means of a transit – when two known objects are in line with each other. Simply join the two objects on the chart, extend the line seaward, and the boat is somewhere along it. It is good practice to take a compass bearing of the transit and to check it against the bearing from the chart, in order to make sure that the objects have been correctly identified. Where the bearings of transits or leading marks are shown on the chart or in sailing directions, they are true bearings from seaward so it is necessary to apply variation. Taking the bearing is also a useful check on the compass.

A transit of two objects and a bearing of another object roughly at right angles gives a useful fix, particularly if as suggested above the bearing of the transit is taken so as to check the total compass error, and this is then applied to the second bearing. The procedure is shown in Fig. 3(19). If the transit is 080° on the chart, but 085°

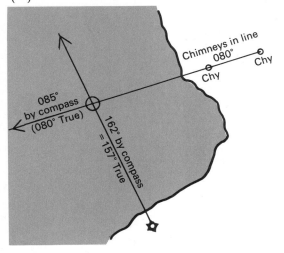

Fig. 3(19) A transit of two known objects, and a bearing of a third object, giving a cut approaching 90°, should result in a reliable fix.

by compass then the total compass error is 5°W. Hence if the bearing of the individual object is 162° by compass its true bearing is actually 157° and should be plotted accordingly.

Visual compass bearings of two or more objects, carefully taken, can give a reasonable fix but it is desirable to take at least three. This is what is involved in plotting one of these bearings – that of the church in Fig. 3(20) – on the chart. Assume that the reading from the hand bearing compass is 073°(M). As indicated, this is a magnetic bearing, so variation must be applied to get the true bearing. If the variation (from the chart) is 7°W the true bearing is 066°.

Place the parallel ruler against the centre of the compass rose and the 066° mark on the outer (true) scale, as indicated by the dotted line on the diagram. Then transfer the parallel ruler carefully to the church and draw a line to seaward. Mark it at the end with a single arrowhead and with the time of observation (1521).

Repeat the process with the other two objects. If all three bearings are completely accurate the three position lines will meet in a point. This seldom if ever happens, and in practice they form a small triangle called a cocked hat. The size of the cocked hat is a good indication of the accuracy of the fix. If a large cocked hat is obtained one or more of the bearings must be wrong or incorrectly plotted. This is why it is important to take at least three bearings; if only two objects are observed there is no check on reliability. It is also important that the objects should be selected so that the position lines from them give a good cut – at a sufficient angle. Ideally when three bearings are taken the position lines should meet at angles of about 60°. Be suspicious of fixes from position lines which cross at less than 30°.

If a cocked hat of a reasonably small size has been obtained, the fix is taken as its centre and is marked with a small circle and the time alongside,

as in Fig. 3(20). If however there are dangers nearby then the fix is taken as the corner of the cocked hat nearest the danger so that the worst situation is assumed.

3.3.6 Running fix

If only one object or one light can be positively identified on a stretch of coast, it is still possible to get at least an approximate idea of the boat's position by a running fix as shown in Fig. 3(21). An initial bearing of a light L shows that the boat is somewhere along the line LA. When this bearing is taken the time and log reading are carefully noted (this should be the practice with any observation). The boat sails on her way, and a

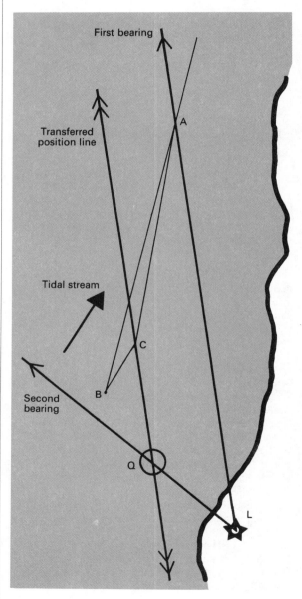

Fig. 3(21) The accuracy of a running fix, from consecutive bearings of one object, depends upon a correct assessment of the effects of tidal stream and leeway.

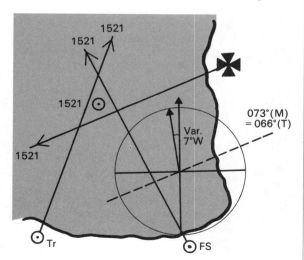

Fig. 3(20) When taking bearings to get a fix, if possible always use at least three objects. The size of the resulting cocked hat indicates the reliability of the position.

little later when the bearing of L has changed by at least 45° a second bearing is taken. Again the time and log reading are noted.

It is then necessary to work out how far the boat has travelled over the ground between the two bearings. This is calculated from the log readings (distance through the water, AB) and from the effect of the tidal stream during this period (BC). So AC represents the movement of the boat between the two bearings. The first position line is transferred by this amount as shown (transferred position lines are conventionally marked by double arrows each end), and crosses with the second position line at Q, which is the position when the second bearing was taken.

3.3.7 Doubling the angle on the bow

This is a special example of a running fix, which is easy to calculate. Assume in Fig. 3(22) that the boat is sailing along the line AC. At A a relative

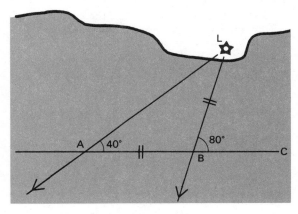

Fig. 3(22) Doubling the angle on the bow is a special type of running fix, and should be used with caution in tidal waters.

bearing is taken of object L which is (say) 40° on the bow at a certain time and log reading. When this bearing has doubled, to 80°, the time and log reading are again noted, at B. It will be seen that ABL is an isosceles triangle and that AB (the distance sailed between the two bearings) equals BL (the distance of the boat from L). Although this is a quick and useful method of getting an approximate position, it is not very accurate and should not be trusted in waters where there is any appreciable tidal stream.

3.3.8 Four point bearing, and other special angles

If, when doubling the angle on the bow as described above, the first relative bearing is 45° and the second is therefore 90°, then the distance run between the two bearings equals the distance which the object is abeam (when the second bearing is taken). This is called a four point bearing fix because under the old method of compass marking a point is $11\frac{1}{4}°$ and four points are 45°.

There are other special pairs of angles of an object on the bow which, if accurately taken and used when there is no tidal stream to consider, result in the distance run over the ground between the bearings being equal to the distance which the boat will pass abeam of the object. These pairs of angles on the bow are 22° and 34°; 25° and 41°; 32° and 59°; 35° and 67°; and 37° and 72°.

It is emphasised that all running fixes should be used with caution. It is important to be sure of the distance the boat has moved over the ground between the bearings, and to be certain that a steady and accurate course has been maintained.

3.3.9 Horizontal sextant angles

Horizontal sextant angles provide an accurate but often neglected method of fixing a boat's position. The method consists of taking the angles between fixed objects with the sextant held horizontally, instead of vertically, when obtaining the altitude of a heavenly body. Since an accuracy of half a degree is quite sufficient, even the cheapest plastic sextant is perfectly suitable.

To obtain a fix by horizontal sextant angles three objects must be visible, and as will be seen their relative positions are important. The method is based on the fact that the angle subtended by a chord at the centre of a circle is double the angle at the circumference. Knowing the angle subtended by two objects gives a position circle, as shown in Fig. 3(23), where the angles AS_1B, AS_2B and AS_3B are all equal.

The position circle can be constructed in various ways. It can be done by plotting, as shown in Fig. 3(23). If, for example, the angle

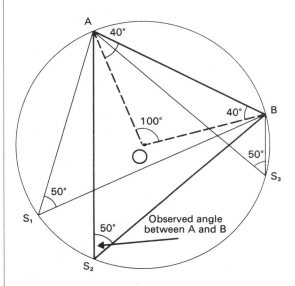

Fig. 3(23) The principle of a position circle, by taking the horizontal sextant angle between two known objects, A and B. If that angle is 50°, as shown, then the centre of the position circle $AS_1S_2S_3B$ is such that the angle AOB is 100°, and hence OAB and ABO are both 40°.

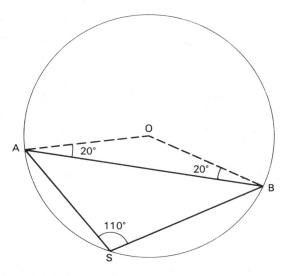

Fig. 3(24) If the observed sextant angle is more than 90°, as shown here, subtract 90 from the figure and construct the two radii OA and OB on the opposite side of the line joining the two objects.

AS_2B is 50°, construct lines at A and B which are each (90 − 50) = 40° to AB. Where they meet at O is the centre of the position circle ABS_2.

Should the angle ASB be greater than 90°, subtract 90° from it and construct AO and BO on the opposite (landward) side of the line AB, as indicated in Fig. 3(24). Here for example ASB is 110°, so OAB and OBA are both 20°.

If the procedure for drawing one position circle is repeated for another angle between two objects B and C, then a second position circle can be drawn cutting the first. The point of intersection gives the fix required.

Another method of using horizontal sextant angles is with a station pointer − an instrument with three arms which can be set at selected angles, in this case the angles taken with the sextant. By adjusting the station pointer so that the bevelled side of each of its arms lies against the three objects which have been observed, the position of the boat is shown at the hole in the centre of the pivot, through which a pencil mark can be made as at S in Fig. 3(25).

If a station pointer is not available it is a simple matter to construct the two angles measured with the sextant on a piece of tracing paper, and then move it about on the chart until the three lines pass over the objects concerned. A Douglas protractor may also be utilised.

It is also possible to construct the position of the boat geometrically, as in Fig. 3(26). If P, Q and R are the objects which have been observed join PQ and QR. Assume that the angles measured of PQ and QR are x and y. From Q construct two lines QT and QU at angles of (90-x) to PQ and (90-y) to QR as shown. From P and R construct perpendiculars which cut QT and QU at V and W. Join VW. Drop a perpendicular QS onto VW, and S is the fix.

If a sextant angle is more than 90°, subtract 90 from it and construct the required angle on the opposite (landward) side of PQ or QR.

The advantages of horizontal sextant angles are that accuracy is not affected by compass errors, log readings or tidal streams. The angles can, with a bit of practice, be measured very accurately and there is no deviation or variation to bother about. Even if no sextant is carried the same method can be used with compass bearings, if only the differences between the bearings are considered and no reliance is placed on individual bearings; this too eliminates any errors due to deviation or variation.

It must be noted however that there are certain limitations on the choice of objects for fixing by horizontal sextant angles. First they should be chosen so that they subtend angles of at least 30°. Also:
(1) The three objects should be on or near a straight line, or
(2) The centre object must be on the boat's side of the line joining the two outer objects, or
(3) The boat must obviously be inside a triangle formed by the three objects.

A satisfactory position will not be obtained when the centre object is beyond the line joining the other two. No fix can be obtained if a circle passes through or near to the three objects and the boat.

3.3.10 Line of soundings
Apart from bearings of shore objects it is often useful to read the echo sounder and record the distance of what is usually the nearest point of land. Most seagoing boats are now fitted with an echo sounder, but the following procedure can be used with a lead and line if necessary.

For navigational purposes soundings must be corrected by the height of the tide at the time and place concerned, so that they can be compared

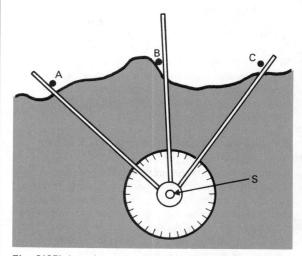

Fig. 3(25) A station pointer provides the simplest method of plotting a position from horizontal sextant angles.

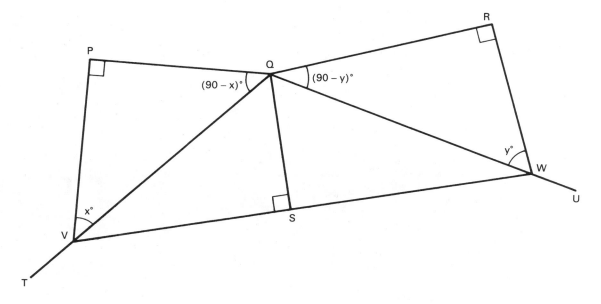

Fig. 3(26) From horizontal sextant angles the position of the boat can be determined geometrically, as it is shown in the diagram above.

with the figures on the chart. Even a single sounding can be helpful on occasions, but it is better to have a line of soundings taken at regular intervals. Having been reduced to datum, by subtracting the height of the tide, mark the soundings at the proper intervals of distance (tidal stream may have to be allowed for here) on the edge of a piece of paper (or better still a piece of tracing paper) and then move it about the chart with its edge parallel to the track of the boat, until it matches the soundings on the chart.

Such a position line should obviously be used with caution, but in thick weather for example it can be very helpful, particularly if the sea bed has distinctive contours.

3.3.11 Bearing and distance

The bearing and distance of a known object which is marked on the chart will give a fix. If radar is available it is a simple matter to get the range of anything which presents a good radar target. Radar gives more accurate ranges than bearings, so it is good practice to take a radar range and a visual bearing with the hand bearing compass, but be careful that the same object is observed in each case.

An alternative to radar for finding the distance of an object is a rangefinder, but reasonably-priced instruments are not very accurate at ranges of over a mile or so. There are however some small distance reading meters on the market.

If the height of an object is known, and if the angle which it subtends vertically can be measured (as with a sextant), its range can be calculated or extracted from tables. The procedure is described in section 3.3.12. Combined with the bearing of the object, this will give a good fix.

The range of a light of known height can be calculated or extracted from tables, for different heights of eye, when the light rises or dips over the horizon. This often gives a useful fix when making a landfall, and the method is described in section 3.3.13.

Should accurate ranges of two or more objects be known, by radar for example, a fix can be obtained by drawing the appropriate arcs on the chart and seeing where they intersect. If the ranges of only two objects are taken it is of course possible for them to intersect in two feasible positions, and for this reason it is sensible to take at least approximate bearings of each.

The use and limitations of radar in yachts is discussed in Chapter 4.

3.3.12 Vertical sextant angles

If the height of an object, such as a lighthouse, is known, and if the vertical angle which it presents to the observer is measured with a sextant, then its distance can be calculated or extracted from the tables provided in *The Macmillan & Silk Cut Nautical Almanac*.

A bearing of the object taken at the same time will provide an accurate fix of the boat's position.

Heights of prominent objects are shown on the chart or are given in sailing directions. On metric charts these are shown in metres (m). In the case of lights do not be confused by their range, shown in miles (M). Heights are above Mean High Water Springs (MHWS) and in the case of lights are to the centre of the lantern.

In practice it is not usual to allow for the height of the tide or for the height of eye, since by neglecting them the object is made to appear a little closer than it actually is, which gives a safety

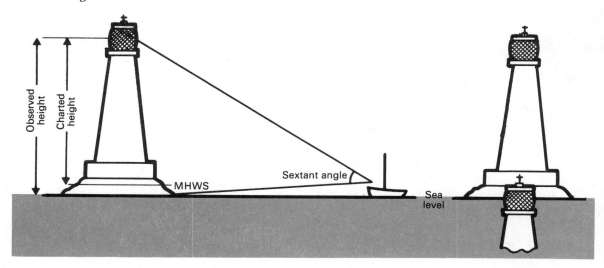

Fig. 3(27) A vertical sextant angle, combined with a bearing, of an object of known height gives a reliable fix. In order to get a really accurate range, the distance sea level is below the level of Mean High Water Springs should be added to the charted height of the object before entering the table.

margin if it is assumed that any danger is inshore of the yacht (but not if it is to seaward). The sextant angle should however be corrected for index error.

The sextant angle to be measured is from the top of the object (the centre of the lantern in the case of a lighthouse) to the sea at its base – not to the horizon, see Fig. 3(27). From a height of eye of three metres or 10ft (which is about the maximum likely to be used in a small yacht) the horizon is only visible to a distance of 3.6 nautical miles. Therefore at a greater distance than this the base of a light tower, for example, is below the horizon

and not visible to an observer. Consequently a measured sextant angle will be less than it should be, making the object appear to be further away than it actually is. Under these conditions vertical sextant angles must be used with caution.

If a more precise range is required, then the distance that sea level is below MHWS should be added to the height of the object (above MHWS) before entering the tables (see Chapter 9). Be sure that the same units (metres or feet) are used in each case.

Knowing the height of the object and the sextant angle (corrected for index error) the

TABLE 3(2) Distance off by Vertical Sextant Angle

Height of object ft	m	Distance of object (nautical miles)															Height of object m	ft
		0.1	0.2	0.3	0.4	0.5	0.6	0.7	0.8	0.9	1.0	1.1	1.2	1.3	1.4	1.5		
		° ′	° ′	° ′	° ′	° ′	° ′	° ′	° ′	° ′	° ′	° ′	° ′	° ′	° ′	° ′		
33	**10**	3 05	1 33	1 02	0 46	0 37	0 31	0 27	0 23	0 21	0 19	0 17	0 15	0 14	0 13	0 12	**10**	33
39	**12**	3 42	1 51	1 14	0 56	0 45	0 37	0 32	0 28	0 25	0 22	0 20	0 19	0 17	0 16	0 15	**12**	39
46	**14**	4 19	2 10	1 27	1 05	0 52	0 43	0 37	0 32	0 29	0 26	0 24	0 22	0 20	0 19	0 17	**14**	46
53	**16**	4 56	2 28	1 39	1 14	0 59	0 49	0 42	0 37	0 33	0 30	0 27	0 25	0 23	0 21	0 20	**16**	53
59	**18**	5 33	2 47	1 51	1 24	1 07	0 56	0 48	0 42	0 37	0 33	0 30	0 28	0 26	0 24	0 22	**18**	59
66	**20**	6 10	3 05	2 04	1 33	1 14	1 02	0 53	0 46	0 41	0 37	0 34	0 31	0 29	0 27	0 25	**20**	66
72	**22**	6 46	3 24	2 16	1 42	1 22	1 08	0 58	0 51	0 45	0 41	0 37	0 34	0 31	0 29	0 27	**22**	72
79	**24**	7 23	3 42	2 28	1 51	1 29	1 14	1 04	0 56	0 49	0 45	0 40	0 37	0 34	0 32	0 30	**24**	79
85	**26**	7 59	4 01	2 41	2 01	1 36	1 20	1 09	1 00	0 54	0 48	0 44	0 40	0 37	0 34	0 32	**26**	85
92	**28**	8 36	4 19	2 53	2 10	1 44	1 27	1 14	1 05	0 58	0 52	0 47	0 43	0 40	0 37	0 35	**28**	92
			4 28	3 05	2 19	1 51	1 33	1 20	1 10	1 02	0 56	0 51	0 46	0 43	0 40	0 37	**30**	
				2 28	1 58	1 39	1 25	1 14	1 06	0 59	0 54	0 49	0 46	0 42	0 40		
				3 06	1 45	1 30	1 19	1 10	1 03	0 57	0 53	0 49	0 45			
					1 35	1 24	1 14	1 07	1 01	0 56	0 51				
						1 18	1 11								

Fig. 3(28) Portion of table of distance off by vertical sextant angle.

TABLE 3(3)		Distance of horizon for various heights of eye					
Height of eye		Horizon distance	Height of eye		Horizon distance	Height of eye		Horizon distance
metres	feet	n. miles	metres	feet	n. miles	metres	feet	n. miles
1	3.3	2.1	21	68.9	9.5	41	134.5	13.3
2	6.6	2.9	22	72.2	9.8	42	137.8	13.5
3	9.8	3.6	23	75.5	10.0	43	141.1	13.7
4	13.1	4.1	24	78.7	10.2	44	144.4	13.8
5	16.4	4.7	25	82.0	10.4	45	147.6	14.0
6	19.7	5.1	26	85.3	10.6	46	150.9	14.1
7	23.0	5.5	27	88.6	10.8	47	154.2	1₄ ͡
	26.2	5.9	28	91.9	11.0	48	157 ͡	
		͡ ͡	29	95.1				

Fig. 3(29) Portion of table of distance of horizon for various heights of eye.

distance can easily be worked out with a scientific calculator from the formula shown in 3.3.16.

Table 3(2) in the Almanac is used as follows. Enter with the height of the object, either in metres or feet, in the column down the side of the page and then read across until the required sextant angle (corrected for index error) is met. Take out the distance of the object (in nautical miles) at the head of the column, interpolating as necessary.

Make certain that the table is entered with the correct units, either metres or feet as the case may be.

Example
Referring to Fig. 3(28), the vertical sextant angle of an object with an elevation of 79ft (24m) is 1°04′ (after correction for index error). How far away is it?

By inspection, for an object with height 79ft (24m) and an angle of 1°04′, the distance is 0.7 nautical miles.

If in this case the sea level was known to be 6½ft (2m) below the level of MHWS, the table would be entered with a height of 85ft (26m). By interpolation, it can be seen that an angle of 1°04′ would then give a distance of approximately 0.75 nautical miles.

Should it be required to keep a certain distance away from an object of known height, it is easy to extract the appropriate 'danger angle' from the table, and then ensure that this is not exceeded.

3.3.13 Distance of the horizon
It is useful to be able to extract from tables (or to calculate from formulae) the distance of the sea horizon for a certain height of eye. The actual distance may be affected by abnormal refraction. The appropriate table and formula for use with a calculator are given in *The Macmillan & Silk Cut Nautical Almanac*. An extract from Table 3(3) is shown in Fig. 3(29). It can be used, for example, for determining the distance of a light when it is on the horizon – see Fig. 3(30).

The distance OL is the sum of the distance of the horizon from the observer at O and the distance of the horizon from L. If the height of eye is 10ft (3m), and the height of the light is 72ft (22m), the distance OL is (3.6 + 9.8) = 13.4 nautical miles.

For convenience Table 3(4) in *The Macmillan & Silk Cut Nautical Almanac* combines selected heights of eye with selected heights of lights, to give the range at which a light may be seen to dip below or rise above the horizon. A portion of this table is shown in Fig. 3(31).

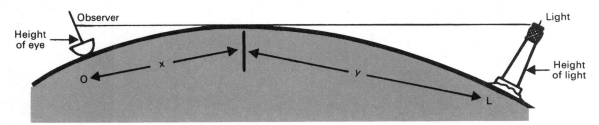

Fig. 3(30) The distance at which an observer can just see a light on the horizon is the sum of x and y above; that is the distance from the observer's eye to the horizon plus the distance from the light to the horizon.

TABLE 3 (4)   Lights — distance off when rising or dipping (n. miles)

Height of light						Height of eye						
		metres	1	2	3	4	5	6	7	8	9	10
metres	feet	feet	3	7	10	13	16	20	23	26	30	33
10	33		8.7	9.5	10.2	10.8	11.3	11.7	12.1	12.5	12.8	13.2
12	39		9.3	10.1	10.8	11.4	11.9	12.3	12.7	13.1	13.4	13.8
14	46		9.9	10.7	11.4	12.0	12.5	12.9	13.3	13.7	14.0	14.4
16	53		10.4	11.2	11.9	12.5	13.0	13.4	13.8	14.2	14.5	14.9
18	59		10.9	11.7	12.4	13.0	13.5	13.9	14.3	14.7	15.0	15.4
20	66		11.4	12.2	12.9	13.5	14.0	14.4	14.8	15.2	15.5	15.9
			11.9	12.7	13.4	14.0	14.5	14.9	15.3	15.7	16.0	16.4
			12.3	13.1	13.8	14.4	14.9	15.3	15.7	16.1	16.4	17.0
				13.5	14.2	14.8	15.3	15.7	16.1			
						15.3	15.7					

Fig. 3(31) Portion of table showing the distance off of lights when rising or dipping, for various heights of light and eye.

TABLE 3 (5)   Time, Speed and Distance Table

Time							Speed in knots											Time	
Decimal of hr.	Mins	2.5	3	3.5	4	4.5	5	5.5	6	6.5	7	7.5	8	8.5	9	9.5	10	Mins	Decimal of hr.
.0167	1				0.1	0.1	0.1	0.1	0.1	0.1	0.1	0.1	0.1	0.1	0.2	0.2	0.2	1	.0167
.0333	2	0.1	0.1	0.1	0.1	0.1	0.2	0.2	0.2	0.2	0.2	0.2	0.3	0.3	0.3	0.3	0.3	2	.0333
.0500	3	0.1	0.1	0.2	0.2	0.2	0.2	0.3	0.3	0.3	0.3	0.4	0.4	0.4	0.4	0.5	0.5	3	.0500
.0667	4	0.1	0.2	0.2	0.3	0.3	0.3	0.4	0.4	0.4	0.5	0.5	0.5	0.6	0.6	0.6	0.7	4	.0667
.0833	5	0.2	0.2	0.3	0.3	0.4	0.4	0.5	0.5	0.5	0.6	0.6	0.7	0.7	0.7	0.8	0.8	5	.0833
.1000	6	0.2	0.3	0.3	0.4	0.4	0.5	0.5	0.6	0.6	0.7	0.7	0.8	0.8	0.9	0.9	1.0	6	.1000
.1167	7	0.3	0.4	0.4	0.5	0.5	0.6	0.6	0.7	0.8	0.8	0.9	0.9	1.0	1.1	1.1	1.2	7	.1167
.1333	8	0.3	0.4	0.5	0.5	0.6	0.7	0.7	0.8	0.9	0.9	1.0	1.1	1.1	1.2	1.3	1.3	8	
.1500	9	0.4	0.4	0.5	0.6	0.7	0.7	0.8	0.9	1.0	1.0	1.1	1.2	1.3	1.3	1.4	1.5		
.1667	10	0.4	0.5	0.6	0.7	0.8	0.8	0.9	1.0	1.1	1.2	1.3	1.3	1.4	1.5	1.6	1.7		
		0.5	0.5	0.6	0.7	0.8	0.9	1.0	1.1	1.2	1.3	1.4	1.5	1.6	1.6	1.7			
				0.7	0.8	0.9	1.0	1.1	1.2	1.3	1.4	1.5	1.6	1.7	1.8				
						1.0	1.1	1.2	1.3	1.4	1.5	1.6	1.7	1.8					
							1.2	1.3	1.4	1.5	1.6	1.7	1.9						
								1.4	1.5	1.6	1.8	1.9							

Fig. 3(32) Portion of time, speed and distance table.

TABLE 3 (6)   Measured Mile Table — Knots related to time over one nautical mile

Secs	1 min	2 min	3 min	4 min	5 min	6 min	7 min	8 min	9 min	10 min	11 min
0	60.00	30.00	20.00	15.00	12.00	10.00	8.57	7.50	6.67	6.00	5.45
1	59.02	29.75	19.89	14.94	11.96	9.97	8.55	7.48	6.66	5.99	5.45
2	58.06	29.51	19.78	14.88	11.92	9.94	8.53	7.47	6.64	5.98	5.44
3	57.14	29.27	19.67	14.81	11.88	9.92	8.51	7.45	6.63	5.97	5.43
4	56.25	29.03	19.57	14.75	11.84	9.89	8.49	7.44	6.62	5.96	5.42
5	55.38	28.80	19.46	14.69	11.80	9.86	8.47	7.42	6.61	5.95	5.41
6	54.55	28.57	19.35	14.63	11.76	9.84	8.45	7.41	6.59	5.94	5.41
7	53.73	28.35	19.25	14.57	11.73	9.81	8.43	7.39	6.58	5.93	5
8	52.94	28.12	19.15	14.52	11.69	9.78	8.41	7.38	6.57	5.92	
9			19.05	14.46	11.65	9.76	8.39	7.36	6.56		
					11.61	9.73	8.37				

Fig. 3(33) Portion of measured mile table – knots related to time over one nautical mile.

The heights of all major lights are shown on the chart. Remember that it is the small m which gives the height in metres, while the large M is the range of the light in nautical miles.

3.3.14 Time, speed and distance

When navigating by dead reckoning it is important to understand the relation between time, speed and distance. To assist, Table 3(5) in *The Macmillan & Silk Cut Nautical Almanac* relates these three quantities – for speeds from 2.5 to 20 knots, and for times up to one hour at one minute intervals. The tabulated figures are nautical miles. A portion of this table is shown in Fig. 3(32).

Example

To determine how far the boat has sailed at 6.5 knots in 8 minutes – select the column headed 6.5 knots and read down to the 8 minute line at the side of the table. Answer – 0.9 nautical miles. Conversely the table can be used to find out how long it will take to cover a known distance at a certain speed, or what speed is required to go a certain distance in a given time.

3.3.15 Measured mile table

Particularly in motor yachts it is important to know the boat's speed in relation to engine rpm. This is best done by running the boat over one of the measured distances which exist around the coast and are marked on large scale charts. Check the actual length of the measured distance from the chart. A few are not exactly a sea mile.

In order to offset the effects of tide, and possibly of wind, it is important to make at least one run in each direction. Calculate the speed from the results obtained.

For accurate figures two or three runs should be made in each direction, and the speed calculated from the mean of means, as follows.

If six successive runs are done in alternate directions, take the speed of each run. Multiply consecutive speeds by 1, 5, 10, 10, 5, 1 and divide the total by 32.

If four runs are done in alternate directions, again take the speed of each run. Multiply the consecutive speeds by 1, 2, 2, 1 and divide the total by 6.

When doing measured mile runs it is important to keep a steady course, on the heading which is marked on the chart (perpendicular to the transit marks each end). Otherwise the distance steamed is greater than indicated.

Most measured distances are along a shoreline, which is sometimes shallow. Make certain that there is sufficient depth of water on your intended course, and remember that inaccurate results will be obtained in shallow water – particularly at higher speeds. Use the greatest depth which is practicable.

Table 3(6) in *The Macmillan & Silk Cut Nautical Almanac* gives speeds in knots for times over a nautical mile at one second intervals from one minute (60 knots) to 12 minutes (5 knots). A portion of this table is shown in Fig. 3(33).

During measured distance runs it is appropriate to take note of the following factors for subsequent reference:

Direction and strength of wind relative to course(s)
State of hull bottom (clean, foul etc)
Loading of boat (fuel, water, crew)
Engine rpm
Turbocharger boost pressure (if applicable)
Readings of log (if fitted) for calibration.
Sea water temperature
Ambient air temperature

Examples
(a) Runs in alternate directions give times of:

$$6 \text{ min } 01 \text{ sec} = 9.97 \text{ knots}$$
$$\text{and } 6 \text{ min } 07 \text{ sec} = \underline{9.81} \text{ knots}$$
$$19.78$$

Hence mean speed ($\div 2$) = 9.89 knots

(b) Four runs are made in alternate directions, giving times of 7 min 02 sec, 7 min 08 sec, 7 min 00 sec and 7 min 06. These times are respectively 8.53, 8.41, 8.57 and 8.45 knots. To determine the speed from mean of means:

$$1 \times 8.53 = 8.53$$
$$2 \times 8.41 = 16.82$$
$$2 \times 8.57 = 17.14$$
$$1 \times 8.45 = \underline{8.45}$$
$$50.94$$

Divide by 6 = 8.49 knots

3.3.16 Navigation by electronic calculator

The formulae below help to solve problems when using scientific calculators. Any calculator used for navigation should be able to work in degrees, minutes and seconds of arc (DDMMSS) as well as Degrees and Decimals (D.d); have the powerful feature of polar to rectangular coordinate conversion, by which a sine and cosine can be calculated simultaneously, or an arc tangent resolved into its proper quadrant without having to apply rules, and sum the results; and be able to evaluate trigonometrical functions for all angles (not just those in the range $0°$ to $90°$).

It must have adequate memory storage and recall facilities. Suggested minimum requirements for memory stores are: coastal navigation, 4; celestial navigation, 6; and advanced navigation or yacht racing aplications, 26. Highly desirable features are statistical functions and accumulations ($\Sigma+$, $\Sigma-$, etc); the ability to add and subtract directly in hours or degrees, minutes and seconds; and a continuous memory facility, which means the ability to retain programmes and/or navigational data when switched 'off'.

For both coastal or celestial navigation, a programmable calculator is highly desirable to reduce potential errors resulting from numerous key operations, as they only require users to key in the required navigational data. There is the choice of two calculator languages – algebraic or reverse polish notation (RPN). The RPN system is unquestionably more suited to solving complex navigational problems. Which system to use is a matter of personal preference.

The most important factors are to thoroughly understand the operation, capability and limitations of the chosen calculator. Regular practice and familiarity with a particular type of calculator should allow any user to devise the best working procedures.

Speed, time and distance

$$\text{Speed} = \frac{\text{Distance} \times 60}{\text{Time (in mins)}}$$

$$\text{Time (in mins)} = \frac{\text{Distance} \times 60}{\text{Speed}}$$

$$\text{Distance} = \frac{\text{Speed} \times \text{Time (in mins)}}{60}$$

Distances and speed

Distance of horizon
(in nautical miles)
$$= 1.144 \times \sqrt{\text{Ht of eye (in feet)}}$$
or
$$= 2.072 \times \sqrt{\text{Ht of eye (in metres)}}$$

Distance a light is visible
(in nautical miles)
$$= 1.144 \times (\sqrt{h_o} + \sqrt{\text{Ht of eye}}) \text{ (in feet)}$$
or
$$= 2.072 \times (\sqrt{h_o} + \sqrt{\text{Ht of eye}}) \text{ (in metres)}$$

where: h_o is the height of object in feet or metres according to formula used.

Distance from mountains etc beyond horizon
(in nautical miles)

$$= \sqrt{3.71(h_o - HE) + (a - 1.76 \times \sqrt{HE})^2}$$
$$-(a - 1.76 \times \sqrt{HE}) \text{ for heights in metres}$$
or
$$= \sqrt{1.13(h_o - HE) + (a - 0.972 \times \sqrt{HE})^2}$$
$$-(a - 0.972 \times \sqrt{HE}) \text{ for heights in feet}$$
where: h_o is the height of the mountain or object, HE is height of eye, and a is the sextant angle (in mins).

Distance to the radar horizon (in nautical miles)

$$= 2.21 \times \sqrt{\text{Ht of scanner (in metres)}}$$
or
$$= 1.22 \times \sqrt{\text{Ht of scanner (in feet)}}$$

$$\text{Boat speed over 1nm} = \frac{3600}{\text{time in seconds}}$$

Horizontal sextant angle

$$\text{Radius of position circle} = \frac{D}{2 \times \sin A}$$

where: D is distance between the objects in nautical miles, and A is the angle between them in degrees.

Vertical sextant angles
Distance off
(in nautical miles)
$$= \frac{\text{Height of object (above MHWS in feet)}}{6076 \times \tan \text{(sextant angle)}}$$
or
$$= \frac{\text{Height of object (above MHWS in metres)}}{1852 \times \tan \text{(sextant angle)}}$$

Note: In the above formulae, sextant angle in degrees and minutes must be corrected for index error.

An approximate distance off, adequate for most purposes, is given by the formulae:

Distance off
(in nautical miles)
$$= \frac{\text{Height of object (in feet)} \times 0.565}{\text{Sextant angle (in minutes)}}$$
or
$$= \frac{\text{Height of object (in metres)} \times 1.854}{\text{Sextant angle (in minutes)}}$$

Coastal Navigation
Where R is the distance run between two relative bearings of an object, the first A degrees, and the second B degrees,

$$\text{Distance (D) of object at second bearing} = \frac{R \times \sin A}{\sin (B - A)}$$

$$\text{To predict distance object will be off when abeam} = D \times \sin B$$

Conversion angle (half convergency)
Radio bearings follow great circle paths and therefore become curved lines when plotted on a Mercator chart. The angle between a great circle and rhumb line bearing is called 'conversion angle' or 'half convergency'. Near the equator, conversion angle is negligible, and as latitude increases, the error is larger.

If using a radiobeacon more than about 60nm away, a correction may be required before plotting on a Mercator chart. A great circle always lies on the polar side of the rhumb line, and conversion angle is ALWAYS applied towards the equator, and may be calculated from:

Conversion angle (half convergency)
$$= \tfrac{1}{2} \text{ d.long} \times \sin \text{ mid latitude}$$
or for small differences in latitude:
tan conversion angle
$$= \sin \text{ mid latitude} \times \tan \frac{\text{d.long}}{2}$$

Latitude of receiver	Radiobeacon lies to	Correction
N	East	+
N	West	−
S	East	−
S	West	+

For further information see 4.6.3.

Course to Steer and Speed Made Good

Several different methods are available for calculating the Course to Steer Co(°T) and Speed Made Good (SMG) given the required Track, Tr(°T), yacht's speed and the Set and Drift. The best methods are to calculate the Course to Steer and SMG in one operation.

The primary equations for this are:

$$Co(°T) = Tr(°T) - \sin^{-1} - ((\text{Drift} \div \text{yacht's speed}) \times \sin(\text{Set} - \text{Drift}))$$

and

$$SMG = \text{Speed} \times \cos(Co(°T) - \text{Track}) + \text{Drift} \times \cos(\text{Set} - \text{Track})$$

Note: The Drift MUST always be less than the yacht's speed.

The relevant key sequences for a TI.57 are given below for solving the two most common navigation problems encountered which involve the triangle of velocity. Other calculators might require slightly different key operation (perhaps no second functions), but the principle applies to all algebraic calculators.

To find Course and Speed Made Good (CMG & SMG)

Example: Course steered 135°T Yacht's speed 6.5kn Set/Drift 075°/1.5kn

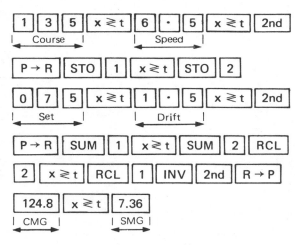

Note: If the course in display is negative (−), add +360°.

To find Course to Steer and Speed Made Good (Co. T & SMG)

Example: (using TI.57)

Track req'd. 042°T Yacht's speed 7.5kn Set/Drift 135°/1.2kn

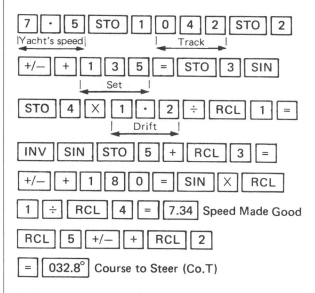

Note: If course in display is negative (−), add + 360° to give the proper Co.T.

The same problems can be solved on an RPN calculator with far fewer key operations. The relevant key sequences to find the Course to Steer and SMG are as follows:

Key in Set	135	ENTER
Key in Track	042	STO 0 − sin
Key in Drift	1.2	×
Key in Yacht's speed	7.5	÷ sin⁻¹ RCL 0
		x ⇄ y −
		= 32.81 Co(T)
Key in Yacht's speed	7.5	→ R Σ +
Key in Set	135	ENTER
Key in Drift	1.2	→ R Σ + RCL 11
		RCL 13 → P
		= 7.34kn SMG

Note: If Course in display is negative (−), key in 360° + to give proper Co(T). In the case illustrated STORES 11 & 13 contain the vector summation.

With any calculations involving solutions to triangle of velocity problems, it is often easiest to use the Polar-Rectangular conversion facility in conjunction with vector addition capability (Σ +, Σ −, etc). Each type of calculator enters the x and y into specific memory stores so, to recall accumulated data, it is essential to identify which stores are used.

To find the Course to Steer and Yacht's speed

Using an RPN calculator: Given Track required 042°T, SMG required 7.3kn and the Set and Drift 135/1 .2kn.

Key in Track   042   ENTER
Key in SMG   7.3   → R Σ +
Key in Set   135   ENTER
Key in Drift   1.2   → R Σ +
                 RCL Σ + (in this case
                 RCL 13, RCL 11)
                 → P =
                 7.5kn yacht's speed required
                 x ⇄ y =
                 32.8 Co(T)

Note: If course displayed is negative (−), key in 360° + to give proper Course (T).

Using the technique of vector summation and polar-rectangular capability, a variety of different navigation vector problems can be solved.

Short distance sailing
(Note: These formulae should not be used for distances over 600nm).

Departure	=	Distance × sin Course
	=	d.Long × cos Mean Latitude
	=	tan Course × d.Lat
d.Lat	=	Distance × cos Course
d.Long	=	Departure ÷ cos Mean Latitude
Distance	=	Departure ÷ sin Course
	=	d.Lat × sec Course
Sin Course	=	Departure ÷ Distance
Cos Course	=	d.Lat ÷ Distance
Tan Course	=	Departure ÷ d.Lat

Long distance sailing
Basic rhumb line sailing formulae are based on the Sphere, but can be modified for use with a Spheroid, commonly called Mercator sailing, for which tables of Meridional parts are published in nautical tables. Mercator sailing techniques should be used for the calculation of rhumb line tracks and distances over 600nm.
The basic formula for use with the Sphere are:

$$\tan \text{Track} = \frac{\pi(\text{Long}_1 \sim \text{Long}_2)}{180°\left[\text{In}\tan\left(45° + \frac{\text{Lat}_2}{2}\right) \sim \text{In}\tan\left(45° + \frac{\text{Lat}_1}{2}\right)\right]}$$

$$\text{Distance} = 60 \times \frac{\text{Lat}_2 - \text{Lat}_1}{\cos \text{Track}}$$

When the track is 090° or 270°, the formula below should be substituted:

$$\text{Distance} = 60\,(\text{Long}_2 \sim \text{Long}_1) \times \cos \text{Lat}$$

Note: The above formula for tan Track uses natural logarithms instead of common logarithms and this is shown by the abbreviation 'In'.

Mercator sailings are usually calculated on the Spheroid using the following basic formulae:

$$\tan \text{Track} = \frac{\text{d.Long (in mins)}}{\text{difference in meridional parts (dmp)}}$$

$$\text{Distance (nm)} = \frac{\text{d.Lat in mins}}{\cos \text{Track}}$$

$$\text{d.Lat} = \text{Distance} \times \cos \text{Track}$$

$$\text{departure (nm)} = \frac{\text{d.Lat} \times \text{d.Long (in mins)}}{\text{dmp}}$$

Before starting, it is necessary to calculate the meridional parts (MP) for the Latitude of departure and destination in order to find the difference (dmp). Remember, that when the latitudes of departure and destination are of contrary name, the SUM of the two MPs is used for dmp.

For the International Spheroid (eccentricity (e) 0.08199189), the value of meridional parts (MP) for any given latitude can be calculated from the formula:

$$\text{MP} = 7915.704456 \times \log \tan \left(45^\circ + \frac{\text{Lat}}{2} \right) - \sin \text{Lat} \times (23.110771 + 0.052051 \times \sin^2 \text{Lat}).$$

If the results are checked against say, Nories tables, a slight difference will be noted between the figures. The reason for this is that Nories tables are based on the Clarke spheroid of 1880, which uses an eccentricity factor of 0.0824834.

Great circle sailing

Great circle sailing is used when it is desired to take advantage of the shortest distance between two points along the great circle, rather than the longer rhumb line distance. For practical purposes, the Earth is assumed to be a sphere. If higher accuracy is required, then great circle formulae based on the Spheroid should be used. The shortest great circle distance on the Spheroid is called a 'geodesic'.

$$\text{Initial Track} = \tan^{-1} \left[\frac{\sin \text{d.Long}}{(\cos \text{Lat}_1 \times \tan \text{Lat}_2) - (\sin \text{Lat}_1 \times \cos \text{d.Long})} \right]$$

Note: If the name of Lat_2 (destination) is contrary to that of Lat_1 (departure), then Lat_2 is treated as a negative $(-)$. The Track angle is calculated from the pole towards east or west.

$$\text{Distance (nm)} = 60 \times \cos^{-1} \left[(\sin \text{Lat}_1 \times \sin \text{Lat}_2) + (\cos \text{Lat}_1 \times \cos \text{Lat}_2 \times \cos \text{d.Long}) \right]$$

Worked example: Great circle

From:	FALMOUTH	50°09′N (50.150°)	05°03′W (05.050°)
To:	ANTIGUA	17°00′N (17.000°)	61°46′W (61.766°)
	d.Lat	33°09′S (33.150°) d.Long	56°43′W (56.716°)

$$\text{Initial Track} = \tan^{-1} \left[\frac{\sin 56.716^\circ}{(\cos 50.150^\circ \times \tan 17.000^\circ) - (\sin 50.150^\circ \times \cos 56.716^\circ)} \right]$$

$$= \tan^{-1} \left[\frac{0.83596}{(0.64078 \times 0.30573) - (0.76772 \times 0.54879)} \right]$$

$$= \tan^{-1} \left[\frac{0.83596}{(0.19591) - (0.42132)} \right]$$

$$= \tan^{-1} \frac{0.83596}{-0.22541}$$

$$= \tan^{-1} - 3.70862$$

$$= S - 74.90955^\circ W$$

$$= 254.9^\circ \,(T)$$

$$\text{Distance (nm)} = 60 \times \cos^{-1} \left[(\sin 50.150^\circ \times \sin 17.000^\circ) + (\cos 50.150^\circ \times \cos 17.000^\circ \times \cos 56.716^\circ) \right]$$

$$= 60 \times \cos^{-1} \left[(0.76772 \times 0.29237) + (0.64078 \times 0.95630 \times 0.54879) \right]$$

$$= 60 \times \cos^{-1} \left[(0.22446) + (0.33629) \right]$$

$$= 55.89242 \times 60$$

$$= 3353.54 \text{nm}.$$

3.3.17 DR computers

With the increasing use of microprocessors in the field of navigational instruments, several new and exciting aids have become available to yachtsmen, and more will follow. Despite the position fixing systems which are now available (described in Chapter 4), many yachts rely largely on DR positions. This is just one of the many functions of the Brookes & Gatehouse Hydra system, which can take inputs from compass and log, and continually provide information on distance and course made good from a certain point. The computer at the heart of the B&G data system accepts inputs from various sensors, and can produce navigational and performance information on a number of analogue indicators or multi-function digital displays, sited where required in the boat.

The days when navigators tediously plotted dozens of small velocity triangles are not perhaps quite over for the average yachtsman, but they may well be in the not too distant future. Microprocessors can do it more quickly and more accurately, and without getting seasick. Although of particular interest to racing yachtsmen, such a system has several applications for cruising boats, whether power or sail. We are likely to see a steady extension in the use and versatility of such equipment even in quite small yachts, and hopefully a steady reduction in price.

3.4 Pilotage

3.4.1 Pilotage—general

Pilotage is the navigation of a vessel using geographical features, buoys and other marks (or their lights) in conjuction with the chart, compass, echo sounder and radar (if fitted). It involves the navigator knowing his approximate position at any moment, and following a pre-determined track so that he can correctly identify objects appearing ahead, or maybe a transit astern for example.

Pilotage is often most difficult when there are a large number of confusing objects available – like the lights of a large sea port when first approached from seaward. But if the position of the boat is known or can be established at any time, it is a comparatively simple matter to take a bearing of an object or a light which appears in order to identify it from the chart. Alternatively it may happen that the object will be in transit with one that has been positively identified.

It is sometimes possible to work ahead by plotting what the bearings of certain future marks will be when the boat reaches a certain position. Then a quick check with the hand bearing compass should tell you which is which.

Pilotage is obviously much easier (and safer) if one person steers the boat and follows the courses ordered, and the navigator is completely free to concentrate on his job. In a difficult situation it pays to use two people for pilotage – one up top taking the bearings, and passing them to the other who is at the chart table. This is particularly helpful in darkness, because it preserves the night vision of the person in the cockpit.

For inshore pilotage always use fixed marks or beacons in preference to buoys, which may not be precisely on station.

3.4.2 Leading marks and clearing lines

Most charts show examples of leading marks – objects placed at a harbour entrance or in a narrow channel, so that by keeping them in line the best water is followed. Where they are lit pairs of leading marks sometimes have the same characteristics, to help identify them. Leading marks are described in the 'Pilot' and are shown on the chart thus 'Ldg Lts 047°'. This is the true bearing of the transit from seaward.

Another common use of transits is as clearing lines to keep a boat clear of hidden dangers. When using any form of transit always take a bearing of it, and check this against the chart or sailing directions, to see if the correct objects are being observed. Not all clearing lines are necessarily shown by transits. In some cases the bearing of a conspicuous object may be given.

3.4.3 IALA Buoyage System (Region A)

International buoyage is now harmonized into a single IALA Maritime Buoyage System which, applied to Regions A and B, differs only in the use of red and green lateral marks. In Region A (which includes all Europe and the Mediterranean) lateral marks are red on the port hand, and in Region B they are red on the starboard hand, related to the direction of buoyage. Shapes of lateral marks are the same for both regions.

Region A uses five types of marks, in any combination, as follows (see page 59):
(1) *Lateral marks* used in conjunction with a conventional direction of buoyage, and indicating the port and starboard sides of a channel to be followed.
(2) *Cardinal marks* used in conjunction with a compass to show where dangers exist or where the mariner may find navigable water.
(3) *Isolated danger marks* to show isolated dangers of limited size that have navigable water all around them.
(4) *Safe water marks* to show that there is navigable water all round that position.
(5) *Special marks* not primarily for navigation, but indicating an area or feature referred to in nautical documents.

The significance of an individual mark depends upon its colour, shape or topmark by day, and the colour or rhythm of any light displayed at night.

Lateral marks (Region A)

Lateral marks are used in conjunction with a direction of a buoyage shown by a special arrow on the chart; in and around the British Isles its

Fig. 3(34) Direction of buoyage around the United Kingdom. In rivers and estuaries the direction of buoyage is normally from seawards inwards.

general direction is from SW to NE in open waters – see Fig. 3(34)- but from seaward when approaching a harbour, river or estuary. Where port or starboard lateral marks do not rely on can or conical buoy shapes for identification they carry, where practicable, the appropriate topmarks. Any numbering or lettering follows the direction of buoyage.

	Preferred channel	
	To starboard	**To port**
Colour	Red, with one broad green horizontal band	Green with one broad red horizontal band
Shape (buoys)	Cylindrical (can), pillar or spar	Conical, pillar or spar
Topmark (if any)	Single red can	Single green cone, point up
Light (when fitted)	Red	Green
Rhythm	Composite group flashing Fl(2 + 1)R	Composite group flashing Fl(2 + 1)G

Fig. 3(35) Preferred channel marks, Region A.

Port hand marks:

Colour	Red
Shape (buoys)	Can or spar
Topmark (if any)	Single red can
Light (when fitted)	Red, any rhythm

Starboard hand marks:

Colour	Green (see note)
Shape (buoys)	Conical or spar
Topmark (if any)	Single green cone point up (see note)
Light (when fitted)	Green, any rhythm

Note: In exceptional cases black may be used instead of green.

At the point where a channel divides, when proceeding in the direction of buoyage, the preferred channel may be indicated by a modified port or starboard lateral mark as shown in Fig. 3(35) (for Region A).

Cardinal marks

Cardinal marks are named after the quadrant in which the mark is placed, in relation to the danger or point indicated. The four quadrants (North, East, South and West) are bounded by the true bearings NW–NE, NE–SE, SE–SW and SW–NW, taken from the point of interest. The name of a cardinal mark indicates that it should be passed on the named side. For example, a North cardinal mark (situated in the quadrant between NW and NE from the point of interest) should be passed to the northward. Similarly you should keep to the east of an East cardinal mark, and so on.

A cardinal mark may indicate the safe side on which to pass a danger, or that the deepest water is on the named side of the mark, or it may draw attention to a feature in a channel such as a bend, junction or fork, or the end of a shoal.

Cardinal marks are pillar or spar shaped, painted black and yellow, and always carry black double cone topmarks one cone above the other. Their lights are white, either very quick flashing (VQ or VQkFl), 120 to 100 flashes per minute, or quick flashing (Q or QkFl), 60 or 50 flashes per minute. A long flash (as used in the light for a South cardinal mark) is a flash of not less than two seconds duration.

North cardinal mark

Topmark	— Two black cones, points up
Colour	— Black above yellow
Shape	— Pillar or spar
Light (when fitted)	— White, VQ or Q.

East cardinal mark

Topmark	— Two black cones, base to base
Colour	— Black, with single horizontal yellow band
Shape	— Pillar or spar
Light (when fitted)	— White, VQ (3) every 5 sec or Q (3) every 10 sec.

South cardinal mark

Topmark	— Two black cones, points down
Colour	— Yellow above black
Shape	— Pillar or spar
Light (when fitted)	— White, VQ (6) plus long flash every 10 sec or Q (6) plus long flash every 15 sec.

West cardinal mark

Topmark	— Two black cones, point to point
Colour	— Yellow, with single horizontal black band
Shape	— Pillar or spar
Light (when fitted)	— White, VQ (9) every 10 sec or Q (9) every 15 sec.

To help identify cardinal marks, the double cones of north and south cardinal marks point north (up) and south (down) respectively. West cones for cardinal marks are point to point, or waisted. East cones have their points apart or extended. So far as the lights are concerned, the number of flashes increases in a clockwise direction – three at three o'clock (east), six at six o'clock (south),and nine at nine o' clock (west).

Isolated danger marks
Isolated danger marks are moored on or above, or erected on, an isolated danger such as a rock or a wreck which has navigable water all around it.

Topmark	— Two black spheres, one above the other
Colour	— Black, with one or more broad horizontal red bands
Shape (buoys)	— Pillar or spar
Light (when fitted)	— White, Fl(2).

Safe water marks
Safe water marks indicate that there is navigable water all round the mark, and are used for mid-channel or landfall marks.

Topmark (if any)	— Single red sphere
Colour	— Red and white vertical stripes
Shape	— Spherical, pillar with spherical topmark, or spar
Light (when fitted)	— White, isophase, occulting, or long flash every 10 secs, or Morse 'A'.

Special marks
Special marks are not primarily intended to assist navigation, but indicate a special area or feature such as spoil grounds, military exercise areas, water ski areas, cable or pipe line marks, Ocean Data Acquisition Systems (ODAS), or traffic separation marks where the use of conventional channel marking may cause confusion.

Topmark (if any)	— Single yellow 'X' shape
Colour	— Yellow
Shape	— Optional but not conflicting with lateral or safe water marks.
Light (when fitted)	— Yellow, with a characteristic different from cardinal, isolated danger, or safe water marks.

Where can, conical or spherical are used they indicate the side on which to pass (i.e. can is port-hand mark; conical is starboard-hand mark; spherical is safe water mark).

New dangers may include naturally occurring obstructions such as a sandbank that has appeared or moved, or man made dangers such as wrecks. New dangers are marked in accordance with the rules above; in the event of a specially grave danger one of the marks may be duplicated. If lit the mark will have the appropriate cardinal or lateral characteristic.

3.4.4 Practical passage making
Apart from using the correct navigational techniques, there are elements of preparation and planning for any passage – even for short coastal trips. These matters are discussed in Chapter 15 (15.6).

3.5 Bibliography

Practical Yacht Navigator by Kenneth Wilkes (Adlard Coles Nautical).
Navigation for Yachtsmen by Mary Blewitt (Adlard Coles Nautical).
Coastwise Navigation by G. G. Watkins (Stanford Maritime).
Basic Coastal Navigation by Conrad Dixon (Adlard Coles Nautical).
Start to Navigate by Conrad Dixon (Adlard Coles Nautical).
Coastal Navigation by Gerry Smith (Adlard Coles Nautical).
High Speed Navigation by Dag Pike (Adlard Coles Nautical).
New Coastal Navigation by David Nicolle (Adlard Coles Nautical).
Navigation Exercises for Yachtsmen by Bill Anderson (Adlard Coles Nautical).
Exercises in Coastal Navigation by G. W. White (Adlard Coles Nautical).
Inshore Navigation by Tom Cunliffe (Fernhurst).
Coastal and Offshore Navigation by Tom Cunliffe (Fernhurst).
The Log Book (International Log Book).
The Shell Guide to Yacht Navigation by J. O. Coote (Faber & Faber).

Chapter 4

Radio navigational aids

Contents

4.1 Aids to navigation

4.1.1 Developments

It is only about 45 years since the first radio direction finding (RDF) receivers became available for use in small boats. Since then the silicon chip and widespread use of microprocessors has revolutionised both electronic equipment and navigation techniques. However, the marine world still lags some way behind the space and aviation communities in its willingness to readily accept the new high technology equipment now available, or to adopt the new navigational techniques necessary to fully exploit the capability and advantages now available.

Since the early 1980s, when the 'Transit' satellite navigation system and Decca became widely available to yachtsmen, there have been considerable developments with various types of navigational aids. RDF is now virtually obsolescent, so is Consol, and these have been superseded by more accurate and reliable systems such as the Global Positioning System (GPS), Decca or Loran-C.

From the outset it should be emphasised that the growing number and bewildering variety of navigational aids and position fixing systems which are available to yachtsmen should always be considered *as* aids, and not as replacements for more traditional or fundamental methods of navigation and pilotage. There may be times, perhaps most awkward times, when an electronic device for one reason or another is not available, or (even worse) when it gives misleading results. Hence, whatever sophisticated equipment is fitted in a small boat, it is essential that the navigator can use and retain the basic navigation skills which have already been outlined in the previous chapter.

Equally important, it should be understood that conventional and electronic navigation techniques need to be used together and not in isolation. In the comparatively near future electronic navigation will become the primary method of navigation, with existing traditional methods being regarded merely as the back-up aid. Doubtless in the coming years we will see even more sensational developments for yachts and small craft. Hopefully we can expect smaller, more accurate, more versatile and more reliable, and fully waterproofed equipment coming on the market, and at prices which will be increasingly competitive in real terms.

4.1.2 Navigational aids and position fixing systems

The present choice of navigational aids for the individual yachtsman depends on the usage of the boat concerned, the user's requirements and interests, and the particular waters in which she operates – apart from the depth of the owner's pocket. For a world-girdling yacht, a satellite navigation receiver which can provide continuous fixes anywhere on the earth's surface, to an accuracy of 100 metres or less, might be worth up to a couple of thousand pounds. The same receiver can equally be used in the average coastal or offshore cruising boat operating occasionally across the North Sea or the English Channel, but it could be also be a waste of money as lower cost terrestrial hyperbolic navigation aids such as Decca or Loran can equally provide continuous fixes within coverage areas, albeit with less accuracy and reliability.

The following is a summary of the radio navigational aids and position fixing systems available:
(1) Satellite Navigation – GPS, Differential GPS, and Transit
(2) Decca
(3) Loran-C
(4) Radar, including radar beacons
(5) Marine and aeronautical radiobeacons
(6) HM Coastguard VHF DF (Emergency only)
(7) Omega, Differential Omega
(8) VHF Direction-finding
(9) Radio Direction-finding stations

Each of the above has advantages and disadvantages when it comes to considering such matters as cost, accuracy, space occupied (including that for the aerial or antenna), power supply, simplicity of operation, reliability, and the way in which the information is presented. It should be noted that in some cases, one set on board a yacht can cover two (or more) of the above. For example, a suitable MF receiver will cover (5) and (9), and a VHF radiotelephone will cope with (6) and (8). At a more sophisticated (and expensive) level, there are hybrid navigation receivers which combine satellite navigation with Decca or Loran-C, or satellite navigation with Omega.

Hyperbolic navigation systems
Since three of the systems listed above (Decca, Loran-C and Omega) all work on this same basic principle, it is useful to understand the theory of

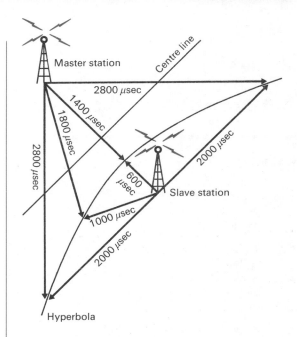

Fig. 4(1) The principle of a hyperbolic position line. For each point on the curve the difference in time between receipts of synchronised signals from the master station and slave station is 800 μ sec.

hyperbolic position lines. A hyperbola is formed by points whose distances from two fixed points always differ by a constant amount. The systems depend on the measurement of the difference in time taken by radio waves travelling from two fixed stations on shore to the vessel. Since the speed of radio waves is constant, from the time difference can be derived the actual difference in range of the two fixed stations, and hence the appropriate hyperbola which forms a position line – see Fig. 4(1). A similar measurement from another pair of fixed stations gives a second position line, and hence a fix.

In practice, three fixed stations in a triangular pattern are typically set up round a master station to form a 'chain'. The two pairs giving the best cut can be selected for a fix. As an alternative to the direct measurement of the time difference, the phase difference can be compared between continuous-wave signals from two fixed stations. Since a hyperbola consists of two parts which are symmetrical about the axis of the fixed stations, means have to be provided for determining which half forms the position line.

Hyperbolic systems display figures which correspond to lines on a latticed chart, from which is derived the position, and this gives the most accurate results. However, most instruments now give a direct read-out of latitude and longitude – not quite so precise, but very convenient. This is discussed in more detail in 4.3.1.

Waypoint
With the advent of modern position fixing systems came the term 'waypoint'. A waypoint is a specified position which can be a departure point,

a selected position along the intended route (perhaps where it is proposed to alter course), or a destination. Before starting a passage, waypoints can be entered as latitude and longitude, or often also as bearing and distance from some position or from another waypoint. On demand the set will then display such information as course and distance to the next waypoint (either by great circle or rhumb line) and estimated time of arrival (ETA). Most receivers provide at least 20 waypoints. The latest receivers now becoming available often possess many more – up to several hundred waypoints in some cases -and also make provision for waypoint names to be entered in addition to geographical coordinates which makes the entry of waypoints much safer.

Accuracy

It is important for the navigator to appreciate the accuracy that can be expected from any navigational system in the prevailing conditions. Although technical specifications may include terms such as Root Mean Square (RMS) error, the commonsense definition of accuracy (absolute accuracy) is the distance between the boat's actual position and the position obtained from the aid or system being used. However, one other term that may be met is repeatable accuracy. This defines the ability of the set to return to a position by repeating readings previously obtained for that position – useful for relocating fishing marks, wrecks or landfall buoys for example.

Do not be misled by the fact that a digital read-out may give figures to two or more decimal places. High resolution of a display does not necessarily imply high accuracy.

4.2 Satellite position fixing systems

4.2.1 Satellite navigation – Transit

The interest of yachtsmen in satellite navigation was stimulated by the appearance of the Walker Satnav 801 at the 1980 London Boat Show. Around 85,000 sets are now in use worldwide, and prices have fallen to about £500.

There is nothing new about satellite navigation, which has been available since 1967 from the US Navy's Navigation Satellite System (NNSS), commonly called 'Transit'. The system comprises seven operational satellites which circle the earth in low polar orbits at a height of about 600 n miles (1000 km), as shown in Fig. 4(2).

The Transit system will be discontinued on 31 December 1996 and will be replaced by GPS. Additional (Nova) satellites which are of an improved design have been launched during the late 1980s and there are currently (1992) a total of 20 satellites in orbit, although only about seven of these are operational at any one time. A number of

Fig. 4(2) The orbits of NNSS Transit satellites, forming a cage inside which the earth rotates. There were originally five operational satellites (as shown) and other non-operational or spare satellites (not shown). Due to launching errors the satellites are not evenly spaced around the world. Further (Nova) satellites of a new design have been launched.

these satellites are now in orbital storage ready to be switched on in the event of any failures occurring.

The rotation of the earth brings a user beneath each orbit in turn, and while a satellite is above the horizon a receiver can compute its own position from data transmitted to it from the satellite. Each satellite circles the earth once every 106 minutes and the time between suitable satellite passes varies with latitude, averaging once every 70 minutes at 50° and every 90 minutes at 30°. The fact that Transit does not provide continuous fixing like Decca or Loran is a drawback. Between satellite passes the better receivers can automatically display the DR position, computed from inputs from the vessel's log and compass via an interface. With many yacht receivers, speed and course have to be keyed in manually which is satisfactory on an ocean passage perhaps, but inconvenient (and often inaccurate) in coastal waters. The best results are always obtained using a calibrated automatic interface of log and compass. Satnav can be used worldwide, regardless of weather conditions. It is simple to use, requires no special charts or tables, and is very accurate – normally within 0.25 n miles at sea and considerably better when the yacht is stationary.

While a satellite is in orbit its transmissions are monitored by ground stations which track it very precisely, and thereby predict its exact orbit in the immediate future. These details are transmitted to the satellite and are stored in its memory. Every two minutes, precisely, the satellite transmits details of its orbit and other ephemeral data on two carrier frequencies of 150 and 400 MHz. The receiver's calculation of the fix is based on the

Doppler effect on the frequency, as the slant distance between the satellite and receiver decreases and increases due to their relative movement. Each satellite pass takes about 10 to 15 minutes depending on its elevation in relation to the vessel. The angle of elevation for acceptable passes varies with receivers, but with most is limited to elevations over 10° and below 75° above the user's horizon. Two frequencies are used to refine the calculations but most yacht receivers work on only one frequency and are consequently not quite so accurate.

The errors associated with Satnav are relatively small. The largest single error in position will be as a result of incorrect input of the vessel's speed. North-south movement has the greatest effect, and produces position errors of up to 0.2 n miles per knot of speed error, while east-west movement has a much smaller effect. It is important to ensure that during a satellite pass the vessel's speed and heading is as accurate as possible and that no major changes in speed and heading take place. Other errors are caused by the lack of a consistent horizontal chart datum all over the world, and by inaccurate surveys in certain areas. The calculation of Transit fixes is based on the World Geodetic System (WGS 72) reference spheroid, but the charts on which the navigator plots the fixes are invariably based on a different datum. When the highest accuracy is required, it may be necessary to correct the displayed coordinates before plotting on the chart in use. Some receivers make provision to key in a datum, in which case it is only necessary to ensure that the receiver and chart datum are the same. British Admiralty charts are being progressively amended to incorporate a note such as follows:

SATELLITE DERIVED POSITIONS
Positions obtained from satellite navigation systems are normally referred to WGS Datum; such positions should be moved 0.05 minutes NORTHWARD and 0.09 minutes EASTWARD to agree with this chart.

The maximum errors likely from this cause are 0'.1 in the European area (including the Mediterranean), 0'.2 in the North Atlantic area, and 0'.4 in the Indian Ocean area. For practical navigation purposes, when passing through several zones, it is probably easiest to use a receiver which is set to WGS 72 or WGS 84 Datum if a choice exists.

In order to compute position fixes, all satellite receivers using Transit need initially to know time within ± 15 minutes and position within 60 n miles. Some receivers can auto-locate, in which case the initial position entry is unnecessary but the receiver may take longer to produce its first fix. It is also necessary that the receiver has been switched on for the maker's recommended period before the satellite pass, so that it is generating a stable reference frequency, against which it can measure the Doppler shift.

4.2.2 Global Positioning System (GPS)

The Global Positioning System (GPS), commonly called 'Navstar', is a new second generation satellite navigation system developed in the USA for military purposes. It is expected to be fully operational in 1995 and will provide highly accurate worldwide, three-dimensional position-fixing coverage (latitude, longitude and altitude), together with velocity and time information in all weather conditions. GPS satellites have a design life of 7.5 years. Mid-1994 the constellation consisted of 24 operational satellites (any model) which are operating in their assigned orbits, are available for navigation, and provide the SPS levels of service shown below. Fig.4(3) shows how these are deployed in six orbital planes, evenly distributed, circling the earth at heights of about 10,900n miles in 12-hour orbits.

Any planed disruption of GPS in peacetime will be subject to a minimum 48-hour notice from the US Department of Transport (DOT) to the US Coast Guard GPS Information Center, from which status information is available on 001 703 313 5907 (or from the UK Civil Satnav Group computer bulletin board on 01602 422111).

GPS provides two levels of service. These are a Standard Positioning Service (SPS) and a Precise Positioning Service (PPS). The SPS will be available to all users at no cost and will provide horizontal positioning within 100 metres on a 95% probability basis (2 drms) and 300 metres on a 99.99% probability basis. It is the SPS which is of interest to yachtsmen. The PPS provides higher accuracy but is intended solely for military purposes and will not be available to the civil

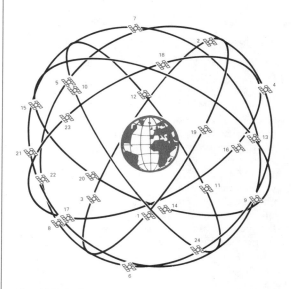

Fig. 4(3) GPS (Navstar) satellites arranged in six orbital planes inclined to the equator at 55 degrees. This configuration should ensure that at least four satellites with suitable elevations are available for a receiver anywhere on earth.

users unless specially authorised for specific applications.

GPS Initial Operating Capability (IOC) was declared in December 1993. This means the system is no longer regarded as experimental, and guarantees operational performance at SPS levels of accuracy for civil navigation, with 24-hour two dimensional fixing (latitude and longitude) adequate for most yachting needs. Full Operational Capability (FOC) is expected in 1995.

Accurate time plays a vital role in GPS, so each satellite is fitted with two caesium and two rubidium atomic clocks which gain or lose less than one second every 300,000 years. Timing accuracy is vital because a timing error of only 1/1000th of a second can produce a distance error of around 161 n miles.

The pattern of satellite deployment will be such that four satellites will always be visible at elevations greater than 5°, and five satellites will normally be above the horizon anywhere on earth. In conjunction with control and monitor stations, satellites will give highly accurate positions anywhere in the world. A marine receiver, whose altitude above the surface of the earth is already known, requires only three satellites to produce a fix.

Each satellite transmits navigation and time data on two downlink frequencies of 1575.42 and 1227.6 MHz. The 1575.42 MHz frequency transmits both the Standard Positioning Service (SPS) code for general civil use and the Precise Positioning Service (PPS) code which is strictly reserved for military and agreed specialist civil use. The 1227.6 MHz frequency transmits the PPS code only.

The principle on which GPS works is the accurate measurement of distance from a receiver to a number of satellites whose precise positions in space are known. In over-simplified terms, each satellite transmits the PPS and/or SPS code saying 'this is my position and this is the time'. By knowing the accurate times of transmission and reception of the signal, it is possible to establish the signal transit time. When this is multiplied by the speed of light (161,829 n miles per second), the distance to the satellite is obtained. If similar measurements are made on three satellites, three intersecting circles each centred on the satellite's position at the time of its transmission are obtained. If no errors are present, the intersection of the circles represents the yacht's position.

The total system errors associated with GPS are relatively small, and are of the order of 7-8 metres using PPS, and 19-20 metres using SPS. Current US plans for the civil use of the SPS are based on a denial of full system accuracy to civil users. This is called 'selective availability'. The SPS accuracy permitted for civil use will be no better than 100 metres (0.054n miles), horizontally and 156 metres (0.084 n mile) vertically, and time to 167 nanoseconds. The accuracy of a GPS fix varies with the capability of the user's receiver and the user-to-satellite geometry. GPS provides continuous global two-dimensional (latitude and longitude), or three-dimensional (latitude, longitude and height) fixing in all weathers.

No user charges will be incurred for the use of GPS SPS for at least ten years, although the next generation of replacement Block III satellites are reported to include encryption facilities which would make it possible for user charges to be introduced later if required.

A wide range of suitable receivers are already being manufactured, including portable handheld instruments. Typically these display: latitude/longitude, course made good and speed made good, an estimate of the error in the position, information on the satellite status, and the best satellites to use for fixes.

GPS fixes are based on a worldwide datum called the World Geodetic System (WGS 84) reference spheroid. WGS 84 is invariably different to the datum used on the majority of marine charts in use today. British Admiralty charts always state which datum a chart is based on, and often incorporate a note to tell you the amount of correction required for that chart. Because of the basic accuracy GPS offers, when a user requires the highest accuracy from the system, it is necessary to correct the displayed coordinates before plotting on the chart. Most good quality GPS receivers now build in datum shift parameters to compensate for the differences between the displayed GPS positions and the local chart positions by offering a large number of local data which the user can select. Always ensure the receiver is selected to the same datum as the chart in use.

In the UK the datum used for Admiralty charts is the Ordnance Survey Datum (1936), abbreviated as OSGB 36. For European waters the datum used is usually based on the European Datum 1950 (abbreviated as ED 50). In practical navigational terms, in the Dover Strait the difference between the ED 50 and WGS 84 would amount to 134 metres, and between the OSGB 36 and WGS 84 the difference is 139 metres. The figures are different for every location and may exceed over 2 kilometres in say the Pacific. The importance of setting a GPS receiver to the local chart datum is obvious when one considers that the average GPS accuracy available is usually under a 100 metres.

4.2.3 Differential GPS

Differential GPS (DGPS) is a technique used to improve considerably the basic GPS SPS system accuracy. Suitably located DGPS monitoring stations will determine the range errors by observing real time GPS signals and comparing them with predicted signals expected at the specified reference point, and then providing corrections to users operating in the local area by transmitting the required corrections over selected marine radiobeacon frequencies without detriment to the DF or homing signals.

A radio receiver capable of receiving marine radiobeacons, equipped with a suitable demodulator for the DGPS messages, is interfaced with the GPS receiver and will automatically apply the transmitted corrections to the navigation data. DGPS is expected to provide navigation accuracy of better than 10 metres.

DGPS monitoring stations in a number of countries are being set up and it is expected that a worldwide network will become available in time. Differential techniques can also equally be applied to Loran-C and Omega. Initially DGPS will appeal to only a limited number of yacht users, such as the racing community for laying out race marks etc., but may well gain more widespread popularity later.

4.3 Hyperbolic position fixing systems

4.3.1 Decca

The Decca Navigator system is a very accurate short to medium range continuous position fixing system for coastal waters and for landfall navigation. It was introduced towards the end of World War II, but since then has undergone considerable extension and refinement. Very good coverage is provided in coastal waters (to a range of about 400 n miles by day, and 250 n miles by night) for most of NW Europe, as shown in Fig. 4(4), and in certain parts of South Africa, the Persian Gulf, Pakistan and Japan. There are now (1994) 32 Decca chains in operation.

Decca transmitters are organised into groups called chains. Each chain comprises a master and up to three slave transmitters which are situated between 85 and 240 n miles from the master station in a geometrical pattern. For identification purposes the slaves are referred to as red, green and purple respectively. The same colours are used on Admiralty Decca lattice charts.

The general principle on which all the hyperbolic aids operate is described in 4.1.2 under hyperbolic navigation systems. With Decca, the method used to determine the time difference is by measuring the phase differences between phase-locked signals transmitted from a master and a slave station. Decca transmitters operate in pairs -master and red, master and green, and master and purple.

Each pair of transmitters provides a large number of hyperbolae which are printed on Decca lattice charts. The area which lies between any two of the Decca lattice lines printed on a chart is known as a lane. For ease of identification, lanes are numbered in sequence from a master station as follows: red 0–23, green 30–47 and purple 50–79.

Since many hundreds of lanes are involved, it is convenient to group lanes into zones, which are denoted by letters A to J. In cases where the master and slave are more than ten zones apart, the zone lettering after J starts again at A. Therefore, any **position line is** identified by colour, zone, lane number and fractional part of a lane, e.g. Purple E 75.34, and this type of display is known as a Decca coordinate.

Most yacht receivers display position in latitude and longitude, or in waypoint form, rather than in Decca coordinates, which is more convenient but not so accurate as using raw Decca coordinates after applying any corrections, and plotting on a Decca lattice chart. If the highest accuracy is required, always use corrected Decca coordinates. From 1 January 1987 the General Lighthouse Authorities assumed responsibility for running the UK Decca chains formerly operated by Racal-Decca. As a result it is now no longer necessary for manufacturers to prevent yacht receivers from displaying Decca coordinates. Any new receivers appearing on the market should now offer displays of both geographical and Decca coordinates. For the best results it is always preferable to purchase a receiver which provides both geographical and Decca coordinates.

When using the Decca Navigator System it is important for navigators to appreciate that errors are present in any radio position fixing system, and they should not just accept displayed readings as being of absolute accuracy. In other words do not confuse high resolution with high accuracy. Just because the position is displayed to two decimal places does not mean that it is that accurate. A practical tip is to treat all Decca positions with extreme caution whenever your TV picture at home is distorted by abnormal radio propagation conditions. Such conditions are quite frequent whenever atmospheric pressure is significantly higher than average.

The propagation of radio waves can be affected by: weather, season, radio noise, time of day and night, the type of terrain over which the radio waves pass, and the range from transmitters to name but some. Such factors may result in interference to the required groundwave causing 'variable errors' in the Decca readings obtained. Errors in Decca readings are generally quite small and, in the best areas of chain coverage, may not be of practical significance. Nevertheless it needs to be appreciated that errors are present and can assume navigational significance. One of the major disadvantages of Decca sets which only display geographical coordinates is that one cannot correct the displayed coordinates for fixed or variable errors as no published data suitable for correcting latitude/longitude displays is available. For practical navigational purposes, it would be unwise to assume an accuracy better than 0.25 n miles at ranges of 50–100n miles from transmitters, and up to 1.5 n miles or more at the limits of coverage. Receivers which display Decca coordinates can always be fully corrected from Decca data sheets.

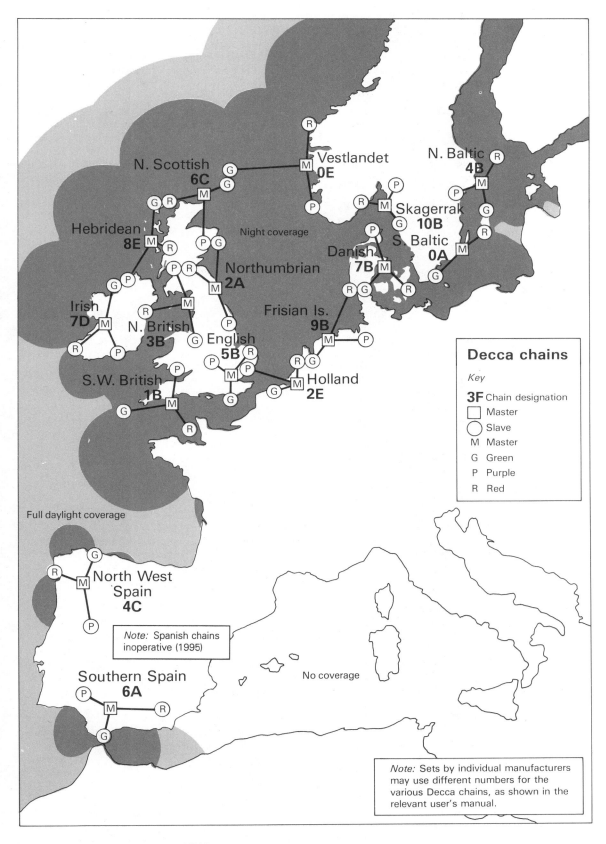

Fig. 4(4) Decca chain coverage – NW Europe.

There are two types of errors to which Decca is subject.

(1) *Fixed errors.* These occur as a result of variations in the velocity of radio waves over different types of terrain. Fixed errors are constant for any given geographical location, and data sheets giving fixed error corrections for each chain are published by Racal-Decca Ltd. The effect of fixed errors can be very pronounced when close to the coast.

(2) *Variable errors.* Variable errors are due to the effect of skywave/groundwave interference, and to the other factors mentioned above. Estimated variable errors for each Decca chain are published by Racal-Decca Ltd. Generally speaking, winter night conditions produce worse results than in summer, and errors are bigger at the extremities of the coverage area than in the centre.

Because such errors are variable, the magnitude at any given location is not constant and no precise figures can be given. For practical purposes, on a winter's night at the centre of the coverage area the error would be of the order of 0.2 n mile, and in summer about 0.1 n mile. At the extremities of coverage, the error on a winter night would be about 1.6 n mile or greater, and in summer about 0.5 n mile based on a 60 per cent probability level (one occasion in three), but statistically there is a 1 in 20 chance that the actual error will exceed twice the values quoted above. Even under the most favourable conditions it would be unwise to expect an accuracy of better than 0.1 n mile.

There is also a possibility of slipping lanes, particularly at night, due to excessive skywave interference of the groundwave, external radio interference or electrical storms. There is little chance of this happening at short distances from the transmitters, but the risk will increase as the distance from the centre of the chain increases. Other possible causes of lane slip are fouling of the Decca antenna or interruption of the electrical supply for a significant period. Most receivers incorporate some form of alarm warning for this condition. The best way of revealing an inaccurate fix due to lane slip is by plotting Decca fixes at frequent intervals and comparing them with positions found by other navigational methods.

The operating procedures vary with individual receivers and it is essential to read the operating manual carefully and to follow the instructions precisely. On switching on for the first time, most receivers carry out a self-test routine which checks out the computer memory, receiver and antenna for correct operation. It then prompts the operator to key in the present position coordinates which shoul‹ be within half the width of a zone in each pattern – that is normally within 1 to 2 n miles of the true position. If a receiver is switched on at sea, and the last position in the memory is some way from the true position, then a new EP must be keyed in.

Most receivers automatically select the best chain to use, but provision is made to key in a chain manually if required. After a receiver has locked-on to the most suitable chain, it displays the current position which is updated at frequent intervals – usually every 20 seconds or less. At this point it is advisable to check that there are no alarm warnings present, that the strengths of the received signals are satisfactory, and to note which slave stations are being used for fixing together with the expected accuracy prediction. If Decca coordinates are available, it is advisable to refer the pair of in-use Decca coordinates to a lattice chart to see that they agree with the true position, especially the zone letters and lane numbers. If the displayed geographical position, or Decca coordinates, agree with the true position, and all the alarms are extinguished, the receiver is ready for navigational use.

Navigational accuracy is vitally important and it is necessary to understand two terms which are commonly used. These are:

(1) *Absolute accuracy.* This is a measure of the receiver's ability to determine geographic position (latitude and longitude), the accuracy of which varies depending on where the vessel is within the coverage area. Use absolute accuracy to keep track of true position.

(2) *Repeatable accuracy.* This is the accuracy with which a user can return time and again to a position whose coordinates have been measured at a previous time, using the same navigational aid. It is repeatable accuracy that helps to find a particular buoy having previously determined its coordinates, or to return safely to harbour when the visibility is poor.

Perhaps the most important principle in navigation is never to rely on one piece of information if it can be cross-checked by another means. Sensibly used, modern position fixing receivers can assist navigators to cross-check the correctness of conventional techniques or other instrumentation.

An adequate power supply is vital to satisfactory performance. Check that the battery voltage and capacity are adequate. It is advisable to have a fused 12V or 24V supply to prevent damage to the receiver caused by voltage surges. It is also advisable to ensure that the boat's electrical supply is 'clean' and that no undue electrical noise is present.

Logs and compasses play an important role with any receiver or DR computer requiring an input of speed or heading. Before such data is used for navigation, either via an automatic interface or manually for dead reckoning, it is essential that the log and compass are accurately calibrated. The best results are always obtained if electronic equipment is automatically interfaced with log and compass. Such a combination provides a more accurate DR plot and takes account of steering errors.

Waypoint navigation, as it is called, is the very basis of electronic navigation. Any error in the entry of position coordinates is likely to result in navigational error if undetected. It is a good idea to develop a system to eliminate blunder error when loading waypoint data into receivers. Waypoints can be keyed into a receiver in two ways – as latitude and longitude, or as Decca coordinates. Some receivers can accept both types of data while others will take only latitude/longitude.

As the procedures vary between receivers, before attempting to load waypoint data it is necessary to understand the format used to key in data and where to position any decimal points. Incorrect placing of the decimal point can result in considerable errors in the calculation of bearing and distance. Another point to watch is whether East or West longitude is assumed by the receiver. If necessary, change the sign by using the $\pm$ or other designated key. Following the simple precautions below can assist in preventing errors being made when loading waypoints:

(1) Check that the positions have been taken off the chart correctly.
(2) Measure the tracks and distances on the chart and record the results on a simplified passage plan.
(3) Check that the waypoints have been entered into the receiver memory correctly.
(4) Get an independent check if possible.
(5) After loading waypoints, cross-check the tracks and distances calculated by the receiver against those measured off the chart and shown in the simplified passage plan.

A simple passage plan showing the bare bones of the intended passage is all that is required. The information might include the following as shown in Fig. 4(5):

(1) Waypoint Number.
(2) Name or identification of waypoint
(3) Charted position in latitude/longitude
(4) Track and distance to next waypoint, from chart
(5) Maximum cross-track error (maximum distance allowable to left or right of intended track, with regard to navigational dangers)
(6) DR time for that leg, at estimated speed

Load the waypoint data into the receiver memory. Having done this, select the interwaypoint calculation facility and compute the tracks and distances between the various waypoints. Check that the receiver display compares with the tracks and distances shown on the simplified passage plan, and investigate any discrepancies. Computed results are rarely identical to measurements taken off a chart, so small differences are acceptable. However if using an advanced calculator the results should be virtually the same as those displayed on the receiver.

With any receiver capable of holding more than about 30 waypoints in its memory for future use, it is advisable to adopt a method whereby it is possible to catalogue and record waypoint data used frequently. For example, allocate waypoints 1 to 10, or 10 to 20 for routine daily navigation purposes and use the remaining memory capacity to hold those waypoints required for permanent use. An indexed address book can be used for that purpose. In it can be recorded, in alphabetical order, the charted geographical and/or Decca coordinates for anchorages, buoys, harbours or turning points. Subsequently, as these places are

Passage plan with electronic navigation aid

									Satellite derived positions (WGS datum, chart *1138*)
Harbour check:	Charted position Lat *49°10'.90N* Long *2°06'.62W*	Aid co-ordinates Lat *49°10'.79N* Long *2°06'.56W*	System error – position to be moved: *0.11* minutes N/S̶ *0.06* minutes E̶/W						to be moved: *0.06* minutes N/S̶ *0.09* minutes E/W̶
Route no: *3*									

WPT no.	Description	Charted position	WPT no.	Charted position	Track °T	Dist nm	Max XTE	DR time @ ___ *5* ___ kn	Remarks
1	*Canger Rock lt Buoy*	*49°07'.40N 2°00'.30W*	2	*49°07'.89N 1°57'.06W*	*078°*	*2.18*	*0'.2*	*0h 26m*	*Plateau de la Frouquie offlier, to S. La Route en Ville, to N.*
2	*Violet lt Buoy*	*49°07'.89N 1°57'.06W*	3	*49°10'.50N 1°57'.34W*	*356°*	*2.66*	*0'.35*	*0h 32m*	*Seal Rocks, to E.*
3	*Gorey front ldg lt 298° 3'*	*49°10'.50N 1°57'.34W*	4	*49°11'.87N 2°01'.27W*	*298°*	*2.93*	*0'.2*	*0h 35m*	*Le Giffard (buoy), to S. Horn Rk Bn, to S.*

Fig. 4(5) Passage plan for use with electronic aid, whereby tracks and distances taken off the chart can be compared with computed tracks and distances to expose any blunder in loading waypoints.

visited, record the actual geographical or Decca coordinates so that full advantage can be taken of the high repeatability, which enables the vessel to return again and again to the same position on the basis of previous readings.

A major advantage of waypoint navigation is that the computer continually displays a variety of valuable navigation information (in addition to current position) such as distance to go, cross-track error, course made good and speed made good, according to the facilities provided. Cross-track error is defined as the distance that the vessel is to left or right of the intended track. This is valuable information in its own right, but even more so if at the planning stage the navigator defines the maximum off-track distance that can be accepted, coupled with the knowledge of how this distance relates to potential navigational dangers.

Once the required waypoints have been entered, it is then a simple matter to call up a display of continuously updated range and bearing as the vessel advances towards the selected waypoint, as illustrated in Fig. 4(6). The range and bearing between WPT 1 and WPT 2 defines the track required. If the vessel remains on track, the bearing does not change; if she goes off-track, then the bearing will increase or decrease. The most useful facility to indicate relationship to the required track is the display of cross-track error (abbreviated as XTE). If cross-track error is indicated and if no navigational danger exists between the present position and the destination waypoint, the boat can sail direct to the destination. But if some danger is present, as is shown in Fig. 4(6), it may be necessary to regain the original track as soon as possible. The golden rule to adopt is that, if off-track, always check the track from the present position to destination for proximity to dangers. On a longer passage, when making an allowance for the effect of tidal stream, the vessel will invariably be to one side of the track or the other and, if no dangers exist, it is pointless attempting to keep rigidly to the required track.

It is well worth checking periodically that the Course Made Good (CMG) and Speed Made Good (SMG) display accords with the track required to reach the next destination.

Finally, when using bearing information, make sure whether it is true or magnetic. Remember that a bearing and distance to a waypoint is not a course to steer. Some sets can accept a tidal input and give a course to steer, but most do not, so the effects of set, drift and leeway will have to be applied manually in the normal way.

4.3.2 Loran-C

Loran-C is a long range hyperbolic fixing system which is suitable for coastal, landfall and offshore navigation within coverage. The original Loran system, known as Loran-A, was invented in the USA during the early 1940s. By the end of World

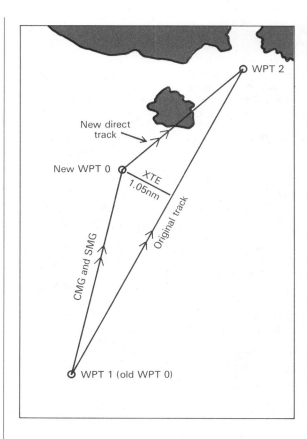

Fig. 4(6) Waypoint navigation does not eliminate the need for conventional plotting techniques. Maximum cross-track error should be related to navigational dangers on the chart. Here a radical alteration of course is needed to regain the original track.

War II, some 70 transmitting stations were in operation, but they have now been phased out apart from a few chains in Japan and China in the North Pacific. The improved version, called Loran-C, was developed after the war and first became operational in 1957.

Loran-C provides continuous fixing coverage in North West Europe, around the east and west coasts of North America, across the northern parts of the North Atlantic and North Pacific, in the Red Sea, in Saudi Arabia, and in India, and north-west parts of the Indian Ocean. Dependent on the power of transmitters and other factors, ground wave reception at ranges of 800–1200 n miles is possible, but a more practical figure for normal operational use would be up to a distance of 600 n miles from transmitters. Loran-C pulses also propagate as skywaves, the incidence of which varies between day and night and from place to place. Skywaves may be received at ranges up to 2300 n miles, but with much less accuracy.

A typical Loran chain consists of three to five transmitters spaced several hundreds of miles apart, and geometrically located so that signals from the master and at least two secondary stations may be received throughout the required area of coverage. One of the stations is designated as the master station (M). The others are called secondary stations and for identification are labelled W (Whiskey), X (X-ray), Y (Yankee) and Z (Zulu) as appropriate. These identification letters are used on lattice charts and in publications.

Loran-C transmitters operate in sequenced pairs: master and secondary W (TD-W); master and X (TD-X); master and Y (TD-Y); or master and Z (TD-Z) depending on the number of secondary stations in the chain. Precise time is the very basis of Loran, so each transmitter is accurately controlled by caesium clocks. The master station transmits its pulses at a fixed repetition rate, called the group repetition interval (GRI). Secondary stations transmit at the same GRI as the master station, but in a predetermined sequence after a fixed time delay. The delay between a master and secondary is known as the coding delay (CD) and is different for each station. Coding delays are so

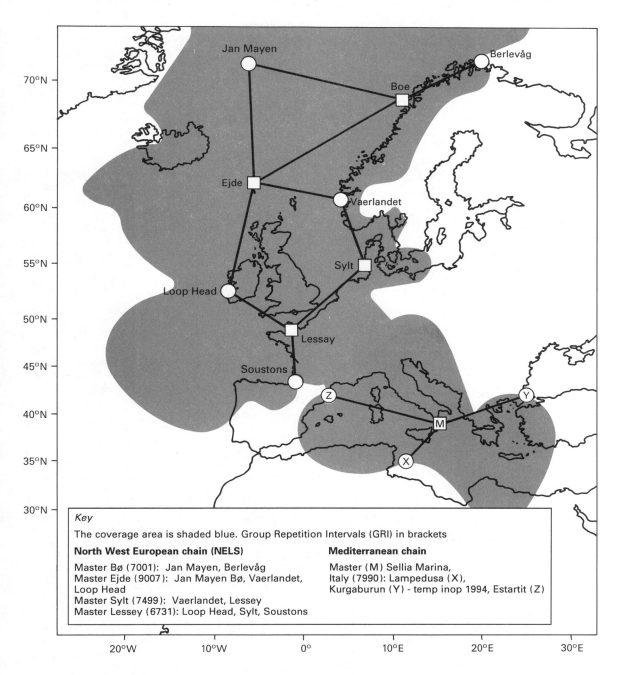

Key

The coverage area is shaded blue. Group Repetition Intervals (GRI) in brackets

North West European chain (NELS)

Master Bø (7001): Jan Mayen, Berlevåg
Master Ejde (9007): Jan Mayen Bø, Vaerlandet, Loop Head
Master Sylt (7499): Vaerlandet, Lessey
Master Lessey (6731): Loop Head, Sylt, Soustons

Mediterranean chain

Master (M) Sellia Marina, Italy (7990): Lampedusa (X), Kurgaburun (Y) - temp inop 1994, Estartit (Z)

Fig. 4(7) Predicted coverage (1995) of Northwest European Loran-C System (NELS). Within the blue area, better than 463m ($\frac{1}{4}$ mile) 2 drms. Over the British Isles, English Channel, North Sea and Irish Sea accuracy will be much improved – better than 50m apart from Northern Ireland and Clyde area (50–199m). The Mediterranean chain no longer operates (1994).

arranged that no matter where the vessel is within the coverage area, she will always receive the signals in the same order. The Loran receiver accurately measures the time difference (TD) in arrival of the pulse signals sent out from the master and secondary stations. These measurements are made initially by measuring the pulse envelopes (coarse difference) and then by matching the phase of the 100 kHz carrier (fine difference). TDs are measured in micro-seconds, or millionths of a second, and the readings are shown on the receiver display which can then be transferred to a Loran lattice chart overprinted with hyperbolic curves for the stations concerned. Selecting the correct hyperbola, or interpolating as required, gives a position line. The procedure is repeated with a different secondary station to get a fix. Most modern Loran-C sets are able to convert the TDs obtained and then compute and display the latitude and longitude. If the highest accuracy is required always use corrected time differences and plot on a lattice chart.

Modern Loran-C receivers also show navigational information such as waypoints, bearings and distances, cross-track information, speed and course made good, and course to steer. Position information is presented continuously.

There are (1994) 18 Loran-C chains in operation, all in the northern hemisphere. It is expected that further chains will be commissioned. The first chain in the southern hemisphere is planned for South Australia, providing coverage in the vicinity of the Bass Strait.

A new Northwest European Loran-C System (NELS) becomes operational in 1995, with nine stations forming four chains. NELS users must update their receivers with the new system parameters for Group Repetition Interval (GRI) as shown in brackets below.

Master: Bø (7001) with secondaries Jan Mayen, Berlevåg. Master: Ejde (9007) with secondaries Jan Mayen, Bø, Vaerlandet, Loop Head. Master: Sylt (7499) with secondaries Vaerlandet, Lessay. Master: Lessay (6731) with secondaries Loop Head, Sylt, Soustons.

Fig. 4(7) shows the anticipated groundwave coverage of NELS. Further information can be obtained from: US Coast Guard Activities – Europe, London. Tel: 0171 872 0943. Loran-C coverage of the Eastern Mediterranean is no longer operational (1994).

Data on the accuracy and coverage of Loran-C is given in publications issued by the US Hydrographic office. These include *Publication No. 221* which contains tables for each pair of stations in a Loran chain, and data for constructing Loran LOPs together with skywave corrections, in much the same way as is used for plotting celestial LOPs. The tables are available from Kelvin Hughes Ltd, New North Road, Hainault, Ilford, Essex, IG6 2UR.

The accuracy of the system, using groundwaves, varies from about 100 metres at a range of 200 miles to about 250 metres or more at 500 n miles

from transmitters. Skywave reception gives greater range but less accuracy. When using Loran-C, similar considerations apply as with Decca, described above in 4.3.1.

4.3.3 Omega

The Omega system is still being developed and is not yet fully operational (1994), but it already gives almost worldwide coverage. It is operational in the North Atlantic, South Atlantic and North Pacific. It is a long range aid, operating on Very Low Frequency (10–14kHz) radio waves from eight stations in Norway, Liberia, Hawaii, North Dakota, La Réunion, Argentina, Australia and Japan.

The extensive global coverage makes the system very attractive, although the accuracy is not so good as either Decca or Loran-C, about 1–2 n miles by day and 2–4 n miles by night.

Omega stations transmit on four frequencies, but the cheaper receivers only operate on 10.2kHz and these must be set with the correct lane number at a known position, and must subsequently track received signals continuously.

Before they are plotted on a lattice chart, Omega readings must be corrected for such phase variations as are predictable, which are given in Propagation Prediction Correction Tables. Other, unpredictable, variations are Sudden Ionospheric Disturbances (SIDs) and Polar Cap Absorption (PCA). Information on these variations is promulgated in Hydrolant and Hydropac messages broadcast by United States stations, in United Kingdom Long-range Radio Navigational Warnings broadcasts, in broadcasts from Rogaland (Norway), in Navtex broadcasts, or by dialling US Coast Guard NAVCEN (USA) on 703 313 5900. The radio time signal station at Fort Collins, Colorado (WWV) also broadcasts warnings on 5000, 10,000, 15,000 and 20,000kHz at H + 16. Kekaha (Kauai), Hawaii (WWVH) broadcasts on the same frequencies at H + 47.

4.3.4 Differential Omega

Differential Omega avoids the principal errors in the Omega system by monitoring the signal at a number of known positions. The difference which is obtained is rebroadcast, and can be used by vessels which have Differential Omega receiving equipment to decode the signal. This can improve the accuracy to about 0.25 n miles when within 50 n miles of one of the following monitoring stations: Cap d'Alprech (50°42′N,1°34′E); Pointe de Créach (48°28′N, 5°08′W); Ile d'Yeu (46°43′N,2°23′W); Cabo Finisterre (42°53′N,9°16′W); Lagos, Portugal (37°10′N, 8°37′W); Cabo de Palos (37°38′N,0°41′W); Porquerolles (42°59′N,6°12′E); Horta (38°31′N, 28°41′W); Porto Santo (33°04′N,16°21′W); Cap Bon, Tunisia (37°04′N,11°03′E); La Isleta (28°10′N, 15°25′W); Port Bouët, Ivory Coast (5°15′N,3°58′W); Tête de Galantry (46°46′N,56°09′W); Pointe-à-Pitre (16°16′N,61°32′W); Punta Tuna (17°59′N,65°53′W); Cayenne (4° 50′N,52° 22′W).

4.4 Radar

4.4.1 Radar in yachts

Radar is being increasingly used by yachtsmen, both as an aid to navigation and for collision avoidance. But in order to make proper use of its considerable advantages, and to enjoy its benefits in safety, it is essential to understand a little about how it functions, and to know how it should be operated. It is important to read the instruction book carefully, so that the various controls are well understood, and to practice using and adjusting the set to give optimum performance in different conditions. Finally, it is necessary to learn how to interpret what is actually seen on the display.

4.4.2 How radar works

Radar (short for RAdio Direction And Range) uses radio waves at super high frequency, concentrated in a series of powerful but very short pulses, each pulse lasting less than a microsecond (a millionth of a second). The number of pulses transmitted per second (the pulse repetition frequency, or pulse repetition rate) is usually between 800 and 3000. The wavelength is very short, 3cm (X-band) in yacht radars, but 10cm (S-band) in larger commercial sets. The pulses, generated by a device called a magnetron, are transmitted in a narrow beam by a rotating aerial, which also receives any echo reflected back from a target within range. The aerial rotates at a steady speed, usually about 30rpm, and the whole assembly is called the scanner. In yachts, aerials are normally of the slotted waveguide type, the pulses and returning echoes passing through accurately machined slots. Radio waves travel extremely quickly (162,000n miles per second, or about 1000ft a microsecond), so it only takes a very short time for a pulse to reach a target and be partially reflected back – 62 microseconds for example for an object 5 miles away, or only 1 microsecond for an object 500ft away. This is why each pulse must be very short, so that it is cut off before any echo returns – increasingly important as the range of the target is reduced. Most radar sets automatically reduce the pulse length when shorter ranges are selected on the range scale.

The range of an object is determined by the time interval between the outgoing pulse and the returning echo, and this has to be measured very accurately. This is done by a stream of electrons in a cathode ray tube (CRT), the larger end of which is the Plan Position Indicator (PPI) of the boat's radar display, normally sited in the wheelhouse. The centre of the PPI represents 'own ship', and a rotating trace on the display is synchronised with the rotation of the aerial. The electrons energise a chemical coating on the inside of the CRT, to give spots of light which persist for a short time after the flow of electrons has ceased. A returning echo received by the scanner is amplified by the

receiver and passed to the CRT, so that the flow of electrons is intensified, and a bright spot or echo shows on the PPI. The distance of this spot from the centre of the PPI (own ship) represents the range of the target. Each outgoing pulse from the scanner is transmitted on a slightly different bearing, and, since the rotation of the scanner and the trace on the display are synchronised, the direction of the target is indicated on a scale graduated round the circumference of the PPI.

A radar beam is typically $2°$–$3°$ in width horizontally, and about $25°$ wide in the vertical plane to allow for the vessel's movement at sea. Echoes are returned from an object so long as it is within the beam: the echo of a ship, for example, therefore appears rather wider than it actually is, and it may be impossible to distinguish (say) a gap in a harbour wall. Put in more technical language – a radar set does not discriminate so well in bearing as it does in range. Also some of the transmitted beam escapes into 'side lobes', which can give spurious echoes.

The effective range of radar is only approximately line of sight, and most yacht radars have a maximum range of 16–24 n miles, although greater ranges are possible with more powerful sets. Under conditions of abnormal propagation radar range may be greatly increased (by super-refraction) or it may be reduced (by sub-refraction). Freak conditions called ducting may on occasions allow targets hundreds of miles away to be detected, or conversely prevent the identification of objects at short range.

There are occasions when radar signals can be self-cancelling, either on their way from the scanner to the target or on the way back, or both. These areas where coverage may be lost or be adversely affected are sometimes referred to as Fresnel zones, or radar extinction zones, and are caused by multipath propagation as illustrated in Fig. 4(8).

The radar signal from scanner to target is transmitted partly in a direct line and partly by reflection off the surface of the sea, particularly when it is smooth. The latter path is longer than the direct route, which can cause the two

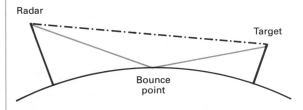

Fig. 4(8) How radar signals arrive at a target in part directly and in part by reflection from the surface of the sea. The latter route is longer, so there is the opportunity for the two transmissions to cancel (or augment) each other in phase.

transmissions to cancel (or augment) each other in phase. This may cause the signal received at a passive target (such as a radar reflector) to be too weak for a return signal to be detected by the radar set, remembering that the returning signal may also suffer a reduction like the outward one. If the target is a transponder, as for example a radar beacon, the outward signal may be too weak to activate it.

Yachtsmen should be aware that they may be in a zone where the radar of a larger vessel cannot detect them for a time, or conversely that the yacht's radar may be unable to pick up a target at certain critical ranges.

The Firdell Tables of Radar Extinction (Fresnel) Zones, which give examples of the size and positions of Fresnel zones relative to a radar scanner and its target, can be obtained free of charge by sending a stamped addressed envelope to Firdell Radar Reflectors, The Grove, Warren Lane, Stanmore, Middlesex HA7 4LY.

The influence of meteorological conditions on radar propagation close to the sea surface is still being documented, and reliable data about the phenomenon would be welcomed by Firdell at the address above. The information required for each observation is date, time, latitude/longitude, radar height, target height, observed width of extinction zone, temperature, atmospheric pressure, visibility, precipitation, and make/model/year of radar.

It is important to remember that radar will not detect a low-lying coastline which is over the radar horizon, but may show up a range of hills several miles inland, as in Fig. 4(9). In this connection it is useful to calculate the distance of the radar horizon in nautical miles from the formula: distance $= 1.22 \sqrt{h}$ where h is the height of the scanner in feet, or $2.2 \sqrt{h}$ where the height is in metres.

From the above it is evident that the scanner should be mounted as high as possible, although topweight is an obvious consideration since the average unit for a yacht weighs about 25kg (55lb), though some are less. With a ketch rig the scanner can be conveniently mounted on the mizzen mast, but it should not be sited at or about the level of the spreaders on the mainmast. In some cases it is essential to use a radome to prevent the rotating

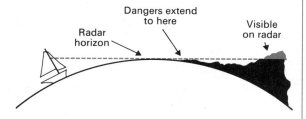

Fig. 4(9) High land, perhaps some distance from the coast, may be the first thing detected on radar when approaching from seaward. Lower ground may be hidden from view, over the radar horizon.

aerial fouling sails or rigging. The scanner must not be sited where people are liable to be in the direct line of harmful emissions of radiation.

The display unit needs to be in a sheltered position, at a safe distance from the steering compass (usually about 0.76m or 30in), and mounted so that it can be viewed from the chart table and/or steering position. Most yacht radars will accept 12/24/36 volts DC, or AC power supplies with a suitable rectifier. Consumptions vary from about 50 watts to over 300 watts for the more powerful sets.

Controls are mounted alongside the PPI, and typically consist of the following, although details vary from make to make:

(1) On/off switch, also controlling the brilliance of the display. Before switching the set on it is necessary to make certain settings to the controls for the warming-up period (usually a minute or two) or damage may occur to the CRT. Then adjust the brilliance so that the rotating trace is faintly visible.

(2) The gain control adjusts the amplification in the receiver, and the brightness of the echoes. Too much gain results in unwanted interference, with speckles over the screen. Too little gain results in weaker echoes not appearing.

(3) The range selector controls the scale, so that the full radius of the display can be made to represent (say) 0.5, 1.5, 3.0, 6.0, 12.0 or 24.0 n miles. With the 6-mile range scale selected, an object at the circumference of the display is 6 miles distant. If the 12-mile scale is then selected, the same object will reappear at half the radius from the centre (own ship). Range rings, which can be varied in brightness, are projected onto the display to help assess the ranges of echoes. A more sophisticated arrangement is a variable range marker (VRM), whereby the operator can measure a range, which is then displayed on a digital read-out.

(4) The bearing cursor is a transparent engraved screen over the face of the PPI, which can be rotated so that the bearing of an echo is read at the circumference. Equally spaced parallel lines each side of the main, diametric line form what is called the parallel index, which can be used for navigational problems and for collision avoidance. Some sets have an Electronic Bearing Marker (EBM) – an electronic cursor which can be placed over an echo to obtain a digital read-out of bearing. At this point it must be noted that yacht radars invariably have a relative motion or 'ship's head up' display. Own ship is at the centre, and any object at the top of the display (at 12 o'clock) is dead ahead. So all bearings, whether from a bearing cursor or EBM, are relative (to ship's head). Thus an echo at 3 o'clock on the display must be on the starboard beam; if own ship alters course 90° to starboard, that echo will then reappear at 12 o'clock, or dead ahead.

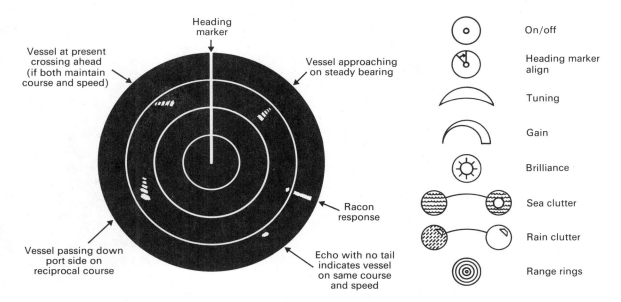

Fig. 4(10) The 'tails' shown by echoes on the radar display can helpt to indicate movement, relative to own ship.

Fig. 4(11) Symbols for controls of radar set.

(5) Sea clutter control is used to reduce unwanted reflections from the sea around the yacht, in order that echoes from objects such as buoys and small craft are not obscured. This is achieved by reducing the gain out to a certain distance from the yacht. If too much sea clutter is applied, no echoes will be received at short range.

(6) Rain clutter control can reduce the echoes from precipitation, which would otherwise obscure the display, or parts of it, but may not be effective for heavy rain. It can be useful in good weather to help improve definition at short ranges, particularly when looking for small objects like buoys.

(7) Heading marker control is used to line up the heading marker (a line representing ship's head) when the set is first switched on, so that it points straight upwards, at 12 o'clock. Some sets have means of suppressing the heading marker, so that it does not conceal an echo directly ahead.

It should be realised that some objects provide better radar targets than others. Radar beams are reflected in much the same way as rays of light on a mirror, and curved or sloping surfaces (such as low shorelines, chimneys or lighthouses) do not give such a good response as abrupt faces (like steep cliffs, breakwaters or buildings). Objects which are conspicuous by radar are marked on Admiralty charts. A ship beam-on will give a better echo than one with an aspect of 45°. Yachts, boats or buoys without radar reflectors do not show up at all well, but most major navigational buoys are now fitted with reflectors.

Due to the angular width of the radar beam, a target near the edge of the PPI will appear wider than an identical target at short range, as shown in Fig. 4(12). Experience will show that, apart from large targets which are nearby, there is little relation between the size of an echo on the screen and the actual size of the target it represents.

Overhead power cables reflect a radar echo at right angles to them, which may be identified as a ship on a collision course, on a constant bearing.

The most positive and identifiable response comes from one of the many radar beacons, or Racons, which are described in 4.4.5.

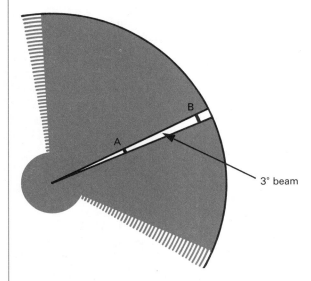

Fig. 4(12) Targets A and B are in fact the same size, but on the radar display B appears to be twice the size of A, because it is further away and due to the spread of the radar beam.

4.4.3 Radar for collision avoidance

At the outset it must be remembered that radar range is more accurate than bearings obtained from the PPI, and that the latter are relative to ship's head. Although true motion displays (where static objects remain stationary on the display, and vessels move relative to them) are found in commercial ships, yacht radars invariably have a relative or ship's head up display, with the boat at the centre, apparently stationary. The shore, buoys and ships at anchor move past as the boat follows her course, which is always towards the top of the display no matter in what direction she is actually heading. If the boat alters course, then all the echoes on the display rotate accordingly.

If the target is moving in the same direction at the same speed, and is therefore stationary relative to own ship, its echo should be sharp and well defined – assuming the set is properly adjusted. But if another vessel is on an opposite course she will paint an echo with a long tail, which indicates which way she is moving relative to own ship.

Initially it is easier to study collision avoidance if it is assumed that own ship is proceeding on a steady course and at a steady speed. For collision avoidance, in fog for example, a long range scale should be used in open water, but reduced from time to time in order to make sure that no echo appears which might have been missed at longer range. When an echo is detected the bearing cursor should be placed over it (or the EBM used) so that its relative bearing is noted, and its progress watched. If the relative bearing is constant (own ship's head being steady), and the range is closing, there is risk of collision. It is advisable to plot an approaching echo at least three times, on a circular plotting chart as shown in Fig. 4(13), say at six minute intervals. Her positions at A, B and C indicate that she is holding a steady course and speed, and when projected to D give the closest point of approach (CPA). The actual course and speed of the other vessel can then be determined from the plot. If the vector AE represents the distance which own ship moves while the echo moves from A to B, then EB gives the course and speed of the target. This course is relative to own ship.

Only at this stage can a proper appreciation be made of the problem, and a decision made as to which vessel is required to keep clear under the Collision Regulations. In restricted visibility these require that 'a vessel which detects by radar alone the presence of another vessel shall determine if a close-quarters situation is developing and/or risk of collision exists. If so, she shall take avoiding action in ample time ...' (see Rule 19(d)). In the example shown in Fig. 4(13) it is evident that the yacht (own ship, in the centre of the display) is bound to keep clear of the vessel on her starboard bow, and if in any doubt about the CPA she should make an early and substantial alteration of course to starboard.

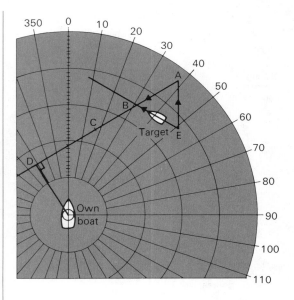

Fig. 4(13) To make proper use of a radar set for collision avoidance it is necessary to plot echoes as shown here, in order to determine their closest point of approach and their actual course and speed. Only then is it possible to make a correct decision about what should be done under the Collision Regulations.

It should be emphasised that the plotting procedure indicated above and in Fig. 4(13) is only valid if a steady course and speed is maintained by own ship. In particular, the existence of risk of collision is established by the fact that the *actual* bearing of an approaching vessel does not alter significantly (not the *relative* bearing). It is of course perfectly feasible to obtain the actual bearing of any object by reading the compass course (ship's head) at the same time as the relative bearing is obtained by radar, but in respect of collision avoidance this introduces undesirable complications in the plotting procedure for a yachtsman.

In restricted waters there is usually not enough time for the procedure described in Fig. 4(13), and often not room for vessels to make significant alterations of course while following a channel. Under these circumstances the proper use of radar for collision avoidance is limited, and the set becomes more an additional and very valuable look-out. In poor visibility yachts should in any case keep out of shipping channels, or skirt along the very edge of them.

4.4.4 Radar as a navigation aid

Properly used, radar can be a useful aid to navigation, but it is necessary to be aware of its limitations. It cannot see behind other objects, or round corners, or over the horizon; also it may not pick up small targets or differentiate between two targets which are close together.

The chart should be carefully studied when making a landfall by radar, to decide what objects may appear first. High cliffs make a good target, but approaching a low coastline the first thing to show on the radar display may be hills some distance inland. Ordinary buildings give good echoes, but smoothly contoured structures do not.

Due to the width of the radar beam, objects like ships or islands appear on the display as wider than they really are. For the same reason harbour entrances may not always be evident from seaward, although they should appear as the range is reduced.

Because radar ranges are more accurate than radar bearings, it is often preferable to obtain a radar range and visual bearing of an object in order to get a fix: be sure that the same object is observed on both occasions. Often a very good fix can be obtained from radar ranges of three different objects, suitably distributed.

Proper use of the range scales helps maintain a certain distance from any danger. As an example if it is desired to pass 3 miles from a headland select the most appropriate range scale, and make sure that the 3 mile range ring does not reach the point concerned.

The bearing cursor can be used to determine the course to steer relative to an object such as a buoy, in order to offset the effect of tidal stream. Set the bearing cursor over the buoy and watch its progress. If its tail is along the bearing cursor, and the cursor continues to cover it as the range is closed, then the relative bearing is steady and the boat will arrive at the buoy. If the buoy drifts either side of the bearing cursor, course can be corrected accordingly.

When using radar in poor visibility, do not forget to watch for echoes other than buoys etc, which may be approaching (or overtaking) ships.

4.4.5 Radar beacons (Racons)

A Racon is a transponder beacon, triggered by the emissions of a vessel's radar set, and sending out a distinctive signal which appears on the display of the set. They are fitted to a number of light-vessels, buoys and lighthouses, and are marked on the chart.

In most cases the Racon flash on the display is a line extending radially outwards from a point slightly beyond the actual position of the Racon, as shown in Fig. 4(10), due to the slight delay in the response of the beacon apparatus. Thus the distance to the mark of the Racon flash is a little more than the vessel's real distance from the Racon. Most Racons give a flash composed of a Morse identification signal, often with a tail to it, the length of the tail depending on the number of the Morse characters.

The maximum range of a radar beacon is usually about 10 nautical miles, but may be more. In practice, picking up a Racon at greater distances depends also on the effective range of the boat's radar. With abnormal radio propagation, a spurious Racon flash may be seen at much greater distances than the beacon's normal range, appearing at any random position along the correct bearing on the display. Only rely on a

Racon flash if its appearance is consistent, and the boat is believed to be within its range. At short range a Racon sometimes causes unwelcome interference on the radar display, and this may be reduced by adjusting the rain clutter control on the set.

The characteristics of radar beacons around the coasts of Great Britain, and the adjacent coasts of Europe, are given each year in chapter 4 of *The Macmillan & Silk Cut Nautical Almanac*. Details shown include:
(1) Reference number.
(2) The type of radar beacon. Unless otherwise stated, all radar beacons sweep the frequency range of marine 3cm (X-band) radar emissions. An increasing number also respond to 10cm (S-band) emissions. The term F Racon indicates a fixed frequency Racon, transmitting on a frequency outside the marine radar band, so that by tuning to that frequency the Racon flash is selected to the exclusion of normal echoes. Some in-band Racons are called frequency agile. Their response is within the band width of a yacht's radar, and they may cease to respond for a short period to allow echoes otherwise obscured by the Racon signal to be seen.
(3) Name of the station.
(4) Latitude and longitude.
(5) The time, in seconds, for a slow-sweep radar beacon to sweep the frequency range of the marine radar band.
(6) The sector within which signals may be received, bearings being towards the beacon, clockwise from 000° to 359°. 360° indicates all round operation.
(7) Approximate range, in nautical miles. This also depends on the effective range of the yacht's radar set.
(8) The form of the beacon's flash on the radar display. Morse signals are shown alphabetically, and are often followed by a 'tail'. Racons coded 'D' are used to mark new dangers.

4.5 Marine and aero radiobeacons

4.5.1 Marine radiobeacons

This system of direction finding is a relatively simple method whereby yachtsmen can establish at least an approximate position from non-directional radiobeacons, using a receiving set which has an aerial with directional qualities. It is useful in poor visibility or when navigating out of sight of land, but the effective range of the system is limited and few beacons give bearings of reasonable accuracy at distances of more than 50 miles.

Very few DF sets now remain available for sale. A simple but adequate DF set can still be bought for under £100 and is likely to be a small hand-held instrument powered by internal batteries. More sophisticated equipment, with better bearing discrimination at longer range, can cost a great deal more – as can the automatic DF set which, once tuned into a beacon frequency, automatically displays the required bearing.

Marine radiobeacons are non-directional and transmit on medium frequencies on a continuous basis or, in some parts of the world, at fixed intervals. The navigator tunes to the listed frequency, identifies the required beacon by its Morse call sign, and rotates the aerial of the set so that it registers the minimum signal, or null. (The minimum signal is chosen because it is easier to identify than the maximum.) The position of the aerial then indicates the direction of the beacon.

The signal modulation for all marine beacons is A1A. This means that receivers need a Beat Frequency Oscillator (BFO) switch to operate properly (see 4.5.7). On Admiralty charts marine radiobeacons are shown by a magenta circle with the letters 'RC'. On some old charts they may still be shown as 'R°.B^n'. *The Macmillan & Silk Cut Nautical Almanac* uses the symbol ⓡ.

4.5.2 DF receiving sets

Most simple DF sets have ferrite rod aerials, which give a minimum signal when they are pointing in line with the direction of the station. Often they incorporate a small compass, so that the magnetic bearing of the beacon can be read at the same moment as the operator identifies the null in his earphones (much better than a loudspeaker for this purpose). Such compasses are just as liable to error as any other magnetic compass, and must not be used close to magnetic objects.

With other sets the receiver itself is fixed and the aerial rotates against a graduated scale which gives the relative bearing (that is relative to the ship's head). The course on the steering compass must then be noted at the same moment that the null point and the relative bearing are obtained. This requires co-operation between the operator and the helmsman. Against this disadvantage there is the benefit of having the aerial in a certain place, so that the set can be properly calibrated for any error – rather like a compass is swung for deviation. This type of set also allows the aerial to be fitted on deck, connected to the set by a long spindle, so that it is well away from magnetic influences. An extension of this principle is to use a cross-loop aerial above the wheelhouse or even at the masthead, connected to the receiver through a goniometer – an electronic device which produces a similar electro-magnetic field at the receiver to the one experienced at the aerial.

An Automatic Direction Finding (ADF) set is tuned to the required frequency, which may be crystal controlled, and will then lock on to any transmission automatically, and indicate the bearing of the beacon on an azimuth scale, a digital display, or a cathode ray tube. If there is a sequence of beacons on the same frequency it will point to each one in turn. Such sets usually have cross-loop aerials, and a sensing device to remove ambiguity about the direction of the beacon. (When a bearing is taken with an ordinary set the null point does not differentiate between a bearing and its reciprocal.) Aerials of this type can be positioned high up, even at the masthead, where they are well removed from undesirable magnetic influences within the boat. ADF sets have another advantage, in that whatever type of unit is fitted for sensing the Earth's horizontal magnetic field can be sited separately, in the part of the boat which is most magnetically neutral.

Radiobeacons must always be positively identified by their call sign, to ensure you are using the correct beacon and to prevent confusion with other beacons operating on similar frequencies, but received as a result of freak propagation, or narrow band separation between frequencies with adjacent radiobeacons. Positive identification is particularly important when using RDF or ADF at night.

4.5.3 Grouping and sequence of beacons

Hitherto two or more marine beacons have often shared a common frequency, transmitting on a strict time schedule. In North West Europe grouping of beacons is no longer used (see 4.5.1). In other parts of the world where such groups still exist, up to six beacons may share a frequency on a six-minute cycle, each transmitting for one minute in a fixed sequence. In all cases the cycle of the group starts at the hour; thus the first beacon to transmit (Sequence Number 1) comes on the air at the hour, and subsequently at 06, 12, 18, 24 etc. minutes past. The beacon which is Sequence Number 6 transmits at 05, 11, 17, 23 etc. minutes past the hour. The table below shows the relation between sequence numbers and the start of transmission times, in minutes past the hour.

Sequence Number	1	2	3	4	5	6
	00	01	02	03	04	05
	06	07	08	09	10	11
Starts to	12	13	14	15	16	17
transmit at	18	19	20	21	22	23
these	24	25	26	27	28	29
minutes past	30	31	32	33	34	35
each hour	36	37	38	39	40	41
	42	43	44	45	46	47
	48	49	50	51	52	53
	54	55	56	57	58	59

4.5.4 Directional Radiobeacons (RD)

In a very few places, all of them overseas, a directional signal is transmitted, to assist vessels making harbour, the signal varying depending on the boat's position relative to the required bearing line. Automatic gain control should be switched off when using such devices: if the set has a direction finding aerial it should be tuned to the position of maximum reception.

On Admiralty charts the bearing is shown as a pecked line, with the legend RD. Allowance should be made for the width of the beam when the bearing line passes close to dangers. In small craft, for collision avoidance, it may often be wise to keep slightly to starboard of the indicating bearing.

It may sometimes be found, when a directional transmission is calibrated, that the observed beam deviates from the promulgated bearing along part of its length. Major deviations of this kind are given in the *Admiralty List of Radio Signals Vol. 2,* where known. On Admiralty charts the bearing line is normally limited to the portion(s) in which the observed beam substantially coincides with nominal or intended bearing line.

4.5.5 Beacons incorporating distance finding

Occasionally yachtsmen may encounter radiobeacons which incorporate radio and sound signals which are synchronised for distance finding. The two signals are usually synchronised at an easily identifiable point in the cycle of each — say at the beginning or end of a long dash and a long blast of the fog signal. A stopwatch must be used, and the difference between the two times in seconds, multiplied by the factor of 0.18, gives the distance off in nautical miles.

Other systems involve the transmission by the beacon of a number of measuring signals, started when the fog signal is sounded. The number of measuring signals received before the fog signal is heard on board the boat is an indication of the distance, the time scale of the beacon being included in information on that station. An interval of 5.5 seconds between measuring signals is equivalent to a unit distance of one nautical mile.

A third form of synchronisation involves transmissions by the beacon of a count of units on RT; then it is only necessary to note the figure heard when the fog signal timing point is heard.

4.5.6 Aero radiobeacons

Aero radiobeacons are established for use by aircraft, but those situated on or very near the coast are useful to yachtsmen. Only selected aero radiobeacons are shown on charts, where they are marked by a small magenta circle and the letters Aero RC. *The Macmillan & Silk Cut Nautical Almanac* uses the symbol $\underset{\text{Aero}}{\overset{\text{RC}}{\ominus}}$. It is necessary to plot the positions of other beacons which are listed, from the latitude and longitude as given.

Aero radiobeacons transmit continuously, but care needs to be taken with their use because the land effect may be unpredictable. They also operate on a wider range of frequencies than marine ones: from 255.00 to 283.50kHz, 315.00 to 405.00kHz, 415.00 to 435.00kHz on primary frequencies, and 285.00 to 315.00kHz, and 435.00 to 495.00kHz used as secondary frequencies.

4.5.7 Types of emission (modes)

New designations for radio signal emissions came into force on 1 January 1982. In the following explanation the new designations are given.

Intelligence is impressed upon a radio emission by modulation. A continuous emission of constant amplitude (or strength) and of constant frequency carries no information, and the simplest way of impressing intelligence upon it is to switch it on and off (or key it), to make Morse Code characters for example. This type of modulation is designated as A1A and is used for the identification signal of radiobeacons and in radiotelegraphy.

The amplitude of the radio emission, however, can be fluctuated at a rate and to a degree corresponding with a sound wave to produce speech, music or a plain musical tone. The latter may be keyed as necessary. These emissions are referred to as 'amplitude modulation' (AM), of which there are various types depending on whether the original (carrier) radio wave is transmitted with the so-called 'sidebands' generated in the process of modulation, or whether it is wholly or partially suppressed. One of the sidebands may also be suppressed to make better use of the transmitter's power and of the radio-frequency spectrum. The resulting 'single-sideband' (SSB) emission is the standard for maritime medium frequency (MF) radio, enabling the number of MF channels to be doubled.

The designation A2A refers to amplitude modulation, the type of transmission being telegraphy by the keying of an amplitude-modulating audio frequency (or audio frequencies), or by keying the modulated emission. It is commonly used for the identification signals of aeronautical radiobeacons.

A second way of impressing intelligence on a radio wave is to fluctuate the frequency, with the amplitude staying constant. This is called 'frequency modulation', and is used in VHF radiotelephones. It suffers less than AM from outside interference, and it is simple and relatively cheap; but it occupies more spectrum width per channel and for this reason is not suitable for the HF and MF bands.

When using a radiobeacon it is important to know what type of radio emission is used in order to receive the transmissions correctly. A1A indicates that the transmissions are unmodulated, which requires a receiver with a built-in oscillator to produce an audible signal. This is usually referred to as a Beat Frequency Oscillator (BFO), which must be switched ON to receive A1A or NON A1A transmissions, and to identify them.

Nearly all British aeronautical radiobeacons are NON A2A — an unmodulated transmission with telegraphy identification by the keying of an amplitude modulating audio frequency, the carrier emission being continuous during the identification period. With a NON A2A beacon, to receive the DF tone any separate BFO control should be ON, and to receive the identification signal it should be OFF.

Where a separate control is provided for BFO it should be adjusted as follows:

Emission	BFO setting	
	For DF use	For ident.
A1A	ON	ON
NON A1A	ON	ON
NON A2A	ON	OFF[2]
A2A	ON or OFF[1]	OFF[2]
A3E	ON or OFF[1]	OFF[2]

Note:
(1) For best performance consult the maker's handbook.
(2) If BFO cannot be switched off, it may be difficult to hear Morse identification.

With any set where the user is expected to listen for a null signal, the BFO should be switched on during the DF period while the bearing is being taken.

4.5.8 Radiobeacons – operating procedure

The detailed procedure depends upon the type of set, but normally includes the following.
(1) First it is necessary to select the beacons to be used, depending on their range and the angle of cut they will give for a good fix. As with taking bearings of land objects, it is desirable to use at least three beacons so that the resulting cocked hat gives an indication of the reliability of the fix. If three beacons are used it is best if the position lines they give cut at angles of about 60°. Extract from the list the frequency and call sign of each beacon, and the time at which it transmits.
(2) Turn on the set, and the Beat Frequency Oscillator (BFO), if there is a separate control for this. BFO makes the signal clearer for directional purposes and produces a more precise null. It should be used in accordance with the table in 4.5.7 above.
(3) Tune the receiver to the required frequency. Often this is done by an ordinary tuning dial, but some new sets have a keyboard rather like a simple calculator on which the required figures are keyed to give precise results. The aerial may incorporate a separate tuning control. Earphones are better than a loudspeaker for direction finding, and they don't disturb other members of the crew, particularly at night.
(4) When the required beacon has been identified from its call sign and the long dash commences, swing the aerial backwards and forwards over a diminishing arc to determine

the null. In some sets a visual null (signal strength) meter assists with this.
(5) With sets fitted with an integral compass mounted on the aerial the magnetic bearing of the beacon can be read directly. Write it down against the name or the call sign of the beacon in the navigator's notebook. Before it is plotted on the chart it will need to be corrected for variation and also for Quadrantal Error (if this is known – see 4.5.10 below). If a compass is not fitted to the set the relative bearing is read and at the same moment the helmsman must read the steering compass. Write them both down – never trust to memory in these matters.
(6) The procedure is then repeated with the other beacons, and the time of the fix and the log reading should be noted before the bearings are plotted on the chart. This is done in exactly the same way as visual bearings are plotted. The likely accuracy of the fix can be judged by the size of the cocked hat.

4.5.9 Errors in radio bearings

Bearings from radiobeacons are subject to errors, which fall into two categories.

Signal errors
(1) The accuracy of a radio bearing decreases considerably with the distance from the beacon. Any bearing taken towards the maximum range of a beacon (particularly at night) should be treated with caution Fig. 4(14).

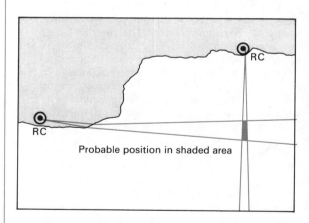

Fig. 4(14) Beams from a radiobeacon (on left) which come along the coast or over intervening land are refracted and less reliable. Due to refraction, the navigator will think that he is slightly further inshore than the shaded area. The diagram also shows how accuracy decreases with distance from the beacon.

(2) Night effect (or sky-wave effect) can cause errors from one hour before sunset to one hour after sunrise, especially near sunset and sunrise. The error increases with distance from the beacon, but is less serious if within about 25 miles.

(3) If the beacon's radio beam passes along the coast or over high ground it may be bent by land effect (or coastal refraction) and thus give an incorrect bearing Fig. 4(14).

(4) Synchronised transmissions of two beacons are a possible source of error.

Errors on board

(1) Quadrantal Error is caused by the magnetic effect of objects in and around the boat, which reradiate the signal being received so that its true direction is distorted. This effect on the radio waves on their way to the receiving aerial is usually greatest on each bow and quarter, and least when the beacon is on the beam or ahead/astern of the boat. With a fixed installation the set can be calibrated for Quadrantal Error in much the same way that a compass is swung. Visual and radio bearings of a convenient beacon are taken at the same time, and are compared on various headings. Beacons which provide a special calibration service are shown in 4.5.10.

(2) Compass error can be an important factor with a hand-held instrument unless it is used in a certain place which is known to be free from any magnet influences.

(3) Unless the set has a sensing device it is possible to take the reciprocal of the required bearing, when the beacon is on a light vessel or a lighthouse in the open sea for example.

(4) The error which may be caused by the operator depends upon his experience with the set concerned, and also on the prevailing weather conditions. Accurate radio bearings are not easy to get when the boat is moving around a great deal.

Radio bearings from a small yacht may therefore be a useful guide when taken by an experienced operator, using a set which has been properly installed and calibrated, as described in 4.5.10. But they can suffer from serious errors, and should not be relied on exclusively unless three or four position lines result in an acceptable cocked hat. Practice and experience help to get good bearings, but the results should always be compared with position lines from other sources (if available) so that they can be properly assessed. It is important to become familiar with the Morse code signals of beacons which are likely to be used.

4.5.10 Calibration

Before it can be trusted (and there is no sense in having navigational equipment which cannot be trusted) a DF set must be calibrated in very much the same way that a compass is swung to establish its deviation.

The easiest way to calibrate a DF set is to get within visual range of a radiobeacon, and then take simultaneous radio and visual bearings of it with the boat on different headings. Unless a pelorus (or bearing plate) is available, and the visual bearings of the beacon can thus be related to the steering compass (which should previously have been corrected and swung), the visual bearings of the beacon will have to be taken with a reliable hand bearing compass, kept well clear of magnetic objects.

The two sets of bearings should be taken, say, every 15°, and it is helpful if the beacon concerned is one which transmits continuously or the process can take rather a long time. As an alternative method radio bearings (only) of the beacon are taken from the boat when she is in a known position, so that the actual bearing of the beacon is known. In either case the object is to plot the Quadrantal Error for, say, every 15° of relative bearing.

The following stations in the British Isles provide a calibration service for DF sets. In each case the service is available from 1 hour after sunrise to 1 hour before sunset, and the range of the station is 5 n miles: Souter Lt, PT, 294.50kHz; Point Lynas Lt, PS, 294.50kHz; Lynmouth Foreland, FP, 294.50kHz; Cloch Pt, CL, 300.00kHz (8 n miles); Old Head of Kinsale, KC, 294.50kHz; Baily Lt, BC, 286.50kHz; Black Head, BA, 294.50kHz.

Other stations provide a service on request, and a charge is made accordingly.

4.5.11 Details of Radiobeacons

A list of marine and aero radiobeacons, for the geographical area covered, is published each year *in The Macmillan & Silk Cut Nautical Almanac*. The information given includes:

(1) A reference number for each beacon, which can be used to assist identification on charts provided.

(2) Name of beacon.

(3) Latitude and longitude.

(4) The Morse Code identification signal (Ident), with the Morse symbols.

(5) The frequency of the transmission, in kilohertz (kHz).

(6) The mode of emission (see 4.5.7).

(7) The range, in miles, at which the field strength produced by the ground wave of the transmission falls to a minimum acceptable value. In some areas, where there are numerous radiobeacons, it is necessary to reduce power output at night, so day and night range are quoted. Elsewhere the ranges shown should be obtained in the absence of skywave effect. MF beacons should not be relied on at ranges of more than about 50n miles in the presence of night effect, particularly near sunset and sunrise.

(8) Notes such as 'Day service', 'On request', or 'DGPS service' with the relevant frequency and range (see 4.2.3).

4.6 Radio direction finding

4.6.1 Principle of operation

Radio direction finding stations (which are few in number) are shown on charts by a magenta circle and the letters RG. They are equipped with apparatus enabling them to ascertain the direction of signals transmitted from a vessel. A charge is usually made for the service.

The procedure is that the vessel calls the station concerned, and is requested to transmit a series of long dashes followed by her call sign. These are processed by the station (or sometimes stations) and the result, either as bearing or if more than one station is involved as a fix, is transmitted to the vessel.

4.6.2 Radio direction finding stations

In Western Europe the only radio direction finding station is situated in Germany (Norddeich). There are also stations in Scandinavia and in the Faeroes. Details are given in the *Admiralty List of Radio Signals, Vol. 2*. There are no stations in the British Isles, other than the VHF DF stations which are described in 4.6.4.

4.6.3 Half convergency

A radio wave moves along a great circle, which is represented on a Mercator's chart by a curved line (unless it is exactly north/south, when it coincides with a meridian). So the bearing of a distant radio station from a vessel is the angle between the circle through the station and the vessel, and the meridian through the vessel. Meridians as depicted on a Mercator's chart are parallel straight lines, but in reality on the surface of the globe they converge towards the poles. The difference in the angles formed by the intersection of a great circle with two meridians is called convergency, and it depends on the differences of latitude and longitude between the two points of intersection. An approximate formula for convergency is:

Conv. (in mins) = diff Long (mins) × sin mid Lat

If the difference in longitude between the vessel and the radio station is more than about 3°, the true bearing of the radio signal should be converted into a mercatorial bearing by adding or subtracting half the convergency, before it is plotted on the chart (see also 3.3.16).

It must be remembered that in north latitudes the straight line bearing as plotted on a Mercator's chart is always to the south of the great circle bearing. It may help to draw a simple sketch as in Fig. 4(15) in order to determine whether half convergency should be added or subtracted, but in north latitudes the following rules apply: For bearings of a radio station taken from a boat –

If the boat is:	Half convergency must be:
east of the station	subtracted
west of the station	added

For bearings of a boat provided by a direction finding station –

If the boat is:	Half convergency must be:
east of the station	added
west of the station	subtracted

The converse applies in southern latitudes.

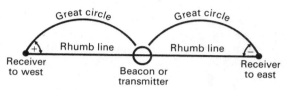

Fig. 4(15) The diagram shows how half convergency is applied in N hemisphere to D/F bearings from a beacon or transmitter, i.e. + if the yacht is to the west, and − if to the east.

Half convergency table

For practical purposes the table below can be used to find half convergency for distances up to 1000 n miles.

Enter with the difference in longitude between the station and the vessel (along the top), and mid-latitude between the station and the vessel (down the side). The figure extracted is half convergency in degrees.

Mid Lat				Difference in longitude (degrees)						
	3°	6°	9°	12°	15°	18°	21°	24°	27°	30°
5°	0.1	0.3	0.4	0.5	0.7	0.8	0.9	1.0	1.2	1.3
10°	0.3	0.5	0.8	1.0	1.3	1.6	1.8	2.1	2.3	2.6
15°	0.4	0.8	1.2	1.6	1.9	2.3	2.7	3.1	3.5	3.9
20°	0.5	1.0	1.5	2.1	2.6	3.1	3.6	4.1	4.6	5.1
25°	0.6	1.3	1.9	2.5	3.2	3.8	4.4	5.1	5.7	6.3
30°	0.7	1.5	2.2	3.0	3.7	4.5	5.2	6.0	6.7	7.5
35°	0.9	1.7	2.6	3.4	4.3	5.2	6.0	6.9	7.7	8.6
40°	1.0	1.9	2.9	3.9	4.8	5.8	6.7	7.7	8.7	9.6
45°	1.1	2.1	3.2	4.2	5.3	6.4	7.4	8.5	9.5	10.6
50°	1.1	2.3	3.4	4.6	5.7	6.9	8.0	9.2	10.3	11.5
55°	1.2	2.5	3.7	4.9	6.1	7.4	8.6	9.8	11.0	12.3
60°	1.3	2.6	3.9	5.2	6.5	7.8	9.1	10.4	11.7	13.0

Example. A yacht in DR position 47°20′ N 06°20′W obtains a radio bearing from a powerful station in position 58°37′N 05°38′E. The difference in longitude between the two positions is 12°. The mid-latitude is 53°. From inspection the half convergency is 4.8°. Because the yacht is to the west of the station, this figure should be added to the bearing taken before it is plotted on the chart.

4.6.4 VHF emergency direction finding service

Direction finding can be applied to VHF radio transmissions in much the same way as to MF transmissions. A VHF direction finding set can in fact be fitted in a yacht, but the equipment is expensive and a rather bulky aerial unit consisting of four dipoles needs to be located at or near the masthead (a position for which other radio equipment makes conflicting demands). It is therefore more feasible to locate VHF DF sets ashore, and several stations are operated by HM Coastguard. There are several French stations.

These VHF DF stations are intended *for emergency use only*, and should not be considered as a normal navigation aid. However in practice the term 'emergency' seems to be interpreted quite liberally. Except for those in Guernsey and Jersey the stations are controlled by a Coastguard MRCC or MRSC (see 8.4.2). On a request, by VHF radiotelephone, from a yacht in distress or difficulty, the station transmits the bearing of the yacht *from the DF site,* which is marked by the symbol RG on Admiralty charts and in *The Macmillan & Silk Cut Nautical Almanac* on Area Maps.

Watch is kept on Ch 16. A yacht should transmit on Ch 16 (for distress calls only) or on Ch 67 (Ch 82 for Jersey and Ch 11 for French stations) for the station to obtain the bearing. The yacht's bearing *from the station is* transmitted on Ch 16 (distress calls only) or on Ch 67 (Ch 82 for Jersey and Ch 11 for French stations). For details see *The Macmillan & Silk Cut Nautical Almanac.*

4.6.5 QTG service from Coast Radio Stations

Certain Coast Radio Stations will, on request, transmit medium frequency signals for use by any vessel equipped with ADF or DF equipment so that it can obtain a DF bearing. The procedure to request this service, for which a charge is made, is as follows:

The yacht contacts the Coast Station, identifies herself, and sends 'QTG . . . . . . (times) . . . . . . (kHz)', meaning 'will you send two dashes of ten seconds each, followed by your call sign, repeated . . . . . . times, on . . . . . . kHz'.

The Coast Radio Station replies 'QTG . . . . . . (times) . . . . . . kHz', followed by the signals requested.

Details of Coast Radio Stations, for the area covered, are given in Chapter 6 of *The Macmillan & Silk Cut Nautical Almanac.* The frequency used for a QTG request may be a special one reserved for the purpose, or any of the station's working frequencies. A request should specify 410kHz (if listed for that station) or a working frequency close to that on which the boat's DF is calibrated. Stations providing QTG service are shown on Admiralty charts by the abbreviation R (or the obsolescent R°) against a small magenta circle indicating the position of the transmitter. There are no stations in the United Kingdom, Ireland, or France offering a QTG service, but a number of stations in Denmark, Norway, and elsewhere are in operation.

4.7 Bibliography

Simple Electronic Navigation by Mik Chinery (Fernhurst).

Using your Decca by Pat Langley-Price and Philip Ouvry (Adlard Coles Nautical).

Using Loran by Conrad Dixon (Adlard Coles Nautical).

Radio Position Fixing for Yachtsmen by Claud Powell (Adlard Coles Nautical).

Electronics Afloat by Dag Pike (Adlard Coles Nautical).

A Small Boat Guide to Radar by Tim Bartlett (Fernhurst).

Radar Mate by Lt Cdr G.A.G. Brooke and Captain S. Dobell (Adlard Coles Nautical).

How to use Radar by H.G. Strepp (Adlard Coles Nautical).

Electronic Navigation by Colin Jones (Helmsman Guides).

Using GPS by Conrad Dixon (Adlard Coles Nautical).

Chapter 5

Astro-navigation

Contents

5.1 Introduction to astro-navigation

5.1.1 General

Astronomical navigation, astro-navigation (or just astro, as it is widely called) remains the most basic method of fixing a vessel's position offshore out of sight of land. To some extent modern electronic and especially satellite fixing aids have lessened its usefulness but it remains a system that is universally available, self-contained and free; further, it is controlled by a non-political body. It continues to fascinate most navigators, perhaps largely because of its independence of outside influence.

The astro-navigator's tools are the sextant, to measure the altitude of a heavenly body above the horizon, a timepiece to give the precise time of observation, the ephemeris which gives the body's coordinates at that time and some form of reduction process (typically tables or an electronic calculator of some kind) by means of which he 'works up' the sight. An electronic calculator can be programmed to give the position in terms of latitude and longitude but with tables position is normally established by plotting the position lines.

In this chapter the sextant is first of all described, with its errors and adjustments. To simplify the explanation of what follows, a summary of the principles of nautical astronomy is then given and, for those who want to go more deeply into the matter, a glossary giving definitions of the principal terms used in astro-navigation. The sextant altitude corrections are then described and illustrated.

The method of sight reduction recommended in this volume is the *Sight Reduction Tables for Air Navigation* published in the United Kingdom as AP 3270 and in the United States as Pub No 249. The tables, in three volumes, are of the inspection or direct entry kind and cater for all bodies to a precision sufficient for all practical purposes at sea. The volumes contain full explanations of use but examples are given here under Sight Reduction (5.6).

Today perhaps a 'dedicated' electronic calculator (often referred to as a navigation computer), which requires neither almanac nor tables and can display the fix in terms of latitude and longitude, is the most convenient form of sight reduction and in time this may well become the standard method. However, such instruments are vulnerable to damage of one kind or another at sea and as things stand it would be unwise to rely solely on them.

The Macmillan & Silk Cut Nautical Almanac produces an Astro Supplement with ephemeris of the Sun, Moon, GHA Aries, 57 stars, Pole star, altitude correction tables, rise/set tables etc. It is envisaged, however, that those who practise astro-navigation regularly will use *The Nautical Almanac* which is issued by HM Nautical Almanac Office and published by HMSO. In addition to tabulations for the Sun, Moon, planets and stars the volume contains a concise set of reduction tables for use when neither more extensive tables nor computer aided solutions are available. The tables are briefly described here under Sight Reduction (5.6). A low-precision ephemeris for the Sun, suitable for programmable calculators, is given in 5.7.7.

Methods of plotting are next discussed with ways of analysing the plot to establish the most probable position. Finally there are some general

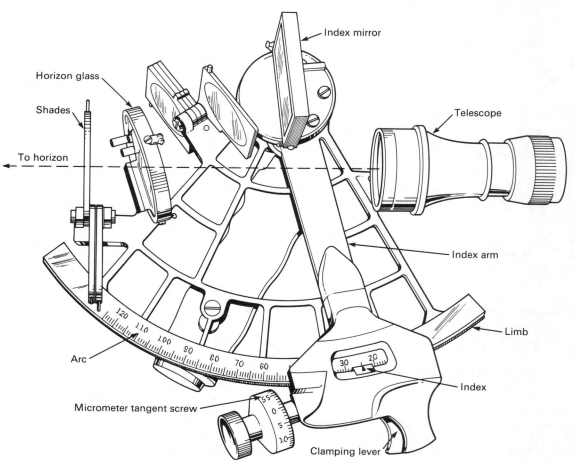

Fig. 5(1) The sextant.

notes on sight taking, the height of altitudes, angles of intersection and so on.

Whether stars are identified for sights by using the appropriate volume of AP 3270 or by planisphere, or even by star globe, most navigators like to achieve a familiarity with the sky at night that will enable them, and indeed other members of the crew, to pick out the principal constellations, the main navigational stars and the planets. The star chart shown in Fig. 5(9) and the accompanying text is intended principally for this purpose.

5.1.2 The sextant

The marine sextant is shown in a simplified form in Fig. 5(1). The telescope and horizon glass are fixed with respect to the frame although minor adjustments can be made by means of adjusting screws. The index mirror is similarly fixed with respect to the index arm. The latter rotates about the centre of curvature of the arc, and at its lower end carries an index against which the graduated arc is read. The index mirror and horizon glass should be parallel when the index reads zero.

The arc of the sextant subtends an angle of $60°$ but, because of the principle of double reflection, the scale is graduated to $120°$. Older sextants carry a vernier scale on the index arm opposite the arc to facilitate reading fractional parts of the smallest graduations on the scale. Most modern instruments have micrometer tangent screws, or drums, which serve the same purpose and are far easier to read.

5.1.3 Sextant errors and adjustments

Sextants are subject to certain errors. Instrument error cannot be corrected by the navigator and, where it exists, is usually tabulated by the manufacturer and applied as corrections to different altitudes. The three principal sources of instrument error are centring error from a faulty location of the pivot of the index arm, graduation error on the scale, and prismatic error where the two sides of the mirrors or shades are not parallel. Instrument error in a good sextant is normally small enough to be ignored.

The errors adjustable by the navigator are perpendicularity, side error, index error and collimation error. Because of their interdependence they should normally be corrected in the order given.

Perpendicularity error

Perpendicularity error arises when the index mirror is not perpendicular to the frame. It is checked by holding the sextant horizontally and sighting the arc simultaneously through the mirror and directly. If the reflected and direct views of the arc do not appear as a single unbroken line there is perpendicularity error. The error is removed by a screw at the back of the mirror.

Side error

Side error is strictly speaking another form of perpendicularity error, arising from the fact that the horizon glass is not perpendicular to the frame. It may be checked by setting the index to zero and sighting the horizon which should appear as a continuous straight line in both the direct and double reflected views. If either moves up or down with respect to the other when the sextant is rotated about the line of sight, side error exists. It is corrected by means of a screw near the base of the glass. An alternative way of checking side error is to use a low-flying (low altitude) star. With the index set to zero two images of the star side by side show side error.

Index error

Index error occurs when the index mirror and horizon glass are not parallel when the index is at zero. It may be determined in the same manner as side error, observing the horizon with the sextant vertical. The horizon glass and index mirror will be parallel when the index reads zero and the direct and reflected image of the horizon appear as a continuous straight line. Several readings should be taken, the sextant being offset in different directions each time. An alternative way of determining index error is by observing the Sun *on* and *off* the arc, the limbs of the two Suns visible just touching in either case. The index error will be half the sum of the two readings, and a useful check on the accuracy of the observations is that the sum should be four times the semi-diameter of the Sun as given in the nautical almanac. Perhaps the best way of all is to use a low flying star and one that is not too bright, which will allow greater accuracy and be less tiring than using the Sun.

Index error may be corrected by means of the screw or screws at the base of the horizon glass. Since it will directly affect the angles measured, index error should be checked each time the sextant is used. However, adjusting the sextant each time index error is found would tend to wear the thread of the adjusting screws and it is customary to allow errors up to 2′ or 3′ as a correction to the observations. If the index correction is *on* the arc of the sextant the reading will be too high by that amount and must be subtracted to get the observed altitude, and of course added if it is *off* the arc. An easy way to remember the sign of the correction is the phrase 'If it's on it's off, and if it's off it's on'.

Collimation error

Collimation error is caused by the telescope not being parallel to the frame and will result in greater angles being measured than the correct values. To determine the error the sextant is placed horizontally on a flat surface and a mark made on the wall or bulkhead opposite in line with the line of sight along the upper surface of the frame. Another mark is made above it corresponding to the distance between the frame and the telescope, and the two will be parallel when the second mark is in the centre of the field of view of the telescope. Where there is provision for correction, adjustment is by a pair of screws on the collar of the telescope.

Regular checks
In the normal course of events the only errors which need to be checked with any regularity are index error and side error; unless it exceeds about 2′ the former is generally included as a correction to the altitude, while the latter will so far as possible be eliminated by adjustment.

5.1.4 Sextant handling
The sextant is a delicate instrument that requires careful handling and treatment. It should only be lifted by the frame or the handle, never by the arc, and should always be replaced in its box after use. The glasses and mirrors should be wiped dry with a clean bit of soft chamois leather or linen to prevent moisture damaging the silvering. Wiping the glasses should be done with great care to avoid altering their adjustment. A bag of silica gel in the sextant box will help stave off moisture. A little light oil applied from time to time to the worm gear at the back of the arc is the only lubrication necessary.

Many modern sextants are made of aluminium alloys which confer a considerable advantage in terms of weight. Plastic sextants are both light and cheap but require careful treatment to prevent the possibility of warping or distortion. The question of telescopes is to some extent a matter for the individual but there is much to be said for having a single telescope suitable for all bodies in preference to a range of telescopes for different purposes (star, inverting etc).

5.2 Principles of nautical astronomy

5.2.1 Introduction
In order to grasp the basic principles of astro-navigation certain concepts and relationships must be understood. It is assumed throughout this chapter that the Earth is spherical; and in practice the navigator will not need to introduce corrections for its oblateness since these are taken into account in the charts, tables etc.

For the purposes of navigation the distances of the heavenly bodies are irrelevant. It is therefore permissible to envisage all of them as lying on the inner surface of a sphere concentric with the Earth which we call the celestial sphere. This is a purely notional device to facilitate the interpretation of position and apparent movement of the heavenly bodies in relation to the Earth's surface.

The plane of any great circle on a sphere will pass through the centre of the sphere dividing it into two equal parts (hemispheres).

The celestial horizon (sometimes called the rational horizon) is the great circle whose plane is horizontal to the observer which cuts the celestial sphere midway between the zenith and nadir.

The true altitude of a heavenly body is the angle at the centre of the Earth between that body and the celestial horizon.

The nautical mile is the average length of a great circle of the Earth which subtends an angle of one minute of arc at its centre. Since the radius of the Earth is known, so is the length on its surface of 1 minute of arc. Minor differences have arisen through accepting different values for the size (and shape) of the Earth and the International Nautical Mile has now been standardised as 1852m (6076ft); this fact, as such, has no navigational significance.

The counterparts of terrestrial latitude and longitude on the celestial sphere are declination, measured north or south, and hour angle, conventionally measured west from a chosen meridian (not east and west as is longitude). Greenwich hour angle (GHA), however, increases with the rotation of the Earth whereas longitude clearly does not, see Fig. 5(3).

The geographical position (GP) or sub-point of a heavenly body is where an imaginary line from the centre of the Earth to the body would cut the Earth's surface. To an observer at that point the body would be at the zenith, right overhead. The latitude of that position would be the body's declination, north or south and the longitude its GHA expressed in angular measure west of the Greenwich meridian.

5.2.2 Angular measure and geographical distance
Fig. 5(2) shows how the measurement of a body's altitude gives the observer's distance from the body's geographical position in nautical miles. The observer at O on the Earth's surface measures, after correction, the altitude of the body X above the celestial horizon H′CH. This measurement in arc subtracted from 90° gives the angle XCZ between the body (X) and the zenith (Z). The arc XZ on the celestial sphere is clearly the same as the arc X′O on the Earth's surface and, since the radius of the Earth is known, this angular measure

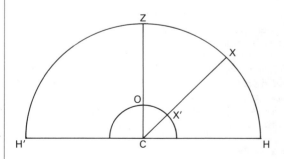

Fig. 5(2) Arc and distance on the Earth's surface.

in degrees and minutes gives the linear distance in nautical miles. This relationship is the basis of all nautical astronomy.

5.2.3 Time and hour angle

If the heavenly bodies were all stationary on the celestial sphere the element of time would not feature in astro-navigation. However, the rotation of the Earth on its polar axis gives the stars, which because of their immense distances we regard as fixed, an apparent motion from east to west across the celestial sphere of one complete cycle approximately every 23 hours, 56 minutes, 4 seconds, the length of a sidereal (or star) day.

The Earth, of course, not only rotates on its axis but also revolves about the Sun completing one revolution every year. This makes the solar day slightly longer than the sidereal day, by about one part in 365.

The movement of the apparent Sun in its orbit is not, for various reasons, entirely regular and for timekeeping the concept of a mean Sun whose passage over successive meridians takes exactly 24 hours has been introduced. The difference between mean time and apparent time is the equation of time given on the daily pages of *The Nautical Almanac*.

Both time and longitude are measured conventionally from the Greenwich or prime meridian and since the Earth rotates 360° relative to the Sun in 24 hours, 15° of longitude is equivalent to 1 hour of time. For every 15° of longitude west of Greenwich the local mean time will be 1 hour earlier than Universal Time = Greenwich Mean Time. (To preserve the Greenwich date an international date line runs, with certain detours round islands, along the meridian 180° E and W.) The entries on the daily pages of the ephemeris are tabulated for Universal Time but the navigator will in general be more directly concerned with local time.

For various reasons the longitude of a heavenly body is specified by its hour angle, that is the angle along a parallel of declination west of a celestial meridian. When the Greenwich or prime meridian is the celestial meridian chosen, the angle will be the Greenwich hour angle (GHA); if it is the observer's meridian it will be the local hour angle (LHA). The ephemeris tabulates GHA of the Sun, Moon and planets. This is converted to LHA by subtracting westerly or adding easterly longitude.

$$LHA = GHA \quad \begin{array}{l} + \text{ observer's longitude east} \\ \text{or} \\ - \text{ observer's longitude west} \end{array}$$

(where necessary adding or subtracting 360°) Fig. 5 (3) illustrates these relationships.

Because the stars may be regarded as fixed, whereas the bodies of the solar system move rapidly on the celestial sphere, the GHA of each navigational star is not usually tabulated in the ephemeris. Instead the GHA of the First Point of

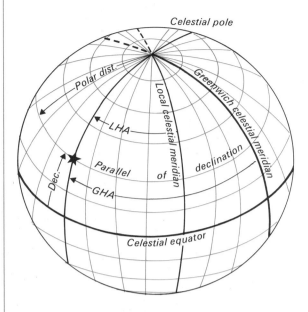

Fig. 5(3) Celestial coordinates relative to the Earth.

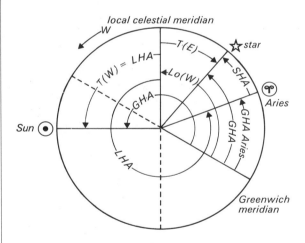

Fig. 5(4) Time diagram (viewed from above the South Pole) showing the relationship between time (T) and hour angle.

Aries, a fixed point in the sky, is given and for each (navigational) star sidereal hour angle (SHA) is tabulated. GHA Aries added to SHA gives the GHA of the star. The time diagram in Fig. 5(4) shows the connection between GHA, LHA and SHA.

In 5.7.7 will be found an approximate ephemeris for the Sun which is suitable for programmable calculators and personal computers.

5.2.4 Glossary of terms

The following definitions relating to nautical astronomy have been adapted, with permission, from *Navigation Afloat: A Manual for the Seaman* by A.B. Moody (Hollis & Carter and U.S. Naval Institute, 1980).

Age of the Moon   The elapsed time, usually expressed in days, since the last previous new Moon.

Altitude   Angular distance, along a vertical circle, from the horizon.

Altitude difference   (1) Intercept. (2) Difference in consecutive tabular entries of altitude.

Amplitude   Angular distance, along a parallel of altitude, clockwise or anticlockwise from the prime vertical.

Apogee   An Earth satellite's orbital point farthest from the Earth.

Apparent motion   Motion, especially of astronomical bodies, relative to a reference point which may itself be in motion.

Apparent time   Time based upon the rotation of the Earth relative to the apparent, or true, Sun.

Astronomical triangle   The navigational triangle solved in sight reduction.

Astronomical twilight   The period of incomplete darkness following sunset or preceding sunrise when the centre of the Sun is not more than 18° below the celestial horizon.

Atmospheric pressure correction   The value applied to a sextant altitude to correct for non-standard atmospheric pressure.

Autumnal equinox   That equinox at which the Sun crosses the celestial equator from north to south.

Augmentation   The increase in apparent semi-diameter of an astronomical body with increased altitude, because of reduced distance of the body from the observer.

Azimuth   Angular distance, along a parallel of altitude, eastward from the principal vertical circle.

Azimuth angle   Angular distance, along a parallel of altitude, clockwise or anticlockwise from the direction of the elevated pole, or occasionally from either this or the reciprocal direction, whichever is nearer.

Back sight   An observation of an astronomical body made facing away from the body.

Calculated (or computed) altitude   Altitude of an astronomical body as determined by calculation or equivalent means.

Celestial equator   The intersection of the plane of the Earth's equator and the celestial sphere.

Celestial horizon   The celestial-sphere great circle midway between the zenith and nadir.

Celestial meridian   A great circle through the celestial poles and the zenith.

Celestial pole   Either of the two points of intersection of the celestial sphere and the extension of the Earth's rotational axis.

Celestial sphere   Imaginary sphere of great radius concentric with Earth on which astronomical bodies other than Earth are imagined to be projected.

Civil twilight   Period of incomplete darkness after sunset or before sunrise when the centre of the Sun is no more than 6° below the celestial horizon.

Computed altitude   Calculated or tabulated altitude.

Co-ordinated Universal Time (UTC)   A precise time scale related to Earth's rotation, periodically adjusted by 'leap seconds' so that it does not differ from Universal Time by more than 0.9 secs. Radio time signals normally relate to UTC.

Corrected sextant altitude   Observed altitude.

Declination   Angular distance north or south of the celestial equator.

Dip   The vertical angle between the horizontal and the line of sight to the visible horizon.

Diurnal circle   The apparent daily path of an astronomical body.

Ecliptic   The apparent annual path of the Sun round the celestial sphere.

Elevated pole   The celestial pole above the horizon.

Equation of time   The difference between mean solar time and apparent solar time.

Equinoctial   Celestial equator.

Ex-meridian observation   An observation of the altitude of an astronomical body taken near the celestial meridian, for conversion to a meridian altitude.

First point of Aries   Vernal equinox.

Geographical pole   Either intersection of the surface of the Earth and the Earth's axis of rotation.

Geographical position   (1) Sub-point. (2) A position defined by geographical co-ordinates, usually latitude and longitude.

Geometrical horizon   The intersection of the celestial sphere and an infinite number of straight lines from the eye of the observer tangent to the surface of the Earth.

Great circle   The intersection of the surface of a sphere with a plane through its centre.

Greenwich apparent time   Apparent time on the Greenwich meridian.

Greenwich hour angle (GHA)   Angular distance, along a parallel of declination, west of the Greenwich celestial meridian.

Greenwich mean time (GMT)   Mean time on the Greenwich meridian. Superseded by Universal Time.

Greenwich sidereal time   Sidereal time at the Greenwich meridian.

Horizon   That great circle of the celestial sphere midway between the zenith and nadir, or a line approximating this circle.

Horizontal parallax   Geocentric parallax of an astronomical body on the horizon.

Hour angle   Angular distance, along a parallel of

declination, west of a reference celestial meridian or hour circle.

Hour circle   A semi-great circle of the celestial sphere connecting the celestial poles and another fixed point on the surface of the sphere.

Intercept   The difference between calculated and observed altitudes.

International nautical mile   The linear unit internationally accepted as the nautical mile; 1852m or 6076ft.

Local apparent noon   The instant of upper transit of the apparent Sun.

Local apparent time   Apparent time at a specified meridian.

Local hour angle (LHA)   Angular distance, along a parallel of declination, west of a specified celestial meridian.

Local mean time (LMT)   Mean time at a specified meridian.

Local sidereal time   Sidereal time at a specified meridian.

Lower transit   The passage of an astronomical body across the lower branch of a celestial meridian.

Lunar distance   The angle between the Moon and another astronomical body

Lunar month   One revolution of the Moon around the Earth.

Mean Sun   A fictitious Sun conceived as moving eastward along the celestial equator at the average rate of the apparent Sun along the ecliptic.

Mean time   Time based upon rotation of the Earth relative to the mean Sun.

Meridian altitude   Altitude of an astronomical body on the celestial meridian.

Meridian transit   The passage of an astronomical body across a celestial meridian.

Nadir   That point of the celestial sphere vertically below the observer.

Nautical mile (n mile)   Generally, the length of 1' of a great circle of the Earth. Specifically, the international nautical mile of 1852m or 6076ft.

Nautical twilight   The period of incomplete darkness following sunset or preceding sunrise when the centre of the Sun is not more than 12° below the celestial horizon.

Navigational triangle   The spherical triangle solved in sight reduction or great-circle sailing.

Nutation   Irregularities in precession of the equinoxes.

Observed altitude   Actual altitude of an astronomical body above the celestial horizon.

Parallactic angle   The navigational triangle angle at the astronomical body or destination.

Parallax   Difference in apparent position of an object as viewed from different positions.

Parallax in altitude   Geocentric parallax of an astronomical body at any specified altitude.

Parallel of altitude   A circle of the celestial sphere parallel to the plane of the celestial horizon.

Parallel of declination   A circle of the celestial sphere parallel to the plane of the celestial equator.

Parallel of latitude   Parallel.

Polar circle   The parallel (N or S) equal to the maximum co-declination of the Sun.

Polar distance   Angular distance from a celestial pole.

Polar motion   Wobbling motion of the geographical poles of the Earth, affecting measurement of universal time.

Precession of the equinoxes   Conical motion of the Earth's rotational axis about the vertical to the plane of the ecliptic, caused by the attractive force of other bodies of the solar system on the equatorial bulge of the Earth, and resulting in a slow drift of the equinoxes and solstices.

Prime meridian   The meridian from which longitude is reckoned.

Prime vertical circle   The vertical circle through the east or west point of the horizon.

Principal vertical circle   The vertical circle through the true north point of the horizon.

Proper motion   The component of motion of an astronomical body perpendicular to the line of sight.

Refraction   Change in direction of a ray of radiant energy as it passes obliquely into a medium of different density.

Retired (transferred) position line   A position line moved back to allow for motion of the observer between the earlier time to which the line is retired and the time of observation.

Right ascension   Angular distance, along a parallel of declination, east of the hour circle of the vernal equinox.

Sea-air temperature difference correction   The correction applied to a sextant altitude to correct for error in tabulated dip because of difference in the temperature of the water and air at their interface.

Sensible horizon   A small circle of the celestial sphere marking the intersection of a plane parallel to the plane of the celestial horizon, through the eye of the observer.

Sextant altitude   Altitude of an astronomical body as measured by a sextant.

Sidereal   Of or pertaining to stars.

Sidereal hour angle   Angular distance, along a parallel of declination, west of the hour circle of the vernal equinox.

Sidereal time   Time based upon rotation of the Earth relative to the vernal equinox.

Summer solstice   The solstice occupied by the Sun about June 21.

Time sight   Observation of an astronomical body for determination of longitude by calculation of meridian angle and its comparison with Greenwich hour angle.

Transferred position line   See Retired position line.
True altitude   Corrected observed altitude.

Universal Time (UT).   For practical purposes the equivalent of GMT.
Upper branch   That half of a celestial meridian through the zenith.
Upper transit   The passage of an astronomical body across the upper branch of a celestial meridian.

Vernal equinox   That equinox at which the Sun crosses the celestial equator from south to north.
Vertical circle   A semi-great circle joining the zenith and nadir.

Zenith   That point of the celestial sphere vertically overhead.
Zenith distance   Angular distance from the zenith.
Zone description   The number, with its sign, applied to zone time to convert it to the corresponding GMT or UT.
Zone time   Mean time at a standard reference meridian whose time is kept throughout a designated area (see 9.3.3)

5.3 Altitude corrections

5.3.1 General
The altitude read off the sextant is corrected first of all for any known instrument error including index error and, where appropriate, for personal error (where the observer has been able to establish the amount he habitually over- or under-reads the sextant). The resultant altitude, the sextant altitude (Hs for Height sextant) is then corrected for altitude corrections to give the true altitude or in modern parlance (which came in with the adoption of direct entry tables) observed altitude (Ho for Height observed). The altitude corrections are applied to the sextant altitude as appropriate for dip, refraction, semi-diameter and parallax. Only semi-diameter and parallax vary with the body concerned. In most methods of sight reduction the true or observed altitude so obtained is compared with the calculated altitude (Hc for Height computed) given in the tables to give an intercept. In using the correction tables, as for example in *The Nautical Almanac* (HMSO), the sextant altitude is first corrected for index error and dip to give an apparent altitude with which the table of correction for refraction and semi-diameter is entered. The altitude corrections will be considered in turn. The various horizon systems are illustrated in Fig. 5(5).

5.3.2 Dip
Dip of the sea horizon arises from the fact that the observer's eye level will be above the surface of the sea which causes the horizon to dip (be depressed) below the horizontal plane at the

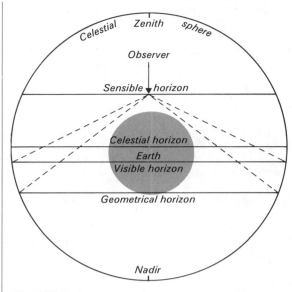

Fig. 5(5) Horizon systems used in astro-navigation.

observer's eye. The correction, which is always subtractive, increases numerically with height. Anomalous conditions, such as a large difference between sea and air temperature, can introduce errors into the calculated dip values. Taking sights on opposite horizons or equally spaced round the horizon are one way of overcoming this difficulty. The dip correction includes an allowance for the fact that light from the horizon will be affected by terrestrial refraction.

5.3.3 Refraction
Astronomical refraction is the angular difference between the true and apparent direction of a heavenly body. The light travelling from a heavenly body into the Earth's atmosphere is progressively bent towards the vertical by the variation of the density of the medium which causes the body to appear higher in the sky than it would otherwise be, Fig. 5(6). The density of the

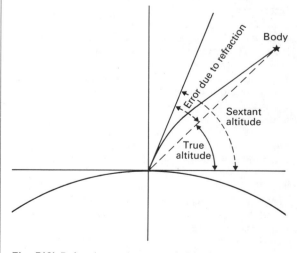

Fig. 5(6) Refraction and measured altitude.

air is affected by temperature and atmospheric pressure and the mean refraction corrections given in the almanac are for temperature 10°C and pressure 1010mb. Refraction decreases with altitude, from about 34′ at the horizon to zero at the zenith. The correction is always subtractive. Anomalous conditions such as will affect the dip also affect astronomical refraction; however, since refraction decreases rapidly with altitude, the effect will be minimised by avoiding low altitude sights, say below 10°. An additional table for non-standard atmospheric conditions is provided in some almanacs and may be used with low altitude sights.

5 3.4 Semi-diameter

Semi-diameter corrections apply only to the Sun and Moon, and arise from the fact that the coordinates for astronomical bodies given in the almanac relate to the centre of each body whereas in the case of the Sun and Moon one or other limb will have been observed. Stars and planets appear in the sextant telescope as points of light, although

Venus at its nearest approach has in fact a semi-diameter of over 0′.5. Semi-diameter will vary with the body's altitude and its distance from the Earth but only in the case of the Moon, with its nearness to Earth, is this augmentation navigationally significant. In *The Nautical Almanac* (HMSO) the position of Venus is corrected for centre of light.

5.3.5 Parallax

Parallax is the angle between the direction of a body seen from somewhere on the Earth's surface and the place it would occupy if seen from the centre of the Earth. Parallax is zero at the zenith and increases as the altitude decreases to a maximum on the observer's sensible horizon, Fig. 5(7). This value is known as the horizontal parallax (HP). In *The Nautical Almanac* corrections for parallax are taken into account in the altitude correction tables for the Sun, Moon, Venus and

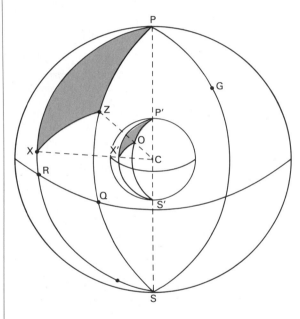

Fig. 5(8) The astronomical triangle.

Fig. 5(7) Parallax, only significant for the Moon, will be zero when it is at the zenith (M_Z) and maximum at Horizontal Parallax (M_H).

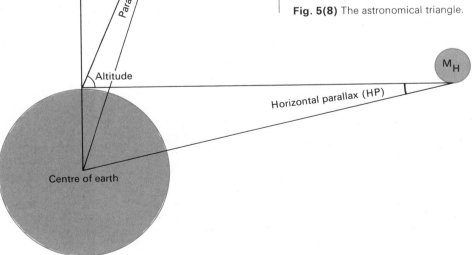

Mars; only in the case of the Moon, because of its proximity to the Earth, is horizontal parallax used as an entering argument in the tables. For stars any correction would be negligible and is ignored.

5.4 Theory into practice

5.4.1 The astronomical triangle

Since, as we have seen (5.2.2), zenith distance measured in arc can be equated with distance on the Earth's surface in nautical miles, it follows that an observation of a heavenly body whose geographical position (5.2.1) can be established will locate the observer on a circle of position whose centre is the geographical position and radius the zenith distance. In Fig. 5(8) the outer hemisphere represents the celestial sphere, the inner one the Earth. The altitude subtracted from $90°$ gives the zenith distance ZX and the arc OX' expressed in nautical miles is the distance on the Earth's surface.

For the instant of observation the navigator extracts from the ephemeris the body's coordinates (declination and hour angle) which will enable him in principle to plot its geographical position and describe a circle of position somewhere along which the observer must lie. In practice, however, except in the case of very high altitudes when the body is within a degree or two of the zenith, the distances involved make plotting to the scale required totally impossible. It is for this reason that recourse is had to the navigational or astronomical triangle, illustrated in Fig. 5(8), where ZX is the body observed, X' its geographical position, O the observer and Z his zenith; RQ is the celestial equator. In the triangle, the angle at Z is the azimuth angle, the angle at P the local hour angle of X from Z and the angle at X the parallactic angle. PGS being the Greenwich celestial meridian, GPX is the Greenwich hour angle of X and GPZ the longitude of Z.

In the triangle, $90°$-XZ has been measured with the sextant, and PX established by the chronometer and ephemeris. To solve the triangle a third part is required, and the various mathematical methods of sight reduction make different approaches to this end. In the Marcq St Hilaire or intercept method which, in a number of forms, is virtually universal today, an approximate position (generally either the DR or a position near it suitable to the method in use) is assumed for Z, which gives two sides and the included angle; the zenith distance of the position chosen is then calculated and compared with the zenith distance observed. The difference is the *intercept* which is applied from the chosen position towards or away from the body according to whether the position is nearer or further away from it. Unless the radius of the position circle is very small, as with very high altitudes, the portion of it in the vicinity of

the observer can be treated without sensible error as a straight line at right angles to the body's bearing.

There are many solutions to the problem of deriving the intercept and azimuth of a heavenly body from a timed observation of its altitude - whether trigonometric, tabular, graphical or by electronic calculator. Only two are considered in any detail here: direct entry or inspection tables (5.6) which, for an assumed position, give precomputed values of altitude and azimuth for integral degrees of declination and hour angle; and electronic calculators of one kind and another programmed to give the intercept and azimuth from the dead reckoning position without reference to almanac or reduction tables and to present the latitude and longitude of the fix and an assessment of its precision.

5.5 Practical sight taking

5.5.1 Notes on observation

In a small boat there is generally little option about the height from which sights will be taken. For the purpose of altitude corrections, the observer's height of eye will be the height of the deck above the sea surface plus the observer's height. However, all things being equal, it is worth remembering that the higher the height of eye the less rapidly the correction for dip of the horizon changes and thus the more reliable the observation. Further, in anything like a seaway the horizon is often hidden from view by the wave tops. On the other hand in thick weather it is often possible to obtain satisfactory observations by getting close to the sea surface where the horizon shrinks to within the range of visibility. Thus at 2ft above the surface, which might be obtained by taking sights from a companionway, or in calm weather from a dinghy, the horizon will only be about $1\frac{1}{4}$ miles.

The best situation for taking sights is to be wedged from the waist down with both hands free. An observation is made by bringing the heavenly body down to the point on the horizon immediately below it. In the case of the Sun the lower limb will generally be used and with the Moon whichever limb is fully visible. The point of tangency is defined by swinging the sextant through an arc of about $20°$ on either side of the line of sight. The higher the altitude the more important this becomes.

Considerable practice is required in the technique of using the sextant from such an unsteady platform as a small boat. To begin with, the advice of an experienced observer can be helpful. There are a number of ways of bringing the body down to the horizon, including initially holding the sextant upside down to allow the horizon to be brought up to the body. With the Sun, and occasionally Moon, quite a good dodge is to half close the eye and be guided by the ambient light as to when the body is in the field of view. Clearly one should be careful not to be blinded.

The random error of the mean of a number of observations, we are told, is reduced as the square root of the number. Averaging a series of observations will not necessarily reduce the error by this amount because the errors will not all be random. However, because of the difficulties of taking sights in small vessels, with rapid accelerations and a low height of eye, it is customary to take a series of observations and mean the times and altitudes. Care should be taken, however, not to include rogues. If the sights are more or less evenly timed, a series of three or five (or even seven) observations allows the middle one to be treated as a yardstick as to how good the series is; the time and altitude should be close to the mean.

It is a great convenience to have another member of the crew as a timekeeper who will record the time of each sight and the altitude the navigator gives him. The time should be recorded to the nearest second, which represents 0.25 minute of arc. It is of course perfectly possible to take accurate times on one's own (as indeed single-handers have to) but it is inconvenient to the extent that sights will not normally be taken in the place where they are most easily recorded. The skill in taking one's own time, which can be acquired with practice, is in counting down accurately in seconds from the time of the observation to the moment the time is read.

Nowadays quartz crystal clocks or wrist watches have almost universally replaced clockwork chronometers or deck watches. Their accuracy is extremely high, they are reliable, and can be water resistant and virtually shockproof. The most convenient sort for navigation has a dual display, one analogue which can be kept on ship's time, the other digital kept on Universal Time for sights. With a digital display there is little chance of a gross reading error.

5.5.2 The accuracy of sights
Many navigators tend to exaggerate the accuracy of sights at sea, perhaps because of some confusion between the accuracy attainable, which is quite high, and the accuracy which on average one might be led to expect. The first thing therefore is to reach an understanding of what is meant by accuracy.

Obviously, by a combination of circumstances any sextant observation can be accurate to within the limits to which the altitude and time can be read, and the resultant position line will then pass near enough through the observer's position. In investigating accuracies the point to establish therefore is on how many occasions is this, or any other predicted result, likely to happen. This confidence level is usually expressed in terms of a percentage. The level with which practising navigators are normally most concerned is the 95

per cent level which defines the number of occasions out of every 100 on which the error is unlikely to exceed the stated value. To say, for example, that the 95 per cent level accuracy of sextant observations at sea is 4 miles is to say that out of every 100 observations only five may be expected to have an error exceeding 4 miles.

The next point is to establish whether the accuracy in question is what may be attained or is that which may be expected in the course of every day seafaring. Unless it is for some special purpose, such as survey, practising navigators will be more interested in the latter.

In 1957 the Royal Institute of Navigation, with the cooperation of the Royal Navy and the Royal Netherlands Navy and of a number of British shipping companies, conducted an investigation into the accuracy of astronomical observations at sea which gave the following results (from an analysis, by HM Nautical Almanac Office, of some 4000 observations).

Percentage error	Average observer	Best observer	Error exceeded in
50	0'.7	0'.5	10 out of 20
90	2.4	1.4	2 out of 20
95	3.1	2.0	1 out of 20

The errors in question are of course position-line errors, not errors in position.

Although the observers in this investigation were for the most part professional seamen observing from a comparatively steady platform and an elevated height of eye, there is no reason to think that results from experienced yachtsmen would differ substantially.

Besides being a useful guide for the navigator these results shed light on the precision requirement for almanacs and tables. Almanacs and tables for marine navigation are normally tabulated to a precision of 0'.1 of altitude and 0°.1 of azimuth, mainly because the next convenient unit is 1' or 1°. It can be shown however that where there is an inescapable error, in this case that of observation, little is gained by reducing other sources of error beyond a certain point. It is for that reason that the standard method of sight reduction proposed in this Handbook is the combined British and American *Sight Reduction Tables for Air Navigation* (respectively AP 3270 and Pub No 249) tabulated to 1' of altitude and 1° of azimuth, a precision sufficient for all practical purposes at sea.

5.5.3 Sun sights
The Sun is the body most frequently observed at sea, generally in successive observations with an allowance for the run between sights.

Except when it is hidden by cloud the lower limb of the Sun will normally be observed. When the upper limb is brought to the horizon the altitude correction for semi-diameter will, clearly, be subtractive. Very occasionally the outline of the Sun is so blurred that it will be easier to estimate when the centre of the disk is on the horizon than to use either limb. In this case the altitude correction may be obtained from the combined altitude correction table by taking the mean of the corrections for the upper and lower limbs.

A firm horizon considerably facilitates accurate observation although it can occur in conditions conducive to abnormal dip. There are generally tell-tale signs of abnormal atmospheric conditions such as the distortion of the outlines of ships on the horizon.

5.5.4 Moon sights
Whether the upper or lower limb of the Moon is observed will depend on which is the more complete. The altitude correction tables for the Moon with argument horizontal parallax give separate corrections for either limb.

In general Moon sights will only be taken in daylight when the resulting position line can often usefully be crossed with a position line from the Sun in order to give a fix. The Moon takes rather longer than other bodies to cross the same meridian and to that extent is marginally easier to observe.

5.5.5 Star sights
Star sights are normally taken in the morning and evening when the Sun is about 8° or 10° below the horizon in the interval between civil and nautical twilights. The limits last about 24 minutes on the equator, longer as latitude increases. In this period of incomplete darkness the brighter stars will be visible in the sextant telescope while the horizon will be firm enough for sight taking. In general stars to the eastward will appear first in the evening and disappear first in the morning. The brightest star should normally be taken first in the evening and last in the morning.

It is usual to plan star sights beforehand by working out the time of twilight for the dead reckoning position, from data given in the nautical almanac, and then by means of a star globe or planisphere or the Selected Star Tables of AP 3270 to calculate the altitudes and azimuths for the approximate time. The stars may then be observed by setting the approximate altitude on the sextant rather than attempting the more difficult task of bringing them down to the horizon.

Although single observations should be the exception rather than the rule, the time for taking stars is limited by the light, and it will generally be better to take single observations of a larger number of stars well distributed in azimuth than to take several shots of a smaller number.

It is sometimes possible to take star sights by moonlight but the results should be accepted with some caution because the horizon can be deceptive. Venus is occasionally visible in daylight through the sextant telescope and can be crossed with a position line from the Sun or Moon. Because of the difficulty of picking it up it is usual to observe Venus at its meridian altitude. Jupiter too is often visible long after sunrise or before sunset.

Because several stars can generally be observed more or less simultaneously, star sights tend to yield the most accurate astro-fix at sea. In principle two well observed stars at a reasonable angle of cut suffice for a fix, but a third will enable any errors in the observation or reduction in either sight to be detected and thus add reliability. Four stars or more, provided the plot is intelligently analysed (see 5.9.2), give the best chance of an accurate and reliable fix.

Star identification
The stars are identified by their constellation, a catalogue designation (within the constellation) and in some cases a name. Their apparent brightness is measured in terms of magnitude: the lower the magnitude, the brighter the star. The constellations, of which there are nearly 90, are groups of stars which appeared to different cultures to resemble mythical figures or objects; for the most part their names are Arabic, Greek or Latin. The designation of a star attaches to the Latin name of its constellation a lower-case Greek letter in descending order of brightness; thus α Leonis would be the brightest star in the constellation Leo, β Leonis the second brightest, and so on. The principal navigational stars have names, so that navigators seldom need bother with constellation and catalogue designations.

There are some 20 stars of the first magnitude, and in good conditions stars down to the sixth or even seventh magnitude are visible to the naked eye. In the normal course of events the navigator will not require to use more than about 20 of the 57 'selected' navigational stars, although there are occasions when it is convenient to be able to identify and observe some of the lesser used bodies.

Of the planets Venus, Jupiter, and sometimes Mars, are of negative magnitude. The navigational planets Venus, Mars, Jupiter and Saturn are easy enough to pick out in the sky since they are relatively bright and shine with a steady light, as opposed to the twinkling light of a star. All planets stay fairly close to the ecliptic. Mercury is sometimes confused with the navigational planets when it is near its maximum elongation (angle from the Sun).

Fig. 5(9) is a star chart of the northern sky, and shows in terms of declination and hour angle, the relative positions of the stars as seen from Earth. The projection obviously distorts the places of the stars near the equator, and the equatorial stars can be displayed separately. The lines joining certain stars show the shapes of the constellations devised by the ancients, and the key gives the meaning of the ways of depicting stars on the chart.

For the beginner, in the northern hemisphere, the simplest way to locate stars is first of all to establish the pole of the heavens, marked approximately by Polaris, the Pole Star, around

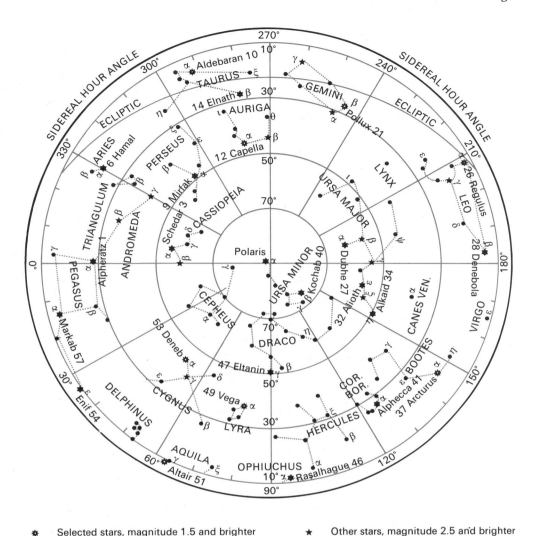

| ❋ | Selected stars, magnitude 1.5 and brighter | ★ | Other stars, magnitude 2.5 and brighter |
| ✹ | Selected stars, magnitude 1.6 and fainter | • | Other stars |

Fig. 5(9) Star chart – northern stars.

which the firmament appears to rotate. This is most easily done by identifying *Ursa Major*, the Great Bear or Plough, and following the line of the two Pointers at the 'front end' of the Plough, from the lower one Mirak through the brighter Dubhe (one of the selected navigational stars) which leads very close to Polaris. Polaris is itself part of *Ursa Minor*, a constellation very similar to *Ursa Major*, which rotates anticlockwise round the Pole with Polaris as its (approximate) pivot. Following round the extension of the handle of the Plough leads to the first-magnitude Arcturus, a reddish star and, continuing the arc, to another first magnitude star, the blush-white Spica.

On a summer evening, to an observer in the northern hemisphere the Plough will lie west of Polaris with the Pointers nearly horizontal. The brightest star in the northern hemisphere, Vega, a brilliant blue-white, will be visible to the east with Altair, an equatorial star, just about midway

between the two Guardians which point towards it. The 'summer triangle' of Altair, Vega and Deneb is conspicuous. Antares, a noticeably red, first-magnitude star, will be found in the constellation of *Scorpius* at about this time, fairly low in the southern sky. In the sky, though not on the star chart, the resemblance to a scorpion is obvious.

In the autumn, the Plough will be low in the northern sky in the evenings, and Cassiopeia's Chair will be picked out on the other side of the Pole at about the same distance. On winter nights the Plough will lie to the right of Polaris, and Cassiopeia to its left. At this season Orion's Belt, with Betelgeuse, a bright yellowish-red star, to the north-east, and Bellatrix, a fainter, white star to the north-west, can be seen to the south. Rigel, a bright bluish star, lies south-west of the Belt. Continuing the line of the Belt south-eastward leads to Sirius, a brilliant blue-white star, the brightest in the heavens.

Undoubtedly the quickest way to become familiar with the night sky is to identify one or two of the constellations and the brightest stars within them, and to follow their progress across the sky, first hour by hour and then night by night. With the aid of the star chart more bodies can be added as time goes on, until recognition becomes virtually automatic once a pattern in the sky is discernible.

5.6 Sight reduction

5.6.1 Sight reduction methods

The term sight reduction applies to the whole process of calculating the observer's position from an astronomical observation (or series of observations). In particular it refers to the use of tables or other means to obtain an astro position line, generally by comparing a calculated altitude with the observed one. The notion of the position line was first conceived by the American shipmaster Thomas H. Sumner in 1837 and it is sometimes known as the Sumner line. The device of comparing the observed and calculated altitudes to obtain the intercept was introduced by the French naval officer Marcq St Hilaire in 1875, after whom the method is named; it is now the standard method of sight reduction, whatever means are used to calculate the intercept.

Tabular methods of solving the astronomical triangle by spherical trigonometry have generally made use of the haversine formula. The azimuth is usually derived from a separate table or diagram as for instance the ABC tables or Weir's azimuth diagram. Books of nautical tables such as Norie's, Inman, Burton and so on cater for sight reduction by such methods, as well as other, sometimes obsolescent, methods such as Longitude by Chronometer. The major disadvantage of all such methods is the amount of calculation involved.

What became known as 'short' methods were devised precisely to shorten the amount of calculation and simplify the sight reduction process generally. They usually involve dividing the astronomical triangle into two right angled triangles by dropping a perpendicular from a vertex to the side opposite. Such tables have generally appeared in comparatively slim volumes devoted entirely to sight reduction. On the other hand the methods have not always been universally applicable and most have involved rules for special cases so that in due course they have been superseded by tables of the modern direct entry or inspection type in which great simplicity is achieved, but at the expense of bulk for all of them run into several volumes. Typical of the 'short' methods were those devised by Ageton, Aquino, Dreisonstok, Myerscough and Hamilton, and Ogura. One of the most notable was perhaps *Hughes' Tables for Sea and Air Navigation*, devised by P.V.H. Weems and produced by L.J. Comrie, a former Superintendent of HM Nautical Almanac Office.

Inspection tables, of which the earliest, *Tables of Computed Altitude and Azimuth* (US HO214=UK HD486) covered the world in nine volumes, give, typically, precomputed values of altitude and azimuth for integral degrees of latitude, declination and hour angle and avoid excessive interpolation by assuming a position such that the local hour angle is a whole number.

The tables recommended in this handbook are the *Sight Reduction Tables for Air Navigation* produced jointly in the United Kingdom (as AP 3270) and the United States (as Pub No 249). In three volumes they cater, to a precision sufficient for all normal purposes, for every astro-navigational requirement at sea. They have at least a marginal advantage over *Sight Reduction Tables for Marine Navigation*, also produced jointly in the United Kingdom (as NP401) and the United States (as Pub No 229) which, in six volumes, tabulate altitude to 0'.1 instead of 1' and azimuth angle to 0°.1 instead of 1°, a precision not relevant to normal requirements at sea.

Programmable and dedicated electronic calculators (navigation computers) are now capable of both storing the astronomical ephemeris and working up sights, so dispensing with both nautical almanac and reduction tables. In addition they can be used for a wide range of navigational problems outside astro-navigation such as dead reckoning, tidal heights, the sailings, speed/distance and so on. Some are purpose-built but most are electronic calculators programmed specifically for navigation. In general all such 'navigation computers' carry the solar ephemeris while others provide for the navigational stars, planets and Moon as well. All give the intercept and azimuth and some the fix with, in the case of the more advanced, an estimate of its accuracy. By allowing for passage during the course of the observations all the sights in a series can be adjusted to the time of the first (or last) and it is possible both to reject a poor sight or add others to a fix. All in all the use of navigation computers of this kind promises a considerable simplification of astro-navigation procedures and once they can be shown to be reliable in all conditions it seems possible that they will replace tables as the standard method. Typical of a purpose-built navigation computer is the Tamaya NC77 and of the more advanced dedicated electronic calculators the Merlin II, CN2000 and astroNavCOMP IQ, although the situation is far from static.

The Nautical Almanac publishes concise reduction tables intended for use when other methods, such as electronic calculator or more extended tables, are not available. Like most of the 'short' methods it is based on splitting the astronomical triangle, in this case by dropping a perpendicular from the observer's zenith. Full instructions for use and an example accompany the tables. The entries are at intervals of one degree for all latitudes and hour angles and the table has to be entered twice, the second time with arguments extracted in the first entry. As with inspection tables an integral degree of latitude is chosen and a longitude such that the local hour angle is an integral degree. The entries, in seven steps, are straightforward but some care needs to be taken to observe the rule of signs. Altitude is given to the nearest minute of arc, although rounding off errors could increase the error to 2′.

5.6.2 Sight Reduction Tables for Air Navigation, AP 3270 = Pub No 249

The tables are in three volumes and tabulate altitude to the nearest minute of arc and azimuth to the nearest degree. As their name implies, they were originally intended for use in the air but they are being increasingly used at sea, as recent modification to some of the correction tables for

LAT 49°N

LHA ♈	Hc	Zn	Hc	Zn	Hc	Zn	Hc	Zn	Hc	Zn	Hc	Zn	Hc	Zn	LHA ♈	Hc	Zn	Hc	Zn	H
	◆DENEB		VEGA		ARCTURUS		◆SPICA		REGULUS		◆POLLUX		CAPELLA			◆Mirfak		Alpheratz		◆
180	13 44	034	23 02	057	49 46	126	27 04	157	46 21	222	37 37	271	27 07	310	270	14 22	025	20 17	069	43
181	14 06	034	23 35	057	50 17	127	27 19	158	45 54	223	36 57	272	26 37	311	271	14 39	025	20 54	069	44
182	14 28	035	24 08	058	50 49	128	27 34	159	45 27	224	36 18	273	26 07	311	272	14 56	026	21 30	070	44
183	14 51	035	24 42	059	51 19	129	27 48	160	44 59	225	35 39	273	25 37	312	273	15 14	027	22 08	071	44
184	15 14	036	25 16	059	51 50	131	28 01	161	44 31	227	34 59	274	25 08	312	274	15 31	027	22 45	071	45
185	15 37	037	25 49	060	52 19	132	28 13	162	44 02	228	34 20	275	24 39	313	275	15 50	028	23 22	072	45
186	16 01	037	26 24	060	52 48	133	28 25	163	43 32	229	33 41	275	24 10	313	276	16 08	028	24 00	073	45
187	16 25	038	26 58	061	53 17	135	28 36	164	43 02	230	33 02	276	23 42	314	277	16 27	029	24 37	073	46
188	16 49	038	27 32	062	53 44	136	28 47	165	42 32	231	32 23	277	23 13	314	278	16 46	030	25 15	074	46
189	17 14	039	28 07	062	54 11	137	28 56	166	42 01	232	31 44	278	22 45	315	279	17 06	030	25 53	075	46
190	17 39	040	28 42	063	54 37	139	29 05	167	41 29	234	31 05	278	22 18	315	280	17 26	031	26 31	075	47
191	18 04	040	29 17	063	55 03	140	29 13	169	40 58	235	30 26	279	21 50	316	281	17 46	031	27 09	076	47
192	18 29	041	29 52	064	55 28	142	29 21	170	40 25	236	29 47	280	21 23	317	282	18 07	032	27 47	077	47
193	18 55	041	30 28	064	55 52	143	29 28	171	39 53	237	29 08	280	20 56	317	283	18 28	032	28 26	077	48
194	19 21	042	31 03	065	56 15	145	29 34	172	39 19	238	28 29	281	20 29	318	284	18 49	033	29 04	078	48
	◆DENEB		VEGA		Rasalhague		◆ARCTURUS		REGULUS		◆POLLUX		CAPELLA			◆Mirfak		Alpheratz		◆
195	19 48	043	31 39	066	23 26	098	56 37	146	38 46	239	27 51	282	20 03	318	285	19 11	034	29 43	079	48
196	20 15	043	32 15	066	24 05	099	56 58	148	38 12	240	27 12	282	19 37	319	286	19 33	034	30 21	079	48
197	20 42	044	32 51	067	24 44	099		150	37 38	241	26 34	283	19 11	319	287	19 55	035	31 00	080	48
223	33 55		47 13	083	40 34			171		244	21 27	264	56 21		313	15 58	036	47 57	100	49
224	34 28	058	49 54	083	41 06	124	59 07	199	38 39	245	20 48	264	55 56	314	314	16 21	036	48 37	101	49
	DENEB		◆VEGA		Rasalhague		ANTARES		◆ARCTURUS		Denebola		◆Dubhe			CAPELLA		◆Hamal		A
225	35 02	059	50 33	084	41 39	125	12 02	160	58 54	201	38 04	246	55 28	314	315	16 44	037	26 02	084	49
226	35 36	059	51 12	085	42 11	126	12 15	161	58 39	203	37 28	247	55 00	314	316	17 08	038	26 41	084	49
227	36 10	060	51 51	085	42 42	128	12 28	162	58 24	204	36 51	248	54 32	314	317	17 32	038	27 20	085	50
228	36 44	061	52 31	086	43 13	129	12 40	162	58 07	206	36 15	249	54 04	315	318	17 57	039	28 00	086	51
229	37 18	061	53 10	087	43 43	130	12 51	163	57 49	208	35 38	249	53 36	315	319	18 22	039	28 39	086	51
230	37 53	062	53 49	087	44 13	131	13 02	164	57 31	209	35 01	250	53 08	315	320	18 47	040	29 18	087	52
231	38 27	062	54 29	088	44 43	132	13 13	165	57 11	211	34 24	251	52 40	315	321	19 12	041	29 58	088	53
232	39 02	063	55 08	089	45 12	133	13 23	166	56 50	213	33 47	252	52 12	315	322	19 38	041	30 37	089	53
233	39 37	063	55 47	090	45 40	135	13 32	167	56 28	214	33 09	253	51 44	315	323	20 04	042	31 16	089	54
234	40 12	064	56 27	090	46 08	136	13 40	168	56 06	216	32 31	254	51 17	315	324	20 30	042	31 56	090	54
235	40 48	064	57 06	091	46 35	137	13 48	169	55 42	217	31 53	255	50 49	316	325	20 57	043	32 35	091	55
236	41 23	065	57 45	092	47 01	138	13 56	170	55 18	219	31 15	256	50 22	316	326	21 24	043	33 14	092	55

Fig. 5(10) Portion of page from AP 3270 Vol 1, Epoch 1990–0, page 63 for latitude 49°N. With argument LHA Aries the calculated altitude (Hc) and azimuth (Zn) are shown for seven stars. The brightest stars are in capitals, and the best combination for a fix from three stars is marked by lozenge-shaped asterisks. (Crown Copyright. Reproduced from AP 3270 with the permission of the Controller of Her Majesty's Stationery Office.)

Example

25 June 1992, DR 48° 55′N, 17° 12′W, civil twilight about 2200 UT. For LHA Aries 227° (GHA 244°-17°W) AP 3270 Vol 1, epoch 1990 shows the following selected stars for latitude 49°N: DENEB (36 10 060) *VEGA (51 51 085) Rasalhague (42 42 128) ANTARES (12 28 162) *ARCTURUS (58 24 204) Denebola (36 51 248) *Dubhe (54 32 314). The following observations were made and reduced by the tables:

	Vega	Antares	Arcturus	Dubhe
UT	22 03 14	22 06 12	22 09 05	22 11 15
GHA	244° 17′.3	244° 17′.3	244° 17′.3	244° 17′.3
Increment	48.6	1 33.3	2 16.6	2 49.2
GHA Aries	245 05.9	245 50.6	246 33.9	247 06.5
Assumed longitude	17 05.9	17 50.6	17 33.9	17 06.5
LHA Aries	228	228	229	230
Hc	52 31	12 40	57 49	53 08
Zn	086	162	208	315
Ho	52 35	12 35	57 25	53 16
Intercept	4′ to	5′ away	24′ away	8′ to

Observed position 49° 15′N 17° 01′W

marine purposes indicates. The tables were designed for use with the *Air Almanac* which tabulates GHA and declination for every 10m of UT but are just as easily used with *The Nautical Almanac*. The tables also include an auxiliary table which, in emergency, enables the GHA and declination of the Sun to be calculated for some years ahead without the use of an almanac. Although for various reasons (see 5.5.2) a tabulated precision of 0'.1 of altitude and 0°.1 of azimuth is normally adopted in marine tables and almanacs, the accuracy that can be obtained with these tables suffices for all practical purposes at sea.

Volume 1, which is for star sights only, gives, for integral degrees of latitude and argument LHA Aries, the calculated (or computed or tabulated) altitude (Hc) and azimuth (Zn) of sets of seven stars selected for their brightness and angle of cut. No interpolation is needed. The brightest stars are shown in capitals and the best combination to obtain a fix with three stars is marked by asterisks. Since both north and south hemispheres are catered for, the azimuth (rather than the azimuth angle) is extracted direct. Because of precession of the equinoxes the star tables become inaccurate with the passage of time and are calculated for a particular epoch and republished every five years; corrections for later years are tabulated as a displacement to apply either to a position line or to the fix, in the case of the correction table for marine use to the nearest degree and tenth of a nautical mile.

To use the star tables a position near the dead reckoning position is assumed with an integral degree of latitude and a longitude such that it will combine (adding easterly and subtracting westerly longitudes) with the GHA to give a whole degree of LHA. The tables are entered at the appropriate latitude page, north or south, with argument LHA, and the tabulated altitude (Hc) and azimuth (Zn) of the stars observed are extracted and the intercept derived in the usual way. The time to take stars is between civil and nautical twilight (see glossary) when the horizon is still firm and the stars

visible.In the evenings this will be from the beginning of civil twilight and in the mornings from the end of nautical twilight. The values for twilight are given in the daily pages of *The Nautical Almanac*. The tables are most effectively used by planning the observations beforehand, estimating according to the DR position and GHA Aries at the time of twilight, the LHA Aries and from the tables seeing the selection of stars available. The navigator can then set the approximate altitude of the stars he intends to take on the sextant, identifying each in turn by its bearing (remembering to apply magnetic variation). This will enable him to see the stars on the horizon well before they can be picked out in the sky, and save the time-consuming business of bringing each down to the horizon.

Volumes 2 and 3 are permanent tables which provide for navigation by the Sun, Moon and planets and for navigational stars with declinations less than 30°. They are similar in principle to Volume 1 but tabulate, for integral degrees of latitude, declination and LHA, the calculated altitude (Hc), a quantity *d* used to adjust the altitude for increments of declination, and azimuth angle (Z). Selection of the page to enter is made according to the chosen latitude, the declination range (0°–14° or 15°–29°) and whether the declination and latitude have the same or contrary names. Volume 2 covers latitudes 0° to 39°, Volume 3 39° to 89°. The tables can also be used to check the compass from a bearing of the Sun, taking the time to the nearest minute.

Each volume carries clear instructions for use. As before an assumed position is chosen such that the latitude is a whole degree and the longitude combined with GHA gives an integral degree of LHA. The GHA and declination of the body are extracted from *The Nautical Almanac* in the usual way and the tables entered at the appropriate page with argument LHA. The altitude is corrected (Table 5) for the increments of declination and the tabulated altitude (Hc) compared with the (corrected) observed altitude (Ho) to give the intercept, towards or away according to whether

Example

At UT 10h 57m 01s on 22 August 1992 in DR position 41° 58'N, 18° 26'W the sextant altitude of the Sun's lower limb was observed as 46° 54'.5. Height of eye 3.2m.

Sextant altitude (Hs)	46° 54'.5	GHA	343° 33'.5
Dip	−3.1	Assumed longitude	18 33.5
Main correction	+15.1	LHA	325
		Declination N.	11 37.0
Corrected altitude (Ho)	47 06.5	Assumed latitude N.	42°

From AP 3270 Volume 3 latitude 42°, declination same name:

	Hc	*d*	Z
	46° 29'	+47'	125°
d correction (Table 5)	+29		
Calculated altitude (Hc)	46 58.0		
Observed altitude (Ho)	47 06.5		

Intercept (Ho-Hc) = 8'5 to 125°

Ho is greater (to) or less (away) than Hc. Where necessary the azimuth angle (Z) is subtracted from 180° to give the azimuth according to the rule printed on each page of the tables.

5.6.3 Sight Reduction Tables for Marine Navigation (NP 401=Pub No 229)

The tables are in six volumes, each covering 16 degrees of latitude from 0° to 90° with an overlap of one degree between each volume. They are intended for use with *The Nautical Almanac* and tabulate calculated (computed) altitude (Hc) to the nearest tenth of a minute of arc and azimuth angle (Z) to the nearest tenth of a degree. The principle is identical with that of *Sight Reduction Tables for Air Navigation* but an integral degree of LHA rather than latitude determines which page to use. The interpolation table for increments of declination printed on the inside covers is necessarily more elaborate than its equivalent in the air tables to match the greater precision of the main tables. Although conceived primarily for astronomical navigation at sea, the tables constitute a fundamental solution to the spherical triangle in which two sides and the included angle are given and can be used for a wide variety of purposes (for instance great-circle sailing) outside sight reduction. For some of these, more elaborate interpolation techniques are available.

Although in the normal course of events the increased accuracy of the tables will be of little practical consequence, they have the marginal advantage over AP 3270 of covering all declinations and not just 0°–29°. On the other hand they lack the convenience of the separate and very much simplified star tables.

5.6.4 Latitude by meridian altitude

By far the simplest form of sight is the determination of latitude by observation of the meridian altitude, usually of the Sun. It is also an easy sight to take because during the period of meridian passage the altitude changes very slowly. At the time of transit the Sun appears to hang in the sky for a period of a minute or so.

The approximate time of meridian passage, generally to the nearest minute, is calculated by applying to the UT (GMT) of meridian passage given in the ephemeris the DR longitude at noon converted into hours and minutes. In west longitudes meridian passage will be later than on the Greenwich meridian, in east longitudes, earlier.

In some circumstances a timed altitude, generally to the nearest minute, is preferable to judging the maximum altitude but it is common practice at sea to observe the meridian altitude by taking a series of, say five, sights over two or three minutes when the Sun appears to be at its highest, before it dips. In that case the sight is not timed and no plotting is involved.

The altitude corrections are applied in the usual way and the zenith distance (90° minus true altitude) added to the declination when it is the same name as the latitude and subtracted when it is not. This gives the observer's latitude.

5.6.5 Latitude by the North Star

Polaris, the Pole Star, is easily picked out in the night sky by following the line of the pointers at the leading end of the Plough. It is not quite in line with the axis of the Earth's rotation and a correction to its altitude has to be made to obtain the latitude, which otherwise would correspond precisely with the true altitude. The star revolves very slowly around the pole of the heavens at an angular distance of about 1°. Its apparent movement is only about 1' in 3 min so that an observation for latitude need only be timed to the nearest minute. For the time of the sight GHA Aries is extracted from *The Nautical Almanac* and the longitude applied to form LHA Aries. With LHA Aries as argument the Pole Star Tables in *The Nautical Almanac* give a correction to the altitude from which the latitude is deduced. Alternatively, when lower precision is acceptable, the Q table in AP 3270, Volume 1 may be used. In each case a separate table gives the azimuth of Polaris.

When the star is above or below the pole of the heavens, near the meridian, its altitude will change least and time be less important. Half an hour either side of meridian altitude, the change in altitude will only be about 1' and this is the best time to observe so that a series of shots can be averaged to eliminate random error.

5.6.6 Plotting the Sun's geographical position

In the tropics when the Sun's declination is not more than about 2° from the latitude, it is possible to obtain an extremely accurate fix by plotting the Sun's geographical position as it passes the meridian and from it describing two (or more) arcs with radius the zenith distance. At about 5 to 10

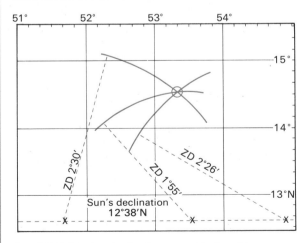

Fig. 5(11) Plotting the Sun's geographical position, a method only available in the tropics, illustrates the principle of astro-navigation. Were the zenith distances not so great in normal circumstances, the method could be employed universally.

minutes before meridian passage, and at about the same time after it, timed altitudes are taken in the normal fashion. The geographical position of the Sun at these times is then plotted with declination as latitude and GHA as longitude (360° minus GHA for easterly longitudes). From the three positions (the meridian altitude can conveniently form the third) as centre, arcs are described with zenith distance as radius; where they intersect constitutes the fix. Fig. 5(11), in tropical latitudes and easterly longitudes, illustrates an example. If it is necessary to transfer the first position circle for the course and distance sailed, as it might be at high speeds, this is most conveniently done by shifting the first geographical position the course and distance made good.

5.6.7 Equal altitudes

In certain circumstances, when the difference between the observer's latitude and the Sun's declination does not exceed about 10°, longitude may be determined by taking equal altitudes of the Sun on either side of the meridian. The latitude may at the same time be conveniently determined by meridian altitude, thus giving a fix. A correction must be made for the change in declination between the successive observations and for any change in latitude between the sights. In this case the assumption that meridian passage takes place at maximum altitude will not lead to significant error. Serious errors will be introduced if the method is used outside the rather confined limits in which it is valid. These are that the Sun should be not less than 20° in bearing from the meridian, not more than 10° in hour angle and at an altitude of not less than 70°.

The time of meridian passage is first worked out in the normal way and the first altitude taken, typically, about 15 minutes before it, and the time noted. The altitude corrections need not be applied, provided the afternoon sight is taken from the same height of eye. The meridian altitude is then observed as usual and (unless a second sextant has been available) the altitude of the first sight is set on the sextant again. At about the same interval after meridian passage the time is noted when the Sun is at the altitude set on the sextant. The mid-time of the observations is obtained by adding the two times together and dividing by 2; the GHA of the Sun for that time is the longitude west (or 360° minus GHA, the longitude east).

If the observer's latitude has changed and/or the Sun's declination has changed between the sights a correction is made to the first altitude to obtain the second. The quantity *d* given on the daily pages of *The Nautical Almanac* is the change of declination, north or south, in an hour; change of latitude will be obtained by working out a DR for the time of the second observation, or from the traverse table. The corrections can be combined and will be added to the first altitude if the Sun is getting nearer to the observer and subtracted if it is getting further away.

5.7 The use of calculators

5.7.1 Calculators – general

It is possible to use a calculator to make a sight reduction and also to solve the astronomical triangle for position without referring to tables. The advantage is that the problem of position can be solved precisely, so that the main errors in the determination of position will then come from errors in the sextant observations. With tables, for example, an assumed position is used that has been specially rounded off to the nearest whole degree of latitude or LHA to simplify or eliminate interpolation, but the solution to the astronomical triangle is for this assumed position and not the true position. With a calculator the position lines can be solved by an iterative process so that provided the correct mathematical equations are used the final solution is exact. Such a method is given in *The Nautical Almanac* under the section on Sight Reduction Procedures.

So-called dedicated calculators are pre-programmed to solve the sight reduction problem. In this section formulae are given which are intended to be programmed into a non-dedicated calculator or personal computer, for the purpose of making a sight reduction. Nowadays calculators are available which can remember many thousands of program steps or instructions to perform the tasks, thereby alleviating the user's mental effort. Some calculators use a high level programming language like Basic, others use standard algebraic notation and it is even possible to key in equations almost in the form that they are written. To be able to program the long-term solar ephemeris in section 5.7.7 the calculator would need to have built in trigonometric functions, like sine, cosine and tangent, and their inverse functions. In order to perform the calendar calculation in the solar ephemeris section a function key is required that will take the whole part of a number in front of the decimal point. Also useful is a function key which converts hours, minutes and seconds to decimals of an hour, and vice versa. In order to be programmable the calculator must also be able to test certain mathematical relations, for example to test if a number is greater than, equal to or less than another number, and then branch to another part of the program, according to the outcome of the test. Such tests are often made to decide if a solution has converged to a definite value or not. For instance, in the calculation of the time of sunrise, the position of the Sun is not known precisely until the time of sunrise is known, and the problem has to be solved in a series of approximations, called iterations. A test is made after each iteration until the new estimate for the time of sunrise is sufficiently close to the previous estimate, which is the required answer.

In this section the standard rules of algebra are assumed, and it is important that they are interpreted correctly. Except in section 5.7.6 and 5.7.10 the multiplication signs have been included to help those unfamiliar with standard algebraic notation. Terms enclosed in brackets are always evaluated first. In general the operation of multiplication and division are carried out before addition and subtraction. Thus, for example, $2 + 3 \times 4 = 14$, while $(2 + 3) \times 4 = 20$. When in doubt always include the brackets when keying into the calculator, so the calculator must also have a key for open and close brackets.

The main purpose of this section is to provide the necessary formulae and method for making a sight reduction using a calculator and to determine a fix from the DR position. The method assumes that the observations have been made in the usual way with a marine sextant and the method of reduction is based on the standard procedure of determining the intersection of position lines on a chart to find a fix. A solar and bright star ephemeris is also provided for use with a calculator so that the whole sight reduction may be made without reference to an almanac. At the end of this section additional procedures are given, for example formulae for calculating amplitudes and a simple method for calculating the times of sunrise, sunset and twilights.

5.7.2 Dip

A general description of the concept of dip is given in section 5.3.2. The correction for dip in minutes of arc is calculated from:

$$\text{Dip} = 1'.76 \times \sqrt{\text{HE}}$$

where HE is the height of eye above sea level in metres. Alternatively:

$$\text{Dip} = 0'.97 \times \sqrt{\text{HE}}$$

where HE is in feet. The correction for dip is always subtracted from the sextant altitude Hs to produce the apparent altitude Ha after applying the sextant index error.

$$\text{Ha} = \text{Hs} - \text{Dip}$$

5. 7.3 Refraction

For a general description of the effects of atmospheric refraction see section 5.3.3. The correction for refraction R_0 in minutes of arc, at a standard temperature of $10°C$ and atmospheric pressure of 1010 millibars, may be calculated from Bennett's formula:

$$R_0 = 1'.0 / \tan\left(\text{Ha} + \frac{7.31}{(\text{Ha} + 4.4)}\right)$$

where Ha is the apparent altitude in degrees at sea level, that is, sextant altitude corrected for instrumental error and dip. The advantage of using Bennett's formula is that it is both simple and

produces smaller errors over the whole altitude range $0°$ to $90°$, when compared with other approximate expressions. Thus the maximum error introduced by using this formula is normally less than $\pm 0'.05$ except in the altitude range $7°$ to $24°$ where a small systematic error of $-0'.1$ is introduced.

An approximate expression for the correction (f) for a non-standard temperature of $T°C$ and atmospheric pressure P in millibars is

$$f = \frac{0.28 \times P}{(\text{T} + 273)}$$

The total refraction correction R is calculated from:

$$\text{R} = \text{R}_0 \times f$$

Refraction is always subtracted from the apparent altitude Ha to produce the observed altitude Ho:

$$\text{Ho} = \text{Ha} - \text{R}$$

5.7.4 Calculation of altitude and azimuth for sight reduction

Several methods are available for calculating altitude (Hc) and true azimuth (*Zn*) for the reduction of a sight using the intercept and azimuth method. The formulae for calculating Hc and *Zn* require the latitude and longitude (Lat and Long) of the observer, and the Greenwich hour angle and declination (GHA and Dec) of the body. The sign convention used in the formulae is: Lat and Dec are plus (+) if North, and minus (−) if South; Long is plus (+) if East, and minus (−) if West.

Calculate the local hour angle from

$$\text{LHA} = \text{GHA} + \text{Long}$$

(1) Hc is obtained directly from

$$\sin \text{Hc} = (\sin \text{Lat} \times \sin \text{Dec}) + (\cos \text{Lat} \times \cos \text{Dec} \times \cos \text{LHA})$$

(2) *Zn* is obtained as follows:

$$\cos Z = \frac{(\cos \text{Lat} \times \sin \text{Dec}) - (\sin \text{Lat} \times \cos \text{Dec} \times \cos \text{LHA})}{\cos \text{Hc}}$$

If $\text{LHA} > 180°$ then $Zn = Z$, otherwise $Zn = 360° - Z$

For calculators that have a function key which converts directly from rectangular coordinates (x, y) to polar coordinates (r, θ), set

$x = \cos \text{Lat} \times \sin \text{Dec} - \sin \text{Lat} \times \cos \text{Dec} \times \cos \text{LHA}$
$y = - \cos \text{Dec} \times \sin \text{LHA}$

Enter x and y into the appropriate stores in the calculator, convert to polar coordinates by pressing the conversion key, then $Zn = \theta$

These same expressions for x and y may also be used in general to calculate azimuth when the altitude is not known or required, as for example when checking a compass, as follows:

$$z = \tan^{-1}\left(\frac{y}{x}\right)$$

If $x < 0$ then $Zn = z + 180°$
If $x > 0$ and $y < 0$ then $Zn = z + 360°$
Otherwise $Zn = z$

5.7.5 Calculating a fix from two position lines

A fix may be calculated from the intercept (p) and azimuth (Zn) of two observations, which is equivalent to finding the point of intersection of two position lines on a chart. The intercept p is calculated from:

$$p = Ho - Hc$$

where Ho is the observed altitude, i.e. the sextant altitude corrected for dip, index error and refraction, and Hc is the calculated altitude. The intercept is plus if Towards and minus if Away. Use 5.7.2 and 5.7.3 to calculate Ho, then use 5.7.4 to calculate Hc and the true azimuth Zn, which requires a DR position (DR Lat and DR Long) and the GHA and Dec of the body taken from an ephemeris. Use 5.7.7 and 5.7.8 for calculating the GHA and Dec of the Sun and navigational stars. If the fix is found to differ from the DR position by more than say 30 nautical miles it is advisable to replace the DR position by the fix position and repeat the calculation, starting from the point where the altitude and azimuth are calculated to obtain an improved estimate of the fix.

The sign convention used in the calculations is as follows: North latitudes are plus (+), South latitudes are minus (−), East longitudes are plus (+), West longitudes are minus (−). If subscripts 1 and 2 refer to the first and second observations, then with the DR position (DR Lat and DR Long), using the methods already described, calculate the intercept and azimuth for the first observation, i.e. p_1 and Zn_1 and for the second observation, i.e. p_2 and Zn_2. If d Long and d Lat are the corrections to be added to the DR position to obtain the fix position (fix Lat and fix Long) then calculate:

$$\text{dLat} = \frac{p_2 \times \sin Zn_1 - p_1 \times \sin Zn_2}{\sin(Zn_1 - Zn_2)}$$

$$\text{dLong} = \frac{p_1 \times \cos Zn_2 - p_2 \times \cos Zn_1}{\sin(Zn_1 - Zn_2) \times \cos(\text{DRLat})}$$

$$\text{FixLat} = \text{DRLat} + \text{dLat}$$

$$\text{FixLong} = \text{DRLong} + \text{dLong}$$

If necessary replace the DR position with the latest fix position and repeat the calculation, starting from the point where the altitude and azimuth are calculated from the DR Lat and DR Long, and the GHA and Dec of the body until the estimate for the new fix lies less than 30 nautical miles from the previous estimate. Repeating the calculation in this way even when the fix is close to the DR position is an ideal check that the calculator has been programmed correctly.

Worked example. If DR Lat = 48° 30′N and DR Long = 08° 48′W, and for sight No 1, $p_1 = 3'.0$ towards, $Zn_1 = 225°.1$, and for sight No 2 $p_2 = 2'.6$ towards, $Zn_2 = 267°.3$, calculate the fix position.

$Zn_1 = 225.1$	$Zn_2 = 267.3$
$Zn_1 - Zn_2 = -42.2$	$\sin(Zn_1 - Zn_2) = -0.6717$
DR Lat = 48.5000	cos DR Lat = 0.6626
$p_1 = +0.0500$	$p_2 = +0.0433$
$\sin Zn_1 = -0.7083$	$\cos Zn_1 = -0.7059$
$\sin Zn_2 = -0.9989$	$\cos Zn_2 = -0.0471$

$$\text{d Lat} = \frac{0.0433 \times (-0.7083) - 0.0500 \times (-0.9943)}{(-0.6717)}$$
$$= -0.0287$$

$$\text{d Long} = \frac{0.0500 \times (-0.0471) - 0.0433 \times (-0.7059)}{(-0.6717) \times 0.6626}$$
$$= -0.0634$$

$$\text{Fix Lat} = +48.5000 - 0.0287$$
$$= +48.4713$$
$$= 48°28'.3\text{N}$$
$$\text{Fix Long} = -8.8000 - 0.0634$$
$$= -8.8634$$
$$= 80°51'.8\text{W}$$

In the above calculation it has been assumed that there is no motion of the observer between the two sights. Moreover, in real situations there will be more than two sights. To solve the position line equation for more than two sights requires the method of least squares. The section on sight reduction procedures in *The Nautical Almanac* gives formulae and method for solving for two or more position lines and also includes the effect of motion of the observer.

It is possible to apply an approximate correction, which is good enough for most purposes, for the motion of the observer to the intercept p. If the observer is moving at a constant speed V in knots on a constant course C the correction MOO, which allows for the motion of the observer from the time of the observation t to the time of fix T, is added to p where

$$\text{MOO} = \frac{V}{60} \times (T - t) \times \cos{(Zn - C)}$$

and where T and t are in hours. Although this part of the calculation is not rigorous it is better than ignoring it altogether.

The speed V and course C should be relative to the ground and not the sea, which may also be moving, so allowance should be made for tidal streams and ocean currents. A few dedicated calculators include this feature in their software. If there is a strong ocean current with speed V and bearing C' the absolute speed W and course C'' is calculated as follows:

set
$$x = U \cos C' + V \cos C$$
$$y = U \sin C' + V \sin C$$

then
$$W = \sqrt{x^2 + y^2}$$
$$c = \tan^{-1}\left(\frac{y}{x}\right)$$

If $x < 0$ then $C'' = c + 180°$

If $x > 0$ and $y < 0$ then $C'' = c + 360°$
Otherwise $C'' = c$

5.7.6 Calculating a fix from two or more position line

If there are only two position lines the best estimate for the fix is at the point where the two position lines intersect. If there are three or more position lines it is unlikely that they will meet in a single point. In this case the best estimate for the fix is to find the position where the sum of the squares of the distances from each position line is a minimum.

In this section the expressions are given for three position lines with intercepts and azimuths p_1, Z_1, p_2, Z_2, p_3, Z_3. It should be obvious from the form of the expressions how to extend the calculation to four or more position lines. The method also works for two position lines, by dropping the terms with subscript 3. The method then produces the same answer as the method described in section 5.7.5.

In this section the multiplication signs have been omitted, which makes the equations easier to read. Form the sums

$A = \cos^2 z_1 + \cos^2 z_2 + \cos^2 z_3$
$B = \cos z_1 \sin z_1 + \cos z_2 \sin z_2 + \cos z_3 \sin z_3$
$C = \sin^2 z_1 + \sin^2 z_2 + \sin^2 z_3$
$D = p_1 \cos z_1 + p_2 \cos z_2 + p_3 \cos z_3$
$E = p_1 \sin z_1 + p_2 \sin z_2 + p_3 \sin z_3$
$F = p_1^2 + p_2^2 + p_3^2$

Then
$$\text{dLat} = (CD - BE)/G$$
$$\text{dLong} = (AE - BD)/(G \cos{(\text{DR Lat})})$$
where $G = AC - B^2$

and as in the previous section

$$\text{FixLat} = \text{DRLat} + \text{dLat}$$
$$\text{FixLong} = \text{DRLong} + \text{dLong}$$

The minimum sum (S) of the squares of the distances to all the position lines is given by

$$S = F - D\,\text{dLat} - E \cos{(\text{DR Lat})}\,\text{dLong}$$

If the fix position differs from the DR position by more than 30 nautical miles, it is advisable as in the previous section to repeat the calculation by replacing the DR position by the latest calculated position for the fix. The calculation continues from the point where the altitude and azimuth are calculated (see section 5.7.4).

5.7.7 A solar ephemeris for sight reduction

A long-term, low precision ($\pm 0'.5$) solar ephemeris is given for programmable calculators and personal computers. Method and formulae are given for calculating GHA, Dec, semi-diameter (SD) and the equation of time (E) for the Sun for the period 1995 to 2000. The maximum errors in GHA and Dec are $\pm 0'.4$ and $\pm 0'.2$, respectively. In the algorithm, angles are expressed in degrees.

Step 1. Calculate n the time interval in days from 1994 December 31 at 0^h UT to the date and time of the observation of the Sun on y-m-d-UT, where y is the year, m is the month, d the day and UT the universal time in hours.

$$n = D + d + \frac{\text{UT}}{24}$$

where D is taken from the table on page 162.
Alternatively calculate D as follows:

if $m > 2$ set $a = y$ and $b = m - 3$
otherwise set $a = y - 1$ and $b = m + 9$, then $D = [365.25 \times (a - 1992)] + [30.6 \times b + 0.5] - 1036$ where $[x]$ means take the whole number in front of the decimal point.

Step 2. Calculate the angles (in degrees) L, G, M, EPS, LNG, and RA as follows:

Mean Longitude $L = 279.190 + 0.9856\,4736 \times n$
Mean Anomaly $G = 356.343 + 0.9856\,0028 \times n$
Lunar Term $M = 221.818 - 0.0529\,538 \times n$
Obliquity $EPS = 23.440 - 0.0000\,0036 \times n + 0.003 \times \cos M$

Apparent Longitude $LNG = L + 1.915 \times \sin G + 0.020 \times \sin(2 \times G) - 0.005 \times \sin M$
Right Ascension $RA = LNG - 2.465 \times \sin(2 \times LNG) + 0.053 \times \sin(4 \times LNG)$

Remove multiples of $360°$ from L, G, LNG and RA

161

Step 3. Calculate GHA, Dec, SD (in degrees) and E (in minutes of time) as follows:

GHA = $99.190 + 0.9856\,4736 \times n + 15 \times$ UT
$\qquad - 0.004 \times \sin M - $ RA
Remove multiples of $360°$ from GHA
Declination   Dec = $\tan^{-1}(\tan EPS \times \sin$ RA$)$
Semi-diameter SD = $\dfrac{0.267}{(1 - 0.017 \times \cos G)}$ in degrees
Equation of time $E = 4 \times (L - RA)$ in minutes of time

Table for D, the number of days elapsed from 1994 December 31 to the beginning of the month.

	1995	1996	1997	1998	1999	2000
January	0	365	731	1096	1461	1826
February	31	396	762	1127	1492	1857
March	59	425	790	1155	1520	1886
April	90	456	821	1186	1551	1917
May	120	486	851	1216	1581	1947
June	151	517	882	1247	1612	1978
July	181	547	912	1277	1642	2008
August	212	578	943	1308	1673	2039
September	243	609	974	1339	1704	2070
October	273	639	1004	1369	1734	2100
November	304	670	1035	1400	1765	2131
December	334	700	1065	1430	1795	2161

The following example showing values of the quantities at main stages of the calculation may be used as a check on the programming.

Example. Find GHA, Dec, SD, and E for the Sun on 1996 February 3 at $13^h\,36^m$ UT

Step 1.
$y = 1996$	$m = 2$	$d = 3$
$a = 1995$	$b = 11$	$D = 396$
UT = 13.6000	$n = 399.5667$	

Step 2.
$L = 313.022$	$G = 30.156$	$M = 200.659$
$EPS = 23.437$	$LNG = 314.003$	RA = 316.470

Step 3.
GHA = $20°.553$ Dec = $-16°.624$
SD = $0°.271$ E = $-13^m.793$

5.7.8 Star places for sight reduction

The table on page 163 gives coefficients for calculating the Greenwich hour angle (GHA) and declination (Dec) of selected navigational stars for the period 1995 to 2000 using a programmable calculator or personal computer. The maximum errors are $\pm 0.'1$ in GHA and Dec.

Step 1. Calculate the time interval n in days from 1994 Dec. 31 at 0^h UT to the required date and time of the observation of the star on y-m-d-UT, where y is the year, m is the month, d is the day, and UT is the universal time in hours, from

$$n = D + d + \frac{\text{UT}}{24}$$

where D is obtained from the table on page 162 or calculated from the expression for D in section 5.7.7.

Calculate the total sidereal hour angle L from 1994 December 31 at 0^h UT to the time of observation from

$$L = n \times 0.9856\,474$$

Step 2. Take the coefficients for the star from the table on page 163 and calculate GHA and Dec from

$$\text{GHA} = G_0 + G_1 \times L/360 + G_2 \times \sin L + G_3 \times \cos L \\ + 15 \times \text{UT}$$
$$\text{Dec} = D_0 + D_1 \times L/360 + D_2 \times \sin L + D_3 \times \cos L$$

Remove multiples of $360°$ from GHA. Note the division of by 360 in the second term on the right hand side of the equations for both GHA and Dec. Also note that multiples of 360 must not be removed from L in this term.

Example. Find the GHA and Dec of *Deneb* (No 53) on 1996 October 3 at 18^h24^mUT.

Step 1.
$D = 639$	$d = 3$
UT = $18^h.4000$	$n = 642.7667$
$L = 633.5413$	

Step 2.
$\sin L = -0.9981$ $\cos L = 0.0618$
$L/360 = 1.7598$ $15 \times$ UT $= 276.0000$
GHA = $148.8740 + 359.9912 \times 1.7598 +$
$0.0038 \times (-0.9981) + 0.0069 \times 0.0618 + 276.0000$
$\qquad = 1058.3964$
$\qquad = 338°.3964$ (removing multiples of $360°$)
Dec = $+45.2651 + 0.0031 \times 1.7598 -$
$0.0048 \times (-0.9981) + 0.0018 \times 0.0618$
$\qquad = +45.2755$
$\qquad = 45°16'.5$N

5.7.9 Amplitudes

The amplitude (AMP) of a body is its bearing measured from true east or west when it is near the horizon, i.e. near rising or setting. Using the formula below, AMP is minus if South and plus if North. It is useful for checking the accuracy of a compass, which is described in section 3.1.8.

$$\sin \text{AMP} = \frac{\sin \text{Dec}}{\cos \text{LAT}}$$

where Dec is the declination and Lat is the latitude. This formula is correct for the apparent

SELECTED STARS, 1995–2000

Name	Mag.	No.	GHA				Dec			
			G_0	G_1	G_2	G_3	D_0	D_1	D_2	D_3
			°	°	°	°	°	°	°	°
Alpheratz	2.2	1	97.1565	359.9872	+0.0059	+0.0008	+29.0639	+0.0050	−0.0023	+0.0024
Ankaa	2.4	2	92.6832	359.9874	+0.0071	+0.0002	−42.3323	+0.0049	−0.0014	−0.0041
Schedar	2.5	3	89.1305	359.9862	+0.0095	−0.0002	+56.5107	+0.0050	−0.0012	+0.0046
Diphda	2.2	4	88.3564	359.9874	+0.0055	−0.0003	−18.0133	+0.0050	−0.0021	−0.0021
Hamal	2.2	6	67.4662	359.9861	+0.0053	−0.0024	+23.4386	+0.0043	−0.0013	+0.0018
Acamar	3.1	7	54.6744	359.9901	+0.0057	−0.0044	−40.3256	+0.0037	−0.0036	−0.0032
Menkar	2.8	8	53.6855	359.9869	+0.0043	−0.0034	+4.0693	+0.0036	−0.0020	+0.0000
Mirfak	1.9	9	48.1961	359.9827	+0.0061	−0.0059	+49.8424	+0.0033	+0.0012	+0.0030
Aldebaran	1.1	10	30.2812	359.9858	+0.0028	−0.0051	+16.4975	+0.0020	−0.0009	+0.0005
Rigel	0.3	11	20.6160	359.9879	+0.0019	−0.0054	−8.2095	+0.0012	−0.0029	−0.0005
Capella	0.2	12	20.1086	359.9821	+0.0027	−0.0077	+45.9910	+0.0010	+0.0020	+0.0012
Bellatrix	1.7	13	17.9743	359.9866	+0.0017	−0.0055	+6.3430	+0.0010	−0.0017	−0.0001
Elnath	1.8	14	17.6954	359.9845	+0.0019	−0.0062	+28.6011	+0.0009	+0.0004	+0.0006
Alnilam	1.8	15	15.2003	359.9873	+0.0014	−0.0055	−1.2074	+0.0007	−0.0023	−0.0003
Betelgeuse	0–1	16	10.4647	359.9865	+0.0010	−0.0056	+7.4038	+0.0003	−0.0016	−0.0001
Canopus	−0.9	17	3.2311	359.9938	+0.0006	−0.0093	−52.6956	−0.0003	−0.0055	−0.0003
Sirius	−1.6	18	357.9582	359.9889	+0.0000	−0.0059	−16.7116	−0.0011	−0.0036	−0.0003
Adhara	1.6	19	354.5831	359.9899	−0.0005	−0.0064	−28.9679	−0.0011	−0.0045	+0.0001
Procyon	0.5	20	344.4300	359.9870	−0.0013	−0.0055	+5.2352	−0.0022	−0.0018	−0.0005
Pollux	1.2	21	342.9376	359.9849	−0.0017	−0.0062	+28.0357	−0.0020	+0.0004	−0.0011
Suhail	2.2	23	322.2360	359.9906	−0.0043	−0.0060	−43.4150	−0.0035	−0.0045	+0.0022
Alphard	2.2	25	317.3545	359.9877	−0.0035	−0.0042	−8.6394	−0.0038	−0.0028	+0.0003
Regulus	1.3	26	307.1640	359.9867	−0.0042	−0.0035	+11.9895	−0.0043	−0.0015	−0.0013
Dubhe	2.0	27	293.3388	359.9846	−0.0101	−0.0048	+61.7762	−0.0048	+0.0008	−0.0048
Denebola	2.2	28	281.9896	359.9872	−0.0053	−0.0012	+14.5987	−0.0050	−0.0019	−0.0018
Gienah	2.8	29	275.3022	359.9872	−0.0055	−0.0004	−17.5152	−0.0050	−0.0023	+0.0013
Alioth	1.7	32	265.7418	359.9885	−0.0093	+0.0008	+55.9864	−0.0049	−0.0015	−0.0049
Spica	1.2	33	257.9573	359.9869	−0.0052	+0.0013	−11.1355	−0.0048	−0.0020	+0.0007
Alkaid	1.9	34	252.3575	359.9896	−0.0077	+0.0027	+49.3383	−0.0046	−0.0026	−0.0044
Menkent	2.3	36	247.5913	359.9856	−0.0061	+0.0028	−36.3452	−0.0045	−0.0007	+0.0027
Arcturus	0.2	37	245.3329	359.9884	−0.0051	+0.0025	+19.2088	−0.0048	−0.0028	−0.0021
Zuben'ubi	2.9	39	236.5390	359.9863	−0.0046	+0.0033	−16.0203	−0.0039	−0.0014	+0.0009
Kochab	2.2	40	236.5208	359.9986	−0.0161	+0.0115	+74.1769	−0.0038	−0.0033	−0.0047
Alphecca	2.3	41	225.5724	359.9891	−0.0042	+0.0045	+26.7328	−0.0032	−0.0036	−0.0022
Antares	1.2	42	211.9141	359.9849	−0.0032	+0.0054	−26.4192	−0.0021	−0.0000	+0.0009
Sabik	2.6	44	201.6669	359.9858	−0.0021	+0.0055	−15.7167	−0.0013	−0.0008	+0.0001
Shaula	1.7	45	195.8717	359.9834	−0.0019	+0.0069	−37.0981	−0.0008	+0.0012	+0.0005
Rasalhague	2.1	46	195.5149	359.9883	−0.0015	+0.0056	+12.5659	−0.0008	−0.0033	−0.0008
Eltanin	2.4	47	190.0692	359.9935	−0.0016	+0.0090	+51.4920	−0.0003	−0.0054	−0.0010
Kaus Aust.	2.0	48	183.2294	359.9838	−0.0005	+0.0069	−34.3846	+0.0003	+0.0011	−0.0002
Vega	0.1	49	179.9984	359.9911	−0.0001	+0.0073	+38.7816	+0.0007	−0.0050	−0.0003
Nunki	2.1	50	175.4510	359.9847	+0.0004	+0.0063	−26.3004	+0.0010	+0.0003	−0.0006
Altair	0.9	51	161.5552	359.9877	+0.0016	+0.0055	+8.8578	+0.0022	−0.0030	−0.0002
Deneb	1.3	53	148.8740	359.9912	+0.0038	+0.0069	+45.2651	+0.0031	−0.0048	+0.0018
Enif	2.5	54	133.2047	359.9877	+0.0038	+0.0039	+9.8544	+0.0040	−0.0028	+0.0003
Al Na'ir	2.2	55	127.2120	359.9844	+0.0060	+0.0049	−46.9831	+0.0043	+0.0009	−0.0036
Formalhaut	1.3	56	114.8475	359.9862	+0.0054	+0.0027	−29.6470	+0.0047	−0.0008	−0.0029
Markab	2.6	57	113.0616	359.9876	+0.0050	+0.0023	+15.1801	+0.0048	−0.0027	+0.0010

Sun when its lower limb is about a semi-diameter above the horizon, and the true altitude $h = 0$.

When h is non-zero use the formula

$$\sin \text{AMP} = \frac{\sin \text{Dec} - (\sin h \times \cos \text{Lat})}{(\cos h \times \cos \text{Lat})}$$

At rising or setting, for a star or the centre of the Sun on the horizon, $h = -34'$. When the lower limb of the Sun is on the horizon $h = -18'$. When the lower limb of the Sun is about a semi-diameter above the horizon, $h = 0$ and the formula reduces to the previous one.

5.7.10 Times of sunrise, sunset and twilights

The calculation begins by making an estimate for the time T_0 (in hours) of the phenomenon. For example, in European waters take $T_0 = 6^h$ for rise and $T_0 = 18^h$ for set.

Step 1. Using the algorithm in 5.7.7, calculate the GHA and Dec of the Sun on the day required at time T_0 in hours. Calculate the local hour angle t of the Sun at rising or setting from

$$\cos t = \frac{\sin h - \sin \text{Lat} \sin \text{Dec}}{\cos \text{Lat} \cos \text{Dec}}$$

where angles are measured in degrees, and $h = -0°.8333$ for sunrise or sunset, $-6°$ for civil twilight and $-12°$ for nautical twilight. Alternatively set $\sin h = -0.0145$, -0.1045, -0.2079 for sunrise or sunset, civil twilight and nautical twilight, respectively.

Step 2. Calculate an improved estimate of the time of the phenomenon T_1 from

$T_1 = (15T_0 - \text{Long} - t - \text{GHA})/15$ for rise, and
$T_1 = (15T_0 - \text{Long} + t - \text{GHA})/15$ for set

If necessary add or subtract 24^h to place T_1, in the range 0^h to 24^h. If T_1 differs from T_0 by more than $0^h.008$ replace T_0 by T_1 and repeat the calculation from Step 1.

In the above calculation the standard sign convention has been adopted for latitude, longitude and declination, i.e. for latitude and declination, North is plus (+), South is minus (−), and for longitude, East is plus (+), West is minus (−).

In step 1 if $\cos t > +1$ set $t = 0$, if $\cos t < -1$ set $t = 180°$. If after several iterations $\cos t > +1$ then the Sun remains above the chosen altitude all day. On the other hand if $\cos t < -1$ then the Sun remains below the chosen altitude all day. The time of transit of the Sun across the meridian may also be calculated using this algorithm by setting $t = 0$ in step 2.

Example. Find the time of sunrise for Aberdeen on 1996 May 7.

First iteration.
Step 1.

$T_0 = 6.0000$	$\sin h = -0.0145$
$\text{Lat} = 57.1667$	$\text{Long} = -2.0667$
$\sin \text{Lat} = 0.8403$	$\cos \text{Lat} = 0.5422$
$\text{GHA} = 270.8691$	$\text{Dec} = 16.8992$
$\sin \text{Dec} = 0.2907$	$\cos \text{Dec} = 0.9568$
$\cos t = -0.4988$	$t = 119.9183$

Step 2.
$T_1 = 4.0853$
$T_0 - T_1 = 1^h.9147$ a second iteration is needed

Second iteration
Step 1.

$T_0 = 4.0853$		
$\text{GHA} = 242.1471$		$\text{Dec} = 16.8772$
$\sin \text{Dec} = 0.2903$		$\cos \text{Dec} = 0.9569$
$\cos t = -0.4981$		$t = 119.8753$

Step 2.
$T_1 = 4.0882$
$T_0 - T_1, = -0^h.0030$ the solution has converged
Time of sunrise $= 4.0882 = 4^h 5^m$ UT

5.8 The position line

5.8.1 The use of a single position line

A single astronomical position line can be used in conjunction with other information such as a line of soundings or a bearing (whether obtained visually by compass or by any radio method) to produce a fix. The accuracy of the fix will, clearly, depend upon both the accuracy of the information and the angle of cut. The accuracy of a visual bearing will depend on the distance of the object; the accuracy of radio bearings on that of the system which is being used.

A useful fix can often be obtained by observing a planet or bright star shortly before sunrise, and crossing it later with an altitude of the Sun when it has reached at least $10°$; the angle of cut should be at least $30°$. In this way the uncertainty in the course and distance used to transfer the first position line will be minimised.

A single position line can also be used to clear a point or danger in the same way that a visual bearing can, due allowance being made for the accuracy of the observation. Where appropriate the position line can be shifted to clear the danger by the required distance; the direction and distance the line has been shifted will then be the course and distance to make good.

5.8.2 Angle of cut

For a two-body fix, whether Sun, Moon, star or planet (and whether obtained from simultaneous or successive altitudes) the optimum angle of cut is $90°$, at which angle the effect of errors in either position line will be minimised. However, the error introduced by smaller angles of cut decreases so slowly that for all practical purposes any angle between about $60°$ and $120°$ will be as good as the right angle. See Fig. 5(12) and the accompanying table. With three position lines the optimum angle of cut is $60°$ and with four position lines, as with two, it is $90°$.

5.8.3 Rate of change of bearing and altitude

In terrestrial navigation it is evident from the practice of doubling the angle on the bow that rate of change in bearing increases until the object is abeam. The maximum rate of change will be on

Angle	Error
°	′
90	1.0
85	1.0
80	1.0
75	1.0
70	1.1
65	1.1
60	1.2
55	1.2
50	1.3
45	1.4
40	1.5
35	1.7
30	2.0
25	2.4
20	2.9
15	3.9
10	5.8
5	11.5

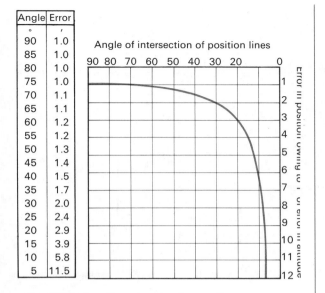

Fig. 5(12) The effect of angle of cut on fix accuracy.

the beam. The same principle applies to a celestial body as it approaches the meridian. The altitude on the other hand changes most rapidly when the body is rising or setting, and very slowly around the time of culmination. Further, the higher the altitude (in other words the closer the declination is to the latitude) the faster the change in bearing.

In low latitudes it is thus possible on occasions to obtain a right-angled cut by successive observations of the Sun on either side of the meridian within the space of a comparatively few minutes.

For historical reasons that go back to before 'the problem of longitude' was solved, the noon position is always logged as the principal position for the day. However, noon is, navigationally, far from the best time to take a fix and whenever possible successive observations should be taken either side of the meridian. The important criterion is the shortest possible run between sights consistent with a sufficient change in bearing.

5.9 Plotting and evaluating the sight

5.9.1 Plotting
In the oceans the chart in daily use is unlikely to be on a scale convenient for plotting sights. Plotting sheets on the Mercator projection for different latitude belts are available from the

Fig. 5(13) The 'Universal' plotting sheet is converted into a blank Mercator chart by joining the outer figures round the compass rose, north and south of the central latitude line, corresponding to the DR latitude. In DR latitude 50° (north or south), for example, joining the two fifties on the outer graduation east of the central meridian (one north and one south of the central parallel) establishes the meridian east of the central one etc.

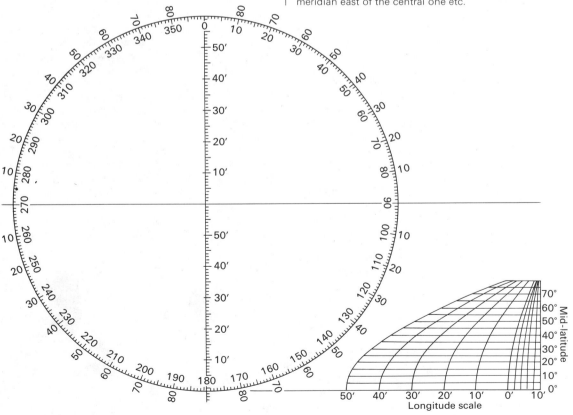

Hydrographic Department but they are not strictly necessary, take up room and represent an additional expense; any navigational chart in the right latitude belt can of course be used to plot sights by simply altering the longitude labels.

If the sight is worked from the DR position (as opposed to the assumed position used with inspection tables) the simplest form of plot is to erect, for example in the work-book, a perpendicular to represent the meridian and use the lines of the work-book on any convenient scale for latitude. (Squared paper can be used just as effectively.) The sights are then plotted, using a protractor, from the DR position and the resultant fix transferred to the chart either as a bearing and distance from the DR position or in terms of latitude and longitude, departure being converted into difference of longitude by the traverse or any other suitable table. If the DR position for successive sights is worked up from that used in the first sight, no account need be taken of the run between the sights.

Undoubtedly the most convenient form of plotting sheet for use with an assumed position, where each sight will be plotted from a separate longitude, is the 'Universal' plotting sheet (Fig. 5(13)) issued by the US Defense Mapping Agency and published by a number of private firms on either side of the Atlantic. The central meridian is graduated in nautical miles and the compass rose is marked on the inside from 0° to 360° and on the outside from 0° to 90° north and south from the central parallel. The parallel is labelled with the latitude chosen and the plotting sheet converted into a Mercator chart by simply joining the graduations north and south corresponding to this latitude, which defines meridians either side of the central one. Minutes of longitude are measured by means of the longitude scale at the bottom of the sheet using the mid-latitude.

A plotting sheet effective over a limited area can be constructed by drawing equally spaced vertical lines to represent the meridians with horizontal lines correctly spaced in relation to the meridians as parallels of latitude (a relationship defined mathematically by the cosine of the latitude or its complement the secant). One such construction is shown in Fig. 5(14): the meridians are drawn to a convenient scale and the spacing of the parallels is determined by drawing a line from one parallel towards the next at an angle equal in degrees to the mid-latitude between them. The length of the inclined line between the meridians represents the correct spacing between parallels; the inclined line can then be graduated to measure nautical miles.

5.9.2 Evaluating position lines

The evaluation of position lines to establish the most probable position plays an important part in the art of astronomical navigation at sea. A plot of six star sights, for example, may show position lines intersecting at nine separate points within reasonable distance of the DR, and some method

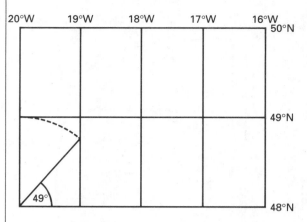

Fig. 5(14) Construction of a plotting sheet for a limited area.

will be required to analyse the plot and see which of the lines is likely to be the more reliable and to detect the presence of gross errors or blunders. Observational errors are of course an integral part of navigation and the first thing to realise is that a position line more accurately represents a band of position the width of which corresponds to the probable error of the observation. Thus if the error from all causes in an observation is estimated, to a given confidence level, to be, say, half a mile, the observer's position should lie within a band of position a mile wide (i.e. half a mile on either side of the position line). The confidence level most generally used in navigation is the 95 per cent level at which the stated error will be exceeded only once in twenty occasions.

When two position lines cross at an angle other than 90°, the bands will form a diamond of error which may conveniently be drawn as an ellipse. When the angle of cut is 90°, assuming equal reliability in each position line, the error configuration will be a box which is generally represented by a circle or ellipse of error of radius slightly larger than the position-line error. Fig. 5(15) illustrates examples. In practice these

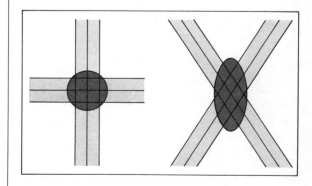

Fig. 5(15) Error configuration and angle of cut.

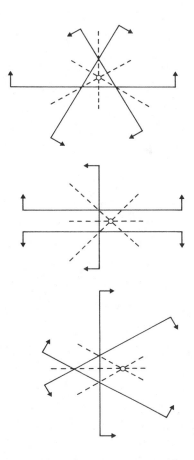

Fig. 5(16) The bisector method of establishing the most probable position. The arrows point toward the body observed.

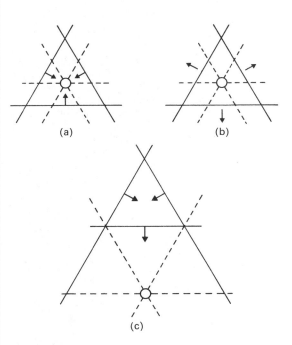

Fig. 5(17) Shifting astro-position lines an equal amount towards or away from the bodies observed to establish the most probable position from a cocked hat.

configurations will seldom be drawn on the chart but the experienced navigator will always think of position lines as bands with a certain width and of the resultant fix as a small area within which his ship lies rather than as a point.

When three position lines intersect at an angle of about 120°, the in-centre of the cocked hat is generally assumed to be the position. This will be so if the errors in each sight are equal and in the same direction, as they usually are; however, if there is a blunder in one of the position lines, the position may well lie outside the triangle.

There are several ways of analysing the astro plot, all of which involve marking on each position line, generally by a small arrow, the bearing of the body observed. The bearing will of course be at right angles to the position line. Unless there is an abnormal cause of error the arrows should all point towards or away from the centre of the figure described by the position lines. In the bisector method the (external) angle between two position lines whose azimuth arrows both point either towards or away from each other is bisected (by eye); the intersection of the bisectors is taken as the fix. The use of bisectors, which are in fact position lines obtained from

equal differences of altitude, eliminates systematic error and averages random errors in the observations. However, there are constraints on the method. The best bisector will be derived from sights separated in azimuth by 180° but, because of the slow variation of the sine curve, this figure can be extended to 150°. The method should not be used where the difference in azimuth is less than 60°.

An alternative to the bisector method is to shift all the position lines the same amount and in the same direction, either towards or away from the body observed, thus closing or opening out the pattern, until they meet at a point. This will both eliminate systematic error and reveal gross errors or a blunder. The two methods are illustrated in Figs. 5(16) and 5(17).

Two position lines constitute a fix. A third line, however, will increase the reliability of the fix; it will not, though, enable the navigator to distinguish between any systematic errors and blunders. A 'cartwheel' fix of four stars whose bearings differ by 45° will give a more reliable fix, but four stars 90° apart will often indicate, by the spacing of the two sets of reciprocal position lines, the size of the systematic error and the probable size of the random error. On the other hand since the bisector method eliminates systematic error, the soundest procedure is to take four stars 90° apart and analyse the plot by that method which will indicate whether the set has been influenced by random error. A fifth sight as a stand-by, which need not be worked up, can indicate a blunder if that is suspected.

5.10 Bibliography

Admiralty Manual of Navigation (HM Stationery Office)

American Practical Navigator, originally by Nathaniel Bowditch US DMA Pub. No. 9 (US Government Printing Office).

Celestial Navigation for Yachtsmen by Mary Blewitt, 10th edition (Adlard Coles Nautical).

The Complete Nautical Astronomer by Charles C. Cotter (Hollis and Carter).

Emergency Navigation by David Burch (Ashford Press).

Lecky's Wrinkles in Practical Navigation, 23rd edition by G. Cobb (George Philip).

Navigation Aftoat by Alton B. Moody (Hollis and Carter and US Naval Institute).

Ocean Yacht Navigator by Kenneth Wilkes (Adlard Coles Nautical).

The Yacht Navigator's Handbook by Normal Dahl (Ward Lock).

Chapter 6

Communications

Contents

6.1 Communications — general

While yachtsmen may not need to be able to communicate at sea with the same facility as professional seamen, it is still very useful to be able to understand and pass simple messages. There is also an increasing need for yachts to be able to communicate with shore stations which control commercial harbours.

Yachtsmen may, for example, wish to receive signals relating to weather forecasts, time signals, navigational matters including radio aids, safety or distress messages from (or concerning) another vessel, personal or business matters, or signals connected with yacht racing.

There are fewer reasons for yachtsmen wishing to send signals, but they include distress messages, being able to communicate with another boat when either is in some kind of trouble, arranging a rendezvous, and passing personal messages. Various methods of signalling are available, as will be explained. Some are slow, but simple and suitable for short distances; others are quicker but more complicated, and usually more expensive.

6.2 International Code of Signals

6.2.1 Explanation

The basis of most forms of communication afloat is the *International Code of Signals*, published by HM Stationery Office. In the following pages is given suffcent information for yachtsmen to understand its working and to pass simple messages. For comprehensive use of the code it is necessary to hold the complete code book.

Although the International Code caters for the increasing use of plain language communication (by voice on VHF radiotelephone for example), it provides for safety of navigation and of persons, particularly where there are language problems.

By its use, seamen of nine nations can communicate with each other without knowing any foreign language.

Before explaining the various methods of signalling, and how the code works, it is helpful to establish certain important definitions.

Defnitions

Addressee. The authority to whom a signal is addressed.

Group. One or more letters and/or numerals which together comprise a signal.

Hoist. In flag signalling, one or more groups displayed from a single halyard. A hoist or signal is *at the dip* when hoisted about half way, and is *close up* when hoisted to the full extent of the halyards.

Identity signal, or call sign. A group of letters and figures assigned to each station by its administration.

Numeral group. A group consisting of one or more numerals.

Originator. The authority who orders a signal to be sent.

Procedure. Rules drawn up for the conduct of signalling.

Sound signalling. Any method of passing Morse signals by siren, whistle, foghorn or other sound apparatus.

Station. A ship, aircraft, survival craft, coast station, or any other place at which communications can be effected.

Tackline. In flag signalling, a length of halyard used to separate groups of flags.

Time of origin. The time at which a signal is ordered to be made.

Visual signalling. Any method of communication, the transmission of which is capable of being seen.

Some of the above definitions are repeated elsewhere, when describing different methods of signalling.

Methods of transmission

The code can be transmitted in the following ways:

(1) *By flags* (see colour section pages 192-193), displayed in groups (or singly for the most important signals), and interpreted in nine different languages. This method is rather slow, and requires good visibility.

(2) *By flashing light*, using the Morse code of dots and dashes (see 6.2.4). This can be transmitted by light (day and night, given a powerful light and good visibility). Messages can be passed in plain language (for preference) or by code groups in the event of language difficulties.

(3) *By sound signalling*, using the Morse code, with the boat's foghorn for example. This is rather slow, and it can cause confusion in poor visibility, when its use should be restricted to the minimum.

(4) *By voice*, over a loud hailer. Whenever possible plain language should be used, but in the event of language difficulties groups from the International Code can be transmitted, using the phonetic spelling tables which are described later.

(5) *By radiotelegraphy*, using the Morse code. Not applicable to the very great majority of yachtsmen, but very high speeds can be achieved by professional operators, over big distances.

(6) *By radiotelephone* — by voice over radio circuits, normally in plain language, but again International Code groups are useful in the event of language difficulties.

(7) *By hand flags* (or arms), using the Morse code.

Types of signals

The present International Code, which came into effect in 1969, provides for nine languages – English, French, German, Greek, Italian, Japanese, Norwegian, Russian and Spanish. Signals consist of:

(1) Single-letter signals which are very urgent, important, or very common.
(2) Two-letter signals in the General Section.
(3) Three-letter signals beginning with the letter 'M' in the Medical Section.

Complements

In principle the Code provides that each signal should have a complete meaning. In some cases however complements are used to supplement the available groups. As explained in the examples below, complements may express variations in the meaning of the basic signal, questions concerning the same subject, answers to a question or a request, or more detailed information on the basic signal.

Example (a) Variations in meaning
'KT' = 'You should send me a towing hawser'
'KT 1' = 'I am sending towing hawser'

Example (b) Questions concerning the basic signal
'CV' = 'I am unable to give assistance'
'CV 4' = 'Can you assist?'

Example (c) Answers to a question or request
'IB' = 'What damage have you received?'
'IB 3' = 'I have not received any damage'

Example (d) Supplementary, specific or detailed information
'CB' = 'I require immediate assistance'
'CB 4' = 'I require immediate assistance: I am aground'

Complements which appear in the text more than once are grouped in Tables I, II and III which appear in 6.2.6. These should be used only as and when specified in the Code.

Example (e) Use of complements tables
'K' = 'I wish to communicate with you'
'K (with one numeral)' (complements table I)
= 'I wish to communicate with you by . . .'

Reference to complements table I shows that it lists the various methods of signalling.

In some groups words appear in brackets. These are either alternatives or information which may be included if it is available, or explanations of the text.

The code is arranged under these headings: Distress, Emergency, Casualties, Damage; Aids to Navigation, Navigation; Manoeuvres; Miscellaneous; Meteorology; Communications; Pratique; Medical.

6.2.2 General instructions

(1) *Numbers* are signalled as follows. By flag signalling – by numeral pendants; by light – usually by Morse numerals, but spelt if important; by R/T or loud hailer – by phonetic code words (see 6.2.4).
(2) *Decimal point* is indicated by flags – by Answering Pendant; by light- by '$\overline{\text{AAA}}$'; by voice – by word 'Decimal'.
(3) *Depths* are signalled in figures followed by 'F' for feet (not fathoms) or 'M' for metres.
(4) *Azimuth or bearing*, signalled in three figures, denoting degrees from 000 to 359. Unless stated to the contrary bearings are True.
(5) *Course* – as for Azimuth with figures prefixed by 'C'.
(6) *Dates* – signalled by two, four or six figures preceded by 'D' (for Date). The first two figures show day of month, the next two month of year, and the final two (when six are signalled) the last two figures of the year.
Example: D1002 means 10 February; D 211081 means 21 October 1981.

(7) *Latitude* – signalled by four figures preceded by 'L' and followed by 'N' or 'S', which may be omitted where obvious. The first two figures indicate degrees, and the second two indicate minutes.
Example: L 5146 N = Latitude 51°46'N.

(8) *Longitude* – signalled by four (or five) figures preceded by 'G' and followed by 'E' or 'W'. The last two figures show minutes and the first two (or three) show degrees.
Example: G 12117 W = Longitude 121° 17'W.

(9) *Distance* – signalled by figures (in nautical miles) preceded by 'R'.
(10) *Speed* – signalled by figures preceded by 'S' (for knots) or by 'V' (kilometres per hour).
(11) *Time* – signalled by 24 hour clock. Preceded by 'T' for Local Time or 'Z' for UT (GMT).
(12) *Local Signal Codes* (when applicable) are preceded by the group 'YV1' – 'The groups which follow are from the local code'.

6.2.3 Yachtsmen and the International Code

Yachtsmen are most likely to use the International Code by Morse or, in the event of language or spelling difficulties, by using phonetic spelling with plain language messages (as by radiotelephone, for example). It is also important to know the meanings of the single-letter signals, which can be made by any method of signalling and which comprise messages which are either of special importance or which are commonly used.

The Morse code, phonetic alphabet and single-letter signals are shown in 6.2.4. Also shown is the figure-spelling table: in practice it is normally only necessary to use the last component of each code word in the figure-spelling table.

6.2.4 Morse code, phonetic alphabet and single-letter signals

Letter	Morse	Phonetic spelling (Emphasize syllables in italics)		Single-letter meaning (May be made by any method of signalling. * see note (1) below.)
A	· —	Alfa	*AL* FAH	I have a diver down; keep well clear at slow speed.
B	— · · ·	Bravo	*BRAH* VOH	* I am taking in, or discharging, or carrying dangerous goods.
C	— · — ·	Charlie	*CHAR* LEE	* Yes (Affirmative or 'The significance of the previous group should be read in the affirmative').
D	— · ·	Delta	*DELL* TAH	* Keep clear of me; I am manoeuvring with difficulty
E	·	Echo	*ECK* OH	* I am altering my course to starboard.
F	· · — ·	Foxtrot	*FOKS* TROT	I am disabled; communicate with me.
G	— — ·	Golf	GOLF	* I require a pilot. (By fishing vessels operating in close proximity it means 'I am hauling nets'.)
H	· · · ·	Hotel	HOH *TELL*	* I have a pilot on board.
I	· ·	India	*IN* DEE AH	* I am altering my course to port.
J	· — — —	Juliett	*JEW* LEE ETT	I am on fire and have dangerous cargo on board; keep well clear of me.
K	— · —	Kilo	*KEY* LOH	I wish to communicate with you.
L	· — · ·	Lima	*LEE* MAH	You should stop your vessel instantly.
M	— —	Mike	MIKE	* My vessel is stopped and making no way through the water.
N	— ·	November	NO *VEM* BER	No (Negative or 'The significance of the previous group should be read in the negative'.) This signal may be given only visually or by sound. For voice or radio transmission the signal should be 'NO'.
O	— — —	Oscar	*OSS* CAH	Man overboard.
P	· — — ·	Papa	PAH *PAH*	In harbour: All persons should report on board as the vessel is about to proceed to sea. At sea: By fishing vessels means 'My nets have come fast upon an obstruction'.
Q	— — · —	Quebec	KEH *BECK*	My vessel is healthy and I request free pratique.
R	· — ·	Romeo	*ROW* ME OH	
S	· · ·	Sierra	SEE *AIR* RAH	* I am operating astern propulsion.
T	—	Tango	*TANG* GO	* Keep clear of me; I am engaged in pair trawling.
U	· · —	Uniform	*YOU* NEE FORM	You are running into danger.
V	· · · —	Victor	*VIK* TAH	I require assistance.
W	· — —	Whiskey	*WISS* KEY	I require medical assistance.
X	— · · —	X-ray	*ECKS* RAY	Stop carrying out your intentions and watch for my signals.
Y	— · — —	Yankee	*YANG* KEY	I am dragging my anchor.
Z	— — · ·	Zulu	*ZOO* LOO	* I require a tug. By fishing vessels operating in close proximity it means 'I am shooting nets'.

Notes:
(1) * When made by sound, must comply with *International Regulations for Preventing Collisions at Sea*.
(2) 'K' and 'S' have special meanings as landing signals for small boats. See 6.4.4.

Figure-spelling table

Figure	Morse	Word	Pronounced
0	− − − − −	NADAZERO	NAH-DAH-ZAY-ROH
1	· − − − −	UNAONE	OO-NAH-WUN
2	· · − − −	BISSOTWO	BEE-SOH-TOO
3	· · · − ·	TERRATHREE	TAY-RAH-TREE
4	· · · · −	KARTEFOUR	KAR-TAY-FOWER
5	· · · · ·	PANTAFIVE	PAN-TAH-FIVE
6	− · · · ·	SOXISIX	SOK-SEE-SIX
7	− − · · ·	SETTESEVEN	SAY-TAY-SEVEN
8	− − − · ·	OKTOEIGHT	OK-TOH-AIT
9	− − − − ·	NOVENINE	NO-VAY-NINER
Decimal point		DECIMAL	DAY-SEE-MAL
Full stop		STOP	STOP

Note: In the figure-spelling table, each syllable should be equally emphasised. The last component of each code word (e.g. 'Zero') is the code word used for figures in the Aeronautical Mobile Service.

6.2.5 Procedure signals
Certain procedure signals are laid down, and are designed to facilitate the conduct of signalling. Certain procedure signals are reserved for certain types of signalling, but the majority can be used for any form of transmission.

A bar over the letters of a signal means that the letters are joined together and made as one symbol.

(1) Procedure signals for voice transmissions (RT or loud hailer)

Signal	Pronunciation	Meaning
Interco	IN-TER-CO	International Code group(s) follow(s)
Stop	STOP	Full stop
Decimal	DAY-SEE-MAL	Decimal point
Correction	KOR REK SHUN	Cancel my last word or group. The correct word or group follows.

(2) Procedure signals for Morse by light

$\overline{AA}$ $\overline{AA}$ $\overline{AA}$ etc	Call for unknown station or general call.
$\overline{EEEEEE}$ etc	Erase signal.
$\overline{AAA}$	Full stop or decimal point.
$\overline{TTTT}$ etc	Answering signal.
T	Word or group received.

(3) Procedure signals for flags, radiotelephony and radiotelegraphy transmissions

CQ — Call for unknown station(s) or general call to all stations.

Note: When this signal is used in voice transmission, it should be pronounced in accordance with the letter-spelling table (i.e. Charlie Quebec).

(4) Procedure signals for use where appropriate in all forms of transmission

AA	'All after . . .' (used after the 'Repeat' signal (RPT)–see below–means 'Repeat all after . . .').
AB	'All before . . .' (used after the 'Repeat signal (RPT) – see below – means 'Repeat all before ...').
$\overline{AR}$	Ending signal, or end of transmission or signal.
$\overline{AS}$	Waiting signal or period.
BN	'All between . . . and . . .' (used after the 'Repeat' signal (RPT)–means 'Repeat all between ... and ...').
C	Affirmative – YES or 'The significance of the previous group should be read in the affirmative'.
CS	'What is the name or identity signal of your vessel (or station)?'
DE	'From . . .' (used to precede the name or identity signal of the calling station).
K	'I wish to communicate with you' or 'Invitation to transmit'.

173

NO	Negative – NO or 'The significance of the previous group should be read in the negative'. When used in voice transmission the pronunciation should be 'NO'.	
OK	Acknowledging a correct repetition or 'It is correct'.	
RQ	Interrogative or 'The significance of the previous group should be read as a question'.	
R	'Received' or 'I have received your last signal'.	
RPT	Repeat signal 'I repeat' or 'Repeat what you have sent' or 'Repeat what you have received'.	
WA	'Word or group after . . .' (used after the 'Repeat' signal (RPT) means 'Repeat word or group after . . .').	
WB	'Word or group before . . .' (used after the 'Repeat' signal (RPT) means 'Repeat word or group before . . .').	

Notes:
1. The procedure signals 'C', 'NO' and 'RQ' cannot be used in conjunction with single-letter signals.
2. When these signals are used by voice transmission the letters should be pronounced in accordance with the letter-spelling table, except that 'NO' is pronounced 'NO'.

6.2.6 Tables of complements
Table I
1. Semaphore
2. Morse signalling by hand flags (or arms)
3. Loud hailer (or megaphone)
4. Morse signalling lamp
5. Sound signals
6. International Code flags
7. Radiotelegraphy, 500kHz
8. Radiotelephony, 2182kHz
9. VHF Radiotelephony-Channel 16

Table II
0. Water
1. Provisions
2. Fuel
3. Pumping equipment
4. Fire-fighting appliance
5. Medical assistance
6. Towing
7. Survival craft
8. Vessel to stand by
9. Ice breaker

Table III
0. Direction unknown (or calm)
1. North-east
2. East
3. South-east
4. South
5. South-West
6. West
7. North-West
8. North
9. All directions (or confused or variable)

6.2.7 Single-letter signals with complements
These signals bear no relation to the single-letter signals already described in 6.2.4. Some have already been mentioned in 6.2.2. They may be made by any method of signalling.

A with three numerals	AZIMUTH or BEARING
C with three numerals	COURSE
D with two, four or six numerals	DATE
G with four or five numerals	LONGITUDE (the last two numerals denote minutes and the rest degrees)
K with one numeral	I wish to COMMUNICATE with you by . (Complements table I)
L with four numerals	LATITUDE (the first two figures denote degrees, the others minutes)
R with one or more numerals	DISTANCE in nautical miles
S with one or more numerals	SPEED in knots
T with four numerals	LOCAL TIME (the first two figures denote hours, the others minutes)
V with one or more numerals	SPEED in kilometres per hour
Z with four numerals	UT (GMT) (the first two figures are hours, the others minutes)

6.2.8 Selected groups from the International Code
AC I am abandoning my vessel.
AE I must abandon my vessel.
AF I do not intend to abandon my vessel.
AN I need a doctor.
CB I require immediate assistance.
CB4 I require immediate assistance; I am aground.
CB5 I require immediate assistance; I am drifting.
CB6 I require immediate assistance; I am on fire.
CB7 I require immediate assistance; I have sprung a leak.
CS Do you require assistance?
CK Assistance is not (or is no longer) required by me (or vessel indicated).
CV I am unable to give assistance.
DX I am sinking.
ED Your distress signals are understood.
EF SOS/MAYDAY has been cancelled.
FA Will you give me my position?

IL   I can only proceed at slow speed.

IM   I request to be escorted until further notice.

IT   I am on fire.

IW   Fire is under control.

IX   Fire is gaining.

IZ   Fire has been extinguished.

JG   I am aground. I am in a dangerous situation.

JH   I am aground. I am not in danger.

JI   Are you aground?

JL   You are running the risk of going aground.

JO   I am afloat.

JW   I have sprung a leak.

JX   Leak is gaining rapidly.

KM   I can take you in tow.

KN   I cannot take you in tow. (See also 15.4.3)

LO   I am not in my correct position (to be used by a lightvessel).

MG   You should steer course. ..

NC   I am in distress and require immediate assistance.

NG   You are in a dangerous position.

NH   You are clear of all dangers.

PD   Your navigation light(s) is (are) not visible.

PH   You should steer as indicated.

PI   You should maintain your present course.

PP   Keep well clear of me.

QO   You should not come alongside.

QP   I will come alongside.

QR   I cannot come alongside.

QT   You should not anchor. You are going to foul my anchor.

RA   My anchor is foul.

RB   I am dragging my anchor.

RN   My engines are out of action.

RY   You should proceed at slow speed when passing me (or vessels making signal).

SC   I am under way.

SD   I am not ready to get under way.

SQ   You should stop or heave to.

UM   The harbour or port is closed to traffic.

UN   You may enter harbour immediately.

UO   You must not enter harbour.

UW   I wish you a pleasant voyage.

VJ   Gale is expected from direction indicated. ⎫

VK   Storm is expected from direction indicated. ⎬ (Complements table III)

YT   I cannot read your . . . (Complements table I)

YU   I am going to communicate with your station by International Code.

YV   The groups which follow are from the International Code of Signals.

ZD2   Please report me to Lloyd's London.

ZK   I cannot distinguish your signal. Please repeat it by . . . (Complements table I).

ZL   Your signal has been received but not understood.

ZM   You should send (or speak) more slowly.

6.2.9 Flag signalling

The International Code flags (see colour section page 192) consist of 26 alphabetical flags, 11 pendants (numerals 0-9 plus the Answering Pendant or Code Flag), and three triangular flags the First, Second and Third Substitutes.

Some definitions already mentioned in 6.2.1 are important. *Group* – one or more continuous letters and/or numerals comprising a signal. *Hoist* – one or more groups on one halyard. *At the dip* – a signal half-hoisted. *Close up* – a signal fully hoisted. *Tackline* – a line separating two groups. *Superior* – a flag or group above another. *Inferior* – a flag or group below another. *Class* — whether a flag is alphabetical or numeral.

The Answering Pendant is used to answer or acknowledge signals from another vessel. It may also be used as a decimal point.

Substitutes allow for the repetition of one or more letters (or numerals) within a group. The First Sub. repeats the first flag of the group in the class immediately superior to it. The Second Sub. repeats the second flag of that class, and the Third Sub. repeats the third.

A substitute can only repeat a flag of the same class as that immediately preceding it. The Answering Pendant used as a decimal point is disregarded in deciding which substitute to use.

Procedure

The basic procedure is that the sending ship hoists the identity signal of the ship she is calling – or she hoists the group 'VF' ('You should hoist your identity signal') or 'CS' ('What is the name or identity signal of your vessel/station') – at the same time hoisting her own identity signal.

The sending ship then hoists her message, and when sighted the receiving ship hoists her Answering Pendant at the dip – and close up when the signal has been understood. The procedure is repeated for subsequent hoists.

6.2.10 Morse code by light

The most likely method for yachtsmen to use the Morse code is by light. It helps to have a good light with a proper flashing key or trigger.

When making Morse it is most important to get the right rhythm and spacing. If a dot is taken as the unit of time, the correct spacing is as follows:

Dot	1 unit
Dash	3 units
Space between each dot or dash in a letter	1 unit
Space between each letter or symbol	3 units
Space between each word or group	7 units

Procedure (Morse by light)

The procedure signals used when sending Morse by light are given in (2) of 6.2.5. Other procedure signals, common to all forms of signalling, are given in (4) of 6.2.5. It should be remembered that where a bar is placed above the letters, they are run together.

A signal made by flashing light comprises the following:

(1) *The call*. This may be either the general call ($\overline{AA}$ $\overline{AA}$ $\overline{AA}$ etc) if it is required to attract the attention of all stations within sight or of a station whose identity is not known, or it may be the identity signal of a known station to be called. The call is repeated until response is made in the form of the answering signal ($\overline{TTTTTT}$ etc) which is repeated until the call stops.

(2) *The identity*. The transmitting station then makes 'DE' followed by its identity signal or name. This is repeated back by the receiving station, which then signals its own identity signal or name. This in turn is repeated back by the transmitting station.

(3) *The text*. This may consist of plain language or code groups, the latter being preceded by the signal 'YU'. Plain language may be included in code groups for the names of places etc. The receiving station acknowledges the receipt of each word or code group by the letter 'T'.

(4) *The ending*. The transmitting station indicates the end of the signal with the letters '$\overline{AR}$', which are acknowledged by the receiving station with the signal 'R', meaning 'Received' or 'I have received your last signal'.

The erase signal ('$\overline{EEEEE}$' etc) indicates that the last word or group was signalled incorrectly. It is answered by the same signal. When answered the transmitting station repeats the last word or group, and then proceeds with the rest of the message.

The repeat signal ('RPT') is used by the transmitting station to indicate that it is going to repeat. If such a repetition does not follow immediately, the signal should be interpreted by the receiving station as a request to repeat the signal received. If used by the receiving station the repeat signal is a request for a repetition of the signal transmitted.

The special repetition signals 'AA', 'AB', 'WA', 'WB' and 'BN' are made by the receiving station as appropriate, after the repeat signal 'RPT'.

A correctly received repetition is acknowledged by the signal 'OK'.

The transmitting station makes the signal 'CS' when requesting the name or identity signal of the receiving station.

The waiting signal, or period signal '$\overline{AS}$', when made independently or after the end of a signal indicates that the other station must wait for further communications; when inserted between groups it separates them to avoid confusion.

The signal 'C' is used to indicate an affirmative statement or an affirmative reply to an interrogative signal. The signal 'RQ' is used to indicate a question. For a negative reply or for a negative statement, the signal 'N' should be used in visual (or sound) signalling. The signals 'C', 'N' or 'RQ' cannot be used in conjunction with single-letter signals. When the signals 'N' or 'RQ' are used to change an affirmative signal into a negative statement or a question, they are transmitted after the main signal.

Examples:

'CY'	—'Boat(s) is (are) coming to you'
'CY N'	—'Boat(s) is (are) not coming to you'
'CW'	—'Boat/raft is on board'
'CW RQ'	—'Is boat/raft on board?'

6.2.11 Foreign Morse symbols

The following foreign Morse symbols may be met, as for example with the identification signals for certain foreign radiobeacons:

Ä (German) or AE (Danish)	· — · —
Á (Spanish) or Å (Scandinavian)	· — — · —
Ch (German or Spanish)	— — — —
É (French)	· · — · ·
Ñ (Spanish)	— — · — —
Ö (German) or Ø (Danish)	— — — ·
Ü (German)	· · — —

6.2.12 Radiotelephony (RT)

Plain language is normally used for communication by radiotelephone, and the procedures are described in 6.6.8. However, in the event of language difficulties it may be necessary to use the International Code, in which case the following procedures apply. Letters and figures are spelt in accordance with the spelling tables (6.2.4).

(1) *Method of calling*. The call consists of the call sign or name of the station called, not more than three times at each call; the group 'DE' (DELTA ECHO); and the call sign or name of the calling station, not more than three times at each call. Difficult names should be spelt. Once contact is established the call sign or name need not be sent more than once.

(2) *Reply to call*. The form of reply consists of the call sign or name of the calling station, not more than three times; the group 'DE' (DELTA ECHO); and the call sign or name of the station called, not more than three times.

(3) *Calling all stations*. The group 'CQ' (CHARLIE QUEBEC) is used to call all stations in the vicinity, but not more than three times at each call.

(4) *Code groups*. The word 'INTERCO' indicates that International Code groups follow. Words of plain language may also be in the text as names, places etc. In this case the group 'YZ' (YANKEE ZULU) meaning 'The words which follow are in plain language' is inserted if necessary.

(5) *Waiting*. If the station called is unable to accept traffic immediately, it transmits the signal '$\overline{AS}$' (ALFA SIERRA), adding if possible the duration of the waiting time in minutes.

(6) *Receipt*. Receipt of a transmission is indicated by the signal 'R' (ROMEO).

(7) *Repetition*. If the transmission is to be repeated in total or in part, the signal 'RPT' (ROMEO PAPA TANGO) is used, supplemented as necessary by:

AA   (ALFA ALFA) – all after . . .
AB   (ALFA BRAVO) – all before . . .
BN   (BRAVO NOVEMBER) – all between . . . and
     . . .
WA   (WHISKEY ALFA) – word or group after . . .
WB   (WHISKEY BRAVO) – word or group before
     . . .

(8) *End of transmission.* The end of transmission is
indicated by the signal '$\overline{AR}$' (ALFA ROMEO).

6.2.13 Morse code by hand flags, or arms

The method of signalling the Morse code by hand
flags or arms is shown in Fig. 6(1). A dot is made
by raising both flags (arms) above the head, and a
dash by extending them horizontally at shoulder
level. Between dots and dashes the flags (arms) are
brought in front of the chest. To separate letters,
groups or words the flags (arms) are extended
downwards at 45° from the body. Circular motion

**1. Raising both hand-flags
or arms**

'dot'

**2. Spreading out both
hand-flags or arms
at shoulder
level**

'dash'

**3. Hand-flags or arms brought
before the chest**

*Separation of 'dots'
and/or 'dashes'*

**4. Hand-flags or arms kept at
45° away from the body
downwards**

*Separation of letters, groups
or words*

**5. Circular motion of hand-
flags or arms over the head**

*Erase signals, if made by
the transmitting station.
Request for repetition if by
the receiving station*

Note: The space of time
between dots and dashes and
between letters, groups or
words should be such as to
facilitate correct reception

Fig. 6(1) Morse signalling by hand flags or arms.

of the flags (arms) overhead indicates the erase
signal if made by the transmitting station, or a
request for repetition if made by the receiving
station.

A station wishing to communicate with another
by this method signals 'K2', or makes the usual
general call for Morse '$\overline{AA}$ $\overline{AA}$ $\overline{AA}$ etc.' On receipt
of the call the station addressed should make the
answering signal ('$\overline{TTTT}$ etc'), or, if unable to
communicate by this method the signal 'YS2' by
any means.

Both arms should be used, but where this is
difficult or impossible only one need be used.

The signal concludes with the ending signal
'$\overline{AR}$.'

6.3 Sound signals

6.3.1 Sound signals – International Code

Sound signalling is one of the ways of using the
International Code, but because of the equipment
used (whistle, siren, foghorn etc) it is necessarily
slow. Also if misused it can cause serious
confusion. Sound signalling in poor visibility
should be reduced to a minimum, and signals
other than the single-letter ones should be used
only in extreme emergency, and never where there
is other traffic around.

The signals should be made slowly and
distinctly. They may be repeated, if necessary, but
at sufficiently long intervals to ensure that no
confusion can arise.

The single-letter signals of the Code, which are
marked with an asterisk, when made by sound
must only be made in accordance with Rules 34
and 35 of the *International Regulations for
Preventing Collisions at Sea* (see the relevant rules
in 2.1).

6.3.2 Sound signals in restricted visibility

The requirement for ships to make sound signals
in fog, mist, heavy rain or other conditions
restricting visibility (whether by day or night) are
in Rule 35 of the *International Regulations for
Preventing Collisions at Sea*, which are stated in
2.1.

By Rule 33 a vessel of 12m (39ft) or more in
length shall be provided with a whistle and a bell.
A smaller vessel is not obliged to carry these but
must have other means of making an efficient
sound signal.

A prolonged blast is four to six seconds'
duration. A short blast is about one second.

Sound signals in restricted visibility are:

Power vessel making way through the water	A prolonged blast at intervals of not more than 2 minutes.

Power vessel under way, but stopped (i.e. not at anchor)	Two prolonged blasts at intervals of not more than 2 minutes.
Vessel at anchor	Bell rung rapidly for about 5 seconds, at intervals of not more than 1 minute.
Vessel over 328ft (100m) at anchor	In addition to above sound, a gong aft at similar intervals.

(In addition a vessel at anchor may sound 'R' on her foghorn to warn an approaching vessel.)

Vessel towed	One prolonged blast followed by three short, every two minutes.
Vessel aground	As for at anchor, plus three separate and distinct strokes of bell before and after.
Pilot vessel on duty	Four short blasts.

Vessel under sail or not under command, or constrained by her draught or engaged in fishing or towing, sounds one prolonged followed by two short blasts ('D') at least every two minutes.

6.3.3 Sound signals by vessels in sight of each other

Rule 34 of the Collision Regulations prescribes the following:

One short blast — 'I am altering course to starboard.'
Two short blasts — 'I am altering course to port.'
Three short blasts — 'I am operating astern propulsion.'

When either of two vessels approaching each other fails to understand the actions or intentions of the other, or is doubtful that sufficient action is being taken to avoid a collision, she shall give at least five short and rapid blasts.

The whistle signals above may be supplemented by an all-round white light, with the number of flashes equivalent to the number of blasts.

In a narrow channel when overtaking can only occur if the overtaken vessel takes action to permit safe passing, a vessel intending to overtake shall indicate her intention by the following whistle signals.

Two prolonged blasts followed by one short — 'I intend to overtake you on your starboard side.'
Two prolonged blasts followed by two short — 'I intend to overtake you on your port side.'

If in agreement the overtaken vessel sounds one prolonged, one short, one prolonged and one short blast and takes the necessary steps. If in doubt she may sound five or more short rapid blasts.

Warning signal

Under Rule 34(e), a power driven vessel is required to sound one prolonged blast as a warning when approaching a blind bend in a river or channel.

6.3.4 Sound signals for distress purposes

Under Annex IV of the Collision Regulations the following constitute distress signals and must not be used for any other purpose.
(1) A gun or other explosive signal fired about every minute.
(2) The continuous sounding of any fog-signalling apparatus.

6.4 Miscellaneous signals

6.4.1 Radio time signals

When seagoing it is necessary to understand the system of standard times, whereby the world is divided in 24 zones, each with a width of 15° of longitude. In each zone, the same time (Zone Time) is kept. The Greenwich meridian is the reference centre of the system, and of Zone 0. Zones to the east of Zone O are numbered −1, −2, −3 etc, and those to the west +1, +2, +3 etc. The twelfth zone is divided into two by the International Date Line, the part to the west being −12, and the part to the east +12. Ashore, zones are adapted to suit geographical areas. For example, all France keeps Zone −1 (−0100) as Standard Time.

The zone number is the hours by which Zone Time must be decreased (east of Greenwich) or increased (west of Greenwich) to obtain Universal Time (UT) or Greenwich Mean Time (GMT). Zone Time may also be indicated by letters. UT (GMT) is Z (zero): zones to the east are lettered A to M (omitting J), and those to the west are lettered N to Y. Further details are given in 9.3.3.

The International Date Line is a modification of the 180° meridian, drawn so as to include islands of particular groups on the same side of the line. When crossing the Date Line heading east, assume yesterday's date: when heading west, assume tomorrow's date.

The standard times kept in different countries, together with indications as to whether or not individual countries observe Daylight Saving Time (DST), are shown in *The Macmillan & Silk Cut Nautical Almanac*, as are the details of time signals broadcast by the British Broadcasting Corporation (BBC). These are transmitted at roughly hourly intervals from 0500–2400 on one of the domestic BBC radio stations-BBC Radio 1, 2, 3 or 4. BBC time signals consist of six pulses representing successive seconds — five pulses each of one-tenth of a second, followed by a final half-second pulse. The start of the final, longer pulse marks the minute.

The term Universal Time (UT) is gradually replacing Greenwich Mean Time (GMT) with which for practical purposes it is equivalent.

Co-ordinated Universal Time (known internationally as UTC) was introduced in 1972 to provide a globally accessible and precisely defined timescale for Earth-rotation time (UT) and International Atomic Time (TAI). TAI is based on the atomic second of fixed duration, established through the quantum resonance of isolated caesium-133 atoms. The master atomic clocks run undisturbed, generating time markers at intervals of exactly one second to give the minutes, hours and days of the TAI scale. TAI was initially set to agree with UT in 1958, but the scales have since slowly drifted apart due to small changes in the Earth's rate of rotation. UTC is formed by occasionally breaking the normal counting sequence to insert or delete a second (known as a 'leap second') to keep UTC within one second of UT. This is done as the final second of a UTC month – December or June as first choice, and March or September as second choice. It happens about once a year on average.

The BBC Time Standard equipment is at Broadcasting House in London. It receives UTC information from the GPS satellites and from MSF at Rugby to generate the 'pips'. These can be received in the United Kingdom with an accuracy better than 1/20 second (50ms). Signals from relay stations abroad which receive their signals through a satellite link will be delayed by about $\frac{1}{4}$ second (250ms).

6.4.2 Pratique messages

All yachts, whether carrying dutiable stores or not, arriving in the United Kingdom from abroad (including the Channel Islands) are subject to Customs, Public Health and Home Office (Immigration Department) requirements. Details are given in Customs Notice No. 8B, which is summarised in 2.3 and is obtainable from any Customs and Excise office or from HM Customs and Excise, Customs Directorate, 1st Floor West, New King's Beam House, 22 Upper Ground, London SE1 9PJ. For these purposes Customs Officers normally act for the Immigration and Health authorities.

The following Health Clearance Messages, from the *International Code of Signals*, apply:

Q or ZS	My vessel is 'healthy' and I request free pratique. (Note: National requirements may require 'Q' to be flown on entering territorial waters and to be illuminated at night.)
QQ (i.e. flag Q over First Substitute) or by night a red light over a white light	I require health clearance.
ZT	My Maritime Declaration of Health has negative answers to the six health questions.

ZU	My Maritime Declaration of Health has a positive answer to question(s) . .. (indicated by an appropriate number(s))
ZW	I require Port Medical Officer.. 'ZW 1' Port Medical Officer will be available at (time indicated).
ZY	You have health clearance.
ZZ	You should proceed to anchorage for health clearance (at place indicated). 'ZZ 1' Where is the anchorage for health clearance?
AL	I have a doctor on board.
AM	Have you a doctor?

Health clearances may be given wholly in plain language, partly in the above signal code and the remainder in plain language, or wholly in the above code.

6.4.3 Distress signals

A complete list of distress signals, as in Annex IV of the *International Regulations for Preventing Collisions at Sea*, is given in Section 2.1. Those which are more appropriate for yachts and small crafts are given in 8.3.10, together with notes on their use. It must be emphasised that distress signals must only be used when the boat is in serious and immediate danger, and when help is urgently required. If help is needed but the boat is not in immediate danger, the proper signal is 'V' (Victor) in the International Code, meaning 'I require assistance'. (See also 6.2.8 for selected groups from the International Code.)

6.4.4 Visual signals between UK shore stations and ships in distress

The following signals should be used if a vessel is in distress, or stranded off the coast of the United Kingdom.

(1) Acknowledgement of distress signal

By day. Orange smoke signal or combined light and sound signal (thunderlight) consisting of three single signals fired at about one minute intervals.
By night. White star rocket consisting of three single signals fired at about one minute intervals.

'You are seen – assistance will be given as soon as possible.' (Repetition has the same meaning.)

If necessary the day signals may be given at night, or the night signals by day.

(2) Landing signals for small boats with persons in distress

By day. Vertical motion of a white flag or the arms, or signalling the code letter 'K' (– · –) by light or sound.

'This is the best place to land'

By night. Vertical motion of a white light or flare, or signalling the code letter 'K' (− · −) by light or sound. An indication of direction may be given by placing a steady white light or flare at a lower level and in line with the observer. — 'This is the best place to land'

By day. Horizontal motion of a white flag or arms extended horizontally, or signalling the code letter 'S' (· · ·) by light or sound. — 'Landing here is highly dangerous'

By night. Horizontal motion of a white light or flare, or signalling the code letter 'S' (· · ·) by light or sound. — 'Landing here is highly dangerous'

By day. Horizontal motion of a white flag, followed by the placing of it in the ground and the carrying of another white flag in the direction indicated, and/or a white star-signal in the direction of a better landing place. Or signalling the code letter 'S' (· · ·) followed by the code letter 'R' (· − ·) if a better landing place is more to the right in the direction of approach, or by code letter 'L' (· − · ·) if a better landing place is more to the left in the direction of approach. — 'Landing here highly dangerous. A more favourable location for landing is in the direction indicated'

By night. Horizontal motion of a white flare or light, followed by the placing of the white light or flare on the ground and the carrying of another white light or flare in the direction to be indicated, and/or a white star-signal in the direction towards the better landing place. Or signalling the code letter 'S' (· · ·) followed by the code letter 'R' (· − ·) if a better landing place is more to the right in the direction of approach, or by code letter 'L' (· − · ·) if a better landing place is more to the left in the direction of approach. — 'Landing here highly dangerous. A more favourable location for landing is in the direction indicated'

(3) Signals used in connection with shore life-saving apparatus

By day. Vertical motion of a white flag or the arms
By night. Vertical motion of a white light or flare. — In general 'Affirmative'. Specifically - 'Rocket line is held' 'Tail block is made fast' 'Man is in breeches buoy' 'Haul away'

By day. Horizontal motion of a white flag or arms extended horizontally.
By night. Horizontal motion of a white light or flare. — In general 'Negative'. Specifically 'Slack away' 'Avast hauling'

(4) Signals to be used to warn a vessel standing into danger

The International Code signals 'U' or 'NF', or the letter 'U' (· · −) flashed by lamp or made by foghorn, whistle etc. — 'You are running into danger'

If necessary the attention of the vessel may be called to these signals by a white flare, a rocket showing white stars on bursting, or an explosive signal.

6.4.5 Signals used by aircraft on SAR operations

With the increasing use now made of aircraft in search and rescue (SAR) it is important that yachtsmen can recognise and understand certain signals which may be used.

Search procedures

The pattern of search and the spacing between tracks flown by an aircraft depends upon the visibility, the characteristics of the object being searched (e.g. yacht or liferaft) and the type, if any, of electronic search aid used. Unless distressed personnel can indicate their position to the aircraft the search may be valueless.

An aircraft normally flies through the search area at 900–1500m (3000–5000ft), or below cloud, firing a green Very cartridge approximately every five to ten minutes and at each turning point. When a green flare is sighted it is most important that the following action is taken:

(1) Wait for the glare of the green flare to die out.
(2) Fire one red flare.
(3) Fire another red flare after about 20 seconds (this enables the aircraft to line up on the bearing).
(4) Fire a third red flare when the aircraft is overhead, or appears to be going badly offcourse.

It is important to note that, in order to comply with the above, a boat or liferaft should carry at least three red flares. Should the aircraft be diverted to the search from another task it may fire flares of another colour (except red). Do not fire pyrotechnics aimed directly at aircraft, particularly helicopters overhead.

RAF aircraft diverted to SAR are equipped with some or all of UHF, VHF, HF WT/RT and MF. Royal Navy SAR helicopters carry HF/VHF/UHF RT equipment, and other Royal Navy aircraft carry HF/UHF RT. RAF search aircraft on SAR operations usually maintain the following continuous watches:

(1) HF WT communications with Rescue Co-ordination Centre, 5695 or 3095kHz.

(2) MF watch (with DF) on 500kHz. This is a listening watch only, the aircraft cannot transmit on this frequency.

(3) RT watch on 121.5 or 243MHz. The aircraft also have homing facilities on 243MHz and in some cases on 121.5MHz and Marine Band FM frequencies.

Designated SAR helicopters in the UK can communicate with RNLI lifeboats, HM Coastguard, Coast radio stations etc on the VHF/FM marine distress calling and safety frequency Channel 16, and on working frequencies.

United Kingdom and most European SAR aircraft use voice call signs comprising the word 'Rescue' followed by two or three numerals.

Directing signals

The following signals may be used by SAR aircraft to direct ships towards another ship, aircraft or person in distress.

(1) In sequence, the aircraft circles the ship at least once. It then crosses low, ahead of the ship, opening and closing the throttle or changing the propeller pitch. Finally it heads in the direction in which the ship is to be directed. The signal may be repeated.	The aircraft is directing the ship towards the ship or aircraft in distress.
(2) The aircraft passes close astern of the ship, at low altitude, rocking the wings or opening and closing the throttle or changing the propeller pitch. The aircraft may repeat the signal as necessary.	The aircraft is indicating that the assistance of the ship is no longer required.

6.4.6 Port signals

General

On the Continent signals to control port or harbour traffic are to some extent standardised, but not at present in the United Kingdom. Signals for individual harbours are shown in Chapter 10 of *The Macmillan & Silk Cut Nautical Almanac*. A new system of International Port Traffic Signals is being introduced – see 6.4.7 – but the process will be gradual.

Increasing use is being made of VHF radio for port operations, pilot services and traffic management; VHF channels used for individual harbours are shown in Chapter 10 of *The Macmillan & Silk Cut Nautical Almanac*. Where appropriate, call on the indicated working frequency – usually Channel 12 or Channel 14. Often however it is very helpful just to listen on the right frequency. Radiotelephone procedures are discussed in Section 6.6.

The following groups in the *International Code of Signals* refer to port operations:

UH	Can you lead me into port?
UL	All vessels should proceed to sea as soon as possible owing to danger in port.
UM	The harbour (or port indicated) is closed to traffic.
UN	You may enter harbour immediately (or at time indicated).
UO	You must not enter harbour.
UP	Permission to enter harbour is urgently requested. I have an emergency case.
UQ	You should wait outside the harbour (or river mouth). 'UQ 1' You should wait outside the harbour until daylight.
UR	My estimated time of arrival (at place indicated) is (time indicated). 'UR 1' What is your estimated time of arrival (at place indicated)?
RZ 1	You should not proceed out of harbour/anchorage.
RV 2	You should proceed into port.

British Isles

The Ministry of Defence might, in certain circumstances, control entry to special ports, and institute an Examination Service for vessels which approach them. In such cases, signals as follows may be displayed ashore or by Examination Vessels or by Examination Vessels or Traffic Control Vessels in the approaches:

By day	By night	Meaning
Three red balls shown vertically	Three flashing red lights shown vertically	Entry to port prohibited
	Three green lights shown vertically	Entry to port permitted
A blue flag	Red, green, red lights shown vertically	Movement of shipping within the port or anchorage prohibited

Vessels of the Examination Service wear a special flag, with a blue border and a square in the centre – the top half white and the bottom half red.

France

The following signals are in general use in France. There are two systems – the simplified code, used where there is not much traffic, and the full code.

(1) *Simplified code.*

By day	By night	Meaning
A red flag	A red light	Entry prohibited

A green flag	A green light	Departure prohibited
A red flag above a green flag	A red light above a green light	Entry and departure prohibited

(2) *Full code*. Each of the following signals is displayed vertically, and should be read accordingly:

By day	By night	Meaning
A cone, point up between two balls	A white light, between two red lights	Entry prohibited
Two cones, points together, above another cone point down	A white light between two green lights	Departure prohibited
Two cones, points together, above a ball	A white light above a red light and below a green light	Entry and departure prohibited

(3) In addition to the usual traffic signals, the following special signals may be shown on occasions:

By day	By night	Meaning
Three red balls, vertically	Three all-round flashing red lights, vertically	Port closed (emergency signal)
The appropriate International Code signal	Three all-round green lights, vertically	Port open

Netherlands

In the event of government control of entry to Dutch harbours, the following signals indicate that entry is prohibited, and that a yacht should proceed towards the examination vessel flying the same signal.

By day	By night
Three red balls, disposed vertically or:	Three red lights, disposed vertically or:
Two cones, points together, over a ball	Three lights, disposed vertically, green over red over white

Germany

The following signals are commonly used in Germany.

Signals at fixed bridges	Meaning
Two diamonds red and white in halves	Indicate limits of navigable width
Yellow diamond over centre of passage	Passage permitted in both directions
Two yellow diamonds, horizontally disposed	Passage permitted in one direction; traffic coming from opposite side stopped

Sound signals at moveable bridges, locks etc	Meaning
· · · ·	Passage or entry forbidden
— —	Please open bridge or lock, or raise lift bridge to first step
— — ·	Please open lift bridge to full extent
— — · —	Vessel proceeding seawards may pass or enter
— — · · —	Vessel proceeding inwards may pass or enter
— — — — —	Channel is closed

Light signals (R-red, W-white, G-green)

R	R	Passage or entry forbidden
	R	Be prepared to pass or enter
W R	R	Bridge closed or down; vessels which can pass under the available clearance may proceed, but beware of oncoming traffic which may have a right of way
W R	W R	Lift bridge will remain at first step; vessels which can pass under the available vertical clearance may proceed
G	G	Passage or entry permitted; oncoming traffic stopped
W G	G	Passage permitted, but beware of oncoming traffic which may have right of way
	R	Bridge, lock or flood barrage closed to navigation
R		Exit from lock forbidden
G		Exit from lock permitted

6.4.7 International port traffic signals

An international system of port signals is being gradually introduced, but their general adoption is likely to take many years, and some existing signals may be retained indefinitely.

The rules for the new system, which is illustrated on page 62, are as follows:

(1) The main movement message given by a port traffic signal shall always comprise three lights, disposed vertically. No additional light shall be added to the column carrying the main message. (The fact that the main message always consists of three vertical lights allows the mariner to recognise it as a traffic signal, and not lights of navigational significance.)
(2) Red lights indicate 'Do not proceed'.
(3) Green lights indicate 'Proceed, subject to the conditions stipulated'.
    Note that, to avoid confusion, red and green lights are never displayed together.
(4) A single yellow light, displayed to the left of the column carrying main messages Nos 2 or 5, at the level of the upper light, may be used to indicate that 'Vessels which can safely navigate outside the main channel need not comply with the main message'. This signal is of obvious significance to yachtsmen.
(5) Signals which are auxiliary to the main message may be devised by local authorities. Such auxiliary signals should employ only white and/or yellow lights, and should be displayed to the right of the column carrying the main message.

From the above it is evident that the basic signals are simple, and easy to memorise. Ports with complex entrances and much traffic may need many auxiliary signals, which will have to be documented, but smaller harbours with less traffic may only need one or two of the basic signals, such as 'Vessels shall not proceed' and 'Vessels may proceed, two way traffic'.

Some signals may be omni-directional – exhibited to all vessels simultaneously; others must be directional, and be shown either to vessels entering or to vessels leaving harbour.

Signal No 5 is based on the assumption that some other means of communication such as VHF radio, signal lamp, loud hailer, or auxiliary signal will be used to inform a vessel that she may specifically proceed.

The 'Serious Emergency' signal must be flashing, at least 60 flashes per minute. All other signals must be either fixed or slow occulting (the latter useful when background glare is a problem). A mixture of fixed and occulting lights must not be used.

6.4.8 Visual storm signals

Visual gale warning signals are now only displayed at a very few places around the British Isles when a gale is expected within 12 hours, or is already blowing, in the adjacent sea area. The signals consist of black cones, point up for a gale from a northerly quarter or point down for a gale from a southerly quarter.

For further information on visual storm signals see 7.6.17. Official visual storm signals have been discontinued in the UK, but they are still shown in a few places by private arrangement.

6.4.9 Tide signals

At some French ports tide signals are displayed, indicating the height of the tide above chart datum. The signals are shown by three different shapes (or lights by night) as follows:

By day	By night	Meaning
A cone, point down	A green light	0.2m (or about 8in)
A cylinder	A red light	1.0m (or about 3.3ft)
A ball	A white light	5.0m (or about 16.4ft)

The three different shapes are disposed horizontally with cones to the left, and balls to the right of the cylinders when viewed from seaward; if more than one of each shape is used they are disposed vertically. Thus three cones, three cylinders, and one ball signify 8.6m. The night signals are disposed in a similar way.

Other signals are used to indicate the state of the tide, as follows:

By day	By night	Meaning
An elongated cone, point up	A green light over white light	Tide rising
A white flag with a black St Andrew's cross	Two white lights, horizontally	High water
An elongated cone, point down	A white light over green light	Tide falling
A blue pendant	Two green lights, horizontally	Low water

6.5 Radio receivers

6.5.1 Requirements for seagoing yachts

The advantages and uses of radiotelephones are discussed in Section 6.6, but any seagoing yacht should at least have a radio receiver. The very minimum requirement is to receive the shipping forecasts broadcast by the BBC on 198kHz (1515m). In many yachts this facility is provided by a set which is also used for direction finding.

6.5.2 Frequencies

It is becoming increasingly common to specify a radio transmission by its frequency rather than its wavelength; this has been the practice in commercial and marine radio for many years, and it is useful to understand the relationship between the two descriptions.

Frequencies are expressed in kiloHertz (kHz), which used to be called kilocycles per second. For frequencies higher than 3000kHz, the term MegaHertz (MHz) is used. One MHz = 1000kHz.

$$\text{Wavelength (metres)} \times \text{Frequency (kHz)} = 3 \times 10^5$$

From this formula it can be seen, for example, that 1500 metres equals 200kHz, and that 200 metres equals 1500kHz.

The various frequency bands in use in marine radio are:

Frequency	Band	Wavelength (metres)
Low (LF)	3–300kHz	10,000–1000
Medium (MF)	30–3000kHz	1000–100
High (HF)	3–30MHz	100–10
Very High (VHF)	30–300MHz	10–1

Typical frequencies (in kHz) covered by a yacht's radio receiver are: 150–400 for radiobeacons, and for shipping forecasts; 550–1600 for 'Medium Wave' broadcast stations; 1600–4000 for receiving radiotelephone messages (e.g. from British Telecom coast radio stations – see 6.6.9).

6.5.3 Weather bulletins
Full details of the various methods of receiving weather information from the radio are given in Section 7.6.

6.5.4 Radio installation
Marine radios need proper, professional installation if they are to perform efficiently and this is often overlooked. Bad aerials are often a cause of trouble. Attention must also be given to the suppression of electrical equipment in the boat; alternators, pumps, fluorescent lighting, windscreen wipers, ignition systems, revolution counters, and even rotating propeller shafts can all cause interference.

6.6 Radiotelephony

6.6.1 Radiotelephones – introduction
The radiotelephone is the modern way to communicate at sea, and there are five distinct types of concern to yachtsmen:
(1) Long Range High Frequency (HF) Service. World-wide communication is provided through Portishead Radio, but HF sets are large and costly so they are only appropriate for yachts making extended cruises.
(2) Medium Frequency (MF) equipment has a range of 200 miles (322km) or more, operating in the 2MHz band. MF sets must be single

sideband (SSB). Double sideband transmissions are prohibited except for emergency-only sets on 2182kHz. For modes of emission see 6.6.6, and for SSB see 6.6.7.
(3) Very High Frequency (VHF) equipment has a range rather more than line of sight between the aerials concerned, but is much cheaper than MF (or HF), simple to install, and also relatively free from interference. The number of VHF shore stations is steadily increasing. See 6.6.4.
(4) Citizens' Band (CB) radio is not a real substitute for VHF afloat, because it has less range and because the CB emergency channel 09 is not monitored in the same way as VHF Channel 16 (see 6.6.4). But legal (CB 27/81) CB radio can be useful for club purposes in organising events, and for social chat. For further details see 6.6.19.
(5) Amateur (ham) radio has some marine applications, and is described in 6.6.20.

Similar considerations to those for radio receivers (6.5.4) apply in the installation of a radiotelephone. A good aerial is most important. Since the power of a VHF transmitter is limited to 25w it is desirable to use an antenna which will transmit the maximum beam in a horizontal direction, and not up into the sky. This, however, can be overdone, so that there is a loss in signal strength when the boat heels appreciably. The antenna must be matched to the transmitter, with the right impedance, expressed in terms of the 'voltage standing wave ratio' which should be as near unity as possible over the range of frequencies employed. Connecting cables must be kept as short as possible (consistent with placing the antenna as high as possible), and be of good co-axial cable: this should normally be 6.5mm ($\frac{1}{4}$in), although 13mm ($\frac{1}{2}$in) may be required for some masthead installations. In the event of dismasting, it should be possible to use an emergency aerial rigged on deck.

Good suppression of all electrical equipment is essential, and should meet the requirements of BS1597, which defines the permitted interference over a frequency range of 15kHz to 100MHz.

The set itself should be mounted where it is accessible, but protected from spray and dampness. A waterproof extension speaker is useful at the steering position.

The battery should be as high as possible, remote from bilge water or from possible fire in the engine compartment, and it must be kept well charged.

MF and HF radiotelephones require some form of earthing arrangement, usually a metal plate in the bottom of the boat.

6.6.2 Radiotelephones – licences
The Radiocommunications Agency regulates the use of radio equipment installed or used on board, with the aim that all who use the airwaves can do so without transmissions being subject to

interference, particularly in emergencies. In general the regulations are contained in the International Radio Regulations and the Wireless Telegraphy Act 1949, as amended, which provides that a licence issued by the Secretary of State is required to install or use any radio apparatus on board a UK registered vessel or one whose moorings are predominantly in the UK. A licence is not needed for a radio receiving set.

From 1 April 1995 a new single licence was introduced, covering all types or combinations of radio equipment including VHF, MF, HF, UHF, satellite communications equipment, radar, on board repeater stations and Emergency Position Indicating Radio Beacons (EPIRBs) operating on 121.5/243 MHz, 406 MHz and 1.6 GHz.

Ship Radio Licences are distributed by Wray Castle, Ship Radio Licensing, PO Box 5, Ambleside, LA22 0BF. Tel: 015394 34662. Fax: 015394 34663, on behalf of the Radiocommunications Agency.

Licence fees (in 1995) are £22 for vessels used solely for pleasure, and £40 in all other cases.

Where transportable equipment is used on vessels which are not covered by a Ship Radio Licence, each item of transportable equipment must be separately licensed.

The revised licence documentation comprises a new version of the Licence Terms booklet, a new Licence Document (previously known as the Validation Document) and Licence Disk. You should destroy old documentation on receipt of a new licence.

Wray Castle collect information on licence holders carrying 406 MHz EPIRBs, to assist the Maritime Safety Agency (MSA) in maintaining their database for search and rescue purposes.

It is a condition of the licence that the equipment meets certain minimum standards in terms of spurious emissions, power output, frequency deviation etc. Before buying a set make sure that it has passed the Radiocommunications Agency Type Approval testing.

Authorised marine radio installations as above must be controlled by an operator holding an appropriate Certificate of Competence and Authority to Operate. The minimum standard is the Restricted (VHF Only) Radio Telephony Certificate of Competence. The Royal Yachting Association is responsible for the conduct of the examination for this certificate, and details can be obtained from them at RYA House, Romsey Road, Eastleigh, Hampshire SO50 9YA. Tel: (01703) 627400.

RYA booklet G22/91 gives advice on how to choose and use the equipment, and G26/89 contains details of the syllabus for the examination. At the examination it is essential to produce evidence of British nationality, and a passport-sized photograph.

Information on other certificates comes from the Radiocommunications Agency, Room 813, Waterloo Bridge House. Tel: 0171-215 2292.

A call sign/VSL (visual signal letters) is allocated when the vessel is first licensed for radio, and remains with the vessel despite change of ownership or change of name.

Channel M (157.850MHz) and Channel M2 (161.425MHz) are 'private' channels that pleasure craft are authorised to use when granted a Ship Radio Licence. Marinas or yacht clubs wishing to use Ch M or Ch M2, or the international Channel 80 (see 6.6.4) must apply for a Maritime Coastal Licence from the Maritime Business Radio Section, Radiocommunications Agency, Room 613, Waterloo Bridge House, Waterloo Road, London SE1 8UA. Tel: 0171-215 2137.

A licence is required regardless of whether the vessel is actually in use, since it is granted for establishing a station. If radio equipment is removed and stored a licence is not required, but it is necessary to apply for one if and when it is refitted. Callsigns are not transferable: it is necessary to apply for a new licence (and therefore a new callsign) when buying another vessel. If you sell your boat write to Wray Castle at address above to give details of the new owner, and return the old licence. Except as approved for a base station (above) a VHF set may only be used when afloat. Use on shore is illegal.

A Ship Radio Licence does not cover television for which a separate licence is required.

There are two other types of licence, other than the marine ones referred to above, that are relevant to yachts. They are:

(1) Citizens' Band (CB) Radio Licence. This is described in 6.6.19.
(2) Amateur Radio Licence, for amateur 'ham' radio, as described in 6.6.20.

6.6.3 Radiotelephones – general provisions

Apart from the licensing arrangements described in 6.6.2, there are various regulations governing RT (other than CB and amateur radio) afloat. They are contained in the *Handbook for Marine Radio Communication* (Lloyd's of London Press Ltd). Here is a brief summary.

(1) Operators are required to preserve the secrecy of correspondence, and not to divulge the contents of any transmissions which they may receive or intercept.
(2) Stations *must* identify themselves when transmitting. Coast stations (see 6.6.9) are normally identified by their geographical names followed by the word 'Radio', e.g. North Foreland Radio. Ship stations are identified by the name of the vessel, amplified where necessary to explain her nationality or occupation. Yacht call signs may be prefaced by the word 'Yacht', e.g. Yacht Seabird, when relevant.
(3) A yacht with a radiotelephone must carry the appropriate Ship Radio Licence; a copy of

Section 11 of the Post Office (Protection) Act, 1884;130 the certificate(s) of the operator(s); a Radiotelephone Log; a list of coast stations with which communications are likely to be conducted, showing watchkeeping hours, frequencies, charges, times of traffic lists etc.

(4) Except in cases of distress, coast stations control communications in their areas, and their instructions should be complied with. For a vessel in distress close to the coast, the nearest MRCC or MRSC becomes the co-ordinating station for the incident – see 8.4.2. and 8.4.7.

(5) While at sea a yacht may call other vessels, and she may call shore stations (or aircraft stations). Messages must not be transmitted to an address ashore except through a coast radio station (see 6.6.9). When in harbour she may not communicate with other vessels, but only with shore stations including a local Port Operations Service, coast station, or station by authorised private channel (e.g. Ch M or M2). Intership calls in harbour are allowed only concerning safety.

(6) It is most important that operators do not interfere with the working of other stations. Before transmitting, an operator must always listen on the appropriate frequency or channel in order to make sure that it is not already in use.

(7) It is forbidden to transmit unnecessary or superfluous signals. Test transmissions must not interfere with other stations, and must include the vessel's callsign.

(8) Absolute priority must be given to distress calls and messages. The transmission of false distress, safety or identification signals is strictly prohibited.

(9) The transmission of profane, indecent or obscene language is strictly forbidden.

(10) Under the regulations any vessel fitted with a radiotelephone should keep a radiotelephone log. The following entries should be made:
— the operator's name
— the time of arrival at and departure from ports, with names
— a summary of communications relating to distress, urgency and safety traffic
— a record of communications exchanged with coast stations and other ship stations
— a reference to any important service incidents (breakdowns of the apparatus)
— the boat's position, at least once each day.

6.6.4 VHF radio

The general subject of VHF radiotelephones for yachtsmen is well covered in RYA booklet G22, which gives the various procedures in detail.

VHF is limited to ranges slightly better than the line of sight between the aerials, so the yacht's aerial needs to be sited as high as possible. The maximum permitted output of a VHF set is 25 watts, and it pays to fit an efficient aerial in order to get the best performance. A low power output, normally one watt, is used for close range communication.

Most UK coast stations, and an increasing number of commercial and yachting harbours, are now fitted with VHF. So are the principal Coastguard stations and other elements of the rescue services.

The frequencies allocated by international agreement for marine VHF are in the range 156.00–174.00MHz. Channel 16 (156.80MHz) is used for distress and safety purposes, and for calling and answering. Once communication has been established the stations concerned must switch to an appropriate working frequency, except for safety matters.

All vessels at sea equipped with VHF are encouraged to keep watch on Ch 16, for safety reasons.

Although there are a total of 57 channels in the international marine VHF band, a small boat needs only about a dozen – the sort of number fitted in the cheaper sets.

Basic VHF sets are 'simplex' which means that they transmit and receive on the same frequency – so that it is not possible to speak and listen at the same time; the 'transmit' button blots out all reception. 'Semi-duplex' sets transmit and receive on two different frequencies, while fully 'duplex' sets can do this simultaneously – so that conversation is normal.

There are three main groups of frequencies, as shown below in order of preference. Certain channels can be used for more than one purpose.

(1) *Public correspondence* (for use with British Telecom coast radio stations). All these can be used for duplex working if the set is so equipped: Ch 26, 27, 25, 24, 23, 28, 4, 1, 3, 2, 7, 5, 84, 87, 86, 83, 85, 88, 61, 64, 65, 62, 66, 63, 60, 82, 78, 81.

(2) *Inter-ship*. These are all simplex channels: Ch 6, 8, 13, 9, 72, 73, 69, 77, 15, 17.

(3) *Port operations* (pilotage, tugs etc). The simplex channels are: Ch 12, 14, 11, 13, 9, 68, 71, 74, 69, 73, 17, and 15. Channels which can be used for duplex are: Ch 20, 22, 18, 19, 21, 5, 7, 2, 3, 1, 4, 78, 82, 79, 81, 80, 60, 63, 66, 62, 65, 64, 61, 84.

It should be explained that the original VHF channel spacings were 50kHz. In 1972 this was reduced to 25kHz, and additional frequencies were interleaved between the existing ones; this has resulted in the rather odd channel designations, since channels between 29 and 59 are allocated to other services.

Ch 70 (156.525MHz) is reserved for digital selective calling for distress and safety purposes. (GMDSS – see 6.6.18.)

Ch 0 (Zero), which is 156.00MHz, is a special channel reserved for communication between HM Coastguard and other rescue services such as lifeboats. It may only be fitted in a yacht if specially authorised by the Radiocommunications Agency in consultation with HM Coastguard.

Ch 10 (156.500MHz) is the Oil Pollution Channel.

Special channels are allocated for marinas, yacht clubs and race control. Ch 80 (Tx 161.625MHz Rx 157.025MHz) is the primary working channel between yachts and yacht harbours, with Ch M (157.85MHz) as a stand-by. Yacht clubs use Ch M2 (161.425MHz) for race control, with Ch M as a stand-by. Special authorisation is needed for the shoreside use of Ch M and Ch M2, see 6.6.2.

Ch 67 (156.375MHz) is an inter-ship channel allocated in this country to communications relating to yacht and small craft safety. The principal coastguard stations are fitted with this channel, which is accessed via Ch 16. When calling HM Coastguard, use the title of the local centre followed by 'Coastguard'. For example: 'Solent Coastguard'.

VHF sets

As can be understood from the number of different channels which are available for VHF communication, to take full advantage of the system a set should be chosen which can use a reasonable number – depending on the intended area of operation. If a boat is only to be used in one locality, then a dozen channels (which are the sort of number fitted in less expensive sets) can be sufficient, if they are sensibly selected.

TRANSMITTING FREQUENCIES IN THE 156–174 MHz BAND FOR STATIONS IN THE MARITIME MOBILE SERVICE

Channel	Ship stations	Coast stations	Inter ship	Single frequency	Two frequency	Public correspondence
60	156.025	160.625			●	●
01	156.050	160.650			●	●
61	156.075	160.675			●	●
02	156.100	160.700			●	●
62	156.125	160.725			●	●
03	156.150	160.750			●	●
63	156.175	160.775			●	●
04	156.200	160.800			●	●
64	156.225	160.825			●	●
05	156.250	160.850			●	●
65	156.275	160.875			●	●
06	156.300		●			
66	156.325	160.925			●	●
07	156.350	160.950			●	●
67	156.375	156.375	Small Ships Safety Channel			
08	156.400		●			
68	156.425	156.425		●		
09	156.450	156.450	●	●		
69	156.475	156.475	●	●		
10	156.500	156.500	Oil Pollution Channel			
70	156.525	156.525	Selective Calling (GMDSS)			
11	156.550	156.550		●		
71	156.575	156.575		●		
12	156.600	156.600		●		
72	156.625		●			
13	156.650	156.650	●	●		
73	156.675	156.675	●	●		
14	156.700	156.700		●		
74	156.725	156.725		●		
15	156.750	156.750	●	●		
75	Guard band 156.7625–156.7875 MHz					
16	156.800	156.800	DISTRESS Safety and Calling			
76	Guard band 156.8125–156.8375 MHz					
17	156.850	156.850	●	●		
77	156.875		●			
18	156.900	161.500			●	
78	156.925	161.525			●	●
19	156.950	161.550			●	
79	156.975	161.575			●	
20	157.000	161.600			●	
80	157.025	161.625			●	
21	157.050	161.650			●	
81	157.075	161.675			●	●
22	157.100	161.700			●	●
82	157.125	161.725			●	●
23	157.150	161.750				●
83	157.175	161.775				●
24	157.200	161.800				●
84	157.225	161.825			●	●
25	157.250	161.850				●
85	157.275	161.875				●
26	157.300	161.900				●
86	157.325	161.925				●
27	157.350	161.950				●
87	157.375	161.975				●
28	157.400	162.000				●
88	157.425	162.025				●

NOTES

1. For intership communication, those channels (i.e. Ch 06, 08, 72 and 77) assigned solely for this purpose should be used in preference to other frequencies. Ch 06 may however be used by ships and aircraft on SAR operations, when its use for other purposes must be avoided.
2. Ch 10, 67 and 72 may be used by ships, aircraft and land stations for SAR co-ordination and for anti-pollution operations.
3. In the UK, Ch 67 is allocated as a Small Craft Safety Channel, for use by small craft and HM Coastguard. Ch 80 is used as the primary working channel between yachts and yacht harbours, with a private channel 157.85MHz referred to as Ch M as a stand-by. Ch M2 (161.425MHz) is used by yacht clubs for race control.
4. Ch 70 is reserved for digital selective calling in connection with the Global Maritime Distress and Safety System (GMDSS).

It is mandatory to have Ch 06 as well as Ch 16. Most boats will probably need Ch 12 and Ch 14 for port operations. Ch 80 is very useful if the boat is kept in a marina which operates this frequency. Ch 67, the Small Craft Safety Channel, is a great benefit in a boat which is used for coastal cruising. In a 12-channel set this leaves six further channels to be chosen – say Ch 08 as an alternative inter-ship channel, and the others from the public correspondence (ship–shore) channels depending on which coast stations are most likely to be used.

A refinement available with some sets is 'dual watch facility', whereby two channels can be monitored by the receiver at the same time: one of these should be Ch 16, and the other can be selected as required. It is also possible to obtain an attachment which will scan a larger number of channels.

Another operational extra available is selective calling (Selcall), which dispenses with the need to monitor traffic lists and allows the set to be used almost like a telephone ashore. When a message is to be passed to the yacht, the coast station concerned transmits a specially coded signal which alerts a decoder attached to the receiver, triggering an audible alarm and an indicator light. In addition to alerting vessels for individual calls, a special signal also gives warning of 'All Ships' calls for safety and urgency messages about to be transmitted by coast stations.

When Selcall is to be fitted to existing equipment, application must be made to the Radiocommunications Agency at Waterloo Bridge House for a Selcall number, or with a new set it can be requested when applying for the licence. Coast stations keep on file the Selcall numbers for all vessels so allocated.

Autolink RT is a service provided by British Telecom to give direct dialling from ship to shore into national and international telephone networks, and is described in 6.6.11.

Using special equipment (IRMA), telephone numbers can be direct-dialled through French VHF coast stations.

6.6.5 MF and HF radio

It is convenient to consider Medium Frequency (MF) and High Frequency (HF) together, because there are basic similarities and because sets are available which overlap the MF band (1.6–4.2MHz) and the HF band (4–25MHz). MF radiotelephones provide communication at ranges of up to 200 miles (320km) or more – considerably greater than can be achieved by VHF. An HF set can give worldwide coverage. But MF/HF sets are larger and heavier than VHF, consume more power, and are more expensive.

As explained in 6.6.7, MF/HF sets must now be single sideband (SSB), and must be type-approved for a licence to be obtained. As for VHF sets, a large number of channels are available at different frequencies. The MF international RT distress frequency is 2182kHz, and is used for distress calls and traffic, signals of emergency position-indicating radiobeacons, the urgency signal and urgency messages, the navigational warning signal, and for the safety signal. UK and many foreign coast stations keep watch on 2182kHz. There is a silence period on this frequency for three minutes commencing every hour and half-hour. During these silence periods all transmissions except distress, urgency and safety communications must cease on 2182kHz.

HF radio

The United Kingdom long range (HF) radiotelephone service is provided by Portishead Radio in Somerset, and gives worldwide coverage. The station controls transmitters at Rugby and reception at Somerton in Somerset.

The channels assigned to Portishead Radio are listed in *The Macmillan & Silk Cut Nautical Almanac*. For mode of transmission R3E (SSB reduced carrier) or J3E (SSB suppressed carrier) working is mandatory in both directions, but on channel 1201 J3E should be used whenever possible, and is the preferred mode for all transmissions. A yacht should be able to use all the channels.

Watch is maintained on bands that are chosen according to the radio conditions from 4, 8, 12, 16 and 22MHz. In general watch is set on higher bands during daylight and on lower bands during darkness. The bands in use are announced after the traffic lists, and major changes are notified during the previous week. A 24-hour watch is kept on the 8MHz band. If traffic so warrants, Portishead Radio opens further channels that are clear of interference.

The current optimum transmitting frequency guide is available on radiotelex from Portishead Radio Databank facility. This predicts at two-hour intervals the best frequency band for contacting Portishead from 25 points around the world. The figures are based on a monthly mean average of predicted conditions, so actual conditions experienced on any one day may not tally and it is essential that the information be checked by monitoring. Select the maritime frequency band at or next below the optimum, listen to the bands either side and use whichever sounds loudest. The letter X in the predictions means that it is not possible to predict a band, but does not imply that communication is impossible.

The table also shows the IF2 index – a measure of the ionosphere's ability to reflect radio raves, ranging from −30 when conditions are very poor to +180 when they are very good. These changes follow an eleven-year cycle.

In general, long distance contacts are better using the highest possible frequency when the path is entirely, or mostly, in daylight. The lagging effect of ionisation allows a station which has just entered darkness to communicate on the daylight high frequencies during the first few hours of darkness. Deep fading of a signal which is strong at peaks usually indicates that a lower frequency should be used. Conversely, if the signal is gradually falling into the noise level the frequency should be increased.

When making a final choice of channel it may help to relate the likely delay with the turn numbers being issued to other callers. When the channel is disengaged or when a call is invited, make a call quoting callsign and name. A short call should suffice for establishing communication. If more than one call is made, cut any carrier between calls. Do not tune the transmitter or make a call when traffic working is in progress between Portishead Radio and another ship. After contact it is usual to continue working on the same channel, but to equalise delays you may be diverted to another. To save time, be sure to tune your receiver to the Portishead Radio transmissions. If you expect a long contact time, say so at the outset. During contact do not use a loudspeaker which may introduce feedback howl. If asked to change channel and contact is not made on the new channel, you will be recalled on the original one and you should not lose your original turn.

Traffic lists are broadcast every H+00 on the primary channel in each band that is open. Callsigns are broadcast of all vessels having outstanding radiotelephone bookings on hand. Ships at extreme range, for example in the Pacific, or having urgent or Medico-type traffic, may arrange schedules at mutually convenient times. Medico is a free service.

6.6.6 Modes of emission
As already discussed in 4.5.7, intelligence is impressed upon a radio signal in various ways – by employing different modes of emission. Examples of those most commonly used in marine radio are given below:

A1A Continuous wave telegraphy, Morse code.
A2A Telegraphy by the on-off keying of a tone modulated carrier, Morse code: double sideband.
H2A Telegraphy by the on-off keying of a tone modulated carrier, Morse code: single sideband, full carrier.
A3E Telephony using amplitude modulation: double sideband.
R3E Telephony using amplitude modulation: single sideband, reduced carrier.
J3E Telephony using amplitude modulation: single sideband, suppressed carrier.
H3E Telephony using amplitude modulation: single sideband, full carrier.
F1B Telegraphy using frequency modulation: Narrow band direct printing (Telex).
F3E Telephony using frequency modulation (Sound broadcasting).
FXX Cases not covered by F1B, F3E nor frequency modulation facsimile, in which the main carrier is frequency modulated.

6.6.7 Single sideband (SSB)
Except for distress purposes, it is now illegal to use double sideband (DSB) transmissions. The old DSB signal consisted of three components – the carrier wave and two speech information sidebands, one on each side of the carrier, thus occupying a fairly broad band. In single sideband (SSB), the carrier and one sideband (usually the lower) are suppressed, thus reducing the width to the upper sideband only. This therefore reduces the band width, and greatly reduces interference with adjacent channels. Also, whereas previously the output power of a transmitter was divided between three components, it is now concentrated on one sideband, thus increasing power output.

A3E DSB transmissions are now prohibited on all channels, except for Emergency-Only equipment using 2182kHz.

H3E full carrier SSB working should be used for calling and listening on 2182kHz, and for all casualty working between ship and shore.

R3E reduced carrier SSB working is seldom used in practice. It is permitted, but tends to be used only at the request of a receiving station which has difficulty in resolving an incoming signal. The injection of partial carrier allows a finer tune on the carrier. It is then usual to request return to J3E – see below.

J3E fully suppressed carrier, SSB working is compulsory on all working frequencies.

All Casualty and other broadcasts on 2182kHz are made in the H3E mode. All other broadcasts (i.e. Weather Bulletins, Gale Warnings and Navigational Warnings) on working channels are made in the J3E mode, as are all link calls and other transmissions on working channels.

In the event of having to make a Distress Call, you are permitted to use any means at your disposal to attract attention. This means that an old DSB set can still be used for Distress working, but only for this purpose. In modern sets H3E is used when 2182kHz is selected.

If using French documentation, the term for SSB is BLU (Bandes Latérale Unique); and for Dutch it is EZB (Enkel Zyband).

6.6.8 General procedures
The following procedures in general apply to all radiotelephones (other than CB). Except for distress, urgency or safety messages, communications between a ship and coast station are controlled by the coast station; ship stations must comply accordingly. Between two ship stations, the station called controls the working, but if a coast station intervenes both ship stations must comply with its instructions.

Before transmitting, a station must first listen to ensure it will not interfere with communications already in progress, and if necessary await an appropriate break. Apart from distress, urgency or safety communications, calling and signals preparatory to the exchange of traffic should not exceed one minute when using 2182kHz (MF) or Ch 16 (VHF).

Calling procedure

To make a call, the calling station must use a frequency on which the other station keeps watch. Normally a ship station calls a coast station, and the frequencies/channels to be used are given in *The Macmillan & Silk Cut Nautical Almanac*.

However a coast station may call a ship station for which it has traffic if it knows the ship is within its area.

A call consists of:

— the name or identification of the station(s) called, not more than three times;
— the words THIS IS (or DE spoken as DELTA ECHO in case of language difficulties);
— the name or identification of the calling station, not more than three times.

For VHF communication the name of the station called need only be given once, and that of the calling station twice. When contact is made the name need only be transmitted once.

If a station does not reply, the call may be repeated at three-minute intervals — assuming that this does not interfere with any communication in progress. Where reliable VHF communication is practicable, the calling ship station may repeat the call as soon as it is known that other traffic has terminated.

Replying to calls

A reply is made on the frequency upon which the calling station keeps watch, unless it has specified another frequency. The exchange of identities is made in a similar form to the initial call. If the station is unable to accept traffic immediately it instructs the other station accordingly — 'WAIT . . . MINUTES', or if other ships are waiting, 'YOUR TURN IS NUMBER . . .'

When a station receives a call intended for it, but is uncertain of the identity of the calling station, it replies as follows:

— 'STATION CALLING . . .' (insert name of called station). 'THIS IS . . .' (insert name of called station). 'REPEAT YOUR CALL – OVER'.

Agreement on working frequency/channel

If the station called agrees with the working channel proposed by the calling station, in the reply to the call it should indicate that from then on it will listen on that working channel and also state the working channel which it will itself use. If it does not agree with the working channel proposed it should indicate a suitable alternative.

'All Ships' broadcasts

Information about gale warnings, navigational warnings etc. for general promulgation from coast stations is generally addressed to 'All Ships' or 'All Stations'. Such a message does not require any reply or acknowledgement.

Voice communication

Before making a radiotelephone call it is important to decide exactly what needs to be said; for those who are inexperienced it is advisable to write the message down, rather as one would write out a telegram. Clear and distinct speech is very important. The voice should be pitched a little higher than normal for best results, avoiding any tendency to drop the pitch at the ends of phrases. Speak directly into the microphone, held a few inches from the face, about as loud as for normal conversation. Speak clearly, and emphasise weak syllables. The rate of speaking should be steady, but complicated words or figures should be given more slowly than other parts of the message particularly if they need to be written down the other end — and may be repeated.

Names or important words should be spelled out by the phonetic table given in 6.2.4. It is normally not necessary to use the full phonetic spelling for figures, as in 6.2.4, but the following pronunciations are helpful:

Numeral	Pronunciation	Numeral	Pronunciation
0	ZE-RO	5	FIFE
1	WUN	6	SIX
2	TOO	7	SEV-en
3	TREE	8	AIT
4	FOW-er	9	NINE-er

Prowords (procedure words)

In RT communication it is important to know certain prowords, which have these meanings:

ACKNOWLEDGE	'Have you received and understood?'
CONFIRM	'My version is . . . is that correct?'
CORRECTION	Spoken during a message, means 'An error has been made in this transmission; the correct version is . . .'
I SAY AGAIN	'I repeat' (normally important words or numerals in the message).
I SPELL	'I will spell out the next part of the message phonetically'
OUT	End of work
OVER	'I have completed this part of my message and am inviting you to reply'
RECEIVED	Receipt acknowledged
SAY AGAIN	Repeat your message (or portion indicated)
STATION CALLING	Used when a station is uncertain of the identity of a station which is calling

6.6.9 Coast radio stations

British Telecom (BT) operates a number of coast radio stations at strategic places around the British Isles. Similar facilities are provided in other countries.

Flag Etiquette – see also Chapter 6 (6.8)

White Ensign

Blue Ensign

Red Ensign

Defaced Blue Ensign

Defaced Red Ensign

Club Burgee

Commodore's Flag

Vice-Commodore

Rear-Commodore

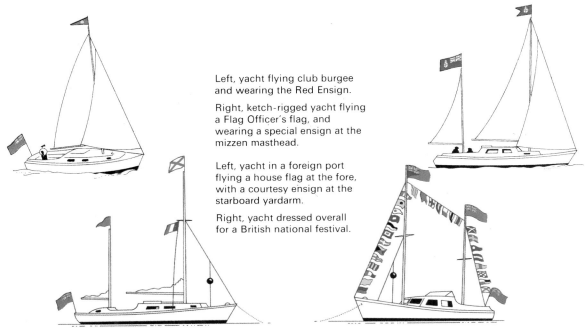

Left, yacht flying club burgee and wearing the Red Ensign.

Right, ketch-rigged yacht flying a Flag Officer's flag, and wearing a special ensign at the mizzen masthead.

Left, yacht in a foreign port flying a house flag at the fore, with a courtesy ensign at the starboard yardarm.

Right, yacht dressed overall for a British national festival.

International Code of Signals
Code Flags, Phonetic Alphabet, Morse Symbols and Single-letter Signals

Notes:
1. Single letter signals may be made by any method of signalling. Those marked * when made by sound must comply with the *International Regulations for Preventing Collisions at Sea*, Rules 34 and 35.
2. Signals 'K' and 'S' have special meanings as landing signals for small boats with persons in distress.
3. In the phonetic alphabet, the syllables to be emphasised are in italics.

A   Alfa   (*AL* FAH)

I have a diver down; keep well clear at slow speed

*B   Bravo   (*BRAH* VOH)

I am taking in, or discharging, or carrying dangerous goods

*C   Charlie   (*CHAR* LEE)

Yes (affirmative or 'The significance of the previous group should be read in the affirmative)

*D   Delta   (*DELL* TAH)

Keep clear of me; I am manoeuvring with difficulty

*E   Echo   (*ECK* OH)

I am altering my course to starboard

F   Foxtrot   (*FOKS* TROT)

I am disabled; communicate with me

*G   Golf   (*GOLF*)

I require a pilot. When made by fishing vessels operating in close proximity on the fishing grounds it means: I am hauling nets

*H   Hotel   (HOH *TELL*)

I have a pilot on board

Code and Answering Pendant

*I   India   (*IN* DEE AH)

I am altering my course to port

J   Juliett   (*JEW* LEE *ETT*)

I am on fire and have dangerous cargo on board: keep well clear of me

K   Kilo   (*KEY* LOH)

I wish to communicate with you

L   Lima   (*LEE* MAH)

You should stop your vessel instantly

*M   Mike   (MIKE)

My vessel is stopped and making no way through the water

N   November   (NO *VEM* BER)

No (negative or 'The significance of the previous group should be read in the negative'). This signal may be given only visually or by sound

O   Oscar   (*OSS* CAH)

Man overboard

P   Papa   (PAH *PAH*)

In harbour: all persons should report on board as the vessel is about to proceed to sea. **At sea**: it may be used by fishing vessels to mean 'My nets have come fast upon an obstruction'

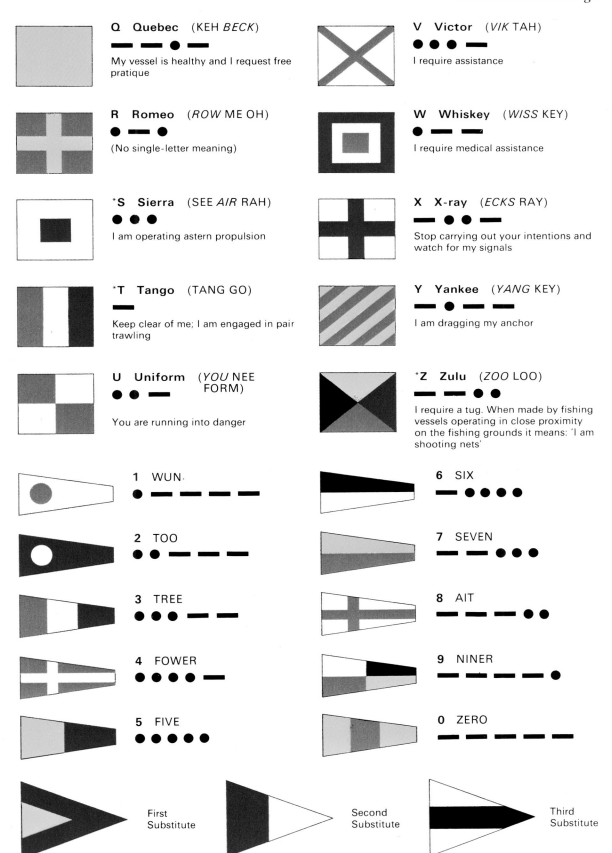

Q Quebec (KEH *BECK*)
● ● ●
My vessel is healthy and I request free pratique

R Romeo (*ROW* ME OH)
● ▬ ●
(No single-letter meaning)

***S Sierra** (SEE *AIR* RAH)
● ● ●
I am operating astern propulsion

***T Tango** (TANG GO)
▬
Keep clear of me; I am engaged in pair trawling

U Uniform (*YOU* NEE FORM)
● ● ▬
You are running into danger

V Victor (*VIK* TAH)
● ● ●
I require assistance

W Whiskey (*WISS* KEY)
● ▬ ▬
I require medical assistance

X X-ray (*ECKS* RAY)
▬ ● ● ▬
Stop carrying out your intentions and watch for my signals

Y Yankee (*YANG* KEY)
▬ ● ▬ ▬
I am dragging my anchor

***Z Zulu** (*ZOO* LOO)
▬ ▬ ● ●
I require a tug. When made by fishing vessels operating in close proximity on the fishing grounds it means: 'I am shooting nets'

1 WUN
● ▬ ▬ ▬ ▬

2 TOO
● ● ▬ ▬ ▬

3 TREE
● ● ● ▬ ▬

4 FOWER
● ● ● ● ▬

5 FIVE
● ● ● ● ●

6 SIX
▬ ● ● ● ●

7 SEVEN
▬ ▬ ● ● ●

8 AIT
▬ ▬ ▬ ● ●

9 NINER
▬ ▬ ▬ ▬ ●

0 ZERO
▬ ▬ ▬ ▬ ▬

First Substitute

Second Substitute

Third Substitute

National Maritime Flags

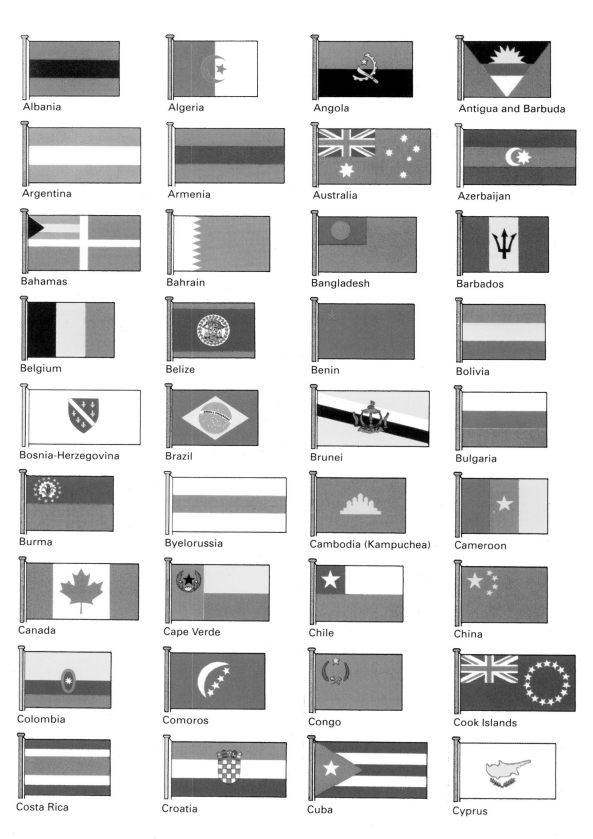

Albania

Algeria

Angola

Antigua and Barbuda

Argentina

Armenia

Australia

Azerbaijan

Bahamas

Bahrain

Bangladesh

Barbados

Belgium

Belize

Benin

Bolivia

Bosnia-Herzegovina

Brazil

Brunei

Bulgaria

Burma

Byelorussia

Cambodia (Kampuchea)

Cameroon

Canada

Cape Verde

Chile

China

Colombia

Comoros

Congo

Cook Islands

Costa Rica

Croatia

Cuba

Cyprus

National Maritime Flags

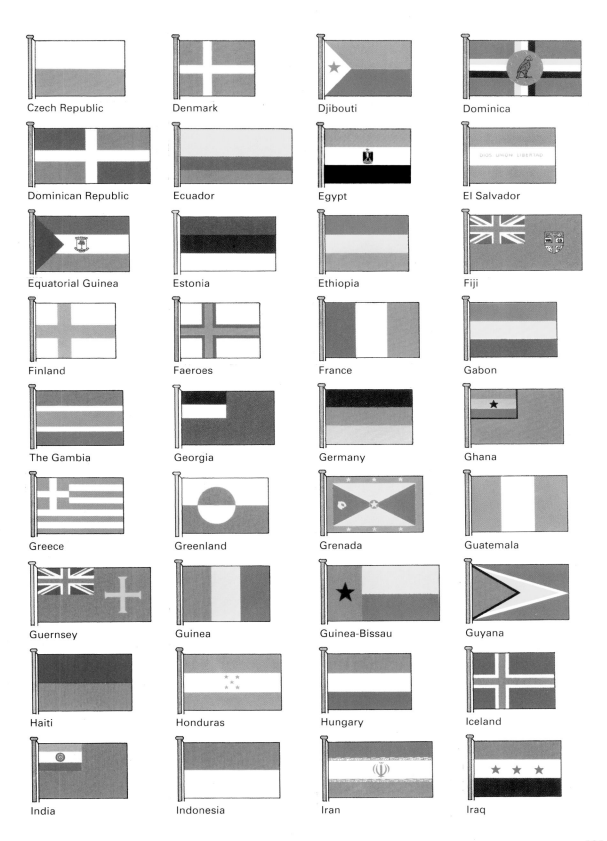

Czech Republic

Denmark

Djibouti

Dominica

Dominican Republic

Ecuador

Egypt

El Salvador

Equatorial Guinea

Estonia

Ethiopia

Fiji

Finland

Faeroes

France

Gabon

The Gambia

Georgia

Germany

Ghana

Greece

Greenland

Grenada

Guatemala

Guernsey

Guinea

Guinea-Bissau

Guyana

Haiti

Honduras

Hungary

Iceland

India

Indonesia

Iran

Iraq

National Maritime Flags

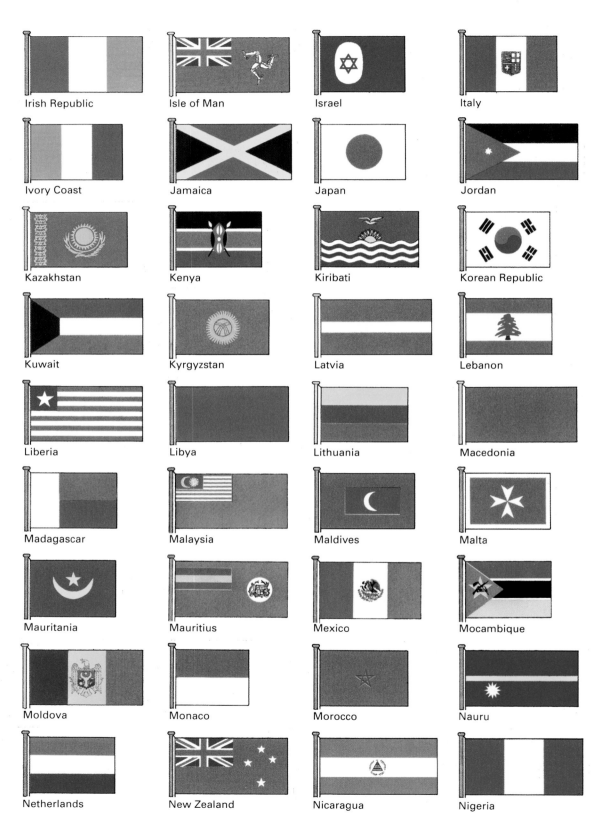

Irish Republic	Isle of Man	Israel	Italy
Ivory Coast	Jamaica	Japan	Jordan
Kazakhstan	Kenya	Kiribati	Korean Republic
Kuwait	Kyrgyzstan	Latvia	Lebanon
Liberia	Libya	Lithuania	Macedonia
Madagascar	Malaysia	Maldives	Malta
Mauritania	Mauritius	Mexico	Mocambique
Moldova	Monaco	Morocco	Nauru
Netherlands	New Zealand	Nicaragua	Nigeria

National Maritime Flags

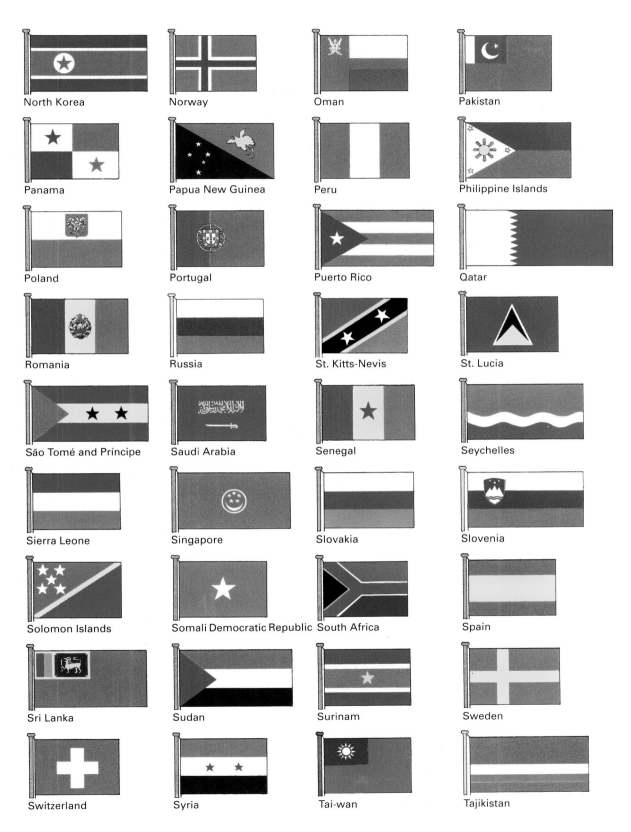

North Korea

Norway

Oman

Pakistan

Panama

Papua New Guinea

Peru

Philippine Islands

Poland

Portugal

Puerto Rico

Qatar

Romania

Russia

St. Kitts-Nevis

St. Lucia

São Tomé and Príncipe

Saudi Arabia

Senegal

Seychelles

Sierra Leone

Singapore

Slovakia

Slovenia

Solomon Islands

Somali Democratic Republic

South Africa

Spain

Sri Lanka

Sudan

Surinam

Sweden

Switzerland

Syria

Tai-wan

Tajikistan

National Maritime Flags

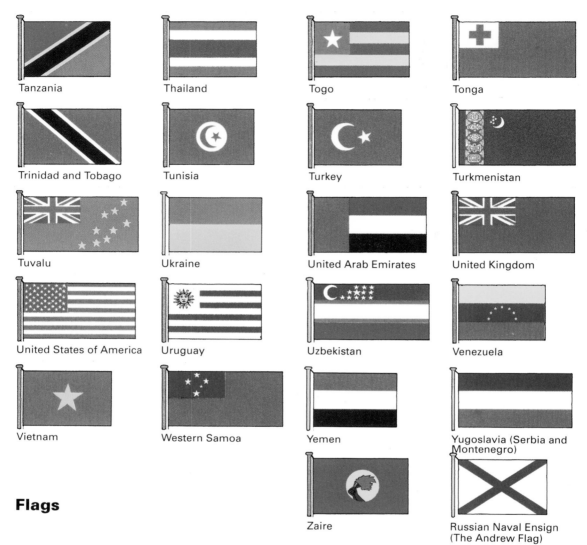

Tanzania | Thailand | Togo | Tonga

Trinidad and Tobago | Tunisia | Turkey | Turkmenistan

Tuvalu | Ukraine | United Arab Emirates | United Kingdom

United States of America | Uruguay | Uzbekistan | Venezuela

Vietnam | Western Samoa | Yemen | Yugoslavia (Serbia and Montenegro)

Zaire | Russian Naval Ensign (The Andrew Flag)

Flags

Flags are divided into two, vertically, the half nearest the flagstaff being the hoist, the other half being the fly. Flags are also divided into quarters, each quarter being called a canton. The upper canton in the hoist is called 'The Canton'. The size of a flag at sea should match the size of the vessel. The Royal Navy measures flags in breadths. It assumes that all flags are in the ratio 1 : 2 (i.e. length is twice the width). Flags for the RN used to be made of strips (breadths) nine inches (23cms) wide and so it is only necessary to give the number of breadths to fix the size of the flag, e.g. an aircraft carrier would wear a 12 breadth ensign (108in x 54in) and a minesweeper a 4 breadth (36in x 18in).

Burgees are swallow-tailed except for club burgees which are triangular and normally in the ratio of 1 : 2. **Pendants or pennants** (always pronounced pennants) are truncated cones. There are 10 numerical pendants and 14 special pendants in naval signalling: there are 10 numerical pendants and one answering pendant in the International Code.
A Union flag with a broad white border is used as a pilot signal.
Ensigns are 'worn' whereas admiral's flags, Commodore's broad pendants, signal hoists etc. are 'flown'.

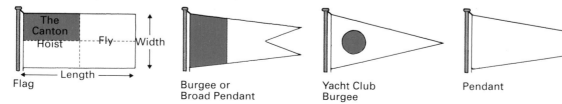

Flag | Burgee or Broad Pendant | Yacht Club Burgee | Pendant

British and Irish Yacht Club Burgees

Aldeburgh Yacht Club

Alexandra Yacht Club

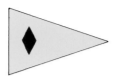
Arun Yacht Club (The)

Association of Thames Yacht Clubs

Ballyholme Yacht Club

Bar Yacht Club

Barry Yacht Club

Bembridge Sailing Club

Benfleet Yacht Club

Birdham Yacht Club

Blackpool & Fleetwood Yacht Club

Blackwater Sailing Club Ltd.

Bosham Sailing Club

Brading Haven Yacht Club

Brandy Hole Yacht Club

Brighton Marina Yacht Club

Bristol Channel Yacht Club

Britannia Yacht Club

British Kiel Yacht Club

British Motor Yacht Club (The)

Brixham Yacht Club

Burnham-on-Sea Yacht Club

Burry Port Yacht Club

Cabot Cruising Club

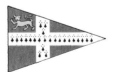
Cambridge University Cruising Club

Cargreen Yacht Club

Chichester Yacht Club

City Livery Yacht Club

Clyde Corinthian Yacht Club

Clyde Cruising Club

British and Irish Yacht Club Burgees

Coleraine Yacht Club

Colne Yacht Club

Coquet Yacht Club (The)

County Antrim Yacht Club

Crosby Sailing Club

Crouch Yacht Club

Cruising Association

Dale Yacht Club

Dartmouth Yacht Club (The)

Deben Yacht Club

Donaghadee Sailing Club

Douglas Motor Boat & Sailing Club

Eastney Cruising Association

Erith Yacht Club

Essex Yacht Club

Fishguard Bay Yacht Club

Forth Corinthian Yacht Club

Guernsey Yacht Club

Hamble River Sailing Club

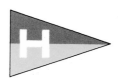
Hardway Sailing Club

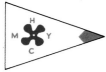
Harleyford Motor Yacht Club

Hartlepool Yacht Club

Household Division Yacht Club

House of Commons Yacht Club

House of Lords Yacht Club

Howth Yacht Club

Humber Yawl Club

Ilfracombe Yacht Club

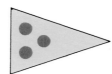
Imperial Poona Yacht Club

Irish Cruising Club

British and Irish Yacht Club Burgees

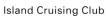

Island Cruising Club

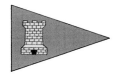

Island Sailing Club

Isle of Man Yacht Club

Itchenor Sailing Club

Junior Offshore Group

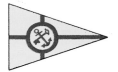

Keyhaven Yacht Club

Law Society Yacht Club

Leigh-on-Sea Sailing Club

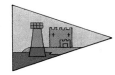

Little Ship Club

Liverpool Marina Yacht Club

Lloyd's Yacht Club

London River Yacht Club

Lough Erne Yacht Club

Lough Foyle Yacht Club

Madoc Yacht Club

Maldon Little Ship Club

Maldon Yacht Club

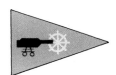

Marchwood Yacht Club

Margate Yacht Club

Medway Cruising Club

Medway Yacht Club

Merioneth Yacht Club

Middle Thames Yacht Club

Minima Yacht Club

Mudhook Yacht Club

Multihull Offshore Cruising & Racing Association

Mumbles Yacht Club

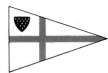

Mylor Yacht Club

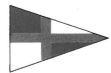

National Yacht Club

Newhaven Marina Yacht Club

British and Irish Yacht Club Burgees

Norfolk Broads Yacht Club   North Devon Yacht Club   Orwell Yacht Club   Parkstone Yacht Club   Penarth Yacht Club

Penton Hook Yacht Club   Perth Sailing Club   Poole Harbour Yacht Club   Poole Yacht Club   Portmadoc & Trawsfynydd Sailing Club

  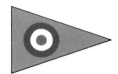  

Portrush Yacht Club   Ribble Cruising Club   Royal Air Force Yacht Club   Royal Anglesey Yacht Club   Royal Artillery Yacht Club

Royal Burnham Yacht Club   Royal Channel Islands Yacht Club   Royal Cinque Ports Yacht Club   Royal Corinthian Yacht Club   Royal Cork Yacht Club (incorporating Royal Munster Yacht Club)

Royal Cornwall Yacht Club   Royal Cruising Club   Royal Dart Yacht Club   Royal Dorset Yacht Club   Royal Eastern Yacht Club

Royal Engineer Yacht Club   Royal Findhorn Yacht Club   Royal Forth Yacht Club   Royal Fowey Yacht Club   Royal Gourock Yacht Club

British and Irish Yacht Club Burgees

Royal Harwich Yacht Club

Royal Highland Yacht Club

Royal Irish Yacht Club

Royal London Yacht Club

Royal Lymington Yacht Club

Royal Mersey Yacht Club

Royal Motor Yacht Club

Royal Naval Club & Royal Albert Yacht Club

Royal Naval Sailing Association

Royal Norfolk & Suffolk Yacht Club

Royal Northern & Clyde Yacht Club

Royal North of Ireland Yacht Club

Royal Northumberland Yacht Club

RNVR Yacht Club

Royal Ocean Racing Club

Royal Plymouth Corinthian Yacht Club

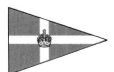

Royal St. George Yacht Club

Royal Scottish Motor Yacht Club

Royal Solent Yacht Club

Royal Southampton Yacht Club

Royal Southern Yacht Club

Royal Tay Yacht Club

Royal Temple Yacht Club

Royal Thames Yacht Club

Royal Torbay Yacht Club

Royal Ulster Yacht Club

Royal Victoria Yacht Club

Royal Welsh Yacht Club

Royal Western Yacht Club

Royal Western Yacht Club of England

British and Irish Yacht Club Burgees

Royal Yachting Association

Royal Yacht Squadron

Royal Yorkshire Yacht Club

Salcombe Yacht Club

Scarborough Yacht Club

Seaview Yacht Club

Severn Motor Yacht Club

Solway Yacht Club

South Caernarvonshire Yacht Club

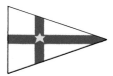
Starcross Yacht Club

St. Helier Yacht Club

Strangford Lough Yacht Club

Sunderland Yacht Club

Sussex Motor Yacht Club

Sussex Yacht Club

Teign Corinthian Yacht Club

Thames Estuary Yacht Club

Thames Motor Yacht Club

Thorpe Bay Yacht Club

Thurrock Yacht Club

Walton & Frinton Yacht Club

Waveney & Oulton Broad Yacht Club

Welland Yacht Club

West Lancashire Yacht Club

West Mersea Yacht Club

West Stockwith Yacht Club

Whitby Yacht Club

Whitstable Yacht Club

Yealm Yacht Club

York Motor Yacht Club

Foreign Yacht Club Burgees

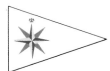

Clube de Vela
Atlântico
(Portugal)

Deauville Yacht Club
(France)

Kongelig Dansk
Yachtklub
(Denmark)

Kongelig Norsk
Seilforening
(Norway)

Koninklijke Jacht Club
Oostende en Motor
Jacht Club van Belgie
(Belgium)

Koninklijke
Nederlandsche
Motorboot Club
(Netherlands)

Koninklijke
Nederlandsche Zeil-en
Roeivereeniging
(Netherlands)

Koninklijke Roei-en
Zeilvereeniging 'De
Maas'
(Netherlands)

Kungl. Svenska Segel
Sällskapet
(Sweden)

New York Yacht Club
(USA)

Point Yacht Club
(South Africa)

Royal Belgian Sailing
Club
(Belgium)

Royal Bermuda Yacht
Club
(Bermuda)

Royal Hong Kong
Yacht Club
(Hong Kong)

Royal New Zealand
Yacht Squadron
(New Zealand)

Royal Nova Scotia
Yacht Squadron
(Canada)

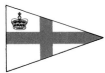

Royal Perth Yacht
Club of Western
Australia
(Australia)

Royal Suva Yacht
Club
(Fiji)

Royal Sydney Yacht
Squadron
(Australia)

Royal Yacht Club de
Belgique
(Belgium)

Segelkamaradschaft
'Das Wappen von
Bremen'
(Germany)

Société des Régates
du Havre
(France)

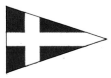

Société Nautique de
la Baie de St. Malo
(France)

Société Nautique de
Quiberon
(France)

Union National Pour
La Course Au Large
(France)

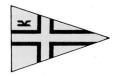

Vlaamse Vereniging
Voor Watersport
(Netherlands)

Watersportvereniging
'Haringvliet'
(Netherlands)

Watersportvereniging
'Texel'
(Netherlands)

Yacht Club
Argentino
(Argentine)

Yacht Club
d'Arcachon
(France)

Foreign Yacht Club Burgees (continued)

Yacht Club de
Cherbourg
(France)

Yacht Club de France
(France)

Yacht Club de Morlaix
(France)

Yacht Club de
Nieuwpoort
(Netherlands)

Yacht Club du Nord
de la France
(France)

Yacht Club du Trieux
(France)

Yacht Klub Polski w Gdyni
(Poland)

Other Flags That May Be Seen

Flag of Europe

or

With appropriate
national flag
in the canton

Many places have local flags (see 6.8.2 and 6.8.3)
including Scotland, Northern Ireland, Wales, Isle of
Man, Jersey, Sark, Alderney, Herm and Normandy –
which should *not* be used as courtesy flags.

Scotland

Northern Ireland

Wales

Isle of Man

Jersey

Sark

Alderney

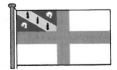

Herm

Also to be seen are some unofficial flags,
not fully recognised in the places or
countries concerned.

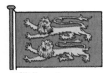

Normandy

Guernsey has an
official maritime
flag. (see p.195)

Brittany (Independent)

Cornwall

Details of all coast radio stations, worldwide, are contained in the *Admiralty List of Radio Signals, Vol 1*. Those in North-West Europe are given in *The Macmillan & Silk Cut Nautical Almanac*.

Coast stations control their respective areas and serve as a link between ship stations and the telephone network. They also transmit routine traffic lists (notifying ships of traffic for them), navigational warnings (of wrecks, lights not functioning etc) for sea regions lettered A–N around the British Isles as described in 6.7.2 below, and weather bulletins. Gale warnings are broadcast at the end of the next silence period and at other scheduled times. Details of these services are given in *The Macmillan & Silk Cut Nautical Almanac*.

Coast stations have an important role to play in respect to distress, urgency, safety and medical messages, which are described in 6.6.16.

Most of the major coast stations in the United Kingdom operate on both MF and VHF, and most control one or more unmanned, remote VHF stations, in order to extend the area of VHF coverage.

Each BT MF coast station has its own separate broadcast-only frequency (for traffic lists, navigational warnings, weather bulletins and gale warnings), and its own separate paired working frequencies. Details are given in *The Macmillan & Silk Cut Nautical Almanac*.

The procedure for making an MF call is as follows: Call the coast station concerned on the designated calling channel. For United Kingdom (BT) coast stations (and for many foreign coast stations) this is 2182 kHz, on which frequency all coast stations keep watch continuously (H24) for distress and safety traffic. The BT service around the United Kingdom is one region for call handling, and a call will be answered by the first available operator wherever he may be, not necessarily at the station called.

Wait for the operator to reply, on 2182 kHz, and he will designate the working channels to be used. For BT coast stations there are paired frequencies for ship and coast station to use for MF RT traffic. Before making any call always listen on the frequency concerned to make sure the channel is not already in use. If a coast station is working 2182 kHz for distress or safety traffic, call on 2191 kHz and listen for reply on the station's broadcast frequency.

The radio officer will request the following information: vessel's callsign, name, accounting code (AAIC), category of traffic (e.g. telegram, telephone call), and the telephone number required (see 6.6.11).

Note: Distress and Urgency calls should always be made on 2182kHz and will be answered on the same channel. This includes urgent medical calls, which should be preceded by the Urgency Signal 'PAN PAN MEDIC' – see 6.6.13. Non-urgent medical calls should be made on working channels.

Except in the case of distress, urgency or safety messages all United Kingdom VHF coast stations should be called directly on a working channel.

Where possible avoid using a station's broadcast channel, particularly around the times of scheduled broadcasts.

The yacht should monitor each working channel in turn until a free one is located, with no transmissions. A channel in use is indicated by either speech or by an engaged signal – a series of pips being transmitted. Having selected a free channel, the call should last at least eight seconds in order to activate equipment at the coast station, whereupon the engaged signal indicates that the call has been accepted. The radio officer will then speak, although not perhaps immediately since he may be occupied with another call on another channel.

If you do not succeed in 'switching on' a coast station's transmitter you may be out of range. Try another channel or another station, or call again when closer.

VHF coast stations called on working channels may listen on Ch 16 for distress and safety calls (but primary cover on this channel is provided by HM Coastguard), and give preliminary announcements of traffic lists etc on this channel.

Queries or comments regarding United Kingdom coast radio stations should be addressed to Maritime Radio Services, British Telecom, 43 Bartholomew Close, London EC1A 7HP.

French and German coast stations should be called on VHF on the appropriate working channel. The calling channel for Belgian and Dutch coast stations depends on the geographical position of the yacht.

6.6.10 'TR' organisation

A radiotelephone provides the best and most convenient way for a yacht to be kept in touch with somebody ashore. Any boat leaving harbour for more than a few hours sailing in local waters - say if she is coastal cruising, or bound foreign – is advised to call the nearest coast station and give the boat's name, her current position, destination, and estimated time of arrival, or return to harbour. This not only enables the coast station to know how to set about passing any traffic to the boat, but it could be vital information if the boat becomes overdue or is involved in a distress situation. It also serves as a test for the boat's radiotelephone, and is an opportunity to train members of the crew in its use. It is equally important to report the boat's safe arrival at her destination.

This is done through what is known as the 'TR' organisation, and a call would take the following form after initial contact has been made with a coast station: 'LEWIS RADIO – THIS IS SEABIRD – TANGO ROMEO – DEPARTED OBAN – BOUND LERWICK – ETA ONE SIX JULY – OVER.'

On arrival at Lerwick *Seabird* reports to the nearest coast station (Shetland Radio):

'SHETLAND RADIO – THIS IS SEABIRD – ARRIVED LERWICK – CLOSING DOWN RADIO WATCH – OVER.'

Shetland Radio would then inform *Seabird*– if there is any traffic for her.

6.6.11 **Radiotelephone link calls**

Radiotelephone services are available, through coast radio stations, from ship stations to telephone subscribers not only in the United Kingdom but also in other countries of the international telephone network. It is possible to make personal calls to certain countries and collect (transferred charge) calls to the United Kingdom.

World-wide accounting for calls made through foreign coast stations (including Jersey and Guernsey) is arranged through one of the several ITU-recognised accounting authorities such as BT, Cable and Wireless plc, Kelvin Hughes Ltd. STC International Marine Ltd, Marconi International Marine Co. Ltd etc. quoting the allocated 'Accounting Authority Indicator Code' (AAIC). Coast stations hold copies of the ITU List of Ship Stations, giving the accounting authority for each vessel, and are then able to charge the accounting authority accordingly. It is not possible to make a call through a foreign coast station on a Ship Radio (Transportable) Licence.

To make a link call through a BT coast station to a telephone number in the UK, Channel Islands or Isle of Man there are different methods of payment. One is by AAIC as in the previous paragraph. However, for VHF calls to numbers in the UK and Isle of Man it is convenient to pay by Yacht Telephone Debit (YTD) whereby the charge is made to the account for your UK home or business telephone number. To use this facility, advise the coast station that you require a YTD call, and quote the telephone number for billing. You can also pay with a BT Chargecard for calls to UK and foreign destinations. It is also possible to make a reverse (transfer) charge call.

Example: To set up a link call from the yacht *Seabird* to a number in the United Kingdom. The yacht calls the nearest coast radio station, say Lewis Radio, on the appropriate working channel, which in this case is Ch 05. Note that this is also the broadcast channel for Lewis Radio, so that calls should be avoided at or near the times of routine broadcasts. The procedure for calling a coast station on VHF is described in 6.6.9 above, and must be followed.

'LEWIS RADIO – THIS IS SEABIRD – SEABIRD – LINK CALL PLEASE – OVER.'

Seabird then listens on Ch 05 for Lewis Radio, which calls back:

'SEABIRD – THIS IS LEWIS RADIO – WHAT NUMBER PLEASE – OVER.'

Seabird replies, quoting 'YTD' and her home telephone number as follows:

'LEWIS RADIO – THIS IS SEABIRD – YANKEE TANGO DELTA – ZERO SEVEN ONE – THREE EIGHT FIVE – SIX ONE FOUR THREE – LINK CALL TO ZERO NINE SIX – TWO SEVEN EIGHT – THREE ZERO THREE – OVER.'

If communications are good, it should not be necessary to repeat the numbers, but do so if in doubt or if so requested.

The coast station would then ring the number required, and when it is obtained make the connection to the yacht. When radio channels are congested calls may be limited to six minutes. The coast station decides the duration of the call for charging purposes, and normally informs the ship station at the end of the conversation with the land number. The timing of a call ceases when the shore telephone is put down, not when the yacht signs off.

Autolink RT

Autolink RT gives direct dialling from ship to shore into national and international telephone networks without going through a coast station operator. It functions through an onboard unit which is easily connected to the radio, and which does not interfere with normal manual operation. This service on VHF, MF and HF gives quicker access, call scrambling on some units where privacy is required, and simplified accounting. Last number redial and a ten number memory store are available.

To make an Autolink call switch on the radio and the Autolink unit. Select a working channel and enter your PIN number (see below) as prompted. Key in or recall from memory the required telephone number in response to the prompt. If the channel is free, press the Send key on the Autolink unit, and connection is automatic. If the radio channel is already in use, either wait until it is free or select another channel if available. Then press the Send key again.

With full duplex radios press the PTT key throughout the conversation. With semi-duplex sets press the PTT key only when speaking. The connection is ended and charging stops when the receiver is replaced on the telephone ashore, but press the Send button if the 'call-off' indicator is not displayed.

To obtain manual assistance from BT coast station, key in one of these two-digit codes instead of a telephone number: 11 for low priority assistance, 00 for high priority assistance.

For the local weather forecast, key in the code 12 instead of the full Marinecall telephone number. To obtain Marinecall numbers for other areas you must dial the full 0898 numbers.

For Distress, Urgency and Safety (including medical) calls use the normal manual procedure on VHF Ch 16 or 2182kHz.

If you own an Autolink unit, on registering with BT you may elect to pay for calls by one of three methods: (1) a nominated UK telephone number, (2) a BT Chargecard, or (3) a ship's Accounting Authority. There is no registration or subscription charge, and you may change your method of payment on request. For charging you are identified by the PIN number allocated. Up to 99 different PIN numbers can be issued with the serial number of each Autolink unit, so the unit is available for 99 different people, each charged individually.

6.6.12 Weather information by radiotelephone

The various sources of weather information are given in Section 7.6, and the proper use of a radiotelephone can be an advantage in this respect. For example, as detailed in 7.6.10, it is possible to make a link call through any United Kingdom coast station.

Similarly actual weather can be obtained by link calls to coastguard stations and lighthouses which make observations for the Met. Office. When in VHF range broadcasts can be received from HM Coastguard as described in 7.6.9.

6.6.13 Medical help by radiotelephone

Medical advice can be obtained by requesting 'Medico' service through any United Kingdom or Irish coast station, which will connect the yacht with a suitable medical authority – usually the nearest hospital. If medical help is needed in the form of a doctor, or if a serious casualty has to be off-lifted, the call will be passed to the Coastguard. In either case the message is passed free of charge, and where appropriate the Urgency Signal 'PAN PAN MEDICO' may be used (see 6.6.16).

Similar arrangements apply in other European countries. Calls to French coast stations should be in French, prefixed 'Radiomédical'. For Belgium call Oostende coast station in English, French, Dutch or German using the address 'Radiomédical Oostende'. For Netherlands call Scheveningen coast station in English, Dutch, French or German, using the address 'Radiomédical Scheveningen'. For the waters of Germany, call the nearest coast station in English or German, prefixing the call 'Funkarzt' (see also 8.6.27).

6.6.14 Radiotelephone calls to ships

By dialling 0800 378389 you will be connected free of charge to the ships radiotelephone service to book calls on a person to person basis on the VHF (Short Range), MF (Medium Range) or HF (Long Range) services. The charge starts only when you speak to the nominated person on board the vessel. At present (1992) all calls are connected and controlled by a radio officer.

You will be asked for your name and telephone number, the name of the person you wish to speak to, the name of the ship, her callsign and position (if known) and the radio station with which the ship is in contact (if known). The vessel is then called. When she responds you will be called back and connected. The booking remains valid for 24 hours, after which it will be cancelled.

Marine-Page
This service allows swift contact with a ship at sea which is suitably equipped and within MF range. Call Portishead on 01278 792850 and give the ship's paging number. The vessel should respond within a few minutes and call back using Autolink RT direct dial or any other means available. You

may even relay a short text message with a maximum of 80 characters.

Marine-Page operates through a unit similar to a Navtex receiver, and can combine Navtex and Weatherfax facilities. When you purchase a unit you register with BT and receive a paging number. A quarterly subscription allows you to receive unlimited paging calls or text messages without further cost. The caller on shore pays normal telephone charges to Portishead.

For further details contact Marine-Page, Customer Services, Portishead Radio Station, Highbridge, Somerset TA9 3JY. Tel: 0800 262283. Fax: 01278 772222.

Inmarsat
For BT Inmarsat service (see 6.6.17) call 155. Ask for an Inmarsat call and give the ship's identification number and ocean region (if known). Calls may be dialled direct from digital exchanges. If the identification number is not known, call 153.

6.6.15 Port operations

Many commercial ports and harbours now have radiotelephone facilities, operating on VHF. A few also operate on MF, mostly in connection with pilotage services which are not normally the concern of yachtsmen.

Certain VHF channels, most commonly Ch 12 and Ch 14, are allocated for port operations. Communications on such channels must be restricted to those relating to operational handling, the movement and the safety of ships and, in emergency, to the safety of persons. They must not be used for public correspondence messages.

In harbour a radiotelephone must only be used on port operations channels, on private channels authorised by the Home Office (e.g. Ch M), and for communication with the nearest coast station. Intership communication is only allowed for safety purposes.

It is very useful to be able to communicate with harbour authorities by VHF – particularly in busy commercial ports where permission is sometimes needed to leave or enter, or in strange harbours when local information is needed on moorings or other facilities.

Call on Ch 16 or, where possible, on a nominated working channel, but since the Port Radio is likely to be listening out on more than one channel it is helpful, when calling, to state the channel being used, e.g. 'Orkney Harbour Radio – This is Seabird, Seabird – on Channel 20 – over'.

Useful information can often be obtained merely by listening out on the appropriate channel in a commercial harbour. In some ports regular information on local traffic, weather and tidal conditions is broadcast at specified times. It is most important that yachts do not use those working channels which are reserved for port operations – berthing/unberthing, ship/tug, pilot/berthing master messages etc.

6.6.16 Distress messages and procedures

One of the greatest advantages of having a radiotelephone on board a yacht is that it is easy to call for help if things go wrong. In such an important matter there are, however, strict procedures to be followed. All the crew should know what they are, and how to use the set in an emergency.

The frequencies of 2182kHz MF and Channel 16 (156.8MHz) VHF are internationally recognised for passing Distress, Urgency and Safety messages. Many stations, ashore and afloat, keep continuous watch on these frequencies.

Note that while cellular radiotelephones may be useful for various purposes in coastal waters, they should not be used for distress or safety communications (unless proper marine equipment for VHF Ch 16 or 2182kHz MF is not available).

The distress signal 'MAYDAY' by radiotelephone indicates that a ship, aircraft or other vehicle is threatened by grave and imminent danger, and requests IMMEDIATE ASSISTANCE. The procedure is as follows:

Check that the yacht's main battery switch is 'on'. Switch on the set, and in the case of VHF ensure that it is on 'high power'. Switch the transmitter to Ch 16 or 2182kHz, as appropriate.

If the boat carries an alarm signal generator (few yachts do), operate this device for at least 30 seconds. Then speak slowly and distinctly, transmitting:

MAYDAY MAYDAY MAYDAY
THIS IS (name of boat spoken three times)
MAYDAY (name of boat spoken once)
MY POSITION IS . . . (Latitude and longitude, or true bearing and distance from a known point)
Nature of distress . . .
Type of assistance required . . . OVER.

The yacht's position is of vital importance, and should be repeated if time allows. It is also helpful to state the number on board. Do not forget to release the 'transmit' button on completion of the message.

An immediate acknowledgement should be expected anywhere in coastal waters, either from another vessel or from a shore station. If not, check the set and repeat the distress call and message. When using MF, and if there is difficulty in passing a distress message, try during one of the three minutes' silence periods which start on each hour and half hour, and which are intended for this purpose. During these silence periods all transmissions on 2182kHz, except for Distress or Urgency traffic, must cease. There is no equivalent on Ch 16.

Use of distress signal (MAYDAY) imposes general radio silence, which is maintained until the vessel concerned or some other authority cancels the distress. A distress signal should be cancelled as soon as (but not before) the emergency is over.

A distress message is acknowledged in the following form:
MAYDAY
The name of the station sending the distress message, spoken three times
THIS IS . . . (name of the station acknowledging, spoken three times)
RECEIVED MAYDAY.

A yacht which hears a distress message from a vessel in her immediate vicinity and is able to give assistance should acknowledge accordingly, but only after giving an opportunity for the nearest shore station or some larger vessel to acknowledge. If a yacht hears a distress message from some more distant vessel, and if it is apparent that it has not been acknowledged, then the yacht should do everything possible to pass on the distress message. The intercepted distress message is preceded by the words:
MAYDAY RELAY, MAYDAY RELAY, MAYDAY RELAY
THIS IS . . . (name of vessel retransmitting the distress message, spoken three times)
Followed by the intercepted distress message.

Control of distress traffic
Should it be necessary, the station controlling distress traffic may impose radio silence by transmitting:
SEELONCE MAYDAY, followed by its own name or other identification on the frequency being used for distress purposes.

If any other station nearby believes it essential to do likewise, it may transmit:
SEELONCE DISTRESS, followed by its own name or other identification.

When complete silence is no longer necessary on a frequency being used for distress traffic, the station controlling traffic may relax the silence by a signal in the following form, indicating that restricted working may be resumed:
MAYDAY
HELLO ALL STATIONS (spoken three times)
THIS IS (the name or identification of the station sending the message)
The time
The name of the station in distress
PRU-DONCE (pronounced as the French word 'prudence').

When distress traffic has ceased, the controlling station lets all stations known that normal working may be resumed, as follows:
MAYDAY
HELLO ALL STATIONS (spoken three times)
THIS IS (the name or identification of the station)
The time
The name of the station which was in distress
SEELONCE FEENEE

Urgency Signal
The Urgency Signal consists of the words 'PAN-PAN', spoken three times, and indicates that the station has a very urgent message to transmit

concerning the safety of a ship, aircraft or other vehicle, or the safety of a person. Messages prefixed by the Urgency Signal take priority over all messages except distress, and are sent on either or both of the international distress frequencies, 2182kHz or Ch 16 – or on any other frequency which may be used in case of distress. In the case of 2182kHz transmit a long message or the repetition of one on a working frequency.

The Urgency Signal is appropriate when urgent medical advice or attention is required, or when someone has been lost overboard. It should be cancelled by the station concerned when the urgency no longer exists.

Safety Signal

The Safety Signal consists of the word SÉCURITÉ (pronounced SAY-CURE-E-TAY) spoken three times, and indicates that the station is about to transmit a message containing an important navigational or meteorological warning, e.g. a drifting buoy, an extinguished light, a wreck, or a gale warning. Such messages usually originate from coast stations, and are transmitted on a working frequency after an announcement on the distress frequency.

Portable RT equipment

Portable RT sets, operating on 2182kHz or on Ch 16, are mentioned in 8.3.10, together with Personal Locator Beacons (PLBs) and Emergency Position Indicating Radio Beacons (EPIRBs).

6.6.17 Inmarsat

The introduction of a global satellite communication system in 1979 opened a new era for marine communications. Since its inception the number of system users has grown rapidly, and in 1992 there were more than 15,500 vessels that were fitted with Satcom terminals, including many large luxury yachts. The availability of low-cost and compact Inmarsat-C and Inmarsat-M receivers (see below) is expected to lead to many small craft using the system.

The system providing world-wide satellite communications is under the control of Inmarsat,

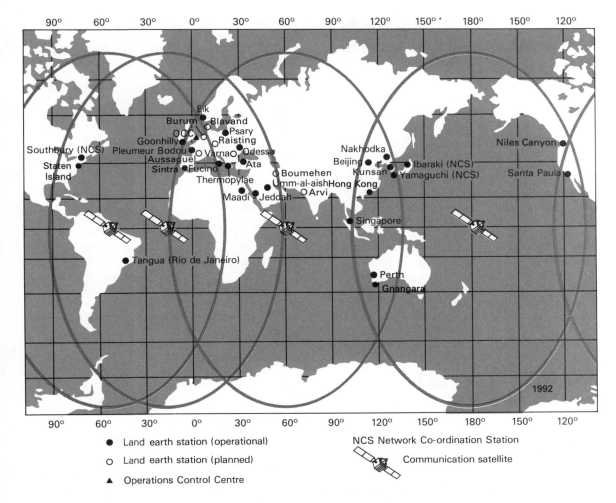

Fig. 6(2) Satellite communications. Four Inmarsat satellites in geostationary orbits over the Atlantic, Indian and Pacific Oceans. The key to the Earth Stations is shown below the diagram.

the global, mobile satellite communications provider, and is made up of three components: the satellites provided by Inmarsat; the Land Earth Stations (LESs) which are owned and operated by the telecommunications organisations in the countries in which they are located; and the on-board terminals, called Ship Earth Stations (SESs). The whole system is operationally controlled from Inmarsat's London headquarters.

Inmarsat operates two satellites over the Atlantic, and one each over the Pacific and Indian Oceans, which provide almost complete global coverage as shown in Fig.6(2). The satellites are located in geostationary orbit approximately 22,300 miles (36,000km) above the equator. In this orbit the satellites circle the earth at the same speed as the earth rotates, so that they remain stationary over one location on the earth's surface. The major advantage of Satcom over conventional Medium or High Frequency Single Side Band radio is the high quality and reliability of communication. Satcom has none of the many limitations associated with HF SSB.

The LESs interconnect the satellite system with the landbased communication networks. Calls or messages to ships originating on land are routed through an LES to one of the satellites, which retransmits them to the required vessels. Messages and calls from vessels are received via the satellite by the LES, and switched to their destinations over landbased networks.

Present Inmarsat-A terminals comprise a parabolic antenna, about 1.2m (4ft) in diameter, with a protective radome, which is connected to a transceiver with a headset and teleprinter below decks. Vessels so equipped can enjoy direct dialling to most countries in the world, automatic ship-to-shore calls, Telex services, data and facsimile transmission, and virtually instantaneous connection to HM Coastguard's Maritime Rescue Coordination Centre (MRCC) at Falmouth.

At present the size of Inmarsat-A terminals limits their use to large yachts. However with the introduction of Inmarsat-C equipment there is now a lightweight, low-cost terminal capable of receiving and/or transmitting data or text (but not voice) anywhere within coverage. The antenna is about 10cm (4in) diameter and 6cm ($2\frac{1}{2}$in) high, and the rest of the equipment is about the size of a shoe box. These terminals can also be used as Enhanced Group Call (EGC) receivers, if optional software is installed, for the receipt of marine safety and other group/area broadcasts.

It is therefore possible for any yacht outside VHF coverage to communicate via Telex or other forms of data exchange, with access to private and public data bases and videotext services such as Prestel. For example, if the owner has a personal computer at home which is equipped with a modem, he can transmit messages to it via Telecom Gold. Inmarsat-C terminals will also be able to use Inmarsat's SafetyNET — a new service providing vital marine safety information to yachts on the high seas. Satellite communications services for the IMO Global Maritime Distress and Safety System (GMDSS) will be provided by Inmarsat and satellite alerting by the COSPAS/SARSAT countries.

More recently Inmarsat have introduced two new systems. Inmarsat-B is a 'top of the range' successor to Inmarsat-A, offering lower charges and enhanced services, while Inmarsat-M makes satellite telephone, fax and data services much more widely available to yachtsmen, combining lower charges with smaller and cheaper equipment.

6.6.18 Global Maritime Distress and Safety System (GMDSS)

Although the ordinary yacht is not required to comply with GMDSS in terms of equipment or operation, the system is of interest to yachtsmen, particularly those who cruise extensively. It is a world-wide communication system, now in course of implementation with completion in 1999, whereby Search and Rescue (SAR) authorities ashore plus shipping near to a casualty can be alerted rapidly and can help to co-ordinate SAR operations speedily. GMDSS will also provide urgency and safety communication and the dissemination of Maritime Safety Information (MSI) including navigation warnings and weather messages.

Under GMDSS all sea areas are divided into four types. A1 is an area within VHF range of coast stations equipped with digital selective calling (DSC) on Ch 70. A2 is an area within MF range of coast stations equipped with DSC on 2187.5kHz. A3 is an area (excluding A1 and A2) within coverage of an Inmarsat geostationary satellite in which continuous alerting is available. A4 comprises other sea areas (i.e. beyond Inmarsat range) not covered by A1, A2 and A3.

The type of radio equipment that will have to be carried by a vessel over 300 tons will depend on the area(s) in which she operates. The timetable for implementation is:

1 Feb 1992. Existing vessels may comply either with GMDSS or current SOLAS regulations.
1 Aug 1993. All vessels required to carry NAVTEX and satellite emergency position indicating radio beacons (EPIRBs).
1 Feb 1995. Vessels built after this date must comply with GMDSS.
1 Feb 1999. All vessels must comply with GMDSS.

Short-range communications will be by VHF, with Ch 16 continuing as the distress and safety channel. Medium-range communications will be in the 2MHz band, with 2182kHz continuing for distress alerting and safety purposes, and 2174.5kHz for Telex. Long-range communications will be by HF, either as an alternative in those areas covered by Inmarsat or as the principal means outside those regions, with vessels keeping watch on 8414.5kHz and the HF frequency most suited to their position.

The International SafetyNET Service is a method based on Inmarsat for promulgating MSI, whereby navigational warnings and weather bulletins can be directed to vessels in fixed or variable areas. It also gives coverage in areas where there is no NAVTEX service. Broadcasts will continue from coast radio stations by radiotelegraphy, radiotelephony and radiotelex for the time being, with the first being gradually phased out.

6.6.19 Citizens' Band Radio

CB radio afloat is not a substitute for proper marine band VHF, if only for the fact that there is no official monitoring procedure for the CB emergency channel (Ch 09) in the way that numerous stations keep watch on VHF Ch 16. Nevertheless it should be recognised that CB radio can be useful in certain circumstances – as a relatively cheap method of communicating between a yacht and a shore station such as a yacht club or marina – or even with the owner's house if within range. In particular CB radio can be used for some of the social talk for which marine VHF is not intended.

A 'CB Licence Information Pack' can be obtained at a Post Office. Send the licence application form and the fee (£15 in 1992) to: Radio Licensing Centre, Subscription Services Ltd, PO Box 885, Bristol BS99 5LG. Tel: (01179) 258333. Unless you are using CB radio under the supervision of another CB licence holder, you must have a licence in your own name. The minimum age is 14. A renewal form will be sent out annually. Information sheets on CB Radio (Licensing, Equipment, and Interference and Abuse) are available from the Radiocommunications Agency at Waterloo Bridge House, Waterloo Road, London SE1 8UA.

The *CB Code of Practice* includes the following instructions:
(1) Read the licence carefully.
(2) Listen before transmitting, with the Squelch control turned down (and Tone Squelch turned off if you have Selective Call facilities), to make sure that the channel is clear.
(3) Keep transmissions and conversations as short as possible.
(4) Leave a pause before replying, so that other stations may join the conversation.
(5) Use plain language.
(6) At all times and on all channels give priority to calls for assistance. Leave Ch 09 clear for emergencies. If you hear a call for help, wait. If no regular volunteer monitor answers, then offer help if you can.
(7) In emergency, if there is no answer on Ch 09, try Ch 14 or 19.
(8) The calling channel is Ch 14. Once contact is established move to another channel.

6.6.20 Amateur (ham) radio

Although 'ham' radio is not a substitute for the official maritime facilities which are available on HF, MF and VHF, it can nevertheless be a useful additional means of communication – particularly for yachts which cruise extensively. There are one and a half million licensed amateur radio enthusiasts in the world, and at least some of them are seagoing. Several 'nets', operating on agreed frequencies, function for specific sea areas such as the United Kingdom, the Atlantic, the Caribbean, and the coastal waters of the United States.

Amateur radio, like other radio services, is controlled by the International Telecommunications Union in Geneva, which allocates strictly defined frequencies. All countries require that amateur radio enthusiasts pass an examination to ensure that they can operate without causing interference to other radio services.

Although most amateur operators communicate by voice, other forms of transmission are by Morse, by slow-scan television, or by teletype. A good set is relatively expensive, and it is essential to have very efficient aerial and earthing arrangements.

In Britain enquiries about amateur licences should be made to the Radio Licensing Centre, Subscription Services Ltd, PO Box 885, Bristol BS99 5LG. Tel: (01179) 258333. There are four licence categories:
(1) Amateur Radio Licence (A). Permits the use of all frequency bands allocated, including HF for global communications. In addition to the Radio Amateurs' Examination it is required to pass a Morse test at 12 words per minute.
(2) Amateur Radio Licence (B). Permits the use only of frequency bands allocated above 30MHz, which does not normally allow communication over more than a few hundred miles (unless the Amateur Satellite Service is used). It is required to pass the Radio Amateurs' Examination, but no Morse test.
(3) Amateur Radio (Novice) Licence (A). Permits use of the limited segments of the allocated bands, including some HF bands.
(4) Amateur Radio (Novice) Licence (B). Permits the use of frequency bands allocated to the novice amateur service above 30MHz.

Full details of the above licences, training courses, Morse tests, and technical details are contained in the booklet *How to Become a Radio Amateur* (RA190), obtainable from the Radiocommunications Agency, Waterloo Bridge House, Waterloo Road, London SE1 8UA.

6.7 Navigational warnings

6.7.1 Navigational warnings – general

The world-wide Navigational Warning Service covers 16 sea areas (NAVAREAS) which are numbered I–XVI in Roman numerals. These are shown in Fig.6(3), which also indicates the Area Coordinator (country) responsible for issuing long range navigational warnings in each area.

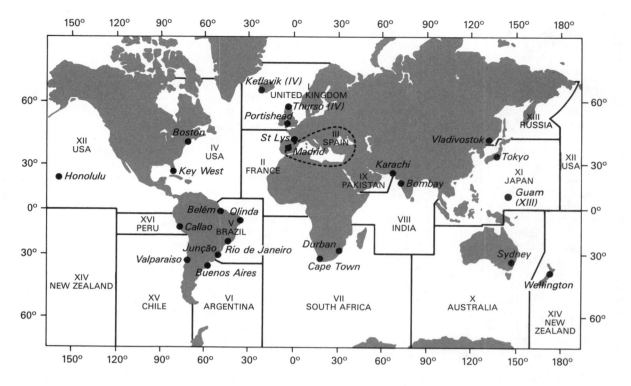

Fig. 6(3) Navigational Warning Service – Limits of NAVAREAS. Area Coordinators are shown in CAPITALS. Transmitting stations for NAVAREA warnings are shown in *italics*.

NAVAREA warnings cover the area concerned, are numbered consecutively through the year, and are transmitted in English and in one or more other languages at specific times by radiotelegraphy. Other forms of transmission (radiotelephony, radiotelex and facsimile) may also be used. They promulgate information which ocean navigators need – such as failures or changes to navigational aids, wrecks and navigational dangers of all kinds, SAR operations, cable or pipe laying operations, naval exercises etc.

Within each NAVAREA, coastal warnings and local warnings may also be promulgated. Coastal warnings, covering waters up to 100 or 200 n miles offshore, are broadcast in English and in the national language by coast radio stations. Local warnings are issued by harbour or port authorities in the national language only.

6.7.2 Navigational warnings – United Kingdom

Radio Navigational Warnings, normally issued by the Ministry of Defence (Navy), provide immediate information on dangers to navigation. Less urgent matters, on dangers within harbour limits, may not be broadcast but are issued in *Notices to Mariners*.

(1) NAVAREA warnings (long range) are broadcast by Portishead Radio (GKA) for NAVAREA I as shown in Fig. 6(3). Messages are numbered in sequence, and the text is published in the weekly *Notices to Mariners*, together with a list of those warnings still in force.

(2) NAVTEX warnings are broadcast from Niton, Cullercoats and Portpatrick Radio. NAVTEX is described in 6.7.4, and the areas concerned are shown in Fig. 6(6).

(3) Coastal warnings are broadcast by radio telephone from coast radio stations at scheduled times for the Sea Regions illustrated in Fig. 6(4). Cancelling messages are not transmitted. Important warnings may be broadcast at any time on the distress frequencies of 2182kHz and VHF Ch 16.

(4) Local warnings may be broadcast by harbour authorities through nearby coast radio stations. HM Coastguard broadcasts local warnings of dangers in inshore waters which are outside the limits of harbour authorities. These local warnings are broadcast on Ch 67 after an announcement on Ch 16, and may be repeated. There is no schedule, and broadcasts do not follow a numerical sequence.

(5) Vessels encountering unexpected dangers to navigation should notify other craft in the vicinity and the nearest coast radio station, prefacing the message by the safety signal as described in 6.6.16.

Further details of radio navigational warnings appear in the *Annual Notices to Mariners*.

6.7.3 Navigational warnings – Europe
The following notes describe the radio navigational warnings which are broadcast by certain countries in Europe. For details of

frequencies and schedules in the area of coverage, see *The Macmillan & Silk Cut Nautical Almanac*. For further information refer to *Admiralty List of Radio Signals, Vol. 3*.

Germany

Navigational warnings commence with the safety signal and the words *Nautische Warnnachricht*, and the warning number. They are broadcast in German and English on receipt and after the next silence period, and may be repeated as necessary. Decca warnings for the German and Frisian Island chains (*Decca Warnnachricht*) are broadcast by Norddeich Radio.

Yachts encountering dangers to navigation should inform Seewarn Cuxhaven through the nearest coast radio station. Oil pollution should also be reported to Seewarn Cuxhaven, prefaced by the word *Oelunfall*.

France

Long range warnings are broadcast in English and French for NAVAREA II in Fig. 6(3) by St Lys Radio.

AVURNAVS (AVis URgents aux NAVigateurS) are coastal and local warnings issued by regional maritime authorities as follows:
(1) Avurnavs Cherbourg for the North Sea and the eastern Channel (Belgian frontier to Mont St Michel, including the Channel Islands).
(2) Avurnavs Brest for the western Channel and Atlantic coast (Mont St Michel to the Spanish frontier).
(3) Avurnavs Toulon for the south coast of France and Corsica.

Avurnavs are broadcast by the appropriate coast radio station, urgent ones being transmitted on receipt and at the end of the next silence period, as well as at scheduled times. RT warnings are prefixed 'Sécurité Avurnav', followed by the name of the station. Latitude and longitude are normally given in three groups. The first of four figures for latitude in degrees and minutes; the second of four or five figures for longitude in degrees and minutes; and the third of two letters to show the sense of latitude and longitude.

Yachts encountering dangers to navigation should report them to the nearest coast radio station, prefixing the message by the safety signal.

Greece

Hellenic Navwarns are broadcast in Greek and English at scheduled times by coast radio stations.

Italy

Warnings are broadcast in Italian on receipt and at scheduled times. The most recent warnings are broadcast first. Urgent warnings are broadcast in Italian and English, on receipt and at scheduled times.

Portugal

Navigational warnings are broadcast by coast radio stations in Portuguese and English, on MF for coastal waters of Portugal, the Azores and Madeira, and on VHF for local areas in Portuguese.

Spain

Long-range warnings are broadcast in Spanish and English by Madrid (EBA) for NAVAREA III in Fig. 6(3). Coastal warnings are broadcast by coast radio stations on MF in Spanish and English. 'Vital' warnings are announced on 2182kHz and are prefaced by the safety signal (*Sécurité*); they are broadcast on receipt, after the next silence period, and at scheduled times. 'Important' warnings are announced on 2182kHz and are prefaced by the safety signal; they are broadcast after the next silence period and at scheduled times. Lesser warnings are only broadcast at scheduled times. Local warnings are broadcast by coast radio stations on VHF in Spanish, and are classified 'Avurnave' or 'Aviso'. Avurnaves are announced on Ch 16 and are prefaced by the safety signal; they are broadcast on receipt and at scheduled times. Avisos are broadcast on the station's working channel at scheduled times.

6.7.4 NAVTEX

The NAVTEX system provides vessels with navigational and meteorological warnings, and with other urgent safety information by automatic print-outs from a dedicated receiver, and is a component of the International Maritime Organisation (IMO) Global Maritime Distress and Safety System (GMDSS) which is in the course of world-wide implementation.

At present, all broadcasts are made in the English language on a single MF frequency of 518kHz, giving excellent coverage of the coastal waters for which the system is intended. Interference between stations is avoided by a combination of time sharing and limiting the power of the transmitters. In practice the range of an individual transmitter is about 300 miles, so only three stations are required to cover the coast of the United Kingdom. IMO is expected to make available a second NAVTEX channel for broadcasts in the local national language.

The use of a single frequency world-wide permits the use of a simple dedicated installation, consisting of a receiver and a printer which uses cash-roll paper less than 102mm (4in) wide. Some yacht receivers utilise a video screen instead of a printer.

Fig. 6(5) shows the NAVTEX system, and the three principal types of information it provides, and how they are co-ordinated and edited before being broadcast. It also explains the functions performed at the receiver on board, partly by operator selection and partly through electronic processes in the receiver- whereby the information printed is limited to a useful minimum relevant to the vessel in question.

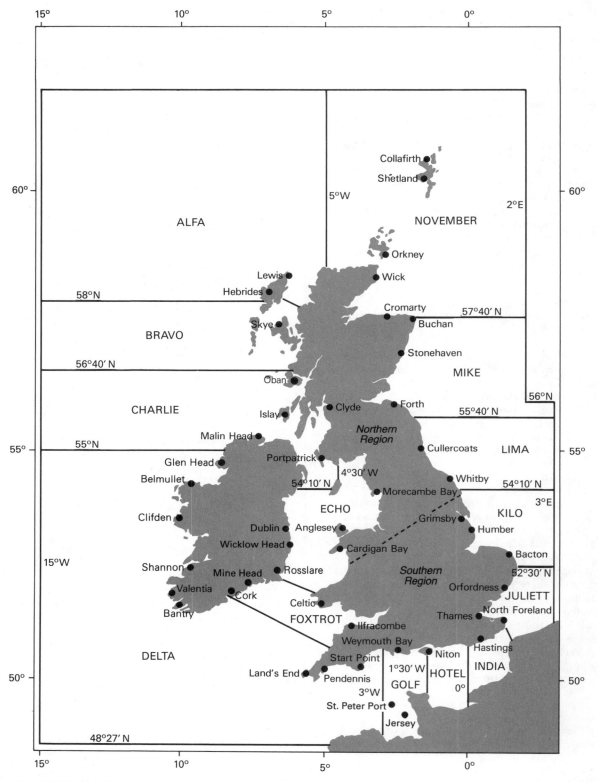

Fig. 6(4) United Kingdom Radio Navigational Warning Service. The diagram shows the Sea Regions (lettered ALFA – NOVEMBER) and the coast radio stations which serve them by radiotelephone (RT). Warnings of special importance may exceptionally be broadcast by stations in adjacent regions. Scheduled times and frequencies are given in *The Macmillan & Silk Cut Nautical Almanac*.

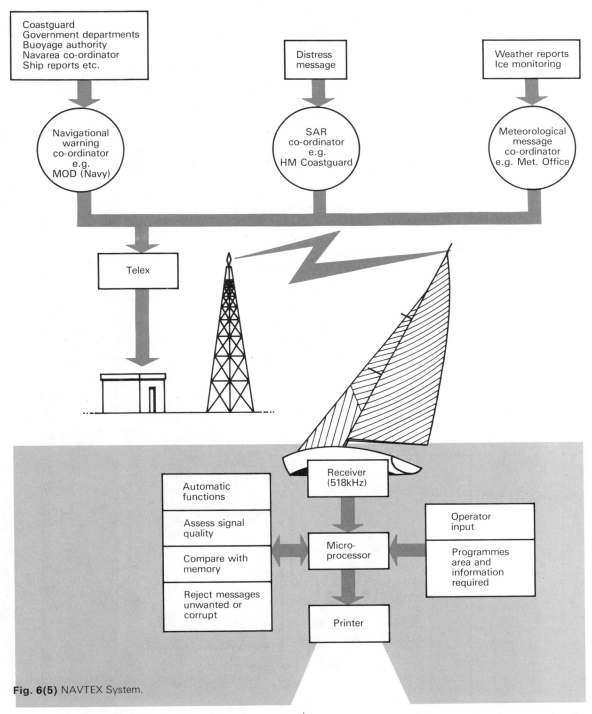

Fig. 6(5) NAVTEX System.

The operator programmes the receiver for the vessel's area and for the types of messages required. For example if Decca is not carried, Decca warnings can be rejected. The receiver will also reject messages which are corrupt or messages already printed out.

To achieve the required selection or rejection of messages, each one is prefixed by a four character group. The first character is the identity code of the station, and the second indicates the category of the message by letters A, B, C etc. as in the code below. The third and fourth characters are message serial numbers, from 01 to 99 in order of receipt. At 99 the numbering starts again at 01 using the numbers of any expired messages. The serial number 00 denotes urgent tragic (for example gale warnings or SAR alerts) which will always be printed, regardless of how the equipment has been programmed. Information in a NAVTEX broadcast applies only to the area for which that station is responsible, as shown in Fig. 6(6). An operator may choose to receive messages from one or more stations depending on his position.

NAVTEX receivers are easy to programme. Having switched on, first select the transmitters required by answering YES or NO to each code letter displayed. A similar process is followed to select the message categories required.

Full details of NAVTEX broadcasts are contained in the *Admiralty List of Radio Signals Vol. 3* (NP 283). The schedules for stations in North-West Europe are given in *The Macmillan & Silk Cut Nautical Almanac*.

Message categories
A Navigational warnings
B Gale warnings
C Ice reports (unlikely to apply in UK)
D Search and Rescue information
E Weather forecasts
F Pilot Service messages
G Decca messages
H Loran-C messages
I Omega messages

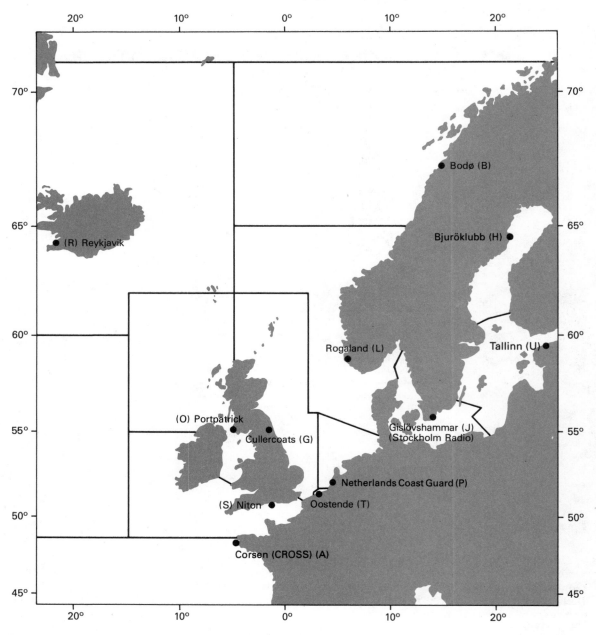

Fig. 6(6) NAVTEX transmitter service areas and station identity letters within NAVAREA I. Routine broadcast schedules are given in *The Macmillan & Silk Cut Nautical Almanac*.

J Satnav messages
K Other electronic navaid messages
L Oil and Gas Rig information
M to Y Not allocated
Z No messages on hand at scheduled time

NAVTEX stations – times UT (1994)

NAVAREA I

R Reykjavik, Iceland
   0318   0718   1118   1518   1918   2318
B Bodø, Norway
   0333   0733   1133   1533   1933   2333
J Gislovshammar, Sweden
   0330   0730   1130   1530   1930   2330
H Bjuröklubb, Sweden
   0000   0400   0800   1200   1600   2000
U Tallinn, Estonia
   0030   0430   0830   1230   1630   2030
P Netherlands Coast Guard
   0348   0748   1148   1548   1948   2348
T Oostende, Belgium
   0248   0648   1048   1448   1848   2248
G Cullercoats, UK
   0048   0448   0848   1248   1648   2048
O Portpatrick, UK
   0130   0530   0930   1330   1730   2130
S Niton, UK
   0018   0418   0818   1218   1618   2018
V Vardø, Norway
   0300   0700   1100   1500   1900   2300
L Rogoland, Norway
   0148   0548   0948   1348   1748   2148
F Arkhangelsk, Russia
   0200   0600   1000   1400   1800   2200
C Murmansk, Russia
   0120   0520   0920   1320   1720   2120

NAVAREA II

A Le Stiff, Corsen (CROSS), France
   0000   0400   0800   1200   1600   2000
R Lisboa, Portugal
   0250   0650   1050   1450   1850   2250
F Horta, Azores
   0050   0450   0850   1250   1650   2050
D La Coruna, Spain
   0030   0430   0830   1230   1630   2030
I Islas Canarias, Spain (planned)
   0100   0500   0900   1300   1700   2100

NAVAREA III

I Izmir, Turkey
   0120   0520   0920   1320   1720   2120
E Samsun, Turkey
   0040   0440   0840   1240   1640   2040
D Istanbul, Turkey
   0030   0430   0830   1230   1630   2030
F Antalya, Turkey
   0050   0450   0850   1250   1650   2050
L Limnos, Greece
   0150   0550   0950   1350   1750   2150
H Iraklion, Greece
   0110   0510   0910   1310   1710   2110

K Kerkyra, Greece
   0140   0540   0940   1340   1740   2140
G Tarifa, Spain
   0100   0500   0900   1300   1700   2100
Z Cabo La Nao, Spain (planned)
M Troodos, Cyprus
   0200   0600   1000   1400   1800   2200
O Malta
   0220   0620   1020   1420   1820   2220
N Alexandria, Egypt (planned)
   0210   0610   1010   1410   1810   2210
Q Split, Yugoslavia
   0250   0650   1050   1450   1850   2250
J Varna, Bulgaria
   0130   0530   0930   1330   1730   2130
P Haifa, Israel
   0020   0420   0820   1220   1620   2020
C Odessa, Ukraine
   0230   0630   1030   1430   1830   2230
B Mariupol, Ukraine
   0100   0500   0900   1300   1700   2100
A Novorossiysk, Russia
   ·0300   0700   1100   1500   1900   2300
W La Garde (CROSS), France
   0340   0740   1140   1540   1940   2340

Further stations are planned, to complete the coverage in Western Europe and the Mediterranean. It is expected that the system will be extended to cover most important coastal areas world-wide.

6.8 Flag etiquette

6.8.1 Flags concerned

The flags which may be displayed by a yacht include the national (maritime) ensign, the club burgee or flag officer's flag of a yacht club, a house flag, a courtesy flag when abroad, and flags connected with signalling or racing.

6.8.2 Ensign

For British yachts this is normally the Red Ensign (*never* the Union Flag). The Union Flag is flown at the bows of warships at anchor or secured alongside, and this is the only occasion when it is correct to refer to it as the Union Jack. Certain clubs (see the *Navy List*, HMSO) have the privilege of using a special Ensign, under strict regulations. There are stiff penalties for contravening them. The special Ensign for a yacht may be the White Ensign (Royal Yacht Squadron only); the Blue Ensign; the Blue Ensign defaced, i.e. with a badge; or the Red Ensign defaced. A special Ensign may only be worn under a warrant issued prior to 1 April 1985, or under a permit subsequently issued to the owner by his club and in accordance with the following rules.

The yacht must be registered under either Part I of the Merchant Shipping Act 1894, or the Merchant Shipping Act 1983. She must be not less

Flag	Cruising Yachts			(4) Racing yacht	(5) Power vessel	(6) Vessel on charter
	(1) Bermudan sloop or cutter	(2) Yawl or ketch	(3) Gaff rigged yacht			
Ensign	(a) Red Ensign (or Special Ensign if all conditions are satisfied). (b) Preferably from ensign staff at stern. (c) If (b) not practicable, e.g. when sailing, from position two-thirds of way up leech of mainsail.	See col (1), (a) and (b). If (b) is not practicable, e.g. when sailing, from a staff at mizzen masthead.	See col (1), (a) and (b). If (b) is not practicable, e.g. when sailing, from the peak of the aftermost sail.	See col (1), (2) or (3) as appropriate. But an ensign is not worn when racing.	See col (1), (a) and (b). Where the vessel has a mast fitted with a gaff, the ensign may be worn at this position when under way.	See cols (1)–(5) as appropriate. But the ensign used must be that of the nationality of the yacht, not of the charterer. Note that where a British yacht has a permit for a Special Ensign, such permit is withdrawn if the yacht is on charter or on loan.
Club burgee	(d) Burgee of club, of which person in charge of yacht is a member, should be flown from staff at the masthead. (e) Where (d) is not practicable, e.g. due to masthead instruments, at starboard crosstree. (f) Where Special Ensign is worn, burgee must be that of club concerned. (g) Only fly one burgee.	See col (1), (d)–(g). Burgee should be flown at main masthead, or, if (e) applies, at starboard crosstree of mainmast.	See col (1) or (2) as appropriate.	See cols (1)–(3) as appropriate, but a burgee is not flown while racing.	See col (1). Where a power vessel does not have a mast, the burgee may be flown from a staff over the wheelhouse or in the forward part of the vessel.	See cols (1)–(5) as appropriate. Any burgee flown must be that of a club of which the charterer is a member (not a club of the absent owner).
Flag Officer's flag	Flown by a Flag Officer instead of a club burgee, in corresponding position. But flown day and night when flag officer is on board, or ashore in the vicinity. If a Special Ensign is worn, it must correspond with Flag Officer's flag.	See col (1)	See col (1)	See col (1). Not normally flown when racing.	See col (1)	See col (1)
House flag	Rectangular flag, not conflicting with design of other existing flags (and particularly official flags). Flown in harbour when owner is on board, at starboard crosstree (inferior to any other flag at this position).	See col (1)	See col (1)	See col (1). At regattas, large 'house flag' may be flown in foretriangle.	See col (1). Normally flown at stub mast over wheelhouse, if so fitted.	See cols (1)–(5). House flag must be that of the charterer (not that of absent owner). In addition, the courtesy flag of the charterer's nationality may be flown at port crosstree, where different from nationality of the vessel.
Courtesy flag	Small version of national maritime flag of foreign country being visited. Flown in harbour at starboard crosstree, but not inferior to any other flag except burgee or Flag Officer's flag.	See col (1). Alternative position is at mizzen masthead.	See cols (1)–(2)	See cols (1)–(2)	See col (1). Normally flown at stub mast over wheelhouse, if so fitted.	See col (1). Not flown if nationality of chartered vessel corresponds with foreign country being visited.

Fig. 6(7) A guide to flag etiquette.

than 2 tons gross if registered by tonnage, or 7 metres overall if registered by length. The owner(s) must be British and be member(s) of the club concerned. The yacht must be a cruising boat (not a houseboat) and must not be used for any commercial purpose. Her name must not incorporate a name, product or trademark used for business purposes. The permit must be carried on board, and a special Ensign may only be worn if the owner is on board or ashore nearby, and if the club's burgee (or Flag Officer's flag) is flown.

If an owner belongs to more than one club eligible to wear a special Ensign, then he must apply for a separate permit for each Ensign. The loss or theft of a permit must be reported immediately, and if the owner ceases to be a member of the club, or if the yacht is sold, the permit must be returned forthwith to the secretary of the club.

Charterer's warrants are no longer issued, but a permit may be issued for short periods in respect of a yacht on charter to a club member. Further details of the issue and conditions for permits for special Ensigns are available from secretaries of clubs concerned.

The Ensign, being the yacht's national colours, should be worn in the most prominent position normally at a staff on the stern. In sailing yachts however this may be impossible: then in gaff-rigged yachts it is usually worn at the peak of the sail on the aftermast (if more than one); in bermudan yawls and ketches on a staff at the mizzen masthead; and in others at a position two-thirds of the way up the leech of the aft sail. In power-driven yachts with a gaff on an aft mast, the Ensign may be worn at the peak of this gaff at sea.

The Ensign should be worn when entering or leaving harbour, and must be worn when a yacht arrives at or departs from a foreign port. At sea it need not be worn except when meeting other craft or when coming near to land – especially when passing coastguard or signal stations etc. Yachts which are racing do not normally wear Ensigns.

In harbour the Ensign should be hoisted, if people are on board, at 0800 in summer (0900 between 1 November and 14 February). It should be lowered at sunset or at 2100, whichever is earlier – or when the crew go ashore if before that time. It is bad form to leave the Ensign flying overnight in harbour.

In a yacht with a permit for a special Ensign, the Red Ensign should be hoisted in the morning if the owner is not present – being replaced by the special Ensign when he arrives. Similarly if the owner departs from the yacht and the port, the special Ensign must be lowered, and replaced by the Red Ensign if the yacht is still manned.

Ensigns should only be used ashore at yacht clubs, where they should be hoisted and lowered at the same times as above.

The maritime Ensigns of the principal yachting and maritime countries are shown on pages 194–198, together with general examples of flag etiquette on page 191.

On occasions of private or national mourning colours are half-masted. This is done by first hoisting them close up, and then lowering them to the dipped position; similarly before hauling them down they are first raised to the masthead. For national mourning only the Ensign is half-masted: for private mourning both the Ensign and burgee.

6.8.3 Courtesy flag

It is customary in a foreign harbour to fly the maritime Ensign of the country being visited – normally at the starboard crosstrees. Some countries insist on this practice. The courtesy Ensign is a small version of the country's maritime Ensign – in the case of yachts visiting Britain, the Red Ensign (not the Union Flag).

Care must be taken that a courtesy flag is not flown inferior to (i.e. below) any flag other than the yacht's own Ensign (if, for example, worn at the mizzen masthead) and burgee (or flag officer's flag).

It is not normal for a yacht to wear more than one courtesy flag. However, parts of the British Isles have local flags including Scotland, Northern Ireland, Wales, Isle of Man, Jersey, Guernsey, Alderney, Sark and Herm (see page 206). Of these, only Guernsey has an official maritime flag (see page 195, which can be used in lieu of the Red Ensign by any boat registered in the bailiwick of Guernsey (which includes Alderney, Sark and Herm). Conversely, it can officially be used by any foreign yacht visiting the bailiwick in lieu of the Red Ensign, as the courtesy flag.

There is no need for a British yacht to wear a courtesy flag anywhere within the British Isles, but if it is considered polite to acknowledge the existence of the local flag, then it can be worn singly. Foreign yachts should wear the Red Ensign at the starboard crosstree and if they desire to wear the local flag, this should be worn at the port crosstree.

Brittany and Normandy both have local flags (see page 206) which should not be used in lieu of the French Tricolour. They indicate support for an independent Brittany or Normandy. They should be treated in the same way as British local flags; if it is desired to acknowledge their existence, the Tricolour should be worn at the starboard crosstree and the Brittany or Normandy flag at the port crosstree.

In the illustrations, the flags of Italy, Poland and Romania are shown with crests in the centre. When these flags are used as courtesy flags, it is customary for the crests to be omitted.

6.8.4 Burgee

Each club has its own burgee – a triangular flag which can be flown on members' yachts. The design is optional provided it does not conflict with official signals or other established flags. A yacht should normally fly not more than one burgee (see also 6.8.6).

It must be understood that the burgee signifies

that the owner, or person in charge of the yacht, is a member of that club, and a club burgee must never be flown under any other circumstances (see also 6.8.6).

6.8.5 Flag officers' flags

Most clubs authorise their flag officers to fly special swallow-tailed flags – of a similar design to the club burgee. The Vice- and Rear-Commodore's flags are distinguished from the Commodore's by one and two balls respectively in the cantons next to the hoist.

Some clubs provide for their past Commodores to fly a special flag at the masthead. This flag incorporates the design of the club burgee but is either a different shape (e.g. rectangular) or has some other distinguishing feature.

6.8.6 Flying burgees etc

Anybody lent or chartered a yacht flies a burgee of a club of which he is a member- not a burgee of the absent owner. In harbour a burgee should be flown at the same times as the Ensign; where a special Ensign is worn the related club burgee should be flown. In recent years, however, the practice has developed of leaving the burgee flying at night in harbour, when the owner is either on board or ashore in the vicinity. At sea a burgee is normally flown in sight of land or other ships.

A flag officer's flag is flown day and night while the owner is on board or in effective control. Yachts which are racing do not fly a burgee or a flag officer's flag.

Normally a flag officer of a club always flies his flag officer's flag (with appropriate special ensign, if any) in preference to the burgee of some other club of which he is a member. But special occasions may arise when it is appropriate to depart from this general rule – as for example when another club stages a rally or regatta which he is attending.

An owner who is not a flag officer of any club but who belongs to a club in the harbour where his boat is lying should use the burgee (and special ensign, if any) of that club. If he belongs to more than one local club he should use the burgee (and special ensign, if any) of the senior one, unless one of the other clubs is holding a regatta or similar function.

6.8.7 House flag

Some owners have a private, distinguishing flag, square in shape, which is normally flown at the starboard crosstrees, but in harbour only. It should be hoisted and lowered at the same times as the burgee and Ensign. The design of a house flag must not conflict with that of any other official or existing flag. The general practice is that a house flag is only flown when the owner is on board.

6.8.8 Yacht racing

The various flags and signals connected with yacht racing are detailed in the rules – RYA booklet YR1.

6.8.9 Salutes

It is customary for yachts to salute all Royal Yachts and all warships, and flag officers of the club whose burgee the yacht is flying (but normally only once a day). Salutes are made by dipping the Ensign (only) – lowering it about two-thirds of the way, but to a position where it will still fly. The salute is acknowledged by the other vessel dipping and re-hoisting her Ensign, when the saluting yacht then rehoists hers.

6.8.10 Dressing ship

Ships can be dressed in two ways – overall (only in harbour), or with masthead flags (normally only when under way in or near a harbour, but may be used as an alternative to dressing overall in vessels not fitted with dressing lines).

Dressing overall is done by flying the flags of the International Code (only) from stem to masthead, from masthead to masthead if there is more than one mast, and down to the taffrail. The triangular flags and pendants should be spaced out between the rectangular flags. The recommended order of flags, from forward, is:

E, Q, p3, G, p8, Z, p4, W, p6, P, pl, I, Code, T, Y, B, X, 1st Sub, H, 3rd Sub, D, F, 2nd Sub, U, A, O, M, R, p2, J, p0, N, p9, K, p7, V, p5, L, C, S.

The Ensign should be worn at its normal position, and there should be a flag (normally another similar Ensign) at each masthead.

For British national festivals (see below) a British Ensign is worn at each masthead, and at the main masthead the Ensign and club burgee fly side by side. But if the owner is a flag officer he flies his flag at the masthead without an Ensign. The principal occasions for dressing ship in this country are currently: Accession Day, Coronation Day, HM The Queen's Birthday, Commonwealth Day, HM The Queen's Official Birthday, HRH The Duke of Edinburgh's Birthday and HM The Queen Mother's Birthday.

For foreign national festivals (at home or abroad), the Ensign of the country concerned is flown – at the masthead alongside the burgee in single-masted yachts, at the mizzen masthead (in place of a British Ensign) in ketches and yawls, and at the fore masthead (in place of a British Ensign) in a schooner-rigged yacht. In the case of a flag officer, flying his flag (alone) at the masthead of a single-masthead yacht, the foreign Ensign should be flown at the starboard crosstrees.

When dressing ship for a local occasion (e.g. a regatta) the club burgee should be flown at the main masthead, and no Ensign. An Ensign should be worn at any other masthead. On all occasions of dressing ship it is important that the same design of Ensign is worn in different parts of the vessel.

Distress Signals – see also Chapter 8 (8.3.10)

Note: Only to be used if the vessel is in serious and immediate danger, and help is urgently required

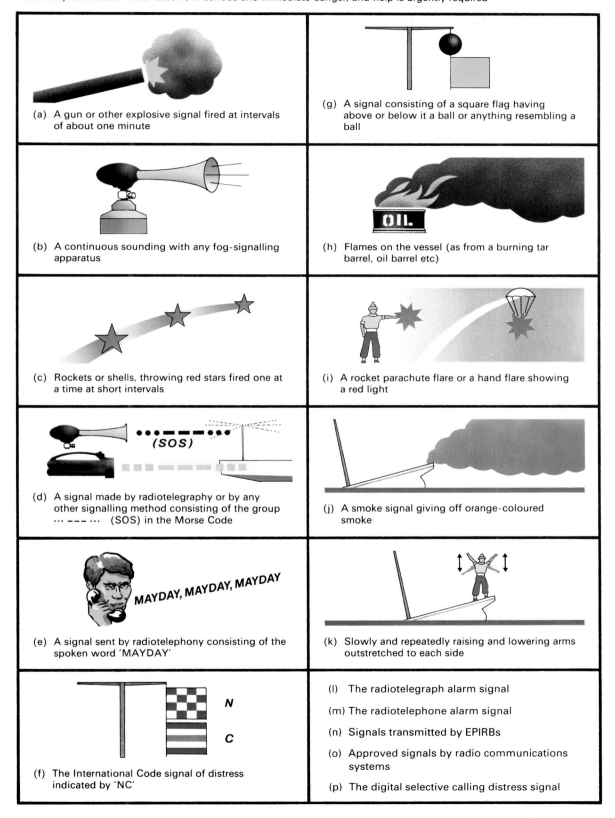

(a) A gun or other explosive signal fired at intervals of about one minute

(b) A continuous sounding with any fog-signalling apparatus

(c) Rockets or shells, throwing red stars fired one at a time at short intervals

(d) A signal made by radiotelegraphy or by any other signalling method consisting of the group ··· ––– ··· (SOS) in the Morse Code

(e) A signal sent by radiotelephony consisting of the spoken word 'MAYDAY'

(f) The International Code signal of distress indicated by 'NC'

(g) A signal consisting of a square flag having above or below it a ball or anything resembling a ball

(h) Flames on the vessel (as from a burning tar barrel, oil barrel etc)

(i) A rocket parachute flare or a hand flare showing a red light

(j) A smoke signal giving off orange-coloured smoke

(k) Slowly and repeatedly raising and lowering arms outstretched to each side

(l) The radiotelegraph alarm signal

(m) The radiotelephone alarm signal

(n) Signals transmitted by EPIRBs

(o) Approved signals by radio communications systems

(p) The digital selective calling distress signal

Types of Cloud – see also Chapter 7 (7.1.9)

1. Typical Cirrus (Mares' Tails) invading the sky, and heralding a warm front when moving rapidly from the North West or West.

2. When Cirrus is thinning out it indicates fine weather, but here Cirrus and Cirrocumulus are increasing and thickening from the West.

3. 8/8 Cirrostratus and a 22° halo round the sun – one of the surer signs of deteriorating weather in the offing.

4. Clouds now thicker and lower – Altocumulus in several layers and gradually increasing, with signs of Altostratus in the distance.

5. Thin Altostratus with a watery sun. The first few spots of rain are felt, and the wind is increasing from the South East or South.

6. 8/8 Nimbostratus – a grey layer of cloud blotting out the sun, and bringing continuous rain with it.

Pictures 1–6 above illustrate a typical sequence of clouds seen with an approaching warm front.

Types of Cloud – see also Chapter 7 (7.1.9)

7. Now in the warm sector – 8/8 Stratus; sometimes sea fog too, when the air is moist and warmer than the water.

8. Stratocumulus in the warm sector, well to the south of the depression. This cloud occurs of course with other air streams.

9. Large Cumulus and Cumulonimbus herald the approach of a vigorous cold front. Be prepared for squalls and a veering wind.

10. Small, fair weather Cumulus shows little sign of growth as the day proceeds. Most Cumulus clouds originate over the land.

11. Typical large Cumulus (Mediocris) in cold air. This type of cloud gives warning of showers occuring, with squally winds.

12. Cumulonimbus and heavy showers, often with rapid wind changes and squalls as the shower passes. Here expect a line squall, with a definite veer.

Pictures 7 and 8 show warm sector weather; 9 the approach of a cold front; and 10–12 the growth of Cumulus.

Lifesaving Signals – see also Chapter 6 (6.4.4)

(1) Landing signals for the guidance of small boats with crews or persons in distress

Manual signals

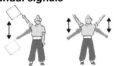

Vertical motion of a white flag (or white light or flare by night) or of the arms

Other signals
International Code letter **'K'** by light or sound

Meaning
'This is the best place to land'
(An indication of direction may be given by a steady white light or flare at a lower level)

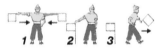

Horizontal motion of a white flag (or white light or flare by night) or of the arms extended horizontally

International Code letter **'S'** by light or sound

● ● ●

'Landing here is highly dangerous'

Horizontal motion of a white flag followed by 2. the placing of the white flag in the ground and 3. by the carrying of another white flag in the direction to be indicated.
  By night white lights or flares are used instead of white flags

1. Signalling the code letter **'S'** (●●●), followed by the code letter **'R'** (●—●) if the better landing place is more to the right in the direction of approach, or 2. Signalling the code letter **'S'** (●●●), followed by the code letter **'L'** (●—●●) if the better landing place is more to the left in the direction of approach

'Landing here is highly dangerous. A more favourable location for landing is in the direction indicated'

(2) Signals to be employed in connection with the use of shore life-saving apparatus

Vertical motion of a white flag (or white light or flare by night) or of the arms

In general: affirmative. Specifically: rocket line is held – tail block is made fast – hawser is made fast – man is in the breeches buoy – haul away

Horizontal motion of a white flag (or white light or flare by night) or of the arms

In general: negative. Specifically: slack away – avast hauling

(3) Replies from life-saving stations etc. to distress signals made by a ship or person

Pyrotechnic signals
Orange smoke signal

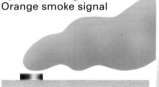

White star rocket – three single signals fired at intervals of about one minute

Combined light and sound signal – three single signals fired at intervals of about one minute

'You are seen – assistance will be given as soon as possible'

(4) Signals to be used to warn a ship which is standing into danger

International Code signals **'U'** [flag] or **'NF'** [flags]

'You are running into danger'

International Code letter **'U'** by light or sound ● ● ▬

Attention may be called to (1) to (4) above by a white flare, a rocket showing white stars on bursting, or an explosive sound signal.

(5) Signals used by Sub-Aqua divers
Left: 'I am OK'   Right: 'I need assistance'

Dressing with masthead flags is carried out by wearing Ensign(s) at the masthead(s), as described above, without dressing lines.

6.8. 11 Mourning

Mourning is indicated by wearing the Ensign and (in the case of private mourning only) the burgee at half mast. When colours are hoisted to the half mast position they should first be hoisted close up, and after a pause lowered to the dipped position. When they are to be lowered they should first be hoisted close up, before being lowered to the deck.

National mourning is observed on such occasions as the death of a member of the Royal Family. The Ensign (only) is half masted when news is received, and kept at half mast until sunset; or if news is received at night, then the Ensign is flown at half mast throughout the next day. Colours are again half masted while the funeral is in progress.

HM Ships half mast Ensigns and jacks when the funeral of an officer or rating takes place in a port where they are lying. Yachts present should conform.

Private mourning may be observed when the owner of a yacht dies, or when for example a flag officer or a past flag officer of a club dies. On such occasions both the Ensign and burgee are half masted, the procedure otherwise being similar to national mourning described above.

Chapter 7

Weather

Contents

7.1 What makes the weather

7.1.1 Introduction
Of all leisure activities, sailing is probably the most weather sensitive. It is therefore in the interests of anyone going to sea that they have a knowledge of how the weather works and to be able to interpret weather forecasts. It is also necessary to show that a certain amount of meteorological knowledge has been acquired before some of the RYA certificates are granted.

Modern aids such as satellites and powerful computers have done much to improve the accuracy of weather forecasts in recent years but weather forecasting is not, and probably will never be, an exact science. In any case, no forecast could be sufficiently detailed to include all the variations within the period and the area covered by the forecast. It follows that it is useful for the mariner to be able to interpret forecasts to obtain maximum benefit from them. Part of the interpretation process is to be able to monitor the weather so that any departure from the forecast can be quickly detected, to allow some anticipation to be made of what is likely to happen in the future and appropriate action taken.

The general principles of weather forecasting are not too difficult to understand and it is a subject that can be studied and practised regularly. A good deal can be learned from a regular study of current weather charts and listening to the more detailed forecasts on radio such as those on BBC Radio 4. Much can also be learned by observing

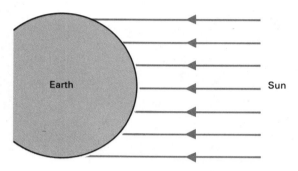

Fig. 7(1) Heat from the sun is not spread uniformly over the globe.

the weather, especially cloud formations and wind changes, and attempting to find the reasons for the various weather phenomena seen. It is, however, necessary to have some knowledge of how the atmosphere works to produce the weather around us.

7.1.2 The air around us

Air is a mixture of gases. By volume, dry air contains about 79% of nitrogen, 20% oxygen and the remainder small quantities of other gases. However, completely dry air does not exist in the free atmosphere – there is also a certain amount of water, variable in quantity and the most important constituent from the aspect of producing 'weather'.

The visible symptoms of the earth's weather and most of the significant changes occur in a relatively thin layer of air near the ground called the troposphere. This extends to about 16km (10 miles) above ground at the equator and to about 9km ($5\frac{1}{2}$ miles) at the poles.

The temperature of the air in the troposphere generally decreases with height, allowing air to move vertically and, as we shall see at 7.1.5, vertical movement is essential for the formation of cloud. The layer of air above the troposphere is called the stratosphere, where there is a gradual increase of temperature with height which means that cloud formation is inhibited.

7.1.3 Transfer of heat

The prime source of heat is of course the sun but as illustrated at Fig. 7(1) the radiation received from the sun is not the same over the whole of the globe. At the poles the incoming radiation energy is spread over a greater area than elsewhere and,

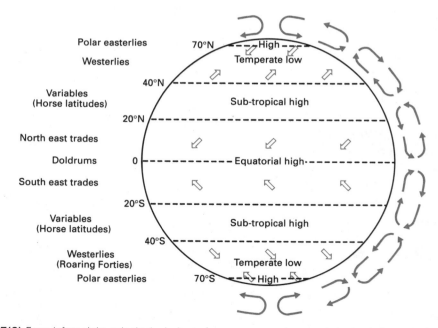

Fig. 7(2) From left to right, principal winds, surface pressure systems and air circulation over the globe.

due to the angle of the sun's rays, there is a greater loss from reflection. The poles show a net loss of heat from the sun throughout the 24 hours but at the equator the reverse is true and there is a net gain of heat. On these considerations alone the poles would become progressively colder and the equator increasingly hotter. The major weather systems around the globe are Nature's way of correcting this potential imbalance.

The 'weather machine' is a phrase sometimes applied to the development, movement and behaviour of weather systems on both global and local scales. Like steam and internal combustion engines, heat energy is used to do work. The movement of air horizontally and vertically and the evaporation of water are examples of work done by the weather machine and these processes play their part in transferring heat around the troposphere and maintaining the general status quo of the climate around the world.

Referring to Fig. 7(2), the excess heat at the equator is initially carried upward by convection. Because the atmosphere is less dense higher up, the rising air expands which leads to cooling. At the top of the troposphere the air can rise no further and it then spreads northward and southward until after further cooling it sinks back towards the ground where some returns to the equator at low level and some flows towards the poles.

While equatorial heat is being dispersed in this manner the cold surface of the poles makes the adjacent air colder and denser. This causes it to flow to lower latitudes where it will meet low level air from the sub-tropics, resulting in upward movement until the troposphere is reached where there is a northward and southward flow again, thus completing the vertical circulation shown at Fig. 7(2). As can be seen in Fig. 7(2), areas of rising air are associated with lower air pressure at the surface and descending air with higher surface pressure.

The general flow of air over the globe described above is a simplified model assuming that the earth has a smooth surface and with the sun over the equator – that is at an equinox; the general flow and the pressure systems shift northwards with the 'thermal equator' during the northern hemisphere summer as the earth tilts seasonally on its axis The reverse happens during the northern winter – see also Fig. 7(3).

The flow from high to low pressure at the surface sets up a circulation of air (more detail of this at 7.1.7). The land masses distort the circulations around the highs and lows breaking them into separate cells and as a result the flow to and from the equator and the poles occurs in bursts.

7.1.4 World weather

A study of local weather patterns must be done in the context of broader considerations – that is, the general distribution of pressure around the world and the weather patterns they produce. The general distribution of pressure areas were considered at 7.1.3. The areas of high and low pressure produce a circulation of wind at the surface. (The relationship of pressure systems and wind is considered in more detail in 7.1.6 and 7.1.7.) It was mentioned in 7.1.3 that land masses disturb the theoretical heat transfer flow of air.

The sub-tropical high pressure belts about latitudes 30°N and 30°S are split into separate regions of high pressure – commonly situated over the eastern part of each ocean – as for example the Azores high. Similarly the belt of low pressure round the world in about 60°N is divided into two regions of low pressure near Iceland and the Aleutians. In the southern hemisphere the belt of low pressure does extend more or less round the world because there are no major land masses in this latitude.

Other factors distort the theoretical picture. Over large land masses pressure tends to build in the winter and to fall in the summer, and these seasonal changes can considerably modify the wind system over nearby oceans – as for example the monsoon winds which blow over the Indian Ocean. Then the belts of high and low pressure drift somewhat north and south during the year, following the sun. To a lesser extent, ocean currents (discussed in 9.10.15) affect the pressure over the world's surface, as they transfer some heat from place to place.

Fig. 7(3) shows the principal regions of high and low pressure, and the main wind systems, throughout the world in January and July, but in the following discussion remarks are confined to the Atlantic Ocean. The Equatorial Trough (Doldrums) represented by the heavy dotted line, is a low pressure area between the NE trade winds north of the equator and the SE trades to the south of it. Although renowned for their light winds, the Doldrums have very changeable weather; their width varies greatly, but is typically 200–300 miles (322–483km).

The NE and SE trade winds blow persistently, mostly about Force 4 and sometimes stronger, but seldom of gale force. The weather is usually fair, with small detached cumulus clouds, described in 7. 1.9, rather wetter on the western side of the Atlantic. The amount of cloud and rain experienced increases towards the Equatorial Trough. Normally the barometer is steady, apart from the diurnal variation described in 7.1.14, but if this diurnal rise and fall ceases, or if the barometer rises or falls to any marked degree, it may portend a tropical disturbance (see 7.1.16).

On the polar side of the trade wind belts lie areas of anticyclones called The Variables (or the Horse Latitudes), with calms, or light to moderate winds variable in direction. Here the weather is usually fine, with only small amounts of cloud and rain.

North of 35°N, and south of 35°S, the winds become more predominantly westerly as latitude increases – more especially in the southern

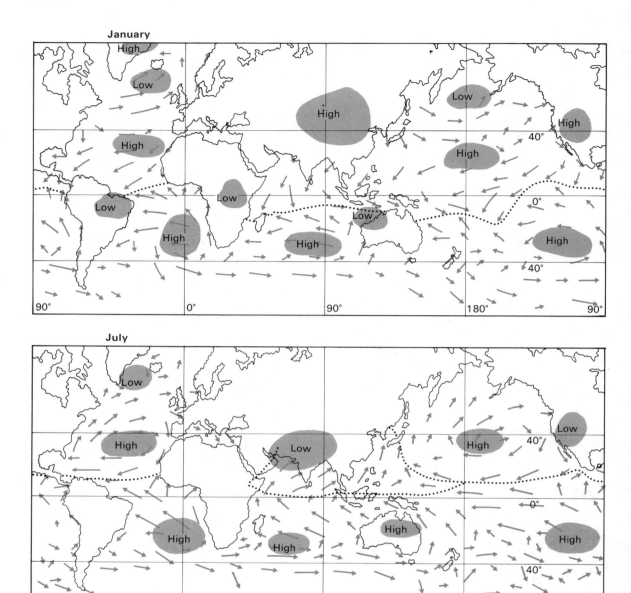

Fig. 7(3) Pressure distribution and wind systems in January and July. The dotted line indicates the Equatorial Trough. The relative strength of wind is shown by the length of the arrows.

hemisphere where the significance of the Roaring Forties needs little explanation. In the northern hemisphere the westerlies in the North Atlantic are in general lighter and not so constant in direction, due to the large land masses and the effects of the depressions which form along the polar front (see 7.1.10 below). Fog is common in summer on the western side of the North Atlantic.

The polar regions are largely unnavigable due to ice. The wind is generally easterly, and the weather often cloudy with frequent fog in summer.

In some parts of the world, particularly the Indian Ocean and the West Pacific, the general distribution of pressure described above is very much influenced by the seasonal heating and cooling of the adjacent land masses.

7.1.5 Air masses

It should always be remembered that weather systems work in the three dimensions of space and the weather will depend largely upon the vertical temperature profile of the air. The temperature profile of the air at any place will depend upon where the air came from, and how it has been changed during its journey.

When air has originated from a polar source it is naturally cold, and a simplified temperature/height graph of such air might look like the solid blue line in Fig. 7(4). If that air is then carried to

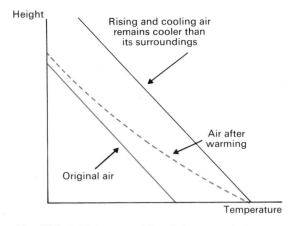

Fig. 7(4) Cold air warmed from below to make it unstable.

lower latitudes (for example in the wake of a cold front) the temperature of the lower layers will be increasingly raised by the warmer underlying surface, thus changing the shape of the graph as indicated by the dotted line. If further heating is applied to the air at the surface – perhaps by sunshine – the air will rise by convection. The rising air cools, but provided that it remains warmer than its environment it will continue its upward motion. This condition is known as 'unstable' air, and is associated with good visibility, cumuliform cloud and gusty wind.

The reverse process occurs when a large mass of air is taken to higher latitudes, as indicated in Fig. 7(5). A situation is reached when any parcel of rising air will soon cool to the temperature of its surroundings, and can rise no further unless mechanically lifted – as it may be by turbulence, or by passing over a mountain range. This condition is known as 'stable' air, which often brings layered cloud, fairly steady winds, and sometimes poor visibility. As shown in Fig. 7(5) the surface cooling can lead to a layer of air with a higher temperature than the layer beneath; this is called a temperature inversion.

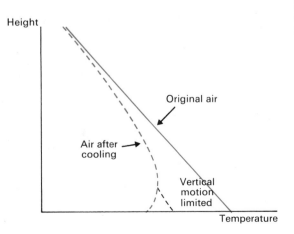

Fig. 7(5) Warm air cooled from below, making it stable.

Air masses can be divided into two main groups: a maritime type, when the air becomes humid as a result of passage over a sea surface, and a continental type, when the air is drier due to its movement over a land mass. Each group can be subdivided according to the source region of the air mass. The main types affecting Britain and northwest Europe are described below.

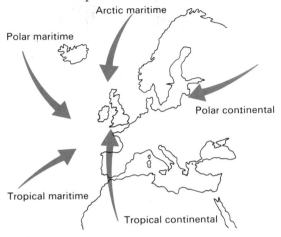

Fig. 7(6) The various types of air masses which influence our weather have widely different characteristics, depending upon their origins.

Tropical maritime air
While it may have started as unstable air, it has been cooled at the surface during its journey over the water towards northwest Europe and become stable and more humid. The weather is typically fairly warm with layered cloud (see cloud colour plates 7 and 8) from which rain or drizzle may fall. The visibility at sea is rarely good and when the humidity is high, sea fog frequently occurs especially during Spring and early Summer with the waters of the near Atlantic, the Irish Sea and the English Channel being most affected. With the air being constrained beneath a temperature inversion near the surface, the wind is usually quite steady.

Polar maritime air
As its title suggests, this air originated over the polar region and has typically moved south towards Greenland before travelling southeastward towards Britain. Naturally it is cold air but has been modified near the surface as it moved over the relatively warmer waters of the north Atlantic. Therefore the air is unstable by the time it reaches Britain. The weather is typically fairly cold with passing showers. The clouds have a good deal of vertical development (see cloud colour plates 11 and 12). The visibility is usually very good (except in any showers). The wind tends to be variable in speed with a large range between gusts and lulls and sometimes very blustery conditions occur, especially in the vicinity of heavy showers with the possibility of squalls. The wind direction will also vary with the gusts and lulls.

Arctic maritime air

This air mass can be considered to be a variation of polar maritime air and it is unstable for similar reasons. The difference is that the air is carried more directly from the polar region and thus it is colder. This air mass is often brought to Britain when there is a low pressure area over Scandinavia which adds to the upward movement of unstable air. This leads to a greater frequency of blustery showers, especially over the North Sea and the waters around northern Scotland. Gustiness is a feature of the winds, particularly to the north and east of Britain. While visibility will be generally good it will obviously decrease during showers, and in the winter half of the year snow showers can bring a sudden and dramatic decrease in visibility.

Polar continental air

There is usually a marked difference in the general weather brought by this air mass to Britain. In summer the skies are often cloudless, especially over waters in the south and west. Although the air tends to become unstable as a result of day-time heating over mainland Europe, the air is normally too dry to produce much in the way of cloud and showers. Visibility is moderate or good but often the air flow backs to the southeast further north over the North Sea, and with a longer sea track the air becomes moister and cooler with a low-level inversion developing. This leads to very low cloud and often to sea fog, known as 'haar' (cloud colour plate 7). These conditions occur mostly over the waters off northeast Britain, especially in the Spring and early Summer, and can persist for many days.

In winter the air has started its journey being cold and remains so as it passes over the cold ground of continental Europe. The sky tends to be either clear due to the dryness of the air or covered with layers of low cloud trapped under an inversion. A generally dry pattern of weather can be expected apart from occasional light rain or snow, although occasionally an introduction of moisture can bring heavier falls of rain or snow to southern Britain. The visibility is usually not good and haar continues to present a problem off the northeast coast. Winds are usually fairly steady depending upon the depth of any inversion, but frequently strong easterlies set in over southern Britain.

Tropical continental air

Like polar continental air the weather produced by this air mass varies seasonally. It occurs infrequently in the winter but when it does it is similar to a warmer form of polar continental air. A low-level inversion tends to develop as the air passes over the cold land and thus any cloud will be layered similar to cloud colour plate 8. The wind tends to be steady and rarely strong. While the visibility is not usually very good, fog is fairly infrequent with western areas being more likely to be affected.

During the summer the precise track of the air is critical with regard to its effect upon the weather. If the air has come from due south or a little east of south the air will be dry with little cloud. Daytime heating results in some instability so there is a degree of gustiness to the wind. The visibility is usually quite good but often hazy. The situation is changed considerably if a veer of the flow brings the air from over the waters off northwest Africa and Iberia. The increased humidity coupled with instability from strong day heating will cause deep clouds to form (cloud colour plates 9, 11 and 12) with thunderstorms over Spain and southwest France. These storms often migrate northwards to Britain with their attendant risks of extreme gustiness and wind shifts and sudden deterioration of visibility. The brunt of these storms is usually taken by the southwestern part of Britain. Thundery weather of this type often occurs at the end of a settled spell when the air flow gradually veers and the air mass changes from polar continental to tropical continental and eventually to a maritime type.

Although the above describes the common air mass types that affect Britain and northwest Europe, every weather situation is unique and there are many variations.

Where different air masses are brought together the boundary between the air masses is called a 'front' with the warmer air mass, being less dense, rising over the colder one. Although some mixing occurs between the air masses they retain their individual identity for several days and the passing of a front is the most common way for a change in air mass over Britain.

7.1.6 Atmospheric pressure

The atmosphere exerts a force upon the earth; the pressure of that force is the weight of air directly above a point on the earth – about 10,000kg (10 tons) per square metre. The pressure can be expressed in several ways: for many years it was expressed as the equivalent height, in inches or millimetres, of a column of mercury that was necessary to balance the weight of the air.

The SI unit of pressure is the pascal but in meteorology 100 pascals (called a hectopascal) is generally used as the standard unit of atmospheric pressure. In recent times the millibar, which is the equivalent to a hectopascal, has been normally quoted in weather reports and forecasts but the term hectopascal is increasingly being used, especially on the Continent.

A conversion scale from millibars or hectopascals to inches and millimetres of mercury is shown in Fig. 7(21). In Britain a surface air pressure of about 950 millibars or hectopascals would be very low and 1050 very high, with the average being around 1013.

The distribution of pressure at a certain time is vital information for the meteorologist who uses reports of pressure readings made at the same time from many places. Because there is less air above, the pressure decreases with increasing altitude and in order that the reports are mutually consistent, pressure readings are adjusted to a datum of mean sea level. From these readings a chart can be produced with lines (isobars) drawn on it that connect places with equal atmospheric pressure. Isobars are usually drawn at equal intervals on either side of 1000mb, the interval between isobars depending upon the scale of the chart. By these means areas of high pressure (anticyclones) and low pressure (depressions) can be identified.

Pressure readings also provide the mariner with valuable information and greatly assist in monitoring weather changes and forecasts received. Any seagoing yacht should carry an aneroid barometer (or better still a suitably mounted barograph that continuously records pressure on a chart). While the changes in pressure are often of most importance it is useful to be able to compare the pressure at one's own location with a weather map or the pressures quoted in shipping forecasts. In order to make a sensible comparison the ship's instrument should be set to mean sea level pressure, and this should be done on board using the present pressure reading for that place. The correct figure to use can normally be obtained by telephoning the local Met. Office.

7.1.7 Wind
Isobars are like contours on a map. When contours are close together the gradient is steep: when isobars are close together the pressure gradient is steep – or pressure is changing rapidly. Since wind is caused by air moving due to changes of pressure it follows that stronger winds will be experienced where the isobars are closely spaced, whereas few isobars which are well spaced out indicate light winds. Thus in Fig. 7(7) the winds at A could be expected to be stronger than at B.

The curvature of the isobars also has an effect on the wind speed. When the isobars are curved cyclonically, i.e. round a depression, the wind

speed is less for the same spacing of isobars than round high pressure. Although in Fig. 7(7) the isobars at C and D are of the same spacing, the wind at D will be much stronger. The extension of a low as shown at C is called a trough while the extension of a high as at D is called a ridge.

Air would like to move directly from an area of high pressure to one of low pressure, but it only does this near the equator. Elsewhere, due to the rotation of the earth (Coriolis Force), it is deflected to the right in the northern hemisphere and to the left in the southern.

It was a Dutchman called Buys Ballot who recognised the relation between isobars and the wind. His law can best be remembered by the fact that if in the northern hemisphere you stand with your Back to the Blast (wind), the Low pressure is on your Left.

However you choose to retain this in your mind, it is important to remember that in the northern hemisphere winds blow anti-clockwise round a low and clockwise round a high, while in the southern hemisphere the circulation is clockwise round lows and anti-clockwise round highs.

Without the earth's frictional effect, winds at about 600m (2000ft) blow freely and roughly parallel to the isobars – the general direction of low cloud (see 7.1.9) movement. At the surface, friction causes the wind to be backed from the free flow wind in the northern hemisphere and veered in the southern hemisphere. The amount of this backing/veering is about 30° over land and 10 to 15° over the open sea.

On some weather maps there is a geostrophic scale against which the spacing of isobars at (usually) 2mb intervals can be read, to give the approximate wind speed or Beaufort force as shown in Fig. 7(8). The scale is placed at right angles to the isobars at the place required, with the highest end of the scale on one isobar, and the reading taken where the next isobar (2mb higher or lower) cuts the scale. Such charts for yachtsmen give the wind speed at sea level, but those used by meteorologists give the wind speed at 600m (2000ft). In this case the wind at sea level is likely to be about $\frac{2}{3}$ the speed shown, due to surface friction.

This raises the point that the wind speed over the open sea can be twice what it is over the land, which needs to be borne in mind when you are in harbour, trying to decide whether or not to put to sea. It applies particularly in sheltered harbours with off-shore winds. It should also be remembered that the wind is less at sea level or ground level than it is even 9m (30ft) above. As we have seen at 7.1.5 the character of the wind, that is, its short-term variability in speed and direction, will depend upon the air mass.

Wind strengths are commonly expressed in forecasts and for other purposes in terms of the Beaufort scale (see 7.3). This originated as an attempt to relate the strength of the wind (when

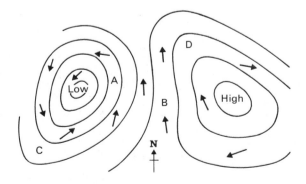

Fig. 7(7) How isobars depict an area of low pressure, (depression) on the left, and an area of high pressure (anticyclone) on the right. The arrows show typical wind circulations in the northern hemisphere.

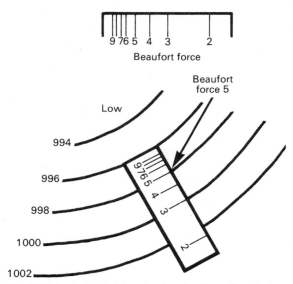

9 7 6 5 4 3 2
Beaufort force

Beaufort force 5

Low

994

996

998

1000

1002

Fig. 7(8) Scale for deriving the Beaufort force from isobar spacing on an RYA weather map.

there were no instruments to measure its speed) to the amount of sail a ship could carry, and later to the effect of the wind on the sea state. It should not be imagined that terms such as 'Force 5' or 'Force 7' have any direct significance in respect of the physical force of the wind − on a sail for example. The actual force exerted on a sail is proportional to the square of the wind speed. Hence a wind of Force 7 (say 30 knots) would have more than twice the weight of a wind of Force 5 (say 20 knots). This explains why even a fairly small increase in wind speed can have a significant effect on a sailing yacht.

7.1.8 Humidity
Passing mention was made earlier (7.1.2) of the important presence of water in the air. It is now considered in rather more detail. Water occurs naturally in three forms: solid (ice), liquid (water or water droplets) and as an invisible vapour. All air contains some water vapour and the amount of vapour it can hold depends upon the temperature of the air. The lower the temperature the less moisture the air can hold in vapour form. For example, air at 0°C (32°F) can hold only half as much water vapour as air at 10°C (50°F). When air is progressively cooled it will eventually reach a condition when it can no longer hold the vapour without condensing into a liquid or solid state − water droplets or ice crystals. The temperature to which air needs to be cooled so that water condenses from its vaporous form to water, is called the 'dew point'. Apart from cooling due to contact with a cold surface, the usual way for air to be cooled is by upward motion. As the air rises into a less dense environment it expands and cools.

The most common manifestation of moisture in the air is the presence of clouds and the various forms are described in the following section.

7.1.9 Clouds
Recognition of the different types of cloud, and knowledge of how they form, move, change and decay, is a great help when studying the local weather or making your own forecast. When observing clouds the extent of cover, the heights and types of cloud present, and their directions of movement should all be recorded. If this is too daunting a task, try to determine the dominant types of upper and lower cloud.

There are four different types of cloud, depending on how the air is made to ascend and is therefore cooled so that the dew point is reached.

Convection clouds
In unstable conditions rising air is cooled to its dew point and forms heaped up cumulus cloud described later.

Clouds due to turbulence
Over the sea turbulence may extend to about 600m (2000ft) when the wind is strong. If the air is sufficiently damp to be cooled to its dew point at this height, a sheet of stratus cloud may be formed.

Orographic clouds
This is the type of cloud formed when damp air is forced up or over the top of a hill. By its nature it is not of much direct consequence to yachtsmen.

Frontal cloud
This is caused by a mass of relatively warm air meeting a mass of cooler air, so that the warm air, being lighter, climbs up over the cold air (or is forced upwards by the cold air driving underneath).

Basically clouds are divided into three levels − high, medium and low levels depending on the height of their base. In some cases it may not be easy to decide the actual heights of clouds, but it is usually simple to decide their other main feature − whether they have vertical development and individual form (cumulus type) or whether they are a shapeless type of spreading cloud (stratus type).

Main cloud types

Cirrus	Ci	High clouds	Typically above 6700m (22,000ft)
Cirrocumulus	Cc		
Cirrostratus	Cs		
Altocumulus	Ac	Medium clouds	2135–6100m (7000–20,000ft)
Altostratus	As		
Nimbostratus	Ns	Low clouds	Usually below 2135m (7000ft)
Stratus	St		
Stratocumulus	Sc		
Cumulus	Cu	ditto	but these may extend vertically into High clouds
Cumulonimbus	Cb		

Where appropriate read the following descriptions of the ten more common types of cloud listed above in conjunction with the coloured cloud pictures on pages 224-225. These pictures show:

1–6   A typical warm front sequence (cirrus, cirrocumulus, cirrostratus, altocumulus, altostratus, nimbostratus)
7–8   Warm sector weather (stratus, stratocumulus)
9   Cold front (cumulus, cumulonimbus)
10–12   The growth of cumulus cloud

In studying cloud types it is helpful to understand the meaning of certain terms:

Cirrus   —   feathery
Stratus   —   layers or sheets
Cumulus   —   heaped
Alto   —   medium level cloud
Nimbus   —   rain bearing
Fracto   —   broken

High cloud

Cirrus (Ci) White, feathery, isolated clouds of ice crystals which cast no shadow. When thin and tufted they are often called 'mares' tails'. Usually indicate strong wind at altitude. Thin, high level cirrus means good weather, but when it thickens and consolidates into cirrostratus and altostratus, it foretells an advancing depression or frontal system.

Cirrocumulus (Cc) Banks or rows of small white flakes, sometimes rippled or patterned (mackerel sky). Thicker than cirrostratus and usually contrasted against the blue sky. May indicate changeable weather. A transient form of cloud which often develops from cirrus or cirrostratus, and then changes back to these or other forms.

Cirrostratus (Cs) A thin white veil of transparent cloud, often giving haloes round the sun and moon. Often follows cirrus and precedes altostratus, heralding a depression and deteriorating weather.

Medium cloud

Altocumulus (Ac) Longish layers or patches of white or pale grey cloud, usually in groups or lines. Rather similar to cirrocumulus, but larger and thicker, with a darker pattern. If much vertical development is evident it is a sign of instability which may give rise to thunderstorms.

Altostratus (As) A sheet of cloud which may follow cirrostratus (although it is lower and thicker), in which case rain almost invariably follows with an approaching front. Altostratus often varies in density — dark in some parts but the sun can be seen through others. It may cover the whole sky.

Low cloud

Nimbostratus (Ns) A dense grey layer of low cloud which forms below altostratus, covering the whole sky and giving steady precipitation; often with scud detached from the main cloud layer.

Stratus (St) Low sheet of uniform grey cloud, like fog not resting on the ground. The sun can sometimes be seen through it. It may cover the whole sky, or only be patches trailing over the sea. Often associated with drizzle and poor visibility.

Stratocumulus (Sc) Irregular masses or rolls of large puffy clouds, with varying degrees of darkness, and often a thick wavy appearance. Common in winter, bringing drizzle rather than rain.

Cumulus (Cu) Clouds with clear outlines, separated from each other. They have flat, grey bottoms; white, puffy sides; and billowing tops, with considerable vertical development. Cumulus comes in all sizes. Small puffy cumulus indicates fair weather.

Cumulonimbus (Cb) Towering and forbidding storm clouds; when well developed, marked by anvil tops indicating powerful rising air currents – often producing squally winds with rain, heavy showers of hail or snow, and frequently thunder. Often embedded in intense cold fronts and vigorous troughs.

7.1.10 Depressions and fronts

Depressions which affect the British Isles mostly originate from a distortion of the polar front (although there are other types of low which can start, for example, from thundery conditions). All frontal depressions have a finite life: some persist longer than others, some become deeper and more vigorous, while others quickly disappear. But during their varying lives the Atlantic depressions are all continually changing as they meet up with or absorb other air masses in their general movement, which is often in an ENE direction passing northward of the British Isles.

Around a depression are formed marked boundaries between the different types of air masses which have helped to get it established. Warm air is lighter than cold, so where a warm air mass advances towards colder air the warm air tends to rise up over the cold before any significant mixing takes place. This is called a warm front, see Fig. 7(9). As the warm air is forced upwards it is cooled and is likely to produce cloud and possibly rain.

Behind the warm front, where colder air is overtaking warm, is formed a cold front – with the cold air driving in under the warm in a wedge action – pushing the warm air upwards even more vigorously. Sometimes the cold air lifts all the warm air off the surface of the land or sea, in which case the front is called occluded.

There are two types of occlusion, depending on whether the air ahead of or behind the occluded front is the colder. With the cold front type of

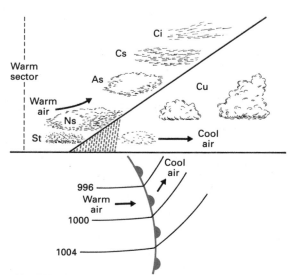

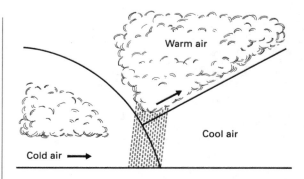

Fig. 7(11) Cross section of an occlusion (cold front type).

Fig. 7(9) Section and plan view of a warm front.

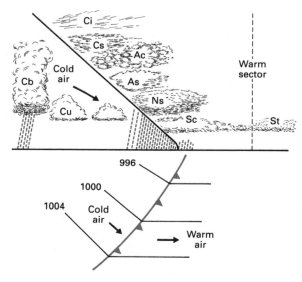

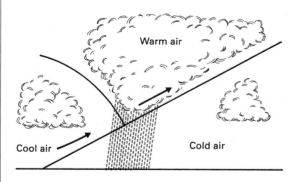

Fig. 7(12) Cross section of an occlusion (warm front type).

Fig. 7(10) Section and plan view of a cold front.

occlusion, as in Fig. 7(11), cold air has overtaken a warm air mass, lifting it off the surface, and has then caught up air which is cool but not so cold as itself. This usually results in rain from the warm front, which continues for a while after the front has passed followed by characteristic cold front wind and cooler weather. This is the more common type of occlusion experienced in the region of the British Isles.

A warm front occlusion, shown in Fig. 7(12), is where the overtaking air is cool but not so cold as the air ahead of the front. The front is not so active as a cold front occlusion and is followed by somewhat warmer air.

Fig. 7(13) shows a typical or 'model' depression with its associated warm and cold fronts. AW (indicated by the rounded marks) is the warm front and AC (with the spiked marks) is the cold front. Between them is the warm sector, behind

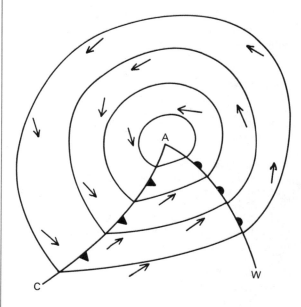

Fig. 7(13) Model depression, showing warm front (AW) and cold front (AC). The arrows indicate wind directions.

the warm front. The arrows indicate the probable wind directions. The frontal symbols are placed on the forward side of a front so they indicate the direction of movement of the front as well as its type. An occlusion is symbolised by alternate

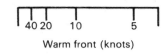

Warm front (knots)

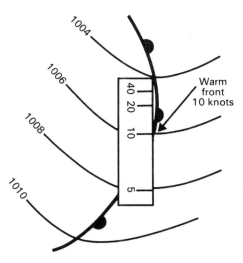

Warm
front
10 knots

Fig. 7(14) Speed of front scales. Above, for warm front.
Below, for cold front or occlusion.

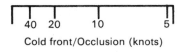

Cold front/Occlusion (knots)

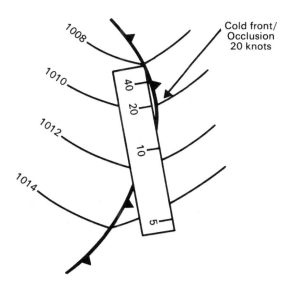

Cold front/
Occlusion
20 knots

round and triangular marks. On coloured charts a
warm front is marked red, a cold front is blue, and
an occlusion is purple.

The speed and direction of movements of
depressions and their associated fronts are
complicated, and it is best to rely on information
given in whatever forecasts are available. However
weather charts such as those supplied by the RYA

have scales, as shown in Fig. 7(14), with which the
speeds of warm and cold fronts can be estimated
in a similar way to wind speeds, as previously
described. Cold fronts and occlusions usually
move faster than warm fronts.

Depressions vary considerably in size and their
speed of movement. They can be a thousand miles
or more in diameter, or barely cover a shipping
forecast area. They can travel at over 50 knots, but
the depressions which cover a large area are
usually the slower moving ones. With the simplest
form of depression the isobars are roughly circular
around the centre, but often a depression is of an
elongated shape, with the worst of the weather in
troughs of low pressure extending from the centre.
All fronts lie in a trough, but not all troughs are
'frontal'.

Sometimes a secondary depression will form in a
trough. This occurs more frequently in a frontal
trough some distance from the parent depression.
Such secondaries can develop and move very
rapidly, causing a sudden and possibly unforseen
increase of wind.

7.1.11 The passage of a depression

Around the British Isles depressions and their
associated fronts typically approach from the west
and pass through to the east, with the centre of
the depression usually to the north, so it is useful
to study the sort of weather sequence this causes,
and which is illustrated in Fig. 7(15).

Initially, with the warm front still well to the
west (A), the weather is fine with a moderate
south-westerly wind; there may be some cumulus
cloud around, and probably cirrus spreading from
the west. The speed and quantity of the cirrus
cloud is a good indication of the depth of the
depression and of resulting strong winds. The
barometer shows a tendency to fall.

As the warm front approaches (B) the wind
backs southerly, the barometer falls, and cloud
cover increases – initially thin cirrus with streaky
white tufts or mares' tails, but steadily developing
into thicker cirrostratus, possibly with a halo.

With the warm front even nearer (C) the cloud
lowers and thickens, first into altostratus and then
nimbostratus; the glass drops faster, and the wind
increases and perhaps backs south east. It starts to
rain and visibility deteriorates.

At the warm front (D) the rain lets up or stops,
the barometer steadies, and the wind veers into
the south west. In the stable air of the warm sector
the visibility is poor, with low cloud and mist. If
the centre of the depression passes some distance
away the cloud may break.

With the passing of the cold front (E) the wind
veers sharply to the west or north west, perhaps
with a squall. The cold front approaches from the
west with a thick bank of cloud, but often this is
not visible due to overcast conditions in the warm
sector, so its sudden arrival may not be expected.
The clouds start to break as the rain ceases and
visibility improves, and the barometer starts to

rise. As the cold front goes through to the east (F) the glass rises further, and the weather brightens with cumulus clouds developing in the unstable air; these may extend vertically into cumulonimbus, causing showers, perhaps with anvil tops and thunderstorms.

Depending on the yacht's position relative to the centre of the depression, very different weather conditions and wind strengths will be experienced, and depressions do not always move as predicted: they can speed up, slow down, deepen, fill or change direction.

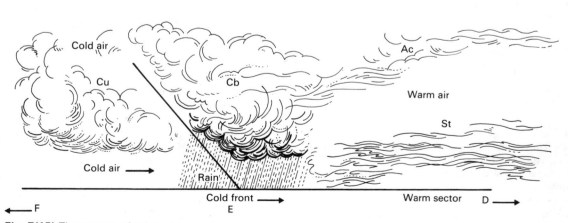

Fig. 7(15) The passage of a depression.

If the centre of the depression passes to the south of the observer there is altogether a smoother transition of weather, without the sudden changes and veers of wind which occur with the passage of fronts south of a depression. Instead the wind continually backs, initially with increasing cloud, as the glass falls. By the time the centre of the low is almost south of the observer the glass is steadier, the wind somewhere from the east, and it is raining. When the centre has passed to the south the wind backs to north east, the barometer rises, and the rain may slacken.

As the depression moves away to the east the wind backs through north to a north-westerly point, and a convective cloud system of cumulus or cumulonimbus becomes established – as behind the cold front further south.

The foregoing describes a 'typical' frontal depression, crossing the British Isles from the west, but each one is unique, with its own variations.

7. 1 .12 Anticyclones

The wind circulation around an anticyclone has been considered in 7.1.7 and as we saw at 7.1.3 an area of relatively high pressure is associated with descending air (called subsidence). This section looks at the behaviour of anticyclones or highs and the general weather characteristics they bring.

A large anticyclone is usually slow to move but a smaller one can move or disperse quite quickly. The summer climate of Britain is often influenced by the northward movement of the semi-permanent high near the Azores (see Fig. 7(3)) causing lows to take a more northern track. Anticyclones are normally associated with fair weather and light winds, but an established high often deflects lows around its periphery where the winds can be quite strong and with occasional poor weather. A ridge has similar characteristics.

As the air subsides it is also warmed thus creating stability and inhibiting upward motion, and hence the general fair weather. As this process continues an inversion often develops near the surface under which the visibility is rarely good and a cloud layer can be trapped, especially in the winter. In winter the low light level resulting from the combination of poor visibility and overcast skies is often referred to as 'anticyclonic gloom'.

The inversion from a well-established high can also affect some radio signals and radar.

7.1.13 Fog

Like cloud, fog is water droplets in suspension in the air. Indeed fog can be considered to be cloud that has formed on the earth's surface. Fog develops in a similar way to cloud by air being cooled to its dew point. It follows that fog is more likely when the air is more humid, that is, when the dew point is relatively high and the air requires less cooling before the dew point is reached. When coastal sailing one should beware any fog banks that are seen offshore; a tidal change can cause the fog to change position with the speed of the tidal flow.

Fogs can be classified according to the way they develop; those of greatest interest to the sailor are:

Advection fog
This is the most common form encountered over the seas of northwest Europe. It occurs typically in moist tropical maritime air that is cooled to its dew point as it passes over a cooler sea surface. It is more likely when there is an inversion, when the sea temperature is relatively low (spring to early summer) and when the air has had a reasonably long sea track to acquire moisture and pick up salt particles which encourage the water droplets to form. Advection fog is not readily 'blown away' and can persist in quite strong winds. A clearance is usually brought about by a change of air mass or occasionally when the fog-laden air is carried over warmer water. See also the comments about fog at 7.1.5 under tropical maritime air and haar in continental air.

Radiation fog
As the earth radiates heat into space, especially on still nights with little or no cloud, the lowest layer of air becomes cooler and when the air temperature falls to, or below, its dew point, fog develops and is trapped below a low-level inversion. By the nature of its development it is most frequent later in the night and during the few hours after dawn, and is most persistent during the winter half of the year. Clearance of the fog comes about by an air mass change, a rise in the temperature, an increase in the wind (when the fog often lifts to become low cloud) or a combination of these events. Radiation fog is only a problem for the mariner when it drifts off the land but the sea temperature is usually sufficiently high to disperse the fog, although occasionally it can be a problem off the coasts of eastern Scotland and northeast England in the spring.

Evaporation fogs
There is a third type of fog which is caused by the cooling of evaporated water; these fogs are rarely either persistent or widespread. Frontal fog occurs when rain falls from relatively warmer air above and evaporates into cooler air close to the surface. Fog sometimes develops in cold weather over estuaries, especially at low water when the exposed land evaporates its water. Cold river water running into the sea can also occasionally produce patchy fog.

7.1.14 Coastal winds
Many yachtsmen cruise largely in coastal waters which can present their own difficulties; there may be many other craft of different types afloat and there may be shoals. Also the yachtsman could be attempting a landfall in an unfamiliar area. To add to the potential problems the coastline itself often produces significant changes

to the general wind. It should always be remembered that these coastal effects rarely occur in isolation but in combination with each other as well as the pressure (geostrophic) wind. The main effects in the northern hemisphere are discussed here.

Sea breezes

The theory of the sea breeze is simple – the sun heats up the land so that it is warmer than the sea, because the two have different thermal properties. The land warms and cools more quickly than the sea. So on a sunny morning the land warms, quickly heating the air above it, which rises so that cooler air from over the sea is drawn in to replace it, thus initiating a wind blowing in towards the land. Fig. 7(16).

The effect depends upon there being little or no cloud over the land; if there is more than half cloud cover the likelihood of a sea breeze developing is remote.

The timing and strength of the sea breeze, and its subsequent behaviour, depend however on other factors. First, and most important, is what wind is already blowing in the morning. If the wind, due to the gradient of isobaric pressure, is already on-shore the sea breeze will intensify it, and by mid-afternoon there may be quite a strong wind blowing. If the gradient wind is off-shore the sea breeze will work in opposition to it, and may or may not prevail. If the off-shore wind is only moderate in strength there is likely to be a period of calm before the sea breeze gets established. If the off-shore wind is more than about 15 knots over the sea then it is likely to continue to blow, but with less force. If the gradient wind is force 5 or more it will inhibit the vertical circulation described and a sea breeze is unlikely to develop.

Sea breezes are encouraged by low coastal areas with hills behind rather than by high cliffs, and are more pronounced on days when the atmosphere is unstable than stable. They start earlier in the absence of cloud over the land, or in the absence of an existing off-shore wind, or on coasts facing east rather than west since they get warmed up more quickly.

The sea breeze begins along the shore, and gradually spreads seawards. Visible evidence of its onset may be the build up of a line of cumulus cloud along the coast and gradually moving inland – formed by the air drawn in from the sea rising by convection over the warm shore – combined with vanishing cloud over the sea, where the air is sinking to feed the on-shore wind which is developing.

Under favourable conditions a sea breeze may be felt 10 miles (16km) or so offshore, although probably not until early afternoon (or later if it has had to overcome an off-shore wind), but its effect may reach much further in some areas. As the sea breeze strengthens during the day, the wind over coastal waters tends to veer.

By early evening, as the power of the sun is reducing, the sea breeze starts to drop and it will be gone by sunset – perhaps earlier due to an increase in the off-shore gradient wind or the spread of cloud across the land.

In British waters sea breezes are most common in late spring, but they are also experienced in summer and early spring.

Land breezes

Land breezes work at night, in the opposite way from sea breezes by day, but they do not usually blow so strongly. They are caused by the land cooling more quickly than the sea – by radiation on a clear night, as often happens in anticyclonic conditions. These off-shore breezes may start a couple of hours after sunset and blow until dawn, or a bit later. Since they depend on the temperature difference between the land and the sea they are more likely to occur in autumn (when the sea is warmest) than in spring or early summer. Their effect does not extend so far offshore as the sea breeze by day – usually not more than about five miles from the coast.

The air which rises over the sea may form some cloud of a cumulus type, while the upper air flowing back inshore and sinking over coastal areas helps to keep them clear of cloud.

The land breeze may be strengthened in some areas by a katabatic wind – caused by air being cooled on the slopes of coastal hills and mountains in settled weather with clear skies, and draining down the valleys to the sea. The effect is local and is usually not very strong in British waters, except in steep-sided estuaries such as Scottish lochs.

Off-shore wind

As an approach is made towards the land with an off-shore wind a backing of the wind can be expected. As we have seen in 7.1.7, due to friction the wind over the land is backed from the wind caused purely by the pressure force (the geostrophic wind), and it is backed by a greater amount than over the sea. There is a lag before the smaller amount of backing over the water takes full effect. When the wind is blowing over cliffs there is also the possibility of an eddy developing so that close inshore the wind can become flukey with an on-shore component.

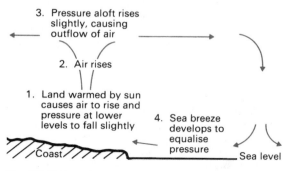

3. Pressure aloft rises slightly, causing outflow of air

2. Air rises

1. Land warmed by sun causes air to rise and pressure at lower levels to fall slightly

4. Sea breeze develops to equalise pressure

Coast

Sea level

Fig. 7(16) How a sea breeze develops.

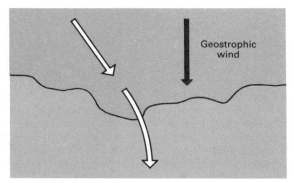

Fig. 7(17) When approaching the land an off-shore wind can be expected to back.

Wind along coastline

The differential in the land and sea friction also has an effect upon the wind when it is blowing more or less parallel to the coastline. There are two cases to consider:

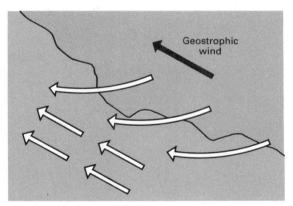

Fig. 7(18) With your back to the wind, and the land on your right, an increase in wind speed can be expected immediately offshore.

(1) Back to wind land on the right
Here the greater backing of the wind over the land causes it to converge with the wind over the sea just offshore leading to an increase in the wind speed.

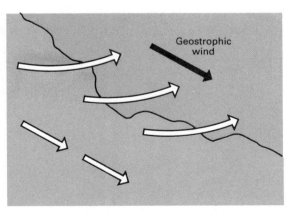

Fig. 7(19) With your back to the wind, and the land on your left, less wind can be expected just offshore.

(2) Land on left of wind direction
This is the reverse case where the difference in the frictional effect causes the flow over the water to diverge from that over the land. The result is that a lighter wind regime could be expected as the shoreline is approached.

Headlands

The air tends to go around obstacles in its path rather than over them. This is more marked when the air is stable, especially when there is a low-level inversion. Near to and on the windward side of a headland the flow will be 'squeezed' causing the wind to be stronger while, as might be expected, there will be a decrease on the leeward side but possibly with an eddy.

Funnelling

The reluctance of air to go over obstacles will also tend to increase the wind when it is blowing up or down an estuary or fjord, especially when there is rising ground on both sides. Added to this there is the effect of the wind blowing along the coastline as described above. As a general rule with the back to the wind, the strongest wind will be towards the right-hand shore.

Diurnal weather variations

Changes to the weather that tend to occur within a 24-hour period are called 'diurnal changes'. Most of these changes are a result of the normal heating and cooling cycle. Thus the onset of sea breezes and the formation of radiation fog have a diurnal pattern.

Such changes are most marked over the land, which responds to daytime heating and night-time cooling, and therefore it is over coastal waters where these effects will be most noticeable. The temperature of the surface of the open sea varies little from day to night so the diurnal effect is negligible, particularly in windy conditions, but some diurnal change can be experienced under light wind or calm conditions with clear skies.

7.1.15 Thunderstorms

Thunderstorms are electrical storms which are caused by areas of electrical charge of opposite polarity within clouds. Lightning is the visible discharge of electricity and thunder is the sound of the sudden expansion of air from the heat of the discharge.

There are two basic types of thunderstorms. Lightning can occur between or within fairly high cloud and does not reach the ground; the path of the lightning is often obscured by the cloud and is commonly referred to as 'sheet lightning'. This sort of thunderstorm does not present the mariner with any particular hazard although it may be an omen of more violent weather to come. The second type of thunderstorm with lightning strikes to earth from cumulonimbus cloud (cloud colour plate 12) is worthy of consideration and respect, and we will look at it in more detail.

Cumulonimbus cloud develops when there is strong vertical motion within most of the troposphere, usually because of high instability, and when the air has an ample supply of moisture. Sometimes the vertical motion is sufficiently enhanced by a cold front or a trough to produce cumulonimbus cloud and thunderstorms.

Cumulonimbus clouds are towering deep clouds often with a dark base rising to a spreading anvil-shaped head of cirrus cloud. A cumulonimbus cloud is a complex structure composed of several cells each having its own updraught which affects the surface wind in its vicinity.

The wind changes around a vigorous cumulonimbus can be sudden and dramatic. As the cloud passes by wind shifts up to 180° can be experienced with extremely gusty conditions and down draughts. As a vigorous cumulonimbus approaches the wind will often turn towards the cloud due to strong updraughts within the cloud, giving rise to the often quoted but misleading comment that a thunderstorm 'comes up against the wind'. A thunder cloud, like all other clouds, is moved by the general wind but the thunderstorm has its own wind pattern around it; this should be borne in mind when deciding the best course to steer to avoid it.

A thunderstorm is capable of suddenly producing very heavy rain and often hail with a rapid deterioration in visibility, so apart from monitoring the progress of the cloud a good lookout for other mariners who may also be changing course is desirable.

A lightning strike can be a hazard, especially with the modern trend to stainless steel rigging and masthead fittings. When lightning is about it is wise to avoid handling metal fittings as far as possible. Damage to the yacht can be minimised by connections to an earthing plate on the vessel's bottom (see 13.3.5).

Occasionally the conditions similar to those necessary to create thunderstorms can lead to the development of a tornado. In northwest Europe these are rarely more than about 100 metres across, unlike their larger and more devastating US cousins. Nevertheless, any violent whirl with intense vertical motion that is capable of uprooting trees, can cause damage or a knockdown to a yacht. A good indicator of their existence is when a funnel-shaped extension to the cloud is observed with disturbed water beneath. A more vigorous tornado will lift the water into a waterspout. Fortunately they are fairly rare over British waters and occur mainly in a very humid late summer southerly.

7.1.16 Tropical storms

Tropical storms are intense depressions which develop in low latitudes. They are of much smaller diameter than a deep depression in (say) the North Atlantic (although covering a larger area than a tornado) and hence the isobars are much more closely spaced and the winds speeds greatly increased. In a tropical storm the wind spirals in towards the centre (anti-clockwise in the northern hemisphere) at all heights, whereas with a normal

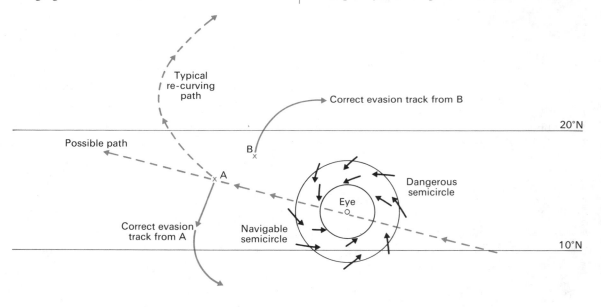

Fig. 7(20) Typical path of a hurricane, showing the dangerous and navigable semicircles.

depression in higher latitudes the winds eventually conform to the higher wind above.

At the centre, or eye, of the storm there is a temporary lull, but near the centre the wind blows at hurricane force, the visibility is almost nil, and the seas are extremely high and confused. Gale force winds are likely to be encountered within 100 miles (161km) of the storm centre.

In general, tropical storms occur on the western sides of oceans. The following remarks apply to the North Atlantic, the Caribbean and the Gulf of Mexico where such storms are known as hurricanes. Hurricanes originate as a rule between 7° and 15°N, but sometimes nearer the equator. Initially they move in a WNW direction, at speeds of 10-15 knots. When in about 25°N they are likely to recurve to the north and north-east, and to increase their speed of advance to about 25 knots. They may continue, gradually diminishing in intensity, for a long way. Some severe gales off NW Europe originated as hurricanes. The hurricane season is from July to September, but tropical storms can occur at other times.

When sailing in low latitudes beware of abnormally low barometric pressure for the time of year. For example, 5mb below the normal mean pressure should arouse suspicion of a tropical disturbance, and it is important to take careful readings of the barometer at hourly intervals, allowing for diurnal variation. Other warning signs are: a significant change in wind speed or direction; swell from a direction indicating the storm centre; cirrus cloud, followed by altostratus and broken cumulus.

With the advent of weather satellites the identification and tracking of hurricanes has improved, and regular information is broadcast by radio. This may allow even a slow-moving yacht to avoid the storm centre. Fig. 7(20) shows the typical path of a hurricane, and identifies the dangerous and navigable semicircles. The dangerous semicircle is on the right of the storm's path, because here the wind is strongest and a yacht tends to be blown into the eye of the storm; also, should the hurricane recurve, the eye of the storm may pass over the yacht. If the wind is steadily veering, it can be assumed that the yacht is in the dangerous semicircle.

Tropical storms are known as cyclones in the Indian Ocean and Bay of Bengal, and as typhoons in the Western Pacific.

7.2 Glossary of meteorological terms

Anabatic wind A wind that blows up a slope as a result of heating. The converse to the more common katabatic wind.

Anaprop Anomalous radio propagation – the interference to radio signals (especially radar) as a result of meteorological conditions.

Anemometer Instrument for measuring wind speed.

Anticyclone An area of high barometric pressure, with isobars encircling the centre of the 'high'.

Aurora Borealis The 'northern lights'-bright streaks of light in the northern sky, caused by electrical discharges in the atmosphere.

Backing A change in the direction of the wind, in an anti-clockwise direction.

Bora A cold blustery northeasterly wind that occasionally blows down the mountains on the eastern Adriatic coast.

Clouds Collection of minute water droplets, or ice, suspended in the atmosphere. For descriptions of different types of cloud see 7.1.9.

Cold front The boundary of advancing cold air.

Corona A series of tinted rings round the sun or moon caused by diffraction of the light by water droplets – not to be confused with a halo which is further from the light source.

Cyclone The name given to a tropical revolving storm occuring in the Indian Ocean, Arabian Sea or Bay of Bengal.

Cyclonic Anti-clockwise circulation over an area associated with a depression.

Depression A discrete area of low barometric pressure.

Dew Water drops formed by condensation of water vapour in the air on surfaces cooled by radiation at night.

Dew point The lowest temperature to which the air can be cooled before condensation (e.g. dew) is formed.

Doldrums The area of light and variable winds over equatorial waters.

Equinoctial gales A phrase sometimes used in the mistaken belief that gales occur with greater severity and frequency near the equinoxes than at other times of the year.

Eye of the storm The area of light winds and often broken cloud in the centre of a tropical revolving storm.

Eye of wind The direction from which the wind blows (now rarely used).

Föhn wind Of Alpine origin, now generally used for a warm dry wind to the lee of a mountain range.

Front A sloping zone separating two air masses of different temperature.

Further outlook A brief description of the general weather conditions for a period following that covered by a more detailed forecast.

Geostrophic wind The wind that would theoretically blow if only the spacing of the isobars is considered (disregarding friction, curvature of the isobars, latitude, and other local effects).

Gust A rapid increase in the wind relative to its general strength.

Haar A name given to sea fog in some eastern parts of Scotland and England.

Hail Small, hard pellets of ice from cumulonimbus clouds – often associated with thunderstorms.

Halo A circle of light round the sun or moon caused by refraction of the light by ice crystals. The angle formed from opposite sides of the common halo to the eye is 22°.

Hectopascal The internationally agreed unit of atmospheric pressure, equivalent to a millibar.

Hurricane A wind of force 12 on the Beaufort scale; also the name given to a tropical revolving storm in the West Indies or off the American seaboard.

Hygrometer An instrument used for measuring humidity in the air.

Inversion When air temperature (contrary to the usual case) increases with altitude. Sometimes a cause of fog.

Isobars Lines on a synoptic chart or weather map joining places of equal barometric pressure.

Isotherms Lines joining places with the same temperature.

Jet stream A fast narrow band of wind in the upper atmosphere usually associated with a front.

Katabatic wind A wind that blows down mountain slopes, due to cooling by radiation.

Land and sea breezes Off-shore and on-shore winds caused respectively by the land cooling and heating up more quickly than the sea under clear skies.

Levanter A humid easterly wind in the Strait of Gibraltar.

Line squall A sudden, violent squall often associated with a cold front; usually identifiable by the low line of black cloud from which it takes its name. Apart from a sudden increase in wind and change of wind direction, its passing is accompanied by a rise of the barometer, a fall in temperature, and usually heavy rain, hail or thunder.

Lull A decrease in the wind relative to its general strength (the inverse to 'gust').

Mackerel sky A sky with cirrocumulus or high altocumulus arranged in a regular pattern like mackerel scales.

Mirage The appearance in the sky of images which are in reality over the horizon, due to abnormal refraction.

Mistral A dry, cold wind over the northwest Mediterranean that blows offshore from the Rhône valley.

Occlusion When the warm sector of a depression has been raised from the surface of the land or sea by the advance of the cold front behind it, the depression is said to be occluded.

Polar front A line of discontinuity in the global weather system where polar air and subtropical air meet, and where as a result depressions often originate.

Precipitation Particles of water or ice which fall from clouds, e.g. rain, drizzle, snow, sleet or hail.

Recurvature Describes the typical track of a tropical cyclone, e.g. in the northern hemisphere such storms, after tracking roughly west, usually swing round to a northeasterly course.

Ridge The extension of an area of high pressure (similar to a ridge running out from a mountain).

Roaring Forties The prevailing westerlies in middle latitudes of the southern hemisphere.

Scirocco A warm southerly wind in the Mediterranean.

Scud Seaman's term for fractostratus cloud – low fragments of racing cloud, often beneath rain clouds.

Sea breeze See land breezes.

Sea fret Used in parts of NE England to describe sea fog.

Sea smoke An evaporation fog formed when cold air moves over warm water. Sometimes called 'steam fog' or 'water smoke'.

Secondary depression An offshoot from a parent depression, often formed by a distortion of isobars along a front, which can cause a quick and unexpected deterioration in the weather.

Showers Periods of rain from cumuliform cloud, interspersed with fair weather and clearer skies.

Sleet In the UK is taken to mean precipitation that has a mixture of rain and snow or snow that melts as it falls. The term has a slightly different meaning in some other countries.

Snow Precipitation of ice crystals, in formations of varying size.

Squall A sudden increase of wind lasting several minutes, usually caused by fronts and large convective clouds, and often associated with a change in wind direction.

Synoptic chart A weather map, showing the distribution of barometric pressure and the principal weather features over a large area for a certain time.

Thunder and lightning Thunder is the noise made by lightning which is a discharge of static electricity within clouds or from a cloud to earth. Most thunderstorms form in cumulonimbus clouds and may result in squalls, hail and heavy rainstorms.

Tornado A violent whirl usually cyclonic and associated with thunderstorm clouds.

Trade winds Winds which blow from the sub-tropical high pressure belts towards the equator – NE winds in the northern hemisphere and SE winds in the southern hemisphere.

Tramontana A term sometimes given in the Mediterranean region to a wind from a northerly direction.

Trough An extension of a depression shown on a weather chart by isobars with increased curvature. A front always lies in a trough. As the trough passes a place the barometer falls and then rises.

Typhoon The name given to a tropical revolving storm in the Western Pacific.

Veer A change in wind direction, clockwise.

Ventimeter A small hand held instrument for measuring wind speed or force.

Warm sector The area of warm air in the circulation of a frontal depression between warm and cold fronts.

Waterspout A cone or cloud extending from the base of cumulonimbus cloud to the sea. Often occurs with a tornado.

Wedge An alternative word for ridge (of high pressure). Now rarely used.

7.3 Beaufort Scale

Force	Mean speed (knots)	Description	State of sea (description in brackets)	Ashore	Probable wave height ft/m	Probable max. wave height ft/m
0	0–1	Calm	Like a mirror (calm)	Calm; smoke rises vertically	0/0	0/0
1	1–3	Light air	Ripples only (calm)	Direction of wind shown by smoke	0/0	0/0
2	4–6	Light breeze	Small wavelets, not breaking (smooth)	Wind felt on face; leaves rustle	0.7/0.1	1/0.3
3	7–10	Gentle breeze	Large wavelets, crests begin to break; a few white horses (smooth)	Leaves in constant motion; wind extends light flag	1.2/0.4	3/1
4	11–16	Moderate breeze	Small waves growing longer; fairly frequent white horses (slight)	Raises dust; small branches moved	3/1	5/1.5
5	17–21	Fresh breeze	Moderate waves, taking more pronounced form; many white horses, perhaps some spray (moderate)	Small trees in leaf begin to sway, crested wavelets on inland waters	6/2	8/2.5
6	22–27	Strong breeze	Large waves forming; white foam crests more extensive; probably some spray (rough)	Large branches in motion; telephone wires whistle	10/3	13/4
7	28–33	Near gale	Sea heaps up; white foam streaks begin blowing from crests (very rough)	Whole trees in motion; difficult to walk into wind	13/4	18/5.5
8	34–40	Gale	Moderately high waves of greater length; crests break into spindrift with foamy streaks (high)	Twigs break off trees; wind impedes progress	18/5.5	25/7.5
9	41–47	Severe gale	High waves with tumbling crests; dense streaks of foam; spray may affect visibility (very high)	Slight structural damage occurs (e.g. slates, chimney pots)	23/7	33/10
10	48–55	Storm	Very high waves with long overhanging crests and dense streaks of foam making surface of sea white; heavy tumbling sea; visibility affected (very high)	Seldom experienced inland; trees uprooted, structural damage occurs	30/9	41/12.5
11	56–63	Violent storm	Exceptionally high waves; sea completely covered with long white patches of foam along direction of wind; visibility affected (phenomenal)	Very rarely experienced; wide spread damage caused	36/11	52/16
12	64 plus	Hurricane	Air filled with foam and spray; sea white with driving spray; visibility very seriously affected (phenomenal)	—	46/14	—

Note: The wave heights above are only a guide to what may be expected in the open sea, away from land.

7.4 Barometer and thermometer conversion scales

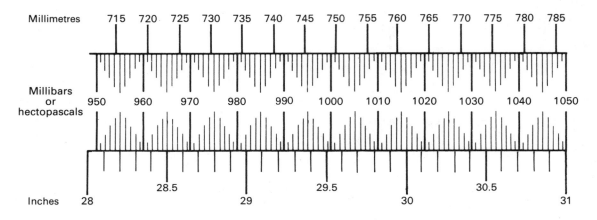

Fig. 7(21) This scale shows the relationship between millibars (or hectopascals), inches of mercury, and millimetres of mercury for atmospheric pressure.

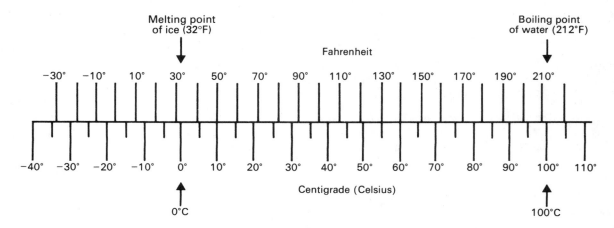

Fig. 7(22) The relationship between temperatures in degrees Fahrenheit and Centigrade (Celsius). For conversion table and conversion factors see 2.5.3.

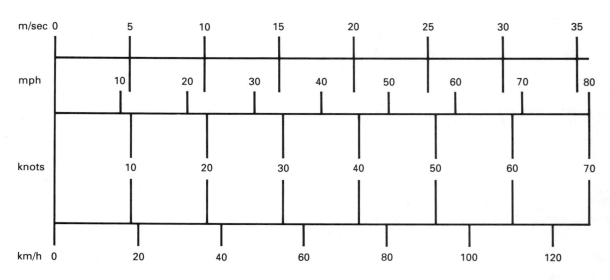

Fig. 7(23) The relation between wind speeds in metres per second, miles per hour, knots and kilometres per hour.

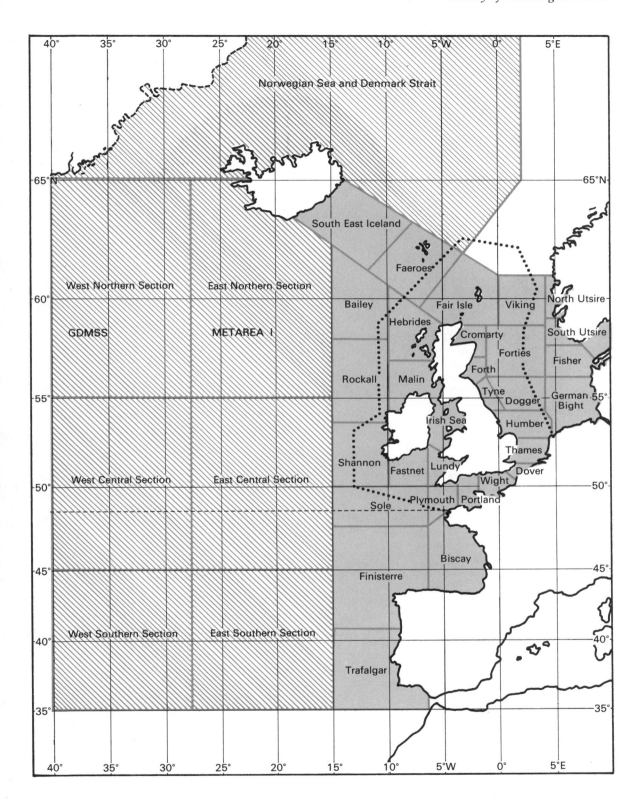

Fig 7(24) British North Atlantic Weather Bulletin and Sea Forecast Areas. The hatched areas, plus Biscay, Trafalgar, Sole and Finisterre are included in the North Atlantic Weather Bulletin transmitted by WT and telex by Portishead Radio (GKA). The other areas (tinted) are included in bulletins broadcast by the BBC and by BT coast stations and on Prestel. The dotted line round the UK coasts encloses GMDSS sea area A2. The dashed line across the Atlantic encloses GMDSS METAREA I, from 48°27′N to 71°00′N.

7.5 Meanings of terms used in weather bulletins

In order to be able to understand a forecast it is essential to know the meanings of certain terms which are regularly used – apart from some of those in the glossary in section 7.2. The following are often used in shipping forecasts.

7.5.1 Visibility

Fog	Less than 1000m (1100yds)
Poor	1000m (1100yds) – 2 n miles
Moderate	2–5 n miles
Good	More than 5 n miles

7.5.2 Timing

Imminent	Within 6 hours of time of issue
Soon	6–12 hours
Later	12–24 hours

7.5.3 Speeds (of weather systems)

Slowly	0–15 knots
Steadily	15–25 knots
Rather quickly	25–35 knots
Rapidly	35–45 knots
Very rapidly	Over 45 knots

7.5.4 Barometric pressure changes (tendency)

Steady	Change less than 0.1mb in 3 hours
Rising ⎫	Means a change of 1.6–3.5mb in 3
Falling ⎭	hours unless qualified by:
Slowly	Change 0.1–1.5mb in 3 hours
Quickly	Change 3.6 – 6.0mb in 3 hours
Very rapidly	Change more than 6.0mb in 3 hours

7.5.5 Gale warnings

Indicate that winds of at least force 8 or gusts reaching 43 knots are expected somewhere in the area. 'Severe gale' implies winds of at least force 9 or gusts of 52 knots. 'Storm' implies winds of force 10 or gusts of 61 knots. 'Violent storm' implies winds of force 11 or gusts reaching 69 knots. 'Hurricane force' means winds of force 12 (64 knots or more). The term 'hurricane' on its own is only used for a true tropical cyclone. Gale warnings remain in force until amended or cancelled ('gales now ceased'). If a gale persists for more than 24 hours the warning is reissued.

7.5.6 Land area forecasts – wind strength

In land area forecasts winds are given in the following terms which relate to Beaufort forces as indicated:

Calm	0	Fresh	5
Light	1–3	Strong	6–7
Moderate	4	Gale	8

7.5.7 Land area forecasts – visibility

The following definitions are used in land area forecasts:

Mist	200–1100yds (183–1000m)
Fog	Less than 200yds (183m)
Dense fog	Less than 50yds (46m)

7.6 Sources of weather information

7.6.1 Weather information

Yachtsmen around the British Isles are well served with various sources of weather information most of which originates from the Met. Office.

The leaflet *Weather Services for Shipping* gives details of weather bulletins and gale warnings from various sources and a summary of other services provided by the Met. Office. It is available from the Met. Office, Scott Building, Eastern Road, Bracknell, Berkshire, RG12 2PW. The sea forecast areas covered by British broadcasts are shown in Fig. 7(24).

The above leaflet is designed primarily for commercial shipping but it contains general notes that are of interest to the yachtsman. It is emphasised that for up-to-date details on all aspects of weather and shipping forecasts reference must be made to the current edition of *The Macmillan & Silk Cut Nautical Almanac* (Chapter 7), published annually.

7.6.2 BBC Radio Shipping Forecasts

Shipping forecasts, primarily designed to give guidance to commercial vessels on passage, necessarily cover very large sea areas, and the spoken bulletins have to be compressed into five minutes. It is therefore impossible, in the time allotted, to include much detail – particularly that associated with the many variations that can and often do occur near land. The ability to convey the right degree of confidence in the development of a particular weather situation is similarly restricted. For these reasons, forecasts for 'Coastal Waters' (see 7.6.3) are usually more helpful to yachtsmen who are cruising near the coast. These forecasts are intended to cover up to 12 nautical miles offshore, and to take some account of local phenomena such as land and sea breezes, and the funnelling effect of the land over inshore waters.

The times, frequencies and contents of the shipping forecasts broadcast by BBC Radio 4 are given in detail in *The Macmillan & Silk Cut Nautical Almanac*.

VHF reception may be useful in certain local areas (such as in the West of Scotland) where 198kHz or medium frequency reception is not satisfactory. A little booklet *BBC television and radio stations*, published annually by the Engineering Information Department of the BBC, gives details and locations of all transmitters. A similar booklet is published by the Independent Broadcasting Authority.

The bulletins include a summary of gale warnings in force; a general synopsis of the weather for the next 24 hours and expected changes within that period; forecasts for each coastal sea area (in a given order) for the next 24 hours, giving wind direction and speed, weather and visibility; and the latest reports from selected stations.

The size of each sea area and the fact that the whole forecast is limited to 300 words mean that it can not include many details of interest to yachtsmen. Some skill and practice is required to make a sensible record of the forecast and this is discussed further in 7.6.4. The meanings of the terms used in the Shipping Forecast can be found in 7.5.

Apart from being included in the shipping forecast, gale warnings are broadcast in the BBC Radio 4 programme soon after receipt.

7.6.3 BBC Coastal waters Forecasts

Forecasts are given for coastal waters (up to l9km/12 miles offshore) of Great Britain each night on English, Welsh and Scottish Radio 4 programmes, and on Radio Scotland. Radio Ulster broadcasts similar forecasts for Northern Ireland. Inshore waters forecasts are also broadcast each morning on BBC Radio 3. Details of the times, frequencies and contents of these forecasts are given in The *Macmillan & Silk Cut Nautical Almanac.*

7.6.4 Recording and interpreting the shipping forecasts

Just to hear the shipping forecast for a particular area may be better than nothing, but much more benefit can arise if the whole of the shipping forecast is recorded and analysed in some detail. This applies particularly when a series of forecasts at six-hour intervals are treated in the same way, because it is then possible to study how a weather pattern is developing and how the local situation relates to what is being forecast for a very much bigger area.

The first requirement is to be able to write down all the essential details of the forecast – any gale warnings in force, the general synopsis (so easy to miss), the forecasts for all sea areas (not just the local ones), and the 'actuals' from the various stations round the coast.

In order to achieve this it is vital to start off with some kind of form on which to write down or tick off the details which are broadcast. Various types are available; one is the Metmap jointly published by the Royal Meteorological Society and the Royal Yachting Association. Pads of 25 can be purchased from the RYA, RYA House, Romsey Road, Eastleigh, Hants SO50 9YA.

Next it is essential to devise some form of shorthand which will allow all the details to be recorded in the very limited time available. This can be a matter of personal choice, although there is an advantage in using the standard international weather map symbols because it is then possible to interpret bulletins which are posted up at harbour offices and other places. A selection of some of the more commonly used symbols is given below.

Wind symbols

Wind direction is shown by arrows, flying in the direction of the wind. The international convention is that each long feather indicates 10 knots, and each half feather indicates 5 knots. A solid triangular feather indicates 50 knots, at which point the long and half feather notation recommences. The examples below show westerly winds.

Symbol	Knots	Symbol	Knots
	1– 2		43– 47
	3– 7		48– 52
	8–12		53– 57
	13–17		58– 62
	18–22		62– 67
	23–27		68– 72
	28–32		73– 77
	33–37		78– 82
	38–42		103–107

Other ueful wind symbols include:

Calm	⊙
Variable force 3	V3
Cyclonic variable force 4	4

Weather symbols

	Beaufort notation	Plotting symbols
Rain	r	●
Drizzle	d	,
Shower	p	▽
Snow	s	✳
Hail	h	△
Thunderstorm	t	ᚱ
Fog	f	≡
Mist	m	=
Haze	z	∞

The symbols may be combined, or elaborated as in the example for rain below:

Intermittent slight rain	r_0	•
Continuous slight rain	r_0r_0	• •
Intermittent moderate rain	r	(symbol)
Continuous moderate rain	$r\ r$	(symbol)
Intermittent heavy rain	R	(symbol)
Continuous heavy rain	$R\ R$	(symbol)

Have everything ready well before the time that the bulletin is going to start, and it is useful to refer to the previous forecast because then one is ready to record the sort of details which are likely in the general synopsis. Once the forecast begins just concentrate on writing down all the details, without trying to analyse them in any way – that comes later. Remember that it is important to write down the various times stated – the time of the forecast and the time at which the actual weather at coast stations was recorded. These are easy to miss.

For navigational purposes it is a good rule to check the time signal which often follows the shipping forecast, and this gives time to draw breath before starting to interpret what has been written down so hurriedly.

It is easiest to construct your own weather map for the time of the actuals recorded. These are usually about two hours before the broadcast. So these reports from coastal stations can be plotted directly on to the chart – wind strength and direction, weather and pressure.

Then plot the information contained in the general synopsis, but with the movements of centres and fronts advanced by the time between the forecast and the time of the actuals on the basis of the speeds given in the forecast.

Finally add the wind, weather and visibility forecasts for the various sea areas. Concentrate on the 'at first' forecasts if there are other predictions for 'later'.

Now all the information is available to start drawing in the isobars, but sketch lightly because almost certainly there will be some rubbing out to do. Begin by joining up the coastal stations with equal pressure, conforming to the general pattern indicated by whatever lows or highs have been given in the general synopsis. More isobars can then be added at suitable angles to the forecast wind directions over the open sea, and at spacings which conform to the geostrophic chart for the forecast wind strengths. Remember that at troughs or fronts the isobars should change direction. It is largely a matter of trial and error, but practice helps to speed up the process so that a very useful weather map can be produced in a few minutes. Armed with this it is much easier to understand what is happening to the weather in one particular small area of sea.

When interpreting the resulting synoptic chart, remember that if the yacht is not far offshore the weather may be affected by a number of variations due to the land. Sea and land breezes are obvious examples, and have already been discussed in 7.1.14. But wherever there is a large lump of land the wind will tend, where possible, to flow round it rather than over the top, and particularly when air conditions are stable. So off large headlands, or in rivers or estuaries, allowance must be made for significant changes in wind speed and direction. The wind can also be greatly affected by purely local cloud conditions.

7.6.5 BBC General Forecasts

Land forecasts can be useful to the yachtsman as they often include the outlook period (up to 48 hours beyond the detailed forecast and the shipping forecast) and often some reference to weather along the coasts. They may also give more recent information which was not available in the previous shipping forecast. The more detailed land area forecasts are broadcast on Radio 4 on 198kHz (1515m).

7.6.6 Local Radio Stations – Forecasts

The details and values of forecasts broadcast by local radio stations vary considerably; some give no more than an indication of the present weather conditions. However, many local radio stations in coastal areas now participate in a scheme for broadcasting 'Small Craft Warnings' when winds of Force 6 or more are expected within the next 12 hours on the coast or up to five miles offshore. These warnings are handled in a similar way to gale warnings on Radio 4, being broadcast at the first programme junction after receipt and then repeated on the next hour or after the next news bulletin.

Details of weather forecasts from local radio stations in coastal areas which are of particular interest to yachtsmen are given in *The Macmillan & Silk Cut Nautical Almanac*.

7.6.7 British Telecom Coast Radio Stations – Weather bulletins by RT

Forecasts originating from the Met. Office (usually those for adjacent sea areas from the latest shipping forecast) are broadcast twice daily – at 0703 and 1903 UT (GMT) or at 0733 and 1933 UT (GMT). The details of times, frequencies and sea areas covered by individual coast radio stations are published each year in The *Macmillan & Silk Cut Nautical Almanac*.

British Coast Radio Stations transmit gale warnings at the end of the next R/T (MF) silence period after receipt. These silence periods are from 00 to 03 and from 30 to 33 minutes past each hour.

Gale warnings are repeated at the next of the following times: 0303, 0903, 1503, 2103 UT (GMT). Gale warnings are preceded by the R/T Safety Signal 'SECURITE' (pronounced 'SAY-CURE-E-TAY').

Gale warnings remain in force unless amended or cancelled. If the gale persists for more than 24 hours from the time of origin, the gale warning is reissued.

7.6.8 Television, Teletext, Prestel

An increasing number of television forecasts now include a synoptic chart, which together with the satellite weather pictures can be a useful guide to the general weather situation at the start of a passage.

Television receivers equipped with teletext can receive a range of information including weather reports and forecasts. Both BBC and ITV operate a teletext service.

Prestel is operated over a telephone link by British Telecom and contains meteorological information provided by the Met. Office. It is accessed by keying the number of the frame containing the information required. All information frames are charged at premium rate except for the main index and explanation frame.

7.6.9 HM Coastguard broadcasts

MRCCs and MRSCs broadcast strong wind warnings (Force 6) on receipt and local forecasts every four hours (every two hours in bad weather) on Ch 67 after an announcement on Ch 16. For scheduled times see *The Macmillan & Silk Cut Nautical Almanac*. They will also respond to telephone enquiries.

7.6.10 Forecasts for ships at sea

Forecasts for areas within the region 65°N to 35°N, and 40°W and the coast of Europe (including the Mediterranean) may be obtained by yachts at sea by contacting the appropriate Met. Office forecasting centre. These are listed, with telephone numbers, in *The Macmillan & Silk Cut Nautical Almanac*. No charge is made by the Met. Office, but a normal RT link call charge is levied by British Telecom.

Alternatively, the request may be addressed to the nearest Coast Radio Station. Such a call might be in the form: 'North Foreland Radio. Request weather forecast next 24 hours for sea areas Dover and Wight on passage Ramsgate to Cherbourg, Yacht Nonsuch'.

When telephoning a forecasting centre it must be realised that during busy periods, such as occasions of bad weather, the staff may be fully occupied and there is likely to be a delay before an answer is obtained.

7.6.11 Special forecasts on request

Forecasts can be specially prepared for an individual yachtsman or organisation for a specified area or route. Enquiries about the services available and the cost should be directed to a convenient Weather Centre or to the Operations Manager, Central Forecasting Office, Met. Office, London Road, Bracknell RG12 2SZ.

Ship routing. For long passages the Met. Office offers a service that advises on the most advantageous route depending upon whether the user wishes to avoid bad weather or make the fastest passage. Details are available from METROUTE, Marine Superintendent, Met. Office, Scott Building, Eastern Road, Bracknell RG12 2PW.

The following private weather forecasting companies also offer services especially for larger vessels on longer passages:
Oceanroutes (UK) Ltd. Tel: 01224 248080 Noble Denton Weather Services Ltd. Tel: 0171-606 4961.

7.6.12 Automatic Telephone Weather Service (Marinecall)

Marinecall is a set of 24-hour forecasts for 15 areas prepared by the Met. Office and provided by the Telephone Information Services branch of British Telecom. The forecasts are updated twice daily (three times in summer). In addition to the 24-hour forecasts, also included are a warnings summary, a general situation, an outlook for a further 24 hours, and a national 5 day outlook. Further details are in *The Macmillan & Silk Cut Nautical Almanac*.

7.6.13 Facsimile Broadcasts

Weather facsimile receivers are available for yachts. They will receive and reproduce the various charts (isobaric, isothermal, wind direction etc) which are broadcast at specific times. While the technique is long-standing, it is only in recent years that the price, size and weight of facsimile equipment has made it suitable for use in yachts. It is simply a method of receiving weather maps by radio. Information from many meteorological stations is sent to major centres such as Bracknell (England), Paris (France) and Offenbach (Germany) where it is processed by computer, codified, and sent out as a radio signal. In the yacht the equipment comprises a suitably stable radio receiver (normally part of the facsimile unit) and a recorder which converts the radio signals into pictures. The correct scanning speed and index of co-operation (ratio of scanning speed to paper feed) must be set on the recorder, but some machines do this automatically.

Each station broadcasts on certain frequencies and at certain times, as promulgated in *Admiralty List of Radio Signals, Vol 3*, and transmits a number of different charts during the day, some of which are unintelligible to the average yachtsman since they require skilled interpretation. Most useful are the Surface Analysis charts, which show the weather map with depressions, anticyclones and fronts drawn in. There are also forecast charts for 24, 48 and 72 hours ahead.

MetFAX Marine. This is a developing Met. Office service following trials during late l991 and early 1992. Weather charts can be received on a standard fax machine by telephoning the appropriate number for the chart required. Calls are charged at the premium rate. Yachts with the equipment to make calls directly without going through one of the coast radio stations can also use a fax machine for this purpose. An enquiry (by fax) about this service can be made on the Helpline number 01344 854018.

7.6.14 Volmet

VOLMET broadcasts provide airfield weather information for aircraft in flight, but can give yachtsmen useful information on conditions experienced at a number of international airports close to the coast in Europe and Western Europe.

The most useful VOLMET is the long range, high frequency SSB (H3E) scheduled broadcast by Shannon. This operates H24 and can be received on any radio capable of selecting the required frequencies and of receiving SSB voice transmissions.

Shannon VOLMET broadcasts on these frequencies:

3413kHz	Sunset to sunrise
5505kHz	H24
8957kHz	H24
13264kHz	Sunrise to sunset

The broadcast operates on a schedule commencing at H+00 at five minute intervals until all airfields have been covered, which takes about 55 minutes. Actual weather reports are transmitted twice per hour for each airfield, and the airfield forecast once per hour. Information on UK and Eire airfields are broadcast at H+05 and H+35. Full details are in the *United Kingdom Air Pilot*, published by the Civil Aviation Authority.

Another useful VOLMET broadcast is the continuous Royal Air Force SSB VOLMET, which operates H24, and broadcasts actual weather reports for a number of military and civil airfields, mostly in the United Kingdom. The frequencies used are 4722kHz and 11200kHz.

7.6.15 W/T Transmissions from Coast Radio Stations

These are intended for ocean going vessels, and the average yachtsman will have neither the equipment nor the ability to receive the information at the speed it is transmitted by W/T, although morse decoders are available for this purpose. Details of transmissions are available in the *Admiralty List of Radio Signals Vol. 3 and Vol. 4.*

7.6.16 Press Forecasts

The delay between the time of issue and the time they are available the following day make press forecasts of limited value to yachtsmen. However the better papers publish weather charts which may include a forecast of the synoptic chart for noon on the day of publication. In the absence of any other chart this can be helpful when interpreting the shipping forecast on first putting to sea.

7.6.17 Visual storm signals

In the British Isles signals hitherto displayed by Coastguard stations, lighthouses, light-vessels etc are now discontinued. A few visual storm signals are still shown by private arrangement, but such signals should be treated with caution, since they may not be up to date.

The signal is lowered when the wind is below gale force if a renewal of gale force winds is not expected within six hours. Thus it is left flying during a temporary lull if a renewal is expected.

The signals consist of black cones. The North cone, point upwards, indicates gales from a point north of the east-west line. The South cone, point downwards, indicates gales from a point south of the east-west line.

A few stations display night signals consisting of a triangle of lights, which are used in the same way as the cones.

Visual storm signals of similar types are displayed in France, Netherlands and Germany. They consist of cones, flags and balls with the following meanings.

Gale expected from	By day	By night
North-west	A black cone point up.	Two red lights shown vertically.
South-west	A black cone point down.	Two white lights shown vertically.
North-east	Two black cones, one above the other, points up.	A red light above a white light.
South-east	Two black ones, one above the other, points down.	A white light above a red light.
Near gale (any direction)	A black ball.	A white light above a green light.

A single black or red flag displayed with any of the above signals indicates that the wind is expected to veer. Two red, or two black, flags indicate that the wind is expected to back.

In some places in France, light signals are shown by day only to warn yachts and small craft that strong winds (above Force 6) are expected:

Quick flashing light	within 3 hours
Interrupted quick flashing light	within 6 hours

At the principal Belgian harbours, small craft warnings are displayed as follows when the wind from seaward is Force 4 or more, and when craft under 6m in length are prohibited to leave harbour:

By day   Two black cones points together
By night   A flashing violet light

7.6.18 Weather information broadcast in English from radio stations in Western Europe

A number of foreign radio stations broadcast weather information in English which is helpful to cruising yachtsmen. Details of these stations including frequencies, times of forecasts, contents and areas covered are given in *The Macmillan & Silk Cut Nautical Almanac*. A vocabulary of some of the more common terms in English, French, German, Dutch and Spanish is given in 7.6.20.

7.6.19 NAVTEX

Certain coast stations in Europe broadcast weather and navigational information by teleprinter. This servicer known as NAVTEX, is the basis of a world-wide system, which is described in Chapter 6 (6.7.4).

The meteorological information from United Kingdom stations (Niton, Cullercoats and Portpatrick) originates from the Met. office at Bracknell, and consists of Weather Bulletins (Area Synopsis and Forecast) and Gale Warnings. There is an obvious benefit in having such information automatically printed out. For details see 6.7.4.

7.6.20 Five language vocabulary of weather terms

English	French	German	Dutch	Spanish
Anticyclone (High)	Anticyclone (haut)	Hoch	Hoge drukgebied	Anticiclón
Area	Région	Gebiet	Gebied	Zona
Backing	Recul de vent	Krimpen	Krimpend	Rolada a la izquierda
Calm	Calme	Stille, Kalme	Stil	Calma
Centre	Centre	Zentrum	Centrum	Centro
Clouds	Nuages	Wolken	Wolken	Nubes
Cold	Froid	Kalt	Koud	Frio
Cold front	Front froid	Kalt front	Koud front	Frente frio
Cyclonic	Cyclonique	Zyklonisch	Cyclonisch	Ciclónico
Decrease	Affaiblissement	Abnahme	Afnemen	Disminución
Deep	Profond	Tief	Diep	Profundo
Deepening	Creusant	Vertiefend	Verdiepend	Ahondamiento
Depression (Low)	Dépression (bas)	Depression (Tief)	Depressie	Depresión
Direction	Direction	Richtung	Richting	Dirección
Dispersing	Se dispersant	Zerstreuend	Verstrooiend	Disipación
Drizzle	Bruine	Sprühregen	Motregen	Llovizna
East	Est	Ost	Oosten	Este
Extending	S'étendant	Erstreckend	Uitstrekkend	Extension
Extensive	Étendu	Verbreitet	Uitgebreid	General
Falling	En baisse	Fallend	Vallend	Bajando
Filling	Comblant	Auffüllend	Vullend	Relleno
Fine	Beau	Schönwetter	Mooi	Buen tiempo, sereno
Fog	Brouillard	Nebel	Mist	Niebla
Frequent	Fréquent	Häufig	Veelvuldig	Frecuente
Front	Front	Front	Front	Frente
Frost	Gelée	Frost	Vorst	Escarcha
Gale	Coup de vent	Sturm	Stormachtig	Viente duro, vendaval
Gale warning	Avis de coup de vent	Sturmwarnung	Stormwaarschuwing	Aviso de viente duro/temporal
Good	Bon(ne)	Gut	Goed	Bueno
Gusty	Vent à rafale	Böig	Buiig	En rachas
Hail	Grêle	Hagel	Hagel	Granizo
Heavy	Abondant	Stark	Zwaar	Fuerte, violento
Increasing	Augmentant	Zunehmend	Toenemend	Aumentando
Isolated	Isolé	Einzelne	Verspreid	Aislado
Light (slight)	Faible	Schwach	Licht, zwak	Ligero, débil
Lightning	Éclair	Blitz	Bliksem	Relámpago
Local	Locale	Örtlich	Plaatselijk	Local
Mist	Brume legère	Dunst	Nevel	Neblina, bruma
Moderate	Modéré	Mässig	Matig	Moderado
Moderating	Se modérant, se calmant	Abschwächend, abnehmend	Matigend, afnemend	Disminuyendo

Moving	Se déplacant	Bewegend	Bewegend	Moviendo
North	Nord	Nord	Noorden	Norte
Occasional (showers)	Éparse(s)	Gelegentlich	Nu en dan	Ocasional
Overcast	Couvert	Bedeckt	Geheel bewolkt	Cubierto, encapotado
Poor	Mauvais	Schlecht	Slecht	Malo
Precipitation	Précipitation	Niederschlag	Neerslag	Precipitación
Pressure	Pression	Druck	Druk	Presión
Quickly	Rapidement	Schnell	Zeer snel	Rápidamente, pronto
Rain	Pluie	Regen	Regen	Lluvia
Rising	En hausse, montant	Steigend	Rÿzend, stygend	Ascendente
Rough	Agité	Stürmisch	Guur	Duro, bravo
Scattered	Sporadiques	Verstreut, vereinzelt	Verspreide	Difuso
Shower	Averse	Schauer	Stort bui	Chubasco
Slowly	Lentement	Langsam	Langzaam	Lentamente
Snow	Neige	Schnee	Sneeuw	Nieve
South	Sud	Süd	Zuiden	Sur
Squall	Grain	Bo	Bui	Turbonada
Stationary	Stationnaire	Stationär, ortsfest	Stationair, stilstand	Estacionario
Steadily	Regulièrement	Stetig, ständig	Regelmatig	Sin parar
Storm	Tempête	Sturm	Storm	Temporal
Strong	Fort	Stark	Sterk	Fuerte
Swell	Houle	Dünung	Deining	Mar de fondo/leva
Thunder	Tonnerre	Donner	Donder	Trueno
Thunderstorm	Orage	Gewitter	Onweer	Tormenta, tronada
Variable	Variable	Veränderlich	Veranderlijk	Variable
Veering	Vent adonnant	Rechtsdrehend	Ruimend	Girando
Warm	Chaud	Warm	Warm	Cálido
West	Ouest	West	Western	Oeste
Wind force	Force du vent	Windstärke	Windkracht	Fuerza del viento

7.7 Forecasting your own weather

7.7.1 Introduction

In preceding sections of this chapter are described the general mechanisms which affect the two weather elements of greatest concern to the yachtsman – wind and visibility. With this knowledge it is possible for the yachtsman to attempt his own predictions using the various sources of weather information available to him, in conjunction with his own observations and any synoptic charts to which he may have access or be able to construct for himself. Strictly speaking this is not weather forecasting but a close and intelligent monitoring of forecasts and weather changes, so that a yachtsman has a greater awareness of how the elements may affect him, and enable him to react to and anticipate weather changes.

7.7.2 Visual observation

It is a sensible and wise tradition among seafarers to keep a good lookout and it is common practice to observe the sky frequently, but not always with conscious thought and analysis. It should be remembered that there is a reason for every weather phenomenon that is seen; the reason may not be immediately apparent in every case, but careful observation and thought can lead to a better understanding of the weather.

The general cloud types and the reasons for their shapes have been discussed in earlier sections. While layered cloud suggests stable air and a fairly steady wind, an increasing depth of instability cloud indicates that winds are likely to become more gusty and variable in direction. When the instability is high as indicated by cumulonimbus cloud it is wise to keep a weather eye on them as squalls are likely in their vicinity (see 7.1.15).

A line of small cumulus developing a little inland is a good indicator that a sea breeze has started to develop.

When sailing offshore it is often noticed that shallow cumulus type cloud forms in lines or 'streets' in the same direction as the wind. This tends to happen most frequently when the wind is in the Force 4 to 6 range. The wind lines up in bands of lighter and stronger winds coincident with the cloud streets with the stronger winds in between the lines of cloud.

7.7.3 Barometric pressure

Generations of mariners have observed 'the glass' to give them some indication of forthcoming weather changes, and regular and systematic barometer readings remain a useful weather guide. The ideal instrument is a barograph which continually records the pressure on a paper covered drum so that the changes of pressure can be readily seen – and it is the changes which are of most importance. Although barographs are now being made for yachts it is not always easy to site them in a small boat so that the boat's movement does not create a blurred and unreadable trace. However a properly set (see 7.1.6) dial type aneroid barometer of reasonable quality is adequate, provided that regular readings are taken and noted. The most convenient way of recording the readings is probably to plot them on graph paper, and on a cruising or offshore racing boat this could become part of a routine log entry and thus provide a record similar to that from a barograph.

A steadily falling pressure can confirm a forecast of the approach of a depression or frontal system with the usual worsening of conditions they bring. Conversely a steady rise of pressure occurs while such systems are moving away. Frequently the rate of pressure change is linked to the intensity of a system – the greater the fall (or rise) the stronger are the accompanying winds likely to be. As a general guide strengthening winds can be expected if the pressure change is more than three millibars in three hours, and gales are probable if a pressure change of more than five millibars in three hours is recorded. Past weather records show that gales rarely fail to develop at a place after a pressure change of ten millibars in three hours has occured. A falling barometer is a better indicator of strong winds to come, because with a rising barometer they are often already being experienced.

It should be emphasised that a steady barometer does not preclude a significant increase in wind. The boat could be between an anticyclone and an advancing depression, so that although the barometric pressure at the place is steady the pressure gradient is increasing.

7.7.4 Wind speed and direction
It is also useful to note the wind speed and direction so that any changes can be readily detected and put in the context of the weather chart. Measuring the wind is easily done if masthead equipment is installed but on any boat under way it should be remembered that it is the apparent wind that is measured, and allowance for the boat's course and speed should be made. Simple hand held instruments such as a ventimeter and a hand bearing compass can be used to measure the wind, taking care to do this on the windward side.

7.7.5 Temperature
This weather element is usually of no great concern to a yachtsman but it is possible to obtain both the dew point and sea temperature to assess whether the conditions are near to those necessary for the formation of fog (see 7.1.13). The dew point is usually obtained by measuring the dry and wet bulb temperatures. A convenient instrument is the whirling psychrometer which is a frame holding two thermometers, the bulb of one being kept moist by dampened muslin. After the

instrument has been whirled like a football rattle, the difference in the thermometer readings is noted, and from tables the dew point is obtained.

7.7.6 Weather lore
Seamen, and especially longshoremen, have traditionally judged the weather outlook in terms of certain visible signs – the only method once available. In any one place the local weather lore may well have some validity, but what applies on, say, the East Coast may have little relevance on the West Coast of Scotland or in the English Channel. So, as generalisations, many of the well-known sayings are not to be trusted. There are, however, a few signs whose meanings are a little more reliable, and which – if used sensibly in the context of the general weather situation – may prove helpful.

There are several sayings which link the forthcoming weather with the colouring of the sky – especially a red sky. As Shakespeare has it:

'A red morn that ever yet betoken
Wreck to the seaman, tempest to the field,
Sorrow to shepherds, woe unto the birds,
Gust and foul flaws to herdman and to herds.'

A reddening of the sky at sunrise could mean an increase of water vapour in the upper troposphere, perhaps also a high level inversion and some cirrus cloud. In other words a frontal depression might be approaching, causing rain and strong winds by and after dusk with the seaman having to navigate under poor conditions in darkness while the shepherd has the problem of gathering a dispersed flock at night. The implications of a red sky at dusk are that any rain and strong winds are more likely to occur during daylight. Sayings that refer to a low or high dawn and dusk (whether the sun is visible on the horizon or not) come into a similar category to the red sky. These sayings are straws in the wind, but could alert a yachtsman to observe more closely any changes in wind and cloud.

One of the most reliable of old saws is 'Backing winds and mare's tails make tall ships carry low sails'. The twisted sheaves of cirrus cloud called 'mares' tails' are caused by the strong winds at upper levels which are often associated with a vigorous frontal depression which, if it is approaching, usually causes the wind to back.

Another reasonably reliable predictor is 'The moon with a circle brings water in her beak'. The circle in this saying is the lunar halo. Remember that the halo occurs around the sun just as frequently as around the moon, but is noticed less often because of the glare. Observing clouds on a bright day is much easier when using sun glasses, and often helps to see cloud formations that cannot be seen with the naked eye.

'Warmth in spring, sea fog will bring' contains an element of truth. As we have seen (7.1.8) air can hold a greater quantity of water vapour with higher temperatures, and in the spring when the sea temperatures have only just started to recover after the winter the air at the surface could be cooled to the dew point – in other words, form fog.

All such sayings should be used with caution although the basis for some can be scientifically explained and can be used by the yachtsman to alert him to possible developments. Listening to the various weather bulletins that are available, drawing a synoptic chart, recording pressure and wind together with careful observation of the sky is the best method of predicting what the weather has in store.

7.7.7 Sea state

Water in motion is an important factor in the safety and comfort of a sea passage but sea state is the result of weather conditions, not the cause of them. The subject is of special interest to yachtsmen and is discussed in Chapter 9(9.10) where it will be seen that an assessment of likely sea state can only be made if certain information is available. It is necessary to know the strength and fetch of the wind and for how long it has persisted. The only way this information can be obtained is to have access to the latest synoptic weather chart and those within the previous 24 to 36 hours.

7.8 Bibliography

The following books are suggested for further reference and reading on various aspects of weather as it affects the yachtsman:

Meteorology for Mariners by the Met. Office (HMSO). A detailed textbook for the professional mariner.

Interpreting the Weather by Ingrid Holford (David & Charles). A practical guide to general weather forecasting.

The Yachtsman's Weather Guide by Ingrid Holford (Ward Lock). An economical description of weather for the yachtsman.

Weather for Yachtsmen by Capt. W. H. Watts (Bosun Books). A good, simple description of the subject.

Weather for Sailing by Ray Sanderson (Adlard Coles Nautical). A guide for all RYA coastal certificates.

Forecasting Instant Weather by Alan Watts (Adlard Coles Nautical). Colour-coded photographs.

Instant Wind Forecasting by Alan Watts (Adlard Coles Nautical). A companion volume to the previous title.

Weather Forecasts (Booklet G5) by David Houghton (RYA). Basic guidance on forecasts. Useful pocket reference.

This is Practical Weather Forecasting by Dieter Karnetzki (Adlard Coles Nautical). Basic knowledge for the cruising yachtsman.

Clouds, Formation and Types: Clouds and Weather by R. K. Pilsbury (BP Educational Services). Photographs and notes available on slides, charts, cards or filmstrips. A useful tutorial aid.

Cloud Types for Observers by the Met. Office (HMSO). A good reference for cloud recognition.

Course in Elementary Meteorology by the Met. Office (HMSO). An excellent general textbook not as basic as the title suggests.

Teach Yourself Weather Forecasting for Sailors by Frank Singleton (Hodder & Stoughton). One of the well-known series of 'Teach Yourself books.

Your Own Weather Map by M. W. Stubbs (Royal Meteorological Society). A guide to producing a weather map from the Shipping Forecast.

Weather at Sea by David Houghton (Fernhurst Books). A good basic description of how the elements behave.

Wind Strategy by David Houghton (Fernhurst Books). A companion publication to the previous title, aimed at the racing yachtsman and race officers

Reading the Weather: Modern Techniques for the Yachtsmen by Alan Watts (Adlard Coles Nautical). How satellite and computer technology help the mariner.

Meteorological Glossary (HMSO). The definitive glossary produced by the Met. Office.

Ship's Code and Decode Book by the Met. Office (HMSO). An essential reference for those wishing to use the W/T Atlantic Weather Bulletins.

Yachtmaster shore-based course notes (RYA). This includes a brief but well-illustrated weather section.

The RORC Manual of Weather at Sea by Dag Pike (David and Charles). A useful guide to weather, forecasts and sea state.

The leaflet entitled *Weather Services for Shipping* is available from the Met. Office Marine Division, Eastern Road, Bracknell, Berkshire, RG12 2PW.

Chapter 8

Safety

Contents

8.1 Introduction

Assuming that a boat is handled sensibly and prudently, implying that good seamanship is used, safety afloat is ultimately a matter of preparation – making sure that the boat is well found and properly fitted out, and that the skipper and his crew are ready to cope with any emergency by knowing how to use the right equipment.

Prevention is always better than cure, and at sea it is easier to forestall an accident than to retrieve the situation. Fire prevention is infinitely preferable to fire fighting: careful pilotage is more satisfactory than having to kedge off the shore: listening to the weather forecast (and interpreting it correctly) is a lot more comfortable than getting caught out unexpectedly in gale force winds: and proper engine maintenance is safer and cheaper

than a tow into harbour. However accidents can
sometimes happen even on board the best
organised boat, and on such occasions it is vital
that all on board know how best to deal with the
particular emergency, and the correct procedures
for seeking help should it be required. In this area
the skipper has an important responsibility for the
proper management and training of his crew.

In earlier years most yachtsmen and
yachtswomen learned the basic skills of
seamanship and navigation by being afloat in
boats belonging to relatives or friends, often from
an early age. Now this is not so common, and
newcomers to the sport are encouraged to obtain
details of the various proficiency and training
schemes which are administered by the Royal
Yachting Association. These cover every aspect of
the sport – dinghy sailing, ski-boats and
runabouts, coastal cruising under either sail or
power, and the RYA/DTp Yachtmaster Certificates
for those who go offshore.

The skipper is responsible for the safety of the
boat and all on board. He must be prepared to
make quick decisions on all matters, and must
learn to anticipate what the next problem may be.

Every boat should have a number of built-in
safety factors. First is her basic design and
construction, which must be suitable for her
intended purpose. Second, she must be maintained
in proper condition. Third, she must have a
competent crew, with some reserve of strength for
unforeseen events. Fourth, she must be fitted with
suitable gear which will withstand all conditions
likely to be met. Fifth, in the event of some
accident, the necessary emergency equipment must
be carried for the crisis to be overcome, and the
crew must know how to use it. All these matters
are the direct and inescapable responsibility of the
owner or skipper.

Individual crew members of a seagoing boat
have a responsibility for taking with them certain
personal items of equipment, some of which are
discussed in more detail below. For comfort and
for the safety of the individual, and ultimately of
the entire crew, it is essential to be properly
clothed at sea. Non-slip shoes or sea boots should
be worn by everybody on board, and even in midsummer all should be in possession of foul
weather clothing with close fastenings at neck,
wrists and ankles, and with a hood or sou'wester
hat. At least two changes of sailing clothing
should be carried, including warm sweaters and
towelling strips as neck scarves. Other personal
items include a sailor's knife and spike, on a
lanyard; a waterproof electric torch, and a personal
supply of anti-seasickness pills for those
particularly afflicted.

Lifejackets and safety harnesses (which are
discussed in 8.3.6 and 8.3.7) are usually supplied
on board, but some individuals prefer to take their
own. If this is the case the owner or skipper
should be satisfied that they are to the required
standard.

8.2 Safety equipment – general

8.2.1 Safety equipment – legal requirements

There are certain legal requirements in respect of
the safety equipment to be carried in yachts.
Owners of larger yachts – 13.7m (45ft) or more in
overall length – must conform to the requirements
in the *Merchant Shipping (Life Saving Appliances)
Rules 1965* and the *Merchant Shipping (Fire
Appliances) Rules 1965*, which are obtainable from
HM Stationery Office.

All yachts must be equipped with the necessary
navigation lights and means of giving sound
signals as required by the International
Regulations for Preventing Collisions at Sea.

Yachts which are racing are usually required to
carry at least a certain minimum of safety
equipment, as prescribed by the class, club or
organisation involved. For example yachts
competing under the International Offshore Rule
(IOR) or in other offshore events must normally
comply with special safety regulations prescribed
for different categories of races by the Offshore
Racing Council (ORC), available from the Royal
Ocean Racing Club Rating Office, Seahorse Building,
Bath Road, Lymington, Hants SO41 9SE. Tel:
Lymington (01590) 677030. Fax: (01590) 679478.

The Department of Transport is seeking to control
yachts used for commercial purposes, such as charter
work. The Sail Training Ship Code of Practice is
being amended to cover all such vessels, with a
parallel code for motor yachts used commercially.

8.2.2 Safety equipment – recommendations for sea-going yachts of 5.5m (18ft) to 13.7m (45ft) overall length

The following is a summary of general
recommendations, agreed by the Department of
Trade and Industry, but precise requirements vary
with the type of craft, where she is used, and the
season of the year. As indicated, certain items of
equipment are dealt with in more detail below.
The suggested type and scale of equipment applies
to seagoing boats; lesser requirements may be
suitable for inshore use or for inland waters.

(1) Normal equipment
For operation and safe navigation.

(2) Personal safety equipment
One lifejacket to the appropriate European
Standard or to BS 3595 or of Department of Trade
accepted type for every person on board, kept in a
safe but accessible place. (For further details on
lifejackets see 8.3.6.) One safety harness to the
appropriate European Standard or to BS 4224 for
each person in a sailing yacht; one or more should
be provided in motor cruisers for use when

working on deck, but experience has shown that a harness may be dangerous if a person goes overboard at speeds greater than about eight knots. In sailing yachts safety harnesses should be worn on deck in bad weather, or at night; they must be properly adjusted, and clipped to a suitable strongpoint. (For further details see 8.3.7.)

(3) Rescue equipment for man overboard
At least two lifebuoys, one within easy reach of the helmsman and with a self-igniting light for use at night. A buoyant line, 30m (100ft) in length and with a minimum breaking strain of 115kg (250lb), should be within the helmsman's reach.

(4) Flotation equipment
For boats going more than three miles offshore (summer or winter), a liferaft of Department of Trade type (or equivalent) should be carried on deck or in a locker opening to deck, *or* a rigid dinghy with permanent buoyancy fitted should be carried on deck, *or* an inflatable dinghy should be stowed inflated on deck. Of these three the liferaft is to be preferred (see 8.3.9) but it must be serviced annually; dinghies should have oars and rowlocks secured in them.

For boats going not more than three miles out in winter an inflatable liferaft (or the dinghy alternatives above) is recommended. In well sheltered waters the summer scale, below, may be adequate. Liferafts may not be necessary in angling boats operating in organised groups when the boats are continually close to each other.

For boats not going more than three miles offshore in summer months (1 April to 31 October), lesser provisions in the form of lifebuoys, buoyant seats etc would be acceptable.

(5) General Equipment
Anchors – two, each with warp or chain of appropriate size and length. Where warp is used there should be at least 5.5m (3 fathoms) of chain between the anchor and the warp.
Efficient compass, and spare.
Charts, covering the intended area of operation.
Daylight distress (smoke) signals (see 8.3.10).
Distress flares (red) – six, with two parachute rockets (see 8.3.10)
Tow rope – of adequate length, say 50m (30 fathoms).
First aid box – with anti-seasick pills (see 8.6.28).
Radio receiver – sufficient for weather/shipping forecasts (see Section 7.6).
Water-resistant torch.
Radar reflector of adequate performance – as large as can be conveniently carried, and mounted at least 4m (13ft) above sea level (see 8.3.1).
Line suitable for general purposes, such as inboard lifeline in bad weather.
Engine tool kit (see 13.5.2).
Name or number, prominently displayed. These should be painted on the vessel or on dodgers in letters or figures at least 220mm (9in) high.

(6) Firefighting equipment
For boats over 9m (30ft) in length and those with powerful engines – two extinguishers each of not less than 1.4kg (3lb) capacity, of the dry powder type or equivalent, and one or more similar additional extinguisher of not less than 2.3kg (5lb) capacity.

For boats of up to 9m (30ft) in length, with cooking facilities and engines – two extinguishers each not less than 1.4kg (3lb) of the dry powder type or equivalent.

For boats up to 9m (30ft) in length, with cooking facilities only or with engine only – one extinguisher of the dry powder type or equivalent, of not less than 1.4kg (3lb) capacity.

Carbon dioxide (CO_2), or foam extinguishers of equivalent capacity are alternatives to dry powder. BCF (bromo-chloro-difluoro-methane) or BTM (bromo-trifluoro-methane) are acceptable but the crew must be warned that fumes from them are dangerous in a confined space, and a notice to this effect should be displayed by each extinguisher.

All craft should also carry a couple of buckets, with lanyards attached, and a small bag of sand for containing or extinguishing a burning spillage of fuel or lubricant.

Your boat should have been designed and built to keep fire risks to a minimum, but the arrangements can be checked by referring to the Home Office pamphlet *Fire Precautions in Pleasure Craft* (HMSO).

Further details on fire prevention and fire fighting in 8.3.5 below.

8.3 Safety equipment – details and usage

8.3.1 Radar reflectors
Objects made of steel or aluminium (the most likely metals encountered in yacht construction) will reflect a radar beam if they are hit at the correct angle, but timber and glassfibre return no worthwhile echo at all. So the average yacht can be considered almost invisible to radar since, due to its shape, even a metal mast is a poor reflector.

To avoid collision a ship should be able to identify and plot an echo from a boat at a range of at least 5 n miles, and to achieve this sort of detection it is essential that the boat has an efficient radar reflector.

Most yachts rely on a simple octahedral reflector, consisting of three metal surfaces (usually aluminium sheet) mounted at right angles to each other. This type of reflector has six points around it, and eight internal corners each of which forms what is called a re-entrant trihedral. When a radar beam encounters one of these re-entrant trihedrals it is reflected off the sides (usually all three) and is reflected back in a direction parallel to that from which it came.

Maximum reflection is obtained when the radar beam is directed into a corner within a cone, as shown in Fig. 8(1). In an octahedral reflector there are eight such corners, and hence eight such cones for maximum reflection. Within these eight cones reflection is good; elsewhere it is not so satisfactory.

To give the best reflection for 360° all round the boat, an octahedral reflector should be mounted in what has come to be called the 'catch rain' position (the attitude it adopts when standing on a level surface). But in this position it can be seen that one of the optimum cones is pointing straight upwards and one is pointing straight downwards. The other six point sideways, three of them angled 20° above the horizontal and three of them 20° below. So that, when the boat is upright, none of the six reflecting corners are working at maximum efficiency.

If the polar diagram is plotted to show the strength of reflection for the complete 360° around the boat, this will typically indicate six equally spaced sectors of about 35° each where reflection is good, with gaps in between where reflection is considerably reduced. A different pattern will emerge when the boat is heeled.

To give adequate responses an octahedral reflector needs to be quite large, with a minimum diagonal length of 460mm (18in), so that each reflecting corner has sides of 230mm (9in). It must be stoutly made so that the plates remain flat and perpendicular to each other. The reflector must be hoisted in the 'catch rain' attitude already described, and at a height of at least 4m (13ft) above the waterline.

Some octahedral reflectors have circular (rather than pointed) corners, formed by the intersection of three circular plates at right angles to each other, instead of three square plates. These have some advantage because the reflecting ability is increased relative to overall size.

Other, more elaborate types of reflectors are available to overcome some of the shortcomings of the standard octahedral. These more elaborate reflectors are however heavier and more expensive. One is the Firdell Blipper 300, consisting of an array of reflecting corners stacked vertically and enclosed in a cylindrical plastic case for protection and to reduce windage.

The most uniform reflection throughout 360° of azimuth (right round the horizon) is provided by the Lensref reflectors, which work on the principle of the Luneberg dielectric lens. This consists of a spherical lens, so constructed that the density of the material is graded as a function of the radius, being greatest in the centre. This has the effect of focusing an incoming radar beam on to a reflecting band, which is fitted round the 'equator' of the sphere and returns the beam along a path parallel to that on which it arrived. The width of the reflecting band dictates the angle of heel which the device can accommodate, but the width cannot be too much or it blanks off an undue proportion of

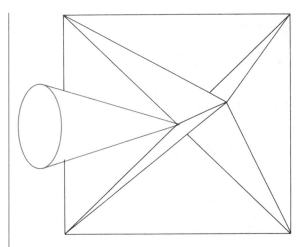

Fig. 8(1) In each of the eight re-entrant trihedrals (reflecting corners) of a standard octahedral reflector, the best reflections are given when the incoming beam is contained within an imaginary cone, as depicted in this diagram.

the incoming beam. Performance is good up to 15° of heel, but then falls off sharply.

8.3.2 Bilge pumps

Modern glassfibre boats should not normally take water into the bilge, but for any boat it is essential that adequate pumping arrangements are provided, and periodically tested, in case they are ever needed for emergency use.

Any seagoing boat should be fitted with at least two suitable pumps, which can be operated off the engine, electrically driven or worked manually. If an engine driven or electrical pump is fitted it must be supplemented with a powerful manual pump in case no power is available. An electrical pump does however have the advantage that it can be float controlled, and therefore cope with any accumulation of water when the boat is lying idle.

A manual bilge pump must be sited where it is easy to use, remembering that considerable and prolonged effort may be called for in an emergency, and also so that it can be conveniently dismantled for cleaning and inspection. The diaphragms, seals and valves of manual pumps should be examined at least once a season, and it is sensible to carry spares for these parts.

Any bilge pump should be fitted with a good strainer in the bilge, and this must be easily accessible for cleaning.

Any opening below the waterline is a threat to the watertight integrity of the boat, and must be fitted with a seacock which can be shut in the event of any failure of pipes or fittings. It is important that these are kept free, and are easy to get at. A few soft wood plugs of different sizes are useful for stopping leaks.

Limber holes in the bilges must be kept clear so that water can drain to the pump suction. Any dirt which is allowed to accumulate in the bilges will soon cause a blockage, and for this reason alone it is important that bilges be kept clear of all forms of dirt and debris.

8.3.3 Underwater damage

Although thankfully it is not common, it is not unknown for a yacht to suffer underwater damage – perhaps due to collision with submerged wreckage, or even a whale. Large baulks of timber are particularly dangerous. If such impact damage results in cracks or splits in the hull, it should be possible to stem most of the inflow of water by driving in small, soft wood wedges wrapped with pieces of rag – always provided that the damaged area is accessible.

If the hull is actually punctured, rather than just cracked or split, a very large quantity of water will start to pour into the boat, far above the capacity of any pumps installed. For example, a hole 150mm (6in) square at 0.6m (2ft) below the waterline will admit about 2275 litres (500 gallons) of water a minute, which is sufficient to sink a small yacht within a couple of minutes. At this point it should be noted that certain smaller yachts (such as the Etap range, built in Belgium, and the Sadler 29 in this country) have two skins with foam buoyancy in between them, to make the boat unsinkable – a commendable safety feature. The survival of an ordinary yacht, however, will depend on the very rapid location of the damage, and immediate steps to reduce the rate of flooding to something that can be controlled by the pumps.

Collision mats were invented more than a century ago, and have proved their efficiency on many occasions. Traditionally made of heavy canvas with ropes at each corner, a collision mat can be drawn over the outside of the hull so that it covers the damaged area, whereupon the

pressure of the seawater presses it tightly against the hull, to stem at least most of the leak. It is obvious, however, that this would need to be done very quickly indeed to cope with a hole of any significant size.

More practical for speedy deployment is a device called the Subrella, made in three sizes by D.C.G. Banbury, 1 Longfellow Road, Banbury, Oxon OX16 9LB. This consists of something looking rather like an umbrella, which is pushed through the hole and then opens on the outside (see Fig. 8(2)). Water pressure spreads the patch over the hole and forms an effective seal. Should it prove impossible to get at the hole from inboard, due to parts of the boat's structure, the Subrella can also be used from outboard. To be effective, it is important that the Subrella be stowed where it is instantly available – not at the bottom of a cockpit locker.

8.3.4 Guardrails

A seagoing boat should have double guardrails, the top one not less than 0.6m (2ft) above the deck, well supported by stanchions at intervals of not more than about 2.15m (7ft). The heel fittings of the stanchions must be through bolted, so that they are securely fitted. The guardrails should be kept taut by bottlescrews or lanyards.

A solid pulpit forward gives much needed security for sail changing or anchor work. It too needs to be firmly bolted through the deck. In cruising boats it is usually feasible to fit some similar arrangement aft, around the stern of the boat. This can be utilised for fitting lifebuoys, and weather cloths with the boat's name clearly painted port and starboard.

8.3.5 Fire prevention and firefighting

Any boat contains a lot of flammable equipment – even discounting such potential hazards as fuel and bottled gas. Hence fire prevention is the first priority. Provided that those who smoke are well disciplined, and that fuel and gas systems are properly installed and maintained, and sensibly used, the risks are not too great.

Smoking within the confines of a small boat should be discouraged. Even if it is acceptable to all concerned, great care is needed with the disposal of matches, ashes and cigarette ends and the skipper should never allow smoking in bunks. Precautions are also necessary on deck to make sure that lighted material does not go down an open hatch or locker lid. Cigarette ends have been known to enter open port holes and cause fires.

Most galley fires are caused by the ignition of hot fat or oil, and deep fat frying should be avoided afloat. Where liquid fuels such as paraffin or alcohol are used there is an obvious danger from spillage.

Gas systems

Bottled gas (normally butane) is the most common galley fuel in British boats. Propane is similar, but

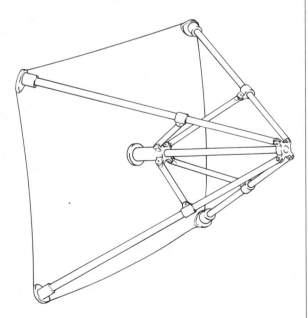

Fig. 8(2) The Subrella leak-stopping device can be pushed through a hole in the hull and then opened on the outside, to make a seal.

can be used in lower temperatures than butane. Both are heavier than air, so if they escape they sink to the bottom of a space or into the bilge, where they can collect until an explosive mixture (about 2% by volume) is built up. It is a sensible precaution to fit a gas detector which will give warning of any leak before a dangerous concentration is reached. The sensor should be fitted down in the lowest part of the bilge, but above the normal level which any bilge water might reach. Gas detectors should be wired up so that they can be switched on before any other electrical equipment in the boat is used.

A 'bubbler' gas leak detector fitted immediately downstream of the regular will indicate the smallest leak in the gas system, and is available from Calor Gas dealers.

All work in connection with gas installations and fittings must be performed by a 'competent person' – somebody with suitable work experience or trained in accordance with the Health and Safety Commission's 'Approved Code of Practice'. The British Standard which currently applies is BS 5482 Part 3, although this is to be replaced by a new European Standard for LPG installations in boats, now in preparation.

The gas cylinder must be fitted outside the accommodation – in a cockpit locker for example with a drain venting overboard above the waterline. Gas piping must be stainless steel or seamless copper, mounted high in the boat and well clipped. Flexible connections should only be used at the cylinder end or at a gimballed stove, and must conform to BS 3212 *Flexible Tubing or Hose for Use in Butane/Propane Gas Installations*. The cylinder must be securely fixed in place with a metal bracket or a strong lashing. Shock cord is inadequate. Should the cylinder be inverted or thrown on its side, liquid gas may enter and pass through the regulator, causing a very large increase in pressure in the low pressure section of the installation.

Gas appliances (water or cabin heaters as well as galley stoves) must be designed for butane/ propane gas and conform to the relevant British Standards. Appliances with pilot lights, such as water heaters, should incorporate a flame failure device to shut off the gas supply if the pilot light is extinguished. Adequate ventilation must be provided to prevent a build up of carbon monoxide or carbon dioxide. When a stove or similar appliance is not in use, or in bad weather, and always before leaving the boat, the gas should be turned off at the bottle. Remote control valves are available.

If gas is smelt prevent all naked lights and smoking, do not run any electrical equipment or the engines, and ventilate the boat thoroughly. It will be necessary to bail the gas from the bilges, or pump it out with a manual diaphragm type bilge pump. Give the entire gas system a careful check for leaks by testing all pipe unions with soapy water, and do not use it until the defect has been rectified.

To maintain safety and efficiency the system should be serviced annually by a competent person. More information on gas systems is given in Chapter 14 (14.1.13).

Fuel systems
A boat's fuel system is the other major fire risk, particularly if the fuel is petrol. Even the smallest leak must be eliminated, and care must be taken with spills when refuelling. The fuel filler must be on deck so that any overflow does not go into the bilges, and so that fumes displaced from the tank are vented into the fresh air. The air vent from the tank should go to a protected place on deck and be covered with a gauze.

There must be a shut off valve (easily accessible) on the fuel line where it leaves the top of the tank, and the entire fuel system should be professionally fitted using materials of approved standards.

Particular care must be taken when refuelling or when working on any part of the fuel system – cleaning filters for example. At such times it is essential to stop smoking and have no naked lights in the vicinity. On completion of the work make quite certain that all joints are tight. In the event of a spill mop up as much fuel as possible and thoroughly ventilate the area.

Before starting an engine, always first run the engine compartment exhaust fan (where fitted) for five minutes, and inspect the engine space for any smell of fuel.

Firefighting
Fire extinguishers work by cooling the fire down, by smothering it, or by reacting with it chemically – or sometimes by a combination of these methods.

Water is an excellent medium for cooling down a fire, and in a boat there is always a plentiful supply, even if just using a couple of buckets with lanyards. Water is less damaging than chemicals to the interior of a boat, and it does not produce harmful fumes. Water can also be useful to prevent re-ignition of a fire which has been temporarily extinguished by other means. But water must not be applied to burning liquids such as fuel or cooking fat since a violent reaction will occur, spreading the fire in every direction. Also, since water is heavier than fuels or cooking fat, the latter will float on the water and continue burning. Neither must water be used on electrical fires where high voltage is present, due to the danger involved.

For general purposes dry powder is best for use below deck since it does not give off any dangerous fumes, does not conduct electricity, is non-corrosive and is suitable for most types of fire. It does make rather a mess, however, although not as much as foam. The powder works chemically to stop combustion, and it also absorbs some heat as it melts, thereby giving at least some cooling effect. When released, the powder emerges as a fine jet which should travel at least 2m (6ft), and when this hits the flames it causes dense white smoke, which can be alarming in the confines of a boat.

Dry powder extinguishers are operated by pressure from a CO_2 bottle, and the best type has a controlled discharge so that all the contents do not have to be released at once. It is useful to be able to keep some back in the event of re-ignition – always something to be watched for when firefighting, but particularly with dry powder, which does not have good cooling properties. With the average extinguisher the total discharge time is likely to be less than 10 seconds, so it is important to get as close as possible and take good aim at the base of the fire, to ensure that the first burst from the extinguisher is really effective.

The powder may consolidate inside if the extinguisher is left standing for a long time. This risk can be minimised by giving it a good shake and by tapping it firmly with a piece of wood every few months.

Galley flare ups are best tackled by smothering with a fire blanket, stowed near (but not above or behind) the stove. Do not use water, which only scatters the burning liquid. If a fire blanket is not available, a towel or blanket soaked in water will serve. Make as good a seal as possible with the blanket round the edge of the pan, and try to prevent the blanket falling into the actual liquid. Leave the blanket in place until the pan and its contents are thoroughly cooled.

Foam extinguishers are best for burning liquids. They form a blanket over the surface, which cuts off the supply of oxygen needed to support combustion and also cools the surface, but generally their use in boats is rather limited.

Vaporising liquids such as halon 1211, or BCF (bromo-chloro-difluoro-methane) and halon 1301, or BTM (bromo-trifluoro-methane) are alternative and good extinguishants, but users must understand that fumes given off by them can be dangerous in the confined spaces of a boat. Halon is an ozone depleting gas and is likely to be withdrawn as an extinguishant in the near future.

Carbon dioxide is good for extinguishing fires of liquids or of electrical equipment, although it acts by blanketing the fire and has no cooling effect. But it needs to be stored under high pressure, and the weight of the cylinders makes it unsuitable for small boats. In larger craft it is often used (like BCF) for fixed installations in machinery spaces. In the event of a fire in the engine compartment of a small yacht, stop the engine(s) plus any ventilation fan(s) fitted, turn off the fuel at the tank, blank off (if feasible) the air inlets to the engine space, and then operate any extinguisher fitted in that compartment. A petrol-engined boat should have an automatic BCF extinguisher in the engine space: heat from the fire activates the sensing head to operate the extinguisher, which floods the compartment with gas. In the event of fire, this eliminates any need to open up the engine space, which can only make matters worse. It is important that the extinguisher should have sufficient capacity in relation to the volume of the space. Manufacturers seem to be divided on this point, but 3lb (1.4kg) of BCF are suggested for every 100 cubic feet (2.8 cubic metres) of engine compartment (no deduction being made for space occupied by engines etc).

Speed is essential in firefighting, so it is important that there should be an extinguisher ready to hand in each compartment of a boat, and that the crew should all know how to use them. A minimum scale is suggested in para (6) of 8.2.2, but one or two extra extinguishers are strongly recommended.

If a serious fire develops, head the boat in a direction so that the wind will not spread the flames further along the boat. Open hatches create a draught which will fan the flames, so far as possible the boat should be battened down.

Fire extinguishers do not remain efficient, or even operable, if left indefinitely in a marine environment. Some (more expensive ones) are fitted with pressure gauges, which should be checked regularly. BCF or BTM extinguishers can be checked by weight, but this is no good for dry powder extinguishers where a leak only causes loss of the propellant, which has negligible weight compared to the powder. It is therefore recommended that extinguishers of this type should be discharged and replenished about every five years.

8.3.6 Lifejackets

Any seagoing boat should carry a lifejacket which conforms either to the new European Standards (see below) or to the previous BS 3595 for every person on board – see Fig. 8(3). The BS 3595 specification requires that a lifejacket has a minimum buoyancy of 16.4kg (35lb) for adults, and 9.4kg (20lb) for children. It must also support the head of an unconscious person so that the mouth is clear of the water, and turn an unconscious or exhausted person from being face down onto his back in five seconds. Another requirement is a lifting becket for raising the wearer from the water.

There have been five different types of lifejackets available up to the introduction of the new European Standards, as follows:

(1) *Inherent buoyancy only.* These are bulky lifejackets of the 'Mae West' variety – simple, cheap and durable, but very awkward to wear and normally only found in commercial ships.

(2) *Part inherent buoyancy, and part oral inflation.* A typical lifejacket of this type must have about 6.8kg (15lb) of built-in buoyancy, which can be increased to a total of 16kg (35lb) by oral inflation. This is a good compromise – reasonably comfortable to wear, and the inherent buoyancy is enough to bring the wearer to the surface if he goes over the side. But oral inflation is needed to give the full support required by BS 3595.

(3) *Full oral inflation.* This type has no inherent buoyancy, and has to be inflated by mouth to

produce any support. Some can be worn partially inflated in reasonable comfort. These are the most compact and were also the cheapest lifejackets conforming to BS 3595, available in vest or halter types.

(4) *Manual gas inflation.* Similar to (3), but with the added facility of inflation from a small CO_2 cylinder, manually operated. Oral inflation available as a stand-by. Gas inflation must not be used if the lifejacket has already been inflated orally.

(5) *Automatic gas inflation.* Similar to (4), except that the lifejacket inflates automatically on entering the water. Alternatively gas inflation can be operated manually, or the lifejacket can be inflated orally. But note that the lifejacket must not be inflated orally before entering the water. This is the most expensive type, but it has the significant advantage that the lifejacket will inflate itself even if the wearer is unconscious on entering the water.

When buying a lifejacket inflate it and try it on. It should provide firm support to the neck, and should not allow the head to fall forward. Special sizes are available for children.

Most lifejackets are a bright orange colour, which makes them more visible in the water. It is a good idea to fit them with strips of reflective tape around the collar. They should also be fitted with a whistle attached to a lanyard, and preferably have some form of automatic light which is switched on when immersed in water. It is recommended that a lifejacket or a combination harness and lifejacket should be fitted with a crotch strap.

Lifejackets should be stowed in a dry place, which is known to the crew, where they are easily accessible if required. They should be checked periodically. The straps should be properly adjusted to suit individual wearers, and this is particularly important in the case of young persons.

For inland waters, where help is readily at hand for a person who goes overboard, a lesser standard of flotation provided by a garment called a Personal Buoyancy Aid (PBA) is acceptable. A PBA is more comfortable to wear than the average lifejacket, but it does not provide so much flotation and is intended to provide buoyancy for a conscious person to help them reach safety.

Good lifejackets are not particularly cheap but they are essential items of equipment for any sea-going boat, and they should be worn when conditions are bad, or by non-swimmers whenever they are on deck or in the cockpit of a boat at sea. Another occasion when lifejackets may well save lives is when proceeding to or from shore in a smaller tender in a tideway – particularly at night or in adverse weather.

New European specifications for lifejackets and buoyancy aids came into force on 1 July 1992, after which a manufacturer should only sell products carrying the CE Mark of Approval.

Fig. 8(3) Putting on a lifejacket – first read the instructions. Hold the jacket up in front of you, put your head through the hole, and secure the waistband at the side or front as appropriate.

However, until stocks are cleared the previous products will remain available for some time. There is no need to replace existing lifejackets or buoyancy aids which are in a good, serviceable condition.

The new standard is measured in Newtons (10 Newtons equal one kilogram or 2.2 pounds). There are four levels of minimum performance, with the higher Newton number giving the higher buoyancy rating. The ratings quoted below are for adults:

(1) A 50 Newton Buoyancy Aid gives 11lb of buoyancy – only suitable for good swimmers in sheltered waters with help close at hand. Inferior to the previous BMIF standard for buoyancy aids.

(2) A 100 Newton Buoyancy Aid gives 23lb of buoyancy, with a better performance than aids previously sold in the UK.

(3) A 150 Newton Lifejacket with 33lb of buoyancy is equivalent in performance to existing UK approved lifejackets (BS 3595).

(4) A 275 Newton Lifejacket is a high performance device providing 62lb of buoyancy for offshore use and severe conditions.

8.3.7 Safety harnesses

In bad weather or at night it is doubly important to prevent any crew member falling over the side; so the skipper must ensure that those on deck are wearing safety harnesses, and that these are clipped to suitable strong points – not to the guardrails or parts of the standing or running rigging.

Safety harnesses should conform to the new European Standards or to BS 4224/82 (BS 4474 for children) or some other recognised standard which requires minimum sizes and strengths for all the component parts – the webbing straps, the securing line, and the snap hook at the end. Apart from being strong enough the metal fittings must be non-magnetic. A harness must be properly adjusted for the wearer, so that the point of attachment for the safety line is high on the chest. It is desirable that a safety harness should be fitted with a crotch strap, and RORC Special Regulations insist on this.

It is useful if the harness has two clips, one on short stay and one on a longer line for working on deck. In poor conditions a crew member should be hooked to a fixed part of the boat's structure before emerging from the cabin into the cockpit. Jackstays rigged along the deck can allow people to move forward and aft without the need to continually alter their attachment to the boat.

The Tupper Latchway system provides the means for a crew member to walk round the yacht, connected by his personal lifeline, with the minimum of restriction. A stainless steel wire is secured round the deck by special fittings. The Latchway 'Transfastener', to which the personal safety line is attached, runs along the wire and traverses the fittings without being detached, see Fig. 8(4). It can therefore give an uninterrupted run, from one end of the boat to the other. All the components meet the requirements of BS 4224/82, and the fittings have a tensile strength in excess of 2200kg (4840lb).

Some sailing jackets incorporate a built-in harness (sometimes an inflatable lifejacket too). These garments help overcome the problem of ensuring that people on deck are wearing harnesses when the weather deteriorates.

Harnesses need to be checked regularly to ensure that there is no wear or damage to the webbing or the safety line. In particular the adjusting buckles and the snap hook need to be kept free and in good condition, and the hinges lightly oiled.

There is not the same requirement for safety harnesses in motor boats, but one or two should be carried in case it is necessary to work on deck in bad weather. It should be remembered however that anybody wearing a safety harness and going over the side at more than about 8 knots is liable to injury.

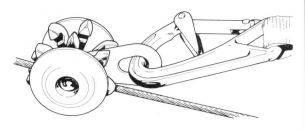

Fig. 8(4) The Latchway safety system permits movement the length of the boat by a crew member attached to a personal safety line.

An experienced crew knows when it is sensible to be hooked on, but often it falls to the skipper or whoever is in charge on deck to insist that everybody conforms.

8.3.8 Man overboard – gear and drill

If, despite all normal precautions, somebody should go over the side, it is important not only to have the necessary gear at hand to help locate and recover him, but to have some prior understanding of the procedure to be followed depending on the circumstances.

The first necessity is to give the alarm, so that all hands are alerted to the emergency. 'Man overboard, port (or starboard) side' should bring everybody on deck immediately. One of the crew on deck, preferably whoever saw him go over the side, should be detailed to keep a continuous watch on the person in the water for as long as possible. Another should release the lifebuoy(s) which should be carried near the stern – preferably fitted with dan buoy and flag, self-igniting light, whistle, dye-marker, and drogue to reduce drift Fig. 8(5). The sooner this can be done the nearer it will be to the person in the water.

There are available small homing beacons that are easily worn by individual crew members, attached to lifejackets or survival clothing. The Locat PLB7 is about the size of a packet of cigarettes; should the wearer fall overboard the transmitter can be activated manually or automatically to set off an alarm on board. A receiving aerial on board the vessel is linked to a simple compass to indicate the bearing of the person in the water. The mini EPIRB (Emergency Position Indicating Radio Beacon) transmits on 121.5MHz for at least six hours.

In a sailing yacht, particularly when running downwind or almost downwind, it may be helpful to start the auxiliary engine if fitted, but before the clutch is engaged care must be taken that no sheets or lines which might foul the propeller are trailing over the side. Great care must be taken with the use of the engine when manoeuvring close to anybody in the water, to avoid injury by the propeller.

Meanwhile, until the boat is fully under control in respect of handling sails etc, so as to be able to return to the place of the disaster, the helmsman should steer a very steady course which he must memorise.

With a well crewed yacht, under sail, the recognised manoeuvre when beating to windward or reaching is to bear away, gybe, and then luff back on a course which will take the boat back to the required spot. The yacht then approaches the person in the water nearly on a close-hauled course, in order that speed may be more easily adjusted to round up alongside him. If stopped just to windward of the person, the yacht will drift down towards him and form a lee for the recovery operation, but there is a danger that the

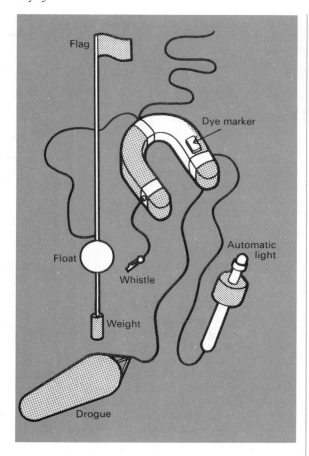

Fig. 8(5) Lifebuoy with dan buoy and flag, automatic light, whistle, dye marker, and drogue.

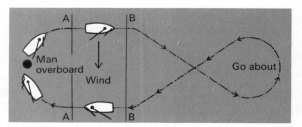

Fig. 8(6) Man overboard drill for a family cruiser, going to windward. The first step is to get the boat on a reach, while getting everything ready to tack and return on a reciprocal course.

boat may either be thrown on to him by a sea, or sail over the top of him. These risks are avoided if the boat is brought to rest immediately to leeward of the man in the water, but in this case it is essential to establish contact with him before the boat drifts away to leeward. Practice is needed in different wind strengths and on different points of sailing to get this manoeuvre right, and it is vital that the sails are trimmed and handled according to the orders of the skipper or helmsman.

If a yacht is running under spinnaker, even with a competent crew, it may be five minutes before the boat is ready to come on the wind and beat back to the place where the man went overboard – perhaps half-a-mile away. Here some accurate plotting is needed to make sure that the tacks which are made will bring the boat as near as possible to the scene.

In a boat such as a family cruiser which is probably not strongly crewed, it may be safer to get the boat on to a reach initially, while things are sorted out, and then go about and return on the opposite tack, sailing a reciprocal course. The distances from the place of the incident to the position of tacking, and from there back to the **person – represented by AB in Fig. 8(6) are equal,**

which may be useful to remember particularly at night. Counting may help. This is mentioned because it is sometimes not feasible to return immediately – if, for example, a spinnaker is set, or a foreguy is rigged on the main boom, or if a mizzen staysail is set in a two-masted boat. Success is more likely to be achieved by keeping control of the boat in such situations, than by precipitate action which may leave her helpless.

When running or broad reaching, especially in a lot of wind, it is probably best to luff gradually until the wind is about on the beam (lowering the spinnaker beforehand, if it is set), and then come about so as to return on a roughly close-hauled course (if originally running) or on more of a reach (if originally on a broad reach), as in Fig. 8(7).

Another approach to man overboard recovery which is gaining increasing acceptance is the 'quick stop' method. On the call 'man overboard' one crew member, if he can be spared, should keep continuous watch on the person in the water. Immediately put all flotation aids available over the side, possibly to aid the victim but also to mark the scene, and put the boat head to wind and beyond – allowing the headsail to back and slow the boat with the wind abeam for two or three lengths. Then bear away downwind and drop the headsail, with the main still sheeted well in. Sail downwind until the victim is abeam, and gybe so as to approach on a course about 45° to 60° off the wind. Make contact with the victim by heaving line or similar device, and recover over the windward side. Particularly with a

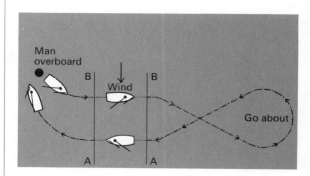

Fig. 8(7) As for Fig. 8(6), but with the boat on a broad reach. In both cases the times to sail from A to B, and from B to A, are equal – useful at night or in poor visibility.

shorthanded crew, the final stages of recovery may be achieved with a 'Seattle Sling' or 'Lifesling' as described below.

In a motor boat it is normally not too difficult to turn the boat round and return to somebody who has gone over the side. If the helmsman sees the incident, or if sufficiently early warning is given by somebody else, the helmsman should apply helm so as to swing the stern away from the person, and thereby reduce the risk of injury from the propeller(s).

As in a sailing boat, a lifebuoy should be released as quickly as possible and somebody should be detailed to watch the person in the water continuously.

Depending on the type and speed of boat the quickest way of getting back to the scene is using the Williamson turn. After the initial helm has been applied to swing the stern away from the person in the water, continue altering in that direction until about 60 degrees off the original course. Then apply full opposite rudder until the boat is steadied on a reciprocal course to that originally being steered. The person should then be right ahead, and it is important not to run him down, with practice in one's own boat this manoeuvre can be made quite precisely. See Fig. 8(8).

Having returned to the immediate vicinity of the person in the water, the next step is to establish contact with him quickly, before the boat starts to drift away. Have two or three lines ready to throw to him, and a lifebuoy if he has not already got one and is not wearing a lifejacket. To reach a person who is more than a few feet from the boat there is a device called the Balcan Emergency Life Line (BELL), which consists of a capsule into which is packed a 40m (130ft) line, which can be thrown quickly and accurately.

The 'Seattle Sling' or similar device consists of a flotation collar, which can also act as a hoisting sling, to which is attached a long floating line stored in a container at the stern of the boat with the end made fast inboard. When the sling is deployed it trails astern, drawing out the rest of the line. The boat then circles the person in the

water until contact is made. The victim puts the sling over his head and under his arms, while the boat drops her sails ready to pull the victim alongside.

Once the person has been got alongside the boat, the next stage of the rescue is to get him inboard. In a boat with any substantial amount of freeboard this can be quite a problem. The first requirement is to get him secured by the becket of his lifejacket or safety harness, or with a bowline round his chest – so that he can't drift away. Some boats have a bathing ladder aft, usually with a hinged lower section which projects down into the water; this is very useful, but remember it is close to the propeller(s). Alternatively a boarding ladder amidships can be used, but since this is unlikely to reach even to the waterline the person will need a loop of rope about 0.6m (2ft) below water, into which he can put one or both of his feet so as to get on to the bottom rung of the ladder. A rope ladder, or any other type of ladder, can be pressed into service.

By this time however he is likely to be cold and exhausted, and will probably need assistance. A strong crew may be able to haul him aboard with the aid of the line already mentioned but otherwise some form of mechanical assistance will be needed. Possibilities include unshackling the lower block of the mainsheet and securing this to his harness/lifejacket, and then winching him in with the topping lift set up; using a small handy billy tackle (preferably fitted with snap hooks each end) attached to him and the main boom for the same purpose; or utilising the falls of davits in the same way. Another suggested method is to lower the jib partly over the side so that the person can be manoeuvred into the bight of the sail and then bowsed inboard by the sheet winch, together with an auxiliary halyard transferred to the clew of the sail.

If none of these methods is practicable an inflatable dinghy or even a liferaft secured alongside the boat will serve to get the person out of the water for the first part of the rescue. In this event it may help to remove the guardrails round that part of the boat in order to transfer him inboard.

It can be seen that such an emergency needs consideration and planning in advance. In order to avoid delay it is essential that all the crew understand the procedure to be used, and know where the requisite gear is stowed.

8.3.9 Liferafts

If because of some disaster it is necessary for the crew to abandon ship (and there are good reasons not to do so prematurely), a liferaft which will accommodate all on board should ensure their safety for a considerable period. Because of the shelter it provides and the survival equipment which it should contain, a liferaft is much better than either a rigid or inflatable dinghy, and is therefore recommended even for coastal waters. It

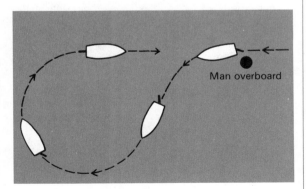

Fig. 8(8) In a motor boat the Williamson turn, pictured here, is a good method of returning with reasonable certainty to a person in the water.

SAFETY CHECK LIST
Before leaving your mooring, check these
items:

- ☐ Boat in seaworthy condition
- ☐ Engine in running order
- ☐ Lubricating oil checked
- ☐ Engine coolant checked
- ☐ Handbook, tools, spares onboard
- ☐ Sufficient fuel onboard
- ☐ Bilge clear and pump working
- ☐ Anchor gear correct
- ☐ Local weather forecast
- ☐ Tidal state
- ☐ Fire extinguishers
- ☐ Flares in date
- ☐ Lifejackets for all onboard
- ☐ Seagoing clothing
- ☐ VHF radio working
- ☐ Safety harnesses
- ☐ Compass and charts
- ☐ Torches and batteries
- ☐ Radar reflector
- ☐ Man overboard gear
- ☐ First Aid box
- ☐ Liferaft
- ☐ Somebody ashore knows where you are
  bound, and estimated time of
  arrival/return

---

is essential that the raft should be capable of
carrying the entire crew. Large yachts may need
more than one raft.

Desirable features include an automatically
erecting canopy to protect the occupants and
prevent total inversion, two independent
buoyancy compartments either of which will
support the raft and occupants, and (particularly
for ocean passages or in cold waters) an inflatable
double floor. To provide stability there should be
water-ballast bags underneath. To help prevent
capsizing and to reduce drift the raft should have
a large and effective drogue of the type developed
by British Marine Technology, made of slightly
porous material and fitted with anti-tangle lines on
the shrouds.

Liferafts are stowed in either a valise or a
canister, which should be secured by quick release
lashings in a place where it can be easily got over
the side. The inboard end of the painter must be
firmly secured to the boat. Once the valise or
canister is in the water (preferably on the leeward
side of the boat) the painter is given a really
strong jerk or series of jerks, whereupon the
liferaft will automatically break out of its
container and inflate itself. Don't worry about the
subsequent wailing sound, which is only surplus
gas escaping so that the raft is not over inflated. It
is possible that the raft may inflate upside down,
but this is easy to rectify although it may mean
somebody entering the water. It is better if the

crew can enter the liferaft directly from the yacht,
and therefore keep dry, rather than via the water.
In any case it is extremely difficult to climb into a
liferaft when wearing an inflated lifejacket.

When first inflated a liferaft is unstable because
it is unloaded, the water ballast pockets have not
had time to fill, and the drogue has not been
streamed. In bad weather the liferaft should be
boarded as soon as possible after inflation, and the
weight of the crew should be evenly distributed.

Even a loaded liferaft can become unstable in
bad weather. Factors which influence instability
include the shape of the canopy in very strong
winds, the design and strength of water ballast
pockets, the position of the access hatch in the
canopy, and (particularly) the design of the
drogue. These and other factors have been the
subject of detailed investigation following the
unsatisfactory performance of liferafts in the 1979
Fastnet Race.

Liferafts are available with a choice of survival
equipment, and the scale carried depends upon
what sort of cruising is intended. Obviously more
items are desirable for an ocean voyage than for a
passage across the North Sea or the English
Channel. As a very minimum it is necessary to
carry water, flares, a pair of bellows for topping
up the raft, repair equipment and a first aid kit,
see Fig. 8(9).

There are now available hand-operated
watermakers, working on the reverse osmosis
principle as described in 14.3.4. Also on the
market is a solar watermaker which works by
condensation only, and is stated to give a pint of
water a day in British waters, and three or four
times that amount in warmer conditions.

Some yachts sensibly carry a 'panic bag'
containing such items as food, clothing, extra

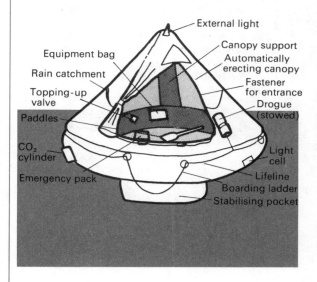

Fig. 8(9) Inflated liferaft.

flares, fishing gear and a signalling mirror, which can be taken into the raft on abandoning ship.

Information about abandoning ship and the use of a liferaft is given in 8.4.8.

Liferafts and the survival equipment which they contain require annual servicing to ensure that they will function correctly in an emergency.

Since cases have occurred of liferafts being found at sea, sometimes being lost from the parent craft in error, it is recommended that the raft should have the yacht's name painted clearly on it in order to assist identification (which otherwise can only be done through the serial number, which takes some time).

It should be noted that for occasional offshore cruises it is possible to hire a liferaft for quite a modest sum.

8.3.10 Distress signals

If (and only if) a situation develops where a boat is in serious and immediate danger, and help is urgently required, a distress signal should be made, as described below.

For a lesser emergency an urgency signal (as described in 6.6.16 and in sub para (e) below) may be appropriate. If help is needed but the boat is not in immediate danger, the proper signal is 'V' ('Victor') in the International Code, which means 'I require assistance'. This can be sent as a flag signal (a white flag with a red St Andrew's cross), or by light or sound in Morse code ($\cdot\cdot\cdot-$). Certain other signals of an 'emergency' nature are contained in the International Code, and a selection is given among the two-letter groups shown in 6.2.8.

A full list of the recognised distress signals is given in Annex IV to the *International Regulations for Preventing Collisions at Sea*, stated in full in Section 2.1. The following are those which are most likely to be appropriate for yachts and small craft, together with some notes on their use. (The letters of the sub-paragraphs refer to Annex IV, mentioned above.) Note that the use of any of these signals is strictly prohibited unless a vessel is in serious and immediate danger, and help is urgently required.

It should also be noted that 999 calls by cellular telephones to HM Coastguard from vessels at sea suffer numerous disadvantages compared to recognised distress calls by VHF radio, and are to be discouraged.

(b) *Continuous sounding with any fog signalling apparatus.* In order to avoid any doubt as to the intention, the continuous sounding should be in the form of a succession of letters SOS ($\cdot\cdot\cdot---\cdot\cdot\cdot$) in Morse.

(d) *A signal made by radiotelegraphy or by any other signalling method consisting of the group* $\cdot\cdot\cdot---\cdot\cdot\cdot$ *(SOS) in the Morse Code.* For a yacht the most likely methods are by sound signal as in (b) above, or by flashing light. The latter is of course particularly effective at night.

(e) *A signal sent by radiotelephony consisting of the spoken word MAYDAY.* The procedure is fully described in para 6.6.16. For ease of reference the basic rules are repeated briefly below. The distress frequencies are 2182kHz (MF) and Ch 16 (VHF). Speak clearly and distinctly, as follows:–

MAYDAY MAYDAY MAYDAY
THIS IS (name of boat, repeated three times)
MAYDAY
(Then restate the boat's name, followed by her position, the nature of the emergency, what assistance is required, and any other helpful information such as the number of persons on board.)
OVER.

Listen for a reply, and if none is heard repeat the procedure. If transmitting on 2182kHz (MF) the distress call should be repeated during the three-minute silence period at each hour and half-hour.

An Urgency Signal indicates a lesser emergency than a Distress Signal, and should be used when there is a very urgent message to transmit concerning the safety of a ship, aircraft of other vehicle, or the safety of a person. The message, which in other respects is similar in format to a distress message, is prefaced by the words 'PAN PAN' spoken three times (instead of 'MAYDAY'). The signal, which has priority over all traffic except distress, should be made on 2182kHz or Ch 16. In the case of a long message, such as when requesting medical advice, it is appropriate to transfer to a working frequency once communication has been established.

Portable, emergency radiotelephones, operating either on 2182kHz or on Ch 16, are available. These are useful because as well as being operable from the yacht they can be taken into the liferaft in the event of abandoning ship.

Also available are Personal Locator Beacons (PLBs) and Emergency Position Indicating Radio Beacons (EPIRBs) which operate on 121.5 and 243MHz. These are primarily for aeronautical purposes, and the maritime search and rescue authorities such as the Coastguard do not keep watch on these frequencies. Reception depends on an aircraft flying nearby and monitoring these channels, and this cannot be relied on. However, they can be very useful as a homing aid for search and rescue aircraft once an alert has been received. Of more value is an EPIRB which transmits on 406MHz, the dedicated COSPAS/SARSAT satellite frequency with full global coverage. The wrong or accidental use of PLBs or EPIRBs can raise problems, particularly in the event of any aircraft being in difficulties in the area. So, if carried, it is important that they are stowed carefully, out of the reach of unsupervised children, and only operated when a distress signal is fully justified. Once activated an EPIRB should not be switched off until instructions are received from the search and rescue authorities. Like any other radio transmitting equipment, PLBs and EPIRBs must have a licence, obtained from the Radiocommunications Agency, Waterloo Bridge House, Waterloo Road, London SE1 8UA. Tel: 0171-215 5000.

Details of a vessel carrying a 406MHz EPIRB must be sent to the Registration Section, DSGIA, Department of Transport, 90 High Holborn, London WC1V 6LP on the prescribed form supplied by the manufacturer.

(f) *The International Code signal of distress 'NC'.* This can be made by flag hoist, N being a blue and white chequered flag and C one horizontally striped blue, white, red, white, blue.

(g) *A signal consisting of a square flag having above or below it a ball or anything resembling a ball.* This should not be too difficult to contrive from any square flag or piece of material, and from a round fender or anchor ball.

(i) *A rocket parachute flare or a hand flare showing a red light.* Undoubtedly a red flare is the most effective visual distress signal at night. Flares are needed for two purposes — first to raise the alarm and then to pinpoint the boat's position so as to guide rescuers to her. Within about three miles from land a hand flare, which gives a brilliant red light for one minute, will do both tasks. At greater distances a red parachute rocket which projects a suspended flare to more than 300m (1000ft) and burns for more than 40 seconds is needed to raise the alarm, but hand flares are useful to indicate the boat's position. A Very pistol needs a firearms certificate from the police.

(j) *A smoke signal giving off orange-coloured smoke.* By day orange smoke signals (hand held for short distances, or the larger buoyant type for greater range) are more effective than flares, although the smoke disperses quickly in a strong wind. The following table suggests minimum outfits of flares for different sorts of usage of a boat. More should be carried by ocean cruising yachts.

White flares are not distress signals, but are used to indicate the presence of a boat — to another vessel sighted on a collision course for example. An outfit of four is suggested for boats which make night passages. Shield your eyes when using them, to prevent loss of night vision.

Flares must be stowed where they are easily accessible, but protected from damp. In good storage conditions they should have a life of three years: replace them by the expiry date. Examine them regularly for any signs of deterioration. All the crew should know where the flares are stowed, and how to use them. Hold hand flares firmly downwind. Rockets turn into the wind: fire them vertically in normal conditions, or aimed about 15° downwind in strong winds. Do not aim them into the wind, or they will not gain altitude. If there is low cloud, fire rockets at 45° downwind so that the flare burns under the cloud.

Flares should conform to SOLAS 83, which should be marked thereon. It is suggested that when parachute rockets are used two should be fired initially with an interval of about one minute. Then wait several minutes before firing another. Do not fire parachute rockets when a helicopter is nearby.

Mini-flares are satisfactory for personal use by dinghy sailors for example, but are not a substitute for proper SOLAS flares offshore.

Outdated flares are not dangerous, but they become increasingly unreliable. Outdated flares must never be thrown overboard, or discharged for practice reasons. Liferaft servicing stations can arrange disposal, but in the event of any difficulty contact the police or the Coastguard. Pains Wessex will accept outdated flares through their agents.

	Inshore (within three miles of coast)	Coastal (within seven miles of coast)	Offshore (more than seven miles from coast)
Red hand flares	2	2	4
Red parachute rockets	—	2	4
Hand held orange smoke	2	2	—
Buoyant orange smoke	—	—	2

(k) *Slowly and repeatedly raising and lowering arms outstretched to each side.* The arms should be raised and lowered together, above and below the horizontal.

It must be emphasised that the use of any of the above signals except for genuine distress purposes is strictly forbidden. Even then they should only be made with the authority of the skipper, and only if in serious and imminent danger and needing immediate assistance, or on behalf of another vessel in such danger which for some reason is unable to make a distress signal.

If subsequently the danger is overcome, the distress call must be cancelled by whatever means are available.

8.4 Search and rescue (SAR) organisation – United Kingdom

Around the coasts of Britain we are lucky to have excellent rescue services, manned by skilled and dedicated personnel, and any seagoer should have some understanding of how these various resources are organised and co-ordinated.

When a vessel (or aircraft) is in distress off our coasts, help may be given not only by other vessels but by the authorities shown in 8.4.1 to 8.4.6.

Increasingly in the coming years, larger vessels and SAR authorities will rely on the Global Maritime Distress and Safety System (GMDSS), described in 6.6.18 and due for full implementation in 1999.

8.4.1 Coast Radio Stations
These are operated by British Telecom, and part of their duties is listening to the international radio distress frequencies. Four stations keep continuous watch on 500kHz (the radiotelegraphy distress frequency). Radio Officers specially assigned to monitor 2182kHz keep a 24 hour watch at Land's End Radio and Stonehaven Radio. These stations can engage and speak over all frequencies and channels of other BT coast stations. Watch may be kept on VHF Ch 16 but primary cover for this is provided by HM Coastguard. Distress calls and traffic have priority over all other communications. When a distress signal is received it is transmitted on all distress frequencies to ships at sea and to the relevant shore authorities.

Full details of Coast Radio Stations are published each year in Chapter 6 of *The Macmillan & Silk Cut Nautical Almanac.*

8.4.2 HM Coastguard
HM Coastguard is responsible for initiating and co-ordinating all civil maritime search and rescue around the United Kingdom and over a large part of the eastern Atlantic (between latitudes 45° and 61°N and out to longitude 30°W). The area is divided into six Maritime Search and Rescue Regions (SRRs), supervised by Maritime Rescue Co-ordination Centres (MRCCs) at Aberdeen, Yarmouth, Dover, Falmouth, Swansea and the Clyde. It also includes 'Shannon' area which is the responsibility of the Republic of Ireland. Each region is divided into Districts, each with a Maritime Rescue Sub-Centre (MRSC).

The relevant telephone numbers of the MRCCs and MRSCs are published each year in Chapter 10 of *The Macmillan & Silk Cut Nautical Almanac.*

Within each district there is an organisation of Auxiliary Coastguard watch and rescue stations, grouped within Sectors under the management of Regular Coastguard Officers.

All MRCCs and MRSCs keep constant watch on VHF Ch 16, at about 100 local and remote radio sites, and are connected to telephone and telex. A visual lookout is maintained when necessary. Some stations have a radar watch facility and the Channel Navigation Information Service (CNIS) keeps a constant radar watch on the Dover Strait, with broadcasts on Ch 11 at 40 minutes past each hour.

In each of the 21 districts are auxiliary coastguard watch and rescue stations, grouped within sectors under the management of regular Coastguard Officers. HM Coastguard also has a cliff and beach rescue role.

Many HM Coastguard stations operate VHF direction-finding equipment, which is for emergency use only and is intended for locating a vessel which is in distress or in difficulty. Details are given in Chapter 4 of *The Macmillan & Silk Cut Nautical Almanac* each year. A yacht should transmit on Ch 16 (distress only) or on Ch 67 for the station to determine the bearing. The yacht's bearing from the station is transmitted on Ch 16 (distress only) or on Ch 67.

HM Coastguard operates three SAR helicopters, based at Lee-on-Solent, Sumburgh and Stornoway.

Yacht and Boat Safety Scheme
HM Coastguard Yacht and Boat Safety Scheme aims at providing useful information for the Coastguard to be able to mount a successful Search and Rescue operation, and at promoting closer links with small boat users. Owners can obtain a post-paid card (Form CG66) from the local Coastguard station, harbour master or marina, on which to fill in details of their boat and her equipment. The information includes club or association, type of boat or rig, colours of hull and sails, sail number, speed and endurance under power, any special identification features, liferaft and serial number, dinghy type and colour, details of safety equipment, radio type and call sign, name of boat and how or where displayed, usual base or mooring, where normally operated, shore contact's name and address and telephone number, owner's name and address and telephone number. It is useful if a recent photograph of the boat can be provided.

This card is then posted to the local Coastguard Rescue Centre, where it is retained so that information on the boat is on file if she becomes overdue or in distress. There is a tear-off section which can be given to a shore contact, such as a reliable friend or relative, so that they will know the Coastguard station to contact if they are concerned for the boat's safety.

It is obviously not easy for the Coastguard to maintain continuous watch for small boats on coastal passages, but they will record any information received by phone before departure, or from intermediate ports, or while on passage by visual signals or VHF Channel 67, which is the small craft safety channel. Access to Ch 67 is via Ch 16. When using Ch 67 for safety messages it is requested that the yacht gives the name of the Coastguard Rescue Centre holding the boat's Safety Scheme card.

The Coastguard must be advised of any change to the planned movements of the boat, if they have been informed of previous intentions. This can be done by telephone, or by visual or radio signals.

Raising the alarm

If you are ashore and see an accident afloat, dial 999 on the nearest telephone and ask for the 'Coastguard'. You will be asked to make a report of the incident, and possibly to stay near the telephone for further communications.

If at sea you pick up a distress signal, or get information about any vessel or aircraft in distress, you are obliged to proceed with all speed to give assistance (assuming you are in a position to do so), unless or until you are specifically released.

When alerted, by whatever means, the Coastguard summons the most appropriate assistance available. They might direct a Coastguard Shore Boat or an Auxiliary (Afloat) if there was one in the vicinity; they might request the launch of a RNLI lifeboat or inflatable lifeboat; the Royal Navy or the Royal Air Force could be asked to send an SAR helicopter; other Coastguard stations might be contacted; or shipping might be alerted through nearby Coast Radio Stations.

8.4.3 Royal National Lifeboat Institution (RNLI)

The RNLI (founded in 1824) is a charitable organisation, supported entirely by voluntary contributions. There are over 200 RNLI stations around the coasts of the United Kingdom, the Republic of Ireland, the Isle of Man, and the Channel Islands. From them are deployed about 130 all-weather lifeboats plus an operational fleet of about 140 inshore lifeboats. Some of the latter are only in service during the summer months. The location of RNLI lifeboat stations in Great Britain and the Republic of Ireland is shown on the 'Diagram of Radiobeacons, Air Beacons, lifeboat stations etc' at the start of each relevant Area in Chapter 10 of *The Macmillan & Silk Cut Nautical Almanac*.

Lifeboats are manned by volunteer crews. At each station there is normally one full-time RNLI servant who may be a motor mechanic or a coxswain-mechanic.

It is a sobering thought that in 1991 28% of the 4935 launches were to assist sailing yachts and 20% were to help powered pleasure craft. In these two categories 465 and 274 lives were saved respectively.

Yachtsmen can help support the activities of the RNLI by joining Shoreline – full details of which can be obtained from the RNLI, West Quay Road, Poole, Dorset BH5 1HZ.

When launched on service all-weather lifeboats keep watch on 2182kHz and Ch 16. They can also use other frequencies for contacting other vessels, SAR aircraft, Coastguard, Coast Radio Stations or other authorities concerned with SAR, and are fitted with MF and VHF direction-finding equipment. Inshore lifeboats are fitted with VHF. All-weather lifeboats and the larger inshore lifeboats show a quick-flashing blue light.

8.4.4 Royal Navy

The Royal Navy assists casualties by means of ships and aircraft, including helicopters (see also 'Helicopter rescue', 8.4.9). SAR Sea King helicopters have a radius of action of 180–285 nautical miles depending on equipment fit, and are generally at 15 minutes' readiness by day and 45 minutes at night.

8.4.5 Royal Air Force

The Royal Air Force operates through Rescue Co-ordination Centres at Edinburgh and Plymouth, providing search and rescue facilities for Service and civil aircraft in and around the United Kingdom, but also helping where possible with other casualties by means of rotary and fixed wing aircraft.

8.4.6 Air Traffic Control Centres

These often first know about aircraft in distress, but they may also be involved in asking aircraft to keep a watch for vessels in trouble.

8.4.7 Response to a distress call

The action taken for any particular incident depends on whether a vessel or aircraft is involved, and the position and whereabouts of the casualty. In the case (for example) of a yacht drifting ashore, the Coastguard may have seen her or have observed her distress signals, or have received a report from a Coast Radio Station. The Coastguard informs the local RNLI Secretary, who decides whether to launch the lifeboat, and also musters the local Coastguard Auxiliary Service with its rescue equipment at the scene. The Coastguard may also request a helicopter, or send a radio-equipped rescue vehicle to the spot.

For a yacht or vessel in trouble offshore, some other ship is most likely to answer her distress call. The Coast Radio Station will re-broadcast a distress message on all the distress frequencies and also inform the Coastguard, the appropriate Area Flag Officer, Lloyd's, RNLI, and the appropriate Rescue Co-ordination Centre at Edinburgh or Plymouth. Each of these authorities will decide whether it can, or should, assist.

It should be remembered that any vessel (including a yacht) which sees or hears a distress signal from some other craft is legally obliged to proceed with all speed to her assistance, unless she is unable to do so in the particular circumstances, or unless and until she is released from such an obligation by other ships or the vessel in distress.

If you hear a distress message, write down at least the more important details such as the vessel's name and position. If you can give help, acknowledge accordingly, but only after giving an opportunity for the nearest Coast Radio Station or a larger vessel to do so. If no other vessel acknowledges you must make a 'Mayday relay' call as described in 6.6.16. Cease all other transmissions that might interfere with distress traffic and continue listening on the frequency concerned. Write down what you hear.

Similarly, if you see a red flare or other distress signal or situation you must render all assistance possible and if necessary relay a distress message to shore (e.g. the Coastguard).

Normally the first vessel to arrive assumes the task of 'on-scene Commander', but a larger or better equipped vessel may take over the job. When rescue craft or a helicopter arrive it is important for other craft not to hinder operations. Due to the noise it is necessary for a boat to be at least 400 metres ($\frac{1}{4}$ mile) away from a hovering helicopter for normal radio communication to be conducted.

8.4.8 Abandon ship

Although preparations should be made, it is unwise to leave a yacht until it is certain that she is doomed. A boat is a much better target for rescue craft than a liferaft and while it is possible to remain on board it may be feasible to use her various resources (such as the radiotelephone for distress calls) to good effect and to select equipment which can be taken into the liferaft, or perhaps be securely lashed into the dinghy — which should be taken too if circumstances permit.

Action needed, if time permits, before entering the raft and cutting it adrift from the yacht:

(1) If a radiotelephone is available, send out a distress message (Mayday call) stating that the crew are abandoning ship in the liferaft, and giving the position. If an emergency radiotelephone is carried it should of course be taken in the liferaft.
(2) Dress warmly with sweaters etc under oilskins and lifejackets on top. Take extra clothes.
(3) Collect any available containers with screw tops or similar, and fill them about $\frac{3}{4}$ full of fresh water, so that they will float.
(4) Collect any additional food that is ready to hand, including tins and a can opener.
(5) Collect any equipment which will help to navigate and manage the liferaft — such as charts, hand bearing compass, pencils and paper, torch, extra flares, bucket, length of line, first aid kit, knife, fishing gear.
(6) If possible, salvage such items as passports, money and ship's papers.

Sea Survival — A Manual by Dougal Robertson (Paul Elek) is recommended reading.

In the liferaft

Around the British Isles it is unlikely that survivors would be adrift in a liferaft for any length of time, but it is best to plan for the worst from the outset. If there has not been time to collect useful items from the parent vessel, there will probably be the opportunity to salvage all sorts of flotsam when she sinks. Almost any item could prove to be useful, but beware of any sharp objects or pieces of wreckage which might pierce the raft.

(1) Get and keep the inside of the raft as dry as possible. In our northern latitudes cold is likely to be a problem even in summer — keep close together for warmth. Close the opening to the raft as necessary, but always keep a lookout for shipping.
(2) Stream the drogue if it is desired to stay near to the scene of abandoning ship, or if the weather is bad.
(3) Ration fresh water to $\frac{1}{2}$ litre ($\frac{3}{4}$ pint) per person per day. Do not drink sea water or urine. Collect any rain water with the arrangements provided.
(4) Use flares sparingly, and only on the skipper's orders. See 6.4.5 and 8.3.10.
(5) Seasickness is likely to be a problem — issue pills as soon as possible.

8.4.9 Helicopter rescue

In the event of a helicopter coming to the rescue of the crew of a yacht in distress, it is essential to understand the procedure. Helicopters have limited endurance and limited lifting capacities (depending on the type) and for safety reasons they cannot hover close to a yacht with a mast.

SAR aircraft use voice call signs comprising the word 'Rescue' followed by two or three numerals.

While hovering the pilot has limited vision of a boat or a survivor below him, and has to rely on instructions from his navigator/winch operator. Normal hovering height is about 8m (25ft) but aircraft may hover lower than this on occasions. Some helicopters have a Hi-Line lifting capability to 90m (300ft), and only larger helicopters can operate at night or in bad weather.

It is essential that the yacht in distress can be identified from the air, particularly if other craft are in the vicinity. An accurate position (latitude and longitude, or range and bearing from some charted object) in the yacht's MAYDAY distress message is the first requirement, so that the helicopter goes to the right area. Dodgers with the boat's name or sail number, an upturned dinghy with the name on the bottom, or the boat's name clearly painted on the hull or superstructure are all aids to identification.

When the helicopter is sighted by a boat in distress, either a flare or a daylight orange smoke signal will assist recognition; even an Aldis lamp trained on the helicopter and flashing SOS will help. If the boat is fitted with VHF radio this may be used to pass a message to the aircraft via the nearest Coast Station or Coastguard station, or via a lifeboat if one is in the vicinity. Remember that parachute rockets must not be used when helicopters are in the vicinity.

Once the helicopter is approaching, final preparations for rescue must be made. In the case of a yacht with a mast it is necessary for survivors to be picked up from a dinghy or liferaft streamed at least 30m (100ft) away from the yacht. It is helpful if the drift of the yacht can be reduced by a sea anchor, or by streaming the anchor and cable over the bows. In a small sailing yacht which does not have any form of dinghy, survivors (who should in any case be wearing lifejackets) may have to take to the water at the end of a long warp so that they can be picked up. This problem does not arise in the case of a motor boat with no mast, or a small sailing dinghy. The latter should, however, if still upright, lower any sails so as to minimise the considerable downdraught from the helicopter's rotor.

Never secure the winch wire to the boat, and beware that it may carry a lethal static charge if not dipped (earthed) in the sea before handling.

The normal way of lifting a survivor is in a strop, as shown in Fig. 8(10). The strop is put over head and shoulders, and fitted under the arm pits with the padded part in the small of the back. The sliding toggle in the front is then pulled down towards the body to tighten the strop. A thumbs up sign indicates that the survivor is ready for the

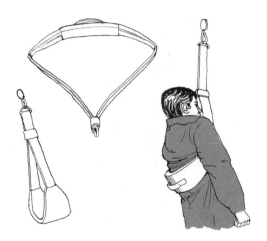

Fig. 8(10) The strop used in helicopter rescue lifts.

Fig. 8(11) Winchman with survivor in double lift.

lift to commence. The survivor's arms should be kept extended downwards, close to the sides of the body. Sometimes two strops may be offered simultaneously, so that two survivors may be raised in one lift.

If the winchman descends to the yacht, or to rescue somebody from a liferaft or from the water, follow his instructions exactly and as quickly as possible, since time may be precious. A winchman will accompany a survivor in a double lift, as illustrated in Fig. 8(11). The survivor in his strop faces the winchman, who puts his legs round the survivor's waist. An injured person is lifted in a Neil-Robertson stretcher, into which he or she is strapped, accompanied by the winchman. Small children are lifted by being carried by the winchman, or by another adult.

If it is not possible to lower the winchman and a strop to the yacht, a Hi-Line technique may be used. The Hi-Line consists of a nylon rope 45m (150ft) in length. At its upper end, where it is secured to the hook on the end of the helicopter's normal winch wire, it has a weak link, intended to break at a load of 90kg (200lb). At its lower end it has a weight, to help it hang as vertical as possible. In effect the Hi-Line is a rope extension to the winch wire. On occasions two Hi-Lines may be joined together to give double the length.

The helicopter hovers well above the yacht, and the Hi-Line is lowered across the deck. The slack should be taken in by the crew as the helicopter pays out the winch wire. Do not make the Hi-Line fast, but coil it down carefully and keep it clear of snags. The Hi-Line is used to guide the winch wire, with its hook and strop, to the yacht. Keep it just taut, but do not pull it in more quickly than the winch wire is lowered, or the weak link will part, with consequent delay. The helicopter pays out the winch wire and descends, while the yacht's crew take in the slack of the Hi-Line (taking care to keep it outboard and clear of all obstructions) until the winch hook and strop are onboard.

The winchman may or may not be lowered with the strop. Two strops may be offered together. When the survivor is secured in the strop, and the thumbs up signal is passed, the helicopter ascends and takes in the wire. Pay out the Hi-Line, keeping it just taut, until the end is reached, when it should be cast off well clear of the yacht. If, however, a further lift is to be made, the end of the line should be retained on board if possible (but not made fast) in order to facilitate the recovery of the strop for the next lift.

On arrival at the door of the helicopter, obey the instructions of the winchman and/or the winch operator. Once the survivor is inside the aircraft the strop will be removed, and the survivor will be directed to a seat where he should strap himself in.

When alighting from a helicopter it is important to obey the instructions of the crew, since it is easy to walk into the tail rotor.

8.4.10 Being taken in tow

When circumstances allow a yacht which is disabled or in difficulties to be taken in tow, the success of the operation depends in part on the effective contribution of the yacht's crew to the evolution of passing the tow − a difficult operation in bad weather. It is important to consider in advance how and where the tow is to be connected, remembering that the average boat has very few strong points that will accept the strains involved in a seaway. Any prior arrangements necessary, such as rigging a towing bridle, should be completed before the arrival of the 'rescue' vessel if possible. Towing is discussed in more detail in Chapter 15 (15.5).

8.5 Search and rescue (SAR) organisation − North-west Europe

In North-west Europe similar SAR arrangements exist as are described in 8.4 for the United Kingdom.

These are summarised in notes about the countries concerned, which appear in Section 7 of the relevant Areas in Chapter 10 of *The Macmillan & Silk Cut Nautical Almanac* each year. Republic of Ireland − Area 12; France − Area 14; Belgium, Netherlands − Area 20; Germany − Area 21. The location of lifeboat stations in these countries is shown on the 'Diagram of Radiobeacons, Air Beacons, lifeboat stations etc' at the start of each relevant Area in Chapter 10 of the Almanac.

Distress signals and procedures are internationally recognised. In the event of language difficulties, use the International Code: selected groups which include emergency signals are given in 6.2.8.

8.5.1 Republic of Ireland

The Marine Rescue Co-ordination Centre for the Irish Republic is situated at Shannon Airport. Tel: (061) 61219 and (061) 61969. If engaged call Air Traffic Control, Shannon (061) 61444, or Cork (021) 313131, or Dublin (01) 379900. In emergency dial 999. The centre can call on the RNLI, Coast Life Saving Service, Irish Army Air Corps helicopters, civil aircraft, the Irish lighthouse service, and the Garda Siochana. The centre liaises with the United Kingdom and France, and acts as a clearing house for all messages received during rescue operations within 100 miles of the Irish coast.

The Irish Coast Life Saving Service is staffed by volunteers who are trained in first aid and equipped with breeches buoys, cliff ladders etc. The telephone number (of the Leader's residence) is given for places quoted in Areas 12 and 13 in Chapter 10 of *The Macmillan & Silk Cut Nautical Almanac* each year.

8.5.2 France

France has five Regional Surveillance and Rescue Operations Centres (Centres Régionaux Opérationnels de Surveillance et de Sauvetage − or CROSS) on the Atlantic coast. These are situated at Gris-Nez, Jobourg, Corsen, Etel and Soulac. They provide a permanent operational presence along the coast and cooperate with foreign equivalents as required. CROSS Etel is linked with the COSPAS-SARSAT centre at Toulon to respond to satellite aided SAR operations.

CROSS coordinates the following tasks:
(1) Traffic surveillance, particularly inshore.
(2) Maritime Search and Rescue.
(3) Fishery surveillance out to 200 n miles.
(4) Monitoring pollution.
(5) Collection of data for future use.

Traffic surveillance includes policing the Traffic Separation Schemes and Inshore Traffic Zones in the English Channel and off Ushant.

Information broadcasts of navigational and traffic information, together with storm warnings and weather bulletins, are relayed from a number of VHF stations along the coast.

CROSS can be alerted on VHF Ch 16, by telex, fax or telephone, through French Coast Radio Stations, through 'semaphore' stations of the French Navy, through the Gendarmerie Nationale, or through Affaires Maritimes.

Details of the CROSS organisation, including broadcast channels and times, are given in *The Macmillan & Silk Cut Nautical Almanac* each year. Some of the more important broadcasts are in French and English.

The French lifeboat service is administered by the Société Nationale de Sauvetage en Mer (SNSM), 9 Rue de Chaillot, 75116 Paris. Tel: 723.98.26.

8.5.3 Belgium

The Sea Rescue Co-ordination Centre is at Oostende. Tel: 70.10.00, 70.11.00, 70.77.01 or 70.77.02. Belgian lifeboats are administered by the Ministerie van Verkeerswezen, Aarlenstraat 104, 1040 Brussels. Tel: (02) 233.12.11. SAR Sea King helicopters of the Belgian Air Force are based as Koksijde.

8.5.4 Netherlands

The Maritime Rescue Co-ordination Centre is at Valkenburg, near Scheveningen. Netherlands Coast Guard keeps watch (H24) on 2182kHz and VHF Ch 16. Lifeboats are operated by the Koninklijke Nederlandsche Redding Maatschappij (KNRM).

There is an SAR helicopter base near Den Helder.

8.5.5 Germany

The SAR service is operated by the Maritime Rescue Co-ordination Centre, Bremen (MRCC Bremen) as a part of Deutsche Gesellschaft zur

Rettung Schiffbrüchiger, Werderstrasse 2, 2800 Bremen 1. Tel: (0421) 50.43.93. The larger German lifeboats are equipped with 'daughter boats' which are used, for example, for rescues in shallower water.

German military SAR helicopters are operated by the Rescue Co-ordination Centre (RCC) at Glücksburg, and are based at Jever, Borkum, Helgoland and Sylt.

8.6 First Aid afloat

The objectives of first aid at sea are to preserve life, to prevent further damage, to relieve pain and distress, and to deliver a live casualty ashore.

8.6.1 Emergency resuscitation – ABC

Immediate procedure to follow for any collapse or unconscious person:

A Airway. Clear mouth of teeth or debris with fingers. Listen at mouth for breathing. Tilt head

Fig. 8(12) Ensuring clear airway: head tilt and chin lift.

Fig. 8(13) Recovery position.

Fig. 8(14) Mouth to mouth ventilation. Maintain head tilt and chin lift. Pinch nose. Blow into victim's mouth; watch chest rise.

Fig. 8(15) Place to feel for the carotid pulse.

backwards, using head tilt and chin lift to maintain clear airway – Fig. 8(12). Place in recovery position if breathing – Fig. 8(13).

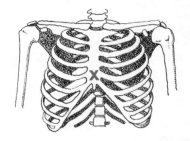

Fig. 8(16) Cardiac massage: hand position on breastbone.

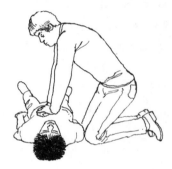

Fig. 8(17) Chest compression: body and hand position. Press firmly, then release.

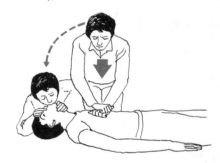

Fig. 8(18) One operator: chest compression rate 80/min, two breaths after every 15 compressions.

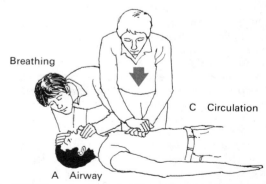

Breathing

C Circulation

A Airway

Fig. 8(19) Two operators: chest compression rate 80/min, one breath every 5 compressions.

B Breathing. If not breathing and airway clear, start mouth to mouth ventilation – Fig. 8(14). Kneel beside patient, maintain head tilt and chin lift, pinch nostrils. Take a deep breath and blow ten full breaths into patient's mouth. Watch for rise and fall of chest. Feel carotid pulse – Fig. 8(15). If pulse present, continue one inflation every five seconds until breathing recommences.
C Circulation. If carotid pulse absent, start external chest compression. Lay patient on hard, flat surface. Kneel beside patient; place heel of one hand just below middle of breastbone – Fig. 8(16). Place other hand on top of this hand. Depress breastbone 40–50mm (1.5–2in) then release – Fig. 8(17).

One operator:
– Fig. 8(18). 80 chest compressions per minute. Two breaths after every 15 compressions.

– Fig. 8(19). 80 chest compressions per minute. One breath after every five compressions.

Children
Blow into both mouth and nose if necessary: use a faster breathing rate (one inflation every three seconds), and smaller breaths. For external chest compression use gentle compression with one hand only, or just fingers for a baby; use a faster compression rate, up to 100 per minute.

Do not stop
Feel carotid pulse every three minutes. Stop chest compression as soon as pulse returns but continue mouth to mouth ventilation if breathing still absent. Continue until both pulse and breathing return or patient is obviously dead after one hour (skin cold and pale, pupils widely enlarged, no breathing, no pulse, no heartbeat). Exception: hypothermia victim (see 8.6.17).

Problems during resuscitation
Bulging stomach. This may result from swallowed air (e.g. during immersion), or from resuscitation efforts. Turn on to side, exert pressure on stomach.
Vomiting. This occurs commonly during resuscitation (especially after immersion). To prevent vomit entering the lungs, turn the patient rapidly on to his side. Clear the airway before recommencing resuscitation.
Fractured ribs. External chest compression moves blood around the body by directly compressing the heart, and by increasing the pressure in the chest cavity. Use your body weight to compress the breastbone, do not lift your hands between compressions and do not press anywhere but directly on the breastbone. Avoid erratic or violent compressions.
Drowning and hypothermia. These casualties may exhibit all the signs of apparent death, yet may still recover totally. Abandon resuscitation reluctantly and only after thorough and repeated attempts have been made to warm the victim.

8.6.2 Blockage of airway and choking
If blockage by some object (e.g. a peanut) is suspected, wrap both arms from behind around the victim's waist, and give five sharp upwards thrusts with both fists into the abdomen above the navel but below the ribs so as to imitate coughing. Clear object from mouth. In unconscious adult administer abdominal thrusts with the victim lying on his back. Attempt mouth to mouth breathing. Do not give up; repeat the abdominal thrusts. Infants and small children should first be given five forceful blows on the back before proceeding to abdominal thrusts.

8.6.3 Shock
Shock can result from almost any accident or medical emergency and, depending upon the cause, may range in severity from a simple faint to near death. Shock results when the delivery of oxygen to the tissues is impaired because of inadequate or inefficient circulation of the blood. Possible causes include:
(1) Loss of blood – internal or external bleeding.
(2) Loss of fluid – diarrhoea, peritonitis, burns.
(3) Heart failure – heart attack.
(4) Lung failure – drowning.
(5) Brain failure – stroke, head injury.
(6) Illness – diabetes.

Signs and symptoms
Thirst, apathy, nausea, restlessness. Pale, cold, clammy skin, sweating. Rapid, weak pulse. Rapid, shallow breathing. Dull, sunken eyes, bluish lips, leads to collapse.

Management
(1) ABC – airway, breathing, circulation (see 8.6.1).
(2) Control bleeding, if present.
(3) Lie flat; elevate legs to 20°. Exceptions:
    (a) Bleeding from mouth – recovery position.
    (b) Unconscious – recovery position.
    (c) Chest injury – sitting may be preferred.
(4) Splint any fractures; avoid movement.
(5) Avoid chilling, keep warm.
(6) Relieve pain – give pain killers. Exceptions:
    (a) Head injury with impaired consciousness.
    (b) Cases with severe breathing difficulty.
(7) Reassure the patient.
(8) Fluids may be life saving in cases of dehydration (e.g. diarrhoea, vomiting, severe burns). Give half a cup of water at 15 minute intervals. Add a pinch of salt and a little sugar. Never give alcohol. Avoid in severe abdominal pain or internal injury.
    Never attempt to give fluids by mouth to an unconscious person.

Collapse and signs of shock after an accident when external blood loss is absent or slight must suggest internal bleeding. Clues may be few. The patient may cough or vomit blood, or pass blood in urine or from bowel. He may complain of worsening pain in abdomen or chest. Urgent help needed.

Medical illnesses, such as diabetes, severe infections or heart disease, may produce shock without giving many clues as to the cause. Urgent help needed. Acquaint yourself with any medical problems of crew before a long passage. There should be a record on board of any medication being taken by any member of the crew, including skipper (see 8.6.21).

8.6.4 Bleeding – open wound

Bleeding is often very dramatic, but is virtually always controllable.

Management
(1) Apply firm continuous direct pressure; bandage on a large pad. If bleeding continues, bandage more pads on top of initial pads; then press directly over wound for at least 10 minutes (blood takes this time to clot).
(2) Elevation if wound is on a limb.
(3) Only use a tourniquet to prevent a patient bleeding to death. The whole limb may be lost if the tourniquet is left on for too long.

8.6.5 Bleeding – internal (closed injury)

Follows fractured bones, crush injuries, or rupture of organs such as the liver or spleen. Shock may appear rapidly. Urgent help needed.

8.6.6 Nose bleed

Lean forwards and pinch the soft part of the nose firmly for at least 10 minutes to allow the blood to clot. Do not blow nose or try to remove clot. If bleeding continues repeat the pressure for longer than 10 minutes. If still bleeding after 30 minutes insert as much 50mm (2in) gauze bandage (moistened with water) as you can, using forceps to feed the bandage into the nose. Urgent help needed.

8.6.7 Cuts and wounds

Often dramatic but only potentially serious if nerves, tendons or blood vessels are severed.
(1) Clean thoroughly with antiseptic. Remove dirt or other foreign bodies in the wound.
(2) Small clean cuts can be closed using Steristrips. Skin must be dry. Use as many Steristrips as necessary to keep the skin edges together. Leave for five days at least. See Fig. 8(20).

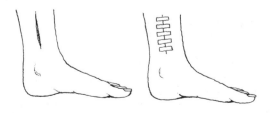

Fig. 8(20) Use of Steristrips to close a superficial wound.

(3) Larger deep cuts may require special suture techniques; apply a dressing and seek help. Do not try amateur surgery at sea.
(4) Ragged lacerations or very dirty wounds. Do not attempt to close these; dead tissues may have to be trimmed away to prevent infection. Clean as well as possible, sprinkle antibiotic powder in wound and apply a dressing. Seek help.

If in doubt a wound is best left open and lightly covered to keep it clean and dry. If contemplating an extended passage, seek tuition from your doctor.

Fingers and toes. Blood may collect under the nail following an injury. Release the blood by piercing the nail with a red hot needle or paper clip. It will not hurt!

8.6.8 Fractures and dislocations – general

Fracture – broken bone. Dislocation – displaced joint. Both result from major trauma and will produce pain (which is worse on attempted movement), localised swelling, abnormal shape, and a grating feeling on movement (when a fracture is present). Blood vessels or nerves around the fracture or dislocation may also be damaged resulting in a cold, pale, or numb limb below the site of the injury. Fractures of large bones such as the femur (upper leg) will result in major internal bleeding and may cause shock. When complications occur urgent help is needed.

Early application of a splint and elevation of the injured limb where possible will reduce pain and minimise complications. Treat for shock and pain.

8.6.9 Specific fractures and dislocations

Skull. See head injury (8.6.12).
Nose. Control bleeding by pinching. Straighten immediately after the accident if possible.
Cheek. Caused by a direct blow. Rarely serious but requires specialist care.
Jaw. Beware of associated brain or spine injury. Remove blood and teeth fragments; leave loose teeth in place; protect broken teeth (see 8.6.22). Ensure airway is clear. Commence regular antiseptic mouth washes and antibiotics. Support jaw with bandage over top of head. Give only fluids by mouth.
Neck. May result from a direct blow, a fall or a whiplash type injury. If conscious, patient may complain of pain, tingling, numbness or weakness in limbs below the injury. Mishandling may damage the spinal cord, resulting in paralysis or death. Avoid movement and support head. Immobilise by wrapping a folded towel around the neck. If movement is necessary then lift the victim as one rigid piece, never allowing the neck to bend. Urgent help needed.
Spine. Fracture of the spine may occur below the neck but the results may be similar and mishandling of the victim may greatly worsen the damage. Avoid movement if possible. Lift the

Fig. 8(21) Sling.

patient without allowing the spine to sag. Urgent help needed.

Upper Limb
(1) Collar bone (clavicle). Support arm in sling – Fig. 8(21).
(2) Dislocated shoulder. If this has happened before, the patient may reduce the dislocation himself; otherwise do not attempt reduction in case a fracture exists.
(3) Upper arm (humerus). Support the arm with a collar and cuff inside the shirt. Tie a clove hitch around the wrist, loop the ends behind the neck – Fig. 8(22).

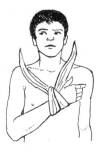

Fig. 8(22) Collar and cuff.

(4) Forearm and wrist. Splint (e.g. with battens or inflatable splint). Do not bandage tightly. Elevate or support in a sling.
(5) Fingers. Elevate hand and, unless badly crushed, leave unbandaged; keep moving. If very wobbly, bandage to adjacent finger.
Ribs. See chest injury (8.6.13). Often very painful. Strapping is not much use.

Lower Limb
(1) Thigh. Shock may be considerable. Splint by strapping to other leg with padding between the legs. Do not bandage too tightly.
(2) Knee. Twisting injuries or falls damage the ligaments and cartilages of the knee. Very painful and swollen. Treat as for fracture.
(3) Lower leg. Pad very well. Splint using oar, broom handle or inflatable splint.
(4) Ankle. Fracture or severe sprain may be indistinguishable. Immobilise in neutral position with foot at right angles. Elevate the limb.

To be really effective a splint should be rigid and extend to the joint above and below the fracture. This is not always possible. The splint must be very well padded. Inflatable splints are useful but may interfere with the circulation.

If the limb beyond the bandage or splint becomes swollen or discoloured, the bandage must be loosened to improve circulation. If you improvise a splint (e.g. fibre glass) it is essential not to enclose the whole limb and risk cutting off the circulation.

8.6.10 Compound fractures
If a deep wound overlies the fracture or the bone ends are visible do not try to close the wound or replace the bone ends. Clean thoroughly with antiseptic and cover with sterile dressing. Seek help. Commence antibiotics if help delayed.

8.6.11 Strains and sprains
Torn ligaments, pulled muscles and other injuries. Rest the injured part; elevate if possible; apply ice packs (wrapped in a towel) if possible at sea; analgesics. If in doubt, treat as a fracture and immobilise.

8.6.12 Head injury
(1) A blow to the head, with or without fracture, may result in immediate unconsciousness or more delayed effects.

Management
(1) Immediate unconsciousness but quick recovery with slight drowsiness or headache. Prescribe rest and watch carefully.
(2) Immediate unconsciousness, no sign of recovery. Put in recovery position (beware of associated spine injury). Check airway. Observe the following and record every 30 minutes: pulse rate, pupil size (both sides), responses to verbal command, response to firm pinching. Urgent help needed.
(3) Delayed deterioration (either not unconscious immediately, or apparently recovering then worsening). Increasing drowsiness, change in mental state and eventually unconsciousness. Treat as (2) above. Urgent help needed.
Scalp wounds may bleed profusely. Control with very firm pressure; cut away hair, and close using Steristrips if no fracture beneath. If in doubt seek help. Avoid giving drugs after head injury.

8.6.13 Chest injury

May result in fractured ribs. These are very painful, and breathing may be uncomfortable and shallow. The fractured ribs may puncture the lung, or if a number of ribs are each broken in two places (e.g. after crush injury) then this flail segment of the chest may seriously impair breathing.

Management
(1) Airway, breathing, circulation (see 8.6.1).
(2) Patient may be more comfortable sitting up.
(3) Plug any hole with a pad if air is sucking in and out.
(4) Support any unstable chest segment with your hand.
(5) For fractured ribs prescribe rest and strong analgesics if necessary. Very painful.
    Beware: tight strapping restricts breathing even further. Urgent help needed for any case with impaired breathing.

8.6.14 Eye problems

All eye injuries or illnesses are potentially serious. *Never* put old or previously opened ointment or drops into an eye. Serious infection could result.
(1) Foreign object. Flush the eye with clean water, pull the bottom lid out to inspect, remove object with a clean tissue. To inspect beneath upper lid, pull the lid out and then roll it upwards over a matchstick. After removal of object, instil sterile antibiotic ointment inside pulled out lower lid. Cover with pad.
(2) Corrosive fluid. Continuous flushing with water for 15 minutes. Give analgesics and chloramphenicol ointment; cover with pad; seek help as soon as possible.
(3) Infection – conjunctivitis. A sticky, weeping eye with yellow discharge. Chloramphenicol ointment four times per day.

8.6.15 Burns and scalds

(1) Move the victim into fresh air to avoid smoke inhalation.
(2) ABC – airway, breathing, circulation.
(3) Stop further injury – dip the whole of the burnt part into cold water for 10–15 minutes. Seawater is excellent but may be very painful.
(4) Remove only loose clothing. Do not pull off clothing stuck to the skin.
(5) Cover with sterile dressing. If skin broken or blistered, use sterile paraffin gauze beneath the dressing. Separate burnt fingers with paraffin gauze. Never use adhesive dressings.
(6) Do not prick blisters or apply ointments.
(7) Elevate burnt limb and immobilise.
(8) Give strong analgesics.
(9) Treat shock – give frequent and copious drinks of water.
(10) Commence antibiotics for major burns.
(11) If burns extensive or deep, urgent help needed.

Sunburn may be very severe. Treat as for any other burn. If skin unbroken apply calamine lotion; give analgesics. For prevention use only filter preparations with high protection factor.

8.6.16 Drowning

The resuscitation of an apparently drowned person may be complicated by two factors. First, a sudden illness (e.g. a stroke) or an accident (e.g. a blow to the head) may have precipitated the fall into the water. Second, the time spent in the water may have produced marked hypothermia. The water around the British Isles is rarely warmer than 15°C (60°F).

Management
(1) *A Airway.* Clear the airway – seaweed, false teeth etc.
(2) *B Breathing.* If not breathing start mouth to mouth ventilation as soon as possible and in the water if practicable. See 8.6.1(2).
(3) *C Circulation.* If pulse absent, start chest compression as soon as aboard. See 8.6.1(3).
(4) If stomach bulging, turn on to side and press to empty, or he may vomit large quantities of water which could be inhaled.
(5) Prevent cooling. Remove wet clothes; wrap in blankets to warm.
(6) Continue resuscitation until victim revives or death is certain. Hypothermia may mimic death. Do not abandon resuscitation until person has been warmed or signs of death persist despite attempts at warming.
(7) Once revived, put in recovery position – Fig. 8(13).
(8) Any person rescued from drowning may collapse in next 24 hours as the lungs react to inhaled water. Urgent help needed.

8.6.17 Hypothermia

Lowered body temperature will follow immersion in sea – Fig. 8(23) – or prolonged exposure on deck. Symptoms include: unreasonable behaviour followed by apathy and confusion; unsteady gait, stumbling, slurring of speech; pale, cold skin; slow, weak pulse; slow breathing; shivering. Leads to collapse, unconsciousness and ultimately death.

Management
(1) *A Airway* control; put in recovery position.
(2) *B Breathing.* If not breathing, start mouth to mouth ventilation.
(3) *C Circulation.* A slow feeble pulse may be present: unwise to use chest compression.
(4) Remove wet clothing. Avoid wind chill. Dry and wrap in blankets or sleeping bag, another person in the sleeping bag will generate heat.
(5) Give hot sweet drinks if conscious.
(6) Do not give alcohol, or rub the skin, or place very hot objects against skin.

8.6.18 Frostbite

Usually affects toes, fingers, ears or nose. The affected part may be very painful, numb, stiff and

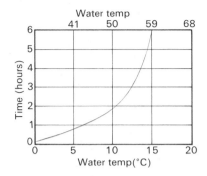

Water temp
41   50   59   68

Fig. 8(23) Estimated survival time after which only 50% of immersion victims would still be alive. Adult males in conventional dress. (By kind permission Surg. Cdr. Frank St. C. Golden, R.N.)

discoloured. Warm gently (e.g. on someone else's back). Immersion in water less than 43°C (110°F) is satisfactory; higher temperatures will cause more damage. Do not rub the affected part with anything.

8.6.19 Poisoning
Poison may reach the body when swallowed, inhaled or injected through the skin (e.g. bites and stings).

General management
(1) *ABC* – airway, breathing, circulation.
(2) Recovery position if unconscious.
(3) Seek help.

Swallowed poison
For swallowed poison the container may have instructions or suggest antidote(s). For corrosive or petroleum products (e.g. acids, alkalis, bleach, detergent, petrol) *do not* induce vomiting. Administer copious fluids (e.g. milk). For other substances (e.g. pills, medicines) induce vomiting – tickle back of throat, or give *one* glass of very salty water. If collapsed or unconscious, urgent help needed.

Inhaled poison
Poison may be inhaled from sources such as carbon monoxide or other exhaust fumes, bottled gas which has leaked into bilge, or fire extinguisher gas. Carbon monoxide inhalation produces cherry red lips and skin. Move into fresh air immediately. If breathing absent, commence resuscitation. Urgent help needed.

Bites and stings
Injected poison from bites and stings usually only causes local swelling and discomfort, but some individuals may react severely. For insect stings, resuscitate if collapse occurs; otherwise give rest, analgesics, antihistamines (e.g. chlorpheniramine). In warmer water, sea snakes and various sea stingers can inject extremely deadly poison: prevent drowning, resuscitate if necessary; if sting caused by jelly fish or Portuguese Man O'War etc, pour vinegar or strong alcohol on to sting to reduce further poison release. If the victim becomes weak and breathless, apply a tourniquet above the bite or wrap a tight bandage around the whole limb to delay spread of poison. Commence resuscitation. Urgent help needed.

Many large cities maintain a 24-hour poison information centre. Use the radio for advice.

8.6.20 Seasickness
Basically an inner ear disturbance caused by motion. Fear, anxiety, fatigue and boredom aggravate the condition. May manifest as lethargy, dizziness or headache as well as nausea and vomiting.

Avoid strong food tastes, and too much alcohol. Take small amounts of fluid and food (e.g. biscuits) frequently if you feel ill. Avoid fatigue; adequate sleep will often relieve the sick feeling. Keep warm. Stay on deck, and concentrate on some task if possible. Ensure that sick crew on deck are secured by lifeline. Retire to a bunk if all else fails. Intractable vomiting may produce serious loss of fluid.

No one remedy is suitable for every person. Try the various preparations until you find one that is effective with minimum side effects. Most tend to cause some tiredness and a dry mouth. Take the first tablet some hours before sailing, and then regularly for as long as necessary. Take a tablet just before a sleep period if possible. Available tablets include: Dramamine (dimenhydrinate), Avomine (promethazine), Marzine (cyclizine), Stugeron (cinnarizine), Kwells (hyoscine). Some preparations can be applied behind the ear or worn as a wrist band.

8.6.21 Sudden illness
Acquaint yourself with any medical problems of the crew (and skipper!) before a long passage. Seek medical advice. Unless forewarned, diagnosis may be very difficult once at sea.
(1) Abdominal pain (minor).
    (a) Upper abdomen, intermittent, burning, no tenderness, otherwise well. May follow large alcohol intake. Eased by milk or antacid. Bland meals. No alcohol.
    (b) More generalised, cramping or colicky pain, no tenderness, may have diarrhoea or vomiting. May be gastroenteritis or food poisoning. Prescribe oral fluid with a pinch of salt added. Avoid dehydration.
(2) Abdominal pain (major). Severe abdominal pain, usually constant and generalised. Abdomen may be rigid or very tender to touch, fever may be present, rapid pulse rate, generally unwell, nausea and vomiting. Make the patient comfortable, give pain relief (injection if possible). Give nothing to eat or drink. Urgent help needed.

(3) Allergies. Mild cases may just have a rash which responds to calamine lotion and antihistamine tablets. Severe cases may collapse with breathing difficulty and require emergency ABC resuscitation.

(4) Constipation. Common at sea. Prevent by eating fruit, vegetables, bran and if necessasry, anti-constipation medication (e.g. senna preparations).

(5) Convulsions. Patient may be a known epileptic. Insert twisted cloth between teeth to protect tongue. Prevent injury. Recovery position; protect airway (he may still look very blue). After fit, allow him to sleep. Urgent help needed.

(6) Diabetes. A diabetic may become unconscious if his blood sugar is too high or too low. For hyperglycaemia (too much sugar) insulin is needed. Hypoglycaemia (too little sugar) may be caused by too much insulin, unusual stress or exercise, or too little food. In either case first give sweets, sugar, soft drinks. Urgent help needed if recovery not rapid.

(7) Diarrhoea. Can become serious, especially in young children if much fluid is lost. Stop food, give plenty of fluid. Kaolin may be useful. Lomotil or Immodium tablets very effective in adults.

(8) Fever. May be associated with anything from common cold, appendicitis, heat stroke to an infected toe. Except for major abdominal problems, prescribe copious fluids, paracetamol or aspirin (not in children) – and antibiotics if infection is present.

(9) Heart attack. Severe central chest pain; may spread to shoulders, neck or arms. Sweating, then bluish lips, then collapse. Breathing and heart may stop (no carotid pulse in neck).
  (a) Early symptoms; rest, reassure. Urgent help needed.
  (b) If unconscious: recovery position; observe breathing and pulse.
  (c) If breathing stops or pulse absent, commence mouth to mouth ventilation and chest compression immediately and *do not stop*. See 8.6.1.

(10) Heat stroke. Cool patient by sponging with cold water; encourage drinking (one teaspoon of salt per pint of water). If patient stops sweating, has a rapid pounding pulse and is becoming unconscious, seek help urgently.

(11) Stroke. Sudden unconsciousness, paralysis or weakness on one side of body, slurring of speech. Recovery position, air way control. Urgent help needed.

8.6.22 Toothache

Dental pain seems worse at sea, and prevention is better than cure. For a long voyage consider carrying a dental mirror, tongue spatula, pen torch, cotton wool rolls, tweezers, zinc oxide powder and oil of cloves (or a ready-mixed temporary filling, e.g. Coltisol).

Management

(1) Throbbing toothache, made worse by hot or cold or when bitten on. If an obvious cavity is present, clean out and apply zinc oxide paste (made by incorporating as much zinc oxide powder as possible into three drops of oil of cloves, to form a thick putty). Take paracetamol.

(2) Dull toothache, tender to bite on; gum swollen or red with possible discharge. Treat as above but also take an antibiotic.

(3) Broken tooth or filling. Cover exposed surfaces with zinc oxide paste.

(4) Bleeding gums. Clean teeth more thoroughly. If accompanied by foul odour and metallic taste, use regular hot salt water rinses and antibiotics.

(5) Pain round wisdom tooth. Toothbrush to clean area; use hot salt water rinses; take antibiotics and analgesics.

(6) Mouth ulcers. Hot salt water rinses.

8.6.23 Children

Children may become ill with alarming rapidity. Ear and throat infections are especially common. Children are also more susceptible to effects of dehydration, so if ill encourage to drink copious fluids. Reduce drug dosage to a proportion of adult dose based on weight. Average adult 70kg (155lb).

8.6.24 Drugs

Drug	Type	Dosage
Paracetamol 500mg tablets	analgesic	1–2 tablets 4 hourly
Dihydrocodeine 30mg tablets	strong analgesic	1–2 tablets 4 hourly
Chlorpheniramine 4mg tablets	antihistamine	1 tablet 8 hourly
Aludrox	indigestion	1–2 before meals
Loperamide 2mg capsules	diarrhoea	2 capsules initially followed by 1 after each loose stool, up to a maximum of 8 per day
Senokot tablets	constipation	2–4 tablets daily
Tetracycline 250mg	antibiotic	1 capsule 4 times daily
Amoxycillin 250mg	antibiotic	250–500mg every 8 hours (beware penicillin allergy)
Cinnarizine 15mg tablets	seasickness	2 before voyage then 1 every 8 hours

8.6.25 Injections

A doctor's prescription is required for injections. Stringent regulations apply to injectable analgesic drugs. Probably only warranted for long passages. It is safest to inject into the muscle on the outer part of the mid-thigh. Clean the area, then plunge the needle swiftly an inch or so through the skin, pull back on the plunger to ensure that a blood vessel has not been entered, then slowly complete the injection.

8.6.26 Normal physiological measurements

(1) Pulse rate. Adults 60–80/min.
                 Children up to 100/min.
(2) Breathing. 12–15/min.
(3) Temperature. 36.7°C (98.4°F)

8.6.27 Seeking medical advice

International Code single letter signal W (Whisky) means 'I require medical assistance'. Use any method of signalling. Medical advice can be obtained through Coast Radio Stations as below. The Coast Station communicates with the most appropriate medical authority. There is no charge. Use the urgency signal Pan Pan (three times) in serious cases.

(1) *United Kingdom and Ireland.* Call nearest Coast Radio Station, requesting 'Medico' service. If medical assistance is required (e.g. a doctor, or off-lifting a patient) the request will be passed to the Coastguard.

(2) *France.* Call nearest Coast Radio Station, with address 'PAN PAN (three times) Radiomédical . . . (name of Coast Station)'. French language should be used.

(3) *Belgium.* Call Oostende Radio, using address 'Radiomédical Oostende'. English may be used.

(4) *Netherlands.* Call Scheveningen Radio, using address 'Radiomédical Scheveningen'. English may be used.

(5) *Germany.* Call nearest Coast Radio Station, using address 'Funkarzt . . . (name of Coast Station)'. English may be used.

(6) *Spain.* Call any Coast Radio Station, using address 'Medrad . . .' Spanish language must be used.

For radio procedures see Chapter 6. Before calling it is best to write down as many details as you can about the patient (e.g. pulse rate, breathing rate, temperature, skin colour, conscious state, site and description of any pain, site and type of any injury, amount of blood lost).

8.6.28 Suggestions for a First Aid kit

Your doctor or chemist may suggest alternatives. Prescriptions are needed for most of the drugs. Out of date drugs are potentially dangerous – destroy them. Special preparations are available for children. Secure items in a waterproof container which is readily accessible.

Triangular bandage × 2 (double as bandage or sling)
Crepe bandage 75mm × 2
Gauze bandage 50mm × 2
Elastoplast 75mm × 1
Band Aids (or similar) various shapes and sizes
Wound dressing bpc, 1 large, 1 medium
Sterile non-adhesive dressing (Melolin) × 5
Paraffin gauze sterile dressings – 5 packs
Steristrips – 5 packs
Cotton wool
Scissors and forceps – good stainless steel
Safety pins
Thermometer
Antiseptic solution (e.g. Savlon)
Sunscreen with high protection factor
Antibiotic powder or spray
Tinaderm powder (athlete's foot)
Calamine lotion (bites, stings and sunburn)
Individual choice of anti-seasick tablets
Chloramphenicol eye ointment
Drugs – see 8.6.24

Additional items for extended cruising
(Do not forget vaccinations – a course may need to start long before departure)
Inflatable splint
Syringes 2ml × 2 (if carrying injections)
Dental kit – see 8.6.22
Moisture cream (for cracked hand and lips)

Yachtsmen cruising abroad may naturally be concerned about the possibility of being given infected blood. Under normal circumstances it is not possible to carry blood or plasma in a yacht. If you are cruising to distant destinations you may wish to take additional sterile needles and syringes, and you would be well advised to seek advice from your local hospital or General Practitioner before departure. Syringes and needles are very attractive to intravenous drug abusers so should be kept in a very secure place.

For cruising in European waters it is sensible to obtain and carry Form E111 from the Department of Social Security (DSS). This can be obtained from an application form (T2) which you can get from a Post Office. It is useful to have a number of photocopies. It allows yachtsmen to obtain medical treatment on a reciprocal basis, although it will not cover the full charge. Details of how to claim in different countries are given on the back of the form.

8.6.29 Recommended books

First Aid at Sea by D. Justins & C. Berry (Adlard Coles Nautical), 1993.
First Aid. Manual of St John Ambulance Association.
The Ship's Captain Medical Guide (HMSO Books).

Chapter 9

Tides and the sea

Contents

9.1 Tides – general

9.1.1 General theory

The tide is the periodical rise and fall of sea level caused by the gravitational attraction of the Moon and, to a lesser extent, of the Sun. The gravitational effect of the Moon is not uniform over the earth's surface. At a point nearest to the Moon it is greater than at the centre of the earth, where it is in turn greater than at a point on the far side of the earth. This causes the sea level to be raised at the points nearest to the Moon and furthest from it – at A and B in Fig. 9(1).

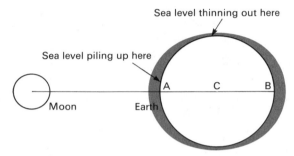

Fig. 9(1) Diagrammatic sketch showing the exaggerated effect of the Moon's gravitational pull on the sea.

When the Moon and the Sun are in the same straight line as the earth their combined gravitational effect is greatest, and this produces the largest rise and fall of tide. These are called spring tides, and occur just after new moon and full moon – see Fig. 9(2).

When the Moon and the Sun form a right angle with the earth their respective gravitational effects

Fig. 9(2) When the Moon and Sun lie in a straight line with the earth, their gravitational forces act in conjunction, and result in a large rise and fall in sea level (spring tides).

Fig. 9(3) When the Moon and Sun form a right angle with the earth, their combined effect is minimised, resulting in a smaller rise and fall in sea level (neap tides).

are acting at places which are one-quarter of the earth's circumference apart, and hence their combined effect is minimised. This results in a smaller rise and fall in sea level, or neap tides which occur just after the first and last quarters.

Since the earth is rotating on its axis every 24 hours, the actual areas nearest to and furthest from the Moon are continually changing. Hence the level of the sea at any point is also continually changing.

A lunar day (the time between two successive passes of the Moon across a given meridian) is about 24 hours 50 minutes. In the Atlantic Ocean, and along the coasts of North-West Europe, two complete tidal cycles occur every lunar day. These are called semi-diurnal tides, with a period of about 12 hours 25 minutes between successive high waters.

Some parts of the world have diurnal tides, with only one high water and one low water every 25 hours or so. Diurnal tides usually have very little rise and fall.

Other parts of the world experience mixed tides, which are partly semi-diurnal and partly diurnal in character. Mixed tides, like semi-diurnal tides, have two complete tidal oscillations per day but often one of the cycles is much more pronounced than the other.

Tides are influenced by the physical details of ocean basins and the surrounding land. For example in the Mediterranean and the Baltic there is virtually no tide, because the entrances to these seas are too narrow to allow the flow of water necessary to create any significant rise and fall in the time available. On open coasts the tide usually rises and falls at about the same rate on any given day, but in estuaries it normally rises more quickly than it falls. See 9.9.6.

The height of the tide is measured against a reference level called chart datum, as defined in 9.2.1. Predictions for the times and heights of high water and low water at places all over the world are published annually in tide tables, which include constants for calculating times and heights at intermediate ports.

Tide refers to the vertical rise or fall in sea level. This in turn causes horizontal movements of water, called tidal streams. Information on the strength and direction of tidal streams is available from various sources, as described in 9.9.

9.1.2 Local tide conditions

Physical details of the coast and the sea bed can cause local tidal conditions which depart substantially from the semi-diurnal (or diurnal) pattern. Often there is no simple explanation for such phenomena, of which a good example is the complex tidal regime between Swanage and the Nab Tower on the south coast of England, and the double high waters which occur at places in that area.

The Coriolis force (induced by the earth's rotation on any object which moves on the surface of the earth, except at the equator) can also affect local tidal conditions, and helps to explain (see 9.10.16) why the French side of the English Channel has bigger tides than the English coast opposite.

Other tidal phenomena, such as bores (or eagres), together with non-tidal changes in sea level caused by abnormal meteorological conditions, are mentioned in 9.7 and 9.10.14.

9.1.3 Equinoxes and solstices
Twice a year, at about the times when the Sun is over the equator at the vernal equinox on 21 March and the autumnal equinox on 23 September, spring tides are larger than normal. These are called Equinoctial Spring Tides, and they occur when all the factors which contribute to big tides – such as the phase of the Moon, the Moon's declination and the Sun's declination – are working in concert. Around the solstices (21 June and 22 December) the tides are smaller than normal.

9.1.4 Tide tables
The Hydrographer of the Navy publishes the *Admiralty Tide Tables* in three volumes. Vol 1 covers all Europe, the Mediterranean and the Black Sea; Vol 2 covers the East Coasts of North and South America including the Caribbean, Greenland, all the coasts of Africa except the Mediterranean, the coasts of Asia up to Singapore and the Malacca Strait; Vol 3 covers the West Coasts of North and South America, Australasia, the Asian coasts east of Singapore, and all the Pacific. Vols 2 and 3 include tidal stream predictions.

Vol 1 is divided into three parts. Part 1 gives tidal predictions for the Standard Ports, being the times and heights of high water and low water for each day of the year, computed by the Proudman Oceanographic Laboratory, or the Hydrographer for certain United Kingdom ports, and by the appropriate authorities for foreign ports. Part 2 gives data for predictions at a large number of Secondary Ports in the form of time and height differences referred to one of the Standard Ports in Part 1. Part 3 gives the harmonic constants for use with the Admiralty method of tidal prediction (NP 159), as discussed in 9.8.5.

The information which a yachtsman needs for the United Kingdom, Eire and the continental coast from St Jean de Luz (near the Spanish/French frontier) to Sylt (near the German/Danish frontier) is in *The Macmillan & Silk Cut Nautical Almanac*.

9.2 Definitions

9.2.1 Chart Datum (CD)
Chart datum is the level to which soundings and drying heights on a chart are referred. The height of the tide at any time is the vertical distance of sea level above (or very occasionally below) chart datum. To find the actual depth of water, the height of the tide at a particular time is added to the depth shown on the chart at the place concerned.

Tidal predictions for British ports are based on Lowest Astronomical Tide – LAT, see 9.2.13. Admiralty metric charts of the British Isles use LAT as chart datum but most fathom charts, of which there are still a small number, were drawn with a chart datum that approximated to Mean Low Water Springs (MLWS). Since MLWS is slightly higher than LAT, it is necessary to make a small correction when using *Admiralty Tide Tables* with most fathom charts. Check the tidal information panel on the chart against the heights given in Part II of *Admiralty Tide Tables* to see if a correction is needed. Any such correction must be subtracted from the predicted height, and may be as much as 0.5 metres.

9.2.2 Charted depth
The charted depth shown on the chart is the vertical distance of the sea bed at that place below chart datum. Depths are shown in metres and tenths of metres on modern metric charts where, for example, 5_2 indicates 5.2 metres. Depths will still be found expressed in fathoms and/or feet on some older charts, where 5_2 would indicate five fathoms and two feet. It is very important to make sure which units are used. Admiralty metric charts have depths in metres printed in magenta in the margins, top and bottom.

9.2.3 Co-tidal and co-range lines
Co-tidal lines are drawn on a special chart through points where Mean High Water occurs at the same time. Co-range lines are drawn through points of equal Mean Spring Range. They enable the height of tide to be predicted at places well offshore, whereas tide tables only give predictions for coastal places (see 9.8.4 for details).

9.2.4 Depth (actual)
The actual depth of water at any place is the sum of the charted depth and the height of the tide at that time and place. If there are no errors in the chart, or in the tidal prediction, the depth as so calculated should correspond to a sounding obtained by lead line or by an accurate echo sounder.

9.2.5 Drying height
The drying height is the vertical distance of the top of any feature which is occasionally covered by water above chart datum. Figures for drying heights are underlined on the chart – in metres and tenths of a metre on metric charts, and in feet on older charts. For example, on a metric chart, $\underline{5}_2$ indicates that the place concerned dries 5.2 m above CD. The actual depth of water at such a place is the height of the tide at the time minus

the drying height indicated. If the result is minus, then that place is exposed at the time selected.

9.2.6 Duration
The duration of a tide is the time between high water and the previous low water, and is normally slightly more than six hours where semi-diurnal tides apply as around the coasts of North-West Europe. The duration can be used to calculate the time of low water where only the time of high water is given in tide tables.

9.2.7 Ebb
The ebb is the movement of tide as it recedes from high water. With semi-diurnal tides it is about six hours' duration and is divided into three parts – the 'first of the ebb', the strength of the ebb' and the 'last of the ebb'.

9.2.8 Elevation of lights etc
The elevations of lights or other structures such as bridges are expressed (in metres on metric charts) above the level of Mean High Water Springs, as is shown in Fig. 9(4).

9.2.9 Equinoctial spring tides
As explained in 9.1.3, unusually big tides can be expected with spring tides at about the equinoxes, which occur on 21 March and 23 September.

9.2.10 Flood
The flood is the movement of tide as it rises from low water. It is about six hours in duration and is divided into three parts, the first two hours being described as the 'young flood', the middle two hours as the 'main flood' and the last two hours as the 'last of the flood'.

9.2.11 Height of tide
The height of the tide is the vertical distance between chart datum and sea level at a given time. In *Admiralty Tide Tables* and in *The Macmillan & Silk Cut Nautical Almanac* the heights of tide at High Water and at Low Water are shown in metres and tenths of metres for the Standard Ports quoted.

9.2.12 Interval
The interval is the time between any given time and the time of high water, expressed in hours and minutes before ($-$) or after ($+$) high water (HW).

9.2.13 Lowest Astronomical Tide (LAT)
LAT is the lowest sea level predicted to occur under average meteorological conditions and under any combination of astronomical conditions. It is only reached very occasionally, but it must be noted that it is not the extreme level. Abnormal meteorological conditions (see 9.7) may cause lower sea levels.

Lowest Astronomical Tide is used as chart datum for Admiralty metric charts of the British Isles. Lowest Astronomical Tide is also the reference level for *Admiralty Tide Table* predictions for ports in Great Britain.

As already noted in 9.2.1, older (fathom) charts were drawn with a chart datum which approximated to Mean Low Water Springs (MLWS). Corrections must therefore be applied to predictions from *Admiralty Tide Tables* when used with most fathom charts.

9.2.14 Making
At neaps the range of a tide (the difference in height between high water and low water, as in

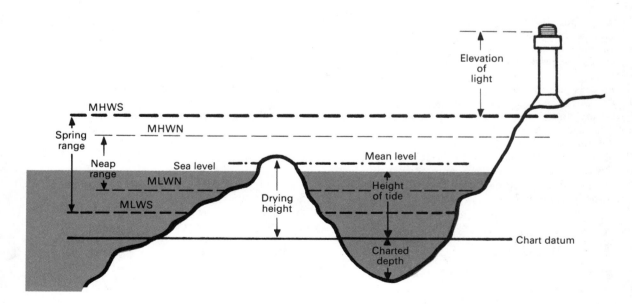

Fig. 9(4) This diagram shows the more important terms used in tidal predictions and calculations.

9.2.17) is relatively small. At springs the range is relatively big. As the range increases from neaps to springs, the tide is said to be making. The opposite is 'taking off'.

9.2.15 Mean Level (ML)

The mean level (ML) at a place is the average height of Mean High Water Springs (MHWS), Mean High Water Neaps (MHWN), Mean Low Water Neaps (MLWN) and Mean Low Water Springs (MLWS). There are seasonal changes in Mean Level, and the monthly variations are shown in Part 2 of *Admiralty Tide Tables*. Where the variation is less than 0.1m it is entered as 'negligible'. For short periods the Mean Level may vary by as much as 0.3m, above or below the predicted figures.

The term 'Mean Level' is also used to describe mean sea level, or the average of a large number of hourly heights. This can produce a different figure.

9.2.16 Neap tides (neaps)

Neap tides occur between spring tides, at the first and last quarters of the moon when (as explained in 9.1.1) the influences of the Sun and Moon are at right angles. At neaps the range of the tide is smallest, i.e. high water is lower and low water is higher than at springs.

9.2.17 Range

The range of the tide is the difference in height between successive high and low waters. Spring range is the difference between MHWS and MLWS. Neap range is the difference between MHWN and MLWN.

9.2.18 Secondary Ports

The term 'Secondary Port' does not imply that the place concerned is of secondary importance. Tidal predictions for Secondary Ports are made by applying time and height differences to predictions for a selected Standard Port (see 9.2.22). The Standard Port chosen is not necessarily the nearest, but one with tidal characteristics which are similar to those of the Secondary Port.

9.2.19 Slack water

Slack water is the period between the completion of the flood and the commencement of the ebb, or similarly at low water between the end of the ebb and the start of the flood. At high water it is also known as the 'stand'.

9.2.20 Sounding

The term 'sounding' is used in two senses. Strictly it means the depth of water as obtained by echo sounder or lead line, but it is also used for the figures on a chart showing the depth of water (below chart datum), because these figures are derived from actual soundings which are adjusted for the height of tide at the time they are taken. To avoid confusion it is best to refer to a sounding on the chart as 'charted depth' (see 9.2.2).

9.2.21 Spring tides (springs)

At springs the tide rises highest and falls lowest from the Mean Level, i.e. the range is greatest. Spring tides occur when the Moon and Sun are acting in conjunction, as described in 9.1.1. During spring tides the tidal streams run more strongly.

9.2.22 Standard Ports

For certain selected Standard Ports, the predicted time and height of every high and low water throughout the year are given in *Admiralty Tide Tables*, and in *The Macmillan & Silk Cut National Almanac*. Predictions are based on observations over a period of at least a year, and usually much longer. Daily predictions for the following Standard Ports are to be found each year in *The Macmillan & Silk Cut Nautical Almanac*: Falmouth, Devonport, Dartmouth, Portland, Poole (low water only), Southampton, Portsmouth, Shoreham, Dover, Sheerness, London Bridge, Burnham-on-Crouch, Walton-on-the-Naze, Lowestoft, Immingham, Tees, Leith, Aberdeen, Lerwick, Ullapool, Oban, Greenock, Liverpool, Holyhead, Milford Haven, Avonmouth, Cobh (Ringaskiddy), Dublin, Belfast, Galway, Pointe de Grave, Brest, St Helier, St Peter Port, St Malo, Cherbourg, Le Havre, Dieppe, Dunkerque, Flushing (Vlissingen), Hook of Holland, Helgoland, Wilhelmshaven and Cuxhaven.

9.2.23 Taking off

'Taking off' is the opposite to 'making' (see 9.2.14). The tide is said to be taking off as the range decreases from its maximum during springs to its minimum during neaps.

9.3 Calculations of times of high and low water

9.3.1 Standard Ports

Daily times of HW and LW for Standard Ports are given in tide tables. The format used in *The Macmillan & Silk Cut Nautical Almanac* is the same as that in *Admiralty Tide Tables*. The Zone Time used for the predictions is shown at the top of each page. In the British Isles, UT (GMT) is used throughout so one hour must be added when BST is in operation. Similar action is required for other daylight saving times (e.g. France), as is explained in 9.3.3.

9.3.2 Secondary Ports

For Secondary Ports, the approximate times of HW and LW are calculated by adding (when +) or subtracting (when −) the time difference shown, to (or from) the time of HW or LW at the Standard Port indicated. Predictions for times falling between those given for the Standard Port at the top of each column must be interpolated. For example, the tidal information for Sark.

Standard Port ST HELIER

Times			Height (metres)			
High Water	Low Water	MHWS	MHWN	MLWN	MLWS	
0300 0900	0200 0900	11.0	8.1	4.0	1.4	
1500 2100	1400 2100					

Differences SARK (MASELINE PIER)
+0005 +0015 +0005 +0010 −2.1 −1.5 −0.6 −0.3

If HW St Helier is at about 0300 or 1500, the correction needed for the time of HW Sark is +0005 (add 5 minutes). If HW St Helier is at about 0900 or 2100, the time difference to be applied to obtain HW Sark is +0015 (add 15 minutes). Similarly for the times of LW. If LW St Helier is at about 0200 or 1400, LW Sark is 5 minutes later. If LW St Helier is at about 0900 or 2100, LW Sark is 10 minutes later.

Such calculations can be conveniently made using the top part of the tidal prediction form shown in Fig. 9(12). The procedure is included in the example given in 9.5.2.

To find the appropriate time difference for the Secondary Port at times which fall between those which are given, it is necessary to interpolate between the columns. For example, when HW St Helier is at 0300, the time difference for Sark is +0005 and when HW St Helier is at 0900 the time difference is +0015. Hence for HW St Helier at 0600, the time difference for Sark will be +0010.

For those who find the business of interpolation difficult, whether by eye or by arithmetic, there is an alternative, graphical method which may be convenient. It is particularly suitable where calculations are required over several tides, and yachtsmen may find it helpful to construct the appropriate graph for their home port if this is governed by tidal considerations.

The figures taken in the example above were convenient ones, because for HW St Helier at 0600 (midway between 0300 and 0900), the Sark time difference was fairly obviously midway between +0005 and +0015, i.e. +0010. The graphical method as illustrated in Fig. 9(5) is a simple way to arrive at more difficult calculations.

The diagram has a vertical scale of hours at the Standard Port, with a horizontal scale of time differences for the Secondary Port. Suppose that, from the data given for the Standard Port St Helier above, it is required to find the time difference for HW Sark when HW St Helier is at 0700.

First establish the Standard Port time bracket in which the required time of 0700 occurs. This is between 0300 and 0900. Using the right-hand scale for Standard Port times, plot the first time (0300) against the associated time difference +0005 on the scale along the top. Then plot a second point for the end of the time bracket (0900) against that associated time difference (+0015). Draw a line between these two points, as is marked HW. The LW line for times between 0200 and 0900 is also shown in the diagram as a dashed line.

To find the HW time difference for Sark when HW St Helier is at 0700, enter the diagram on the right at 0700 and draw a horizontal line until it meets the HW (sloping) one. From that point proceed vertically to the scale at the top and read off the required time difference which is +0012.

Any suitable squared paper can be used, but the scale for time differences needs to be selected according to the figures for the Secondary Port concerned. A similar procedure can be used for interpolating height differences, as illustrated in Fig. 9(8) and described in 9.4.2.

The time differences given for Secondary Ports are approximate, as will occur in normal weather. Although normally given to the nearest minute, they should not be assumed to be that accurate. It is important to note that the times thus obtained are in the Zone Time of the Secondary Port, as is explained more fully in 9.3.3 below.

9.3.3 Zone time and time differences
There are 24 time zones in the world, each of which covers 15 degrees of longitude, as illustrated in Fig. 9(7). The zero time zone, in which the Standard Time (see below) is Universal Time (UT) or GMT, is centred on the prime meridian and extends from $7\frac{1}{2}°$E to $7\frac{1}{2}°$W. The other time zones, in which the time kept differs from UT by an integral number of hours, are sequentially numbered and have either a negative prefix if they lie east of Greenwich or a positive prefix if to the west. A time zone may be described by its zone number (+ or −) or by its letter designator as shown in the diagram.

The twelfth time zone is divided into two parts by the International Date Line, the part to the west of the line being zone −12 and the part to the east +12. Mostly the Date Line follows the 180th meridian, but it is modified so that islands of a particular group (for example Fiji) are all on the same side of the line. When crossing the Date Line heading east, assume yesterday's date; when heading west, assume tomorrow's date.

Fig. 9(5) Graphical interpolation of time differences.

To convert zone time to UT (GMT), the number of hours as given by the zone number is added to (if positive) or subtracted from (if negative) the zone time. For example in Zone -1 (-0100) the time kept is one hour in advance of UT, and so 2000 local time is 1900 UT.

Ashore a uniform time is used for convenience throughout a given country, even if it does not lie wholly within a time zone. Usually this Standard (or Legal) Time is that of the zone within which the country mosty lies. Larger countries may adopt more than one Standard Time.

Many countries introduce Daylight Saving Time (Summer Time), to extend daylight in the evening, as legal time for part of the year. Normally this is the Standard Time of the zone to the eastward.

During the winter months in the United Kingdom, clock time is UT (GMT). During summer months in the United Kingdom, clock time is BST which is Zone -0100, i.e. one hour ahead of UT. The reference timescale UTC (a language-independent abbreviation of Coordinated Universal Time) is for practical purposes the same as UT.

During winter months in France, Belgium, the Netherlands and Germany local (clock) time is

Zone -0100. In all four countries daylight saving time (DST) operates from the last Sunday in March until the last Saturday in September. During this period, local (clock) time is -0200, or two hours ahead of UT (GMT). The relationships between UT (GMT), Zone -0100 and Zone -0200 are shown in the table in Fig. 9(6).

Tidal predictions given in tide tables take no account of BST or other Daylight Saving Times. Standard Port predictions are given in the Standard Time normally kept at the place, and in the British Isles this is UT (GMT). The zone time used is shown on each page of tidal predictions in *The Macmillan & Silk Cut Nautical Almanac*.

Time differences for Secondary Ports, when applied to the predicted times of high water and low water at Standard Ports, will give times of high and low water *in the zone time tabulated for the Secondary Port.*

Any change in zone time at the Standard Port, or any difference between zone times at Standard and Secondary Ports has no significance. Only changes in zone time at the Secondary Port, where different from those tabulated, may be corrected for. In some parts of the world it should be verified that the zone time tabulated for a Secondary Port is in fact valid, since changes are not always notified in time for inclusion in tide tables.

Care is needed in some places, as for example with certain French harbours (Zone -0100) adjacent to the Channel Islands if these are referred to St Helier (UT) as the Standard Port. This difficulty has been overcome in *The Macmillan & Silk Cut Nautical Almanac* since the 1991 edition by including predictions for St Malo (Zone -0100) and referring adjacent French harbours to this Standard Port, and not to St Helier.

Universal Time (UT) or Greenwich Mean Time (GMT) Tide tables for UK, Ireland and Channel Isles	Zone -0100 British Summer Time, (BST) from last Sun in March to 4th Sat in Oct Standard Time in France, Belgium, Netherlands and Germany. Used for tide tables in these countries	Zone -0200 Daylight Saving Time (DST) from last Sun in March to last Sat in Sept, for France, Belgium, Netherlands and Germany
0000	0100	0200
0100	0200	0300
0200	0300	0400
0300	0400	0500
0400	0500	0600
0500	0600	0700
0600	0700	0800
0700	0800	0900
0800	0900	1000
0900	1000	1100
1000	1100	1200
1100	1200	1300
1200	1300	1400
1300	1400	1500
1400	1500	1600
1500	1600	1700
1600	1700	1800
1700	1800	1900
1800	1900	2000
1900	2000	2100
2000	2100	2200
2100	2200	2300
2200	2300	2400
2300	2400	0100
0000	0100	0200

Fig. 9(6) Table showing relation between UT, BST, and the standard and daylight saving times (DST) kept in Western Europe.

9.4 Calculations of heights of high and low water

9.4.1 Standard Ports
For Standard Ports the daily heights of HW and LW are shown in metres, referred to chart datum at the port concerned.

9.4.2 Secondary Ports
For Secondary Ports heights of HW or LW are found by applying the height differences, given in the tidal information for each harbour, to the height of HW or LW at the Standard Port indicated. These average differences are shown for Mean Spring and Mean Neap levels, heights for intermediate dates being obtained by interpolation. The resulting heights are referred to chart datum at the Secondary Port concerned.

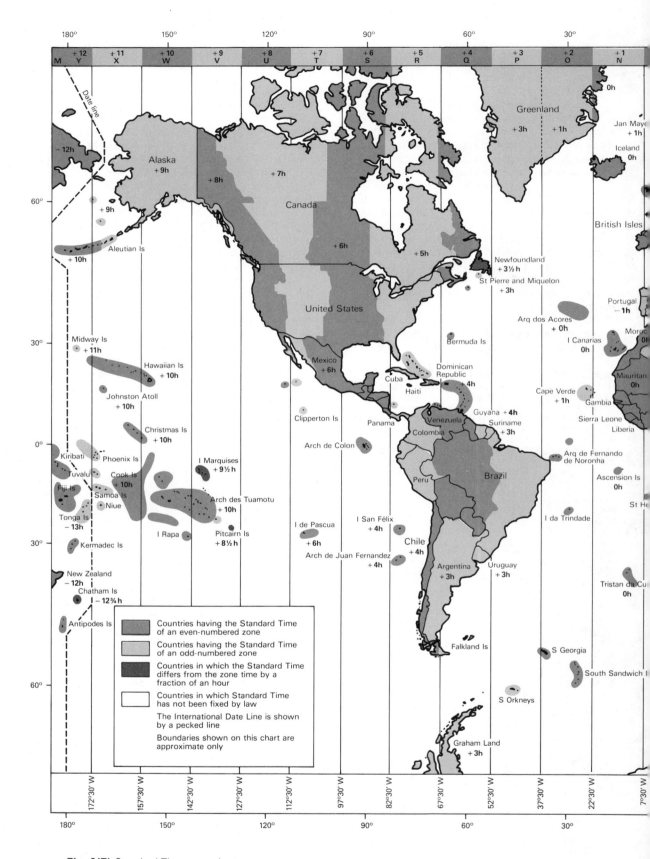

Fig. 9(7) Standard Time zone chart.

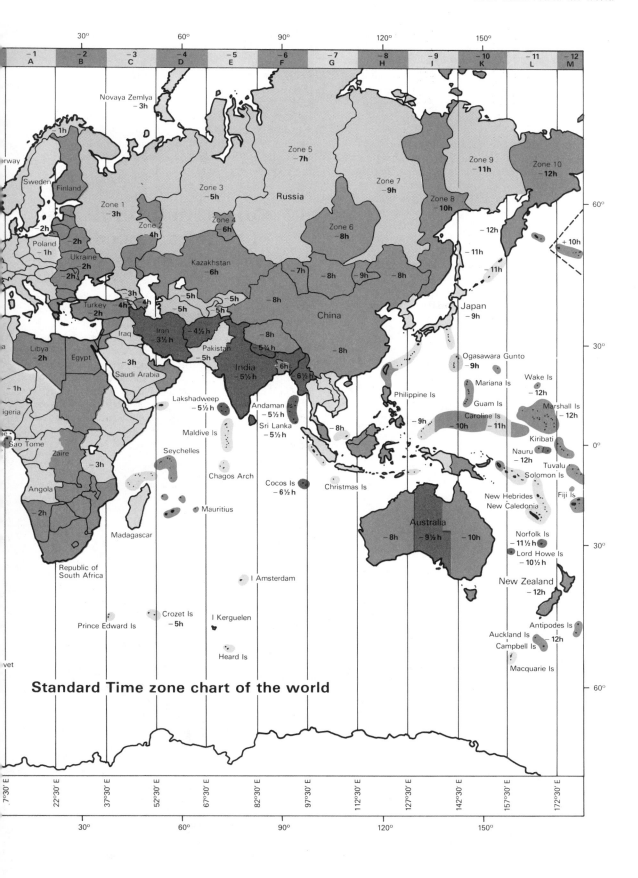

Standard Time zone chart of the world

Referring to the tidal data for Sark in 9.3.2, the height of MHWS at Sark is 11.0 − 2.1 = 8.9m. The height of MLWN is 4.0 − 0.6 = 3.4m. To determine the height (say) of LW at Sark midway between springs and neaps, take the mean of 4.0 and 1.4 (2.7m) to give the predicted height of LW St Helier, and apply the mean of the corrections −0.6 and −0.3 (−0.45m), giving a height of 2.7 − 0.45 = 2.25m.

The height differences shown for Secondary Ports are average values, and predicted heights so obtained are approximate. It is assumed that the variation in height differences is linear.

Height differences for HW or LW at dates between springs and neaps can be interpolated graphically in a similar way to time differences as explained in 9.3.2.

The procedure is shown in Fig. 9(8), which is based on the predictions given in 9.3.2 for St Helier and Sark.

For example, it is required to find the HW height difference for Sark on a date when the

predicted height of HW at St Helier is 9.0m. Select suitable scales for Standard Port heights (vertically) and for height differences (horizontally) as indicated in Fig. 9(8). Plot the Standard Port heights of 11.0m (MHWS) and 8.1m (MHWN) against the height differences of −2.1m and −1.5m respectively, and join these two points by a straight line. Enter the diagram at the required Standard Port height of 9.0m, proceed horizontally to the sloping line, and thence vertically to the scale of height differences to give the required figure of −1.7m.

9.5 Calculations of depths of water at specific times, and vice versa

9.5.1 Standard Ports

As shown in Fig. 9(4), the depth of water is the height of the tide plus the charted depth. The height of tide at intermediate times between high and low water is best predicted by using the Mean Spring and Mean Neap curves, as are shown with the daily predictions for each Standard Port in *The Macmillan & Silk Cut Nautical Almanac*.

The example in Fig. 9(9) is the curve for Galway, and shows the factor of the range which is reached at certain time intervals before and after HW. By definition a factor of 0 relates to LW, and a factor of 1 is HW.

The spring curve is shown as a solid line and the neap curve, where it departs from the spring curve, is pecked. Interpolation between the spring and neap curves can be made by eye from the

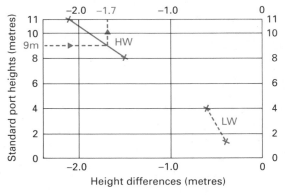

Fig. 9(8) Graphical interpolation of height differences.

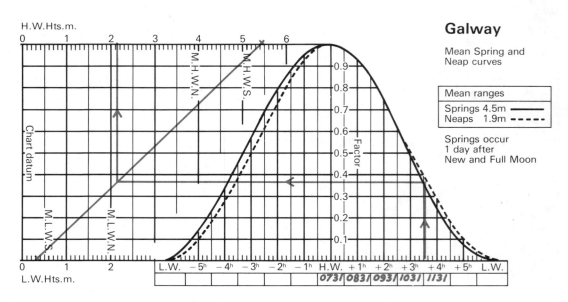

Fig. 9(9) Galway — Mean Spring and Neap curves.

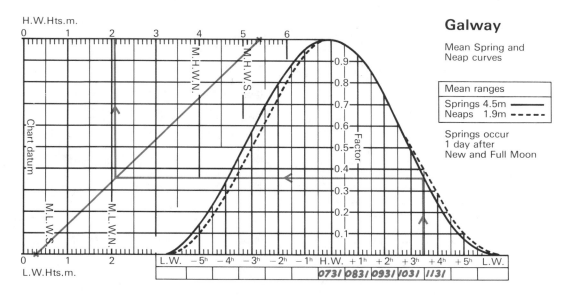

Fig. 9(10) Calculation of height of tide at a certain time.

plotted positions of the heights of HW and LW, compared to the reference figures for MHWS/MHWN and MLWS/MLWN shown on the left of the diagram, explained below. Do not extrapolate beyond the spring or neap curves – for ranges greater than springs use the spring curve, and for ranges less than neaps use the neap curve.
Example To find the height of tide at Galway at 1100 on a day when the predictions are:

21 0107 0·3
    0731 5·4
Su 1331 0·3
    1955 5·0

(1) On the diagram for Galway in Fig. 9(10) plot the heights of HW and LW either side of the required time (i.e. at 0731 and 1331) at the top and bottom respectively on the left-hand side of the diagram, and join the two by a sloping line.
(2) In the boxes below the curves, enter the time of HW (0731) and complete such other boxes as are necessary to embrace the required time (i.e. 0831, 0931, 1031, 1131).
(3) From the required time of 1100 ($3\frac{1}{2}$h after HW) proceed vertically to the curves. In this case the spring (solid) curve applies.

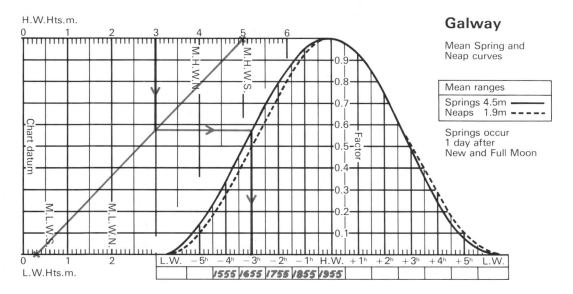

Fig. 9(11) Calculation of time that tide reaches a certain height.

(4) From the curve proceed horizontally to the sloping line, and thence vertically to the scale for height. Read off the height – 2.1m.

Example To find the time in the afternoon, on a day when the predictions are as in the previous example, when the tide rises to a height of 3m at Galway.

(5) On the diagram for Galway in Fig. 9(11) plot the heights of LW and HW either side of the required time (i.e. at 1331 and 1955) at the bottom and top respectively of the left-hand side of the diagram, and join the two by a sloping line.

(6) In the boxes below the curves, enter the time of HW (1955) and complete sufficient other boxes to cover the required event.

(7) From the required height (3m) proceed vertically to the sloping line, and thence horizontally to the curves. In this case the spring (solid) curve applies.

(8) From the curve proceed vertically down to the time scale. Read off the time, which is HW – 3h (i.e. 1655).

The use of factors

As an alternative to the graphical method described above, it is possible to calculate the height of tide at times between HW and LW by simple arithmetic by using the vertical factor scale which appears up the centre of the tidal curves for Standard Ports. The factor may be regarded as the percentage of the mean range which has been reached at that particular time. By definition a factor of 0 implies LW, and a factor of 1 implies HW. A factor of 0.5 means that half of the mean range has been reached at the time shown on the curve, either before or after HW. Multiplying the mean range by the factor gives the rise (height) of the tide above LW at the time concerned.

$$\text{Factor} \times \text{range} = \text{Rise above LW}$$

In tidal calculations with factors, use the tidal prediction form illustrated in Fig. 9(12). The procedure is described in 9.5.2 below.

9.5.2 Secondary Ports

For Secondary Ports along a coast where there is little change in the shape of tidal curves between

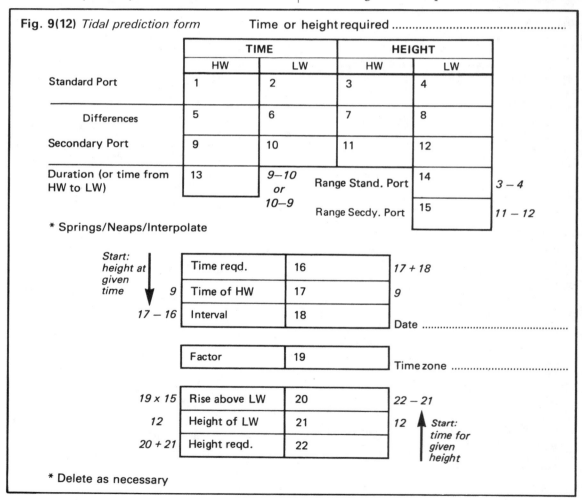

Fig. 9(12) Tidal prediction form for tidal calculations when using *Admiralty Tide Tables* or *The Macmillan & Silk Cut Nautical Almanac.*

adjacent Standard Ports, and where the duration of rise or fall at the Secondary Port is like that of the appropriate Standard Port (where HW and LW time differences are nearly the same), intermediate times and heights may be predicted from the Mean Spring and Mean Neap curves for the appropriate Standard Port in a similar manner as described in 9.5.1.

The curves are entered with the times and heights of HW and LW at the Secondary Port, calculated as in 9.3.2 and 9.4.2 above.

Interpolation between the curves (where necessary) can be made by eye, using the range at the Standard Port as argument. Do not extrapolate – use the spring curve for spring ranges or greater, and the neap curve for neap ranges or less.

Special curves are provided for certain places along the South Coast of England, between Swanage and Selsey, where tides are particularly complex. Such curves are included and described in *The Macmillan & Silk Cut Nautical Almanac*. *Example* To find the height of tide at Fanad Head at 1300 GMT, and the time when the afternoon tide rises to a height of 2.5 metres, on a day when the predictions for the appropriate Standard Port (Galway) are:

5 0326 4.2
0919 1.6
Sa 1536 4.4
2143 1.5

The tidal information for Fanad Head, as in *The Macmillan & Silk Cut Nautical Almanac* is as follows:

Standard Port GALWAY

Times				Height (metres)			
HW		LW		MHWS	MHWN	MLWN	MLWS
0200	0900	0200	0800	5.1	3.9	2.0	0.6
1400	2100	1400	2100				
Differences		**FANAD HEAD**					
+0115	+0040	+0125	+0120	−1.1	−0.9	−0.5	−0.1

First establish the time and height differences for Fanad Head on Galway Bay, from the data above, either by arithmetic or by the graphical solution already described in 9.3.2, as illustrated in Fig. 9(13), which gives the HW time difference as +0107 and the HW/LW height differences as −1.0 and −0.4m respectively. Enter these differences in boxes 5, 7 and 8 of the tidal prediction form beneath the figures for Galway as shown in Fig. 9(14). The resulting figures for Fanad Head (HW at 1643, HW height 3.4m, LW height 1.2m) can then be used to enter the Galway diagram for Mean Spring and Mean Neap curves, as shown in Fig. 9(15).

Enter the Fanad Head heights for HW (3.4m) and for LW (1.2m) top and bottom on the left of the diagram, and connect the two points by a sloping line as shown. Enter the time of HW Fanad Head (1643) in the central HW box, and complete the boxes to the left, before HW, by inserting 1543, 1443, 1343 and 1243.

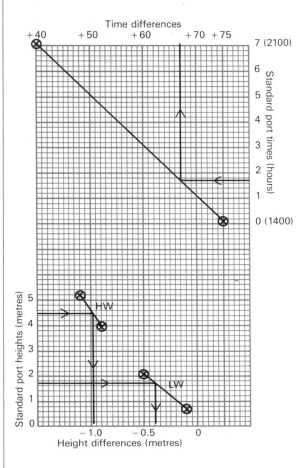

Fig. 9(13) Example of graphical interpolation of time and height differences (Fanad Head on Galway).

The time required (1300) is 3h 43m before HW. From this point proceed upwards to the curves. By examination, the range is rather nearer neaps than springs, and so a point between the two curves is selected accordingly. Then proceed horizontally to the sloping line, and down to the height scale to give the required figure of 2 metres.

To determine the time at which the afternoon tide rises to 2.5 metres, enter the diagram at this point and proceed vertically to the sloping line. Then proceed horizontally to the curves, again selecting a point rather nearer the neap curve than the spring one. Then proceed down vertically to the time scale at the bottom, which gives HW − 2h 40m, i.e. 1403.

Although the graphical method above is very simple, some people may wish to continue with the use of factors – which since the same curves are used should give the same answer. The procedure to find the height of tide at 1300 is as follows.

First complete the top part of the tidal prediction form as already described above, Fig. 9(14). In box 16 enter the time required (1300). In box 17 enter the time of HW at the Secondary

Tidal prediction form   Time or height required ...*1300 and 2.5m*.............

	TIME		HEIGHT	
	HW	LW	HW	LW
Standard Port _Galway_	1 1536	2 0919	3 4.4	4 1.6
Differences	5 +0107	6	7 -1.0	8 -0.4
Secondary Port _Fanad Head_	9 1643	10	11 3.4	12 1.2

Duration (or time from HW to LW)	13	9–10 or 10–9	Range Stand. Port	14 2.8	3 – 4
			Range Secdy. Port	15 2.2	11 – 12

*Springs/Neaps/Interpolate

Start: height at given time ↓ 9	Time reqd.	16 1300	17 + 18
	Time of HW	17 1643	9
17 – 16	Interval	18 -0343	Date ....5 May..........

	Factor	19 0.37	Time zone .....UT.....

19 x 15	Rise above LW	20 0.8	22 – 21
12	Height of LW	21 1.2	12 ↑ Start: time for given height
20 + 21	Height reqd.	22 2.0	

* Delete as necessary

Fig. 9(14) Example of use of tidal prediction form.

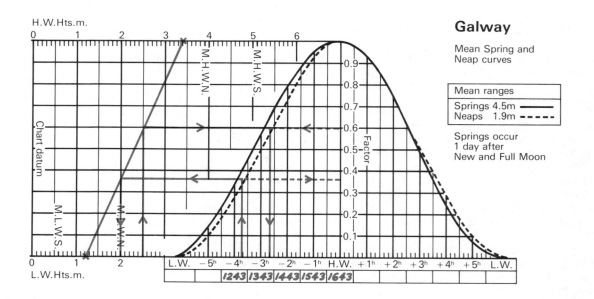

Galway

Mean Spring and Neap curves

Mean ranges	
Springs 4.5m	——
Neaps 1.9m	- - - -

Springs occur 1 day after New and Full Moon

Fig. 9(15) Example of use of Mean Spring and Neap curves for Secondary Port calculations.

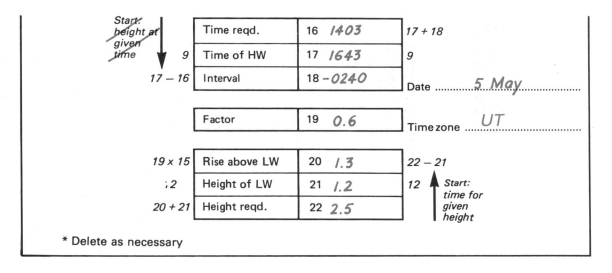

Start: height at given time ↓	Time reqd.	16 *1403*	17 + 18	
9	Time of HW	17 *1643*	9	Date .... *5 May* ....
17 − 16	Interval	18 *−0240*		
	Factor	19 *0.6*	Time zone .... *UT*	
19 × 15	Rise above LW	20 *1.3*	22 − 21	
÷ 2	Height of LW	21 *1.2*	12 ↑ Start: time for given height	
20 + 21	Height reqd.	22 *2.5*		

* Delete as necessary

Fig. 9(16) Example of use of tidal prediction form to determine the time at which the tide reaches a certain height.

Port (1643). By subtracting box 16 from box 17, enter in box 18 the interval from HW (−0343).

Turning to the Galway Mean Spring and Mean Neap curves as in Fig. 9(15), enter at the bottom with the interval (0343 before HW) and proceed upwards to the curves. Interpolate as before between springs and neaps, but instead of proceeding left to the sloping line proceed to the right, as indicated by the dashed line, to the vertical factor scale to determine the factor (0.37). Enter this in box 19.

Rise above LW = Range (2.2m) × Factor (0.37)
= 0.8m

Enter this in box 20. Insert the height of LW (1.2m) in box 21. Add boxes 20 and 21 to give the height required, which is 2.0m.

To determine the time at which the tide rises to 2.5 metres, the lower part of the tidal prediction form is completed in reverse, as illustrated in Fig. 9(16).

In box 22 enter the required height (2.5m). In box 21 enter the height of LW (1.2m). By subtracting box 21 from box 22 determine the rise above LW (1.3m) and enter in box 20.

Factor = Rise (1.3m) ÷ Range (2.2m)
= 0.6

Turning to the Galway Mean Spring and Mean Neap curves as in Fig. 9(15), locate the factor of 0.6 on the central, vertical scale. From this point proceed to the left to the curves, as indicated by the dashed line. As before, it is necessary to interpolate between the spring and neap curves, so select a point nearer the neap curve. From this point proceed down vertically to the time scale at the foot, and read off the interval required, which is −0240 (i.e. 2h 40m before HW). This gives the time of 1403.

9.6 Calculations of clearances under bridges etc

It is sometimes necessary to calculate whether a boat can pass underneath such objects as bridges or power cables. The heights of such objects are shown on the chart are MHWS, so the clearance will nearly always be greater than the figure shown. The height is shown in metres on metric charts, but in feet on older charts. It is sometimes useful to draw a diagram, as illustrated in Fig. 9(17), which shows how the measurements are related to chart datum.

Clearance = (Elevation of object + height of MHWS) − (height of tide at the time + height of mast above water).

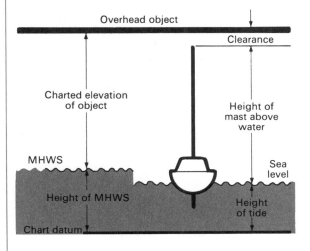

Fig. 9(17) Calculating clearance under bridges etc.

9.7 Meteorological conditions

Meteorological conditions can have a significant effect on tides and tidal streams. Sea level tends to rise in the direction towards which the wind is blowing, and to be lowered in the other direction. The stronger the wind and the longer it blows, the greater the effect. If the wind changes direction significantly – say from south to north – it can cause an oscillation of sea level that greatly affects predicted heights of tide.

Strong winds blowing along a coast can establish long waves which raise sea level at their crest and lower it at their trough. Under exceptional conditions this can raise the height of the tide by two or three metres in what is known as a storm surge; conversely a negative surge can lower the height of low water by one or two metres, which may be more serious for yachtsmen. The southern North Sea is an area which is particularly affected by storm surges and by negative surges, especially in winter months.

Tidal heights are predicted for average barometric pressure. When the barometer is high, tidal heights are likely to be lower than predicted, and vice versa. A change of 34 millibars (2.5cm or 1in of mercury) can cause a change of 0.3m (1ft) in the height of sea level, although this may not occur immediately. Severe conditions giving rise to a storm surge, as described above, are likely to be caused by a deep depression, and the low barometric pressure tends to raise sea level still more. The result of these abnormal conditions is naturally more serious at springs than at neaps.

An intense depression or the passage of a line squall can have local effects on the height of water by setting up what is known as a seiche, which can raise or lower sea level a metre or more in the space of a few minutes. Seiches quite often occur around the British Isles, particularly in winter months.

In some parts of the world seasonal changes in the weather, such as the monsoon, can affect sea level. Where sufficient data is available this is taken into account in tide table predictions.

9.8 Other prediction methods

The procedures described previously for calculating times and heights etc of tide are based on the methods recommended when using *Admiralty Tide Tables*, or the equivalent tables published each year in *The Macmillan & Silk Cut Nautical Almanac*. Alternative methods of calculating tides are given below. In other countries, tide tables may employ different methods for calculating heights at intermediate times and resolving similar problems.

9.8.1 Twelfths Rule

To obtain a rough approximation to the height of the tide between high water and low water, it is possible to use the 'Twelfths Rule'. It must be remembered, however, that unless the tide at the place in question follows a regular pattern (as for example in Fig. 9(9), where the rate of rise and fall is proportional to the interval, defined in 9.2.12) the method can be very misleading. The rule assumes that the rise and fall of the tide is:

1/12 of the range during the first hour
2/12 of the range during the second hour
3/12 of the range during the third hour
3/12 of the range during the fourth hour
2/12 of the range during the fifth hour
1/12 of the range during the sixth hour

9.8.2 Tides by pocket calculator

Assuming a sinusoidal variation in tide height, a calculator can be used to determine the height correction to be applied relative to the nearest high water or low water, using the formula:

$$\text{Height correction} = \frac{R}{2}\left(1 - \cos\frac{180 \times t}{T}\right)$$

where
- R = range of tide concerned
- t = interval from nearest HW or LW
- T = duration of rise or fall

More advanced scientific calculators can be programmed to provide heights of tide for a limited number of places at any time required.

A calculator can also be used for applying the Admiralty method of tidal prediction, which is described in 9.8.5.

9.8.3 French tidal coefficients

In France a coefficient is used to show the size of each tide on each day of the year. These figures are based on a scale for which the reference coefficients are as follows:

C = 120 for the biggest range of tide
C = 95 for Mean Spring tides
C = 70 for an average range of tide
C = 45 for Mean Neap tides
C = 20 for the smallest range of tide

The ratio of the coefficients of different tides equals the ratio of their ranges. Thus the range, for example, of the largest spring tide (120) is six times that of the smallest neap tide (20).

French tide tables provide similar information to that contained in *Admiralty Tide Tables*, albeit in a different form. Time and height differences are given for secondary ports on their appropriate standard port for *vives eaux* (springs) and *mortes eaux* (neaps). The tidal coefficient for the day in question may be used to decide which correction(s) to apply. In general it is satisfactory to use the *vives eaux* correction(s) for coefficients over 70, and the *mortes eaux* correction(s) for the others. Where it is necessary to obtain more accurate corrections (as for example in estuaries), this can be done by interpolating or extrapolating.

Tidal coefficients may also be used to determine rates of tidal streams on any given day, on a similar principle to that described in 9.9.2 and illustrated in Fig. 9(19). Tidal coefficients form the vertical scale from 20 at the bottom to 120 at the top. The horizontal scale is the tidal stream rate from zero to (say) five knots. From the tidal stream atlas or chart plot the neap rate against coefficient 45, and the spring rate against coefficient 95. Draw a sloping line through these two points. Then, using the coefficient for the day in question, the required rate can be determined by drawing a horizontal line to meet the sloping line, and then reading off the required rate from the horizontal scale.

The French also publish a very useful table which gives the height of tide every 15 minutes at certain places where the tidal regime is irregular.

The terms shown in the table below are useful in order to understand tidal information displayed in French ports:

High water	Pleine mer (PM)
Low water	Basse mer (BM)
Springs	Vives-eaux (VE)
Neaps	Mortes-eaux (ME)
Chart datum	Zero des cartes
MHWS	Pleine mer moyenne de VE
MHWN	Pleine mer moyenne de ME
MLWN	Basse mer moyenne de ME
MLWS	Basse mer moyenne de VE
GMT	Temps universel (TU)

9.8.4 Co-tidal and co-range charts

These charts show lines of equal times and equal range of tides for certain selected areas, including the United Kingdom (chart 5058), Dungeness to Hoek van Holland (chart 5057), and the southern North Sea (chart 5059).

Some tidal systems centre round what is called an amphidromic point, where the range is very small but increases in an outward direction, while the times of high and low water progress in either a clockwise or anti-clockwise direction round this centre. A system of this type is centred in the southern North Sea.

Near the amphidromic points the range of tide may change quite considerably in only a short distance – as for example in the North Sea by as much as 1m (3ft) in 15 nautical miles. Co-tidal and co-range charts enable predictions for the times and heights of tide at positions offshore to be obtained, whereas tide tables only provide predictions for coastal places.

The actual lines on the chart show Mean High Water Interval, defined as the mean time interval between the passage of the Moon over the Greenwich meridian and the time of the next high water at the place concerned, and Mean Spring Range, defined as the difference in level between Mean High Water Springs and Mean Low Water

Springs. Instructions for use are given on the charts.

9.8.5 Harmonic constituents

Harmonic constants are quoted in Part 3 of *Admiralty Tide Tables* for a large number of Secondary Ports, and are for use with the Admiralty Method of Tidal Prediction (NP 159). Harmonic constants are also given for Standard Ports. These figures enable the most accurate prediction possible to be made, both in times of high and low water and in hourly heights between. The degree of accuracy produced by this method is not normally needed by yachtsmen, since meteorological conditions probably produce a greater difference to the prediction which he already has, than the increased accuracy provided by this method. The following brief summary is for interest or for the purist.

The study of tides has been considerably facilitated by the fact that tidal movements are to all intents and purposes linear with respect to the tide generating forces. This means that the resultant tide is the direct sum of all the constituents; for example, if the lunar tide is calculated and then the solar tide is calculated, the resultant tide will be the direct sum of the two, there being no inter-action between the two.

The *Admiralty Method of Tidal Prediction* is given in full in NP 159 where a graphic method is used, and a variation on this is given in the introduction to *Admiralty Tide Tables* for those who prefer to use a pocket calculator. The harmonic method of tidal analysis and prediction is based on the principle that a complex curve can be broken down into a number of sine curves and that these can be calculated for future dates, reassembled in their correct relationships and so give predictions of hourly heights of the tide. From these values it is possible to determine the times and heights of the turning points of the curve, which are, of course, high water and low water. The four most important constituents are:

M_2	The Lunar semi-diurnal constituent
S_2	The Solar semi-diurnal constituent
K_1	The Luni-Solar diurnal constituent
O_1	The Lunar diurnal constituent

These four are the ones used for the Admiralty method. Many others can be discovered and normally up to 60 are used in calculating tidal predictions for a Standard Port; in some complex cases up to 120 are used. Distortions of the tidal curve are included by the use of higher harmonics of the basic constituents usually consisting of the Quarter and Sixth diurnals. These are allowed for in the Admiralty method by the use of F_4, f_4, F_6 and f_6.

As the Admiralty method provides hourly or half-hourly heights, details of the shape of the tidal curve can be found. In some cases programs have been written for programable machines so that the user has only to insert the program, insert the data and then run off hourly heights. As this method is universal, it has been used for ports where no suitable Standard Port is available.

Using a computer or programable calculator for tidal prediction is increasingly popular as home computers and laptop portables become more widely used and their value for producing tidal predictions becomes more apparent. The computer is simple to operate, accurate, and is able to produce tabulated or graphical predictions spanning many hours or several days in far less time than it would take to undertake just one hour's prediction using manual methods. Another advantage is that data can be produced for Standard or Secondary ports world-wide using one standardised prediction method.

The NP 159 *Simplified Harmonic Method of Tidal Prediction* is basically a graphical system requiring the use of a pencil, protractor, proforma, and a set of *Admiralty Tide Tables*. The method can be very time consuming if a number of predictions are required; the method can be drastically improved by the use of computers and calculators. Several programs are now available which use the NP 159 Admiralty simplified harmonic method of tidal prediction. The Hydrographic Office markets its own tidal prediction program (called NP 159A version 2.0) for use on the IBM PC XT, AT and 100% compatible machines. About 336K of memory is required as is a graphics adapter to CGA, EGA or VGA standards. The program is available on both 3.5 and 5.25in discs.

Predictions are displayed graphically as hourly plots of height versus time together with tabulated predictions for each hour. To obtain a prediction, it is only necessary to key in the day, month and year, and the relevant port harmonic constants obtained from the *Admiralty Tide Tables*, or NP 160 which lists the tidal harmonic constants for selected ports in European Waters. Since harmonic constants change from time to time, for best results use those listed in the latest tide tables. Other commercially produced programs for NP 159 are now available and can be obtained from Positron Navigation, Dolphin Software, or PC Maritime. Pilotage Software also market good programs for use on the Psion LZ or XP hand held calculator. Programs are also available for use on the old Hewlett-Packard HP41 series calculators and are published in the Nautical Institute's book *Computers at Sea*.

The Hydrographic Office has also recently released a world-wide tidal prediction program called Tidecalc (NP 158), a version of the program used by the Hydrographic Office to compute the daily tidal predictions published in *Admiralty Tide Tables*. It has been adapted for use on an IBM PC and runs on IMB 286/386/486 processors and 100% compatible computers. It requires a memory size of 640K together with a graphics adapter to VGA standard, and runs in colour or monochrome. The software consists of one main program disc, and there is a choice of 12 area discs (NP 158 A1 to A12). Each area disc stores the harmonic

constants for 350 to 400 ports. The Area 1 disc covers the UK, Republic of Ireland, and the Channel Islands, and Area 2 covers Europe from Russia to Gibraltar, including the Channel Islands and the Mediterranean. The Hydrographic Office will also produce special customised discs to order which contain up to a maximum of 400 sets of port harmonic constants to suit individual user needs. As changes are regularly made to the port harmonic constants, users should always ensure that only the latest versions of the area disc are used. These are promulgated from time to time in *Admiralty Notices to Mariners*.

Tidecalc is completely different to the NP 159A program mentioned above; it does not make use of the NP 159 method but utilises many more harmonic constants than NP 159 and is procedurally much closer to the mainframe computer used to compute the *Admiralty Tide Tables*. In addition to computing the times and heights of high and low water for periods of one to three days at a time, predictions can be displayed graphically as a continuous plot of height against time, or as a tabulated list of times and heights. Optional selections possible include displaying heights at 10, 20, 30, 40, 50 minutes, or one hour intervals; metres or feet; the ability to insert the vessel's draught, make an allowance for daylight saving time, or give a pictorial colour indication on screen of daylight, twilight and darkness periods superimposed on the graph. The computations are very fast and in a relatively short time users could undertake a whole month of predictions for all the ports required during a cruise.

9.8.6 Tidal data on Admiralty charts

Large scale charts of the British Isles have a panel which shows the mean heights of high and low water at springs and neaps (i.e. MHWS, MHWN, MLWS and MLWN). This indicates the approximate depths that may be expected at springs and neaps under average conditions, but on occasions the range may be increased by 20 per cent or more.

All vertical survey measurements need a reference, just as latitudes are referred to the equator and longitudes to the Greenwich meridian. The relation between permanent benchmarks ashore and a careful determination of mean sea level gives important information on changes in the relative levels of land and sea.

Large scale Admiralty charts therefore usually show the relation between chart datum and the local land levelling datum. The original British network of levelling was undertaken by the Ordnance Survey in 1840–60, but was based on very limited observations of mean sea level at Liverpool, and was found to be unreliable.

A much more thorough levelling, based on six years' records of mean sea level at Newlyn, was carried out from 1915–21. Hence the relation generally shown between chart datum and Ordnance Datum (Newlyn) on large scale

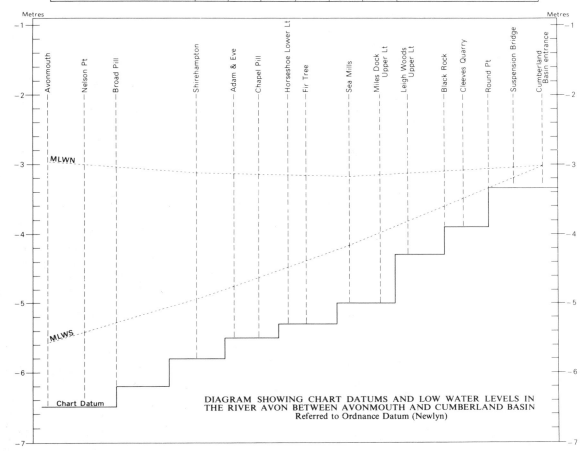

Tidal levels referred to Datum of Soundings

Place	Lat N	Long W	Heights in metres above datum				Datum and remarks
			MHWS	MHWN	MLWN	MLWS	
Portishead	51°30'	2°45	13·1	9·9	–	–	6·50m below Ordnance Datum (Newlyn)
Avonmouth	51 30	2 43	13·2	10·0	3·5	0·9	6·50m below Ordnance Datum (Newlyn)
R Avon – Shirehampton	51 29	2 41	12·5	9·3	2·7	0·9	5·80m below Ordnance Datum (Newlyn)
Sea Mills	51 29	2 39	11·8	8·5	1·8	0·8	5·00m below Ordnance Datum (Newlyn)
Bristol (Cumberland Basin)	51 27	2 37	10·3	7·0	–	–	3·35m below Ordnance Datum (Newlyn)

DIAGRAM SHOWING CHART DATUMS AND LOW WATER LEVELS IN
THE RIVER AVON BETWEEN AVONMOUTH AND CUMBERLAND BASIN
Referred to Ordnance Datum (Newlyn)

Fig. 9(18). Tidal information panel from Admiralty chart 1859 for the Port of Bristol, showing relation between chart datum (the solid, stepped line) to Ordnance Datum (Newlyn) on the left and right. Crown Copyright. Reproduced from portion of Admiralty Chart 1859, with the permission of the Controller of Her Majesty's Stationery Office.

Admiralty charts of United Kingdom waters. In most instances the chart datum (LAT) is shown as so many metres below Ordnance Datum (Newlyn), but occasionally above. The principle is well illustrated in the example shown in Fig. 9(18), published with acknowledgement to the Hydrographer of the Navy and Her Majesty's Stationery Office.

9.8.7 Establishment of a port

For many centuries seamen have undestood that there is a connection between the Moon and the tide. In the Middle Ages mariners predicted the tide from the bearing of the Moon, and in principle this method continued until quite recent times.

Although now only of historical interest, a port's establishment refers to the interval between meridian passage of the Moon and the next high

water at the port, and the associated terms (described briefly below) may be found in old pilot books or on charts. Since this interval is nearly constant for any port, it allowed the approximate time of high water to be determined from the age of the Moon.

High Water Lunitidal Interval (HWLI) was normally considered to be the time between the local transit of the Moon and local high water. The mean value of this figure over a lunation of 29 days was defined as the Mean High Water Interval (MHWI), or the corrected establishment.

High Water Full and Change (HWF&C), otherwise referred to as the establishment or the vulgar establishment of the port, was the high water lunitidal interval on the days of full and new moon. Though often used, this quantity was not so convenient as MHWI, but it could be obtained from fewer observations.

9.9 Tidal streams

9.9.1 Tidal streams – general

Tidal streams are the horizontal movement of water caused by the vertical rise and fall of the tide. With semi-diurnal tides, as occur around the British Isles, the tidal streams reverse their direction every six hours or so, and can be predicted by reference to a suitable Standard Port. Tidal streams are quite distinct from ocean currents, which run for long periods in the same direction and are described in 9.10.15.

Tidal streams are important to yachtsmen in many parts of North-West Europe, because they often run at over two knots, and much more strongly in a few areas and at spring tides. In some places they can attain rates of six to eight knots.

Along open coasts the turn of the tidal stream does not necessarily occur at high or low water, but more often near half-tide. The stream usually turns earlier inshore than offshore, sometimes resulting in significant eddies. In open waters round the British Isles, non-tidal currents are not included in tidal stream predictions. However, in rivers and estuaries there is often a permanent current caused by the flow of river water; such currents are included in tidal stream predictions.

Tidal streams (and currents) are described by the direction towards which they flow, i.e. a tidal stream setting 180° is flowing from north to south.

9.9.2 Tidal stream atlases

For Nort-West Europe the rate (strength) and set (direction) of tidal streams is shown in 15 booklets of Admiralty *Tidal Stream Atlases*. Each atlas has a set of 13 charts covering the same area, and each chart shows the rate and set of the tidal streams for each hour before and after high water at a Standard Port (usually Dover). It should be remembered that tidal atlases cannot show details of inshore eddies, and that the tide often sets towards the coast in bays.

The set of the stream is shown by arrows which are graded in weight to indicate the rate. Thus → indicates a weak stream, and ⟶ indicates a strong stream. The figures against the arrows give the mean neap and mean spring rates in tenths of a knot, Thus 19,34 indicates a mean neap rate of 1.9 knots, and a mean spring rate of 3.4 knots. The comma indicates the approximate position at which the observations were taken.

For predictions referred to HW Dover it is possible to compute the rate at times between neaps and springs by using the table shown in Fig. 9(19). This table assumes that rates vary directly with the range of tide at Dover. First extract the mean spring and neap rates from the tidal atlas for the position and time required. Then obtain the range of the tide at Dover that day from the tide tables. Join the dots representing the mean neap and spring rates with a ruler, and find the point where the ruler intersects the horizontal line representing the range at Dover that day. From that point follow the vertical line to the top or bottom scale and read off the rate.

Example

It is required to predict the rate of the tidal stream off the northerly point of the Isle of Skye at 0420 on a day when the tidal predictions for Dover are:

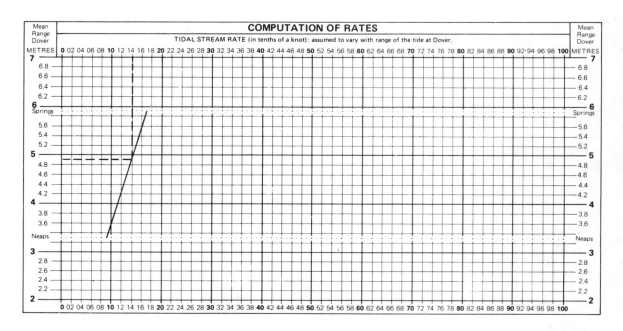

Fig. 9(19) Table for computing tidal stream rates at times between neaps and springs, for tidal stream predictions referred to HW Dover.

0328	1.4
0819	6.3
1602	1.1
2054	6.4

The range of tide is therefore 6.3 − 1.4 = 4.9m. The appropriate chart in the *Tidal Stream Atlas* NP 218, or in Chapter 10 Area 8 of *The Macmillan & Silk Cut Nautical Almanac*, is that for '4 hours before HW Dover' and this gives a mean neap and a mean spring rate of 09 and 17 respectively (0.9 and 1.7 knots). Referring to the table in Fig. 9(19), Computation of Rates, on the horizontal line marked Neaps, mark the dot above 09 on the horizontal scale; similarly on the line marked Springs, mark the dot below the figure 17 on the horizontal sale. Join these two dots with a straight line. On the vertical scale 'Mean Range Dover', find the range 4.9. From this point follow across horizontally until the pencil line just drawn is cut; from this intersection follow the vertical line to the scale of Tidal Stream Rates, either top or bottom, and read off the predicted rate − in this example it is 14, or 1.4 knots.

A perspex sheet or a sheet of tracing paper can be used on top of the table so as to preserve it for future use.

	Hours	Dir	Rate Sp	(kn) Np	Dir
		◈A	51°41'.8N 5°05'.5W		◈B
Before HW	6		slack		
	5	013	0.3	0.1	
	4	023	0.8	0.4	
	3	027	1.1	0.5	
	2	023	1.0	0.5	
	1	017	0.7	0.	
HW		354	0.3		
After HW	1	214	0.5		
	2	207	0.9		
	3	207			

Fig. 9(20) Tidal stream information on Admiralty chart.

9.9.3 Tidal stream diamonds on Admiralty charts

On some Admiralty charts there are diamonds to indicate the rate and set of tidal streams at the positions concerned. On the chart a diamond is shown with a letter inside it, thus: ◈B. In a box insert, under a similar diamond, there is shown the latitude and longitude of the position where the observations were made and a table which gives the set, spring rate and neap rate for each hour before and after HW at the Standard Port nominated. Where appropriate the normal river current is included.

The example shown in Fig. 9(20) is for position ◈A on chart 3247, where tidal streams are referred to HW at Milford Haven.

9.9.4 Tidal stream predictions in tide tables

In some parts of the world, tidal streams are not related to the predicted times of high water at any Standard Port, or are completely unrelated to the tidal pattern. For such places daily predictions of maximum rates, slack water and set are given in *Admiralty Tide Tables*, Vols 2 and 3. The information also includes typical tidal stream curves (dominant semi-diurnal, mixture of semi-diurnal and diurnal, and dominant diurnal), and any currents not included in the predictions.

9.9.5 Tidal stream information in Sailing Directions

General descriptions of tidal streams for the areas concerned are given in Admiralty Sailing Directions. In these volumes time references are in four-figure groups, where the first two figures are hours and the last two are minutes. Such references are usually to the nearest five minutes. Those preceded by a minus (−) sign are intervals before HW; those preceded by a plus (+) sign are intervals after HW.

9.9.6 Tidal streams in rivers

In general the flood stream is slightly stronger than the ebb, but its duration is less. Tidal streams in rivers are influenced by local weather conditions as well as by the phases of the Moon. Strong and prolonged winds blowing up an estuary will increase both the rate and duration of the flood stream, and correspondingly reduce the ebb. This may increase the height of tide within the river, at least temporarily. When the wind decreases the ebb stream runs more strongly until the normal level is restored.

At or near springs, in a river which is obstructed for example by sandbanks at the entrance, the time of high water gets later going up river. The time of low water also gets later, but more rapidly. So the duration of the rise of tide becomes shorter, and the duration of the fall of tide becomes longer. At the entrance the flood stream starts at an interval after low water which increases with the degree of obstruction to the channel, and this interval between low water and the start of the flood increases with the distance up river. However, the ebb begins soon after local high water along the length of the river. Thus the duration of the flood is less than that of the ebb, and the difference increases with the distance up river.

The flood stream is normally stronger than the ebb, and it runs harder during the first half of the rise of tide.

At neaps the flood and ebb both start soon after local low water and high water respectively, and their durations and rates are roughly equal. Both at springs and neaps the stream can be affected by recent precipitation, whereby the duration and rate of the ebb are increased, and of the flood are reduced.

9.10 The sea

9.10.1 How waves are formed

Any sensible yachtsman prefers to sail in smooth water, but once at sea it is inevitable that waves will be encountered. A little knowledge of the subject helps to understand their behaviour and their possible dangers.

Waves are created by wind. Friction between the water and the air moving over it causes energy to be transferred from the wind to the surface of the sea. This energy manifests itself by forming waves, and is the reason that wind speed at sea level is less than at the top of a mast. When wind first starts to blow over a calm sea, small ripples are formed. These result in pressure fluctuations and turbulence above the surface of the water, both of which help to increase the size of the ripples into wavelets and eventually into proper waves. The windward side of each wave is more affected by the wind than the leeward side, and hence each wave collects extra energy from the wind, causing it to grow in size.

The wave making process does not continue indefinitely however. As the size of a wave increases so does its speed of movement, which reduces the speed of the wave relative to the wind, and energy is lost within the wave itself due to the motion of the water, particularly if the wave breaks. So there comes a time when a state of equilibrium is reached, and unless the wind speed changes or the wave reaches shallow water or some other obstruction the wave will continue at a steady state.

9.10.2 Wave forms and definitions

Although waves at sea comprise an infinite variety of sizes and types, it is necessary to consider a train (succession) of theoretical waves in order to study their form and behaviour. Initially it is also necessary to consider waves in deep water, not influenced by the bottom of the sea.

Fig. 9(21) shows in diagrammatic form a wave, and some of the key terms and dimensions which are used to describe it.

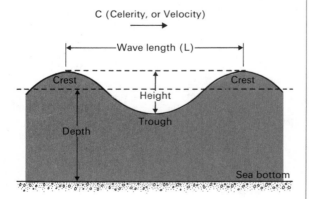

Fig. 9(21) Diagrammatic representation of a wave.

In the diagram, C is the celerity (velocity) in ft/sec of the wave, which is moving from left to right. The period of a wave (T) is the time in seconds between two successive crests passing a given point. If the wave length in feet is L,

$$C = \frac{L}{T}$$

In deep water it can be shown that:

$$C = \sqrt{\frac{gL}{2\pi}}$$

(where g = 32.2ft/sec/sec, and π = 3.14) and hence

$$C = 2.26 \times \sqrt{L}$$

From the equations above it follows that:

$$L = 5.12 \times T^2 \text{ and}$$
$$C = 5.12 \times T$$

Thus it is shown that whereas the celerity (velocity) of a wave varies directly with its period, its length varies as the square of the period.

If celerity is expressed in knots

$$C = 3.03 \times T$$

Fig. 9(22) shows the relationships between celerity (knots) and wavelength (feet) with wave period (seconds).

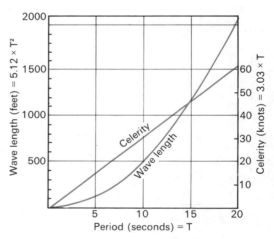

Fig. 9(22) Relationships between celerity and period, and wave length and period of waves.

When a wave passes, any particle of water on or near the surface moves in nearly a circular orbit. Although the wave moves forward, the surface of the sea does not – or only very slightly. If the movement of an object, such as a floating can, is observed it will be seen to move in an almost closed orbit, in a vertical plane: not quite a closed orbit because, as suggested above, there is a small movement of the surface water in the direction of wind and wave.

Particles below the surface also prescribe orbits, the end of each orbit being approximately the same as its starting point. The size of these orbits decreases very quickly with depth below the surface, and becomes negligible at a depth equal to $\frac{3}{4} \times$ the wave length.

9.10.3 The sizes of waves

In the open sea, the sizes of waves that are encountered depend on the strength of the wind, the length of time for which it has blown, and the fetch (distance upwind of the observer) over which it is blowing. Thanks to data collected and published by the Marine Information and Advisory Service, of the Institute of

Oceanographic Sciences, who have kindly agreed to the publication of Figs. 9(23), 9(24) and 9(25), it is possible to predict wave heights and periods with reasonable accuracy. Such predictions must, however, be for some kind of average value and, as explained below, larger waves can be expected to appear from time to time.

Sometimes strong winds blowing for only a short duration produce higher waves than lesser winds blowing for a long time; on other occasions moderate winds blowing for a considerable time produce larger waves. To use Fig. 9(23), enter the

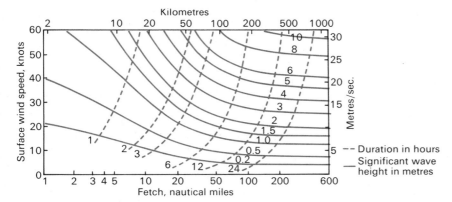

Fig. 9(23) Wave height prediction graph for coastal waters (depth typically 20–200m).

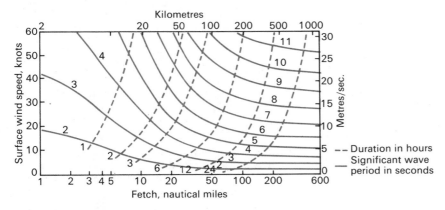

Fig. 9(24) Wave period prediction graph for coastal waters (depth typically 20–200m).

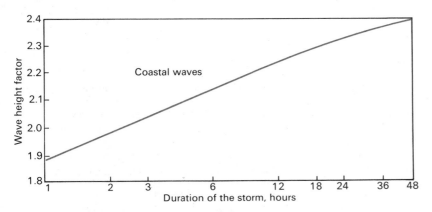

Fig. 9(25) Curve relating wave height factor to duration of storm (coastal waves).

diagram on the left with the surface wind speed in knots. Follow a horizontal line until it meets either the dotted curve for the appropriate duration (in hours) or the vertical line corresponding to the fetch (in nautical miles) as shown on the bottom scale, whichever is reached first. The predicted height in metres is read from the solid curve intersected at that point. As an example, consider a 30 knot wind blowing for 12 hours over a fetch of 60 nautical miles. Entering the diagram on the left at 30 knots, and moving horizontally to the right, the 60 mile fetch line is reached before the duration of 12 hours, and the resulting height is 3m. Fig. 9(24) is used in a similar way to determine the period. Both these graphs give predictions for coastal waters, with depths typically 20–200m. Except in very strong winds the predicted wave heights are only slightly too small for deeper waters, but in deep water the wave periods will be about 10–20 per cent longer than suggested by Fig. 9(24).

The predicted height (H$_S$) obtained from Fig. 9(23) is the 'Significant Wave Height', defined as the average value of the heights of the one-third highest waves. If, for example, 60 waves are observed, H$_S$ is the average height of the 20 biggest. The 'Significant Wave Period' is the average value of the periods of those same (one-third highest) waves. Theory, together with actual measurements at sea, show that on average the highest single wave in any ten-minute period is likely to be about 1.6 times the significant wave height, as expressed in the formula:

$$H_{max(10 \ min)} = 1.6 \times H_S$$

Hence, if the significant wave height (H$_S$) is 3m, as determined in the example above, H$_{max(10 \ min)}$ will be 4.8m. Having calculated this figure, it is then possible to refer to Fig. 9(25). This is a graph of 'Wave Height Factor' for coastal waves plotted against the duration of gale conditions in hours. If, as in the example used above, the wind has blown for 12 hours, the factor from the curve is 2.23 and this figure is used to multiply H$_{max(10 \ min)}$ to give the most probable height of the highest wave in the storm, thus:

$$4.8 \times 2.23 = 10.7m.$$

9.10.4 Freak waves
Observation at sea makes one realise that waves vary considerably in height. This is because any individual wave in practice consists of a large number of wave components, each with its own height and period. In any wave system the faster components (with longer periods) continually overtake the slower components. When crests get into step with each other, exceptionally large waves occur. When crests of some components coincide with troughs of others, there is a brief spell of relative calm.

In a small yacht it is very difficult to judge the heights of waves with any accuracy, but wave recording stations are established at many points around the United Kingdom. It has been shown that about one wave in 23 is twice the average height, and one in 1175 is three times the average height. Only about one wave in 300,000 (the equivalent of about a month at sea) exceeds four times the average height, and such a wave is very seldom encountered by yachtsmen or recorded on any instrument. In the foregoing the average height corresponds to about 0.6 times the significant wave height, as defined previously.

9.10.5 Breaking waves
As the wind speed increases, some waves become too steep, and tend to break. In a theoretical train of waves this happens when the wave height is one-seventh of the wave length, although in reality (due to the fact that waves are not uniform in character) a figure of one-twelfth is quite typical. In the open sea, once the wind blows force 7 or more, breaking seas are likely to be encountered. When a wave breaks, its kinetic energy is partly absorbed by the following wave, causing it to grow.

9.10.6 Swell
Swell consists of waves that are generated by meteorological disturbances, and which persist after that disturbance has ceased. Swell can travel a long way from where it originated, and in deep water it will maintain a constant direction. With distance travelled its height decreases, but its length and speed stay the same. The following terms are used to describe the length and height of swell:

Length – Short		0–100 m
Average		100–200 m
Long		over 200 m
Height – Low		0–2 m
Moderate		2–4 m
Heavy		over 4 m

It is not uncommon for swell from one direction to converge with swell from another. In these circumstances, even in deep water, there will be occasions when two crests (or two troughs) are superimposed – resulting in abnormal waves. When these sorts of conditions already exist, and a strong wind starts to blow from some other direction, a very confused and dangerous sea is likely to result.

9.10.7 Wind against tide
When a wave system encounters an adverse tidal stream (or current) the wave length becomes shorter. Hence the waves become steeper, and more likely to break. The situation is aggravated because the waves also tend to become higher. These conditions can produce a very dangerous sea, particularly where there is a strong tidal stream running over a shallow and uneven bottom.

Conversely, when the wind is blowing with the tidal stream (or current), the length of the waves increases and their height reduces.

9.10.8 Waves in shallow water

When waves move into shallow water they start to feel the effect of the sea bottom once the depth equals three-quarters of the wave length. Due to friction against the bottom, the orbiting movement of the water beneath the wave is upset and the celerity of the wave is reduced.

Because C = L/T (see 9.10.2 above) the wave length is reduced, and the waves become steeper — to the point where they break, a process which is also assisted by the diminishing depth of water.

When a wave breaks upon a beach its total energy content is destroyed, as anybody who has experienced heavy surf can testify. The force generated by breaking waves can be very considerable, and has been known to shift structures weighing hundreds of tons. As a wave starts to break some of the surface water moves forward with the wave form itself. In the open sea this energy, from a breaking wave, is transferred to other overtaking waves, but when approaching a beach the whole accumulated force is spent upon the shore. This moving mass of water is called a 'wave of translation'.

A special situation arises when waves of translation are approaching an estuary. As they meet the outflowing river current the breaking wave can continue for a great distance upstream as a special form of bore — see 9.10.14.

9.10.9 Bars

When, due to the local configuration of the shelving bottom, waves tend to break repeatedly at a certain distance from the shore, a bar may be formed. Smaller waves may pass over the bar without breaking, but they are affected by the shallow water, which shortens their wave lengths. Larger waves break on the bar, throwing large quantities of water over it so that there is a tendency for the sea level inshore of the bar to rise. This water has to return seawards, often through one or more channels scoured through a narrow part of the bar — an extremely dangerous area for boats and swimmers.

Many popular yachting harbours are fronted by a bar. In moderate weather most such bars do not present any great hazard, but it is normally advisable to cross them before (and not after) local high water. Some bars are potentially very dangerous however, and a stretch of harmless-looking water can soon be transformed into a death trap once the ebb starts to run, particularly if there is any strength of wind blowing onshore.

9.10.10 Overfalls and tide races

Some of the worst sea conditions that can be experienced occur quite close to land — off headlands where the tidal stream runs strongly. Any promontory (or a narrow channel, say between two islands) constricts the natural flow of the tidal stream, and hence speeds it up. If at the same time the sea bottom is irregular in depth,

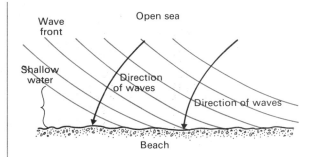

Fig. 9(26) Refraction of waves approaching a beach.

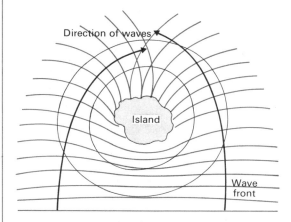

Fig. 9(27) Refraction of waves round an island.

considerable turbulence can be created in the area concerned. These factors, combined with wind blowing against the tidal stream, can create tide races where very dangerous overfalls are formed — conditions naturally being worst at spring tides and in gale force winds.

The more significant tide races can be unpleasant for a small yacht even in good conditions and should be avoided at all times. Others are passable in safety in good weather at the right state of the tide — usually at slack water. Any tide race, or area where there are heavy overfalls, should be given a wide berth in bad weather, or when wind of any strength is against the tide.

9.10.11 Refraction of waves

When waves pass from one depth of water to another — as happens when they meet a coastline at an angle, or when they pass the end of a headland, or down either side of an island — they are refracted (or bent) in much the same way as a ray of light is bent when passing from one medium to another.

The most common example of this is where a train of waves approaches a beach at an angle, as illustrated in Fig. 9(26). As soon as the inshore end of a wave gets into shallow water, it slows down so that the whole wave train eventually alters course somewhat, and the waves approach the shore roughly parallel to it.

Refraction can be very pronounced round the sides of an island. Where the two refracted wave trains meet on the leeward side of the island there can be an uncomfortable stretch of confused water, just where a peaceful lee might have been anticipated, see Fig. 9(27).

The diffraction of waves occurs as waves spread out after passing an obstruction such as a pronounced headland or a breakwater, tending in general to reduce wave height.

9.10.12 Reflected waves

Where waves which are not in shallow water meet a vertical object such as a cliff or harbour wall, they are reflected back in a seawards direction, much as light is reflected by a mirror. This can set up an area of standing waves, wherein both the peaks and the troughs are very pronounced. An unpleasant and confused sea can result — particularly if it should happen that two separate wave trains are being reflected at the same time. Care is needed in the approaches to harbours, where these conditions are relatively common.

9.10.13 Tsunamis

This Japanese name is given to waves which result from submarine earthquakes, volcanic eruptions or similar seismic disturbances. They occur (mostly in the Pacific) on a scale far surpassing any waves generated by the wind, and can be over 100 miles in length, with a height of only a few feet, and travelling at speeds of 500 knots.

In the open sea they present no danger, but once they enter shallow water the series of waves become shorter and very much higher, and their effect can be disastrous. The first crest is often preceded by a trough, so any abnormal lowering of sea level could give warning of a tsunami arriving within a few minutes. If possible, get out to sea fast. Due to their great wave length the waves arrive at intervals of several minutes, and often the third to eighth waves are the largest of the series.

9.10.14 Bores or eagres

A bore, or eagre, is a form of wave induced by resonant tidal oscillations, which rolls up certain estuaries and rivers. In simple terms they are caused either by the meeting of two tides or, more commonly, by the general constriction of the advancing tide into a narrowing and shelving channel. The effect is increased by spring tides, previous heavy rainfall, following winds and low barometric pressure.

The most impressive bores occur on the Rivers Hooghli, Amazon, Petticodiac (Bay of Fundy), and Chien Tang Kiang in China. In Europe the most noteworthy bore used to be the *mascaret* on the lower Seine, but this is now much reduced due to improvements in the channel and is only significant at springs between Villequiers and Rouen. In Britain the Severn bore starts above Sharpness, but does not fully develop until it reaches Longney, 14km (9 miles) from Gloucester,

where it rushes upstream at a height of some 1–1.5m (3–5ft) and is dangerous to boats where it breaks along the banks. The eagre on the River Trent is only slightly less impressive.

9.10.15 Ocean currents

Currents are movements of water that are not caused by the tide. In the navigational context we are concerned with horizontal movement, although out at sea sub-surface currents may have vertical components. Currents are caused by either seasonal or more permanent wind systems blowing over the sea, or by changes in the density of sea water brought about by differences in temperature (rather like air temperature affects the wind). The set of a current is described by the direction in which it flows, so a westerly current flows *to* the west but a westerly wind blows *from* the west.

The established atmospheric circulations over the oceans, such as the north-east and south-east trade winds which blow either side of the equator, are the principal causes of currents — the north equatorial currents which flow in the Atlantic, Pacific and Indian Oceans and which in turn result in the flow of compensating counter-currents.

A simplified diagram of the principal currents of the world is shown in Fig. 9(28). This indicates how, in the Atlantic, the north equatorial current is augmented by a split in the south equatorial current off the coast of Brazil, and flows into the Caribbean and the Gulf of Mexico before swinging north up the east coast of North America to form the Gulf Stream. Off Newfoundland the Gulf Stream is deflected by the cold Labrador current, and swings towards Europe. In the North Atlantic part of it divides to form the Canaries current and then to rejoin the north equatorial drift. The rest flows past the British Isles towards Norway.

In southern latitudes there are no land masses to disrupt the west wind drift caused by the Roaring Forties, resulting in a general easterly current running round the bottom of the world.

Currents are important considerations for major passage making, and more detailed information is available in *Ocean Passages for the World* and in *Meteorology for Mariners*. Notes for particular areas are contained in Admiralty Sailing Directions.

9.10.16 Coriolis effect

Except at the equator, any body moving on the earth's surface is affected by the earth's rotation, and this applies to the water in both ocean currents and tidal streams. This effect, called the Coriolis force, deflects moving water to the right in the northern hemisphere and to the left in the southern hemisphere. The effect is greater in higher latitudes, and in practice typically results in a deflection of 20°. It is the reason that north-flowing currents such as the Gulf Stream and the Kuro Siwo current off Japan, or the south-flowing ones like the Brazil and Agulhas currents, drift away from their respective coasts.

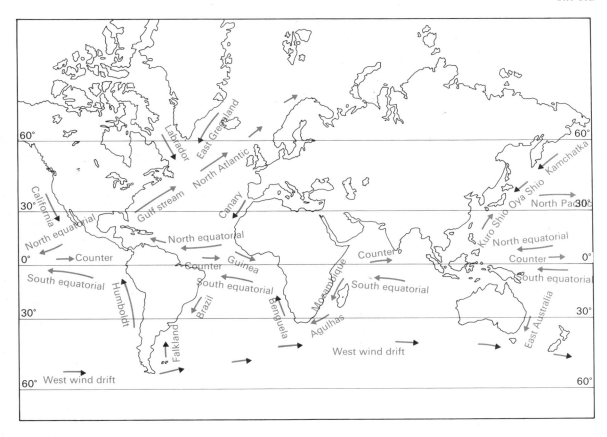

Fig. 9(28) Principal ocean currents of the world (black arrowheads indicate cold currents).

The Coriolis force also influences the bigger range of tide on the French side of the English Channel. Coming up Channel the flood is diverted to the right – towards the French coast. Conversely, on the ebb it is diverted towards the English coast.

9.10.17 Density of sea water

The density of sea water depends on temperature, pressure and salinity. As temperature rises, the density decreases; as pressure rises (with depth below the surface), the density increases; as salinity rises, the density increases.

For normal calculations the density of fresh water at surface level is taken as $1000 kg/m^3$. Sea water varies from about $1021 kg/m^3$ in equatorial regions to about $1027 kg/m^3$ at the poles (at surface level). In general the density of sea water is less in coastal regions than in the open sea. In the depths of the ocean it can reach $1070 kg/m^3$.

For convenience, density is often expressed in the form *sigma-t*, where:

$$sigma\text{-}t = (\text{Density in } kg/m^3 - 1000)$$

Hence a density of $1025.6 kg/m^3$ has a value of 25.6 in *sigma-t* terms.

9.10.18 Salinity of sea water

For our purposes, the salinity of water may be defined as the amount of dissolved solids present, expressed in parts per thousand. In fresh water the figure is zero, and in the open sea it is typically 35 parts per thousand and generally within the 33–37.5 range. The salinity is less in higher latitudes, in regions of high rainfall, or where there is dilution by rivers or melting ice. Where there is considerable evaporation the figure may reach more than 40 parts per thousand.

The North Atlantic has a higher salinity than the South Atlantic, and the Atlantic as a whole is more saline than the Pacific Ocean.

In estuaries, where rivers and streams flow into the sea, changes in salinity have a great influence on plant and animal life. Salinity fluctuates with the tides, and with the prevailing weather conditions. The well-defined zones in which different species live and breed depend largely on the tolerance of the species concerned to varying degrees of salinity. Nature finds ways to meet these natural changes, but not to resist man's pollution of rivers and estuaries with sewage, pesticides, industrial chemicals, oil and other destructive matter.

9.10.19 The colour of the sea

In the open ocean the natural colour of the sea is a very intense blue, but this is modified in higher latitudes and in coastal regions to a green or blue/green colour due to the presence of plankton (very small animal and vegetable life, floating in the sea).

In a few areas, such as the Red Sea, the density of the plankton may produce a brown or red/brown colour.

Temporary discolorations may be caused by a number of factors: plankton dying (due, for example, to changes in temperature); sand or dust particles carried offshore by the wind; or sand or mud produced by submarine earthquakes.

The shadows of clouds can often cause what appears to be a change in colour of the sea, and may be mistaken for shoal water.

Around coral reefs the colour of the sea is a good indication of the depth of water if the sun is high. Depths over 18m (60ft) show as a deep blue-black colour, which becomes a deep blue over sand or more dark green over rock. In 9m (30ft) rock shows as a mottled brown, and sand as light green. In shallower water, sand shows up as very pale green, and rock as light yellow-brown and probably distinguishable by eye.

9.11 Bibliography

Admiralty Manual of Tides (NP 120).

Admiralty Method of Tidal Prediction (NP 159).

Admiralty Tide Tables, Vols. I, II and III (NP 201, 2, 3).

Admiralty Method of Tidal Prediction, Personal computer version (NP 159A).

Tidal Harmonic Constants – Europe (NP 160).

Tidecalc – Tidal Prediction Program Disk (NP 158).

Tidecalc Area Disks – UK, Ireland, Channel Islands (NP 158A1); *Europe and Mediterranean* (NP 158A2).

Dynamic Oceanography by J. Proudman.

Seastate and Tides by Ken Duxbury (Stanford Maritime).

The Tide by H. A. Marmer (Appleton & Co).

The Tides and Kindred Phenomena by G. H. Darwin (Murray).

Waves and Beaches by W. Bascom (Doubleday & Co.).

Chapter 10

Hulls

Contents

10.1 Design considerations

In any discussion on hull types and forms it is necessary to understand the meaning of terms like displacement, centre of buoyancy, stability, balance etc. Like many technical terms the jargon obscures what is often simple and straightforward.

10.1.1 Displacement

This is simply the weight of the vessel in tons, tonnes, pounds or kilograms, complete with everything on board. That includes ballast, stores, engine, water, fuel, personal gear etc, so that a boat's displacement varies from day to day. However, if a displacement is quoted it can be assumed to mean the weight of the craft ready for sea (excluding items of personal gear) with half-full tanks.

If a boat were lowered into a tank brim full of water, some of it would spill over the edge as the craft settled down to its floating level. If the weight of that displaced water were measured it would be found to be the same as the weight of the boat. The denser the liquid in which a vessel is floating the smaller will be the amount (volume) required to equal the weight of the boat. Thus, since salt water is slightly denser (or heavier) than fresh water less volume will be required to support the craft which will consequently float slightly higher in the water.

10.1.2 Centres of buoyancy and gravity

If the water in that tank had been frozen solid after the boat had been lowered in, and she was then taken out again, a hollow would remain representing the shape of the underwater hull of the craft. That hollow must have a centre of area, both longitudinally and vertically. After all, if a cast of the shape were taken in concrete, for example, it would have a balancing point which would be its centre of area. The longitudinal position of that centre of area is called the longitudinal centre of buoyancy (LCB) and its vertical position, the vertical centre of buoyancy (VCB). Since the concrete balanced about that point, so must the boat, and her fore and aft centre of weight, the longitudinal centre of gravity (LCG), must fall in the same line as the LCB.

10.1.3 The lines plan

Of course a designer cannot rely on floating a model of his proposed creation in a tank and then finding the weight of water displaced. Nor can he fiddle with lumps of concrete trying to find a balance point (which would be very difficult anyway) so he draws the boat in three-dimensional

form and does the necessary calculations from that plan. This drawing is called the lines plan and Fig. 10(1) shows the basic lines of a simple 3m (10ft) dinghy. Three views are drawn: the profile (a view looking from one side of the boat which has been sliced down the middle); a plan view (looking down from above on to the deck); and a sectional view with the cross-section shape of the boat shown at various equally-spaced points (known as stations) along its length. Convention has it that the bow points to the right and one side only is drawn. The sections forward of midships and that of midships are shown on the right-hand side of the centreline, and the aft sections on the left-hand side.

Buttocks

It is assumed that the boat is again sliced longitudinally but at some specified distance out from the centreline. This slice will produce a definite shape on the profile view but will only be seen as straight lines on the other two views. One buttock is shown on the dinghy plan.

Waterlines

Sometimes called level lines, waterlines are the shapes produced if the boat were sliced longitudinally on a plane parallel to the line at which she floats. Waterlines will thus have a definite shape on the plan view but will show up only as straight lines on the profile and sectional views. Two waterlines, one above and one on the LWL (which is the load waterline and is the actual level at which the vessel is intended to float) are shown.

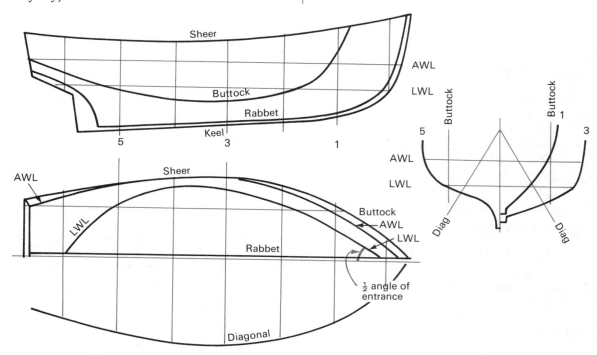

Fig. 10(1) An outline lines plan of a 3m (10ft) dinghy. This is a wooden boat and so the rabbet line is shown. That is where the planking joins the backbone of the vessel and is, presumably, a corruption of the word rebate.

Diagonals

Further slices may be taken running diagonally out from the fore and aft centreline, and one is shown. Their shape will normally be plotted on the plan view and their angle defined on the sectional view.

Fairing up

The general shape of the boat and of the buttocks, waterlines and so forth are drawn to suit the designer's beliefs as to what is required to get the best performance from the boat in whatever role she is cast. However, each of the different lines must be fair and smooth and agree with other lines. A buttock, for instance, must have a fair curve in profile but at the same time it has a definite height above or below the load waterline at each station along its length. The sections must correspond exactly. Waterlines must have a fair curve in plan view but they also have a definite width out from the centreline at each station. So a line drawn through the buttock heights and waterline widths must produce a fair and desirable curve at each section. The same principle applies to diagonals. Ensuring that all this is so is the basic task of the fairing processes that a designer has to go through.

Results

From the lines plan the area of the hull below LWL can be calculated in cubic feet or cubic metres and also the position of the LCB and VCB. The designer will have judged from past experience the best position of the LCB, and he will have totted up the various weights that comprise a boat to discover the probable actual displacement. This must agree with, or be near enough to, the displacement calculated from the lines plan. If he is wrong the boat will float higher or lower in the water than planned. Though at this stage he has probably not worked out exactly where the longitudinal centre of gravity of all the weights lies, he will have a good approximate idea and now knows how the final and shiftable weights will have to be disposed to put the LCG over the LCB. When that figure of volume in cubic feet below the LWL is known it can be divided by 35 to give tons displacement (there being 35cu ft of sea water to the ton). Using the metric system, one cubic metre of underwater volume represents 1000kg of displacement by weight.

10.1.4 Offsets

A lines plan itself is not of much use to a builder, who will not want to have to scale off dimensions from a small-scale plan. So the designer does the job for him, giving dimensions out from the centreline for the deck line and all waterlines; heights from a base line outside the vessel or above and below LWL for all the buttocks plus the keel and deck lines; and distance down the diagonals from centreline. The bow and stern profiles will also be dimensioned.

All these measurements are set down on what is known as an offset table. The builder then makes patterns from these or draws out the whole boat again, full size, on the mould loft floor. He can then make templates for anything he wants at any position he wants (not just at the stations drawn by the designer) off the floor. The designer will have been working to quite a small scale ranging, perhaps, from 1/5th to 1/8th full size on a dinghy to 1/24th or 1/25th full size on a biggish boat, so that some inaccuracies are bound to creep into his offsets.

10.1.5 Tonnage measurement

As stated in 10.1.1, displacement is the actual weight of the boat in whatever state of readiness for sea has been decided upon. There are, however, other forms of tonnage, the principal ones being gross tonnage and register tonnage. Neither is a weight at all but is the estimated internal volume of the boat less exemptions and deductions. Either the internal volume in cubic feet is divided by 100 when using imperial units or the volume in cubic metres is divided by 2.83 to give the same result in notional tons. The word tonnage is confusing but probably derives from the fact that cargo vessels were once assessed on how many tuns, or casks, of wine they could carry. Anyway, from the total internal volume certain exempted spaces such as double bottom tanks and the wheelhouse are subtracted to give gross tonnage. From the gross figure are deducted spaces such as crews' quarters, chart room and so forth to give register tonnage. Passenger ship tonnages are normally quoted in gross tons.

Cargo ships, on the other hand, usually deal in what is called deadweight. This is the weight in tons, or tonnes, that a ship can carry when loaded to her maximum permitted draught and includes provisions, fuel and water as well as cargo. What a ship weighs when completely empty is called Lightship, and therefore Lightship + Deadweight = Load Displacement. When warship tonnages are quoted these are usually actual displacement tons.

The principal types of tonnage, as applied to yachts are as follows. Despite the use of the word 'ton', only two of them (displacement and deadweight) refer in any way to the weight of the boat, and deadweight tonnage is seldom if ever used in respect of yachts.

Displacement

This is the actual weight of the yacht, or more correctly the weight of the water displaced by her which is of course the same thing. Displacement varies depending on how the boat is loaded – whether she is fully stored and full of fuel and water for example.

An approximate formula for displacement (in tons) is:

$$\frac{L \times B \times D \times C_b}{35}$$

where L = waterline length in feet, B = waterline beam in feet and D = draught amidships in feet, and C_b is the Block Coefficient.

The Block Coefficient is the ratio of the immersed volume of the hull to the volume of the cube formed by the waterline length, the maximum beam and the draught (excluding the keel). It is typically about 0.45 for a boat of moderate displacement, but less for modern light displacement types.

In metric units displacement in tonnes is:

$$L \times B \times D \times C_b \times 1.025$$

where the measurements are expressed in metres.

Displacement can be calculated much more accurately from the lines of the boat, by taking the areas of the different sections and applying Simpson's First Rule. This is a method of obtaining the approximate area under a curve, where there are an odd number of ordinates, equally spaced, of known quantities. The area equals the sum of the first and last ordinates, plus twice the sum of the remaining odd ordinates, plus four times the sum of the even ordinates, the whole being multiplied by one-third the distance between the ordinates.

Thames Measurement (TM)

This is an approximation of the internal capacity of the yacht. The formula (unique to this country) was evolved by the Royal Thames Yacht Club in 1854, and amended in 1962.

$$\text{Tonnage (TM)} = \frac{(L - B)^2 \times B^2}{188}$$

where L = the length from the forward side of the stem at deck level to the aft side of the stern-post at deck level. (Where the stern-post does not extend to deck level, the measurement is taken to the prolongation of the aft side of the stern-post, or the centreline of the rudder stock at deck level. If there is no stern-post or fixed rudder stock, or if the rudder stock is wholly abaft the transom, the measurement shall be taken to the aft side of the transom at deck level.) B = maximum beam, excluding rubbing strakes, chain plates or other protrusions.

The measurements are taken in feet and decimals of a foot, and the resulting tonnage is expressed to the nearest ton. The rule does not apply to yachts with more than one hull.

Net and Gross Tonnages

These terms apply to the official registered tonnage of yachts which appear on the registry. Since 1 June 1975 new regulations have applied to the calculations of tonnage for British registered yachts under 13.7m (45ft) in length, so that only one tonnage is now computed and this is known as registered tonnage. This tonnage may be measured by surveyors of Lloyd's Register of Shipping (Lloyd's Register of Shipping, Yacht and Small Craft Services, 71 Fenchurch Street, London EC3M 4BS), or of the Yacht Brokers, Designers and Surveyors Association (Wheel House, Petersfield Road, Whitehill, Bordon, Hants GU35 9BU), or by official measurers of the Royal Yachting Association, RYA House, Romsey Road, Eastleigh, Hants SO50 9YA. Tonnage measurements of yachts over 13.7m (45ft) in length must be done by surveyors of the Department of Trade.

Lloyd's Register Tonnage (LT)

This is used for estimating hull survey fees for yachts classed at Lloyd's, according to the formula:

$$LT = \frac{LOA \times B \times D \times 0.45}{100}$$

where LOA = maximum length (feet), B = maximum beam (feet), excluding protrusions, and D = moulded depth (distance from top of floors to upper deck beams, amidships) in feet.

If the measurements are expressed in metres, the formula is:

$$LT = \frac{LOA \times B \times D \times 15.9}{100}$$

Deadweight tonnage

This is the number of tons of cargo, bunkers and stores that a ship will carry, or in other words it is the difference in displacement when the vessel is light and fully loaded.

One Ton Cup etc

Some offshore yacht racing is conducted under the handicap provisions of the International Offshore Rule, with systems of time allowance to permit yachts of different ratings and potential speeds to race together. In recent years however a number of 'level rating' classes have emerged, in which the competitors race boat for boat with no handicap. Since the first such major event was raced for an old trophy called the One Ton Cup, these level rating classes have all adopted similar names, as follows:

For boats with maximum rating of

One Ton	30.55ft	Half Ton	22.05ft
Three-Quarter		Quarter Ton	18.55ft
Ton	24.55ft	Mini Ton	16.55ft

It will therefore be seen that the description 'One Ton' in this context refers only to the rating measurement of the boat, and has nothing to do with her weight or displacement.

10.1.6 Centre of lateral resistance

From the lines plan, or more specifically from the underwater profile, the centre of lateral resistance (CLR) can be found. In essence this is the centre of area of the underwater profile and is assumed to be the spot around which the vessel pivots under the influence of wind, waves or sail power. If that below-water profile were traced out on a piece of tracing paper and then cut out to shape, folded longitudinally a few times to stiffen it and then balanced on a compass point, that balancing point would be the centre of area, centre of lateral resistance or CLR.

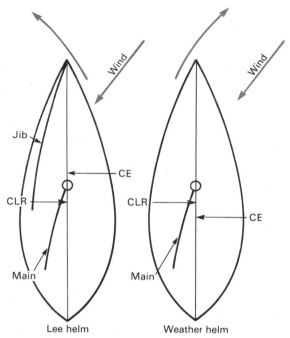

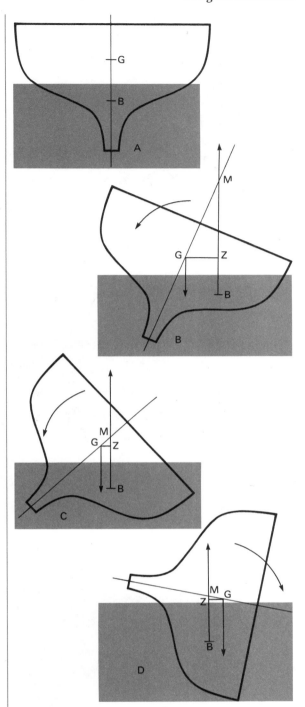

Fig. 10(2) The left-hand sketch shows a yacht with jib and mainsail set, but the centre of effort of the sail plan is so far forward that it causes lee helm. With the jib doused the situation changes and the boat has weather helm.

10.1.7 Centre of effort

The centre of effort (CE) is the combined, overall centre of area of all the sails and is taken to be the centre through which the wind pressure acts, though even a motor boat can have a centre of effort which would be the centre of profile area of hull and superstructure. On yachts the sails are assumed to be fore and aft as they would be shown on a profile drawing of the craft.

The distance between the centre of lateral resistance and the centre of effort is known as the 'lead' and is generally expressed as a percentage of the waterline length. Both these centres move with the boat under way and as Fig. 10(2) shows, for the boat to have 'weather helm' (that is, for the bows to have a bias towards turning into the wind) the centre of effort must be aft of the centre of lateral resistance. In fact when designing a sail plan the opposite is assumed to be the case for the CE is nearly always positioned well ahead of the CLR. The amount these two centres move is impossible to predict and the correct amount of 'lead' is judged by past results. A certain amount of weather helm is desirable because it causes the bows to swing into the wind once the helm is put down and so speeds tacking. The opposite would be the case with 'lee helm' where the bows want to swing away from the wind and have to be forced round when turning through the wind. Weather helm is also safer since if the tiller is abandoned the boat will come up into the wind and stop. A yacht with weather helm can also sail closer to the wind than one with lee helm.

Fig. 10(3) A section through the midship section of a yacht showing the shift in the centre of buoyancy (B) at different angles of heel and its effect on stability. In the bottom, right-hand sketch the position of M has changed from being above G to being below it, and the twisting forces through G and B are now acting to capsize the vessel.

10.1.8 Aspect ratio

Technically this is the length of the chord of any surface measured normally to the direction of motion divided by the chord in the line of motion.

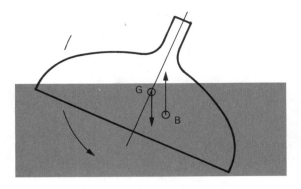

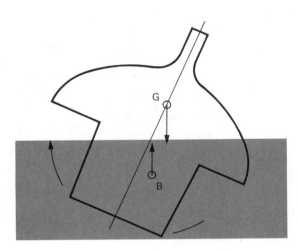

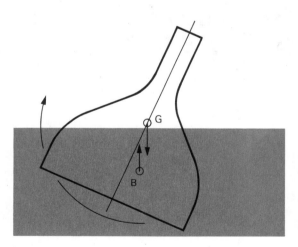

Fig. 10(4) The addition of a deckhouse to a hull will often convert it into a self-righter. Note how in the middle sketch the forces through B and G have changed sides. Old-fashioned boats which were deep and narrow (bottom sketch) were often natural self-righters.

In practice this means, for instance, that the aspect ratio of a rudder is its depth divided by its fore and aft length; of a sail, its vertical height (e.g. the luff) divided by its foot length; for a bilge keel, its depth into the water divided by its fore and aft length. Generally the higher the aspect ratio the

more efficient the object will be. Thus a mainsail with a luff five times as long as its foot will be more efficient than one with a ratio of only 2:1, whatever its other disadvantages.

10.1.9 Stability

As a boat heels her underwater shape changes since a new length of hull is immersed and an original length emerges. The centre of buoyancy moves across to be the centre of area of this new immersed volume. Fig. 10(3) shows this on one section through the hull. The centre of buoyancy will move forward or aft too, since the boat will trim by bow or stern to accord with the entirely new underwater shape, but that is a complication best ignored at the moment. Only its transverse shift need be considered in this section on stability. The buoyancy of the water keeping the boat afloat will act vertically upwards through that centre of buoyancy (B) while the weight of the boat acts vertically downwards through its centre of gravity (G) and however much the boat heels, in theory at any rate, the centre of gravity does not shift. That implies that nothing breaks loose and falls to leeward and there is no loose water in the bilge. Anyway, those two forces through G and B are acting in opposite directions and trying to twist the boat upright or to capsize her.

On a self-righter the forces through G and B are working to right the boat whatever her angle of heel. The craft will recover from a complete inversion and the three sketches in Fig. 10(4) show how this happens and what can be done to encourage it. The top drawing is through a modern shallow, beamy hull and illustrates it nearly upside-down. The forces through G and B are working to complete the capsize.

The next sketch shows the effect of adding a deckhouse. Provided this remains reasonably watertight during the capsize it will eventually cause the boat to float very high in the water when inverted. The forces through B and G are now acting to twist the vessel back upright, and in this they will be successful. Remember that B is the centre of volume of the immersed hull (including the upperworks) and that G is the position of the centre of gravity. The height of G (above the keel perhaps) will have been increased by adding the deckhouse, but as long as that structure was not excessively heavy the shift in G will have been more than compensated for by its added buoyancy. If a deckhouse did not fit in with the scheme of things, a large buoyancy bag inflated after capsize would have the same effect.

The bottom sketch shows the narrow, deep hull form of years gone by. The twisting forces through G and B are working to right the craft. As is mentioned in 10.1.13, increasing beam normally increases initial stability but reduces the range of stability. If a hull is narrow it is bound to be fairly deep in order to accommodate the needed displacement. Modern, beamy hulls are generally not natural self-righters. The essence of self-righting is to have a hull where the natural buoyancy of the immersed form is working to lever the hull back to an upright stance at all angles of heel.

10.1.10 Metacentric height

A vertical line (representing the forces of buoyancy) extended up through B, the centre of buoyancy, will cross the inclined centreline of the vessel at some point M, and that point is known as the metacentre. The distance between G (the centre of gravity) and M is called the metacentric height, or GM. As shown on Fig. 10(3) the distance from G to M will vary according to the angle of heel but as long as the twisting forces are acting to urge the boat back on to an even keel, she is stable. At some angle of heel on most craft, though, the forces change sides in relation to each other and the twisting moment they exert is trying to capsize the vessel, and she is then unstable.

10.1.11 Curves and range of stability

The distance from G to M may be plotted on a base of angle of heel and is known as a stability curve. A self-righting yacht would have positive stability up to 180° (that is, the twisting couple will always be trying to right her) and a representative curve showing such stability together with a curve for a more normal boat is shown on Fig. 10(5). The angle to which a yacht

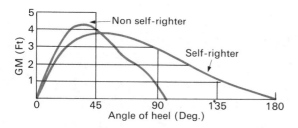

Fig. 10(5) A stability curve for self-righting and non self-righting craft. The latter would capsize at an angle of heel of greater than about 95 deg. The former would right herself from any angle of heel.

may heel before she becomes unstable is known as her range of stability.

10.1.12 Righting levers and moments

Though GM is a measure of stability, an even better one might be the distance between the lines through G and B, Fig. 10(3). This is GZ and is called the righting lever. The length GZ at different angles of heel may also be plotted on a base of heel angle. If the distance GZ were multiplied by the boat's displacement, the result would be called the righting moment and would be a measure of the force actually trying to twist the boat back upright (or to capsize her when she was past her range of positive stability).

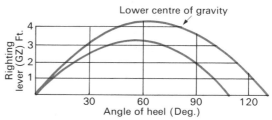

Fig. 10(6) The effect of lowering the centre of gravity (probably by adding weight to the keel or installing inside ballast on an unballasted boat) is nearly always to improve stability at all angles (the distance between the forces acting through G and B being greater) and to increase the range at which the craft is still stable.

10.1.13 Factors affecting stability
Height of centre of gravity

On any boat the lower the centre of gravity the better as far as stability is concerned, and Fig. 10(6) shows the stability curves for two vessels with different VCG heights. The marked effect on the righting levers can be seen. A low centre of gravity is normally achieved by installing ballast as low as possible and many yachts with a big outside ballast keel are self-righting in theory. The words 'in theory' are used advisedly since if, as the boat rolls, water can come aboard and flood the accommodation its effect will be to raise the position of the VCG once the boat is well heeled.

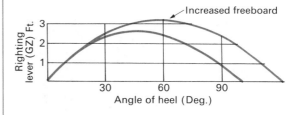

Fig. 10(7) Increasing freeboard – as long as it can be done without raising the height of the centre of gravity too much – generally increases stability a modest amount and, more importantly, lengthens the range of stability.

Freeboard

Increasing freeboard will normally give greater stability provided that the VCG does not rise too far in sympathy. As the boat heels, there are more topsides available than on a boat with lower freeboard to increase the buoyancy and strive to push her back on an even keel.
Fig. 10(7) shows the likely result of increasing freeboard on stability curves.

Beam

Increasing beam will also improve stability for much the same reason as increasing freeboard, but the usual effect is also to reduce the range of stability, see Fig. 10(8).

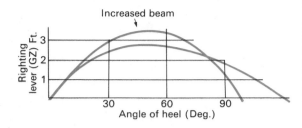

Fig. 10(8) Increasing beam normally gives better stability (the boat is stiffer) at normal angles of heel but reduces the range of stability.

Watertightness

It should be emphasised that the greatest aid to stability is watertightness. If hatches leak or are left open, if hatch boards collapse or are displaced, or if skylights or ports are broken during a knockdown to allow water to flood below, the most convincing self-righter in the world (on paper) may still capsize.

The unsinkable boat

There is increasing interest in yachts that will stay afloat even if holed or swamped. This is of course a requirement for many commercial craft, and is achieved by the use of watertight bulkheads.

Basically the theory is that if a boat is holed between two bulkheads, that volume no longer contributes to buoyancy and the vessel will sink until the new volume added by the length of undamaged hull entering the water equals the lost volume. The siting and spacing of the bulkheads determines at what new draught the yacht will float. There must be watertight doors in the bulkheads, and deck access into each compartment.

The alternative scheme is to install buoyancy in the form of foam, watertight spaces or inflatable air bags in sufficient quantity to keep the craft afloat even if swamped. Here the impermeable volume of the boat and her associated equipment is assessed and compared with its weight. Impermeable volume means the actual cubic volume of material as contained in the hull and equipment. Thus, the shell has a thickness and a superficial area. Multiply these two and a volume is obtained with the same applying to, say, a fuel tank or a refrigerator. Total all the volumes and compare with the overall weight of the vessel. If the weight, for example, was 5050lb, this is the equivalent of 5050/64 = 79cu ft of sea water. So 5050lb needs 79cu ft of water to support it. But suppose the impermeable volume was found to be 59cu ft, then some 20cu ft of added buoyancy would be needed to float the boat. More would be better to give some worthwhile freeboard.

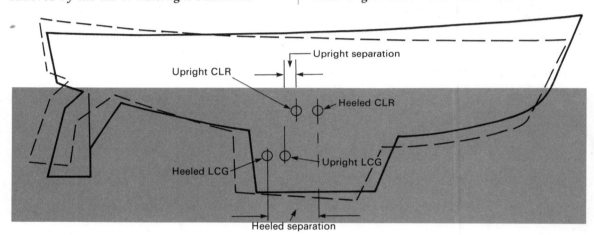

Fig. 10(9) The sections above the waterline aft are generally more full and buoyant than those forward. So as a yacht heels her stern tends to lift and the bow to drop, so that she is trimming bows down. This has the effect of moving the CLR forward and increasing the separation between the LCG and the CLR.

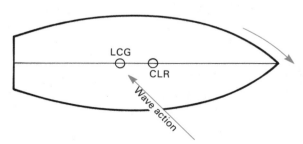

Fig. 10(10) External forces, such as waves, act through the LCG of a yacht but the vessel tends to pivot about her CLR.

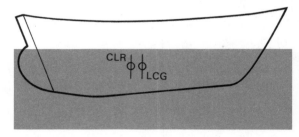

Fig. 10(11) With a full-length keel the CLR is often astern of the LCG when the boat is upright. Heeled, the CLR moves forward but its separation from the LCG should never be great.

10.1.14 Hull balance

Though in the section on transverse stability (10.1.10) it was said that no account was taken of the fore and aft shift of the centre of buoyancy and change of trim as a boat heeled, in fact this trim change has a considerable effect on hull balance and handling characteristics. Generally speaking as a modern yacht is heeled she trims bows down because above the LWL her aft sections are full and her bow sections fine. Thus a very buoyant length aft and less buoyant length forward is being pushed into the water, and the hull will adjust itself in the water accordingly. This change of trim has the effect of moving the centre of lateral resistance forward as in Fig. 10(9).

The CE (centre of effort) of the sail plan is nearly always ahead of LCG. It is also generally forward of the centre of area of the load waterline about which the vessel may be considered to pivot in a fore and aft direction. Thus, as the wind blows the sails tend to force the bows down, adding to the natural bow-down inclination of the heeled hull. Once the sheets are started the centre of effort of the sail plan will move further ahead and the trim will become greater, as will the separation between the centre of lateral resistance and centre of gravity. If for any reason a yaw, or turning moment, is set up (perhaps by a wave), the turning forces will act through the LCG while the boat pivots about its CLR, Fig. 10(10). Hence the craft will try and swing through a circle in the same direction as the induced yaw. This can only be counteracted by fierce rudder action and is the classic cause of broaching. Fig. 10(10) shows the forces causing the swing to be coming from off the bow and the more extreme racing yachts today can broach in these conditions, but the more common cause is a wave from the aft quarter overtaking the yacht and, acting through the LCG, causing the stern to swing round so that it ends up broadside to the seas.

Fig. 10(11) shows the profile of an old-fashioned sailing workboat with the keel line becoming progressively deeper all the way to the stern. The old-timer will probably have her CLR further aft than the modern craft and the tendency for it to move forward when heeled under sail will be far less dangerous, for its separation from the LCG will never be as great. The old boats, too, had better balanced ends than today's yachts in that neither bow nor stern were exaggerated in shape and the change in trim caused by heeling was less. All this partly explains why the long keel, classic underwater profile, tends to be easier on the helm and less liable to broach.

It is not only sailing craft that have unbalanced ends. The modern planing motor boat is a supreme example. The wide, deeply immersed transom, which is necessary for speed, is coupled with comparatively fine lines forward, and she can be a dreadful boat to handle in following seas when speed has had to be reduced. The overtaking sea lifts her great, buoyant transom and in doing so shoves her bows deep into the water where they act as a brake. The waves continue to travel forward and carry the stern along with them. The boat then pivots about the bow and swings round to lie broadside on to the seas – an unhappy situation.

10.1.15 Speed/length ratio

Speed on its own is not a valid comparison between two crafts, length must also be taken into consideration. Hence speed and length are linked by the speed/length ratio which is $V/\sqrt{L}$ where V is speed in knots and L is waterline length in feet. A yacht doing 6 knots on a waterline length of 25ft would thus have a speed/length ratio of $6/\sqrt{25} = 6/5 = 1.2$.

10.1.16 Resistance in general

As a boat moves through the water the passage of her hull creates waves (shown by the wash). If the energy contained in those waves could be measured it would be found to equal the amount of energy expended in making them. That is one type of resistance and is known, with unusual obviousness, as wave-making resistance. At the same time the friction of the water rushing past the bottom, rudder, shaft, propeller and so on has to be overcome. This is called frictional resistance. The two types of resistance to forward motion occur at the same time but the proportion of each to the total resistance varies with the speed/length ratio. Fig. 10(12) shows a typical example in graphical form, and note that the resistance is measured in lb per ton of displacement.

Most of the world's merchant fleets travel at speed/length ratios of not more than about 0.8

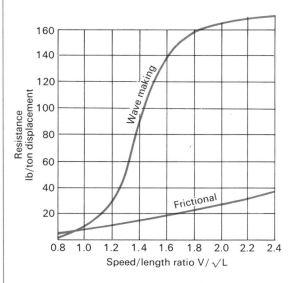

Fig. 10(12) At low speed/length ratios frictional resistance plays a greater part in overall resistance than wave-making but the situation changes as speeds climb.

where total resistance may be around 7lb to 8lb per ton. Incidentally, a $V/\sqrt{L}$ of 0.8 for a 300-footer is $V = \sqrt{300} \times 0.8 = 13.8$ knots. Warships tend to be faster, as do some passenger liners and ferries, but no commercial vessel is likely to be economical at a ratio of more than 1 which is 17.3 knots on our mythical 300-footer. At this speed resistance has risen to 20lb per ton, or thereabouts. Yachts commonly sail at ratios of up to 0.8 to 1.0 (4 to 5 knots on a craft 25ft on the waterline) but may reach a speed/length ratio of 1.2 or 1.3 on rare occasions when resistance will be 50lb to 75lb per ton — or some 10 times its earlier value, which maybe explains the rarity of these bursts of speed. Certain yachts can exceed even these limits without resorting to surfing or other exceptional conditions but at, say, a speed/length ratio of 1.4 (7 knots on a 25-footer) resistance will have increased perhaps 14 times over that at 4 knots.

Resistance can be translated into horsepower: in this case brake horsepower or the power of an engine needed to push the boat along.

$$BHP = \frac{R \times V \times 2}{550}$$

For the sake of an example assume a 25-footer is displacing 5 tons. At 4 knots total resistance (R) will be about 8lb per ton so with a displacement of 5 tons resistance will be $5 \times 8 = 40$lb. At 7 knots it will rise to 108lb per ton or $5 \times 108 = 540$lb total resistance for the 5-tonner. V is speed in feet per second and 4 knots = 6.8ft/sec

while 7 knots = 11.9 ft/sec.

So, for 4 knots,

$$BHP = \frac{40 \times 6.8 \times 2}{550} = 1.0$$

and for 7 knots

$$BHP = \frac{540 \times 11.9 \times 2}{550} = 23.3$$

Above those speed/length ratios come the majority of motor boats — even those of the notional slow speed variety — and way up in the realms of speed/length ratios of maybe 5 or 6 are the fast planing cruisers. As can be seen from Fig. 10(12) the resistance curve is flattening out from a speed/length ratio of about 1.7 and though it continues to rise inexorably with increased speed, the rate of increase will not be very high, partly because a planing boat (which commences true planing at a ratio of 2.5 to 3) lifts in the water so that her high speed waterline is significantly above its level at rest. Thus there is less hull in the water, and frictional resistance is reduced. Further, and as observation will show, as high speeds are reached the tremendous wash that has been dragged along at low speeds is considerably reduced, indicating that wave-making resistance is also reduced.

10.1.17 Frictional resistance

Everything that is in contact with the water leads to frictional resistance. This includes the bottom, keel, bilge keels, rudder, propeller shaft and the propeller itself. It also includes, on fast power boats, that part of the topsides that may be wetted by the sheets of water thrown up in high speed running. Hence the need for an abrupt change in shape between bottom and topsides on such craft. Water running up the bottom flies off into space at the corner, known as the chine, rather than attempting to climb up the sides. Spray rails along the bottom, which will be dealt with in greater detail under 10.3.4 are there mainly to reduce wetted surface.

The shape that gives least wetted surface (or area in contact with the water) for any given displacement is the arc of a circle. That means that for least frictional resistance a boat ought to have semi-circular bottom sections. That would be fairly hopeless in practice since it would produce a barrel-shaped craft that would roll like a barrel too, but some racing yachts have sections that approximate to a circular form underwater though towards the centreline they are generally flattened to give a shape with some resistance to rolling.

A long, inclined propeller shaft with a bracket towards its aft end, all exposed to the water, is quite a large contributor to wetted surface and frictional resistance. It also prduces unwanted turbulence. In many cases sail drives, or outdrives in the case of motor boats, produce less resistance. That is one reason for their efficiency. Another is that they allow the propeller to be set with the blades vertical rather than at an angle to the water flow. This is an advantage when it comes to effective propulsion.

10.1.18 Fouling

An important element in reducing friction is the smoothness of the bottom. Back in the late 1800s William Froude, who made the first proper experiments in model testing and many of whose findings are still relevant today, towed a series of planks in his test tank. The planks were coated with a variety of substances ranging from varnish and enamel to coarse sand. He found that the latter produced double the frictional resistance of enamel and since a barnacle-encrusted and weed-festooned bottom is likely to be very much rougher than coarse sand, the importance of a clean bottom is obvious. In a year without docking, frictional resistance due to fouling can be expected to increase by 100 per cent in temperate waters and 200 per cent in tropical seas. Around the coasts of the United Kingdom resistance may increase by 0.5 per cent per day between July and September, when bottom growth is generally at its worst.

Even on a fast-moving vessel the bottom can become a home for unwelcome visitors, because a boat drags a thin film of water (known as the laminar film) along with her however fast she is moving. This film of water has just the same percentage of spores in it as the rest of the ocean, and these will make a home on the bottom without difficulty since the water is not moving in relation to the boat.

10.1.19 Wave-making resistance

Two principal wave forms are generated by a boat in her passage through water. The first is a divergent wave system running at some 30° to 40° to the bow, and to a lesser extent, the stern. The second, and generally more important, is the transverse wave system which can be seen running along the vessel's sides. This form commences with a wave crest near the bow, caused by increased pressure at this point, followed by a trough and then another crest.

The energy content of a wave is proportional to its length and to the square of its depth. In turn, wave length is governed almost entirely by its speed; and its height or depth by displacement and general hull form (the heavier the boat the bigger the wave she will make).

The following table shows the speed of a boat that produces a wave of a certain length, and since the faster she is travelling the longer the wave she makes, the more the power needed to produce it.

Speed (knots)	Wave length (metres)	(feet)
3	1.5	5
4	2.75	9
5	4.3	14
6	6.1	20
7	8.2	27.2
8	10.85	35.6
9	13.7	45
10	16.95	55.6

Since wave length and speed are linked it is perfectly possible to judge the speed of a vessel by the distance between the wave crests, provided that the length of the boat is known and so can be used as a guide. If a boat 12.2m (40ft) was developing a transverse wave system that appeared to be about three-quarters as long as the boat between crests, Fig. 10(13), that would mean that the wave was some 9.15m (30ft) long and the craft was consequently travelling at a bit over 7 knots. All this can most easily be seen on a heavy displacement vessel because her wave system will be deeper (and more power sapping) than on some

lightweight flyer. It also shows up clearly on the weather side of a yacht heeled under sail.

The length of that transverse wave system governs the likely top speed of a conventional sailing boat. As speeds increase and the wave lengthens there comes a point where there is a crest at the bow and another at the stern. This occurs at a speed/length ratio of 1.34 (6.7 knots on a boat 25ft on the waterline; 7.3 knots on one 30ft and so on) and a further speed increase moves the aft crest past the stern. The boat is then beginning to settle with her bows on a crest and the stern in a trough – at 8 knots, for instance, the aft crest would be some 10ft beyond the stern of a 25-footer. In a sense she would now be sailing uphill and would need a wide, deeply immersed transom to give buoyancy plus plenty of power to be able to climb that hill. Not many sailing craft, other than dinghies where the crew balance the heeling effect of a large sail area and sit in a lightweight hull making a reasonably shallow wave formation, can manage to generate sufficient power for that struggle. The limiting speed dictated by speed/length ratio is sometimes known as displacement speed.

10.1.20 Towing speeds

Past sections have dwelt on hull balance and wave-making resistance. The two could now be combined for a brief aside as to why a yacht may tow so badly and even dangerously at speed. Let us assume that she is of normal sailing or slow motor boat shape (that is, high speeds were not envisaged in the design stage), is 7.6m (25ft) on the waterline and is being towed at 9 knots. The aft wave crest is now some 6m (20ft) behind her and the tow is pulling her up on to that forward wave crest with the consequence that the centre of lateral resistance moves forward. Fig. 10(14). The longitudinal centre of gravity remains where it always was and is now well aft of the CLR.

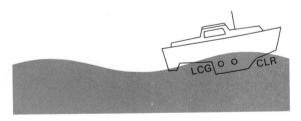

Fig. 10(14) A yacht being towed at greater speeds than her natural or displacement speed is hauled on to the forward wave of her transverse wave system. This causes her CLR to move forward and give rise to possible dangerous yawing from side to side.

The forces acting on the boat are concentrated at the LCG with the result that the slightest deviation off course will cause her to pivot about the CLR and sheer off violently to one side. The towing vessel will unceremoniously drag her back,

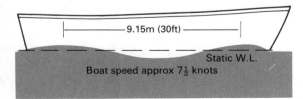

Fig. 10(13) The length of the transverse wave system is governed by the speed of the boat and this fact may be used to estimate the speed of a boat.

only for the process to be repeated endlessly until damage is caused or speed is reduced. Ideally, towing speed should not exceed a speed/length ratio of about 1.3 on the towed craft.

10.1.21 Computer aided design (CAD)

There is no aspect of yacht design that cannot be carried out on a suitably programmed computer. Even the most basic of models could do the straightforward sums for displacement; longitudinal centres of buoyancy and gravity; centre of effort; and tons per inch immersion (the weight that would need to be added or removed to change draught by one inch). Conventionally these sums are the designer's lot; without a computer they are done longhand, aided by a calculator.

Taken one stage further, a designer involved in offshore racing yachts finds a computer of considerable assistance in the calculations needed for IOR ratings where numbers have to be juggled in assessing the likely effect on final rating of many possible hull measurements.

However, in most people's minds a proper yacht computer draws lines plans (under human guidance), sail plans and what-have-you; allows these to be viewed from any angle and in perspective; rattles off those sums previously mentioned at the touch of a button; and finally, when the designer is satisfied, produces a table of offsets. Certain programs to do all this and a lot more are readily available and now form an integral part of many designers' office equipment.

Different programs tackle the method of producing a new design on the computer screen in slightly different ways but most attempt to simulate the procedures of a designer working in the traditional way on a drawing board. Put simply, the design is created by modifying a rectangular box which first appears on the screen representing, say, the boat in plan view. What are called control points are added to define, roughly, intended curve of the deckline. The computer will remember this first view while attention moves to a similar operation to produce the desired shape in profile. U-shaped sections are assumed by the computer and these can next be modified or changed to chine form as desired. Eventually the basis of a rough lines plan emerges from this work to which may be added waterlines, buttocks and diagonals to form a traditional-looking lines drawing from which the computer will give the offsets.

Rather than start from scratch, a program can be used that allows the entry of offsets from an existing design and from them create a lines plan which can be modified as wished. Further programs are available which, for instance, make trim and stability calculations or, as a complete contrast, draw out full-size sections for use as patterns for building moulds. Virtually anything is possible, at a price, of course, for yacht design programs and their associated hefty computers are not exactly in everyday demand.

10.2 Hull forms

10.2.1 Hull forms in general

Broadly speaking boats can be divided between those that have a V-bottom, or hard chine, form and those that are round bilged. The object of having a boat with a definite angle between the topsides and bottom may be to simplify construction when using a sheet material such as ply, steel or alloy; or it may be to achieve better performance on certain types of craft under certain conditions. The notion that a hard chine shape automatically has to have sections composed of straight lines is wrong – in fact there cannot be straight line sections in areas where there is a lot of curve and change in shape (such as towards the bow) without strenuous work being required to deform the sheet. It will naturally fall into concave curves in these regions and Fig. 10(15) shows the general hull form of a single chine yacht. Fig. 10(16) does the same for a double chine vessel and though it would be possible to build three chines or more, needlessly proliferating chines bring the cost close to genuine round bilge form. Though the curves in the sections below the waterline may be discerned, on such a small scale drawing it is difficult to see that most of the sections above the waterline have some shape to them, too.

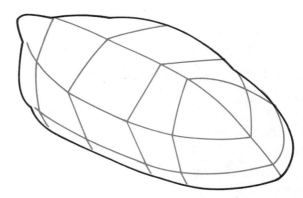

Fig. 10(15) A single chine double-ender.

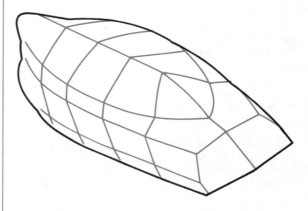

Fig. 10(16) A double chine craft with short counter stern.

A drawback to the chine sailing boat is that the abrupt change in shape between sides and bottom creates a certain amount of turbulence in the water flowing past and this increases drag to the detriment of speed. The difference between a chine boat's performance (especially of a double chine craft) and that achieved by its round bilge counterpart is quite small but significant when planning a racing machine. On the other hand, the V-bottom may be slightly faster downwind in the surges when the stern is starting to drop, simply because a flattish underwater surface will react to water rushing past it more positively than will a curved one. The water flow will have some upwards component which can act more readily on a flat surface to produce lift. Further, a bottom whose sections are formed of straightish lines will resist rolling better than if they were composed of curves.

Sometimes there is found a combination of round bilge and hard chine form. Forward, the bottom sections are rounded to give an easy motion as the bow slices into a head sea in bad weather. Aft, the shape changes to V-bottom to give a better downwind, or motoring, performance. This dual shape is most often seen on motor boats but it sometimes occurs on sailing craft.

On fast motor boats the V-bottom is almost mandatory, partly for frictional resistance reasons and partly to allow the water streaming under the bottom to generate maximum lift. If, for any reason, the hard chine form is not selected, spray rails run along the sides at a height that corresponds to the position of some notional chine to deflect water away from the sides. Spray rails are not really as effective as building in a change of shape, but are much better than nothing. Fig. 10(17) illustrates a section towards the stern of two motor boats; one hard chine and the other round bilged with a spray rail.

The V of the V-bottom may be flattened out to give a completely flat bottom, and this allows very speedy and economical building. Flatties can be successful as sailing boats provided they are light and narrow (the length to beam ratio should not

be less than 4:1, and 5:1 would be better) and have low freeboard including the superstructure. Since a boat heels under wind pressure, flatties present a corner to the water under sail and not their flat bottom, and so do not pound in head seas nearly as much as might be imagined. The same flat-bottomed form can be used for power boats, again provided that the craft is light and low. Motor flatties can be pushed along at quite high speeds and are widely used with outboard power by commercial fishermen in the USA.

10.2.2 Sheer

Conventionally, boats have a hollow sheer, or deck line, viewed in profile but sometimes reverse sheer is employed, Fig. 10(18). The looks of this latter shape are unexpected but it has some practical

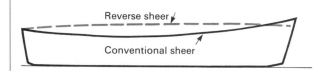

Fig. 10(18) Reverse sheer allows greater space in a boat before side decks intrude.

advantages. From the seagoing point of view the critical height above water is around the forward ending of the load waterline. What happens aft of this point will not affect weatherliness very much, and normally the deck line drops to a point about three-quarters of the length of the boat aft of the bow and then climbs again. However, if it went back some distance parallel to the waterline from that critical forward point, or even had a hump in it, the hull would be more spacious and perhaps allow for better accommodation. Another point in favour of reverse sheer is one connected with stability. Once the deck edge is submerged during heeling there is little further buoyancy available to shove the boat back upright again until the superstructure enters the water. So, if the moment the deck edge is immersed can be delayed by raising the freeboard at its lowest point, the better able to resist heeling the boat will be.

As a matter of aesthetics it is worth remembering that to an observer looking at a boat sideways on, the bow is further away from his eyes than the point of widest beam. Through optical illusion this makes the bow appear to be lower than it actually is. Boats drawn with straight sheerlines thus look as if the bow is drooping, and an illusion of straightness can only be achieved by drawing a slight conventionally-hollow deck edge. With reversed sheers the bow is often drawn as having a downwards slope and this feature is accentuated to the observer.

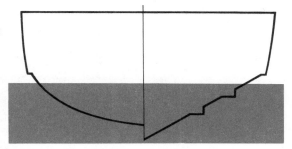

Fig. 10(17) Half sections through two craft: one with a round bottom and the other hard chine, but both intended to reach planing speeds. The chine rail of the round bottom boat will deflect water away from the topsides, though not as effectively as the same rail on a chine boat, while the bottom will clearly not allow as much 'lift' from the water streaming under it.

10.2.3 Overhangs, bows and sterns

At low speeds – up to a speed/length ratio of
about 0.9 – resistance is mainly frictional (10.1.17)
but above that figure wave-making resistance
becomes the more important and thus length is the
main factor in governing speed, with the longer
the boat the higher the potential speed. This is the
reason for building a boat with long overhangs,
Fig. 10(19). When the wind is light and the boat
sailing reasonably upright there is comparatively
little length of hull immersed, and so wetted area
and frictional resistance are low. As the wind and
heel increase a greater length is presented to the
water and since length has increased so has
potential speed. Also, for any given speed if length
is increased the speed/ratio drops to reduce
resistance. The reason why few boats are built
with long overhangs today is simply that there is
little useful space in these drawn-out ends, and so
length is being paid for without compensating
gains in accommodation. The theory behind
overhangs is as sound these days as it ever was.

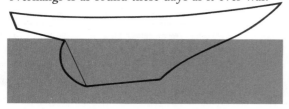

Fig. 10(19) This would have been quite a normal amount
of overhang on a cruising yacht of the 1950s.

Clipper bows

There are various types of bow shape, the most
famous of which is the clipper bow, Fig. 10(20).
This style is a natural adjunct to a bowsprit and
is markedly hollow in profile. It needs to be
carefully designed if it is not to look a mere
affectation, and can be achieved either by
incorporating the shape as a part of the hull lines
and structure or by planting a knee on to the face
of a normal stem.

Pram bow

Though quite often seen on dinghies the pram, or
scow bow, Fig. 10(21), has never been popular on
yachts in the western world. It has the advantages

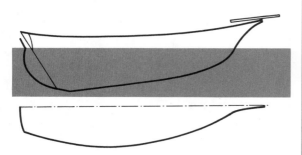

Fig. 10(20) A clipper bow matched with a raked transom
stern.

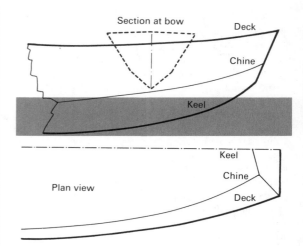

Fig. 10(21) Though pram bows are frequently used on
dinghies, for no very good reason they are almost
unknown in this country on bigger craft.

that it gives plenty of interior space forward and,
on bigger craft, a spacious area for foredeck work.
Provided this bow transom is set well above the
waterline there are few drawbacks except that
people are not used to seeing it and so tend to
distrust the form.

Transom stern

There are a variety of possible stern
configurations. The cheapest to build in any
construction other than where a mould is used, is
the transom stern and it also gives the greatest
interior and deck space for any waterline length.
The boat is simply sawn off at the aft ending of
the waterline (or close to it) though the transom
may lie at quite a steep angle as shown on Fig.
10(20).

Counter stern

If the body of the hull is continued past the aft
waterline ending and then terminates in a
transom, the result is a counter stern, Fig. 10(22).
This has an advantage over the pure transom stern

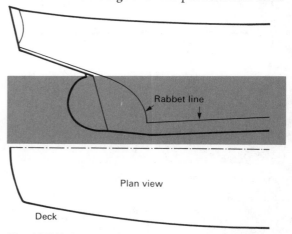

Fig. 10(22) Counter stern on a timber yacht.

that as the stern starts to drop at high speeds, or the boat heels, an additional length of hull is set down into the water to increase length and potential top speed as well as lowering the speed/length ratio and resistance. This is the same argument as that applied to the advantages of overhang, and a counter stern is the usual form used in association with an aft overhang.

Canoe stern

On the other hand, the aft overhang could consist of the stern drawn out beyond the aft waterline ending but terminating in a point. This would give a canoe stern, Fig. 10(23), which is perhaps the most attractive of all the options from an aesthetic viewpoint. It is a waster of space both below and on deck but is reckoned by some to be the most seaworthy form of all. It provides a reasonable amount of reserve buoyancy aft, although not as much as that given by the counter stern, and balances the buoyancy of the bow quite well.

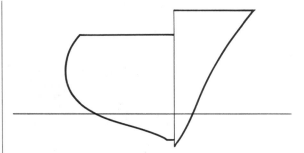

Fig. 10(24) On the left is a half section at the stern of a yacht with tumblehome and, on the right, a half section through a flared bow.

of the boat as well, and is then used to denote how much a structure slopes in towards the centreline. A superstructure, for instance, would look as if it were leaning outwards if the sides were built vertically. Thus it slopes in and the amount of this slope is written, for instance, as 1:10 or 1:12 tumblehome. Bow sections that are markedly concave are said to be flared, Fig. 10(24). A reasonable amount of flare tends to throw water downwards and keep the deck dry, but an exaggerated flare often leads to water running along the hollow until this dies away. The water then comes aboard over the deck edge.

10.2.4 Sailing hull forms

Most production craft today are designed unashamedly around a combination of requirements and beliefs. First, the accommodation must be as spacious as possible within a given length, with length itself important since marina charges have to be taken into account. Secondly, the price must be competitive and since weight costs money, especially if achieved by heavy construction rather than by the addition of ballast, the boat must be light. Thirdly, it is believed that it is a selling feature if the hull form is recognisably similar to that used by successful competitors in the racing fleets. These constraints commonly lead builders to produce craft that are beamy (for superior accommodation and in deference to racing trends) and, because they are also light, to having small hull draught. That is, the main body of the hull has comparatively little depth in the water, whatever may be added to it afterwards in the way of keels or skegs. The hull will also have considerable freeboard to give headroom and the impression of space below. Since this combination of shallow hull draught and high freeboard would lead to a hopeless performance under sail – with the boat preferring to drift sideways rather than marching forward in the desired direction – a fin keel is added, so called to differentiate it from the traditional long keel. This also allows some ballast weight to be carried low down and so promotes stability. The weight may be an addition to the fin keel or it may be provided simply by the weight of the structure itself.

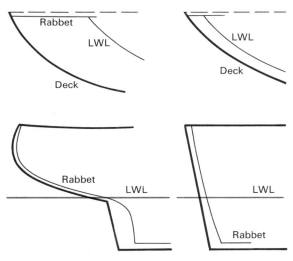

Fig. 10(23) On the left is a canoe stern and, on the right, a lifeboat stern. Both are shown in profile and plan views.

Lifeboat stern

If the hull had been chopped off at the aft waterline but the deck line ended in a point this would give a lifeboat stern, Fig. 10(23), which, as its name implies, is the form traditionally used on lifeboats. Since it was also the type found on Viking ships it has a long and honourable history but it is not as popular now as it once was. Lifeboats and fishing boats increasingly use transom sterns without apparent loss in seaworthiness and, in fact, there is no 'best' bow or stern configuration. Prejudice comes into the reckoning as does the useful space that can be offered on a production boat.

Tumblehome and flare

An aft section that has a marked convex curve above the waterline is said to have tumblehome, Fig. 10(24). That term can be applied to other parts

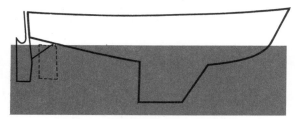

Fig. 10(25) Transom hung and spade rudders on a fin-keeler. A skeg-supported rudder is shown in Fig. 10(9). A spade rudder has no support other than the rudder stock.

The boat has to be steered and so a rudder is arranged. This is sometimes hung on the transom; sometimes emerges from the bottom of the hull with no external support, the bottom bearing being within the hull (in which case it is called a spade rudder); and sometimes has an external support incorporating a bearing. This support is in the form of a miniature fin keel and is called the skeg. Thus a hull with quite low wetted surface has been achieved and frictional resistance is low. Fig. 10(25) and Fig. 10(9) show the possible arrangements.

The speed of this boat is governed by her length and she enters speed/length ratios of about 0.8 and upwards, where wave-making resistance is climbing steeply, sooner than would a longer boat which would also have a higher top theoretical speed. Though it would be quite possible to build that longer boat, with the narrow beam that would be a further requirement for high ultimate speed, as cheaply as the typical beamy, shallow type, her accommodation would be poor by comparison and berthing charges be higher. So a builder who wants to cash in on a worthwhile section of public demand has little choice.

Of course boats are still produced similar in form to the classic yachts of yesteryear and which, by having more headroom and beam than once would have been considered suitable, can have an accommodation quite as good as their more fashionable rivals. They are likely to be good to look at, steady on the helm and easy for a family crew to handle. But if of the same length as their competitors are likely to be not quite as fast, due to their greater wetted area, and to cost a bit more.

10.2.5 Beam
Where sheer speed has priority over everything else, narrow beam is desirable. The resultant boat may be hard to handle to windward where a good sail area will heel the boat uncomfortably and too much for efficiency, but off the wind the craft will come into her own. The reason why narrow beam pays is mainly that water does not like to be disturbed and the more it is forced apart by the boat's passage the greater will be the shock to it and the bigger the waves created. The power absorbed in making those waves leaves a little less available for driving the yacht forward.

On Fig. 10(1) is marked the half angle of entrance, and for speed/length ratios of 1 and above this should not exceed 10°. Such a figure is hard to achieve on a beamy boat without compensating steep curves somewhere aft along the waterline, and water will not appreciate that big change in direction.

In the USA a new breed of lightweight offshore yachts has appeared. Unhampered by the International Offshore Rule (IOR) rating restrictions, they are remarkably narrow. On a waterline length of 24ft (7.3m) for example, beam may only be 5ft 8in (1.7m) and a 40-footer may have a beam of 8ft, a length/beam ratio of 5:1. This contrasts with the 3:1 ratio of more conventional craft. The combination of narrow beam and light weight is unbeatable. Nearer to home, for example the 17ft (5.2m) single-handed International Canoe with a beam of 3ft 2in (0.95m) and a sail area of about 107sq ft (10sq m) is as fast as the two-man Flying Dutchman which is nearly 3ft (0.9m) longer, far beamier and sets 190sq ft (17.7sq m) of sail.

10.2.6 Keels
As with sails, rudders, centreboards and the like, the higher the aspect ratio of a keel the better it will reduce leeway, and with less wetted area. A good example of such a keel may be expected to contribute only 25 per cent of the total drag of the hull (the main body of the hull causing the rest) while providing about 70 per cent of the lateral force acting against leeway. It need not be very thick – about 15 per cent as wide as it is long, fore and aft, being about right – and such types abound, wedded to shoal draught main hulls. They are, though, just necessary excrescences, adding to the draught without the redeeming feature of being wide enough to allow some accommodation to be dropped into them. The old-time yachts could have a low profile above water while still having headroom, because the cabin sole could be arranged in the wide keel which was much more a genuine part of the hull structure and form than it is on today's shapes. Fig. 10(26).

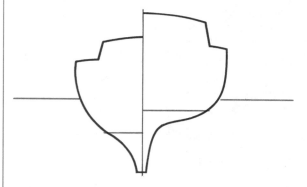

Fig. 10(26) The long keel form of the classic yacht allowed the cabin sole to be deeper in the hull and the overall height above the waterline to be lower than is possible on the shallow hull of the modern fin-keeler.

Recent competition for the America's Cup has given prominence to 'upside down' or inversely tapered keels, which have the advantages of improving the lift/resistance characteristics and of allowing more ballast to be carried as low as possible. Another innovation has been the introduction of winglets (fins extending each side at or near the bottom of the keel, usually pointing slightly downwards). The main function of winglets is to reduce the induced drag, by moving the tip vortex away from the bottom of the keel itself to the tips of the winglets. Winglets also allow more ballast to be carried low down, but they add to the wetted area and hence to frictional resistance so their size and shape need to be carefully considered.

Keels have also been developed with a tandem or canard formation, in effect with a small keel ahead of the main keel, rather similar to the jib and mainsail of a sail plan, and with an end plate of delta configuration which bridges the tips of both foils and accounts for at least half the total weight. The gap between the two foils is carefully shaped – wider at the top than at the bottom, so that the aft (main) foil has an inverse taper as already discussed above. The function of the leading foil is to accelerate and smooth the flow of water past the aft foil. The end plate lowers the centre of gravity, reduces the tip losses from the high pressure to low pressure sides of the foils, and also reduces pitching and rolling. Another bonus is that the end plate provides a good platform for the boat to stand on when dried out. Such keels are likely to be increasingly popular for cruising boats, if only because they permit a shallower draught: this in turn raises the centre of lateral resistance and reduces heeling.

Yet another form of keel found in some cruising yachts is the Scheel keel, where the bottom of the (long) keel is flared outwards to reduce the tip vortex and to carry ballast low down.

10.2.7 Bilge keels

In the place of a single, central keel, whether of the fin or full-length variety, two keels can be substituted, one under each bilge. Their function is exactly the same as for any keel – to reduce leeway and increase stability. Though two keels like this are not as efficient as one of the same total area their combined lateral plane should be sufficient to allow them to be less deep than a central keel. Thus draught is reduced without worsening leeway though at the expense of added surface area. Since the water flooding along the bottom runs roughly on a line with the diagonals, bilge keels are angled out to lie in the same plane, Fig. 10(27). If they are vertical they cause turbulence as the natural flow of the water is disturbed. The forward end of the bilge keels toe-in a matter of a degree or two to help windward performance. Bilge keels have become associated with light, high-sided, beamy yachts at the cheaper end of the market, which naturally sag off to leeward under sail more readily than a heavier, deeper vessel. If bilge keels do not cure this condition entirely that is not a reflection on the scheme itself, for nothing would work any better except for a deep, central keel and this would immediately put paid to the shoal draught advantage. Bilge keels are also popular because in the right conditions of river or harbour bottom they allow the boat to sit upright, or nearly so, when dried out and balancing on her keels. It is worth remembering, though, that the LCG of the boat and all its equipment must lie approximately in line with the middle of the keels in profile, or the boat may tip backwards or forwards.

10.2.8 Centreboards, daggerboards and bilgeboards

For a genuinely shoal draught craft it is obvious that all appendages beneath the hull should be eliminated, and the keel replaced by something that can be lowered into the water to combat leeway only when needed. The amount of wetted area could then be adjusted to suit the course on which the yacht is sailing. On a run this movable wetted area could be lifted right up inside the boat; on a reach it would be set half-way down; and going to windward it would be fully lowered. On a suitable designed hull the boat could take the ground more or less upright without the need to perform a balancing act on bilge keels. All the requirements of altering wetted area are provided by centreboards, which pivot about a bolt near their forward ends and are housed in a case; daggerboards (which slide straight up and down

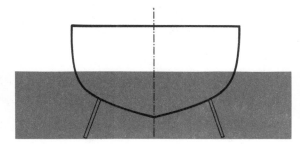

Fig. 10(27) Bilge keels provide resistance to leeway and the ability to take the ground reasonably upright.

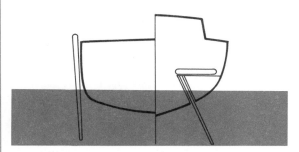

Fig. 10(28) A leeboard (on the left) is sited outside the hull but bilgeboards (on the right) are set in cases like a centreboard. If suitably planned the cases can form the berth or settee fronts for much of their length.

in their case with no pivot); and bilgeboards which either pivot or lift but whose cases are set out one each side of the centreline where they do not intrude badly into the accommodation. If the bilgeboards are canted as shown in Fig. 10(28) one of them becomes vertical as the craft heels and so is more effective than a centreline board in reducing leeway. Unlike bilge keels, which they resemble, only one board need be lowered so that wetted area can be controlled. Still on bilgeboards, which deserve to be more popular than they are, the slots in the bottoms of their cases will be above keel level and so less likely to get clogged with stones and mud than where the case is set into the keel.

In some cases boards have ballast attached to their bottom face and this particularly applies to daggerboards. The ballast might be in the form of a bulb of iron or lead which recesses into a hollow built into the hull, or it might be that the bulb simply pulls up against the hull. The welcome addition of weight low down can also be achieved by making the board hollow and filling some part of it with a dense material, or by making the board of thick steel plate. In all cases the structure must be strong and able to resist the shock of a sudden grounding without bending and staying bent. The argument for having the board of wood is partly that it will break rather than bend in these circumstances. Also, since the board will naturally float up into the case it only requires light tackle to push it down into the water. If the tackle breaks, the board will house itself which can be advantageous.

Heavy centreboards, daggerboards and bilgeboards should have a built-in stop to prevent them dropping down out of their cases if the raising mechanism breaks. It should also be possible to lift them out of the tops of their cases, rather than having to make some elaborate arrangements to drop them through the bottom when inspection, painting or repair is needed.

As with rudders, keels and all suchlike objects, boards with a high aspect ratio are most effective. That is, when lowered, they should be deep compared with their fore and aft length. Such theoretical advantages need to be approached with caution because the strength of the board must be of paramount importance. Sheer surface area, however inefficiently disposed, is better than none at all.

Centreboards and daggerboards are hardly ever of an area that enables them to equal the effectiveness of proper bilge keels or central keel, and so are best used on craft that present a low profile and thus have the least possible windage. They are sometimes used in conjunction with a shallow ballast keel – dropping down through a slot in the keel – and so allow a boat of modest draught to have a potentially good windward performance. Otherwise, in the case of non-ballasted boards, ballast is stowed inside the hull.

10.2.9 Leeboards
The best examples of these are found on Thames barges where boards, pivoting at the deck edge and set outside the hull, can be lowered to reduce leeway. A leeboard being wholly outboard does not take up any useful space and on craft designed to accept them can be quite effective. The pressure of water on the lee side holds them against the side of the vessel and they can be adjusted in a fore and aft position by tackles made fast to the board. The windward board in some cases is left to its own devices, in which case it will fan out from the boat's side and skitter across the surface. Otherwise it is hauled clear of the water on each tack, Fig. 10(28).

10.2.10 Rudders
The rudder, in association with the keel or centreboard, acts to provide a transverse lifting force to counteract the sideways thrust of the sails. Thus it does more than simply steer the boat. A high aspect ratio is good for efficiency and may be as high as 5 on a deep draught yacht. Unlike other high aspect boards such as centreboards, a rudder can be supported down its leading edge from either the aft end of the keel or from a rudder skeg. A skeg also allows a slightly smaller rudder to be used than would otherwise be needed.

Modern racing boats with their high speeds and somewhat wayward handling characteristics can place enormous strains on rudders and associated skegs. Unhappily the obsession with saving weight extends to these items and there have been many failures. Since a rudder can be thick and still be efficient, the soundest way to construct one is to take the stock right down to the bottom of the rudder and build up the blade round that. The stock is the bar or tube that extends up inside the boat, and to which the tiller or quadrant is fastened. Suitable scantlings for different sizes and types of rudder and stock are given by all the classification societies, so there is no excuse for failure. A rudder blade should be aerofoil shaped for efficiency. A flat blade slotted through the stock is cheap but not very effective. Two typical rudders are illustrated in Fig. 10(25).

10.2.11 Multihulls
From what has been written so far on matters of beam, resistance and balance it would seem that a multihull, and especially a catamaran, should be the ideal sailing machine. She does tend to run straight, because of the long, widely spaced hulls, and so may not turn as promptly as a conventional single hull vessel and may present structural problems in joining up the hulls, but those two factors apart (and discounting the real difficulty in ensuring that the craft can be righted after a capsize) the multihull has everything going for it.

The following paragraphs discuss some of the design features of multihulls. For more general matters concerning this special breed of boats, see Chapter 20.

Catamarans

The conventional yacht has more beam than is desirable, from the resistance point of view, to allow a generous sail area to promote speed without undue heeling. The catamaran's two hulls can be very narrow and efficient without prejuducing her ability to sail upright. On the same theme, bottom sections can approach the ideal of being semi-circular, for least wetted area, since they do not need to be shaped to resist heel. The huge initial stability of two hulls placed at some distance from one another means that ballast is not required, and so the boat can have a low overall weight – again disregarding the problems of righting after a capsize. And because a light, narrow hull will only have a shallow transverse wave system, she has the potential for velocities well above her displacement speed. The ends can also be reasonably symmetrical to make a well-balanced hull.

As with other yachts the catamaran, especially in the smaller sizes, may need some additional lateral plane to reduce leeway. This is commonly provided by a daggerboard in each hull, though there have been types built with fin keels. The justification for the latter would be that, in conjunction with a masthead float (of which more later), they can make for a boat that will right

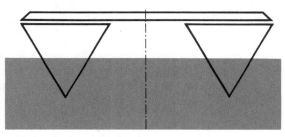

Fig. 10(29) The Wharram type of catamaran relies on steeply vee'd hulls to prevent excessive leeway.

herself from any angle of heel. Other than in that role a fin keel is a nuisance since it adds draught and wetted surface at all times – even when not needed. A big catamaran may not even need daggerboards since her hulls can be very narrow in proportion to their length and so will have a reasonable draught and grip of the water on their own. Big catamarans, too, and especially those designed for racing will probably not have any accommodation planned for the bridgedeck – the structure joining the two hulls – and so will have quite low windage. Again this reduces the need for additional lateral plane below water.

The catamarans designed by James Wharram deal with this problem in a different way. Apart from eliminating all structures on the bridgedeck their hulls are V-shaped, Fig. 10(29), which allows them to be deeper in the water and to resist leeway by that depth alone.

The structural difficulties of a catamaran have been mentioned. The strains on the connections between two widely spaced hulls can be enormous and are aggravated by additional stresses set up by the rigging. It can be appreciated that setting a

mast on the bridgedeck and then tightening up shrouds attached to the hulls tends to pull those hulls upwards, and some clever engineering may be needed to sort that problem out.

As far as stability is concerned it is fairly obvious that an upside-down catamaran is just as stable as one the right way up; more stable in fact, because the mast may be deep down in the water adding weight just where it is not needed. There have been many solutions or partial solutions to the problem of righting a capsized catamaran; the most usual being to attach a float to the top of the mast. Assuming the mast did not break during the capsize, the float will try to rise to the surface bringing the catamaran on her beam ends with it. In this attitude it may be possible to right the boat completely. The weight of a fin keel would assist in getting the craft upright, or it may be feasible to flood the upper hull for the same result. In some cases an inflatable bag replaces the permanent float at the masthead. This can be activated when required. Uninflated it does not have as much windage as the float but has potentially greater buoyancy, which is a good thing. High performance catamarans are also sometimes equipped with automatic sheet releases so that as the load on the mainsail approaches that at which it would capsize the craft, the sheet is let go and the load abruptly diminishes.

Trimarans

A catamaran carries its weight equally distributed between two hulls, but a trimaran's main load carrier is her central hull with the floats port and starboard acting more as balancing sponsons. A trimaran has fewer accommodation problems than a catamaran as, though the central hull will be narrower than on a monohull since it does not need to counter heel with its own beam, everything is under one roof, so to speak. Headroom in the hull is not difficult to achieve either as the main, weight-carrying hull is likely to be quite deep. On a catamaran living quarters tend to be very elongated unless the bridgedeck can be used. If it is, then excessive windage invariably follows since the floor of that accommodation starts at a fair distance above the waterline and then soars upwards.

Structural difficulties are less marked on a trimaran. The floats are comparatively close to a stout main hull and so are easily braced. Even righting after a knock-down does not present quite the same problems and, all in all, the trimaran has many virtues. She may not turn as swiftly as a monohull nor have quite the same accommodation or top speed potential as the catamaran, but will be comparatively safer and fast enough for virtually all purposes.

10.2.12 Motor sailers

The modern motor sailer has most of the characteristics of the true sailing yacht including, in some cases, a fin keel and skeg underwater form. The rig is generally slightly undersize by comparison, and windage is allowed to rise with the provision of a sheltered steering position or even a small wheelhouse-cum-deck saloon, but a reasonbly powerful engine overcomes any difficulties. The craft will generally perform well under sail alone but the biggish motor is there for speedy passages or for when the wind drops. Used in conjunction with the sails when turning to windward it will permit greater speed and closer footing. However, as on all craft of sailing yacht form whose aft waterlines come to a point, top speed is limited to a speed/length ratio of 1.4 or thereabouts. Applying more power than is necessary to reach this speed simply causes the stern to drop and the uphill battle to commence. A slight increase in speed might be possible but at the cost of a huge waste of power and fuel.

The more traditional motor sailer, of which there are still examples being built, relies on the engine to do most of the work most of the time. Under sail only the boat will perform tolerably on a reach or a run and so in an emergency some harbour can be gained, even though it may not be the one originally envisaged. To windward the sails are usually trimmed flat and the engine provides virtually all the drive. On these occasions the sails act mainly as roll-dampers and, to a slight extent, fuel savers. The hulls of these motor sailers are generally of traditional yacht or slow motor boat form without much in the way of keels or other aids to reducing leeway. Since they are not usually expected to reach speed/length ratios over that magic 1.4, the aft waterlines will come to a point to allow an easy flow of water round the hull. Where slightly higher speeds are planned the transom may be lightly immersed for additional stern buoyancy but once this has been done all pretensions to a reasonable sailing performance disappear. A sailing boat develops little enough effective horsepower from its sails at the best of times. The extra drag and turbulence created by a transom being towed through the water is more than it can bear with equanimity.

10.3 Power craft

10.3.1 Motor boats

Vessels that rely purely on engines come in all speed ranges from those that plod along at a very economical speed/length ratio of 1 or a little over (these tend to be biggish craft where even a measured gait – $7\frac{1}{2}$ knots on a boat that is 18m (60ft) for example – is still a worthwhile speed) to those that commonly cruise at ratios of 3 or more and may be capable of reaching ratios of 6 or 7. Even these extremes leave out offshore racers where a boat 9m (30ft) on the waterline might be capable of 80 knots ($V/\sqrt{L} = 14.6$) in the right conditions, and record breakers where boat shape is as much affected by aerodynamics as hydrodynamics. It follows, then, that there must

be a wider variation of hull shape than on sailing yachts. But, unlike them, the form of pure racing boats has comparatively little influence on those designed for more mundane uses.

As speeds increase from a speed/length ratio of about 1.4 up to ratios of 2.5 to 3 (when the boat may be considered to be planing) there is a pressing need for a wide buoyant transom to counteract sinkage of the stern. This transom is then dragging through the water creating a massive amount of turbulence and wash. Above planing speeds, though, the transom will run dry with wash and wave-making resistance greatly reduced. At the same time the boat will have risen bodily under the influence of the lifting component of the water rushing past the bottom, and so the wetted area of the bottom will also have been reduced. Consequently frictional resistance drops. A resistance curve of a planing boat will show a steep climb to the point where the craft is just about on the point of planing. Resistance will then suddenly drop before starting to climb again, though much less steeply than it did initially. The point of maximum resistance is sometimes called the hump speed – because there is a hump in the resistance curve.

10.3.2 Trim

In the course of its progress towards full planing a motor boat will behave in precisely the same way as any other boat. First it settles in the water with the bow usually sinking a little more than the stern. As the aft transverse wave crest passes the stern (speed/length ratio just over 1.34), the bow rises and the stern sinks but then things begin to change. Whereas the sailing vessel or low-speed power boat (which have very much the same sort of shape though the motor craft has no outside keel) would find themselves with an exaggerated bows-up attitude, the planing boat by virtue of its buoyant stern will lift and then start to flatten out. A speed/length ratio of 3.5 to 4 will now have been reached and from there on lift occurring at the LCG, which is normally well aft of midships, will raise the stern more than the bow and the boat will start to run almost level. Though this might seem to be a desirable state, in fact frictional resistance with all that length immersed will be higher than necessary and most planing boats run most efficiently with a bows-up attitude of 3° to 4°.

It is most important to get trim right if power is not to be wasted. A boat will normally plane earlier and thus be more efficient if an excessive bows-up attitude can be avoided. This can be accomplished either by the use of transom flaps which, pivoting on the transom, have their aft edges forced down into the water flow and thus try and lift the stern, or by wedges under the hull. Both are shown in Fig. 10(30). The latter are effective but inflexible in that as speeds rise they will continue to depress the bow until the craft is running much too flat for efficiency. Transom flaps

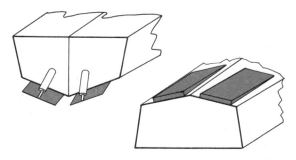

Fig. 10(30) On the left are transom flaps which may be hydraulically, electrically or even manually operated. On the right are wedges fastened to the boat's bottom to force her bows down at speed.

can be raised to allow the hull to assume its natural planing attitude at any time.

Flaps are useful, too, in bad weather. Going to windward a boat will be most comfortable and least liable to violent pounding if she is running level. Too level for greatest efficiency, perhaps, but at an attitude that the crew can stand. Downwind the bows should be high to bring the CLR (centre of lateral resistance) back towards the LCG (longitudinal centre of gravity) to aid handling. That high bows-up attitude is probably the one naturally adopted by the craft at moderate planing seeds and should not be spoilt with wedges.

10.3.3 Planing hull forms

Not all planing hull types have the same trim characteristics. Fig. 10(31) shows the three main types with typical chine and keel lines. The first is the warped bottom type where the deadrise angle is lessening all the way aft to the transom. This shape produces a hull that tends to plane early but flattens out too quickly for really high speeds to

be achieved with efficiency. The second type, the monohedron, has a fairly constant deadrise from a little way aft of midships back to the transom. This form generally planes later than the warped bottom type but never trims with quite such a bows-up attitude. The third type, known as a deep V, where the least deadrise angle is 22° or more, has a chine line similar to that of the monohedron – only higher of course. The steeply angled bottom produces less lift than the other two types and consequently the vessel planes later and less efficiently, but is what is known as a high trimmer. In other words the bows are high further along into the speed range. The warped bottom and monohedron forms will start to flatten out with an increase in resistance comparatively early in the speed range and just when the deep V is becoming efficient – having had too steep a bows-up attitude earlier on. Thus the deep V is suited to really high speeds.

10.3.4 Beam

Motor and sailing boats share many of the same criteria for best performance. Thus, for instance, a very narrow, lightweight power boat can reach high speeds efficiently despite not having a planing form. It is simply that she creates such low transverse waves that it is no effort for her to break through the displacement speed barrier. But in general, while the shape of a motor boat will resemble that of a yacht without a keel at speed/length ratios below 1.4 or so, above that and up to a ratio of 3 or thereabouts, beam becomes increasingly important. The more of it, within reason, the better. At higher ratios again the maximum beam of the planing surface ought gradually to reduce. Fig. 10(32) shows what would be the ideal planing beam for a craft 7.6m (25ft) on the waterline, displacing 3 tons and with the LCG 3m (10ft) forward of the transom. The requirement has dropped from getting on for 4.5m (15ft) at 15 knots (which is ridiculously wide) to a little over

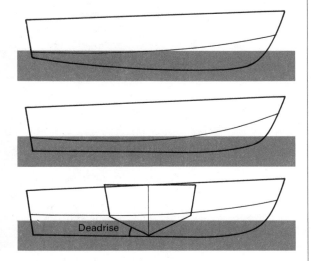

Fig. 10(31) Top, a warped bottom form; centre, a monohedron type; and bottom, a deep V planing hull showing also what is meant by deadrise angle. This is the angle the bottom makes with a horizontal through the base of the keel.

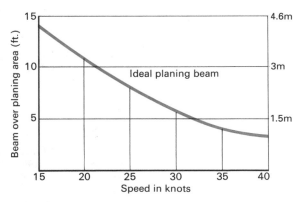

Fig. 10(32) Ideal planing beam (maximum beam over the chine rails) plotted against boat speed for a craft 7.6m (25ft) on the waterline displacing 3 tons, and with an LCG 3m (10ft) forward of the transom.

1m (3ft) at 40 knots. The latter beam would be impossible to attain on a monohull if the boat was not to be hair-raisingly unstable at rest and at low speeds. However, a deep V in conjunction with spray rails, Fig. 10(33), can effectively reduce beam as speeds increase. The boat rises in the water as the throttles are opened and with a number of spray rails running along the bottom at various widths out from the centreline, one pair in succession will define the edge of the waterline beam. A more conventional boat with lower deadrise cannot manage this feat as water breaking away from one set of rails will re-form on the bottom a little higher up.

Consequently a deep V, despite its lack of lift compared with its flatter floored brethren, comes into its own at high speeds because it is a high trimmer and can effectively reduce its waterline beam. It will also have a slightly easier motion in a head sea since the narrow, steeply V'd forward sections will drop into the water without too much shock.

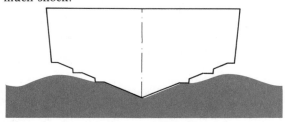

Fig. 10(33) The spray rails on a deep V hull can define a new, narrower waterline beam as speeds rise and the craft lifts in the water.

10.3.5 Windage
Though windage due to the hull and superstructure is considered an important feature in depressing the performance of a sailing yacht it is treated in a very cavalier fashion by designers and builders of fast motor boats, probably because it is believed that its power-sapping proclivities will pass unnoticed. It can be a significant factor, however, and on a boat of 9m (30ft) sporting a flying bridge for example, steaming at 25 knots into a 12 knot headwind the power absorbed in counteracting wind resistance alone would be about 37kW (50bhp). This might rise to 48kW (65bhp) or thereabouts with the wind at 20° to 30° off the bow. Streamlining would have little effect on this total. It is interesting to reflect that only about 6bhp would have been expended in overcoming the wind resistance of the hull alone.

10.3.6 Catamarans
Twin-hulled forms have never made much of an impact on the fast cruising fraternity of the motor boat world. This is somewhat surprising since a power catamaran has advantages in reduced roll at low speeds and, incorporating the bridgedeck, the potential for spacious accommodation. But catamarans show their paces in the racing world by exploiting the advantages of very narrow,

steeply V'd hulls to the hilt, without having to worry about stability at rest and low speeds. Further, on those boats designed for inshore and sheltered water racing the bridedeck can be set low down so that the air being forced into the gap between the bridgedeck and water surface has a strong upwards or lifting component. This is known as the ground effect and in action lifts the boat bodily upwards. These circuit racers at full speed run with daylight showing beneath their hulls, only the drive units of their outboards being immersed. Resistance is consequently at a minimum. The low bridgedeck form is not so suitable for offshore work where rough water and the constantly changing trim of the boat reduces the ground effect. In addition, waves hammering on the underside of the bridge do it no good at all. Speed offshore can be obtained by relying on the narrow hulls and, forgetting ground effect, siting the bridgedeck well above water level.

10.4 Construction

10.4.1 Construction – general
The construction of all boats may be loosely divided into two types – that where a mould is used (for example GRP, cold moulding and some forms of ferro-concrete construction) and that where it is not (such as with traditional timber, steel and alloy building). The former can be subdivided again into whether a female mould is used (as with GRP) or male (as with foam sandwich and cold moulding).

10.4.2 Moulds
When a female mould is required (where laying-up or whatever is done on the inside face of the mould) a wooden version of the boat is made first. The timber used must be as stable as possible so it does not shrink or swell too much in changing atmospheric conditions. This hull, known as the plug, is sanded and smoothed to as good a finish as can be achieved since every imperfection is likely to be faithfully reproduced on the production craft. The plug is then coated with a release agent, and layers of glassfibre and resin are laid over it in the normal moulding process until a sufficient thickness has been achieved. This laminated structure, known as the mould, is then lifted off the plug and with supports bonded to it is stood on the floor for work to commence.

Small boat moulds are normally made in one place but for bigger craft they may be split longitudinally down the middle and bolted together so that after the hull has been laid up inside, it can be supported from above while the two halves of the mould are unbolted and moved apart. Such a split mould is also necessary if there is appreciable tumblehome in the sections. If a one-piece mould were used the hull could not be lifted out since it is wider at some distance below the deck line than it is at the deck line itself. Moulds are sometimes arranged so they can be tipped. This allows the men laying up the layers of glass and resin inside to work downhand from a staging projecting into the mould. Failing such a set-up they have either to scramble about in the bottom or work from stages lowered from above.

A mould has a limited life since it is sometimes damaged when a hull sticks while it is being lifted out – due, maybe, to the laminating resin penetrating the release agent. The damage can be repaired but it may be difficult to get the repair to match exactly the contours of the mould. Further, the mould is frequently polished to achieve a good finish on the hull taken from it and this polishing can wear flats into surfaces that were originally curved.

This description is, of course, of a female mould where the best surface will be that on the outside of the hull – the side that was in contact with the mould. The smoothness of the inside face depends entirely on the skill of the laminators.

Matched moulds
In a few cases another mould is made which represents the inside face of the hull, taking lay-up thickness into consideration. Dry glassfibre is laid between the two. Resin is then sucked up between the two moulds to permeate the glass and give a good finish to both inside and outside surfaces of the finished hull. Traditionally the difficulty with this scheme is determining whether the resin has actually penetrated every nook and cranny of the glassfibre and it is, of course, expensive in mould making costs.

Male moulds
A male mould is virtually the same thing as the plug used when creating a female mould, though it is built to give the hull shape to the inside of the skin and not the outside. It may be an accurate representation of the hull completely planked up, or it may consist of frame patterns covered in closely-spaced though not necessarily touching battens. Though it must be faired and cleaned off it is not usually necessary to bring it to the high degree of finish of a plug, since it acts more as a former against which veneers or sheets of foam may be laid and attached than as a genuine mould. Hence it is cheap by comparison. The finished hull is lifted off the mould which can then be used again if required.

10.4.3 GRP construction
The term GRP stands for glass-reinforced plastics and so defines the great majority of small craft being built today. However, as owners strive after the greater speed potential given by light weight, materials other than glass fibre are being used for reinforcing, and even the standard polyester resin is being replaced on high performance craft by stronger resins which are also more water and

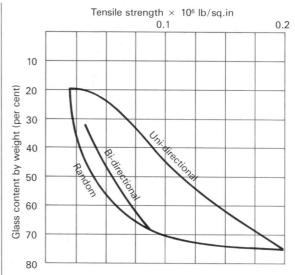

Fig. 10(34) The diagram gives an idea of the effect of type and quanity of reinforcement on tensile strength. Basically, the strength is proportional to the amount of glass fibre; as the orientation increases the maximum glass content possible in a laminate is raised; as the reinforcement becomes more random the effective strength is less.

weather-proof. So maybe the alternative term, FRP (fibre-reinforced plastics) is the better one.

However that may be, most boats are bought by those who simply want to enjoy themselves afloat and whose pockets have restricted depth. For them GRP still applies. The glass reinforcing is made up from filaments extruded to a diameter of something like 0.01mm (0.0004in) and then bundled together to make strands. From there on the reinforcing can take on various guises. The strands may be randomly deposited and bound together with a high solubility binder to form a sheet, known as chopped strand mat. This is the cheapest, easiest to work, and least strong of the reinforcings that are normally used. Remember that it is the reinforcing that gives most of the strength to the laminate. The resin plays a small part, but it is mainly there to bind things together and to keep the water out. There is nothing wrong with an all-chopped strand mat laminate, it will simply be heavier for equal strength than most of the alternatives.

The glass strands may be woven together into a square pattern without twisting or spinning, rather than being randomly deposited, and in this form they are called woven rovings and are the basis of a strong laminate. Because it is difficult to work resin through successive layers of woven rovings in the mould to achieve good uniform resin penetration and bonding, woven rovings are usually combined with chopped strand mat in alternate layers. This mixture forms the basic laminate for most production yachts with some leaning towards good performance.

Glass strands may also be twisted and doubled and then woven into a cloth. This is stronger than woven rovings but is even more difficult to work resin through, and so it is not often used in normal boatbuilding. High strength in one direction is given by uni-directional rovings where the majority of the strands lie in parallel bundles. This form of reinforcing is used in high stress areas, perhaps along the keel for instance, or along frame and stringer faces. Like woven rovings, uni-directional rovings are commonly used in conjunction with chopped strand mat.

One other form of glass reinforcement is rovings deposited from a special gun which chops them up and sprays them out. This method is dealt with in the section 'The laminating process' below.

All the description so far has been of normal glass reinforcement whose strands have a tensile strength of about 37,000kg/cm^2 (500,000lb/sq in). This is called E-glass, probably because it was first developed for electrical applications. But, as mentioned, alternative reinforcing materials are now available for those who have high strength requirements allied to deep pockets. With these reinforcements hull and superstructure weight may be reduced by 12–15% over conventional GRP building, and by even more if sandwich construction is employed (see below). It is difficult to be dogmatic about weight saving since its potential varies with how far the builder is prepared to go in exploiting new materials and with the size of the vessel. It is easier to save weight on a big boat than a small one. Though weight saving on the hull is only part of the story – there being great scope on the fitting-out side as well – dedicated racing men are prepared to pay handsomely for even quite small reductions.

Exotic reinforcings

'Exotic' probably because they are expensive and were first produced for the aerospace business, these reinforcings are generally used in conjunction with one of the high strength resins such as epoxy or vinylester, of which more later.

One such reinforcement is S-glass which has 30–40% higher tensile, impact and flexural strengths than the usual E-glass. It is used mostly in uni-directional form to add strength to stringers and to stiffen up the needy areas of the hull. Better known than S-glass is Kevlar. This is an organic fibre closely linked to nylon chemically, but called an aramid. Its weight is about half that of E-glass, though it is stronger in tension as well as being stiffer. It is less good in compression, however. Kevlar is gold in colour, and when saturated with resin simply becomes a deeper gold. This makes for problems in laminating as compared with normal glass fibre which becomes transparent when resin-wetted. In this state it is quite easy to see if areas are dry or resin-starved, which is not the case with Kevlar. This material is available in various forms but is frequently used as a woven roving to replace layers of glass fibre woven roving. Thus its use saves weight as well as adding strength.

Even stiffer than Kevlar and having a greater compressive strength is carbon fibre, another lightweight organic fibre material. Carbon fibre, though, is rather brittle and so has low impact resistance. Its use in boat hulls is mainly confined to local stiffening on structural items such as frames and stringers with uni-directional rovings. It is also employed on unstayed masts where its stiffness, or resistance to bending, is a prime asset. It is also sometimes used in engineering items like rudder stocks.

Hybrid reinforcing

It is possible to obtain reinforcing containing two different types of reinforcing, such as Kevlar and S-glass or Kevlar and carbon fibre. Such reinforcements are often used in uni-directional rovings designed to exploit the different advantages of different materials. Thus Kevlar with high impact resistance and tensile strength can be combined with the compressive strength and stiffness of carbon fibre.

Resins

The standard laminating resin is what is called an unsaturated polyester resin. Unsaturated means that it is capable of being converted from a liquid to a solid state in the right conditions. The resin on its own is not particularly strong (typical tensile strength being 6.3kg/mm^2 (9000lb/sq in), and compressive strength 14kg/mm^2 or 20,000lb/sq in) but it does keep the water out. If the ratio of resin-to-glass reinforcing is too low the resulting laminate will have poor weather and waterproofing whatever the strength of the laminate may be. This resin-to-glass ratio (by weight) will depend to a large extent on the type of reinforcing used. Chopped strand mat needs quite a weight of resin to consolidate it properly. Woven rovings needs less, and the infrequently used woven cloth less still. On a hull having chopped strand mat only, the ratio by weight will be something like $(2\frac{1}{2}$–3):1. With interleaved layers of woven rovings the resin-to-glass ratio can be expected to drop to $(1\frac{1}{2}$–2):1 and, on high performance racing machines, where longevity is not a vital ingredient but weight-saving is, it may be feasible to reduce the ratio a little further.

Normal boatbuilding resins burn spectacularly as any witness to a boat fire can testify. There are self-extinguishing resins on the market which will not support combustion and will cease to burn once the source of ignition has been removed, but they are less weather resistant and less waterproof than conventional resins. It may be worthwhile employing them on the innermost laminations in the engine space but they are not really used much in yacht building. One application is for the hulls of tankers' lifeboats.

Epoxy resins

The unsaturated polyesters are good, moderately priced all-rounders. Great strength, adhesion and waterproofing qualities can be had by using epoxy resins, though for the penalties of greater cost and more difficult application. Where weight (and thus resin) saving is of paramount importance epoxy resins are used. Resin-to-glass ratios can be reduced by their application, but they are not often found on production boats.

Vinylester resins

Vinylester resins are a sort of halfway house between polyesters and epoxies both in regard to cost and performance. They are almost as easy to work as polyesters but, like the epoxies, will stretch more and are consequently less brittle and will take a greater load before failure. So far they have not been used very extensively in boatbuilding but their day may come.

The laminating process

Assuming a female mould, this is first polished and then coated with a release agent. As the name implies this is used to prevent the laminate sticking to the mould. After that, the gel coat is brushed or sprayed on. The durability of a GRP moulding is mainly dependent on the quality of its exposed surfaces, and every effort must be made to prevent the layers of reinforcement straying too close to that surface where they are liable to act as magnets for moisture. Thus a thick layer of resin is needed on the outside and this is called the gel coat. It may be reinforced with a thin surfacing tissue of glassfibre to hold the resin and help balance the laminate. After the gel coat has been applied and is sufficiently hard comes a coat of laminating resin, on which is laid the first layer of glassfibre reinforcement. Another coating of resin follows, worked past the glass strands by the combination of a stippling action with a paintbrush and rolling with a special roller to get rid of air bubbles. This done, further coats of glassfibre and resin are applied in the same way until the desired number of layers has been reached.

The weight of a laminate is usually defined by the glassfibre weight alone. Thus its final weight will be given as so many ounces per square foot or grammes per square metre. This weight will vary over different areas of the boat and is normally at its greatest along the keel. The bottom will be heavier than the sides, and the middle of the boat heavier than her ends. All this is achieved by adding layers of glass and resin to the basic laminate. In addition there is usually a length of heavier laminate at the top of the hull, extending a little way down the sides and extending over about half the length. When the shell has been laid up, stiffeners in the form of stringers and frames are added. These are usually formed from an expanded foam and glassed over to the required weight. Finally the inside of the hull may have a coat of surfacing tissue applied to hide the coarse weave of the glassfibre and to provide a reasonable surface for painting.

Though hull lay-ups are mostly defined by weight, a rough approximation of thickness can be made by taking 1oz of glass (combined with the appropriate amount of resin) as being 1/32nd of an inch thick. In metric terms that means that a 300 gram per square metre laminate will be about 0.8mm thick. So, for example, an 8oz lay-up will be 8 × 1/32 = 1/4in thick.

As an alternative to this hand lay-up method the glass and resin may be sprayed on. Here the rovings are chopped up and fed out through the nozzle of a special gun. Resin is sprayed out simultaneously from the same gun in the correct proportions. Though the mixture still needs consolidating with rollers, labour costs are reduced. The difficulty, which can be overcome by a skilled operator, is in ensuring that a uniform thickness is achieved.

Resins may be clear or pigmented to the desired colour. Common practice is to use clear laminating resins throughout but to pigment the gel coat on the topsides. On the bottom even this coat may be unpigmented since the bottom has to be painted anyway (with antifouling). The reason for using clear resins is that it is then easier to spot dry patches as laminating proceeds than if the resin is coloured.

Dry or resin-starved areas are sources of both weakness and potential trouble. Water will travel up the strands of dry reinforcement as if along a wick. This can, in serious cases, lead to the breakdown of the laminate. If voids are left in the laminate, as air bubbles perhaps, water migrating through the gel coat will build up pressure in these voids through osmosis and cause blistering. To prevent further damage these blisters then have to be ground off and left to dry completely. The cavities must next be filled (preferably with an epoxy putty), ground smooth, and subsequently coated with several layers of epoxy resin – the epoxy being more waterproof than the original gel coat. All this is expensive and indicates the need for careful workmanship. It also suggests that painting the inside of the laminate with a weather-proof coating is very advisable, since on most boats water is present both inside and outside the hull.

Vacuum bagging

This is a scheme where a plastic bag (generally disposable) is placed over the mould and the air evacuated from it to allow the atmospheric pressure of some 1kg/cm² (14.7lb/sq in) to press evenly on the laminate, which is between the bag and the mould face. This pressure will squeeze the resin into the reinforcing absolutely equally and consolidate the laminate.

So far so good, but it will be obvious that on a normal GRP construction the whole laminating procedure must have been finished before the bag is applied, and none of the resin must have started to gel or cure. It also means that by some method the resin that was applied to the sides must be prevented from running down into the bottom before the air has been pumped out of the bag. All this can be achieved by a few builders but it is not easy, and so vacuum bagging is normally confined to small boats where the lay-up can be done quickly. More appears about vacuum bagging below.

Pre-pregs

Another offshoot from the aerospace industry is pre-impregnated reinforcing. The reinforcing may be woven roving, uni-directional roving or even chopped strand mat. Whatever form the reinforcing takes, it is saturated with resin to the desired resin-to-glass ratio by the makers and then refrigerated to stop the resin curing. The builder then gets this pre-preg with a protective film on each side, and he stores it in a cold or refrigerated room. When required it is cut to shape from patterns, and the desired number of thicknesses are laid in the mould (after removing the protective film). At room temperature the material will have a useful life of a week or two. Anyway, the mould is next vacuum bagged and then placed in an oven where everything is heated to about 120°C (250°F) for several hours, and the laminate is then cured.

This form of building (though expensive) means that laminators do not have to crawl about in the bottom of the boat getting messy and distributing unequal amounts of resin through the structure. The resin-to-glass ratio is determined by the factory. Foam or sandwich honeycomb construction can be used by placing pre-pregs each side of the core.

Foam sandwich construction

An alternative way of building a GRP vessel is to use a male batten mould and foam sandwich construction. Here a complete layer of some foamed plastic sheeting is laid over the mould and fastened down. Even string will do for this fastening, tying the foam tight to the battens from which it can eventually be cut. Over this foam is laid the appropriate weight of glass and resin. When this has cured the hull is lifted off the mould and further layers of glass and resin applied inside. The batten mould is comparatively cheap but, since neither GRP skin has been in contact with a smooth surface, there is a considerable amount of work involved in finishing off the hull to an acceptable standard of smoothness. This means that the final hull is not likely to be any cheaper than one made in a normal, female mould though this method is well suited to 'one-offs' where the cost of a conventional mould, which would have to be written off in the price of one boat, would be prohibitive.

Decks, superstructures and bulkheads

Decks and superstructures are generally laminated together in a single mould. The moulding will often incorporate the cockpit as well. Since GRP is not a very rigid material, areas which tend to be wide but poorly supported, such as cabin tops, often incorporate some depth-giving material in the laminate. This might be foamed plastics, end-grain balsa wood or even honeycomb paper, and its object is to make the laminate deeper and stiffer without increasing weight dramatically. The core material is sandwiched between layers of glassfibre and resin. Reinforcing pads in the way of deck fittings and the like are also bonded into the laminate while it is still in the mould. The pads are generally of thick marine ply. The final moulding is bonded and bolted to some suitable connection on the hull.

Bulkheads are nearly always of marine ply. Though it would be possible to have them of a foam or honeycomb core construction (solid GRP would not be stiff enough without being excessively heavy), the weight saving is not normally considered worthwhile when set against the extra cost and complications.

10.4.4 Cold and hot moulded timber

In this construction a male mould is used. The hull is made up of several layers of thin ply or veneer (three thicknesses being the minimum) all bonded together with, these days, an epoxy glue or resin. The first layer of timber runs at about 45° to the keel; the second layer at right angles to the first; and the third, if the outermost layer, runs fore and aft or at right angles to the keel or in the same direction as the first, Fig. 10(35).

The keel, stem and sometimes the transom framing are let into the mould which is covered with something to prevent the hull sticking to it — even newspaper will do. This is carried up to but not over the keel and stem. The first layer of planking is then close butted, glued to keel and stem and stapled to the mould. The planks will normally be not more than about 4in (100mm) wide so that there is not a lot of shaping to do. The staples are fastened through scraps of thin ply or straddle a piece of thin cord, so that by levering the ply or heaving the cord they can be easily removed. Another thickness of planking is stapled and glued to the first with the original staples being removed as work progresses. The next layer is completed the same way, and so on. Finally the hull is sanded down and probably given some coats of epoxy resin which permeate the outer fibres of the timber and give a hard, waterproof finish. The whole job has been most likely done upside down, so the hull is finally lifted off the mould and inverted for the framing to be added. The inside surface of the hull is also given a coat of epoxy.

The result is a boat of superior strength and one which comes out lighter than almost any other form of construction, barring foam sandwich GRP which might equal it. With the epoxy resins used, rot and water soakage no longer present the problems they did on traditionally-built timber hulls.

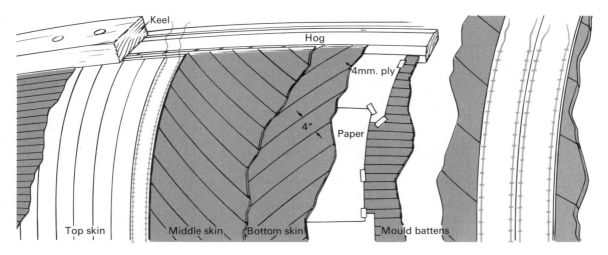

Fig. 10(35) Cold moulding consists of glueing several skins of veneer or thin ply together over a mould. Staples may be fastened over a cord for easy removal.

Boats like the Fairey Huntsman, Fisherman, Atalanta and others were built in a similar manner, though epoxy glues were not available in those days. The building process went one stage further in that a rubber bag was placed over the glued-up hull and the air inside exhausted. This created an even pressure over the whole hull and virtually ensured good contact between all timber/glue/timber faces. The boat and bag were then wheeled into an oven, or autoclave, into which steam was introduced to supply heat and more pressure, and to ensure that the glue permeated every crevice and finally set hard regardless of conditions in the workshop. This was an excellent form of construction but the cost of autoclave, rubber bag and heating equipment in the end made it uneconomic.

10.4.5 Ply construction
In the 1950s and 1960s, before the rise of GRP construction, marine plywood was widely used as a boatbuilding material. It is strong and light but to use it economically in sheet form demands a hard chine or V-bottom hull. There is little wrong with such a shape but today it is unfashionable. The use of epoxy resins and glues at all joints, scarphs and faying surfaces should cure the previous tendency of the ply to delaminate and then rot. Provided the ply is to BSS1088 (and preferably inspected during manufacture as being up to that standard) and epoxies are employed, a marine ply boat should have a long life. It can, of course, be sheathed in nylon or glassfibre as an additional precaution.

As a rule plywood boats are framed conventionally, with timber longitudinals at the keel, chine, and gunwale; but on small craft these are largely eliminated in favour of glassfibre and resin corner pieces. What happens is that the sheets of ply that form the hull of the boat are butted up and sewn together with twists of copper wire. Glassfibre tape or chopped strand mat is then laid over the sewn edges and coated with resin. The process of laminating can be done in as many layers as needed and duplicated on the inside of the craft. This angle of GRP sticks well to the ply and makes for a strong and lightweight structure. Polyester resins are usually used though the more expensive epoxies will do a slightly better job. If the ply forming the sides, bottom and deck is cut accurately from a template this is a simple and quick form of building. It is impossible to put a boat together in any but the intended form if the panels forming the hull are the correct shape.

10.4.6 Steel construction
Steel boats are slowly but steadily finding favour among the cruising fraternity. The reasons for this are that with modern coatings (epoxies or chlorinated rubber) applied after thorough shot blasting, maintenance requirements are low and rusting is no longer the problem it once was. Steel is very strong and will merely bend under an impact that would shatter a GRP or timber hull, and which might tear a hole in aluminium alloy. With good design a 'one-off' single or double chine vessel in steel need cost no more than a production GRP yacht, because the material itself is comparatively inexpensive and is quickly converted to boat form with proper thought in the design and planning stages. Steel is stiff and on small craft the shell requires little additional stiffening or framing other than that which is needed to form the boundaries of bulkheads. But it is indisputably heavy. The hull will weigh maybe twice as much as one of GRP or alloy, and though the completed boat will not weigh twice as much, since fitting out weights will be similar on boats of every form of construction, the additional hull weight may not be acceptable on performance craft. Distortion can be a real problem when welding steel plates less than about 3mm ($\frac{1}{8}$in) thick. This prevents steel boats competing with

rivals built of lighter materials simply by cutting down on plate thickness. In the days of riveting though, very light plates could be and were used (the Thornycroft-built launch *Ariel* of 1863 vintage had iron hull plates 0.6mm ($\frac{1}{40}$in) thick) but today a riveted hull would be expensive as compared with welding, not least because rivets for very thin plating would probably have to be specifically made.

Steel used in boatbuilding is usually to BS4360 43A which is a fairly conventional mild steel. Special steels such as Corten, which has a low carbon content and additions of copper and manganese, have been tried but have not been found to offer sufficient advantages to outweigh their higher initial cost.

Framing on small craft is normally flat bar, and on bigger boats angle bar with the toe welded to the shell. The same types of section are used for the longitudinal stiffeners. Because large, flat areas of steel are unattractive to look at, may even be wavy and anyway are heavy, bulkheads are usually of marine ply. The exceptions are the forward collision bulkhead and possibly another just forward of the engine room. These will be steel and watertight. Decks and upperworks are often of steel, too, though an all-steel boat can have compass problems, especially if the compass cannot be mounted on the centreline. Though a compass adjuster can usually cope, if cost is not of primary importance there is a case for making the surrounding structure (such as the wheelhouse or indeed the whole superstructure) of timber or aluminium alloy. Failing that, the compass can always be mounted at some distance from magnetic materials, and it is normally happy enough set in a pedestal on deck.

Integral tanks are simple to arrange on steel boats but it is important to ensure that there are adequate manholes in them to allow inspection and repair as required. Too many steel boats are built without real thought, using traditional wood building as a basis for construction. This leads to a proliferation of unwanted objects such as chine, keel and stem bars. It is easier, cheaper and just as satisfactory simply to butt plates together in these areas and weld. Welding may be of the simple electric arc type, or the more sophisticated and slightly more expensive shielded arc process where the arc is shrouded in an inert gas such as CO. This last type of welding makes for less distortion.

10.4.7 Aluminium alloy construction

Despite its many attractions and advantages aluminium boats have never been very popular in this country. From time to time 'one-offs' have been built and occasionally some brave soul announces a limited production run, but generally the material is treated with grave suspicion or ignored altogether. This must be partly due to the attitude of the manufacturers who seem to make no serious effort to promote its use and who, by their complicated pricing structure, ensure that costing a boat in its early stages is as difficult as possible; waverers are thereby quickly eliminated.

Aluminium alloy cannot rust or rot. It needs painting, apart from antifouling, only for cosmetic purposes and it is light and strong. Its principal disadvantage is that it is incompatible with many other of the traditional non-ferrous materials used in boatbuilding, such as the brasses and bronzes. In their presence under water it is quickly eaten away through electrolytic or galvanic action (10.5.7). However it is generally possible to substitute some other material. Thus, seacocks may be bought made in aluminium alloy, and stainless steel (which produces no fierce reaction) can often be used. As a last resort just about anything can be hard chrome plated for complete protection. Aluminium alloy is popular with companies working in the less developed countries, where boats may have a bad time in the hands of unskilled crews and get minimum maintenance.

Just like steel, an alloy vessel may be of any shape desired but if she is of single or double chine form labour costs will be reduced. Alloy is normally welded (with an inert gas type of welder), though it is often riveted on small boats to eliminate distortion and to allow thin plates to be used. A typical hull structure will weigh about half as much as steel and about the same as GRP. An alloy plate with equal resistance to bending as steel will be about $1\frac{1}{2}$ times as thick, but about half as thick as ply or a GRP laminate. An alloy boat is built in very much the same way as a steel boat, with frames and longitudinals reducing unsupported panel size. Since it is non-magnetic, alloy presents no compass problems. The aluminium alloy used is normally a British Standard alloy 5083 and though a hull might cost two or three times as much as the steel equivalent, the hull alone represents only a small percentage of complete boat cost and so this figure is not as damning as it first appears.

10.4.8 Ferro-concrete construction

This is a labour-intensive and somewhat heavy form of building that was once all the rage amongst amateur builders of cruising vessels, but which is now less so. The materials are cheap and since conscientious rather than particularly skilled work is required (up to the final stage where the concrete is plastered over the framework) it has its attractions for those who feel they cannot cope with the more traditional forms of boatbuilding. The plastering can be done by professional teams so that a good standard can be achieved at this vital stage, and since it is not really a lengthy process (it is generally reckoned that it is best completed in a single day) the cost involved is not prohibitive. If properly built, a ferro-concrete hull is strong and does not suffer from defects which can afflict other materials: it will not burn, rot, corrode, be eaten by worms, or develop osmosis. It is also easy to repair.

On the debit side, though the work is straightforward enough it is very time consuming and very hard as some builders discovered to their dismay. Secondly, since the actual building materials are cheap people are tempted to turn their hands to craft which are far too big for their pockets, forgetting that the hull alone represents only a fraction of overall cost and that fitting out a big boat is expensive regardless of its constructional material. Thirdly, the re-sale value of the amateur-built ferro-concrete yacht tends to be low since prospective buyers cannot judge the overall standard of workmanship. Everything is hidden under the concrete and that itself, since it has been made on site, might not be up to scratch. It is difficult, even with professional plastering, to ensure that there are no voids or cavities which can cause problems with corrosion, strength and leakage, and such faults are not easily disclosed by surveys. And finally, though conscientious work will produce a fair hull and one that accords with the designer's drawings, slipshod work will result in a bumpy abomination.

Ferro-concrete boats may be built on a full, male mould (that is, they are constructed on the outside of the mould); on a batten mould (though one that has considerably fewer battens than the type used in cold moulded timber); or the boat's own frames may be erected as a basis (as in traditional timber and steel construction). Basically the idea is that to a backbone of, generally, steel pipe, with pipe transverse frames and closely-spaced round bar longitudinals, several layers of chicken wire or similar steel mesh are fastened. This mesh is lashed to the framing with twists of wire, with the same scheme being used to tie the individual layers of mesh to each other. Everything is then faired and smoothed until it gives an accurate representation of the contours of the hull. The mesh acts as a reinforcement for the concrete and obviously can be formed to the correct shape more easily if it can be hammered against a full mould than if simply draped round a framework. However it is said that when the concrete is applied (and this is a very solid mix with a water/cement ratio of about 0.35 with $3\frac{1}{2}$ gallons of water to each 112lb bag of cement (15.4 litres per 50kg) and a sand/cement ratio of roughly 2:1 by weight) it is difficult to avoid air entrapment even where vibrators are used.

On this count the open batten or open frames methods where concrete is applied from inside and outside the hull are preferred. Various additions may be made to the cement/sand/water mix to delay curing (which may be important in hot weather); to reduce water requirement and so to increase strength; and by imparting minute air bubbles, to prolong the life of the concrete where alternate freezing and thawing cycles occur. But such additions are controversial and many builders prefer to use simple Portland cement and to rely on a good standard of workmanship for prolonging life and achieving adequate strength.

It is most important that none of the reinforcing mesh pierces the surface of the concrete or indeed comes very close to it, or it will start to rust and so bring about the eventual breakdown of the structure. Careful workmanship is thus very necessary. In addition the hull is normally painted with an epoxy resin to reduce water absorption.

Decks and even deckhouses may be ferro-concrete but more usually the latter are of timber bolted to a suitable flange formed in the structure. Slow curing is vital with this type of construction, and the hull should be kept moist for at least 28 days after concreting. This is normally achieved by tying sacks round the outside and draping other sacks inside. These are kept continuously moist with fine sprays of water. The water that collects in the hull drains out through previously prepared holes in the bottom into which can be rammed wooden plugs.

Some ferro-concrete boats are built commercially but their price, due to the large labour content in construction, is not very different from craft built in more conventional ways.

10.4.9 Timber construction

With timber planking various options are open. A close relative to cold moulding for instance, is the double diagonal planking once used throughout the RNLI fleet, on ships' lifeboats and on many small naval craft. Here the planking is put on in two layers, the first at about 45° to the keel and the second running at about 90° to the first. Between the two is laid a layer of unbleached calico soaked in thick white lead paint. The planking is fastened with copper nails and roves (rather like riveting over a washer) as Fig. 10(36) demonstrates. This type of planking makes for a strong hull with only comparatively short lengths of planking needed. Another short plank method is long diagonal, where the planking runs up at an angle to the keel but there is only one skin. The scheme here is to butt succeeding planks against one another, run a spindle up the jointing faces to cut away wood and ensure a perfect fit, and then edge-glue.

When planking runs longitudinally it might be carvel (a flush outside surface with caulking cotton and white lead stopping between the plank edges) or clinker, where the planks overlap along their edges. Plank fastenings with the latter method are normally copper nails and roves. No stopping or caulking is used except along the planks which are fastened into the keel. Everything depends upon a good fit and the natural swelling of wood in water.

Carvel planking has its own variations. In top class building the caulking between the planks is sometimes replaced by a thin strip of wood, glued into place. This is known as splined planking, while if the seams in the planking have a batten fastened along inside the hull to cover them this is called seam batten construction. Shortly before

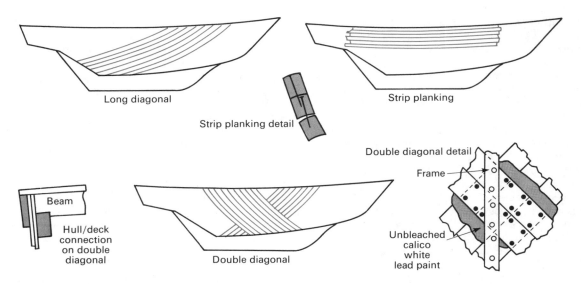

Fig. 10(36) Various types of flush timber planking are possible and three are illustrated here.

cold moulding became popular a common method of planking was to employ what is known as strip planking. With this the planking is in quite narrow strakes which may be rounded or hollowed, as shown in Fig. 10(36), and is the method recommended by Lloyd's, or they may simply be accurately bevelled. All these glued and multi-skinned types of construction make for strong and watertight hulls where it is often possible to save weight in the framing but which are rather difficult to repair.

The two basic methods of framing are to use either sawn frames (originally sawn to shape from the solid, though using natural crooks and following the grain of the timber as far as possible, but now often laminated to shape) or steam bent timbers. In the former the keel, stem, transom and other items of the boat's backbone are erected on the shop floor and the frames next set in place and attached, via their floors, to the keel. They are then faired and the planking fastened. With steamed timbers the backbone is erected as before but in place of the frames are building patterns to give the shape of the hull at a few different positions along its length. If clinker planking is being used this is now set up and fastened. Only then are the closely spaced frames, which are quite small and steamed to make them supple and easy to bend, put in position.

On other forms of construction (such as double diagonal) the frame patterns may have ribbands or longitudinal stringers let in to give more bearing surface for the planking while it is being fastened. With the hull complete and steamed timbers in place the building moulds can be removed for use on another boat. Of course there are variations and even outright contradictions of the methods described, but they illustrate the normal difference between sawn and steamed frame construction. Some craft have a mixture of sawn and steamed

frames, in which case the frames are erected first and the steamed timbers put in later.

WEST

Timber has an excellent strength-to-weight ratio, particularly where woods like spruce, ash, fir and cedar are concerned. In this respect they are generally superior to any rival boatbuilding material apart perhaps from advanced foam/GRP sandwiches. But to take advantage of this strength and to produce a correspondingly light boat the hull must be a homogeneous whole and the timber must be dry. Strength properties fall off rapidly with every increase in water content of the wood. Further, if that content can be held below 20 per cent rot will be very unlikely to develop.

What all this means in practice is that rather than the vessel consisting of masses of individual bits of wood nailed, screwed or bolted together everything must be bonded into a single structure, which acts as a whole to resist stresses and strains. It also means that the wood must be artificially dried (in this country at least) to a low moisture content (say 12 per cent), assembled in a warm and dry workshop, and then completely coated in a substance that repels both water and water vapour. Repelling water is not too difficult and many paints and sheathings do it quite well, but water vapour is a gas that penetrates the cell walls much more readily than water itself. This vapour is obviously present inside the boat as much as, or even more than, on the outside in the form of bilge water, condensation, human breath, wet clothing, cooking and sundry other items. All are adding to the relative humidity and something better than paint is needed in order to combat it.

The Gougeon brothers in the USA developed epoxy resins that would seal timber very effectively, and could be used as strong, gap-filling adhesives. They termed this the WEST (Wood

Epoxy Saturation Technique) system. The term 'saturation' is misleading since the resin does not saturate the timber, but encapsulates it and penetrates to the level of the firmly attached fibres. There are now rivals to the WEST system, but in every case it is important that every piece of timber both inside and outside be thoroughly coated with resin, so that it is completely sealed and cannot absorb moisture. These systems are most commonly used in cold-moulded construction (10.4.4).

Because the epoxy resin has very good gap-filling properties without loss of strength, accurately fitting joints are not so important as in conventional timber construction. Very little clamping pressure is needed, and staples are usually enough to hold strips of timber for the moulding operation. The resin is clear and glue lines are not evident, which allows exterior surfaces to be left varnished and showing a nice timber finish.

There are disadvantages; first epoxy resins are expensive. They also require careful handling because they can cause dermatitis, and need accurate mixing. Careful control of the moulding operation is required because the resins have a short pot life.

10.4.10 Classification and certification

All yachts built to Lloyd's requirements may be assigned the classification of 100A1, while if they are also built under the Society's special survey they are entitled to put the symbol ✠ before the 100A1. The figure 1, incidentally, denotes that equipment in the way of cables, anchors, hawsers and warps accord with the Rules. A yacht with this full classification must have a full survey every four years and intermediate biennial surveys to remain in class. A machinery classification, ✠ LMC or ★ LMC, may also be assigned.

Where owners do not want to get involved with these surveys their boats may have a Hull Construction Certificate and a Machinery Installation Certificate. If they have both of these then the craft carries a Lloyd's Register Building Certificate, or LRBC for short. Though there is no requirement for a survey (apart from that involved during construction) Lloyd's will carry out one at any time after completion if requested. More information on Lloyd's Register of Shipping is given in Chapter 1 (1.5.6).

10.5 Practical considerations

10.5.1 Hulls in practice

The previous sections have dealt with basic design considerations and brief descriptions of building methods. However, most owners are stuck with what they have and though with a bit of knowledge of hull balance, stability, resistance or trim, or any of the other subjects already covered, they may be able to improve their craft in various ways, they cannot profoundly change its in-built qualities. What they might be able to do, on the other hand, is to make minor changes to create, perhaps, a safer or even drier boat.

10.5.2 Decks

With GRP construction it is extremely difficult to mould in a really satisfactory non-slip deck surface. It is often tried but, though the result may be quite good on the first few craft of the production run, gradually the non-skid pattern becomes less prominent in the mould and less effective in practice. Moulding in a pattern is cheap, but a better result is normally achieved by bonding one of the excellent non-skid materials available on to a smooth deck. The material need not cover the whole deck but should be placed wherever people are likely to walk or be standing to work the boat. Thus areas round the mast and the forestay for instance, should be covered, with patches on deck providing a safe walkway to these spots.

The alternative to sticking on specially designed materials is to use a non-skid deck paint. In commercial form this is basically a low gloss paint in which is mixed silver sand. Stirred vigorously and painted all over the deck it is effective and not expensive. A similar effect can be achieved by sprinkling sawdust on wet paint and subsequently painting again over everything. Sawdust tends to have unexpected lumps in it which are painful to bare feet, so it should be put through a fine sieve before use. Deck paints work equally well on all surfaces, but a scrubbed wooden deck (preferably of teak) has built-in non-skid properties and does not need touching.

10.5.3 Windows, ports and hatches

Windows, especially when bent round the curve of the cabin side and then bolted to the non-uniform thickness of the average cabin side GRP moulding, tend to leak. This tendency is exaggerated if the windows have alloy frames, which become distorted in the bending, and if they were also designed to slide open. Cabin sides, ideally, are straight, changing angle occasionally to give the required side deck width, but generally all that can be done with a leaking window is to take it off and re-bed it.

Ports are generally smaller and better, and as their opening capability is achieved through top hinging plus side and bottom clamps, they can generally be persuaded to stay tight. Ports do not have to be round; there are rectangular versions available which work well. On steel, alloy and wood the tendency to leak is minimized by the fact that the cabin sides are uniformly thick.

Hatches tend to leak too, and the only type with a reasonable prospect of keeping all the water

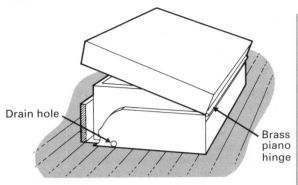

Drain hole

Brass
piano
hinge

Fig. 10(37) The Maurice Griffiths type of hatch has two coamings with a gap and water drainage between the two.

out even in bad weather is the double coaming type, Fig. 10(37), originally developed by Maurice Griffiths.

10.5.4 Cockpit drains
Too many cockpit drains are based on standard household waste systems for reasons of economy, and are consequently hopelessly inadequate in area. According to the Norwegian authorities, all craft with cockpit soles 35cm (14in) or more above the waterline should have drains in accordance with the following formula:
Total drain area (sq cm) = 40 + (15 × area of cockpit sole in square metres).
That could be written in imperial units as:
Area of drains (sq in) = 0.155 × (40 + 1.4A) where A is the cockpit sole area in square feet. If the cockpit sole was, for example, 6ft × 3ft (18sq ft) the drain area should be:
Area = 0.155 × [40 + (1.4 × 18)] = 0.155 × 65 = 10sq in
That means two drains each 63mm (2½in) diameter. They can be crossed if desired so that the port side drain exhausts on the starboard side and vice versa. This means that the leeward drain outlet, which may well be under water, will not flood the cockpit. On the other hand it will not drain it very well either. On a cockpit with its sole well above the waterline it is probably better to have straight-through drains with as short a pipe length as possible, exiting above the waterline. The two last suggestions are to help speed the flow of water through the pipe.
A rough guide to the length of time taken to empty a cockpit is given by the formula:

$$T = \frac{A \times \sqrt{D}}{2B}$$

where T is the time taken to empty, in seconds; A is the sole area of the cockpit in square feet; D is the depth of water to which it is flooded, in feet, and B is the drain area in square feet.
If a 1.8m × 0.9m (6ft × 3ft) cockpit were flooded to a depth of 0.6m (2ft), two 75mm (3in) diameter drains would empty it in about 2 minutes; with twin 38mm (1½) drains it would take about 10½ minutes; and with 25mm (1in) drains

about 21 minutes. The last two are clearly not very comforting figures.
Cockpit drains should have seacocks at their outlets.

10.5.5 Stanchions and toerails
These are safety items and need to be substantial and very well fastened. Stanchions below about 0.6m (2ft) in height are not a lot of use in preventing a body catapulted from one side of the deck to the other from going overboard. If they are 0.75m (2ft 6in) they will be better and anything more is better still. The strains that a flailing body puts on the stanchion base fastenings are enormous, and they must be through-bolted, not screwed. On a GRP craft there must be thick and wide backing plates (usually of marine ply) under the bolts, which might otherwise be pulled straight through the deck. Toe rails bounding the deck edge are a safety feature too, and not merely to stop small items rolling over the side. They should be something like 75mm (2½ to 3in) high and again be through-bolted.

10.5.6 Maintenance and repair
If a boat is to have a long and useful life it pays to have a look at things in detail from time to time, rather than simply standing back and admiring the general picture. Small blemishes in paint or varnish work can turn into large blemishes unless attended to in their early stages, and the same applies to cracks in the gel coat of GRP craft. Stress cracks, like those that sometimes appear in regions of high stress – an instance being in the area round the chain plates – should be looked at by an expert and some remedial action taken. After all, these show that everything is not quite as it should be, and the chain plates might need to be lengthened or have arms welded to them to distribute their load over a wider area. Check that the bow roller runs freely in the stemhead fitting, or raising the anchor will be doubly difficult, while all shackles should be looked at to spot undue wear. The loss of a small and cheap item like a shackle can lead to the loss of a boat easily enough.
With the boat hauled out the opportunity should be taken to examine the sacrificial anodes (see also 10.5.7) for excessive wasting; to check on the state of the propeller shaft and its bearing (seize the prop and shake it violently – if there is much movement the shaft or bearing or both need renewing); and to check on rudder bearing wear. If these bearings are bolted to the hull the bolts themselves ought to be examined. Take a couple out and see if they are wasted, which may be the case if they are brass or stainless steel. If the bearing cannot be removed hit the heads of the bolts hard with a hammer to see if they fall off – they might! All sorts of afflictions can occur among metal items below the waterline, from rusting and stress corrosion to dezincification. (See also 10.5.7.)

Blisters on the bottom of a GRP vessel should be viewed with the gravest suspicion as they may well indicate the onset of osmosis (see also 10.4.3) which needs quick remedial action. Pitting on the bottom plates of a steel boat probably means that the mill scale that is present on the surface of all steel plate after rolling was not properly removed during shot blasting, and a more thorough examination is indicated. On a wooden boat a sharp bradawl or something similar should be poked into the planking, especially along the length between wind and water and at the ends where the planking is rebated into the stem, keel and transom, to check for softness or rot. In fact, have a good look at everything that will all too soon be hidden from view again below the water. Seacock fastenings should be checked and, if possible, a keel bolt drawn for examination. If this cannot be done hit the heads with a hammer, as with the rudder bearings, to check on the state of the metal.

Leaks round deck erections are a curse on wooden boats and occur, too, on GRP craft which have timber deckhouses. Fresh water leaks can lead to rot and not just discomfort below. If the joint or connection is at all suspect clear away all the previous water-stopping treatment, which might take the form of an ineffective quarter-round beading lightly bedded on some compound, and glue a strip of nylon along the joint with resorcinal glue. Ordinary shirt nylon will do quite well, but an alternative is to use glassfibre tape, and polyester or epoxy resin. The nylon method is very effective on an all-wood structure but no use where GRP is concerned. Epoxy putties are great fillers of holes and dents in all materials, but take a great deal of sanding

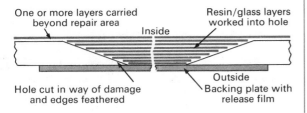

One or more layers carried beyond repair area
Inside
Resin/glass layers worked into hole
Hole cut in way of damage and edges feathered
Outside
Backing plate with release film

Fig. 10(38) If damage has penetrated right through a GRP hull, then it is best to work on the repair from the inside.

off afterwards so probably the car body repair kits are best for work on GRP construction. On major repairs to GRP the damage needs to be ground back to sound laminate and thoroughly cleaned out. When this has been done the area should be dried and degreased. If the damage has not penetrated right through the hull the repair consists of filling the hole with resin and glassfibre mat — as if normal laminating were being carried out (10.4.3) — until the repair is slightly proud of the surface. Then a plastic sheet like cellophane is smoothed on and taped over the repair and everything is left to dry. Lastly the surface can be

ground smooth and the appropriately-coloured two-pot polyurethane paint applied. If the damage extends right through the hull, it is best tackled from inside. The damaged area is ground out and feather-edged as indicated in Fig. 10(38). A backing piece of ply or something similar is attached to the outside of the hull (or wedged against it). This is coated with a release agent and then, if possible, gel coated. The hole is made good with layers of glassfibre and resin with a few layers taken beyond the damaged area. This is covered with a cellophane film and everything allowed to dry, when the backing piece and film are removed and the repair ground smooth on the inside and painted outside if gel coat was not available.

All GRP work should take place in reasonably calm and certainly dry conditions. Warmth assists rapid resin cure, and an electric fire pointing at the repaired section will help things along. Plastic hulls respond well to regular washing off and polishing with one of the many proprietary polishes on the market, but avoid the silicone variety which is difficult to remove if the boat ever needs painting.

Repairs on other forms of construction consist of seeing how the job was done in the first place and then copying the method as far as possible. Much use can often be made of the modern gap-filling epoxy resins which will disguise many deficiencies in workmanship. They will easily fill gaps of up to 6mm ($\frac{1}{4}$in) in width, and even more if extended with a suitable filler. Epoxy paints can be used on all forms of construction and are very waterproof and hard. After a while even wet and dry paper does not seem to touch them, but they do tend to 'chalk' quite quickly. For this reason a final coat of two-pot polyurethane is often applied over an epoxy where a good finish is wanted.

10.5.7 Electrolytic action

Sea water is an admirable electrolyte and that being so two dissimilar metals in close proximity under water tend to form a cell with the current flowing from one to another. This has the effect of wasting away the anodic or more base of the metals. The following table puts some typical boatbuilding metals in a rough electrochemical series with the noble, or cathodic materials at the top.

Galvanic series in sea water
Noble or cathodic end
    Stainless steel type 316 (2 per cent molybdenum)
    Stainless steel type 304
    Stainless steel type 321 (0.4 per cent titanium)
    Monel
    Gunmetal
    Phosphor bronze
    Admiralty brass
    Red brass
    Copper
    Naval brass
    Manganese bronze

Muntz metal
Lead
Stainless steels with oxide destroyed
Cast iron
Mild steel
Aluminium alloys
Cadmium plating
Galvanised steel
Zinc
Magnesium
Base or anodic end

Stainless steel appears in two positions in the table, which is confusing. As delivered, and in normal use with the oxide film that forms naturally to protect the metal intact, stainless steel is among the most noble and corrosion resistant of materials. However the maintenance of that oxide film requires the presence of oxygen which in certain places (such as under a barnacle) may be absent. In other areas as, for instance, where a shaft passes through a rubber bearing, the oxide film may be worn away and the oxygen prevented from reaching the surface. Here what is known as crevice corrosion may occur, and where this happens stainless steel drops down the galvanic series towards the base end and is liable to corrosion. The metal does not change; it is simply that its protective skin (which is formed in other alloys, such as aluminium alloy, in much the same way) is destroyed locally. The addition of molybdenum, as in the 316 alloys, minimises crevice corrosion. The presence of titanium, on the other hand, though it makes for easier welding, reduces resistance to corrosion. If the oxide film is restored the material will again move to the noble end of the scale.

It is clear why zinc anodes are used. They will be attacked before any other of the usual metals and, that being so, will protect them. Magnesium anodes are generally preferred in fresh water, incidentally. The size, positioning and installation of all such sacrificial anodes is best left to the professionals. These anodes should never be painted. Paint acts as a protection against galvanic corrosion (and so is very important) but anodes are meant to be attacked and corroded. Even where cathodic protection is fitted, leakage from insulation faults in electrical circuits can cause rapid corrosion under water, see Chapter 13 (13.3.4).

When deciding on what metals to use underwater the distance they are apart on the galvanic series is one important factor (the greater the distance the more serious the action); the other is their relative bulk. Thus, for instance, if a yacht were copper sheathed and iron fastenings were used, the iron would be attacked which would be dangerous. On the other hand if for some reason gunmetal bolts were put through an iron keel, though the iron would still be wasted that would not be too serious. Taking an even more extreme example, stainless steel shafts are sometimes used

in conjunction with aluminium alloy hulls, and though the aluminium will be attacked, because there is such a vast area compared with that of the shafts the effect is generally not serious. Aluminium alloy shafts in a stainless hull (if such could be imagined) would be asking for trouble.

Mill scale on steel plating is another example of dissimilar metals in action. Mill scale, which occurs as the plates are being rolled, comprises various ferric oxides, among them magnetite. This is about as cathodic to iron as copper, and where paint has been removed and sea water can get at the scale, the plating will be attacked and eaten away. Thus the removal of mill scale by shot blasting or other means is most important on steel craft, just as is the maintenance of a protective film of paint.

Brass is an alloy of copper and zinc. It can be guessed that in the presence of sea water the zinc will be wasted away. This is called dezincification and leaves the metal copper-coloured, crumbly and quite lacking in strength.

10.5.8 Painting
Painting is still extensively used on yachts, both to protect surfaces above and below the water and for cosmetic purposes. Even a GRP hull needs antifouling unless the boat is normally kept out of the water, and epoxy paint systems are being increasingly used on GRP hulls to combat osmosis, or to restore and protect the surface after osmosis has been treated (see 10.5.6).

Terms like two-pot polyurethane, wet edge time and pot life do sound rather forbidding, and modern paint systems are chemically very complex – so it is vital to follow in detail the instructions which are issued by paint makers. Nevertheless, there are some general rules which apply, no matter what paint or varnish is being used.

First, it is essential to choose a suitable paint covering for any particular application. Certain paints are not compatible with others, and cannot be satisfactorily applied on top of them, so it is important to keep a record of what products are used year by year on various parts of the boat – bottom, boottopping, topsides, upperworks, deck, spars, varnished surfaces, deck fittings, interior surfaces, chain locker, bilges etc. It is also necessary to use the right type of paint system for the material being covered, be it GRP, timber, alloy, steel or ferro-cement for example. All paint manufacturers provide literature on these matters, and if this is carefully read and followed there should be no problems, but do not hesitate to seek their advice if in doubt.

Great care needs to be taken when handling most of the substances used in painting a boat and in the previous preparation of the surfaces. Paints, strippers and the like should come with safety notes indicating the risks that they present and how they should be used. Good ventilation is important, but special precautions are needed with antifoulings even when these are removed or applied in the open air. Get advice on the choice of a proper industrial respirator to the appropriate FFB (Filtering Facepiece Particulate) standard. Eye protection is also important and goggles should be worn for applying poisonous liquids, or whenever a power tool is used for sanding etc. Many substances can irritate the skin or cause dermatitis, so it is sensible to wear a pair of disposable gloves. Paints, thinner and the like all present a fire risk, so due care needs to be taken in this respect.

Good surface preparation is absolutely essential for all paintwork, and is likely to account for 75 per cent of the work involved, probably more when applying a single-coat, epoxy resin-based paint. The surface must be smooth, clean and free of grease. Depending on the paint being applied, it may be necessary to remove every trace of the previous paint film. Dust must be removed by washing with water or white spirit, and finally wiping off with a tack rag. The atmosphere must be dust-free: damp down the floor, and do not wear woollen garments which are liable to shed small particles of hair.

With most paint systems a primer or undercoat must be overcoated within a certain interval of time (say with 6–24 hours) which means that careful planning is needed. The weather and temperature must also be considered: never paint in damp conditions.

Paints and varnishes either contain, or need added to them, thinners which allow the covering to spread evenly in a thin film and which then evaporate. Consequently the final film may only be half as thick as the wet film that is applied – one reason that dust particles mysteriously appear when the paint dries. Make sure that the correct thinners are used, and in the right proportions. If a can of paint is to be used which has been previously opened, it is important to strain it carefully to remove any portions of skin which have formed. Mix the components of the paint and/or thinners as directed, and allow the pot to stand for a few minutes to get rid of air bubbles.

Most paints can be applied by brush, roller or spray. Professional painters may use spray systems, for which proper equipment and precautions are essential. Paint spraying can be extremely dangerous unless proper safety precautions are taken. The amateur is therefore likely to use brush or roller; the latter is quicker but does not give such a good finish as a brush, properly used. Also a brush is better for priming coats, which need to be brushed well into the surface. Some paints can be applied satisfactorily with a pad.

Brushes must be best quality and, of course, scrupulously clean. Because speed is important in applying paint (a polyurethane, for example, sets quite quickly) it is necessary to use as large a brush as can be easily handled for the area concerned. If a roller is used, have one of the shaved mohair type.

It is essential to plan the work, dividing the area to be covered into manageable sizes, and working from one to another while the paint is still wet and the boundaries can merge together. Immerse the bristles of the brush not more than half-way into the paint, and do not wipe off the brush against the sides of the tin which causes loss of thinners from the paint running back into the tin. Transfer the paint to the surface as evenly as possible, using fast horizontal strokes, but finally laying off in one direction with the brush angled at about 45°. Do not reverse the brush while it is in contact with the paint film, or air bubbles will be trapped.

After about half-an-hour, paint may start to gel in the top of the brush, so either wash the brush with thinners or change brushes to prevent bits of dried paint getting to the paint film.

Brushes must be thoroughly washed out with thinners after use, and then with warm water and detergent. After rinsing and drying they should be wrapped in greaseproof paper and stowed carefully away, not left stuck in a tin.

With respect to antifouling, it is claimed that electronic resonators can provide good and non-polluting protection against marine growth. One established system is BARNAKiL, marketed in the UK by Roadadd Limited, 308 Upper Richmond Road West, London SW14 7JG. Tel: 0181-878 9250. Fax: 0181-878 7290. Each resonator protects an area 3m (10ft) in diameter, so for an 11m (35ft) boat half-a-dozen would be needed – drawing a total (with the control unit) of only 20 milliamp from the boat's battery. The system has no effect on other electrical systems in the boat, and does not cause electrolysis. No antifouling paint is needed, but to reduce the adhesion of slime and algae (and to guard against osmosis) a hard epoxy paint is recommended for the bottom.

10.6 Bibliography

Boat Data Book by Ian Nicolson (Adlard Coles Nautical).
The Boatbuilding Book by Geoffrey O'Connell (Ashford).
The Boatbuilding Manual by Robert M. Stewart (International Marine).
Boatbuilding with Steel by Gilbert Klingel (International Marine).
Build the New Instant Boats by Harold Payson (Adlard Coles Nautical).
Build Your Own Boat by Ian Nicolson (Hyman).
Cold-Moulded & Strip-Planked Wood Boatbuilding by Ian Nicolson (Adlard Coles Nautical).
Complete Amateur Boatbuilding by Michael Verney (Adlard Coles Nautical).
Design Your Own Yacht by Ben Smith (Adlard Coles Nautical).
Modern Boat Building by Steve Sleight (Adlard Coles Nautical).

Practical Small Boat Designs by John Atkin (International Marine).

Small Steel Craft by Ian Nicolson (Adlard Coles Nautical)

Start With a Hull by Loris Goring (David & Charles).

Principles of Yacht Design by Lars Larsson and Rolf Eliasson (Adlard Coles Nautical).

The Fibreglass Boat Repair Manual by Allan Vaitses (Adlard Coles Nautical).

Osmosis and the Care and Repair of Glassfibre Yachts by Tony Staton-Bevan (Adlard Coles Nautical).

Chapter 11

Spars, Rigging, Ropes and Sails

Contents

11.1 Spars

11.1.1 Masts – general

The mast of a sailing yacht supports the sails which drive her through the water. Most yacht masts depend on standing rigging to hold them in position, but a few are unstayed. In a typical cruising yacht the mast is relatively sturdy, and is kept as straight as possible by the standing rigging. But in a modern racing yacht the mast is made as light and thin as possible, and can be bent by varying amounts in order to optimise the set of the mainsail. This type of rigging is more complicated, often with hydraulic devices, and must be carefully controlled since any error may cause dismasting.

11.1.2 Masts – manufacture

Originally masts were made of solid timber – usually pine, or spruce for small racing yachts. It was not always easy to find suitable timber, and to ensure that it was of uniformly good quality, so as better glues were developed it became feasible to build up a mast in sections. Short lengths of timber which might have been a source of weakness could then be rejected, and by reversing the natural grain of the wood in adjacent sections it was possible to minimise the risk of distortion as the timber matured. Hollow wooden masts were developed.

Masts for large vessels, such as sailing ships and the bigger yachts, were built up from steel plates, originally rivetted together but later of welded construction.

Aluminium alloy began to be generally adopted for yacht masts in the 1950s, and is now in almost universal use. The material has a tensile strength of about 20 tons per square inch, and an alloy spar can be about two-thirds the weight of a hollow one laboriously fashioned in silver spruce. Masts are manufactured from extruded tubes of the required section, incorporating a track or groove for the mainsail as required. Spars for smaller yachts are made up from one extruded length, but bigger masts can be constructed from two or more sections joined together.

The top of a mast may be tapered, by removing a thin vee from each side of the spar, closing the gaps, and welding the seams so formed. Partly to resist the pull of the luff of the mainsail, but also because they have better support athwartships, masts are usually made with a bigger section (and hence more resistance to bending) fore-and-aft.

Special procedures have to be adopted for welding aluminium alloy, because the oxide film which gives the metal resistance to corrosion interferes with the fusion of the joint: consequently the welding process has to be performed within a shield of inert gas, usually argon, which isolates the area of the weld from atmospheric oxygen. Even minor repairs to masts (or other aluminium alloy spars) which involve welding must be done with equipment which is not likely to be available in the average boatyard.

Particular attention also has to be given to avoid dissimilar metals in contact with aluminium alloy, due to the probability of galvanic action. No brass or other copper-based alloys must be used. Stainless steel fittings such as mast tangs and

spreader heel fittings should be insulated from the mast with zinc chromate paste. Many winches have bronze bases, which must be isolated from the pad on which they are mounted by some suitably inert material such as Tufnol. Rivets should be monel metal or alloy, and stainless steel self-tapping screws should be avoided even for the lightest fittings.

After a mast has been polished and chemically etched it is anodised. This is an electrolytic process to prevent corrosion and to give a harder surface which will resist abrasion. Then the shroud and spreader fittings, winch pads, gooseneck, spinnaker fittings etc are attached, and internal halyards and electric wiring are fitted. The interior of the mast may be lined with polystyrene to reduce the noise from wire halyards.

Although aluminium masts are strong and relatively cheap, aluminium is not an ideal material in one important respect. An extrusion does not allow any variation in the wall thickness of a mast from heel to truck, which means that the upper sections of the spar are unnecessarily heavy. A considerable reduction in weight can be achieved by producing spars in carbon fibre but cost is increased by a factor of about four since material costs are high and the different methods of construction available are very labour intensive. Therefore, at present, the technique is confined to very special applications.

11.1.3 Booms and spinnaker poles

The construction of a boom is similar to that of an alloy mast. The section used depends on the method of reefing (see 11.5.3). A round section should be used for roller reefing, since the sail rolls better and the boom has the same strength no matter in which direction it is rotated. Booms for slab reefing are not turned on their sides, so they can be thinner but taller in section.

Spinnaker poles are of circular section. The only point of note is to check and lubricate the end fittings at regular intervals.

11.1.4 Standing rigging

Standing rigging is intended to hold the mast straight and upright, or to control its required bend in the case of racing yachts. The rigging wires which hold the mast in the athwartships direction (sideways) are called shrouds; those which hold it fore-and-aft are stays.

The beam of a yacht in the neighbourhood of the mast, together with the height of the mast, determines what angle a shroud will make to the mast at its point of attachment. In order that the shroud may provide sufficient athwartships pull, this angle needs to be as large as can be arranged: otherwise the shroud tension must be increased, which puts undue compression on the mast. A mast is essentially a strut in compression and under well established mechanical laws it will buckle at a certain load – depending on its length,

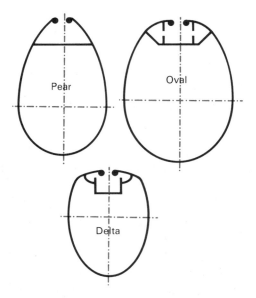

Fig. 11(1) Typical common mast sections. The chain dotted lines indicate the neutral axes of each section – about which the areas of material on either side balance. In general the pear and oval sections are preferred for masthead rigs, and the delta for fractional rigs because it gives more fore-and-aft flexibility.

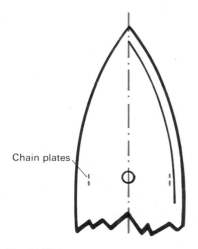

Fig. 11(2) Narrower sheeting angles for headsails require the chain plates to be set inboard from the deck edge, thereby narrowing the angle which a shroud makes with the mast aloft.

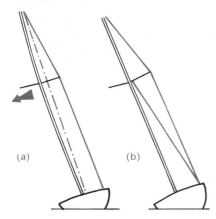

Fig. 11(3) In (a) the upper (cap) shroud bearing against the spreader bends the mast to leeward. The addition of a lower shroud (b), joining the mast at the spreader, holds the mast up to windward at that point, and keeps it straight.

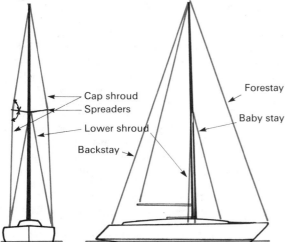

Fig. 11(4) Typical rigging suitable for a masthead sloop.

the moment of inertia (or strength) of its cross-section, the material, and how it is stepped (on the keel or on deck). The problem is exacerbated by the modern tendency to reduce the sheeting angle of headsails making it necessary to set the chain plates (to which the shrouds are attached at their lower ends) inboard from the deck edge, see Fig. 11(2).

Consequently it is necessary for shrouds which run to or near the masthead to be provided with spreaders (or crosstrees) in order to increase the angle which they make to the mast. In Fig. 11(3) it is evident that the tension of the shroud bearing against the end of the spreader is forcing the mast in the direction of the arrow. Hence, in order to keep the mast straight, it is essential for a lower shroud to be fitted at this point so that it holds the mast (and the spreader attached thereto) up to windward. In cruising yachts there are commonly two pairs of lower shrouds, one set leading to the deck slightly forward of the mast and the other set slightly aft of it.

Fig. 11(4) and Fig. 11(5) show typical rigging arrangements in cruising yachts, and the names of the various components. In Fig. 11(4) the mast has only one pair of spreaders, and this layout would be suitable for the average masthead sloop. In Fig. 11(5) two pairs of spreaders are provided, as would be appropriate for a larger yacht, or one with cutter rig (two headsails). In special cases, particularly for racing yachts or in the case of larger vessels, more than two pairs of spreaders may be used. These two diagrams also show the stays which hold the mast fore-and-aft. With the sloop rig this is done by the forestay and the backstay; in addition the lower shrouds help to steady the centre of the mast in the fore-and-aft plane, while an inner forestay (now usually referred to as a baby stay) may also be fitted to the height of the spreaders. The baby stay may be portable, so that it can be brought back to the mast in light to moderate conditions.

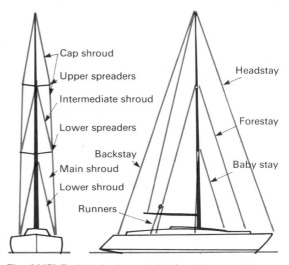

Fig. 11(5) Typical rigging suitable for a larger yacht, or one with cutter rig.

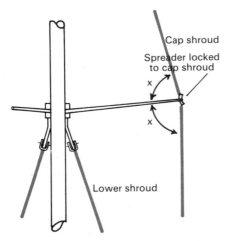

Fig. 11(6) It is important that the spreader bisects the angle of the cap shroud, and that it is locked to same.

With a cutter rig it is necessary to have running backstays to hold the mast aft at the point where the forestay meets it. In order not to restrict the boom and mainsail, the running backstays (or runners) are set up in turn – the windward one being tensioned by a winch or lever, and the leeward one being slacked away. Racing yachts with bendy masts may also have one or more sets of runners to control the rig.

There are a few types of seagoing yacht which have unstayed masts – such as those with modified Chinese junk rigs, and cat rigged yachts as in Fig. 11(37) with no headsails. These unsupported masts must necessarily be bigger and heavier, even though they are not subject to the compression which rigging imposes on an ordinary mast.

11.1.5 Spreaders
The length of spreaders is usually determined by the need to clear overlapping headsails. Spreaders

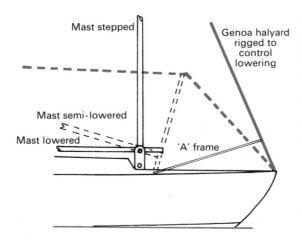

Fig. 11(7) 'A' frame rigged to control lowering of mast stepped on deck in tabernacle, using genoa halyard. The sideways movement of the mast must also be controlled as it is lowered.

must be carefully designed, and well engineered in respect of their attachment to the mast. If they are firmly fixed to the mast the spreaders must be very strong, and consequently large and heavy. More usually they are arranged to swing fore-and-aft. It is most important that the outer end of the spreader is securely fixed to the cap shroud, and that it bisects the angle of the shroud, which means that it normally needs to be cocked up about 5° or 6° above horizontal, see Fig. 11(6). Some spreaders have clamps at the outer end for this purpose, otherwise bulldog grips can be used, well taped over to prevent any damage to sails.

Spreaders and their attachments should be items which are subjected to routine examination aloft, since spreader failure is a common cause of dismasting.

11.1.6 Mast step
Most masts are stepped on the keel, thereby obtaining support at the partners where they pass through the deck. A mast stepped on deck needs to be a bigger section, but has the advantage of not passing through the accommodation, of eliminating leaks at deck level, and being shorter for transportation.

Some yachts have their mast stepped in a tabernacle or hinged heel fitting on deck, so that it can be lowered for passing under bridges etc. As the mast is lowered the effective angle of the forestay to the mast soon diminishes, so it is necessary to erect some kind of frame forward of the mast to serve as a strut, as is shown in Fig. 11(7). Also, as the mast is lowered the tension on the shrouds is removed, and so it is necessary to steady the mast athwartships in order to avoid damage to the tabernacle or heel fitting.

11.1.7 Masts – maintenance
During the sailing season there is little actual maintenance to be done on aluminium alloy spars, but there is a continual need for inspection aloft to ensure that all is in order and to prevent trouble developing. Maintenance of standing rigging is discussed in 11.2.5, and should be done at the same time.

For going aloft a good bosun's chair is needed, preferably one with a safety belt round to prevent the occupant slipping out. Modern bosun's chairs have handy pockets for tools and spares, but otherwise these can be hoisted separately in a bucket. Normally the main halyard is used – make sure that the shackle is properly screwed up. It is advisable to have a second halyard attached for safety, or the person going aloft may take a safety line which can be secured aloft. While anybody is aloft one of the crew should be permanently in attendance at the foot of the mast: it has been known for somebody else to come along and let go the halyard by mistake.

Starting at the masthead check that halyard sheaves are free and in good condition. Take the weight of the halyard off each sheave in turn, to check the clearances in the bearings. Worn bushes should be renewed before further trouble develops with jammed sheaves and worn halyards. A good wash down with fresh water to remove salt deposits from bearing surfaces will not come amiss, followed by the application of an aerosol lubricant.

Examine all the fittings secured at the masthead, to make sure that pins are in good order and that the holes through which they pass are not elongated. Check all split pins for security. Look for any signs of cracks in the mast itself or in castings of fittings attached thereto, and for any movement in screws or rivets. Unless these details are inspected methodically it is easy for something untoward to be overlooked.

Coming down the mast check the security of the mast track, if externally fitted, and wash out the track so that the slides can run freely. Inspect each shroud fitting, check the security of any through-mast bolts, and look for any sign of distortion to the mast itself.

At the spreaders, check that they bisect the shroud angle correctly, that the tips are secured to the shrouds where appropriate, and that anti-chafe arrangements are in place. See that the spreaders are secure in their sockets, and that the latter are properly attached to the mast with all securing arrangements tight and correct.

At deck level check round the main boom gooseneck, winch pads, cleats, sheave boxes etc, for any visual sign of deterioration. Only close inspection may detect a tiny crack in some weld or fitting of a mast, or an elongated hole which should be round, but these are the little details which might save your mast, or even your life.

When spars are laid up for the winter they should be washed with warm, fresh water to remove salt deposits. Use soap, but not detergents which may react with the alloy. When thoroughly dry, the spar can be polished with silicone wax. Lightly oil all moving fittings.

11.2 Standing rigging

11.2.1 Standing rigging – materials
The materials most commonly used for standing rigging are stainless steel rod, 1 × 19 wire and 7 × 7 wire rope.

Cold drawn stainless steel rod is the simplest but most expensive type of standing rigging. It is usually round, but for use as shrouds it may be lenticular in section. The ends of the rod are threaded, and can be used with screwed or rotary-hammer-swaged terminals (see below). Rod rigging has very little stretch for a given strength, and because it is thin it has minimal windage. But it does have some disadvantages, apart from its high cost. Because it is very rigid it must be laid out straight or carefully coiled in a big circle, and it is more prone to fatigue than other types of rigging.

It is also brittle, and even minor damage to the surface can cause loss of strength. Trying to straighten a bent stainless steel fitting or rod rigging is likely to lead to early failure.

Wire rigging can be manufactured from either galvanised wire or 316 specification stainless steel wire. Galvanised wire, which has a zinc coating, is much cheaper, rather stronger and more flexible than stainless steel wire. But it is not nearly so durable and does not look so nice.

Most yachts have standing rigging of 1 × 19 stainless steel wire, to specification 316. Stainless steel can in fact stain under certain conditions, and particularly if it is starved of atmospheric oxygen which initiates crevice corrosion: for the same reason rigging or terminals should not be taped over with adhesive tape. Stainless steel wire is weakened by bending or scratching it, and it is more liable to fatigue failure than galvanised wire. A slight rusty-brown discoloration of the material itself is not serious, and can easily be removed, but such symptoms from inside a terminal or any sign of a broken strand indicate that the rope has reached the end of its life at that point.

Details of the construction and strength of wire ropes are given in 11.4.15 – 11.4.18.

11.2.2 Wire rope terminals
Apart from splicing, which is not practicable for 1 × 19 wire, there are various ways of attaching terminals to wire rigging.

Swaged terminals are commonly used with stainless steel wire, and consist of a sleeve which fits closely over the end of the wire and which has an eye, or a fork or a threaded stud at its other end. The wire is then inserted into the sleeve, which is then squeezed on to the wire at very high pressure in a rotary-hammer machine. If the correct procedures are followed the joint is as strong as the wire, but sometimes salt water may cause corrosion along the grain boundaries of the work hardened stainless steel, so that after a period of service the swage (sleeve) develops hair-line cracks which will lead to failure. Salty moisture may also settle in the minute spaces between the terminal and the wire, creating hidden pockets of corrosion which will, however, be revealed by stains around the lip of the sleeve before they reach a critical stage. Hence it is most important to examine such fittings very carefully, and at regular intervals. At the same time look closely at the wire rope for any signs of flattened and shiny strands adjacent to the swage, which indicate failure at this point.

Swageless screwed terminals, as produced by Norseman, are good alternatives to swaged terminals for stainless steel wire. They are attached to the wire without cold working in a press or work hardening of the stainless steel – the main cause of stress corrosion problems – and they require no special tools or equipment, so they are ideal for use afloat. Routine inspection of the terminal can be done by dismantling the assembly.

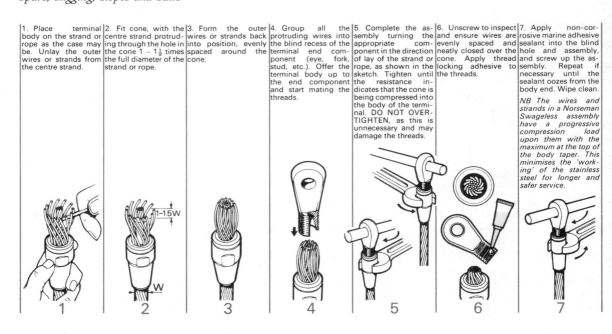

1. Place terminal body on the strand or rope as the case may be. Unlay the outer wires or strands from the centre strand.	2. Fit cone, with the centre strand protruding through the hole in the cone 1 – 1½ times the full diameter of the strand or rope.	3. Form the outer wires or strands back into position, evenly spaced around the cone.	4. Group all the protruding wires into the blind recess of the terminal end component (eye, fork, stud, etc.). Offer the terminal body up to the end component and start mating the threads.	5. Complete the assembly turning the appropriate component in the direction of lay of the strand or rope, as shown in the sketch. Tighten until the resistance indicates that the cone is being compressed into the body of the terminal. DO NOT OVERTIGHTEN, as this is unnecessary and may damage the threads.	6. Unscrew to inspect and ensure wires are evenly spaced and neatly closed over the cone. Apply thread locking adhesive to the threads.	7. Apply non-corrosive marine adhesive sealant into the blind hole and assembly, and screw up the assembly. Repeat if necessary until the sealant oozes from the body end. Wipe clean. NB The wires and strands in a Norseman Swageless assembly have a progressive compression load upon them with the maximum at the top of the body taper. This minimises the 'working' of the stainless steel for longer and safer service.

Fig. 11(8) Norseman swageless terminal fitting instructions.

The complete fitting comprises the end portion (available with eye, fork or stud ends), a cone, a lock nut, and the terminal body. It is important to follow the fitting instructions, summarised in Fig. 11(8).

With the Talurit (or pressed ferrule) system the wire passes through a ferrule (copper for stainless steel wire, or light alloy for galvanised wire), round a thimble, and back into the collar in the reverse direction. The ferrule is then squeezed round both parts of the wire in a hydraulic press. Provided that the ferrule is correctly placed (not close against the thimble) and is not cracked, this system gives good results for rigging which is more lightly loaded, but it does not have the inherent strength of the systems described above. Security can be improved by using two ferrules per eye.

Emergency repairs to rigging can be done with bulldog grips. A seagoing yacht should carry a selection of these, in the correct sizes for the wire rope fitted. The grip, shown in Fig. 11(9), consists of a U-shaped clamp, the two legs of the U being threaded. A drilled cross-piece fits over the legs of the U and is serrated on its inner edge to engage

with the lay of the wire. The two lengths of wire within the U are compressed into the bend of the U by two nuts on the outside of the cross-piece. The short end of the wire should be against the U bend, and the standing part against the cross piece. Three grips should be fitted alongside each other, and it is important that they are the right size for the wire concerned.

11.2.3 Rigging fittings
At their upper ends shrouds are secured to tangs, usually fitted to the mast with through bolts, by means of clevis pins. For a single tang the rigging wire must have a fork terminal, or for a double tang an eye terminal. Whichever arrangement is fitted the clevis pin, see Fig 11(10), must be a close fit in the holes, and must be held in position by a good split pin. Split pins for such essential services should not be re-used after rigging has been removed for any reason, but should be replaced with new. Added security is given by taping them over, which also avoids the possibility of sails or running rigging snagging on the ends of

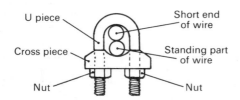

Fig. 11(9) Bulldog grip, for emergency rigging repairs. It is important that the wires be assembled as shown, with the short end in the U of the grip. The grip must be the right size for the wire concerned, and three should be fitted.

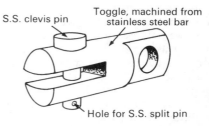

Fig. 11(10) Toggle with clevis pin. With all such rigging fittings it is most important that the clevis pin is an accurate fit within the toggle (or the fork end of a bottlescrew), and that it is also the correct length with the minimum longitudinal movement when secured by the split pin.

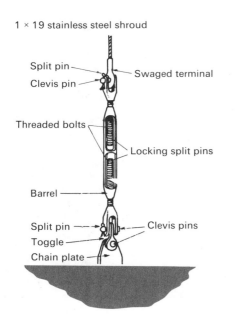

1 × 19 stainless steel shroud

Split pin

Clevis pin

Swaged terminal

Threaded bolts

Locking split pins

Barrel

Split pin

Clevis pins

Toggle

Chain plate

Fig. 11(11) Shroud attachment to chain plate. The 1 × 19 stainless steel shroud ends with a swaged terminal. This is connected by a clevis pin (secured by a split pin) to the upper fork end of the bottlescrew. The lower fork end of the bottlescrew is connected to the chain plate by a toggle, which gives freedom of movement in all directions.

the split pin. All such fittings aloft should be examined at regular intervals.

Racing yachts may have a more sophisticated arrangement for shrouds whereby, in order to reduce windage and turbulence round the mast, the shrouds disappear through holes in the side of the mast and are secured inside.

Shrouds are tensioned at their lower ends by bottlescrews, which must be secured to the chainplates by toggles, as shown in Fig. 11(11). Chainplates must be carefully designed and engineered, securely fastened to the hull, and at the correct angle for the pull to be exerted on them. Like other rigging fittings, they are liable to wear and should be examined regularly.

A toggle, shown in Fig. 11(10), is a form of universal joint which allows the bottlescrew to move in any direction – both to avoid damage to the bottlescrew and also to minimise fatigue in the rigging wire where it enters the terminal above the bottlescrew. The clevis pins in toggles must of course be secured by split pins and inspected as for those in mast tangs referred to above. Forestays should be fitted with toggles at their upper and lower ends.

Bottlescrews (otherwise referred to as rigging screws or turnbuckles) are available to various designs, and in different materials, but basically they all consist of a central body which is threaded internally, right-handed at one end and left-handed at the other, Fig. 11(11). Into this central body are threaded bolts which have either eye, fork or stud ends – to match up with the

rigging and with the toggle attached to the chainplate. Obviously, one of these bolts is threaded right-hand, and the other is threaded left-hand. When the central body is turned, the threaded ends protruding from it are either pulled together or pushed apart. Some means must be provided to prevent the bottlescrew rotating under load: this may be arranged by lock nuts fitted on the threaded ends, but a more positive locking device (e.g. using split pins) is to be preferred.

In most sailing yachts the forestay is fixed (although some means may be provided for making adjustments to it, and hence to the rake of the mast), and the fore-and-aft tension of the rig is controlled by the permanent backstay. Modern rigs for racing yachts depend very much on proper control of backstay tension – whereby mast bend, the shape of the mainsail and tension of the forestay (supporting the genoa) are correctly adjusted for optimum performance. In smaller yachts the backstay may be controlled by a simple purchase, but more commonly tension is adjusted by a handwheel, somewhat resembling the steering wheel of a car, which is screwed internally and carries a threaded shaft connected to the bottom of the backstay. Such tensioners are available in various sizes – from those suitable for backstays of 5mm diameter ($\frac{5}{8}$in circumference) and capable of loading to 1600kg (3500lb), to those for 9mm diameter ($1\frac{1}{8}$in circumference) wire which will develop tensions of 7800kg (17,200lb).

More sophisticated are hydraulic backstay tensioners, with which even higher loadings can be achieved for larger yachts. It is important that such tensioners incorporate some form of pre-set maximum load device, to avoid possible damage to the rig by overloading.

11.2.4 Setting up rigging

These notes are not intended to apply to the more detailed tuning required for the mast of a racing yacht, which is a continuing process, but rather to give guidance on setting up the standing rigging for the average cruising yacht so that it is first of all safe and secure for any weather likely to be met, and second allows the sails to set as well as possible.

The exact procedure depends on the type of rig, and every yacht needs somewhat different treatment according to the type of mast, how it is stepped, and details of the rigging plan. For our purpose we will assume that the yacht is a masthead sloop, and that the mast has a single pair of spreaders with two pairs of lower shrouds.

There is only one way that standing rigging can be properly set up, and that is under sail in smooth water in a breeze of about force 3–4. But previously certain initial adjustments must have been completed in harbour.

First adjust the mast fore-and-aft so that it is standing with a slight rake aft – that is not quite perpendicular, but leaning very slightly aft. This can best be judged by letting the main halyard hang down the aft side of the mast, so that in a boat of 10m (33ft) length it lies about 200mm (8in) aft of the mast at deck level. This, it should be emphasised, is only an initial setting which may need adjusting later, and when checking it be sure that the boat is in normal trim – not down by the bow or by the stern. Tighten and lock the forestay and backstay accordingly: they should be quite tight, because the forestay has to support the luff of the genoa when sailing.

Now tighten the upper (cap) shrouds equally each side, so that they both have almost the same tension as the forestay, but not quite so much. Remember that if the rigging is new it is going to stretch somewhat as soon as the boat is sailing. At this point it is important to make sure that the mast is not leaning to port or starboard. This can easily be checked by taking the main halyard down to the chainplates on each side in turn, and adjusting the cap shrouds until the two measurements are the same. Then adjust the lower shrouds each side so that the forward pair are just taut, but with no real weight on them, and the aft pair are just slack.

If the mast is stepped on the keel it should now be chocked in position at the partners (where it passes through the deck). This can be done with specially shaped wooden wedges, carefully fitted so that they hold the mast evenly, but do not misalign it; alternatively hard rubber strips can be used, but they will need to be held in position in some way – by a large jubilee clip or similar strap.

Now the boat is ready to go sailing – as soon as conditions are suitable. If the rigging is new it will stretch, more especially the upper (cap) shrouds. Increase their tension alternately on the leeward side, as the boat sails on each tack in turn, until most of the slack is taken up in the lee rigging, but being careful to tighten both sides an equal amount by counting the turns of the bottlescrews. It then remains to adjust the lower shrouds so as to eliminate any bend in the mast – which can be checked quite easily by squinting up the mainsail groove or mast track from a position underneath the gooseneck. When the boat is on the wind most of the weight will be on the windward, forward shroud so far as the lowers are concerned; both the leeward lowers will be slack. If the mast falls away to leeward at the spreaders, then both the windward lowers need tightening: in a small yacht the effect of doing this can be judged by racking the two shrouds together. If, however, the mast bends to windward in the area of the spreaders, both the windward lowers need to be slackened.

Sail to windward on alternate tacks, adjusting the lowers on the lee side and then checking the result on the next tack. This can take some time to get right, and it is best to have one person doing the adjusting and one person looking up the mast, while a third sails the boat. During this procedure check the balance of the boat on the helm. Mast rake is not the only cause of weather (or lee) helm

but it can be a major factor, and initial sailing trials may show that the masthead should be moved slightly forward or aft. Depending on the type of fitting, adjusting the forestay to achieve less or more rake may have to await return to harbour. When the best possible adjustments have been made to the lower shrouds be sure to lock all the bottlescrews, and to tape them over.

The rigging of a new boat takes a little time – and a good breeze or two of wind – to settle down. So it will certainly be necessary to repeat the above procedure for adjusting both the upper and lower shrouds while sailing.

Rigs with two (or more) sets of spreaders are obviously more difficult to tune, since there are more variables, but the same basic principles apply. To facilitate adjustments it is best if all bottlescrews are at deck level. The cap shrouds (which run to or near the masthead) must be fixed to the ends of the upper spreaders, but be free to run through the ends of the lower spreaders. The intermediate shrouds (which terminate on the mast at the height of the upper spreaders) must be fixed to the ends of the lower spreaders.

11.2.5 Standing rigging – maintenance

Routine inspections of the standing rigging aloft should be carried out at the same time as the inspection of other mast items, as described in 11.1.7. Standing rigging which can be inspected from deck level should be examined more frequently.

Inspection of standing rigging should cover:

(1) The wires themselves, to check for any signs of stranding or deterioration – particularly with stainless steel wires adjacent to rigging terminals, where flattened strands with a shiny appearance indicate failure. Whereas stainless steel wire requires no real maintenance, galvanised wire will have a longer life if it is washed down periodically, and treated with boiled linseed oil. Any wire which is rusty or has broken strands should be condemned, and the condition of galvanised wire can also be judged by bending it and seeing how it reacts: if it stays bent, or straightens very slowly, it should be replaced.

(2) Rigging terminals (swaged or swageless), for any signs of cracks, hole elongation, security of clevis pins and split pins.

(3) Winches, tackles or other tensioning devices for backstays.

(4) Chain plates, forestay fittings, backstay fittings – for general condition of securing arrangements, welds etc.

A portable electronic testing system is available for yacht rigging, which passes a very small current through the item on test and measures the resistance at the terminal connection. This can detect faults not visible by eye, and there is the advantage that every fitting can be itemised and the resistance readings printed out for future comparison.

If the mast is unstepped for the winter the opportunity should be taken for a thorough examination of all the standing rigging. Ideally it should be labelled, removed from the mast, well washed and dried, and (for galvanised wire) treated with boiled linseed oil. Before storing away in the dry, examine each wire closely throughout its length, and bend it slightly where it enters the rigging terminals to see if there are any signs of broken strands.

The life of standing rigging depends somewhat on the use of the boat, but in general terms it is recommended that a forestay should be replaced after eight years and other items after eleven years.

11.2.6 Rigging failures and dismasting
In the event of a rigging failure the first action is to try to save the mast by minimizing the strain on it. For example, if a weather shroud parts, go about on the other tack; if the forestay carries away, run off before the wind. Then attention must be given to reducing sail, and either repairing the damage or rigging a jury shroud or stay. A genoa halyard can be set up as a temporary forestay, while the main halyard or even the topping lift might be utilised as a backstay. A halyard or the spinnaker pole lift can be pressed into service as a temporary shroud, sufficient to steady the mast on the leeward side while more permanent repairs are done.

Provided it can be reached, and this may be a problem, a break in a wire can be repaired by using bulldog grips to form loops at the two broken ends, and then shackling a handy-billy between the two loops and setting it up tight. If a mast fitting fails it may be possible to pass a strop round the mast and over a spreader, to provide a temporary anchorage for a jury shroud.

Often however, when an item of standing rigging fails, the mast will break and/or go over the side. If a mast is actually falling it is better to bear away so that it drops into the sea, than to luff so that it lands on deck and possibly injures somebody. The first priority is to try to recover the wreckage from the sea, so that it does not damage the hull. If this is not possible it must be cut adrift, for which purpose special wire cutters such as Felco should be carried onboard; try to salvage whatever is available for use as a jury rig. Do not start the engine until it is certain that all the rigging has been removed from the water, and there is no possibility of fouling the propeller.

What sort of jury rig can be contrived depends very much on what items, particularly spars, are available. If the mast has been lost completely it should be possible to use the spinnaker pole or perhaps the main boom as a jury mast (set up with shrouds rigged from sheets or warps), on which at least a small headsail can be set as a form of trysail.

11.3 Running rigging

11.3.1 Running rigging – general
Running rigging comprises the numerous lines such as halyards, sheets, guys, lifts, downhauls, outhauls etc (together with their various snap shackles, blocks, cleats and the like) which hoist and control the set of the sails of a yacht. In a small boat all of these can be controlled by hand, or with the benefit of simple tackles, but in larger yachts powerful winches and other mechanical devices have to be used. Fig. 11(13) shows a handy-billy tackle which can be used for a variety of tasks.

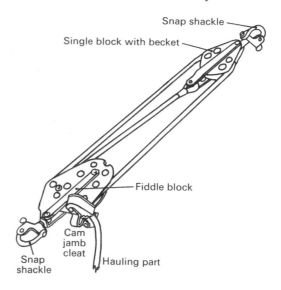

Fig. 11(13) A handy-billy (or luff tackle) is made up of a single block with a becket, to which is attached the standing part, and a fiddle block. That shown in the sketch has a cam jamb cleat on the fiddle block – a modern aid which replaces the old method of 'choking the luff' by jamming the hauling part across the sheave of the block. Snap shackles each end allow the handy-billy to be used easily for a number of tasks. When rigged to advantage (with the single block fixed) the mechanical advantage is 4:1. When rigged to disadvantage (with the fiddle block fixed) it is 3:1.

Fig. 11(12) Jury rigged mast – from spinnaker pole lashed to foot of broken mast, and stayed by lines leading to deck fittings such as samson post, spinnaker blocks etc. On such a mast could be set the yacht's smallest headsail, with its foot along the jury mast and the head of the sail attached to some kind of sheet.

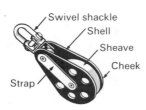

Single block with swivel. Modern blocks are typically manufactured from glass fibre filled nylon, with stainless steel reinforcement and sheaves mounted on ball bearings.

Fiddle block with fixed eye. Since the sheaves are in the same plane, this type of block is less likely to twist than a double block, if the sheaves turn in the same direction.

Turning block. The sheave runs on stainless steel ball bearings. One heavy fastening goes through the sheave spindle and two others through the body.

General purpose cleat. All deck fittings must be through bolted, with generous pad pieces and washers under the deck. A cleat should be secured so that the centreline is about 15° to the line of pull of the rope belayed to it.

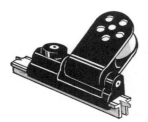

Genoa sheet lead block – position adjustable on deck-mounted track. This type of block gets the sheet as near the deck as possible.

Fig. 11(14) Items of gear for use with running rigging.

Double block with swivel and becket. When choosing any type of block, make sure the sheave is wide enough for the rope, and that the diameter is sufficient to allow the rope to render round it easily. The sheave diameter should be at least five times the rope diameter for fibre cordage.

Snatch block with swivel. The shell is hinged so that one side can be opened to allow the bight of a rope to be inserted.

Snap shackle with swivel eye. Note the short lanyard attached to the ring which releases the plunger. Suitable for loads up to 7000lb (3200kg).

Fiddle block with swivel and becket. The standing part of the rope is made fast to the becket.

Descriptions of types of cordage and wire rope, together with their properties and strengths, and notes on their splicing, handling and maintenance, are given in 11.4.

An increasing variety of fittings are used with running rigging, all aimed to combine strength with lightness, and mechanical simplicity with ease of operation. For full details of what are currently on offer it is best to consult the illustrated catalogue of a good chandler. Fig. 11(14) shows just a few of the more common items of gear.

In Fig. 11(15) can be seen the principal running rigging of a modern masthead sloop. Some of the

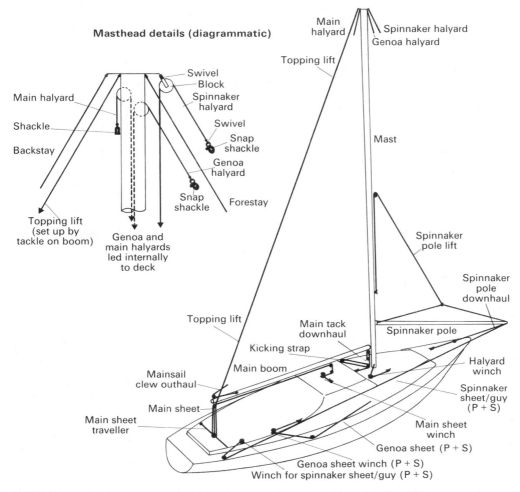

Masthead details (diagrammatic)

Main halyard

Swivel

Block

Spinnaker halyard

Shackle

Swivel

Backstay

Snap shackle

Genoa halyard

Snap shackle

Topping lift (set up by tackle on boom)

Genoa and main halyards led internally to deck

Forestay

Main halyard

Spinnaker halyard
Genoa halyard

Topping lift

Mast

Spinnaker pole lift

Spinnaker pole downhaul

Topping lift

Main tack downhaul

Kicking strap

Spinnaker pole

Main boom

Halyard winch

Mainsail clew outhaul

Spinnaker sheet/guy (P + S)

Main sheet

Main sheet winch

Main sheet traveller

Genoa sheet (P + S)

Genoa sheet winch (P + S)
Winch for spinnaker sheet/guy (P + S)

Fig. 11(15) Diagrammatic sketch showing the main items of running rigging of a 10m (33ft) masthead sloop. For clarity, standing rigging and other details are omitted. Running rigging which is duplicated port and starboard (P&S) is only shown on the starboard side.

lesser items will be described separately. Halyards need to maintain a uniform tension on the luff of a sail, often for long periods, so they should stretch as little as possible.

Consequently they are made up from wire, but for ease of handling they are fitted with a rope tail. The length of the wire should be such that four turns can be taken on the winch, and the wire to rope splice comes between the winch and the cleat when the sail is fully hoisted. Because wire rope for running rigging has to pass over sheaves and round winches, it needs to be much more flexible than the wire used for standing rigging. This is achieved by using a rope which has a larger number of smaller wires – typically 6×19 construction with a fibre core. Sheaves for this type of wire should be 12 times the diameter of the wire in the case of halyards.

The windage of halyards can be reduced by running them down inside the mast, and this is now common practice. The main halyard is shackled to the headboard of the mainsail, whereas genoa and spinnaker halyards are normally fitted with snap shackles: these need to be cleaned and

lightly oiled from time to time to keep them free and secure.

Sheets have to be continually adjusted, so a slight amount of stretch is more acceptable. In any case they need to be easy to handle, so they must be made of rope – except for the largest yachts, where wire may be found. Sheets take a lot of wear, and this should be minimised, both for safety and economy, by making sure that blocks are of sufficient size (with sheaves at least five times the diameter of the rope), and correctly aligned for the direction of pull, and by fitting plastic tubing or similar anti-chafe protection round shrouds, bottlescrews and the like. It pays to buy sheets which are slightly overlength, because the points of wear can then be moved round to give a longer life.

The mainsheet must be sufficiently powerful to control the mainsail in all foreseeable conditions, with large sheaves in blocks which swivel as required to take up the necessary alignment according to the position of the boom. In modern yachts the lower block of the mainsheet is usually secured to a traveller, mounted on a track which runs athwartships. The position of the traveller can be controlled by tackles, and can have a considerable influence on the set of the mainsail. Going to windward in moderate conditions the traveller should be about the middle of the track, but in stronger winds or when reaching it should be moved to leeward. In light airs the traveller may be brought up to windward, and the mainsheet eased, to give more fullness in the mainsail. Other items of running rigging which control the set of the mainsail are the clew outhaul, the main tack (gooseneck) downhaul, and the kicking strap (or boom vang).

The main clew outhaul controls the tension in the foot of the mainsail, which has a big effect on the shape of the whole sail. It may be a simple lashing, or it may be controlled by a tackle which runs either along or inside the boom, or it may be controlled by a screw gear. The clew outhaul should be set up to the required tension before hoisting the mainsail, adjusted as required while under way, and always slacked off when the mainsail is lowered on return to harbour. More tension is required in the clew outhaul when sailing on the wind in a strong breeze, and less when sailing on the wind in lighter airs or when sailing with the wind free. It should be adjusted in conjunction with the main tack downhaul (see below).

In some yachts the tension on the luff of the mainsail is adjusted by the halyard, but more usually the main boom gooseneck slides up and down on a short track attached to the aft side of the mast, and is controlled by a tackle rigged down to deck level. By setting up on this tackle the tension in the luff of the mainsail is increased, pulling the flow in the sail further forward.

The function of the kicking strap (or boom vang) is to keep the boom down, and reduce the twist in the mainsail towards the head. In a small yacht it may also help to impart mast bend. So far as reducing twist is concerned, this mainly applies once the mainsheet is eased – in other words when the boat is reaching. In most yachts the kicking strap consists of a tackle, leading from the underside of the boom forward to a position on the aft side of the mast at deck level. A more sophisticated arrangement, found in some racing yachts, is a hydraulically operated strut which combines the function of kicking strap and topping lift.

One other item of gear deserves mention in respect of the mainsail, and that is a boom guy (or preventer) which is led from the end of the boom forward to a block near the bow, in order to steady the boom in a following wind and sea, and to prevent an accidental gybe.

Details of reefing systems and roller furling for headsails are given under 'Sails' in 11.5.3 and 11.5.4.

In smaller yachts the spinnaker sheets/guys are interchangeable, the windward one to the end of the spinnaker pole being called the guy and the leeward one to the clew of the spinnaker being the sheet. On the opposite gybe their roles are reversed. Larger yachts have separate guys (wire) and sheets (cordage). The sheets/guys are led outboard of all other rigging to blocks which are fitted right aft each side of the boat, and thence to winches.

The spinnaker pole is clipped to a traveller on a track secured to the forward side of the mast, so that the height of the heel of the pole can be adjusted according to the wind strength and the point of sailing. A lift and a downhaul control the height of the outer end of the spinnaker pole.

When the spinnaker pole is trimmed well forward, with the wind almost on the beam, the effective angle of pull of the guy is greatly reduced, making it difficult to pull the spinnaker pole aft. So a jockey pole is rigged athwartships at the mast, with a sheave at its outer end on which the guy bears, in order to push the guy further outboard and thereby increase its effective angle relative to the pole. The jockey pole also keeps the spinnaker guy clear of shrouds, guardrails and stanchions – avoiding mutual damage.

11.3.2 Running rigging – maintenance

Chafe is the greatest enemy of running rigging, and it is not difficult to guess where the maximum wear is likely to occur in any particular rope. For example, a halyard suffers most where it bears on the masthead sheave, where it passes round an exit sheave on the mast, and where it is turned up on winch and cleat when the sail is hoisted. These areas are likely to fail long before the rest of the rope, unless this is crippled in some way by careless handling – kinks in wire rope can be permanently damaging.

Where feasible to do so, it therefore pays to make up running rigging slightly longer in the first place, so that its life can be extended by removing a worn end, as for example the extremity of a halyard which suffers undue wear in the masthead sheave, or by equalising the wear along the rope. Some items of running rigging can be turned end for end to extend their life.

For a yacht which makes extended cruises it is advisable to carry sufficient wire (carefully preserved) to be able to make up a replacement halyard of the maximum length required, as well as spare cordage for other items such as sheets.

If a sheave does not turn freely in a block it will soon damage the rope passing over it. All sheaves should be examined and lubricated at frequent intervals.

If a halyard has to be removed from inside the mast, it should be replaced by a thin line as a messenger – so that the new halyard can be rove easily. If a halyard is broken inside a mast, and needs to be replaced, it will be necessary to pass a messenger through the mast for the purpose. This can be done using a short length of thin but flexible chain, which will pass over the masthead sheave and which can be attached to a suitable messenger to be pulled down the mast. First set up all other internal halyards as tight as possible, to avoid twists in the halyard inside the mast.

11.3.3 Winches

Winches provide the necessary power for hoisting and setting sails, and for other tasks connected with the running rigging of a yacht. The power which a winch develops is the relationship between the distance moved by the handle compared to the distance moved by the circumference of the drum. The power ratio of a simple direct action sheet winch in a small yacht might be 7:1. Power ratio is more meaningful than gear ratio, which is the number of turns of the handle for one turn of the drum.

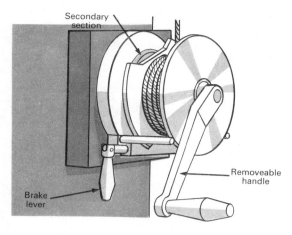

Fig. 11(16) Main halyard self-stowing winch. When hoisting, the turns must be led on evenly with the disengaged hand, and the final two or three turns must be led over the secondary section of the drum, nearest the mast. Remove the handle before releasing the brake to lower the sail.

Larger yachts need much more powerful winches to sheet home big genoas, for example. But a winch with a power ratio of, say, 30:1 would take a long time to take down the slack of a sheet before the higher power is really needed. So bigger sheet winches are two speed, or even three speed. A two speed winch might have power ratios of 7:1 and 30:1, obtained by rotating the handle in opposite directions. A three speed winch might give 5:1, 17:1 and 48:1, selected by a button on top of the winch drum in addition to reversing the direction of the handle.

Usually one person 'tails' the sheet or halyard, maintaining the tension of the rope round the drum, while another operates the winch handle. The lead of a rope on to and off the drum of a winch must be such as to avoid the risk of a riding turn — when a turn rides up over the one above it and jams. Often a riding turn can only be removed by taking the load off the winch. One way of doing this is by securing another line to the sheet with a rolling hitch, and then leading this line to another winch. Another method is by passing a stopper

(see 11.4.8). Modern sheet winches are often 'self-tailing', whereby the sheet is automatically kept taut on the winch drum and the winch can then be operated entirely by one person.

Winches normally turn clockwise, viewed from above, and the turns must be put on in that same direction. When pulling in a sheet or hauling a halyard first take in as much slack as possible, then put on a single turn and continue to haul. Always keep your hands well away from the winch drum in case the rope takes charge and traps your fingers. As soon as any real strain comes on the rope put on a second turn, still hauling. Then put on a third and a fourth turn before inserting the winch handle. Putting on too many turns too soon is one way to encourage riding turns — as is pulling on the rope before it reaches the winch drum. When winching is completed, cleat up the rope, remove the winch handle, and place it in its proper stowage.

Main halyard winches are often self-stowing — the wire being reeled on to the drum as the sail is hoisted. These winches incorporate a brake, and the drum has a secondary section on to which the halyard should be led for the last few turns in order not to damage the wire, see Fig. 11(16). Unless operated correctly such winches can be dangerous, so it is important to familiarise yourself with the brake mechanism. The brake should be on except when lowering the sail.

When it is required to let go a sheet (say) which is under tension round a winch, be careful to keep tension on the tail while uncleating it. Then, still keeping tension on the tail, Fig. 11(17), gradually reduce it slightly while easing the turns round the drum with the flat of the other hand (with fingers clear of possible danger). Once the main load has been released from the winch the turns can be thrown off the drum by raising the tail vertically.

Winches are accurately machined, with close working fits, and to be reliable they must be regularly stripped down, cleaned and lubricated according to the maker's instructions. Manufacturers provide packs of spares for the internal parts of their winches, and it is sensible to carry these on board.

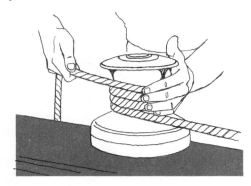

Fig. 11(17) Releasing a sheet. To loosen a taut rope, gradually reduce the tension on the tail while easing the turns slowly round the drum with the flat of the other hand.

11.4 Ropes

11.4.1 Ropes – general

Rope is a vital material for yachtsmen. In one form or another it is used for mooring a boat, or for anchoring her safely, while sailing yachts of course rely on it in many ways for hoisting and setting their sails. There is also a fascination in its construction, and in the very many ways in which it can be used and knotted. Anybody going to sea needs to have some knowledge of rope – how to use and handle it, and how to take care of it. It is also necessary to understand what type and size of rope is required for a given task.

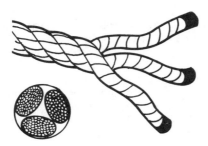

Fig. 11(18) Three-strand rope hawser laid – three strands twisted together to form a rope, normally right-hand construction, with individual strands twisted left handed.

Technical information in compiling this section on ropes has been kindly supplied by Bridon Fibres and Plastics Limited, makers of Marina yacht ropes. The illustrations are taken from their *Marina Manual of Yacht Ropes*, available at most chandlers. The editors are grateful to Bridon for their kind co-operation.

11.4.2 Ropes – construction

Most yacht ropes were traditionally made of three strands, and this form of construction is still used for certain applications such as mooring warps. Fibres are twisted in one direction to form yarns, and a bundle of yarns is twisted in the other direction to make a strand. Then the three strands are twisted in the original direction to make a rope. This alternate twisting produces a rope of stable construction which does not tend to unravel, and where the load is distributed evenly. Three-strand rope is usually hawser laid, which means that the strands are twisted together right-handed as in Fig. 11(18). Three-strand rope will kink unless it is properly coiled in the direction in which the strands are laid – clockwise for a right-handed rope.

For sheets and other running rigging, however, there is increasing use of plaited or braided ropes made from intertwined strands in various forms of construction. In racing yachts their use is universal because they function better in the stoppers, clutches and jammers which are now

used so extensively. They may consist of a three-strand rope surrounded by a braided cover, quite possibly of different materials. Double braided (or braid on braid) rope is made up of two single braided ropes, one inside as a core and the other forming a protective outer sheath, as illustrated in Fig. 11(19). Or, for example, a low-stretch rope may have an outer braided polyester jacket, with an inner braid around a core of parallel fibres – perhaps of polyester but increasingly of more exotic and expensive materials such as Kevlar or Spectra (see 11.4.3).

Plaited ropes consist of eight or more strands plaited together to form a close woven cord, with or without a central core depending on the application. In general, plaited ropes have less stretch than laid ones of the same size, and are less prone to distortion. For some special applications a rope's cover can be 36-plait, giving a good feel to the rope and providing excellent protection against chafe.

Fig. 11(19) Braidline – a double braided rope. A braided sheath and braided core combine to give very high strength.

11.4.3 Ropes and cordage – materials

Nowadays all yacht ropes are manufactured from synthetic fibres. Nylon was the first man-made fibre to be used for boats, and it is still the strongest rope available in general use, although more exotic (and much more expensive) materials have been developed for special applications in racing yachts. Nylon has excellent shock absorbing properties – which make it very suitable for anchor warps particularly in braidline or multiplait form. It is a soft rope, made from fine fibres, and is nice to handle; but it is too stretchy to be used for running rigging. In either three-strand or multiplait form it is good for mooring warps.

Poplyester (Terylene or Dacron) is also made from multifilament fibres; although slightly less strong it does not stretch so much as nylon. It has good resistance to wear, and is widely used for warps and cordage. In plaited or braidline form it is very suitable for halyards and sheets. In small boats halyards may be entirely of pre-stretched polyester, which is heat set during manufacture to reduce stretch in service.

Polypropylene ropes are of lower strength than nylon or polyester, but they are lightweight and buoyant – which is an advantage in some applications. They are available in soft, multifilament form and in a hard monofilament or split film form. The latter is usually only used for water ski lines. In its three-strand form polypropylene can be used for mooring warps but should be a slightly larger size than polyester for the same purpose. It also suffers rather more from light degradation (attack by the sun's rays).

Kevlar and Twaron are trade names for an aramid (aromatic polyamide) fibre with low stretch, and with a strength about three times that of polyester. However, it is expensive and very vulnerable to ultra violet light, so it is normally used only as a core material. It is also brittle so that it must not be bent round small diameter sheaves, and it does not knot well.

For the above reasons the use of Kevlar in ropes has been overtaken by HPME (High Modulus Polyethylene) materials known as Spectra and Dyneema, made respectively in the USA and the Netherlands. The disadvantages of these two materials are that they are slippery by nature, and care must be taken in the construction of the rope to avoid the sheath slipping over the core. Also they have a tendency to creep (extend) if left under load for long. However they are claimed to be ten times stronger than steel, and lighter than water. They knot well, are resistant to light, have good resistance to abrasion, and take up very little weight of water when wet.

Various terms connected with ropes and their different parts are described in Fig. 11(20), and should be understood by any seaman. Although less likely to get damaged than natural cordage, even synthetic ropes must be used and handled carefully to give long service. Although they are waterproof and do not rot they should be stowed away from any source of heat. They can also be damaged by chemicals or dirt; even salt crystals can hurt the internal structure, so ropes should be washed with clean, fresh water (do not use detergents) and dried naturally.

Sheaves which are too small in diameter, or too narrow, will damage ropes passing over them. A seized sheave can ruin a rope very quickly, so it is important to check and lubricate all sheaves regularly.

Most damage to ropes is usually caused by chafe – at fairleads for example in the case of mooring warps. Wherever a rope may be exposed to a rough surface it should be protected by parcelling or by a short length of plastic hose slipped over it.

When buying rope it pays to get slightly more than the minimum length required. It can then be moved around a little from time to time, to equalise the wear and extend the life. A rope can also be turned end for end for the same purpose.

With ordinary use polyester and nylon ropes acquire a slightly fluffy appearance, due to minor damage to the outer surface; this is not harmful to the main structure of the rope and in fact gives additional protection against abrasion.

Periodically the servings (bindings) should be removed from wire rope splices for inspection, since water can be trapped here. If the splice is sound and not corroded, regrease, parcel and serve.

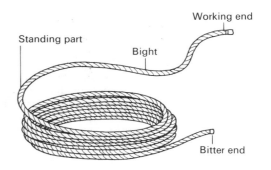

(a) Rope coiled down right-handed (clockwise). The bitter end is the extremity or inboard end of a line (or cable). The working end is used for knotting etc. The standing part is the fixed (as opposed to hauling) part, or the part of a rope about which the working end is turned to make a knot or hitch. A bight is an open loop in a rope.

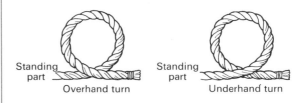

(b) The end of a rope looped over the standing part (left) forms an overhand turn. When looped under the standing part (right) it forms an underhand turn.

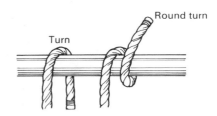

(c) When a rope is passed part way round an object, such as a bollard or a spar, it is said to form a turn. When it goes completely round the object it forms a round turn. However, the instruction 'Take a turn' (round a cleat or bollard, for example) normally implies taking a round turn.

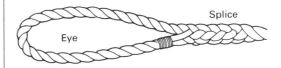

(d) An eye is formed in rope when the working end is brought back and secured to the standing part – either temporarily by a hitch, or more permanently by splicing or seizing.

Fig. 11(20) Rope terms.

11.4.4 Recommended sizes of rope
All rope is now measured by its diameter in millimetres. A diameter of 8mm corresponds to a circumference of one inch. The recommendations which follow should only be taken as a general

guide; certain factors such as design, displacement, sail ratio, use etc. may necessitate variations.

Anchor warps

The length of anchor chain carried should be three times the maximum depth of water for anchoring. If anchor warp is used, five times the depth should be carried. Always use at least 5 metres (3 fathoms) of chain between the anchor and the warp, to add weight and reduce chafe on the bottom.

Halyards

Overall length of boat (m)	Main mm	Jib mm	Spinnaker mm	Burgee mm
5	6	6	6	3
7	8	8	8	3
10	10	10	8	3
12	12	12	10	3
15 and over	12	12	12	3

Sheets

Overall length of boat (m)	Main or jib mm	Genoa mm	Spinnaker mm	Light weather spinnaker mm
5	10	10	8	6
7	10	10	10	6
10	10	12	12	8
12	12	14	14	8
15	12	16	16	10

Mooring warps

Overall length of boat (m)	Nylon mm	Polypropylene mm
5	8	10
7	12	14
10	14	16
12	16	20
15	18	22
17	20	24
20	24	28

Overall length of boat (m)	Nylon mm	Polyester mm	Anchor weight- Danforth or CQR kg	Anchor chain diam. mm	Kedge warp (nylon) mm
7	12	14	10	8	8
8.5	14	16	16	8	8
10	16	18	20	9	10
12	18	20	25	10	10
15	20	22	35	11	10
17	20	22	40	11	10
20	24		45	12	12

11.4.6 Useful knots, bends and hitches

A bend joins the ends of two ropes together, while a hitch makes a rope fast to some other object. A stopper knot is tied at the end of a rope to prevent unreeving, while a binding knot constricts a single object or holds two or more objects snugly together.

11.4.5 Yacht ropes – minimum breaking loads (kg)

Diam (mm)	Super braidline		Marina Spectra Hylite	Marina Squareline Nylon	Plaited dinghy ropes		Three-strand construction		
	Super polyester braidline	Super nylon braidline			Polyester matt finish/ continuous filament	Multifilament polypropylene	Polyester	Nylon	Polypropylene (all qualities)
4	–	–	–	–	–	180	295	320	250
5	–	–	–	–	225	225	400	500	350
6	690	950	1540	–	295	295	565	750	550
7	–	–	–	–	–	–	770	1020	740
8	1220	1450	2575	–	565	565	1020	1350	960
9	–	–	–	–	635	635	1270	1700	1150
10	1920	2725	3100	2080	905	905	1590	2080	1425
12	2780	3400	5750	3000	1360	1250	2270	3000	2030
14	3780	4300	7825	4100	–	–	3180	4100	2790
16	4950	5400	10350	5300	–	–	4060	5300	3500
18	6400	7700	13000	–	–	–	5080	6700	4450
20	–	–	–	–	–	–	6350	8300	5370
21	8720	9525	–	–	–	–	–	–	–
22	–	–	–	–	–	–	7620	10000	6500
24	11400	12700	–	–	–	–	9100	12000	7600

The above figures refer to Marina yacht ropes, from a table kindly supplied by their manufacturers, Bridon Fibres and Plastics Limited.

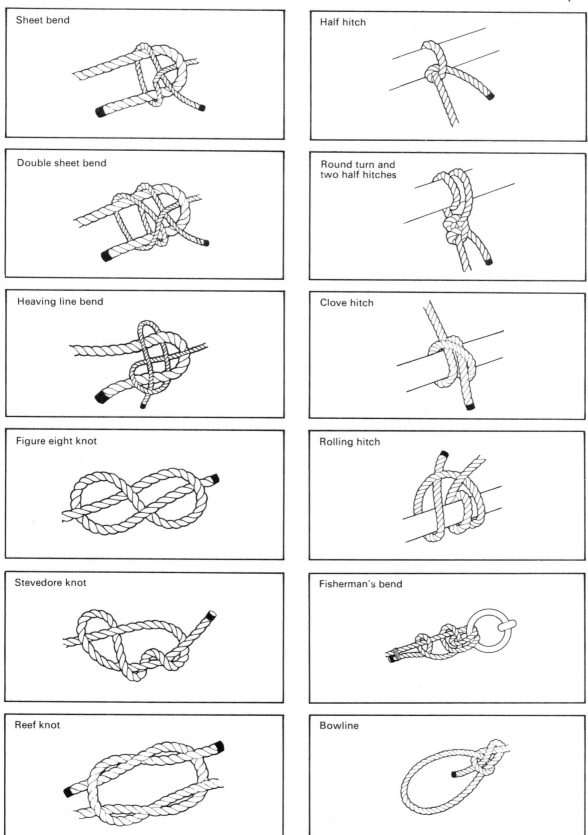

Fig. 11(21) Different types of bends and hitches.

It is always important to use an appropriate knot, bend or hitch – first for security, and second so that it can be undone when required. It must be stressed that knots do reduce the breaking load of a rope – by as much as 50 per cent.

Sheet bend. A most useful general purpose bend, which does not damage the rope, and unties readily. If used to join ropes of different materials, the ends should be seized or the bend may spill.

Double sheet bend. No stronger than the sheet bend, but more secure. If the rope is stiff and large, seize the eye and reeve the working end twice.

Heaving line bend. Used when bending a heaving line to a hawser.

Figure of eight knot. The sailor's most usual stopper knot.

Stevedore knot. Another single strand stopper knot, more suitable for synthetic rope than a figure of eight.

Reef knot. An admirable binding knot, as for reefing sails, but not as a bend. If tied with ends of unequal size, or if one is stiffer or smoother than the other, the knot is almost bound to capsize.

Half hitch. Usually the first stage in tying a more elaborate hitch, and should not be used unsupported.

Round turn and two half hitches. Suitable for securing a rope to a bollard or pile. If employed aloft or in ground tackle, the working end should be seized to the standing part. It is easily untied.

Clove hitch. Often used as a binding knot, but it is not very secure for use afloat. Will unwind under a steady rotating pull.

Rolling hitch. Simple to tie, and the most reliable knot under a lengthwise pull in the direction of the round turn. When bending this knot to another rope, the round turns should be crossed.

Fisherman's bend. Useful as an anchor bend.

Bowline. A popular and useful loop knot. When properly tied there is little or no danger of this knot capsizing before the breaking point of the rope is reached.

11.4.7 Handling ropes

Ropes should always be stored or stowed ready for immediate use. Three-strand rope is normally laid up right-handed, and should be coiled down right-handed (clockwise). Braidline should be hanked up in a figure of eight, ensuring that subsequent turns cancel out the kinks caused by previous turns.

The tails of sheets or halyards, or the ends of warps, should be coiled so that the running part of the rope is on top, and not underneath or at the back of the coil. There are various techniques for making up a halyard on a cleat, but one simple method is shown in Fig. 11(22). When the halyard has been coiled the inner loop is pulled forward through the centre of the coil, and twisted several times in a left-handed direction. The loop so formed is slipped over the top of the cleat, to hold the coil tight. There must be sufficient twists in

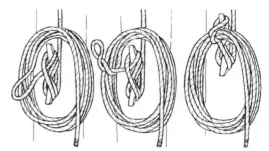

Fig. 11(22) Simple method for making up a halyard on a cleat.

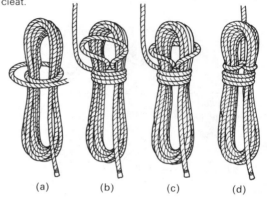

(a)   (b)   (c)   (d)

Fig. 11(23) Another way of securing a halyard.

the loop to make it just possible to slip it over the cleat.

Fig. 11(23) illustrates another way of securing a halyard, suspended by its standing part. When it has been coiled down, a short length is brought from the back of the coil and turned three or four times round the coil, as in (a). Then a loop is brought out from the back of the coil, above the turns and slipped over the head of the coil, as in (b) and (c). The standing part is then pulled tight (d).

When warps etc are stowed away, they should be coiled down so that they are ready for use, but the coil needs to be secured in some way. One method is shown in Fig. 11(24). The final coil of the rope is doubled to form a loop, as shown in (a), which is passed over the head of the coil and then up, under its own part. A turn is then taken with the end of the loop, as in (b). When the turns

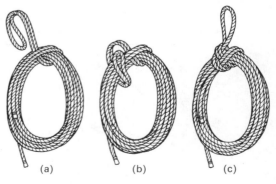

(a)   (b)   (c)

Fig. 11(24) Method of stowing a warp.

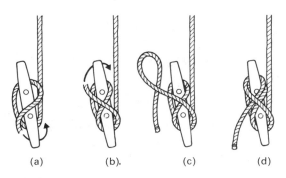

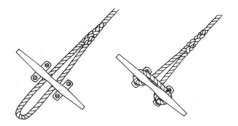

(a)   (b).   (c)   (d)

Fig. 11(25) How to belay a line to a cleat.

Fig. 11(26) Where a line with an eye spliced in the end is to be secured to a cleat with an open base, pass the eye through the base, and then put the loop over the horns.

are pulled tight, the free end of the loop (c) can be hung over a hook.

When belaying a line to a cleat, Fig. 11(25), the first turn should be round the base, and by convention this should be right-handed in case the line has to be handled by somebody else in the dark. The next turn is made with a figure of eight, as shown in (b). The final turn, (c) and (d), may be half-hitched for lines such as halyards or mooring warps. For sheets omit the half-hitch, and replace by a final turn round the base.

When heaving a line, Fig. 11(27), do not rely on a previously coiled line being free of turns, but coil it down yourself into your left hand, in right-

Fig. 11(27) Preparing to heave a line.

Fig. 11(28) Heaving a line.

handed (clockwise) loops about 450mm (18in) in diameter. Plaited or braided rope may fall into figures of eight. Before heaving the line secure the standing part to a cleat or similar fitting, and make sure that the line is long enough for the job. For any lengthy throw it is advisable to use a light (heaving) line as a messenger, in order to pass across a heavier warp. These instructions assume that the rope has a right-hand lay, and that the thrower is right-handed. Before heaving, transfer about half the coil to the right hand, Fig. 11(28). Stand sideways to the direction of throw, bring the throwing arm well back, and swing it forwards with a round arm motion, or more overarm if a long throw is involved. Keep the coil in the other hand facing forward so that it can uncoil easily.

11.4.8. Passing a stopper

A stopper is used to take the strain on a rope temporarily, as for example when it is necessary to clear a riding turn from a winch. The stopper should be a smaller rope, and it should be applied so that the direction in which it pulls is as near as possible the same as the direction of the rope which is to be relieved. If that is a laid rope a single stopper can be used, as shown in Fig. 11(29). First half-hitch the stopper round the rope against the lay, and then dog (wrap) it several times round the rope in the other direction so that the stopper lies closely into the lay of the rope: the

Stopper led to another winch, or to a tackle (hand billy)

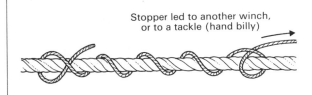

Fig. 11(29) Passing a stopper.

end of the stopper can then be seized to the rope, or held against it by the hand.

If the rope under load is a plaited or braidline rope, without any lay, a double stopper must be used. One end of the stopper is half-hitched round the rope as for a single stopper, above. The other end is then half-hitched alongside it, but in the opposite direction. The two ends are then criss-crossed in opposite directions round the rope several times, and the two ends either seized to the rope or held round it as before.

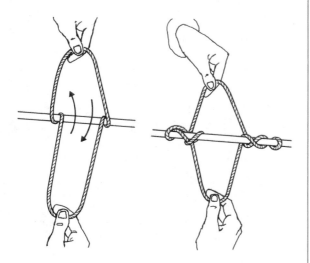

Fig. 11(30) An alternative method of passing a stopper.

An alternative way of passing a stopper is shown in Fig. 11(30), by using a loop of rope thinner than the rope to be relieved, and passing it round and round as illustrated. The relieving tackle should be shackled to both loops of the stopper.

11.4.9 Whippings
The end of a rope should always be neatly whipped, to prevent it unravelling. In most cases a whipping is better than a back splice, which may snarl up when a rope is required to run through a block or fairlead.

When synthetic rope is first purchased the ends of the strands and the strands themselves can be prevented from unravelling by securing them with waterproof boat tape and fusing the ends with a match. This should only be regarded as a temporary measure.

A sailor's whipping can be made by laying a short length of twine along the rope, and towards its end, as in Fig. 11(31). About half-a-dozen tight turns are taken round the rope and against its lay. The short length S can then be cut off. The longer length L is then laid back along the rope, and further turns are continued with the loop is formed. Finally L is drawn tight (a pair of pliers may be useful) and cut off close to the turns on the rope.

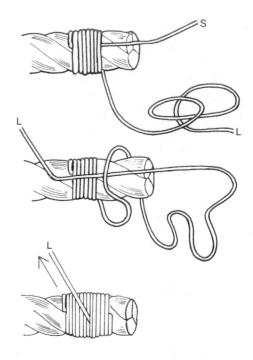

Fig. 11(31) Sailor's whipping.

A common whipping is made by laying a loop along the rope and making a number of turns over it. The working end is put through this loop and pulled back out of sight. The two ends are then cut off short. See Fig. 11(32).

The length of either of the above whippings should be about the same as the diameter of the rope.

A sailmaker's whipping is the most secure, but it really needs a palm and needle. These are items which should be on board any sailing boat. The end of the twine is first anchored by stitching it through a strand, after which turns are taken

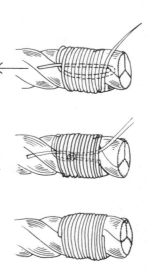

Fig. 11(32) Common whipping.

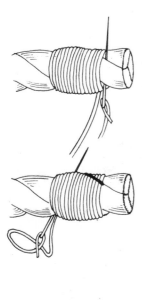

Fig. 11(33) Sailmaker's whipping.

tightly round the rope – working towards the end and against the lay, as shown in Fig. 11(33). The needle is then passed under a strand, and brought back along the groove between strands so that the turns of whipping are frapped tight. It is then stitched under the next strand, and the procedure repeated with each groove in turn. The end of the twine is then secured by stitching it through a strand, and the end cut off short.

11.4.10 Eye splice – three-strand rope

To make an eye splice in three-strand rope, first apply a seizing at the point where the rope is to be unlaid. Five full tucks are necessary with synthetic ropes, and six inches of rope are allowed for every inch circumference: (A 8mm diameter rope is 1in in circumference). Secure the thimble (if one is to be used) in the bight of the rope, as in Fig. 1. The numbered instructions below refer to the appropriate diagrams.

1

(2) Unlay the rope back to the seizing, and temporarily whip each strand. The centre strand will be tucked first. The back of the thimble has been marked black, so that rotation of the work can be followed.

2

(3) Insert the spike, with the lay of the rope, and open up the bight of the strand next to the one to be tucked; pass this strand through this bight from right to left, as looking back along the length of the rope, or in other words against its lay.

3

(4) Haul the centre strand taut, insert the left hand strand underneath the next bight to the left, and haul taut.

4

(5) Now turn the thimble over. Open up with the spike the remaining bight, and pass the remaining strand through, as indicated. All tucks are made from right to left, against the lay of the rope, keeping the lay of each strand correct and maintaining an even tension in the strands.

5

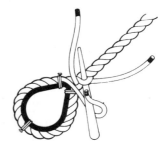

(6) Turning the thimble over again, haul taut on each strand to ensure that the splice fits snugly at the toe of the thimble.

6

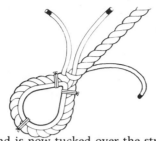

(7) Each strand is now tucked over the strand to its left and under the next one. Continue tucking over and under with each strand in turn until five full tucks are completed.

7

(8) Then unlay each of the ends, and divide into two. Each half is matched with its partner of the next strand, and seized together over the intermediate strand. The surplus tails are cut off, and the ends fused together. The stops holding the thimble are removed, and the splice rolled in the hands so as to even it out.

8

11.4.11 Eye splice – braidline

For splicing braidline a special fid and pusher are required, and can be obtained from chandlers. The fid must be the right size for the rope, e.g. size 10 for a 10mm rope.

Three marks must be made on the sheath, and three on the core. These are best done with a felt tip pen, using the fid as a measure. One fid is the overall length of the fid; one short fid is the distance between the two marks on the fid and the hollow end.

It is important during all stages of the splice that the slack in the sheath be removed,

particularly after extracting the core and in completing the splice. Braidline is a balanced rope, with about half the strength in the sheath and half in the core, so it is important that the tension is equally applied. The instructions (1), (2), (3) etc which follow refer also to the diagrams so numbered.

(1) Marking the sheath (3 marks).
Tape the end of the sheath with adhesive tape, and cut off heat sealed end, if applicable. Measure one fid length from end of rope, and mark (R). Form a loop and mark size of eye required opposite the one fid length – X, where the core is extracted. For instructions when fitting a thimble see under (8). Measure about five fid lengths from core extraction point (X) and secure to cleat or similar. From R count ten double strands back towards the taped end, and mark all way round the rope (T). This is the crossover point.

1

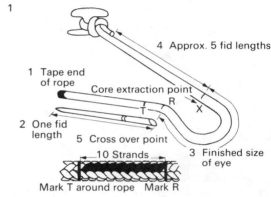

(2) Extract core and mark (3 marks).
Take out the core at X by folding the rope and working the outer strands aside to expose the core. Pull out the core from the end of the rope, and tape the end. Holding the core, slide the sheath towards the knot and then smooth all of the slack of the sheath from the knot, back over the core. This ensures that all slack is removed from both core and sheath, and that tension is equal on both, which is most important. Mark the core where it comes out of the sheath (Mark 1). Slide the sheath back towards the knot and from mark 1 on the core measure towards the knot one

2

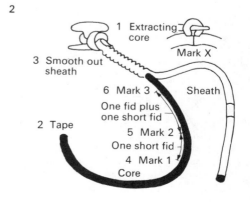

short fid length (Mark 2). From mark 2 measure one full fid length plus a short fid length (Mark 3).

(3) Insert sheath into core.

Lay the work out flat, and ensure the rope parts are not twisted. Place the fid into the core at mark 2, and carefully guide it through the centre and out at mark 3. Flatten the taped end of the sheath and fold it double; now place it in the hollow end of the fid, ensuring a smooth surface that will not catch the yarns as it is pushed through. Place the pusher into the hollow end of the fid, and slide the fid and sheath through the core. When the sheath protrudes at mark 3, remove the fid and pull the sheath through until mark 2 meets the crossover point (T).

3

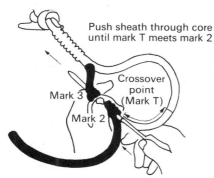

Push sheath through core until mark T meets mark 2

Crossover point (Mark T)

Mark 3

Mark 2

(4) Insert core into sheath.

Place the fid into the sheath at the crossover point (T), along the centre and out of the same hole that the core was extracted from. Place the end of the core into the fid, and pass the fid and all of the core through the sheath. Remove the fid.

4

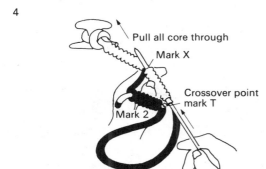

Pull all core through

Mark X

Crossover point mark T

Mark 2

(5) Lock crossover point and taper sheath.

Important – the core end must now be pulled bunching the sheath back against the crossover point. Now pull the sheath end and bunch the core back to the crossover point, making sure that the crossover point is pulled tight. Take off the tape from the end of the sheath and unlay the sheath strands as far as possible. Take a quarter of the strands and cut off as far back as possible. Cut the next quarter of strands at two-thirds length, and the next quarter at one-third, leaving a quarter of strands at full length.

5

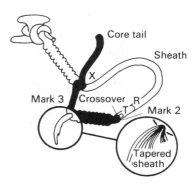

Core tail

Sheath

X

Mark 3   Crossover   R

T   Mark 2

Tapered sheath

(6) Smooth out eye.

The slack parts of the rope are now smoothed out either side of the crossover point. Hold the crossover point as you do this making sure it does not slip. The tapered sheath will disappear into the core.

6

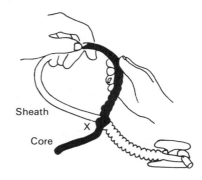

Sheath

X

Core

(7) Bring back slack of sheath from knot.

Hold the core in the right hand and maintain tension against the knot. The left hand smooths the slack of the sheath from the knot, over the core and the crossover point. The right hand maintains tension on the core at all times, and it is necessary to slide the hand back as the sheath progresses. If you cannot get the sheath over the crossover point, slide the sheath back towards the knot, and smooth out the eye from the crossover point as in (6), and continue as above. Go over the rope several times from the knot to ensure that all of the sheath slack is removed. Marks X and R should now coincide.

7

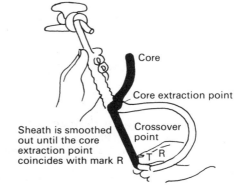

Core

Core extraction point

Sheath is smoothed out until the core extraction point coincides with mark R

Crossover point

T R

(8) Finish the splice.

Smooth out the eye towards the core, and cut off the core leaving 6mm ($\frac{1}{4}$in) protruding. This is now tucked away into the throat of the splice. Fit thimble if required. Check once again that all of the sheath is smoothed out. Place a sailmaker's whipping on the neck of the splice, as near to the throat as practicable. Note that the taped end of the sheath and core must fit neatly into the fid so that they do not catch yarns as they are pushed

8

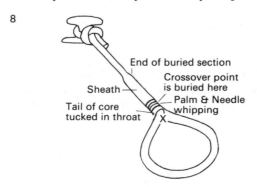

End of buried section
Crossover point is buried here
Sheath
Palm & Needle whipping
Tail of core tucked in throat
X

through. If difficulty is found in placing the taped end into the fid, several strands may be removed from the end – but do not cut off. Should the sheath distort or ruck during the splicing operations, this may be due to a joined strand. The strand ends at the join will be buried between the core and the sheath. Locate the join, and remove the strands by pulling out of the rope. Continue the splice. Smooth out the rucked area with the hands. When the splice is finished, bury the two join strands between the sheath and the core for a minimum distance of 125mm (5in) each way.

To fit a thimble in a braidline splice it is necessary to measure the size of eye around the thimble, as in (1) above, and continue the splice as instructed. Fit the thimble after cutting off the core (8). Carefully slide the sheath towards the knot just enough to insert the thimble. Now ensure that all of the slack is smoothed out towards the eye. Place a sailmaker's whipping at the neck of the splice. If it is found that slack remains in the sheath after the throat is tight on the thimble, then this slack must be worked out through the tail of the rope after whipping, as instructed.

11.4.12 Splicing used braidline rope

First soak the section of rope in water for several minutes, to lubricate and loosen the fibres. When extracting the core, as in (2) above, thoroughly loosen three to four sheath strands at point X, to obtain a large and flexible hole for the extraction.

Before burying the sheath at the crossover point, anchor the loop of slip knot to a firm object before starting to bury: both hands and weight of body can then be used to assist in burying sheath over core at crossover. Holding the crossover tightly, milk all the excess sheath from R to X. Cut off the core tail at X. Pull above crossover with one hand to reduce diameter of the crossover and core, then milk the sheath with the other hand. The use of a small cord in a rolling hitch around the sheath assists in the final burying process. Pulling on the hitch should be towards the eye until the sheath slackness is removed.

11.4.13 Centre eye splice

Measure the circumference of eye required, and mark the rope accordingly. Pierce the rope and pass rope end A through mark 2, and rope B through mark 1. The two rope intersections should be drawn as close together as possible. The eye will take a thimble if required.

11.4.14 Braidline to wire splice

This splice is simple and quick, and extremely strong because it does not rely on the tucks alone for strength but also on the hollow braids gripping the wire as tension is applied. See illustrations (1) and (2).

1

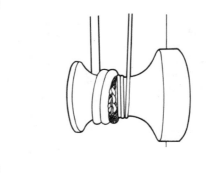

2

If neatly made, little bulk is formed, and the lay of the wire is disturbed to a minimum. Measurements are not critical, providing enough wire is covered and the core tuck is made sufficiently deep to allow enough length for the sheath splice and length of tucks for working. In this case a 6mm diameter 6 × 19 galvanised wire is spliced to a 10mm diameter Marina Super Polyester Braidline. The numbered instructions refer to the diagrams.

(3) The tools needed are a sharp knife, tape, and a hollow or Swedish fid to separate the wire strands. A Marina Braidline splicing fid will help, but is not essential.

3

(4) Tie a knot about two metres from the end of the braidline, securing it to a solid object. Bind the end of the wire with tape, and put a tape marker about 400mm (16in) along it. This amount of wire will be buried inside the rope. Lightly bind the rope about 25mm (1in) from the end and fray the strands out. Separating the core strands from the sheath, the sheath can be slid back along the core towards the knot, exposing about one metre (39in) of core.

4

(5) Bury the wire in the core, with the rope ends overlapping the marker tape.

5

(6) Tape the core firmly to the wire about 150mm (6in) from the wire marker, and carefully unlay the strands back to this tape.

6

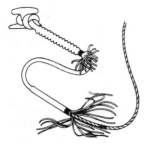

(7) Neatly divide the loose strands into three, and bind each group together.

7

(8) Pass the Swedish fid under two wire strands and tuck the first rope strand, making sure the strands lay flat and neat.

8

(9) Follow round the wire taking the next two wire strands, and make the next tuck and the third the same.

9

(10), (11), (12), (13) Continue until three full tucks are completed, and then cut off the loose ends of rope.

10

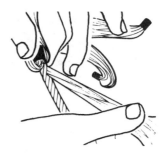

11

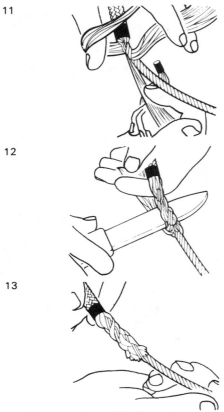

12

13

(14) Smooth the sheath back over the splice, taking care not to ruck the cover over the wire, and make sure that all the slack sheath is worked back from the knot.

14

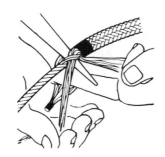

(15) Tightly bind the sheath where the core splice finishes, and unlay the rope strands and divide into three. Proceed as for the core splice, but add a fourth tuck, cutting out half of the strands to form a taper before tucking.

15

(16) Binding the tucks is not essential but waterproof tape can be used with advantage for this purpose. Keep the rope tucks neat and flat.

16

11.4.15 Wire rope – general
Wire is used for both standing and running rigging, for which the requirements are different. Running rigging needs to be flexible, whereas for standing rigging the prime requirement is minimum stretch for a given size.

The construction of wire rope is described by the number of strands and the number of wires in each strand. For example, a 6 × 7 steel core rope has six strands over a steel core, and each strand consists of seven wires (six wires twisted round a central one) – as illustrated in Fig. 11(34).

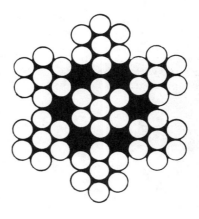

Fig. 11(34) 6 × 7 steel core.

11.4.16 Standing rigging – wire
The simplest, and most expensive type of standing rigging is steel rod, which may be either round or lenticular in section. It has very little stretch, but is easily damaged.

More usual is single strand, 1 × 19, made up of six wires twisted round a central core with an outer layer of twelve further wires, as shown in Fig. 11(35). Although more flexible than rod rigging, 1 × 19 cannot be bent round a thimble for splicing, so special end fittings are required, see 11.2.2. This form of construction gives a good smooth surface to reduce wind resistance, and to allow sails and sheets to pass smoothly with little chafing. 1 × 19 is made of stainless steel which lasts longer than galvanised wire, but is not so

Fig. 11(35) 1 × 19 steel core.

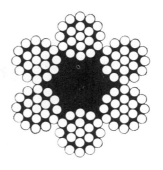

Fig. 11(36) 6 × 19 fibre core.

strong and a good deal more expensive. It needs to be handled carefully when stepping or unstepping the mast.

11.4.17 Running rigging – wire
Many types of ropes are used for running rigging. Wire rope is usually found in halyards because of its non-stretch properties, resistance to chafe, and small windage for a given strength. Its main disadvantages are that it can and does rust, and it does not like sharp bends. Obviously wire used for running rigging needs to be a lot more flexible than that used for standing rigging, but even so sheaves over which it passes should be not less than 26 times the diameter of fast moving rope, or 12 times the diameter of wire used for halyards.

A typical wire rope used for running rigging is the 6 × 19 with fibre core, as illustrated in Fig. 11(36). This may be made of galvanised or stainless steel wire, the former being slightly stronger.

All wire rope needs to be examined regularly for any signs of corrosion or broken strands. If it is lightly oiled from time to time its life will be prolonged. With galvanised wire surface rust can be removed with a wire brush. If the rusting is serious, try bending the wire; if a strand breaks it should be discarded.

11.5 Sails

11.5.1 Sails – general
The correct shapes of sails, combined with their strength and reliability, are important matters for any sailing yacht. For one which races, the precise set of the sails and their proper interaction are major factors in success, and modern racing yachts aim to control the trim and camber of their sails very closely, depending on the relative speed and direction of the wind. The names of the more common sails, and the various parts of them, are shown in Fig. 11(37) and in Fig. 11(38).

The efficiency of modern sails (which make boats more close-winded than hitherto, and faster in a wider range of conditions) depends on the chemical processes which have produced the materials now in use; modern weaving techniques and heat treatment which provide tough and stable cloths; and on ever-increasing sophistication in the actual design of sails in terms of putting them together.

It should be understood at the outset that racing and cruising yachts have quite different requirements. The former can sacrifice almost everything to speed, but cruising yachts need sails

11.4.18 Wire ropes – minimum breaking loads (tonnes)

Size		Galvanised wire rope		Stainless steel wire rope		
		Standing rigging	Running rigging	Standing Rigging		Running rigging
diam. (mm)	approx. circ. (in)	6 × 7 with steel core	6 × 19 with fibre core	1 × 19	6 × 7 with steel core	6 × 19 with fibre core
2	$\frac{1}{4}$	0.28	–	–	0.24	–
3	$\frac{3}{8}$	0.63	0.50	0.72	0.55	0.43
4	$\frac{1}{2}$	1.12	0.88	1.28	0.97	0.77
5	$\frac{5}{8}$	1.75	1.38	2.00	1.51	1.20
6	$\frac{3}{4}$	2.52	1.99	2.88	2.18	1.73
7	$\frac{7}{8}$	3.43	2.71	–	–	–
8	1	4.48	3.54	–	3.87	–
9	$1\frac{1}{8}$	5.04	4.48	–	–	–
10	$1\frac{1}{4}$	7.00	–	–	–	–
12	$1\frac{1}{2}$	10.10	–	–	–	–

which are more versatile (because fewer are carried) and which are easy and safe to handle, are not too expensive and have a long life.

11.5.2 Sailcloth and sailmaking

To understand sails, and how to make the best use of them, it is necessary to know something about their design and manufacture. Most fore-and-aft sails are now made from Terylene (Dacron), a product of the petro-chemical industry. Very fine filaments of polyester are formed by extruding a liquid at high pressure and temperature, and a number of these filaments make up the polyester

fibre, which has several very desirable properties. It has good tensile strength, it resists abrasion, and it is not affected by moisture. The fact that the resulting cloth is hard can be a disadvantage, because stitches tend to stand proud of the surface and therefore wear more easily than if they bedded down into the material. Terylene is also subject to degradation by ultra violet light, so it should not be exposed unnecessarily to bright sunlight.

Spinnakers are made from nylon, which has more stretch but is just as strong and resistant to rot as Terylene. More recently other synthetic

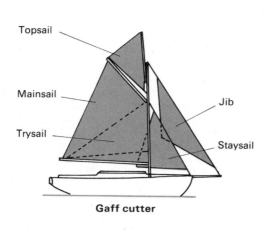

Gaff cutter

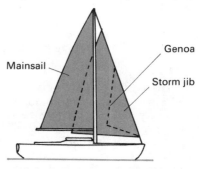

Bermudian masthead sloop

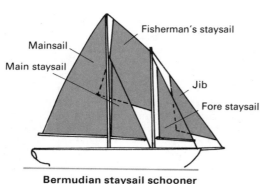

Bermudian staysail schooner

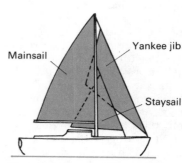

Bermudian masthead cutter

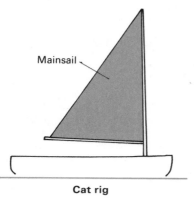

Cat rig

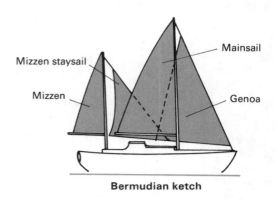

Bermudian ketch

Fig. 11(37) Different rigs.

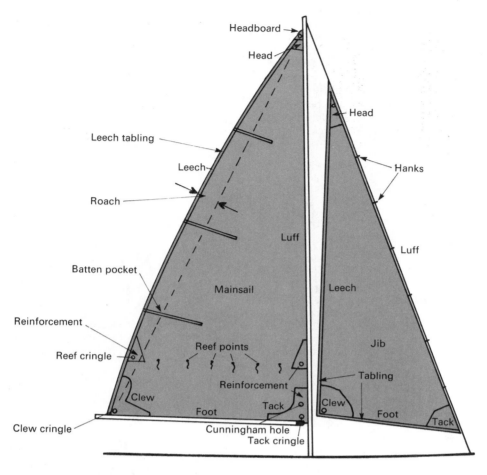

Fig. 11(38) The parts of a sail.

materials such as Kevlar and Mylar have been used for sails, but mostly in specialist racing applications.

Terylene, like other woven materials, is woven from threads at right angles to each other – the warp running lengthwise, and the weft across the length. A certain weight of cloth may consist of heavier threads with rather an open weave or a larger number of thinner threads which are more compacted. The latter type of cloth, more closely woven, is more stable and durable; it also has less porosity, although this quality depends too on the dressing the cloth receives from fillers in the finishing stages.

While sailcloth will quite strongly resist any deformation if tension is applied uniformly along either the warp or the weft, it is a different matter if it is pulled on the bias – at an angle, say, of 45° to the warp and weft. What then happens can be demonstrated by pulling two opposite corners of a handkerchief along the diagonal, when folds can be seen to appear close to the line of tension. This fact can be utilised in sailmaking, as one way of getting the required shape into a sail. But if the stretch cannot be limited the sail will pull out of shape, so it is necessary to use a certain minimum weight (strength) of cloth for each

application, and to control the stretch along the luff of a sail (and the foot of a mainsail) by attaching the cloth to a rope or a tape.

Sailcloth is specified according to its weight per unit area. In Britain this is measured in ounces per

British	American	Metric
(oz per sq yard)	(oz per yard, width 28½ in)	(gram per sq metre)
1	0.8	34
2	1.6	68
3	2.4	102
4	3.2	136
5	4.0	170
6	4.8	203
7	5.6	237
8	6.4	271
9	7.2	305
10	8.0	339
11	8.8	373
12	9.6	407
13	10.4	441
14	11.2	475
15	12.0	508

Fig. 11(39) Equivalent sailcloth weights in British, American and metric units.

square yard, but the Americans use a different unit which is ounces per yard of a cloth which is only 72cm (28½in) wide. Comparative figures for cloths in British, American and metric weights are shown in Fig. 11(39).

Shape is also induced into a mainsail by rounding the luff and the foot, so that when the sail is set on straight spars the surplus cloth is absorbed into the body of the sail, as shown in

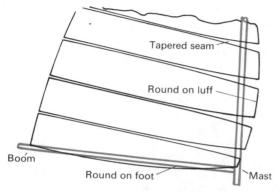

Fig. 11 (40) Exaggerated sketch showing how fullness is worked into a mainsail (a) by tapering the seams, and (b) by the rounded shapes of luff and foot.

Fig. 11(40). This can be seen quite clearly if the sail is spread out on a clean surface. Similar considerations apply to headsails, but here allowance has to be made for the fact that the forestay sags somewhat, which in itself makes the sail fuller so that the luff needs to be hollowed to allow for this.

Fig. 11(40) also illustrates another way of putting fullness into a sail – by tapering the seams. This method has some advantage over rounding the luff and foot because the position of the fullness in the sail is better controlled, but the two are used in combination.

In Fig. 11(41) are shown various ways that a headsail can be cut, to combine the techniques mentioned briefly above and the properties of the sailcloth in order to produce the required shape of sail.

Although sailmaking can still be something of an art, science plays an ever-increasing part. Modern developments have been much influenced by computer design, better cloths, and improvements in sail handling systems. Computers are now used extensively to analyse the loading on different parts of a sail in order to optimise the panel layout and the use of any special materials that may be included for extra strength along the lines of greatest stress.

For racing sails there is increasing use of exotic materials such as Kevlar. These are expensive and although they are very stretch-resistant they have a depressingly short effective life. More recently carbon fibre has appeared in the manufacture of sophisticated sailcloth. For more general purposes, laminates are being used in cruising sails, with films such as Mylar or Tedlar sandwiched between

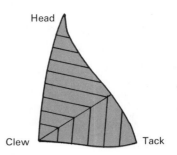

(a) Mitre cut. The traditional cut for headsails, with seams meeting the leech at right angles.

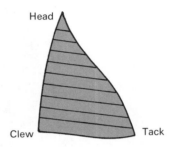

(b) Horizontal cut. The most common cut for mainsails.

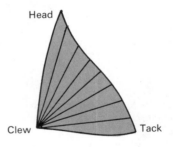

(c) Radial or sunray cut.

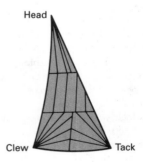

(d) Tri-radial cut.

Fig. 11 (41) Different cuts of headsails. The drawings depict sails as laid out on the loft floor, and shapes of sail edges are exaggerated for clarity. The luff of a jib is hollowed towards the head, for it to set flat while allowing for the sag in the forestay. Lower down the luff is rounded, to give the required flow to the sail. Similar cuts are also used for mainsails, but since there is no forestay to consider the mainsail luff has a slightly rounded convex curve.

Dacron to improve the stability of the cloth, which looks and feels like ordinary Dacron. Such cloth holds its shape better, but is more expensive. The firm of Sobstad makes Genesis sails which consist of a laminate of Tedlar film, Kevlar fibres and polyester scrim, the number of layers depending on the strength required. This material can be transparent or white, and can be used for spinnaker cloth and cruising chutes as well as for fore and aft sails.

A striking development in recent years has been the increased popularity of fully-battened mainsails, combined with lazyjacks to facilitate lowering and reefing. Fully-battened sails do not flog which is kinder to the cloth, they hold their shape well, and they are easy to trim. But attention needs to be paid to the fittings at the forward ends of the battens, and the pockets are liable to chafe against shrouds etc when the sail is squared off.

11.5.3 Mainsail reefing arrangements

There are various methods of reefing the mainsail:
(1) Roller Reefing, where the sail is wrapped round the boom by rotating the latter by worm gear at the main gooseneck fitting. The procedure is simple: remove the kicking strap; take the weight of the boom on the topping lift; check the mainsheet slightly if sailing on the wind; ease the halyard as the turns are taken on the boom. With a mainsail which has sliders on the luff it is necessary to open the gate in the mast track, and it is helpful if one member of the crew keeps the leech of the sail pulled well aft and is available to remove the lower batten should this be necessary. When the required reduction in sail area has been made, set up the halyard tight, ease the topping lift, and close the mast gate. For unreefing, follow the reverse procedure. Despite its simplicity, roller reefing does have some disadvantages. The kicking strap has to be removed, although there are ways of getting round this by using a clawfitting on the boom (but this is inclined to wear the sail), or by winding in a webbing strap as the rolls are taken in the sail: the reefing gear requires regular maintenance, and could fail; the reefed sail does not set very well; and roller reefing really requires a boom with a round section, which is not the best shape from other considerations.
(2) Through-mast roller reefing is a variation of (1), in which the reefing gear passes through the mast and is operated by a handle on the forward side. It can be quicker to use than the worm gear type, but suffers from the same disadvantages. Furthermore it requires a fixed gooseneck, so that tension of the mainsail luff is not so easy to control.
(3) Point reefing is the traditional method. It involves reeving reef pendants through special cringles on the luff and leech of the mainsail, and hauling them down to the level of the boom as the halyard is eased. Reef points in the sail are then tied (preferably passing between the sail and the

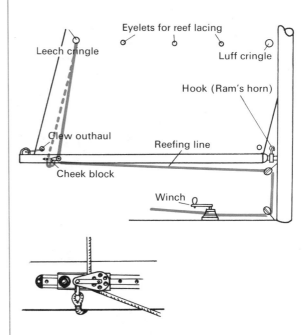

Fig. 11(42) Diagrammatic sketch of slab (or jiffy) reefing system. In practice the gear is often more complicated, with two or more reefs, adjustable cheek blocks mounted on tracks along the boom, and reefing lines led internally through the boom.

boom, where possible) to bunch up the surplus sail; alternatively a reef lacing may be used. The kicking strap is not affected, and if the system is well laid out it is possible to get a better setting sail than with roller reefing, but the work involved is difficult when short-handed. Also, although there are usually two depths of reef, and sometimes three with mainsails of high aspect ratio, point reefing is not as flexible as roller reefing, where the reduction of sail can be adjusted roll by roll.
(4) Slab (or jiffy) reefing is a variation of (3), using modern materials and equipment. The gear is illustrated diagrammatically in Fig. 11(42). Only one reef is shown, but two or more can be provided. The procedure is to ease the kicking strap and set up the topping lift, then ease the main sheet. Heave in on the reefing line so that the boom is pulled up to the leech cringle, and make fast. Then slacken the main halyard until the luff cringle can be slipped over the hook at the gooseneck (it helps if the halyard is marked, so that it is slackened the right amount). Tighten the halyard again. Ease the topping lift, tighten the mainsheet, and set up the kicking strap. The spare folds of the bottom of the mainsail can be gathered by a lacing passed through the eyelets in the sail for that purpose. The gear needs to be good and strong, and it is important that the cheek blocks on the boom are properly positioned so that the sail is pulled to the boom and also kept stretched along the foot.

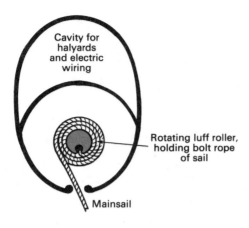

Fig. 11(43) Mast section for internal roller reefing/furling gear.

(5) Roller furling for mainsails is a comparatively new system, and there are two distinct methods: in-mast and in-boom. With the former the luff of the sail is rolled up either inside the mast or on a jackstay running down the aft side of the mast. Operation can be manual or by electric motor, and the sail can be partially rolled up for reefing or fully rolled for furling. An interior roller needs a special mast, see Fig. 11(43), but an exterior roller can be fitted to most masts that are not of the bendy variety. Although they are becoming quite popular and are easy to operate these systems have certain disadvantages – loss of sail area, poor performance, extra weight aloft when the sail is furled (compared to other methods), increased chafe in the cloth, and uncertainty about what to do if something jams. Another disadvantage is that as the sail is reefed the centre of effort moves progressively forward which can upset helm balance. In-boom systems do not have so many snags, and they can cope with fully-battened sails which is a distinct advantage.

Any reefing system depends on proper maintenance of the gear, and its availability in an emergency. Roller reefing gear must be lubricated and worked regularly; if a separate handle is used it must be stowed in a safe place, and a spare provided. With slab reefing the various pendants and sheaves must be kept in good condition, so that even a third reef (which is probably seldom, if ever, used) is readily available should it be required.

11.5.4 Headsail furling and reefing

Traditionally sail area in the foretriangle of a yacht has been reduced, as the wind speed increases, by changing to a smaller sail. This process was made easier in recent years by the advent of forestays with grooves to take the luff of the jib, which speeded things up by eliminating the need to hank and unhank sails on a pitching foredeck. Now the development of efficient roller furling/reefing gear means that a cruising yacht can conveniently set a large genoa, progressively reef it, or totally furl it, without the need for anybody to venture on the foredeck at all.

Headsail reefing gear, as an integral part of the standing rigging, requires regular maintenance (see 11.2.5). Drum bearings, swivels and luff spar joining links have a limited life, particularly in some models.

Roller reefing headsails are now often of radical cut, either bi-radial with the panels radiating from the clew and head, or even tri-radial with panels radiating from all three corners. Radial cut sails, with modern cloths where the strongest fibres are aligned with the loading in the sail, hold their shape better with increasing wind speed. Although the sails themselves last well, the sacrificial strips along leech and foot need regular replacement. Opinion seems divided on the efficiency of Dacron treated to be resistant to ultra violet light. Various devices are used to eliminate the belly which otherwise forms in the body of the sail during the rolling up process. Provision should always be made for setting a storm jib on a separate inner forestay.

11.5.5 Spinnakers

In a cruising yacht, which can if necessary afford to make temporary changes of course while the spinnaker is hoisted or lowered, it should be perfectly easy to handle this sail with just a little foresight and practice.

The basic items of spinnaker gear are described in 11.3.1 and illustrated in Fig. 11(15). To hoist the spinnaker first make sure that it is properly flaked down in its bag with no twists. Attach the bag to the pulpit, or to the guardrails on the lee side, under the jib. Rig the spinnaker guy along the windward side, outboard of everything, through the pole end fitting, and clip it to the tack of the sail. Rig the sheet on the lee side, outboard of everything, and clip it to the spinnaker clew. Pass the halyard under the foot of the headsail, outboard and clear of everything, and clip it to the head of the sail, which has a swivel. Attach the heel of the pole to the mast and heave on the pole lift so that the pole is at right angles to the mast. Take down the slack on the pole downhaul. With the boat running roughly downwind it is easy to hoist the spinnaker quickly under the lee of the headsail and mainsail, then trim the guy and the sheet to set the sail. Then drop the headsail. The pole should be trimmed at right angles to the apparent wind, and its height on the mast adjusted so that the tack and clew of the sail are about the same height. Keep the spinnaker sheet eased out as far as possible without the luff of the sail falling in.

Gybing procedure depends on the gear fitted. With the main sheeted well in amidships and the boat's stern to the wind, the spinnaker guy is released from the pole end fitting and becomes the new sheet. By controlling the two sheets the spinnaker should be kept drawing while the pole is moved across and clipped onto the new guy (the previous sheet). The gybing of the mainsail can then be completed.

Lowering (handing) the spinnaker is simple if the boat is running downwind. First hoist the headsail. Then ease the guy so that the pole

(a) Horizontal cut. Tends to become fuller in stronger winds, and performs best on a run.

(b) Tri-radial construction minimizes distortion, and gives a good all-round sail.

(c) Star cut. A flat, but broad-shouldered spinnaker which is best for use with the wind on or ahead of the beam.

(d) Radial head. A compromise sail, with a radial head and a flat, horizontally cut bottom, which combines good reaching and downwind performance.

Fig. 11(44) Different types of spinnakers.

swings forward near the forestay. Release the tack of the sail from the pole end fitting. One crew member then gathers in all the foot of the sail somewhere aft of the shrouds on the lee side. When he is ready to gather in the rest of the sail, lower the halyard steadily. The sail is then pulled inboard and stowed down below. Clear away the spinnaker pole and secure all the gear.

Different cuts, and hence shapes, of spinnaker are available for best performance on different points of sailing. Originally the spinnaker was essentially a running sail; now, using modern sailcloth and new cutting techniques, spinnakers can be carried effectively with the wind well forward of the beam. The more common types of spinnaker are shown in Fig. 11(44).

Since one of the requirements of a spinnaker is that it must support itself in the air, it is necessary to use a material which is as light as possible, consistent with strength and resistance to stretch. Normally nylon cloth is used, typically about 1–1½oz/sq yard, reinforced to discourage it from ripping. Reaching spinnakers are made of slightly heavier cloth because it is more important that they retain their shape. It is important not to carry a spinnaker in wind speeds greater than that for which it is designed. The suggested maximum wind speeds in Fig. 11(45), are rather lower than might have been expected.

To improve their performance under spinnaker, racing yachts use supplementary sails such as the big boy, or blooper, see Fig. 11(46). This is a very light triangular sail, set on the same side as the mainsail. It has a very full skirt, near the water, and it collects wind which passes under the foot and round the leech of the mainsail. It can only set effectively when the wind is not more than about 30° out on the quarter. Mutual adjustment

Nylon weight	Boat size	Run	Broad reach	Beam reach	Close reach
0.5 oz	Under 9m (30ft)	6	6	5	–
	Over 9m (30ft)	5	5	4	–
0.75 oz	Under 9m (30ft)	22	17	14	12
	9–12m (30–40ft)	16	13	12	11
	Over 12m (40ft)	13	12	11	9
1.5 oz	Under 9m (30ft)	30	26	22	15
	Over 9m (30ft)	26	23	17	13

Fig. 11(45) Suggested maximum apparent wind speeds in knots for different weights of spinnaker cloth and on different points of sailing.

Fig. 11(46) A yacht, bows-on, running downwind with tri-radial spinnaker (left) and big boy or blooper (right).

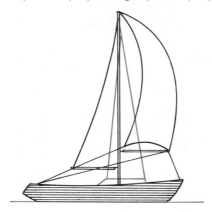

Fig. 11(47) Tallboy.

Fig. 11(48) Spinnaker staysail.

between sheet and halyard is necessary in order to get the sail as far out to leeward as possible. In light winds the blooper may set better by slightly over-trimming the mainsail or by taking down a reef in the main.

The tall boy, Fig. 11(47), is a long, narrow sail sometimes set forward of the mast in conjunction with a spinnaker (or during a headsail change). Its function is to smooth the airflow over the leading edge of the mainsail. It is set flying (not hanked to a stay), and is normally tacked down to windward of the centreline of the boat, in similar fashion to the more traditional spinnaker staysail, as shown in Fig. 11(48).

11.5.6 Running in strong winds

Downwind in strong winds it is best to use a narrow-shouldered, flat spinnaker – smaller than normal and of heavier cloth. The halyard should be hoisted close up, with no drift, the pole should be lowered somewhat, and the sheet kept trimmed in more than usual – so that the spinnaker is well stretched out and made more stable.

There should be a preventer rigged to the end of the boom, and an efficient boom vang is needed to keep the boom from rising and to eliminate undue twist near the head of the sail, which can push the masthead to windward and help induce rolling. For preference the boom vang should be controlled from a cockpit winch, so that it can be eased quickly if the boom dips in the sea, which could cause breakage.

If the boat is surfing, gybing can be risky. It may be better to hand the spinnaker, and rehoist it on the new gybe.

Broaching is usually caused by a combination of circumstances, but in bad conditions any one of them may result in the helmsman losing control of the yacht, which rounds up, beam on to wind and sea, and lies over on her side. The causes are: carrying too much sail, resulting in excessive heel; imbalance of the immersed shapes of the hull forward and aft, and producing a turning couple between the centre of lateral resistance and the centre of effort of the sail plan; the diminished effect of the rudder as the boat heels; the diminished effect of the rudder as the crest of a wave passes under the stern of the boat, thereby reducing the flow of water past the rudder; the turning effect on the boat when the bow ploughs into the trough of a wave and the stern is swung round by the following crest, which is moving faster.

Action to counter a broach should be to let the mainsheet run (if the boom is not already squared off), ease the boom vang to allow the mainboom to sky and thus spill some wind, and let go the spinnaker sheet. When the boat rights, get the boom vang and the spinnaker sheet in again, so that the boat can be brought under control.

In a cruising yacht it is more comfortable, safer, more sensible (and not a lot slower) to goosewing the genoa, or perhaps a smaller headsail, when running downwind in heavy weather, instead of having to cope with a spinnaker when probably short-handed. Rig the spinnaker pole on the mast, with lift and downhaul attached, and pass the genoa sheet through the pole end fitting. It may also be sensible to steady the pole and stop it swinging about by rigging the appropriate spinnaker guy to the pole end.

Yachts intended for long downwind passages are often fitted with twin running foresails – a rig which minimises chafe with the mainsail lowered. But it is important to remember that it takes time to hoist the mainsail and get back to windward in the event of somebody going over the side.

11.5.7 Cruising spinnakers

Many sailmakers now provide asymmetrical cruising spinnakers, which are easier to handle. With the wind well aft such sails are set on the opposite side to the mainsail, with or without a bearing out spar. Or with the wind on or somewhat abaft the beam they can be used as a reaching headsail, either set flying or hanked to the forestay.

There are also devices to facilitate handling a conventional spinnaker. A British invention is the Spee-Squeezer, marketed by Parbury Henty & Co Ltd, Kingswick House, Sunninghill, Berkshire SL5 7BJ. It consists of a glassfibre bell mouth, on the end of a long nylon sleeve. When required, the sleeve with the spinnaker packed inside it is hoisted on the spinnaker halyard, like a long sausage. An uphaul, attached to the bell mouth at the bottom of the sleeve, is then pulled so that the sail is progressively unpeeled from the bottom up. While the spinnaker is set and drawing the bell mouth and the bunched up sleeve remain at the masthead. When the spinnaker is to be furled the uphaul is released and a downhaul is pulled, so

that the bell mouth and sleeve progressively smother and house the sail as the sheet is eased. The sleeve can then be lowered, with the spinnaker inside it. If it is required to gybe, the sail can be temporarily furled inside the sleeve, while the mainsail and spinnaker pole etc are moved across, and then unfurled on the new gybe.

11.5.8 Why a boat sails

Before trying to understand how a boat sails (particularly towards the direction of the wind) it is necessary to appreciate the difference between true and apparent wind. The true wind is what is experienced when standing on the shore, or in a stationary boat on her mooring. But once the boat starts to move, whether under power or under sail, an observer experiences a different wind – the apparent wind which is the vector sum of the true wind and the boat's velocity. This is shown in Fig. 11(49) where a boat is sailing with the wind abeam. RQ represents in length and direction the true wind (V_T). RP similarly represents the boat's velocity (V_s). From the vector triangle so established PQ then gives the direction and strength of the apparent wind (V_A) as experienced by a person on board – and more important by the boat's sails, or by an electronic wind indicator or burgee at the masthead.

Another example is shown in Fig. 11(50), where the boat is sailing more closely into the wind. Comparing the two diagrams it will be noted that in both cases the boat's velocity pulls the apparent wind further ahead than the true wind. It will also be seen that when the wind is abaft the beam the apparent wind is less strong than the true wind, but that when the wind is ahead the apparent wind is stronger than the true wind.

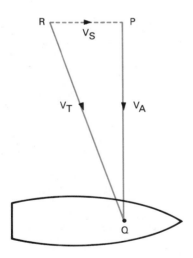

Fig. 11(49) Sails react only to the apparent wind, as shown above by V_A. The apparent wind is always further ahead than the true wind V_T, due to the velocity of the boat, V_s. In this example, with the wind aft, the apparent wind is less in strength than the true wind.

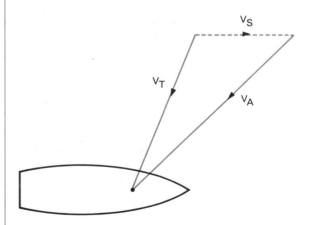

Fig. 11(50) When the wind is forward of the beam the apparent wind is stronger than the true wind.

An extreme example of the effect of boat speed on the apparent wind is when the wind is dead aft. If the wind speed is, say, 15 knots and the boat is sailing at 6 knots, the actual wind speed affecting the sails is only 9 knots.

With modern technology computers will work out the true wind, given the apparent wind and boat speed and course. This is useful to know when, for example, faced with a future alteration of course in order to know which gybe will apply or which sails to set. However, it is quite simple (and more rewarding, and certainly a lot cheaper) to produce such answers graphically.

It is not difficult to understand how a sailing yacht can blow away to leeward off the wind, but the mechanics of what takes a boat to windward are more complex, and the following is only a brief and simple explanation. Fig. 11(51) shows how the air stream is deflected by a single sail when beating to windward. Along the lee side of the sail the air is speeded up and the pressure falls. Over the windward surface the air flow slows down and pressure rises. It is well established that the 'negative pressure' on the lee side has greater effect on propelling the boat than the positive pressure on the windward side. The net effect is to produce a total force in the horizontal plane indicated by the vector R_A. This can be regarded as having two components – L_A representing the lift from the aerofoil shape of the sail, and D_A the drag at right angles in the direction of the apparent wind, V_A. The major contribution to forward movement comes from the first third of the sail from the luff, while the rest of the sail (increasingly towards the leech) only provides heeling and drag forces but this area cannot be dispensed with.

When sailing the constant aim is to reduce D_A as much as possible and to maximise L_A. This is done by altering the shape of the sail depending on the conditions, as described in Chapter 21 (21.6). Maximum lift is obtained when the sail is set to deflect the wind as much as possible, while still maintaining a smooth air flow. But as more curvature is put into the sail, not only is the forward drive increased but also the force pushing the boat sideways, to the point that the boat will heel over excessively and may even capsize. Hence as wind speed increases it is necessary to flatten the sail to reduce the power.

Fig. 11(52) shows the principal horizontal forces on a boat sailing upright at a steady speed on the port tack. R_A has already been described, and is balanced by an equal and opposite force R_W which is the sum of the total hydrodynamic forces exerted by the hull and its appendages (principally the keel). Not only must R_W be equal and opposite to R_A, but both must pass through the same point or the boat would rotate, which is to say that the centre of effort of the rig must be over the centre of lateral resistance of the hull.

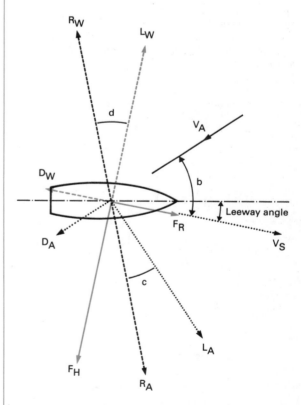

Fig. 11(52) The principal horizontal forces acting on a close-hauled upright yacht are shown above, as R_A by the air (wind) and R_W by the water. R_A is composed of air drag (D_A along the line of the apparent wind, V_A) and air lift (L_A at right angles). R_W is composed of water drag (D_W along the line of the boat's velocity) and water lift (L_W at right angles). Also shown are the drag angles, c and d, which together comprise b, the angle between the apparent wind and the course made good (including leeway).

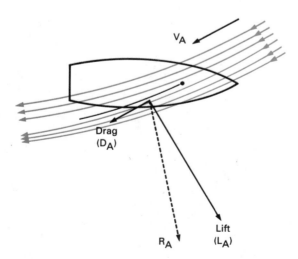

Fig. 11(51) The air stream round the leeward side of a sail is speeded up, and the pressure drops. Over the windward side the air stream slows down, and pressure is increased. The total effect is shown as lift, L_A, with a small forward component and drag, D_A, acting in the line of the apparent wind.

R_W may be considered as composed of two forces, D_W and L_W, at right angles to each other. D_W is the drag of the hull and appendages, acting in the opposite direction to which the boat is moving. This is not along the centreline of the boat but slightly to leeward, as dictated by the leeway angle. Leeway is a necessary evil because it gives the keel the necessary angle of incidence to generate lift, as shown by L_W in the sketch. Rather similar to the rig, it is important that hull and keel produce the necessary lift to counteract the sideways force of the rig, but with the minimum of drag and the smallest possible amount of leeway.

It is also possible to consider R_A as resolved into two different components of more obvious application: one, a force F_R driving the boat ahead, and the other, F_H at right angles pushing the hull sideways and heeling the boat over. The angle between R_A and L_A is termed the (air) drag angle and is shown in the diagram as c. If, for a given lift L_A, the drag and consequently the drag angle can be reduced then R_A would be angled further ahead to increase F_R. In much the same way the hydrodynamic drag angle, d, is an indication of the efficiency of the keel and hull to generate the necessary side force at the expense of minimum resistance and leeway. From the diagram it can be determined that $c + d = b$, which is the angle between the apparent wind and the course made good (including leeway). So in terms of heading ability the sum of the drag angles therefore needs to be as small as possible, too.

In the very brief discussion above no serious consideration has been given to the heeling forces acting on the boat from the sail plan. Heeling is resisted by the moment of the centre of gravity about the centre of buoyancy (see 10.1.9). In seeking from the sail plan a combination of maximum forward drive with minimum drag we are at the same time reducing the undesirable heeling effect of the rig. This means that with an increasing wind optimum sail settings can be retained for longer before it is necessary to depower the rig.

Given the necessary finance, designers will go to extraordinary lengths to experiment with various appendages in full-scale yachts, as has been seen in recent America's Cup competitions in which the extravagant changing of keels was commonplace.

The ordinary yachtsman cannot change the keel of his boat every few races, but he can change the shape of the sails to suit the prevailing conditions and this is something which requires constant attention, particularly when racing. Wind and sea conditions seldom stay the same for long, especially when sailing near the coast. Offshore conditions may be steadier, but even then the good sailor will have learned to detect quite small changes in wind speed or direction, or in the form and behaviour of the waves.

In light winds it is important to have enough flow (fullness) in the sails, by easing the sheets a trifle. As the wind increases so the sheets are steadily hardened in to make the sails flatter. Details of these and other sail controls are given in Chapter 21 (21.6).

In strong winds the boat must be kept on her feet and balanced on the helm, first by flattening the sails and then by changing the headsail and/or reefing the mainsail (see 11.5.3). Many modern yachts are comparatively beamy for their length, and do not perform well if allowed to heel excessively.

11.5.9 Sail care

Examination of a new sail should convince its owner that much skilled workmanship has gone into it. The sailmaker having done his bit, it is up to the yachtsman to look after and make the best use of this new addition to the boat's wardrobe. A good sail can easily be spoiled by bad practices and careless handling.

A sail will only set as well as the mast and rigging allow, and notes on rigging adjustment are given in 11.2.4. In order to avoid creases and unfair strains, a mainsail must fit the mast and boom properly, with clew and tack cringles correctly positioned for the pins which are to hold them. The sailmaker should have taken detailed measurements of the gooseneck etc on board. Headsails are easier to fit, but it is important that the tack fitting is aligned with the forestay, and that the sail does not foul fittings such as the pulpit.

Even though a Terylene sail is reasonably robust, it should first be set and broken in for 2–3 hours in a wind not exceeding force 3–4, and it should not be reefed during this period. A sail should always be hoisted or lowered by pulling on the luff – never along the leech. When a mainsail is hoisted or lowered the weight of the boom should be taken on the topping lift (or by hand in a small boat), to avoid the leech stretching. The leech is not reinforced with roping or tape, or with a luff wire as in the case of a headsail, so it is particularly vulnerable to maltreatment. When sails are hung up to dry they should be hoisted by the head and the tack, not by the clew. Sails should not be allowed to flap unnecessarily, since this damages the cloth structure – particularly in the leech area where the flutter is greatest.

It is easy to put too much tension on halyards or outhauls. A mainsail should only be hoisted and pulled out along the foot enough to allow it to take its designed shape. In light to moderate winds only tension the halyard enough to remove any horizontal creases, and adjust the outhaul so that sufficient flow is given to the lower part of the sail. In stronger breezes they should both be tensioned more, so that little folds appear close to the luff and foot when the sail is hoisted. In strong winds maximum tension is needed to flatten the sail, and in order to keep the flow in the sail well forward extra luff tension may be applied by taking down on the Cunningham hole

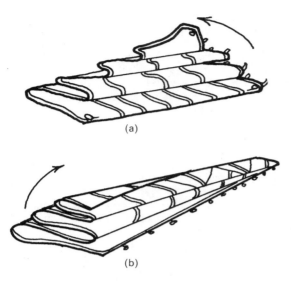

Fig. 11(53) Folding a mainsail. A mainsail should be flaked down either towards the foot (a), or towards the luff as in (b). If there is a window in the sail (a) is preferable, the first fold being taken over it so that it is not creased. Two people are needed, so that the fold is straight and even. Then roll neatly towards the clew (a), or towards the head (b), to fit in bag.

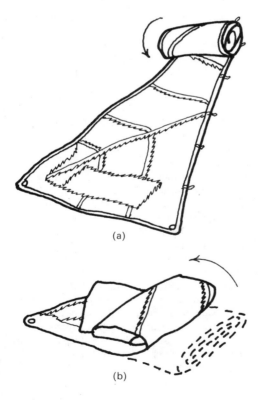

Fig. 11(54) Folding a jib. Headsails can either be flaked down towards the foot – as for a mainsail – or rolled down the luff from head to tack, as shown in (a), and then rolled as shown in (b).

– a device near the tack of the sail which in effect shortens the luff.

Similar considerations apply with headsails. Before hoisting check that the halyard is clear aloft and that the sail is correctly hanked onto the forestay. It is also important to see that the sheeting positions are correct each side. Do not sheet the sail in before it is fully hoisted. Headsails which have a wire luff rope, or a wire on which the luff can slide, need to have the halyard set up tight, so that the luff is as straight as possible. Headsails which have a stretchy luff should have the halyard adjusted according to the wind strength – harder in heavy winds and less in lighter winds. If fitted, it is important not to overtighten the leech line of a sail.

While sailing, do not allow the running backstay or the topping lift to flap against the lee side of the mainsail, nor allow the sail to press unnecessarily against the lee rigging when running off the wind – this all causes damage to the cloth and to the stitching. Done properly, reefing should not damage a sail but if (for example when unreefing) the full weight is taken by reef points or the reef lacing, instead of by the reef pendants at luff and leech, the sail may be seriously distorted.

When a sail is lowered, bag it and stow it away below as soon as possible: sails left lying around on deck only get damaged by being walked on, or made damp from spray. Sail bags should be roomy, so that sails do not get unduly crushed or creased. Sails should be bagged so that they are ready for instant use – e.g. the tacks of headsails on top.

Any sail, but particularly a light nylon spinnaker, will rip on sharp objects such as split pins which are not taped over, so it pays to check all rigging, guardrails, spreader ends etc regularly.

On return to harbour, release the tension on the clew outhaul of the mainsail, remove the battens, flake the sail down over the boom and secure it with ties, and put on the sail cover (even if it is only overnight – it keeps the sail clean and dry, and protects it from the sun). If the mainsail is taken off the boom, flake it down carefully to the foot, roll it up from tack to clew, and put it in its bag. When flaking a sail avoid putting a crease across any window, and avoid flaking to the same creases on each occasion. See Fig. 11(53) and Fig. 11(54).

Modern sails with a hard finish should be rolled up from the head down to the foot, and stowed in a long bag without any further folding or flaking. Try to keep the bag as straight as possible at all times – when stowing the sail or moving it from place to place.

It is bad to dry sails by allowing them to flap in the wind – this causes chafe and damages the structure of the cloth. If sails are wet it is better to leave them spread out in the boat, should it not be possible to dry them on deck. Do not leave wet nylon sails bagged up, since sometimes the colours will run.

Salt and dirt form an abrasive surface on sails, which damages the cloth and the stitching. This can be reduced by keeping the deck and rigging clean, as well as by washing the sails themselves regularly with fresh water.

At the end of the season, or if sails get really dirty, they should be washed properly in warm water (not more than about 120°F or 50°C) using ordinary soap or a mild liquid detergent, and scrubbing gently with a sponge or a soft brush. After washing, sails must be very well rinsed with fresh water, and dried carefully. Then they should be closely inspected for the smallest signs of damage before being stowed away – or sent to the sailmaker. Check both sides of each sail, panel by panel, seam by seam, for any small holes in the cloth, broken stitches, wear on the roping or tabling, loose hanks on headsails, worn or damaged cringles at the corners, and defective slides or batten pockets on mainsails.

It is not easy to wash and inspect sails properly on board, and the work is better done if they can be spread out on a clean surface ashore. If this is not available most sailmakers will undertake the service, and store your sails for the winter.

Certain stains on sails need speedy attention and special treatment. These notes refer to white sailcloth; coloured sails which need special cleaning are best treated professionally. Some of the solvents such as carbon tetrachloride are poisonous and others may involve a fire risk, so it is best if any cleaning is done in the open air and away from naked lights. After cleaning be sure to wash that area of the sail very thoroughly in order to remove all traces of the chemical used.

Oil or grease can usually be shifted by carbon tetrachloride or trichloroethylene in the form of proprietary stain removers like Thawpit – or by rubbing with Swarfega followed by washing in warm water with a mild detergent added.

Rust stains can be stubborn, but try a 5 per cent solution of oxalic acid or 2 per cent hydrochloric acid in warm water. Mix the solution in a plastic container, wear rubber gloves, and do not let the acid solution come into contact with metal fittings or the luff wire of a sail.

Tar or pitch stains can be treated with a solvent such as Polyclens, trichloroethylene, carbon tetrachloride or white spirit.

Paint or varnish should be removed as soon as possible using white spirit or turps substitute. If this fails try Swarfega with a liquid detergent and warm water. Polyurethane varnish can be softened with chloroform, and ordinary varnish with surgical or methylated spirit. Never use alkali-based paint strippers on Terylene cloth.

Blood stains should, if possible, be washed off immediately with plenty of cold water, and then with soap powder. Old stains should be soaked in cold water containing 0.15lt ($\frac{1}{4}$pt) of ammonia to 2.2lt ($\frac{1}{2}$ gal) of water. Residual stains can be treated with a 1 per cent solution of pepsin in water with a few drops of hydrochloric acid added.

Mildew is caused by dirt, a damp atmosphere and poor ventilation. On synthetic sailcloth it is more unsightly than harmful, but it can be removed by scrubbing when dry with a stiff brush, and then soaking in a cold solution of 1 part household bleach to 15 parts of water.

11.5.10 Sail repairs.

Any sailing yacht or motor sailer should carry sufficient repair gear in the form of needles, threads, spare material and a palm, so that even a moderately torn sail can be made serviceable once more. Small holes or splits, which if left unattended would soon extend, can often be given a temporary patch which will last until the chance occurs for a sailmaker to make a more finished and permanent repair. On occasions the safety of a boat may depend upon somebody being able to re-stitch a mainsail seam, or reconstruct the torn out clew of a headsail. In any case, sails are expensive items, and regular examination of them and prompt attention to minor defects will help to prolong their life.

Sail repair gear suitable for the average yacht should include the following items.
(1) Terylene thread, ranging from lightweight machine thread for spinnaker cloths to (say) 6lb thread suitable for cloths of 12oz/sq yd. The upper limit depends upon the size of boat. Roughly the weight of thread needed is half the weight of the cloth. So a 3lb thread is right for a cloth of 6oz/sq yd, and so on.
(2) Needles, similarly, must be selected for the weight of the cloth and the work to be done. They vary from domestic size (No. 19) to No. 13 for very heavy cloth. Two No. 18 and two No. 16 should suit a small yacht. Bigger boats need larger needles, as for example when sewing several thicknesses of cloth, but try not to use too large a needle for the job in hand, since it will make too large a hole in the cloth and thereby weaken it. When repairing highly stressed parts of a sail such as head, tack or clew, use a heavier thread and a larger needle than the weight of cloth would otherwise require. The thread should normally be doubled, or sometimes even quadrupled, to give strength with the minimum number of stitches.
(3) Beeswax is needed for treating the thread, partly for protection and partly to make it easier to work. The thread should be pulled through the beeswax three or four times. If no beeswax is available candlegrease makes an acceptable substitute.
(4) A palm is needed, with which to push the needle through the material.
(5) Repair material – off cuts of sailcloth in the form of strips of different sizes and weights – can usually be obtained from your sailmaker. They are used for patches which, as explained below, give a stronger repair than a simple darn.

(6) Special adhesive tape is useful for temporary repairs to sails in light weather, and also for holding a patch or a tear together while it is being stitched.

(7) A bench hook, with a line attached, is useful for tensioning the work while it is being stitched.

The sailmaker's darn is a form of herringbone stitch, as shown in Fig. 11(55), used for pulling together the edges of a rip in a sail. The thread should be doubled and waxed, and the end knotted. Then, working from the left, the needle is passed up through the cloth on the far side of the rip, and down through the cloth on the near side. It is then brought up through the gap, to the left of and over the top of the first stitch, and down under the cloth on the far side of the gap. It is then passed up again through the cloth on the far side of the gap, and the process is repeated. The stitches should be about 5mm ($\frac{1}{4}$in) from the edges of the cloth each side of the rip, and spaced about that far apart or slightly closer. As each stitch is formed it should be tightened just enough to pull the edges of the tear together. When the end of the tear is reached, the repair is finished off with a couple of half-hitches, stitched over.

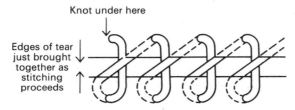

Fig. 11(55) Sailmaker's darn.

A patch will produce a stronger repair than a straight-forward darn, but it involves correspondingly more work. The material for the patch should ideally be the same as the sail – both in weight and texture – but in emergency a near equivalent will suffice. The patch should overlap the tear by 50mm (2in) each end and on each side, and should be positioned so that its weave (warp and weft) corresponds with the sail.

Unless the edges of the patch can be heat sealed to prevent them fraying (by using a hot knife, which is a specialist bit of sailmaking equipment), they will need to be turned under and secured with pins or tape for stitching.

A patch must be worked from one side of the sail so an overhand stitch is used as shown in Fig. 11(56). Starting off with a knot in the end of the thread, the needle is pushed down through the sail, and up through the sail and the patch opposite as indicated. Then take a rather longer diagonal stitch, down through the sail outside the edge of the patch, and repeat. Spacing should be similar to a sailmaker's darn. The stitching is continued right round the rectangular patch, working from left to right, until the starting point is reached.

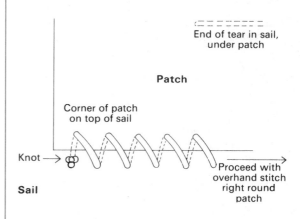

Fig. 11(56) Sewing a patch.

The sail is then turned over, and a rectangle is cut around the tear with its sides parallel to the edges of the patch which have been stitched, and at least 40mm ($1\frac{1}{2}$in) from them. See Fig. 11(57). At each corner of the rectangular hole thus formed, make a diagonal cut in the sail, about 20mm ($\frac{3}{4}$in) long towards the corner of the patch underneath. Turn the four edges under, so that they are between the sail and the patch, and then stitch round the rectangle (securing the turned in edges of the sail to the patch) in just the same way as the patch was originally stitched from the other side. Work from left to right as before, and take care to keep the tension of the stitches uniform.

Fig. 11(57) Finishing a patch.

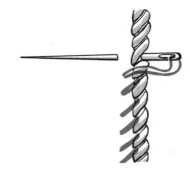

Fig. 11(58) How to re-sew a bolt rope to a sail.

If it is necessary to re-sew part of a bolt rope to a sail, first make sure that any twists are removed from the rope. If more than a very short length is to be re-stitched, it should be temporarily attached about every foot, so that it is sewn on evenly. The stitch used for hand roping is shown in Fig. 11(58), the needle being passed between the strands of the rope. To rope more than a short length properly takes experience if the correct tension is to be applied evenly.

11.6 Bibliography

Spars
Rigging by Enrico Sala (Adlard Coles Nautical).
Sailing Rigs and Spars – Installation, Maintenance and Tuning by Matthew Sheahan (Haynes).
Understanding Rigs and Rigging by Richard Henderson (Adlard Coles Nautical).

Sails
This is Looking at Sails by Bruce Banks & Dick Kenny (Adlard Coles Nautical).
Sails by Jeremy Howard-Williams (Adlard Coles Nautical).
The Best of Sail Trim (Adlard Coles Nautical).
More Sail Trim (Adlard Coles Nautical).
This is Downwind Sailing by John Oakley (Adlard Coles Nautical).
Small Boat Sails by Jeremy Howard-Williams (Adlard Coles Nautical).
Practical Junk Rig by H. G. Hasler & J. K. McLeod (Adlard Coles Nautical).
Racing Performance by Dick Hewitt (International Log Book).

The Art and Science of Sails by Tom Whidden & Michael Levitt (Adlard Coles Nautical).
How to Trim Sales by Peter Schweer (Adlard Coles Nautical).
The Big Book of Boat Canvas by Karen Lipe (Ashford).
Sails – Choice, Trim and Improvement by John Heyes (Fernhurst).

Ropes and knots
Ashley Book of Knots by Clifford Ashley (Doubleday).
Colour Book of Knots by F. Hin (Adlard Coles Nautical).
Handling Ropes and Lines Afloat by Paul & Arthur Snyder (Adlard Coles Nautical).
Knots and Splices by Cyrus L. Day (Adlard Coles Nautical).
Modern Rope Seamanship by Colin Jarman & Bill Beavis (Adlard Coles Nautical).
The Knot Book by Geoffrey Budworth (Elliot Right Way Books).
Knots in Use by Colin Jarman & Bill Beavis (Adlard Coles Nautical).
Alternative Knot Book by Dr Harry Asher (Adlard Coles Nautical).
The Art of Knotting and Splicing by Cyrus L. Day (Airlife).
Knots and Splices by Jeff Toghill (Fernhurst).
The Marlinespike Sailor by Harvey Garrett Smith (Ashford).
Sailing Knots by J. Altimiras (Pelham).
The Shell Combined Book of Knots and Ropework by Eric C. Fry (David & Charles).
The Splicing Handbook by Barbara Merry (Adlard Coles Nautical).

Chapter 12

Deck gear

Contents

12.1 Anchors and equipment

12.1.1 Anchors and cables

Anchors come in various shapes and each has its supporters but just as in the case of sterns, for instance there is no 'best' shape. The traditional anchor is known these days as the fisherman (or stocked) type and though it needs to be rather heavier than modern types for equal holding power and is rather awkward to haul aboard it is still a versatile anchor worthy of consideration. It is essential that the key which holds the stock in place is securely fastened. The fisherman anchor will hold well in any reasonable bottom, and once aboard with the stock unshipped it stows neatly and without the projections of the more modern shapes. A disadvantage is that the upper fluke may be fouled by the cable when the yacht swings (e.g. at the turn of the tide), possibly causing the anchor to drag. Performance is improved if the flukes are sharpened somewhat with a file and the

exposed bare metal given a couple of coats of epoxy paint for protection. Though one of the common zinc-rich paints (such as Galvafroid) will preserve it excellently on deck, they are rather soft and soon wear off if the anchor is used at all frequently. Fig. 12(1) shows the principal parts of a fisherman anchor, and the stock should weigh about 20 per cent of the total weight.

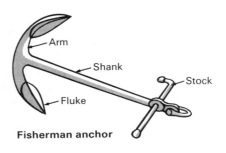

Fisherman anchor

Fig. 12.(1) The various parts of a fisherman or stocked anchor.

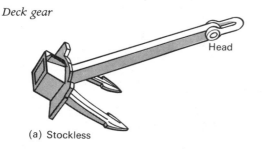

(a) Stockless

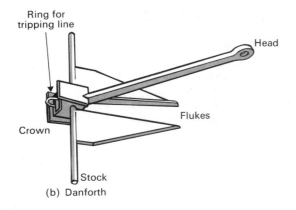

Ring for
tripping line

Head

Flukes

Crown

Stock

(b) Danforth

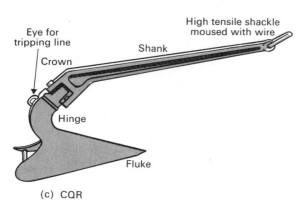

Eye for
tripping line

High tensile shackle
moused with wire

Shank

Crown

Hinge

Fluke

(c) CQR

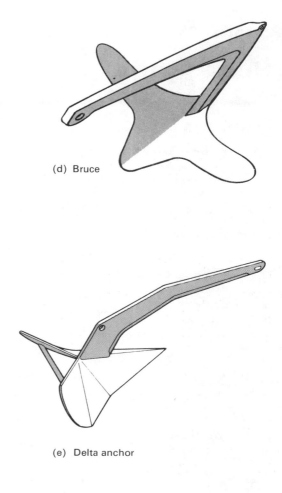

(d) Bruce

(e) Delta anchor

Fig. 12(2) Anchors in common use include: (a), the stockless type which is normally stowed in a hawse pipe; (b), the Danforth, sometimes also known as a spade anchor; (c), the CQR or plough anchor; (d), the Bruce anchor; and (e), the Delta anchor.

Fig. 12(2) shows five other types of anchors: the stockless, Danforth, CQR, Bruce and Delta. The stockless variety is the one normally seen hanging from a hawse pipe where it stows easily. That is its greatest and almost only advantage, for its short shank and the absence of a stock to turn it so that the flukes are in the digging position mean that it has to be heavier than any of its rivals for equal holding power.

The Danforth is a design that dates from 1939. It can also be stowed in a hawse pipe, but one of its attractions is that it lies nice and flat on deck. Its wide flukes can pivot about 30° either way, and have sharp points to dig into the bottom, while its long stock runs through the crown. It is a good general purpose anchor but, like the CQR below, it can skate over a weed-infested bottom rather than dig in. Once set it can be difficult to break out, so a tripping line can be useful.

The CQR (ploughshare) anchor was designed in the 1930s for mooring flying boats. The ploughshare fluke is hinged at the crown so that it tries to dig into the bottom no matter in what attitude it lands. The genuine CQR anchor is drop-forged for reliable strength and is another type of anchor designated as 'High holding power' by Lloyd's. It should weigh about the same as the Danforth. This good general purpose anchor is popular with yachtsmen and holds well on most bottoms except weed. If it does drag it tends to reset better than most other types. It can be arranged to stow neatly in the bow roller fittings at the stemhead - see Fig. 12(3).

Imitations of both the Danforth and CQR types are available, the latter coming under the general heading of 'plough' anchors. Although some are good, others are not, and if there are any doubts it pays to buy the genuine article.

The Bruce anchor originated as mooring for oil rigs. Its rather clumsy claw-like shape is such that it will always lie with the weight on one of its three flukes. As the anchor then drags over the seabed this fluke digs in and turns the anchor so that the other flukes do likewise. It is awkward to stow on deck or down below, but will lie quite well in a suitable stemhead fitting. It is claimed that for the same holding power it can be lighter than either a Danforth or CQR.

Since its introduction in 1990 the Delta anchor has received many commendations. It results from many years of research, development and testing on the part of Simpson Lawrence who examined the merits of all existing anchor types for different types of boat and seabeds before finalising a design which gives good performance and ease of handling combined with maximum durability. It is designed for easy self-launching and self-stowing, while the configuration gives quick setting once on the seabed, with the blade having a sharp point to improve penetration and a stable performance under load. Even more recent than the Delta, the Steadfast anchor was launched at the 1992 Southampton Boat Show. It is claimed to have exceptional holding power, plus the ability to re-orientate itself should it land upside down.

The table overleaf shows suggested sizes of anchors and cables for various boat lengths but

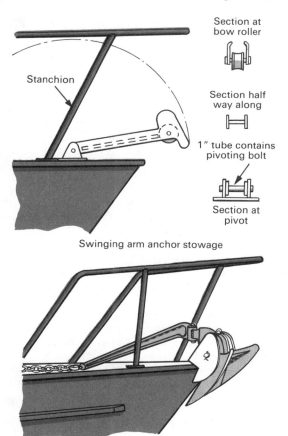

Swinging arm anchor stowage

CQR anchor in bow chock

Fig. 12(3) Rather than stow an anchor on deck it may be pulled against a bow chock as with this CQR type. On the other hand if deck stowage is a requirement the work of getting the anchor aboard can be reduced by using a swinging arm arrangement.

these, it should be noted, are minimum sizes and anything larger will be a bonus. A normal person can man-handle a 23kg (50lb) anchor without too much difficulty and some people can manage up to maybe, 34kg (75lb). Above that size things get difficult and the anchor will either have to be hauled aboard via an anchor davit of sufficient height for the anchor to clear the top rail or guard wire, or hawse pipes will have to be considered. Other than those two schemes it may be possible to arrange for the anchor to haul up flush with the deck, or to reach up to a swinging arm which is finally swung back on board complete with anchor. Fig. 12(3) shows those two methods. The fittings themselves can be fabricated from steel and subsequently galvanised or epoxy-painted. The swinging arm must have a very secure attachment through the deck.

Opinions vary about whether it is best to anchor to a long length of a springy rope like nylon or to a shorter scope (but still at least three times the depth of water) of comparatively heavy chain. If nylon is chosen, and it is important that the rope is just that and not an unreliable polypropylene, for instance, 3.3m (2 fathoms) of chain should be shackled on between the rope and the anchor itself to lend a bit of weight and to take the chafe that might occur on the sea bottom. Nylon is susceptible to chafe and its lead over the deck edge should be as smooth as possible. Lloyd's require 55m (30 fathoms) of chain or nylon for each anchor and actually require two anchors per boat. The second anchor, which might be considered to be the kedge anchor, may be 70 per cent of the weight of the main, or bower, anchor. The weights shown in the table are not necessarily those recommended by Lloyd's incidentally, and in many instances are probably lighter. To make use of Lloyd's requirements it is necessary to know what is called the Equipment Numeral for the boat concerned, and that is something best left to the designer.

A genuine cruising yacht which anchors frequently needs a minimum of three anchors and four are better, with a range of types and sizes.

Should it be necessary to join two lengths of chain cable this is best done with what is called a chain joining link, this being a good deal stronger than using a shackle. The chain should be clearly marked (e.g. with coloured paint) at intervals of about 9m (5 fathoms). The inboard end of the chain, known as the bitter end, should be lashed, not shackled, to an eye or some other secure anchoring point. If the chain stows in an inaccessible chain locker it is sensible to have the lashing long enough for it to show through the chain pipe on deck. Then, if the chain and anchor have to be abandoned in a hurry, it can be quickly cut (preferably after attaching some kind of buoy and line to it).

Chain cable which is to be used with a windlass (see 12.1.4.) must be calibrated chain which, when under tension, fits the indentations of the gypsy concerned. Since there is no universal standard, care is needed when matching chain to gypsy or vice versa.

Minimum sizes for anchors and cable
(Note: Figures are based on craft of average displacement)

Overall boat length m (ft)	6	(20)	7.3	(25)	9	(30)	11	(35)	12	(40)	14	(45)
Bruce kg (lb)	5	(11)	7.5	(16)	10	(22)	15	(33)	20	(45)	30	(66)
CQR (plough) kg (lb)	6.8	(15)	9	(20)	11	(25)	16	(35)	20	(45)	27	(60)
Delta kg (lb)	6	(14)	6	(14)	10	(22)	10	(22)	16	(35)	25	(55)
Danforth kg (lb)	7	(15)	10	(22)	14	(30)	18	(40)	25	(55)	35	(77)
Brittany kg (lb)	8	(18)	10	(22)	12	(26)	20	(45)	25	(55)	35	(77)
Fisherman kg (lb)	12	(26)	14	(31)	18	(40)	23	(51)	32	(70)	41	(90)
Stockless kg (lb)	13	(30)	18	(40)	22	(50)	27	(60)	36	(80)	45	(100)
Chain, short link, diam. mm (in)	6.5	$(\frac{1}{4})$	8	$(\frac{5}{16})$	8	$(\frac{5}{16})$	8	$(\frac{5}{16})$	9.5	$(\frac{3}{8})$	11	$(\frac{7}{16})$
Chain weight kg/m (lb/fathom)	1.1	(4.5)	1.5	(6.0)	1.5	(6.0)	1.5	(6.0)	2.2	(8.9)	2.8	(11.3)
Nylon warp diam. mm (in)	10	$(\frac{3}{8})$	12	$(\frac{1}{2})$	16	$(\frac{5}{8})$	16	$(\frac{5}{8})$	18	$(\frac{3}{4})$	18	$(\frac{3}{4})$

12.1.2 Stemhead rollers and chain stoppers

On all but the smallest of boats a stemhead roller is a necessity. It keeps in place the chain or anchor warp when anchored, and allows it to be retrieved reasonably easily. The roller itself should be of good size and free-running on its spindle. The lips that bound it each side should be canted in at the top to keep the cable down and prevent it jumping out when the lead is not exactly fore and aft. The whole fitting needs to be solidly bolted down.

Though rarely seen these days, a stemhead fitting incorporating a pawl can be a great advantage where chain cable is used. Fig. 12(4) shows one way of fitting the pawl. With it lifted the chain can run out freely. When it is dropped the chain can be hauled in but is prevented from running out. This is a useful attribute on a sailing craft with no windlass but even with one, it allows the operator to take a breather without having to make the cable fast with the risk of jamming his fingers. Stemhead rollers can be bought separately

from the stemhead fitting, and an arrangement such as that shown can be made easily enough by any competent blacksmith. It can be galvanised after fabrication. The two points worth noting when designing it are that the pawl should drop into the chain at the point where it passes over the roller, and it must be possible to lift the chain out if required past the pawl pivoting point. The pawl itself must be robust and of a thickness that allows it to sit neatly into the chain. The bolt on which it pivots should also be stout.

A chain stopper or compressor, also shown on Fig. 12(4), is another useful, though rarely seen, item. It allows the foredeck man to check the run of the chain by leaning or pulling on a handle. He does not have to try and surge the chain round a bollard, which can be difficult. Like the pawl fitting, compressors are not often seen and may be hard to acquire but they, too, can be made up by a blacksmith.

12.1.3 Capstans

Though windlasses are just about universal these days, a capstan whose drum axis is vertical like that of a sheet winch has advantages in that the lead to it can be taken from any angle. This is useful, especially when warping a boat into a berth. The snag with capstans and presumably one reason why they are not more popular is that on the small sizes that would be used on yachts the handles, which operate on a horizontal axis, tend to be rather low. This means that the operator is usually reduced to kneeling on deck, in which position he cannot exert nearly as much force as he can standing up and working the to-and-fro motion of a windlass handle. Powered capstans are widely used in ships, and also for handling stern lines in large yachts.

12.1.4 Windlasses

Windlasses may be had with single or double action. That is, they may operate on only the pulling stroke or on both strokes. They may also be had with two speeds - one for when the work is easy and the chain can come home fast, and the other for when there is a real load on the chain.

Pawl on stemhead fitting

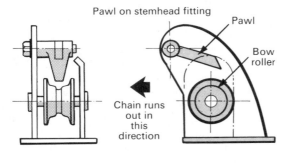

Pawl

Bow roller

Chain runs out in this direction

Chain stopper

Fig. 12(4) A pawl at the bow roller will help when retrieving anchor, while a chain compressor allows the chain to be paid out under complete control.

The gypsy (the drum at the side round which the cable runs) can be designed to suit chain only or a combination of chain or rope, which is useful where rope is the main anchor cable but is joined to the anchor with a short length of chain. There is also normally a separate rope drum on the opposite side of the windlass from the chain gypsy. The spindle may be vertical.

Hand operated windlasses in the larger sizes can be used for loads up to 450kg (1000lb) or more and are capable of handling chain up to 12mm ($\frac{1}{2}$in) diameter with a mechanical advantage of 40:1 in low gear, but once the requirement for such a powerful piece of equipment is reached, people tend to start thinking of electrical or hydraulic windlasses. Normally, smallish boats use electric types but as craft get bigger with more elaborate engine arrangements, the tendency is to switch to the, perhaps, slightly more reliable and robust hydraulic types. The requirement then is for a hydraulic pump to be driven off the main engine or a generator (usually by belt) which transmits power through a hydraulic hose to another pump in the windlass itself. Clearly nothing will work unless the engine is running.

Typically, the battery drain using an electric windlass would be, on a 12-volt system, 34 amps for a pull of 45kg (100lb); 69 amps for 135kg (300lb); and 100 amps for 225kg (500lb). The corresponding figures for 24 volts would be 20 amps, 33 amps and 44 amps, while at 450kg (1000lb) the drain would be 80 amps. These pull figures are a bit confusing but for smallish boats that use up to 8mm ($\frac{5}{16}$in) chain, the maximum likely pull would be 135kg (300lb), while for those with 10mm ($\frac{3}{8}$in) chain the figure rises to 180kg (400lb), and on those that have 12mm ($\frac{1}{2}$in) chain the maximum likely is 225kg (500lb). Most electric windlasses can be fitted with an overload protection unit which will trip if the windlass is overloaded other than briefly, and some are equipped with a gear change mechanism. To conserve battery power, an electric windlass should normally only be operated when the engine is running and the alternator is charging. Both hydraulic and electric types can normally be fitted with a lever for hand operation in an emergency. Some have an indicator which shows how much cable has been veered.

12.1.5 Chain lockers
Allowing anchor chain to collapse into the bottom corner of an undrained chain locker is asking for trouble and unpleasant smells. The locker should have a perforated tray in it on which the chain sits, and a good sized drain plug at the bottom. A hose can occasionally be squirted into the locker to wash off the mud. which can then be collected from a suitable place in the bilges to where it has drained. If the locker is not directly under the chain pipe on deck, the chain should be led to the locker in a trough, not through a pipe in which it is bound to jam eventually.

12.2 Deck fittings

12.2.1 Pulpits and guardrails
A pulpit is fitted to allow people to work round the forestay in safety and with reasonable ease. This means that a man must be able to get forward of the stay and be sustained in that position. If the pulpit does not extend far enough forward things may be difficult, and if it is too wide he may be flung from side to side in bad weather. There is more to the design of a pulpit than simply running a railing round the bow. Remember, too, that it will probably be necessary to haul the anchor on to the foredeck and this may be difficult if the lower rail is fixed at an inconvenient height. A pulpit must be at least 600mm (24in) high and its bases should be designed to take transverse loads as well as fore and aft.

Stanchions were discussed in 10.5.5 but it is worth repeating here that they should be at least 600mm (24in) high (and are better if even more than that) and must be very securely through-bolted at their bases. Stanchions have a top wire (or rail in bigger craft) and, lower down, a second wire at just above mid-height. The lead of these wires should be checked to see that they do not chafe. The wires themselves are probably best made of a plastic-covered stainless steel. Somewhere along their length they should be arranged to clip to, rather than pass through, the stanchions to make a gateway for getting aboard. Stanchions may be of mild steel (epoxy painted after fabrication), stainless steel or aluminium alloy tube.

12.2.2 Mooring bitts and bollards
A bitt is usually taken as having one vertical post with a horizontal member of some form through it, while a bollard has two vertical posts. Either is much more acceptable on the foredeck than a cleat since there may be a multiplicity of lines attached (such as breastlines and springs) while at different times the anchor chain or warp will need securing other than to the windlass. A cleat can really only handle one line at a time without risk of everything jamming up. Of the bitts available, those which are made up of tubes are preferable to those which have a solid bar as the horizontal member, since a bar can cause nasty wounds round the ankle as life gets hectic on the foredeck. Fig. 12(5) shows the various types most often seen. Whatever is fitted should be as large as practical and very well bolted down. The RNLI constantly complain that if they have to tow a yacht there is often no adequate fixing point for their tow rope. Even the bottom of a deck-stepped mast is not always man enough for the job, and they often have to resort to wrapping the rope right round the superstructure. In the old days boats commonly had a sampson post forward which was a stout timber post (usually oak) which was stepped on the keel and ran up through the

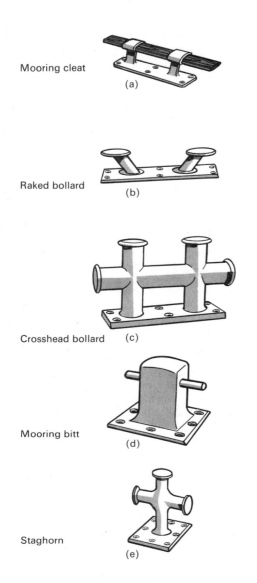

Mooring cleat (a)

Raked bollard (b)

Crosshead bollard (c)

Mooring bitt (d)

Staghorn (e)

Fig. 12(5) Rope and chain require good attachment points, particularly on the foredeck. Typical of these are (a), a mooring cleat; (b), a raked bollard; (c), crosshead bollard; (d), a mooring bitt, though the horizontal bar can be dangerous; and (e), a better type of mooring bitt, or staghorn.

foredeck. This could take immense strains and though it might not be practical today on some small yachts, the need remains for a secure fixing point forward that is big enough to take a number of light warps or one really hefty one. Stout bollards or bitts on the foredeck should be complemented by a pair aft with two more, though perhaps of a lesser size, port and starboard somewhere near midships. These last are the principal securing points for the springs (warps that lead diagonally out from the boat and help to prevent her surging backwards and forwards when moored).

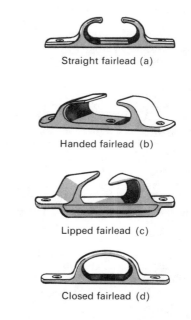

Straight fairlead (a)

Handed fairlead (b)

Lipped fairlead (c)

Closed fairlead (d)

Fig. 12(6) Fairleads come in many guises. Common ones are (a), the straight type which may be mounted to port or starboard; (b), handed fairleads which must be installed on the correct side; (c), a lipped type from which a rope is unlikely to be loosed accidentally; and (d), a closed fairlead which is absolutely secure but through which the warp has to be threaded.

12.2.3 Fairleads

These allow warps to be retained at some predetermined position along the vessel's sides (or transom) as they run in towards a bollard or cleat. They may be had in various types, such as straight, handed, lipped and closed, and all are shown in Fig. 12(6). Handed types must be used on the appropriate sides of the craft and if this is done are good; lipped types need the warp slotting through the lips but once in place it is unlikely to jump out; while the closed models require the warp to be threaded through the fairlead, which is sometimes a nuisance though it can be guaranteed to stay in position. The larger and better made the fairlead is, the less it will chafe the rope.

12.2.4 Lifelines

Unless a yacht is very securely bounded by bulwarks and stanchions supporting guardrails, lifelines are a wise precaution. These generally take the form of a wire starting at the aft end of the cabin top running forward as far as practical towards the mast and anchored both ends. On bigger boats, or those with a centreline hatch, two lines may be necessary. These lines, which are probably best of plastic-covered stainless steel wire, may be used as handholds when going forward or to provide a securing point for safety harness. Obviously their anchoring plates fore and aft must be through-bolted and not merely screwed down.

12.2.5 Latchway Safety System

Though lifelines are a good aid to safety their limited scope is restrictive and running along the deck or cabin top as they do, they can trip the unwary. Better on nearly all counts is the Latchway Safety System. Here the normal lifeline is replaced with a wire which, with specially designed fastenings, can bound the deck and be fixed to stanchions, shroud plates, toe rails, standing rigging or other similar fittings. What is known as a 'transfastener' is attached to the safety harness and can traverse these fastenings without needing to be undone. Since the wire can run from stern to bow, cross the deck, and then run back the other side there is no part of the yacht that is out of reach of the wearer of the safety harness. The transfastener can only be removed from the wire at entry/exit terminals at each end of the span. Maintenance consists of washing off salt deposits with fresh water from time to time.

12.2.6 Ventilators

Very little attention is paid to natural ventilation on most small craft. It is hoped that the provision of an opening port or two, or sliding windows, plus a couple of hatches will do the trick. And so they would if they could be left open, but in bad weather or when the craft is deserted things are generally tight shut. This leads to an unpleasant atmosphere which induces condensation below decks and, in the case of a wooden boat, provides good conditions for the development of dry rot.

Properly there should be one air change every 20 minutes or so, and that is a reasonable figure on which to base calculations. If the cabin of a yacht were, say, 23 cu m (800 cu ft) in volume and an average 1-knot wind speed 30m/min(100ft/min) was estimated while she was closed up, the ventilators must be able to cope with 23/20 = 1.15 cu m(40cu ft) of air for there to be a change every 20 minutes. If that 30m/min (100ft/min) figure is taken then the cross-section area of the vents must be 1.15/30 = 0.038 sq m (0.4 sq ft). That would be given by two 75 mm (3in) diameter vents matched by a further two vents of the same size to get rid of the old air.

The figure of 30m/min (100ft/min) is a low one but the average yacht ventilator is so full of chokes and restrictions that it is probably realistic. In bad weather, though the wind may be blowing hard, some of the vents will probably be closed and what remains will have to cope with a wet and heavy-breathing crew below.

There are various types of special mushroom ventilators available, such as the Aeolian, that permit air to pass while keeping out all but solid water. Such types are claimed to be able to move approximately 0.23 cu m (8 cu ft) per minute in even a light wind. The Aeolian Solarvent is a solar powered extractor ventilator, in which a silicon cell generates sufficient electricity during normal daylight hours to drive a small motor and blade: this will remove 0.3 cu m (11 cu ft) per minute even in still air.

Normal mushroom ventilators have a central bolt projection downwards, so that they can be shut tight when required and at other times opened as far as seems reasonable. Cowl vents are more efficient, as might be expected, but have the drawback that their projection above deck makes them a prime target for errant sheets which tend to take a turn round them, and then whisk them overboard. The classic type of nearly-watertight vent is the Dorade, Fig. 12(7), where a cowl vent is mounted on a box while some little distance from the cowl in the same box is a simple tube. Water getting in through the cowl will simply swill around the box, from which it can drain away, and will not find its way below unless so deep that it overflows the tube. Cowl vents should have some provision made so that the cowl can be removed from its spigot and a watertight cap snapped on in its place.

Fig. 12(7) A Dorade ventilator which is watertight in all but extreme conditions. Water getting down the cowl will normally drain through holes cut in the surrounding box.

12.2.7 Davits and other boat lifting gear

The usual modern yacht is too small to carry a davit-hoisted dinghy anywhere but over the stern, where it tends to be a nuisance (especially when mooring stern-to) and to put weight just where it is not wanted (at the end of the boat). However, unless the dinghy can be swung inboard from a single arm swivelling davit, it is probably even more of a nuisance hanging over the side than it is on the stern. Further, its height above deck when in side davits would probably preclude its use on most sailing craft. So if davits are required they will be of the fixed type and mounted at the stern, and all that can be asked of them is that they are light and strong. Certain types have extending arms which can be valuable when trying to accommodate different dinghies while, once the dinghy is lowered, davit arms can be shortened, with advantage. A davit can be used to sling an aft gangway, when its arms may be used as handrails.

Dinghies can often be lifted aboard via the main halyard though it is a two-man operation - one to push the boat away from the parent vessel's sides and the other winching or heaving down the

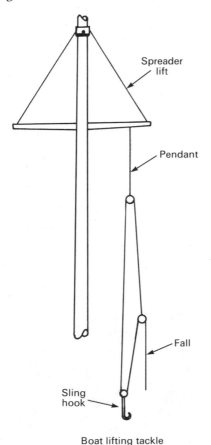

Boat lifting tackle

Fig. 12(8) American fishermen hoisted their dories aboard via a tackle mounted on a spreader.

halyard. Incidentally, if the dinghy is to be stowed upside down it is best to fix the falls or slings on to eye bolts on the outside of the stem and transom. It can be then be turned over in the air with the slings still attached. American fishermen usually bring their dories aboard via a tackle on a spreader, Fig. 12(8), while yachts with a stout boom and a topping lift may be able to employ the boom as a lifting derrick.

12.2.8 Boarding ladders

Some form of rigid boarding ladder is an essential item on all but the very smallest of cruising boats. The ladder may be of plastic, aluminium alloy, stainless steel or teak (a rope ladder is not an easy thing to use without practice), or it may be built on to the yacht in the form of rungs up the transom. Whatever form it takes, it acts as the base for operations in getting a man aboard. Someone who has been in the water for some time is unlikely to be in his first flush of strength and vigour and will almost certainly be unable to pull himself over the deck edge. The crew leaning over the side cannot exert much useful lifting power, and there have been cases of people simply being swept away from the tired arms of their would-be rescuers. A ladder down the boat's side or

transom, that can be unshipped when not required, will give the unwilling swimmer a chance to get himself aboard, or failing that, will provide a footing from which a crew member can act in a useful manner.

The bottom rung of the ladder should be at least 30 mm (12in) below the water level at rest, as the craft may well be heeling away from the person in the water. In quieter times a boarding ladder makes getting aboard from a dinghy less of a scramble. It should be strong and demonstrably capable of taking the strains likely to be put on it. There may be two men on the same rung at times and at least one of them may have added weight in the form of waterlogged clothing.

12.2.9 Tabernacles

The traditional tabernacle, which allows the mast to pivot backwards or forwards on a bolt through the spar passing through the cheeks of the tabernacle, allows the pivoting point to be at any convenient height, within limits. This facility can be useful in that it may permit the mast to lie horizontally when lowered aft over a doghouse, for instance, or to have its truck no higher than the highest point of its parent yacht when lowered forward and sitting on the pulpit. This is worthwhile when the mast has been dropped so that the craft can pass under a low bridge where it is important to have the minimum overall air draught. As opposed to modern deck-stepping methods the tabernacle also gives some degree of control over the mast as it is being raised or lowered since the cheeks extend a little way above the pivoting point and the spar is confined within them.

In practice some of the load is taken off the bolt by driving a wedge under the heel of the mast once it is raised but this wedge sometimes jams while the bolt hole in the mast gradually becomes worn and elongated. Both factors make handling

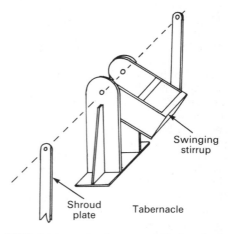

Fig. 12(9) A tabernacle allows a mast to be raised or lowered under reasonable control. Even greater control is assured if shrouds are set on the same plane as the mast with their attachment points to the shroud plates in line with the pivoting point on the tabernacle.

the mast more difficult than it should be. Fig. 12(9) shows the set-up of a modern tabernacle where the mast sits in a stirrup which swings about studs in the main structure. When lowered it can simply be slipped out of the stirrup. To ship it again, the stirrup is angled correctly and the mast slipped back. There is no awkward lining-up of bolt holes needed.

Though it may not always be possible, if a pair of shrouds can be arranged such that they lie in the same plane as the mast, and if their connections at the chain plates are in line with the pivoting studs, these shrouds can be kept tight when lowering or raising the mast and will thus prevent it swinging from side to side. Achieving this set-up usually means extending the chain plates well above deck level.

Tabernacles of this type work best if the bottom of the mast is square. This implies a timber spar which can be made to change from a square to a round or oval section without problems.

12.2.10 Gallows

Rather like the tabernacle (12.2.9), boom gallows have fallen from favour despite their real utility. They can be made from timber and steel pipe and can often be sited at the aft end of the superstructure where they will provide a good handhold. A boom stowed in gallows is much more secure than if supported by a topping lift and restrained with the sheet. If the gallows incorporate three stowage positions the boom can be hauled over to one side when required so as to keep the cockpit clear. Fig. 12(10) shows a type built up from pipe frames (which drop through and into supports rather like deck stanchions) connected by a stout timber cross-piece. The gallows can thus be unshipped and the cross-piece unbolted when the time comes to stow it. The whole structure should be robust and securely fastened but there are endless variations on the theme.

12.2.11 Warps and hawsers

Any craft may have to be towed at some time,

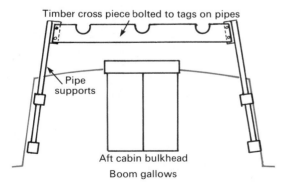

Fig. 12(10) Boom gallows will hold a boom and sail securely in place when stowed. The gallows themselves can be made to slot in place and to be taken apart for easy stowage.

hence the need for a stout bollard or bitt forward. Equally, though, she may be called on to tow another vessel and should be equipped to do so. For both purposes a towing hawser is needed and this, on the average yacht, should consist of some 55m (30 fathoms) of 16mm ($\frac{5}{8}$in diameter) nylon rope, which has a breaking load of about 5 tonnes. This hawser could also be streamed astern in a bight when running downwind in bad weather. Towing procedure is discussed in 15.5.1.

Every yacht should also have two mooring warps of about one size down from the towing hawser and at least twice the length of the vessel plus a further length of light line (about 6mm or $\frac{1}{4}$in diameter) as a heaving line. This should be about 15m (50ft) in length and be weighted at one end. The weight might consist of a big brass nut or something similar worked into a monkey's fist knot. Recommended sizes of warp (and other ropes) for yachts of different sizes are given in 11.4.4

12.2.12 Fenders

All yachts need fenders to absorb any impact and spread the load. Hence the larger they are the better. The modern air-filled types are very good and the cylindrical models which can be hung vertically or horizontally are the most generally useful supplemented by large spherical fenders for use at bow and stern. When mooring against piles a short plank is need to suspend outboard of a couple of fenders and to bear against the piles. Fenders should always be brought inboard when under way. If left hanging they cause damage and spray, can be lost in rough water, and look untidy swinging about with the boat's motion.

12.2.13 Awnings

While sadly not needed in UK waters, a good awning is an important requirement in lower latitudes - certainly in the Mediterranean during summer and in the Caribbean, for example. If it is to be regularly used an awning must be easy and quick to erect, and this depends a good deal on the configuration and cockpit layout of the boat. In a sloop or cutter athwartship spreaders are likely to be needed across the forward and aft ends of the cockpit, unless the layout allows for a hinged Bimini-type structure.

In the tropics some shelter must be provided at least for the helmsman when under way. This may be a small separate awning or part of the main structure. The latter should be designed for the collection of rain water, and detachable sidescreens are a bonus when the sun is lower during longer spells in harbour. They can also preserve privacy when lying alongside a jetty,

Awnings need to be made of a fairly heavy, rotproof material which will resist penetration by the sun's rays and which will not flap about noisily. An awning is often needed on a day which is quite windy but where the sun is still beating down from a clear blue sky.

12.3 Tenders

Until comparatively recently very few yachts had berths from which the crew could step ashore dry-shod. Rather, at the end of a cruise they would pick up a mooring and then row to a boatyard in a dinghy. This had, more often than not, been towed astern for the duration of the trip since anchoring or, as a special treat, picking up a vacant mooring, was the order of the day at every port of call. Outboards were not much in use being considered noisy and smelly (which they still are, of course) and, above all unreliable (which is much less true these days). Consequently people had to row, and there is considerable pleasure to be had from drifting down through an anchorage studying and criticising the assembled craft. Such an occupation is much less attractive in an outboard-powered dinghy, which is much too fast and whose noise prohibits quiet conversation.

Though there have been inflatable boats in existence for a long time, the sort of thing so widely used today was only properly developed after World War II. Today few cruising boats go to sea without an inflatable dinghy which despite its high cost and short life compared with the normal rigid type can at least be stowed on board all but the smallest vessels. It is thus always available as a makeshift liferaft in emergencies and as a conveyance of sorts. There is no pleasure and little progress to be had from rowing an inflatable and it makes a poor vehicle for, say, laying out a kedge anchor, but it is better than no dinghy at all.

12.3.1 Rigid dinghies

The main advantages a rigid dinghy has over an inflatable are that it is better suited to rowing and, having some worthwhile depth of hull below the floorboards, it is drier inside. Since it has more freeboard it can be used in worse weather without soaking the occupants and their baggage while propelled by oars, and it is a better vehicle for rowing out an anchor than is the inflatable. With added buoyancy in the form of buoyancy bags, slabs of foam or an inflatable collar round its gunwale it is nearly as good a makeshift liferaft. Few small cruisers, however, can stow a dinghy on deck with any ease, and towing it may cause difficulties when manoeuvring in the confines of a marina. In any case a towed dinghy is always a potential source of trouble in that during bad weather it may fill with water and break away. A proper cover reduces this risk but does not completely eliminate it and such a thing is a nuisance to have to fit. Unless specially designed for the job a dinghy will not tow at all happily behind a motor cruiser which would normally be travelling too fast, causing the dinghy to sheer from side to side until it eventually started to tow broad-side on, when it would capsize.

Thus for most yachts (and especially those that are berthed in marinas) a rigid dinghy is not worth having unless it can be stowed on deck. Its occasional real advantages would be outweighed by its general drawbacks. If a dinghy is to stow on deck it will have to be quite small, with something like 2m to 2.3m (6ft 6in to 7ft 6in) overall being the maximum that could be accommodated aboard the average cruising yacht. Although at that length it will not be a good rowing boat it will be tolerable if the craft has been properly designed. A stem dinghy is not very sensible since a lot of useful space forward has been lost, and the boat either sheers away or capsizes if anyone is unwise enough to step aboard near the bow. A normal pram dinghy will be better - this has a transom at the bow as well as the stern - while a W-cross-section hull should be better still. With the last-named shape the buoyancy of the hull is out at the sides so that the boat will be more stable and with what amounts to twin hulls will tend to row and tow in a straighter line than will a more conventional type.

Fig. 12(11) shows the dimensions that should be adhered to, or nearly so, on a small dinghy and they demonstrate why the usual inflatable cannot ever be rowed with much success - it is simply too shallow. On most really small dinghies of the type under discussion feet will be braced against the transom while rowing. If this cannot happen there should be some type of alternative brace on the floorboards since rowing is done as much by the leg, stomach and back muscles as by the arms. When sitting on the rowing thwart legs should be slightly flexed with feet against the transom or brace. Beam of the dinghy would be about 1.2m (4ft) and the oars as long as will stow inside the dinghy. Thus 2m (6ft 6in) oars will fit neatly in a dinghy which is 2.15m (7ft) long. If thwarts and floorboards are easily lifted out this will make the dinghy lighter for slinging aboard and to that end there should be stout eyebolts fore and aft. It

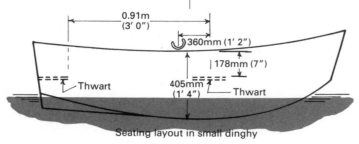

Seating layout in small dinghy

Fig. 12(11) Some minimum height and lengths for easy rowing in a small dinghy.

should be possible to fasten the rowing thwart down in alternative positions so that the balance of the boat is roughly right whether there is one person or two aboard, and whether a mountain of baggage is being carried forward or the boat is empty. This means two rowlock positions as well. There should be a sculling notch in the transom. Sculling is a useful art to acquire but the notch is also useful if the anchor, or its cable, is to be laid out while under way. If the dinghy is to be towed very often, the forward eyebolt should be supplemented on pram and W-type hulls with a further two eyebolts somewhere near the bottom, outside corners of the forward transom. On these can be fastened a bridle and the towing warp taken to the centre of this, or twin towing warps used. The dinghy will travel better under such an arrangement than if towed only from its centreline.

There is no best material for building a dinghy. Probably the lightest will be stitch and glue ply, and lightness is always a virtue in such craft.

12.3.2 Collapsible and folding dinghies

Carrying on from the conception of a small, rigid dinghy that can be lifted aboard, one way to increase its length and thus its usefulness, and to better its rowing performance is to have a further, short length of hull that can be bolted on to the stern transom. Thus an easily stowed dinghy 2m (6ft 6in) in length could be converted into one 3m (10ft) in length with the addition of a 1m (3ft 6in) length of hull. That extra length of separate hull would not present too many problems in stowage on board and it might even be stowed inside the main hull.

Collapsible boats of various kinds appear on the market from time to time. Some have rigid sides that fold down flat on to the rigid bottom, so making a very shallow package; others fold up lengthways, concertina fashion. Some are made almost entirely of a flexible plastic, but whatever the building system the thwarts and transom are usually used to brace the sides apart. For some reason these craft never seem to find much favour with the public, though if robustly built of good materials there is much to recommend them. The hinging medium is usually canvas or, these days, heavy duty plastic. Buoyancy bags could be fitted after erection, and if the erecting can be done really quickly and does not require much space to lay out the individual parts the type is worth investigating. It should have a reassuringly solid feel about it when put together and in the water.

12.3.3 Inflatables

There is a wide range of inflatable dinghies on the market, most of which follow the same basic idea of multi-chamber inflatable tubes set on a fabric floor. There may also be an inflatable keel to reduce leeway while wooden floorboards are usually available. The transom is of timber so it can take an outboard. Rather basic rowlocks are provided to go with stumpy oars. At the expensive end of the market buoyancy tubes are normally a hand-glued Hypalon/nylon material, but a bit lower down the price scale there are craft available with welded Dynalon tubes. Welding is cheaper than hand-glueing. The craft may be pump-inflated but CO_2 inflation bottles are also available with most types; these will speed up the operation enormously.

A good quality inflatable is expensive and is not to be confused with the toy boats that are blown off beaches complete with their young occupants. The materials used are of far better quality; there are separate buoyancy chambers so that springing a leak does not mean the collapse of the whole craft; and the whole dinghy is much more robustly built.

The British Standards specification for inflatables, MA16, covers both materials and manufacture and insists, for example, that any ply used in the craft - such as for transoms and floorboards - should be to the marine ply specification BS1088.

Inflatables for use as tenders come in sizes ranging upwards from about 2.4m (8ft) to a maximum of roughly 3.6m (12ft). Much bigger types are also made for commercial applications. All this excludes rigid bottom inflatables which are dealt with in 12.3.4. Some inflatables can be had with sailing gear. They make a very safe sailing dinghy which is unlikely to capsize under normal wind pressure alone. In fact one of the inflatable's advantages is that it is very stable. It requires deliberate action by the crew, or exceptional action by wind and waves, to turn one over. And, of course, the tubes that bound the edges ensure a soft landing against the parent yacht's sides when getting aboard.

Though an inflatable is not a liferaft some are offered with a canopy that can be lashed in place to give the occupants a measure of protection against the elements. For a craft set on a lengthy cruise where the expense of a liferaft would be the straw that broke the proverbial camel's back, a canopied inflatable complete with sailing gear might be worth considering.

All reputable inflatable manufacturers can supply a repair outfit with their craft and the instructions should be followed, but in an emergency a bicycle puncture repair kit will do a temporary job. The glue supplied with the manufacturer's outfits has a useable life of only about a year, so after that it should be replaced. Bostik No. 3 is suitable and this is available from many ironmongers or yacht chandlers. If a big tear has occurred it is best to sew the edges together using a herringbone stitch and a thin fishing line as the thread before applying the patch.

Before an inflatable is stored for any length of time it should be washed down in fresh water. If it can be stored partially inflated so much the better, but if it has to be put back in its valise fold it carefully and in the same manner as it was originally packed.

12.3.4 Rigid bottom inflatables

The normal inflatable with its soft floor cannot make a very satisfactory motor boat because the bottom is all the wrong shape and changes what shape it has with every wave that passes under it. Thus the rigid bottom inflatable was developed, where the buoyancy tubes are mounted on a GRP hull that stops at cockpit sole level. This level is above the waterline so that it can be made self-draining, and with the very buoyant tubes round the deck edge the result is a safe boat and one that can be driven as fast as any other high speed motor boat. On a parent vessel big enough to sling such a craft in davits, the rigid bottom inflatable is excellent for towing water skiers. It is widely used by the RNLI, the Royal Navy and many commercial companies as a patrol and rescue boat.

The fact that the bottom is rigid means that this type of craft loses the advantage the normal inflatable has of being capable of being folded into a small package where it can be stowed on even quite small yachts. Hence it is not a substitute for the inflatable nor, really, for the normal rigid dinghy. However, types are available that will sail and row quite reasonably.

12.4 Self steering

12.4.1 Steering by sail

Anyone who has played around with model yachts will know that if the craft is reasonably well-balanced it can be made to steer quite an accurate course with the rudder free, downwind, upwind or reaching, simply by freeing or hardening the main and jib sheets. The mainsail tries to drive the boat's bows into the wind while the jib has the opposite effect, and these opposing forces have to be balanced. This is normally achieved by sheeting in the jib harder than would otherwise be desirable and freeing the main. What can be achieved on a model can usually be achieved on a full-size yacht, and this is one form of self-steering. Joshua Slocum must have done just this during his single-handed circumnavigation. Certainly he did not have any sophisticated vane gear (after all, he set out in 1895) but was still able to leave the helm untouched for days on end. Though a modern fin and skeg form would not respond to this basic treatment as well as did his traditional, long keel vessel, even so, experimenting with different main and headsail areas and sheeting ought to bring reasonable results.

12.4.2 Linking the rudder and sails

Using sails alone, their drive must be adjusted to the demands of self-steering rather than to maximum efficiency, and so a reasonable development is to link the main sheet to the tiller in an attempt to allow the sails to develop their

full power. Fig. 12(12) shows one such scheme. Here the sheet leads through a block on the weather side of the boat and then back to the tiller. Under way the main tries to turn the yacht's head into the wind but is resisted by the rudder being pulled in the opposite direction. The harder the wind blows, the greater the pull on the sheet and thus on the rudder via the tiller.

The point at which the sheet joins the tiller is adjustable so that the leverage can be altered, and there is normally a length of shock cord made fast on the opposite side, as shown, whose tension can also be adjusted and whose main function is to speed the return of the tiller to its correct angle, In practice two sheets are used with blocks on

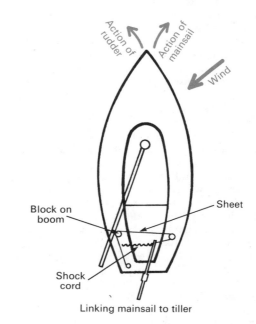

Linking mainsail to tiller

Fig. 12(12) The most basic form of positive self-steering is to link the main boom sheet to the tiller via a quarter block.

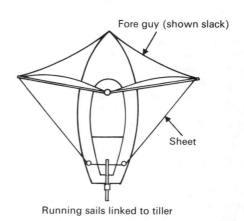

Running sails linked to tiller

Fig. 12(13) Running sails may be linked to the tiller for downwind self-steering.

both quarters so that the system can be used on either tack. It works well enough on most small yachts when beating or close reaching and as the whole arrangement is finally adjusted with the headsails pulling hard there is little loss in efficiency, but it does not act so satisfactorily on a run or with a quartering wind. Hence single or short-handed sailors may link their running sails (usually twin staysails or twin spinnakers) to the tiller as shown in Fig. 12(13). The way it works is clear. If the yacht veers off course the pressure on one of the sails is increased and on the other, reduced. These pressures are transmitted back via lines and quarter blocks to the tiller, which then automatically heads the boat back on course where the pressure in both sails is the same. Such running sails can be reefed through Wykeham-Martin furling gear (still available) which rolls them up on their stays. There are many variations on this basic theme.

12.4.3 Self-steering by vane and apparent wind

The French yachtsman and artist, Marin-Marie, who crossed the Atlantic under sail single-handed in 1933, made the return, west-east, run in 1936 but this time in a motor boat, the 13m (42ft) *Arielle*. He was again single-handed. On board he had a hastily installed and experimental autopilot plus vane steering of his own devising. This must have been the first vane steering ever used on a yacht, and even the autopilot was a considerable novelty though the system was even then in use on aircraft and big ships. Anyway, during an average 24 hours he used the vane for about 15 hours; the autopilot for four or five hours; and the rest of the time he took the wheel himself. The pilot was switched on when there was no wind, and Marin-Marie steered generally when there was not much wind but a big sea was running. In those conditions the mechanism of the autopilot tended to be overworked.

The wind vane is illustrated in Fig. 12(14) and its action is uncomplicated. First the vane, which was V-shaped, of ply and about 1.2m (4ft) high, was unclamped from the spindle and allowed to rotate until it faced the apparent wind. This is the wind felt on board and is neither the same strength nor (generally) from the same direction as the actual or true wind. If a boat was sailing directly downwind at, say 6 knots in a 13-knot breeze, the apparent wind on deck would be 13 − 6 =7 knots and would still appear to be coming from directly astern. However, if the boat was going to windward at 6 knots in a 13-knot breeze which was blowing at 45° to the boat's course, the apparent wind would be 17.7 knots at 33° to the yacht's heading. Fig. 12(15) shows this in diagrammatic form. Apparent wind is described in more detail in Chapter 11 (11.5.8).

When the vane on the *Arielle* was steady it was clamped on to the spindle. If the boat got off course the wind acted on the vane from one side

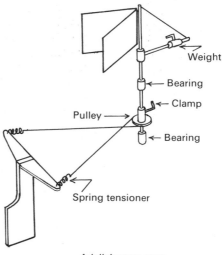

Arielle's vane gear

Fig. 12(14) The French painter and author, Marin-Marie, built what must have been the first practical wind vane steering and installed it on his motor boat *Arielle* for his 1936 west-east single-handed Atlantic crossing. It was entirely successful.

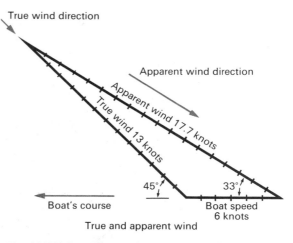

Fig. 12(15) The difference between true and apparent wind with a yacht working to windward. The apparent wind is from further ahead and stronger than the true wind on this heading.

or the other, and would turn the vane (and thus the tiller) until it once again faced the wind and equalled the pressure on both sides of the V. This wind vane acted on an auxiliary rudder hung on the transom, and while it was in operation the wheel steering was locked to keep the main rudder fore and aft. There have been many systems since similar to Marin-Marie's.

12.4.4 Other wind vanes
These days vertical axis vanes are usually more complicated than their originator's and more directly linked to the rudder they steer. Perhaps the most common types have the vane set on a vertical, or nearly vertical, axis operating a trim tab which may be mounted on the main, transom-hung rudder or hung separately but still directly linked to the rudder. The trim tab system is illustrated in basic form in Fig. 12(16). What happens is the vane turns the trim tab. The rush of water past the tab causes the rudder to turn in the opposite direction and to steer the boat back on course.

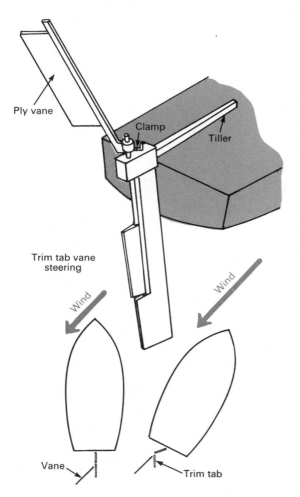

Ply vane

Clamp

Tiller

Trim tab vane steering

Wind

Wind

Vane

Trim tab

Fig. 12(16) A vertical wind vane operating a trim tab on the main rudder. Its action is fairly obvious but a commercial model would have a more refined method of setting the wind vane on the spindle than a clamp. In all probability it would be operable from the cockpit.

Pendulum type
Another type of vertically-mounted vane steering is the pendulum gear developed by 'Blondie' Hasler. It works on the principle that if an auxiliary rudder blade could pivot sideways on a fore and aft axis (like an athwartships pendulum) and could also be turned into the water stream in the same manner as a normal rudder, it would swing sideways when turned. This swing could be used to operate lines fastened to the tiller of a main or auxiliary rudder. The general arrangement of this pendulum system is shown in Fig. 12(17).

Horizontal axis vanes
An alternative type of wind vane steering has the vane mounted on a horizontal axis, which gives more power. The blade of a vane pointing directly into the apparent wind, with a counterbalancing weight below, will stand vertically. If the boat changes course or the wind changes direction, the resulting breeze will blow on one side of the vane causing it to tilt about its horizontal axis. This tilt can be translated into movement on tiller lines linked to the main or auxiliary rudder. Fig. 12(18) shows the scheme in sketch form.

Modern vane gear
A good example of vane gear currently on the market (in 1992) is the Monitor Windvane from Scanmar Marine Products in California, combining the principles of the servo-pendulum gear with a vane mounted on a near-horizontal axis as described previously. The Monitor has taken over the mantle from the Aries vane gear to which it is similar but which is no longer available. Apart from the wind vane, fabricated in marine ply, the rest of the structure is almost entirely stainless steel to minimize corrosion. Remote control of the wind vane setting is by stainless chain and sprocket drive. The pendulum is hinged in the middle to allow it to be swung up and out of the water when not in use. If necessary it can be locked in the central position and used for emergency steering. Maintenance-free roller and ball bearings are used to reduce friction between the wind vane and the servo-pendulum. Any self-steering system needs some form of feedback to prevent over-steering, and this is done through the master gearing which gradually neutralises the rotation of the pendulum blade as it swings outwards - bringing it back into alignment with the hull. Thus the force of the water on the pendulum blade reduces progressively. The gear can be used for either tiller or wheel steering, and in both cases arrangements are made for quick disconnection if required.

12.4.5 Vanes in general
The better balanced and easier to steer a boat is, the more chance a vane has of working well. To that end it is usually worth experimenting with shifting ballast, altering the rake of the mast and even, perhaps, trying different proportions of sail

area ahead and astern of the mast to improve balance if the yacht is hard on the helm and good vane steering is a major requirement. Shifting ballast aft, for instance, will move the CLR aft by putting the stern deeper in the water and should reduce weather helm. Raking the mast aft, on the other hand, will shift the CE astern and may increase weather helm. A larger headsail and smaller main (adding up to the same working sail area) will move the CE forward and reduce weather helm.

Except for the servo-pendulum type, a wind vane can only produce a limited amount of power unless it is so large that it is cumbersome and a nuisance on board. Hence a balanced rudder (that is, one with some blade area forward of the stock) which takes less power to turn than an unbalanced rudder will be a good thing and bearings should be examined to make sure they are as friction-free as possible. The power required from the vane can be reduced if it is connected to an auxiliary rudder (if the yacht's rudder is forward, at the aft end of the keel), or to a trim tab if the rudder is transom-hung.

Many people have made their own vane systems with complete success. The criteria must always be to produce a robust structure with low friction, though the vertical axis vanes seem to be able to cope with friction better than the horizontal axis types. The vane gear must incorporate some method of disengagement that can be operated very quickly so that a helmsman can take over. And however good the design, it will probably not be too effective in really light winds; nor in big seas where the vane may be blanketed from time to time, nor where a big slop left over from a dying wind knocks the boat about to the extent that the breeze on the vane cannot control her. A vane will not usually work as well downwind as

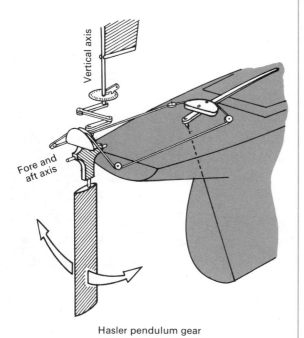

Hasler pendulum gear

Fig. 12(17) The Hasler Pendulum gear translates the swing of a rudder about a fore and aft axis into pull on tiller lines.

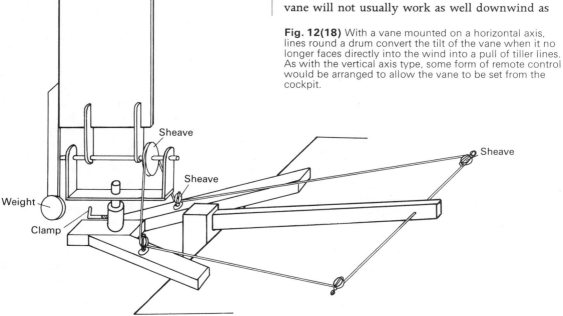

Horizontal axis vane

Fig. 12(18) With a vane mounted on a horizontal axis, lines round a drum convert the tilt of the vane when it no longer faces directly into the wind into a pull of tiller lines. As with the vertical axis type, some form of remote control would be arranged to allow the vane to be set from the cockpit.

upwind (remember that the apparent wind is less than the true wind when running but is greater when going to windward) but on longer voyages the system is a great boon. It is not, however, a substitute for a man on deck keeping watch. It simply allows him to do that more efficiently since he does not have to bother about steering. The Amateur Yacht Research Society publish an excellent book on the whole subject, called *Self Steering*.

12.5 Wheel-steering gear

12.5.1 Wire and cable

The simplest and (generally) the cheapest form of steering gear is that where flexible wire cables are led back from the wheel via sheaves along the hull side to a quadrant on the rudder stock. The quadrant may be replaced by a tiller with a sliding collar attachment for the cables on an even cheaper system. The mechanical advantage can be varied by altering the size of the quadrant (or length of tiller) and the diameter of the wheel.

In its simplest form the wires may be attached to a drum on the wheel but a more usual arrangement is to fit a chain sprocket on the wheel. The wire cable is made fast to the ends of the chain and a typical layout is shown on Fig. 12(19). A system like this is positive and if all the sheaves are carefully aligned and lubricated it is sensitive to pressures on the rudder. This is important on sailing vessels where 'feel' at the wheel makes for more responsive handling. It is important that the tension in the cables can be adjusted - even though everything is normally set up quite slack. To this end there are rigging screws or other tensioners at the quadrant or, alternatively, a similar device somewhere along the cable. Rudder stops should be fitted to prevent shock loads to the rudder (as in a broach) being transmitted directly to the cables. Though the basic components in this system are comparatively inexpensive and there is very little to go wrong (and if it does it is easy to repair), the chain and cable gear may not be very much cheaper than more sophisticated systems if installed professionally. This is simply because siting, aligning and bolting down the sheaves is quite a time-consuming business. Autopilots and dual steering positions can be arranged in the layout.

Many fishing boats and similar commercial craft used chain throughout. This was because nearly all the gear was on deck at the deck/bulwark edge and chain would last much longer than the wire then available.

12.5.2 Conduit wire cable gear

Basically similar to the normal wire and chain steering is the type where the wires are led to the quadrant in a conduit. At the quadrant there is a

Fig. 12(19) The basic chain and wire wheel-steering system shown on a Simpson-Lawrence gear.

special box designed to take the end of the conduit, and this box moves with the quadrant, transmitting the cable movement through sheaves. Autopilots and twin steering positions can be incorporated into the steering gear which is very quick to install since the conduit can lead along any convenient path and needs no sheaves to guide it. A typical layout is shown in Fig. 12(20). Rudder stops are vital.

12.5.3 Single cable steering

In essence this type of steering moves the tiller through a single push-pull cable very similar to that used for the operation of gears and throttle on modern marine engines. The cable is contained in a conduit fastened at both ends, and is generally actuated by a rack and pinion at the wheel. The system is positive in operation and simple to install. Maintenance requirements are low and consist of checking on the free-running of the cable and on lubrication of exposed moving parts, but there is virtually no 'feel' with such an arrangement and it is thus most suited to motor boats where it is widely used on craft up to about 15m (50ft) in length.

12.5.4 Mechanical steering

Mechanical steering may be achieved through a gearbox and simple rod to the tiller as in

Fig. 12(21), this being a very effective and comparatively low-cost system where the wheel is sited close to the rudder stock. Where greater distances are involved torque tube steering is usually used. On this the rotary movement of the wheel is converted to rotary movement in a series of connected tubes, known as torque tubes. The rotary motion is finally converted to a back and

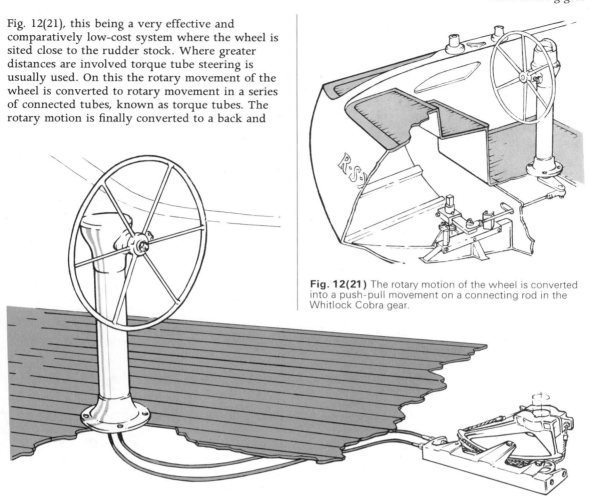

Fig. 12(21) The rotary motion of the wheel is converted into a push-pull movement on a connecting rod in the Whitlock Cobra gear.

Fig. 12(20) If the wire of a steering gear is enclosed in a conduit, installation will be simplified as accurately aligned sheaves will no longer be required. This is the Whitlock Constellation arrangement.

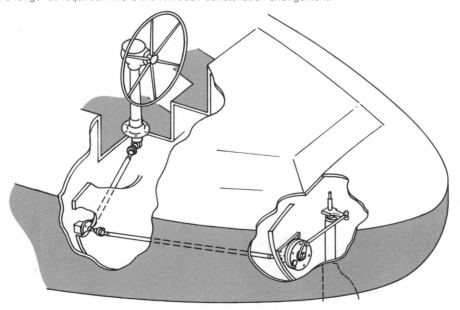

Fig. 12(22) A torque tube mechanical steering system. As shown the torque tube runs directly to the helm unit near the tiller. If this cannot be achieved the line of the torque tube can be changed by the use of universal joints or angled transfer boxes between bearings.

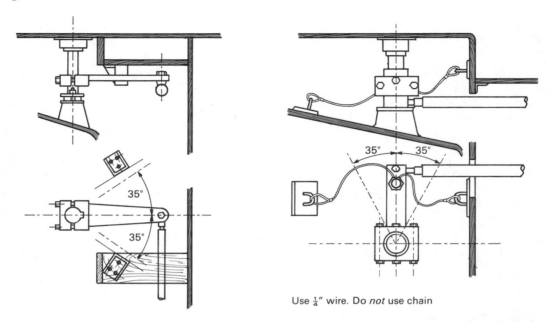

Use ¼" wire. Do *not* use chain

Fig. 12(23) Rudder stops are essential on virtually all steering gears. Two possibilities are shown which prevent the gear from being damaged under the extreme circumstances of, for instance, a high-speed broach. Stops also prevent the rudder from assuming an extreme angle when going astern under power.

forth movement on an arm linked to the tiller. The torque tubes themselves require bearings to support them if they are over about 2.4m (8ft) long but can change direction between bearings by the use of universal joints or, in more extreme cases, through angled transfer boxes. Various gear ratios are normally available in the bevel boxes below the steering wheel and in the final, aft end box, so that different mechanical advantages can be obtained. In addition the number of turns of the wheel to achieve a hard-over helm can be selected.

With a mechanical system, power assistance can be added as well as the gear for an autopilot and, if necessary, dual station steering. It is a strong and reliable system, and in many cases the various gearboxes are sealed and lubricated for life. Some attention has to be paid to the universal joints, bearings and ball joints to keep them greased and clean but this is a straightforward process.

Fig. 12(22) shows a layout and Fig. 12(23) two types of rudder stop.

12.5.5 Rack and pinion and worm gears

There are two other types of wheel-steering gear in general use. The first is the rack and pinion type, where the pinion on the wheel drives the rack on a circular path pivoted about the line of the rudder pintles. This movement can be transmitted directly to the rudder Fig. 12(24) or can be linked to a push-pull rod side mounted on the rudder, as shown in Fig. 12(25). The system is smooth and normally has a fair amount of 'feel'. It is usually used in craft where the wheel and rudder are reasonably close together, though universal joints may be employed to allow the wheel to be mounted out of line with the rudder pintles so that wheel angle may be adjusted.

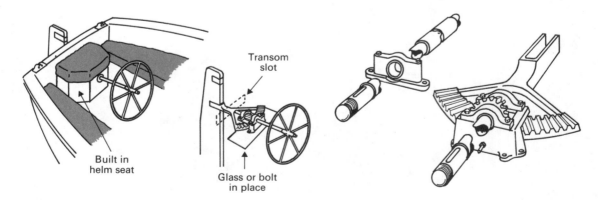

Fig. 12(24) Rack and pinion steering is direct and simple. With a universal joint on the shaft forward of the pinion, the wheel can be mounted at any reasonable angle.

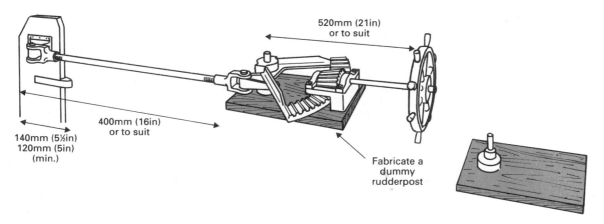

Fig. 12(25) Rack and pinion gear may be mounted at some distance from the rudder using a push-pull rod as in this Edson system.

Worm gears are best suited to motor boats or to sailing yachts where steadiness at the wheel is more important than 'feel'. Such might be the case with a long-distance cruiser where the ultimate in responsiveness could be sacrificed in return for a steering system where the wheel, on a well-balanced craft, can be left unattended for short periods in modern conditions, without it being turned by the heaving of the boat. The gear tends to be heavy and very robust and usually requires more turns of the wheel from hard-over to hard-over than do other types. Fig. 12(26) shows a typical installation.

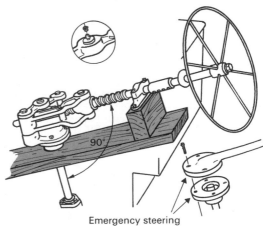

Emergency steering

12.5.6 Hydraulic steering

There are various types of hydraulic steering available which have different features, but basically they all consist of a hydraulic pump near and directly actuated by the wheel, leading via hydraulic hoses to a ram near the rudder stock.

Fig. 12(27) shows the basic layout.

Fig. 12(26) The Edson worm gear is robust but offers little 'feel' at the wheel. It is thus most suited to motor boats and to sailing yachts where 'feel' is less important than the ability to hold course for an appreciable time without much attention at the wheel.

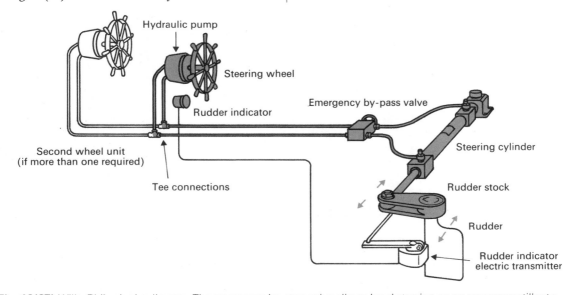

Fig. 12(27) Wills-Ridley hydraulic gear. The emergency by-pass valve allows hand steering on an emergency tiller to override the hydraulics. This can be important in the event of a malfunction.

Powered versions can be had for bigger craft and such things as autopilots and dual station steering can easily be incorporated in the layout. Hydraulic steering is quick to install since the hoses can follow any reasonable path and need no lining-up. Maintenance requirements are low. For power craft this type of steering has the advantage that a locking valve prevents kick-back from the rudder, allowing it to be held in one position for considerable periods with little attention since it cannot drive the wheel. This feature is not wanted on sailing craft where some feedback from pressure on the rudder is desirable.

An emergency by-pass valve should be incorporated so that in the event of malfunction tiller steering can be used.

12.5.7 Emergency steering

However good and sound the basic wheel-steering system, there should always be some way of hand steering by tiller. This is best done by extending the rudder stock up to just short of the deck or cockpit sole level. A hole is cut in the deck or sole sufficiently large for an emergency tiller to be shipped over the end of the stock. When the tiller is not required the hole is covered by a reasonably watertight plate held down with thumb screws or wing nuts. It is important that the helmsman

using the emergency tiller has a reasonable view, and is not confined to an aft cabin or has to steer with his head in a locker.

12.5.8 Autopilot

There are two basic types of autopilot. One is known as a course follower and the other as a compass follower. With the former the boat is steered manually on to the desired course and the pilot then engaged. It will maintain that course until disengaged and a new course steered and set. With a compass follower, though, the desired course is set on the autopilot which will then keep to that course until it is changed, which can be done at any time. On some types it can be changed by remote control, which is useful in bad weather when someone is keeping a watch from on deck.

An autopilot is best selected and installed by an expert who can assess individual requirements. In action a properly adjusted model can steer a better course than the normal helmsman, and keep doing it for hours or days on end - provided the power supply can be sustained. However useful this facility is it does not reduce the need to have a man on deck, who can keep a better lookout if he does not have to steer. He should also make an occasional check on the pilot to confirm that it is doing its job properly. Fig. 12(28) shows the basic

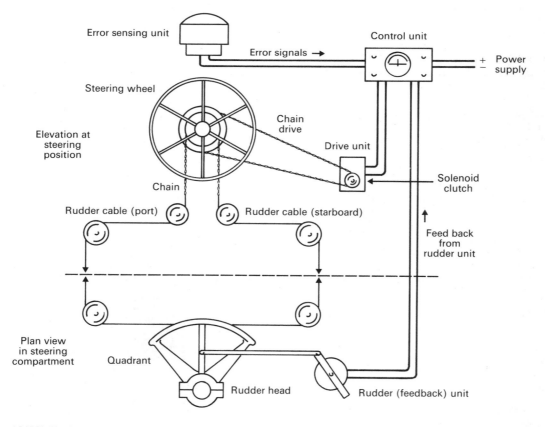

Fig. 12(28) The layout of a typical autopilot system. On some types various of the functions may be incorporated in one unit and items such as the rudder feedback unit may be dispensed with; the information it supplies being gained from other sources.

layout of an autopilot. In principle it functions as follows: the desired heading is set on the course selector (if it is of that type) or the boat is steered to the required course and the autopilot engaged. The true heading is sensed by the course or error sensor (which usually has its own compass). The difference between the steered course and the set course - the course error - is calculated. Should the course error become greater than some pre-set valve the drive of the autopilot operates the rudder sufficiently to bring the boat back on course. The drive motor may be a fractional horsepower electric type with an electro-magnetic clutch or an electrically driven hydraulic pump type which can be coupled directly into the system of a boat with hydraulic steering.

On some models there is a rudder feedback unit which monitors the rudder angle and passes the information back to the control unit, but in other models this information comes from the output of the control unit itself or from the drive of the steering motor.

On modern autopilots there are various refinements and additions. Thus, for instance, the amount of deadband (the angle through which the craft is allowed to veer off course before the rudder starts to correct) can be selected to take into account sea state and the general qualities of the boat.

The rudder control can act rather like a human helmsman in that it can react to course error and correct accordingly before it builds up sufficiently to require major rudder movement, while the rate at which the rudder is applied can be selected and automatically controlled.

Overswing may be automatically counteracted by applying counter rudder during course changing. The autopilot in some cases can be overridden in an emergency after which it will bring the craft back on the original course. Navigational systems (such as Loran) can be incorporated with the pilot so that the vessel will be steered from one position to another automatically rather than simply steering a selected course. Off-course alarms may be fitted as well as display units showing the rudder angle at any time (and so judgement may be made on how hard it is having to work). The actual course, not just the selected one, may be shown as a further guide. Corrections for trim, weather helm and helm bias can be set to allow for the fact that most craft under sail or power have a tendency to pull to one side or the other. Some makes of autopilot also incorporate wind vane steering.

Pilots for tiller steering work on the same principles as those for wheel steering, but are modified so that the mechanism is linked to the tiller.

The maintenance requirements on an autopilot are low, being mainly concerned with keeping all working parts of the steering gear free and eliminating backlash as far as possible. A radio transmitter close to the autopilot can cause uncontrolled course changing, and it should go without saying that any magnetic objects close to the boat's compass or autopilot's sensing unit can lead to major trouble.

12.5.9 Bow thrusters

Bow thrusters are becoming popular on power boats and, to a lesser extend, on biggish sailing yachts and motor sailers. As a generalisation a propeller is sited inside a transverse tube near the bow and below the waterline. The propeller is symmetrical, giving equal thrust whichever way it rotates, and by having this transverse thrust

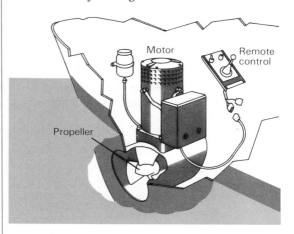

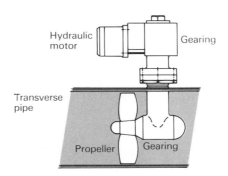

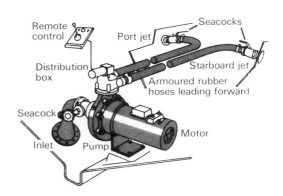

Fig. 12(29) Top, a fairly conventional arrangement for a bow thruster powered by an electric motor; middle, a hydraulically-powered bow thruster; and bottom, the arrangement of a jet bow thruster.

available so far forward quite precise manoeuvring is possible - a boon when berthing in a crowded marina or attempting to moor stern-to, Mediterranean style.

The amount of thrust needed is not great, and small models developing some 45kg (100lb) of push are normally quite sufficient for craft up to 13.7m (45ft) or so in length. In these sizes power is usually supplied by an electric motor, but in bigger types hydraulics are common.

Details vary between manufacturers but a typical small bow thruster has an athwartships tube about 185mm ($7\frac{1}{4}$in) in diameter. It has a 3kW motor, and assuming a 35amp alternator it will take about ten times as long to recharge the battery as the period over which the bow thruster is used. Thus a ten second burst on the bow thruster will need 100 seconds to recharge the battery.

Not as effective and more expensive, but reducing installation problems to a minimum and with smaller holes in the hull to reduce unwanted drag when sailing, are jet bow thrusters. Here water is drawn up through the bottom and pumped to outlets port and starboard near the bow. The water pick-up can be almost anywhere convenient, and since the hoses are only about 30mm ($1\frac{1}{4}$in) diameter very little space is taken up for installation purposes.

Another form of installation consists of a retractable impeller which can be rotated on a vertical shaft to give omni-directional thrust. When housed the impeller is retracted into an aperture in the forefoot which is closed off by a fairing. However, this arrangement takes up more space inside the boat, and when in use the rotating impeller can foul anchor and mooring warps.

Yet one more form of bow thrust is achieved by releasing large numbers of air bubbles one side or other of the hull, up forward. Although the power achieved is low, the system shows some promise for smaller craft.

Chapter 13

Engines and Electrics

Contents

13.1 Marine engines – construction

This chapter emphasises what a yachtsman can do to look after the engine of his boat, and to ensure that it gives long and reliable service. But to achieve this it is first necessary to have some understanding of how the engine works, and some knowledge of the various systems associated with it.

13.1.1 Petrol engines

Many reader will be familiar with the principle of the petrol engine. Air and petrol, mixed together in the carburettor in the correct proportions for efficient combustion (about 15 parts, by weight, of air to one of petrol), are drawn into the combustion chamber above each piston of the engine in turn. The upstroke of a piston compresses the mixture, which is ignited by a spark-plug when that piston is nearing the top of its stroke. The burning mixture expands and forces the piston down. The reciprocating movement of the pistons is transformed into rotation by connecting rods between the pistons and the crankshaft. Off the crankshaft is driven a camshaft, which runs at half the speed of the crankshaft, and controls the opening and closing of the inlet and exhaust valves for each cylinder.

Most petrol engines work on the 4-stroke cycle. On the downward (induction) stroke the inlet valve is open, allowing the air/petrol mixture to be drawn into the cylinder from the carburettor. During the (upward) compression stroke both valves are closed, so that compression heats and vaporises the mixture in the combustion chamber. After the mixture has been ignited by the spark-plug both valves remain closed for the (downward) power stroke. When the piston is near the bottom of the power stroke, the exhaust valve opens so that on the (upward) exhaust stroke the burnt gases are expelled. The cycle is then repeated. With the 4-stroke cycle each cylinder produces power every fourth stroke, or every two revolutions of the crankshaft. Hence with a four-cylinder engine there are two power strokes per revolution of the crankshaft, a typical firing order being 1,2,4,3.

The great majority of outboard engines (see 13.4) and a few other marine units work on the 2-stroke cycle, where the various operations described above are arranged to occur within one complete revolution of the crankshaft. The sequence of events is described in 13.4.2.

For a given power, a 2-stroke engine is compact and light in weight, but it consumes more fuel than a 4-stroke, mainly because the scavenging of the exhaust gases is inefficient, a proportion of the incoming charge being lost with the exhaust.

The power output from an engine depends on the weight of air/fuel mixture that can be drawn into each cylinder, and how much it can be compressed. A typical compression ratio when using ordinary petrol is 9:1. Too high a compression ratio results in uneven burning of the fuel (detonation), which is inefficient and can result in damage. An additional weight of air/fuel mixture can be pushed into the cylinder by a supercharger, either driven off the engine or from a turbine operated by exhaust gases.

13.1.2 Diesel engines

Outwardly a diesel engine looks very similar to a petrol one, but there are essential differences in its operation. Nearly all diesel engines work on the 4-stroke cycle, but on the induction stroke only air is drawn into the cylinder, see Fig. 13(1). On the compression stroke this air is heated to a temperature which will ignite a very fine spray of diesel fuel, injected into the combustion chamber just before the piston reaches the top of the stroke. The fuel then burns and performs useful work on the power stroke, after which the exhaust gases are expelled on the next upstroke. In order to achieve the necessary temperature for ignition of the fuel, very high compression ratios are needed in diesel engines - roughly double those for petrol engines: this means that their construction must be more robust, and consequently they are heavier for a given power output.

Instead of the carburettor, ignition system and spark-plugs of the petrol engine, a diesel unit has a fuel injection pump which supplies very accurately metered quantities of fuel at very high pressure and at precisely the right time to fuel injectors which are situated at the top of each cylinder - see 13.2.3.

13.1.3 Choice of engine

The choice of a petrol or diesel engine depends on the application. In general terms petrol engines are cheaper and lighter for a given power, and are more easily maintained; but they involve a greater risk of fire, and the electrical ignition system does not react kindly to salt water. Diesels are safer, potentially more reliable, and cheaper to run; but they are more expensive, heavier, noisier and smellier, and maintenance of fuel injection equipment needs proper workshop facilities.

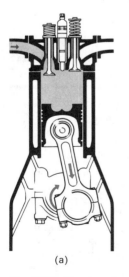 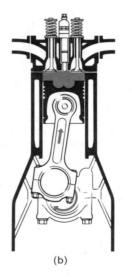 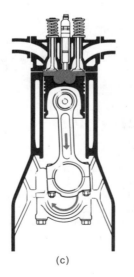 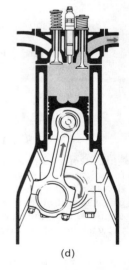

(a)	(b)	(c)	(d)

Fig. 13(1) Diesel engine, 4-stroke cycle. (a) On the inlet stroke air is drawn into the cylinder, through the inlet valve. (b) On the compression stroke both valves are shut, and the air is compressed and heated. Near the top of the compression stroke, fuel is sprayed into the combustion chamber by the injector. (c) The fuel ignites in the hot air: the burning gases, expanding, force the piston down on the power stroke. (d) Near the bottom of the power stroke, the exhaust valve opens, and on the exhaust stroke the burnt gases are evacuated.

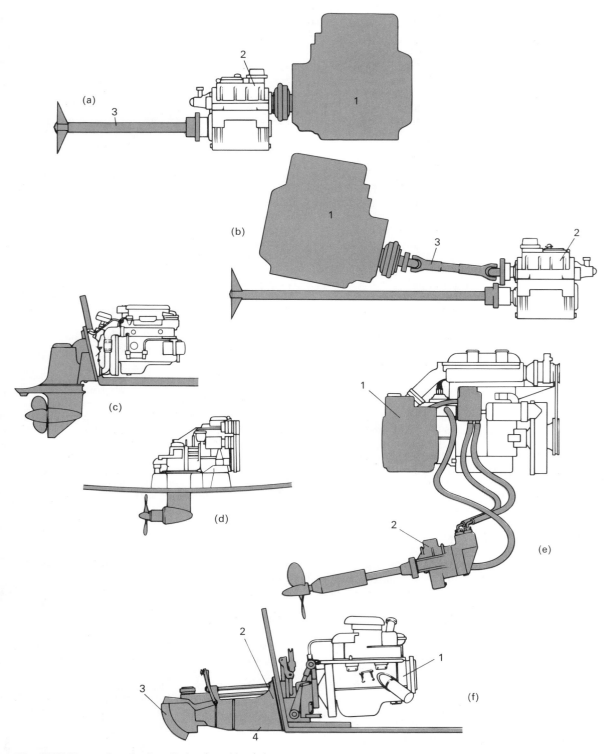

Fig. 13(2) Types of engine installation found in yachts.
(a) Conventional gearbox and shaft layout. 1 — engine, 2 — gearbox, with drop centre transmission, 3 — propeller shafting.
(b) V-drive installation. 1 — engine, 2 — separately mounted V-drive gearbox, 3 — articulated shaft connecting engine and gearbox.
(c) Outdrive power unit. Engine and transmission are installed as a single unit.
(d) Sail drive unit, with (non-steerable) folding propeller.
(e) Hydrostatic drive. 1 — hydraulic pump coupled to the engine, 2 — hydraulic motor connected to the pump by flexible pipes, and driving propeller shaft.
(f) Water jet propulsion. 1 — engine, 2 — pump, 3 — jet, 4 — water intake.

If it is used intelligently and properly maintained, the fire risk of a petrol engine should not be over-emphasised. The merits listed above make petrol engines very suitable for auxiliary propulsion, certainly for smaller yachts, while weight considerations make the choice essential for smaller high-speed motor boats. Larger craft are normally powered by diesel engines.

Most yachts have a conventional inboard engine installation, where the power unit is mounted in the bottom of the boat (usually about two-thirds of the way aft) and is connected to a gearbox which provides ahead/neutral/astern operation - Fig. 13(2) (a). To the output side of the gearbox is bolted the propeller shaft which passes through a watertight gland in the hull to drive the propeller. Such an installation has several advantages: the weight of the engine is low, and roughly amidships, and if it is situated under the cockpit or below the wheelhouse it does not occupy useful space within the hull; the engine is well protected from the elements, or from unwanted interference; and the propeller is well immersed below the waterline.

If, for considerations of weight distribution, it is necessary to mount the engine further aft, it can be turned through 180° and the drive taken forward to a V-drive gearbox where the direction is reversed to a conventional propeller shaft, as shown in Fig. 13(2) (b).

Instead of a normal gearbox, hydraulic drive may be fitted between the engine and the propeller, which allows the engine to be fitted anywhere within the hull. The engine drives a hydraulic pump, from which the power is transmitted through flexible pipes to a hydraulic motor connected to a shortened propeller shaft, as is shown in Fig. 13(2) (e). Apart from giving flexibility in the layout, hydraulic drive eliminates problems with alignment of engine and shafting, but there is some loss in efficiency.

Another version of inboard installation is provided by water jet propulsion, replacing the normal propeller and shafting. A pump, driven off the engine, takes in water through the bottom of the boat and forces it out astern. The resulting reaction drives the boat. Provision for steering and for astern power is made by deflectors, which aim the thrust of the jet in the required direction. Such installations are normally only found in specialist craft, designed, for example, for shoal waters, or for rescue work or water skiing, where the lack of a vulnerable or dangerous propeller is a distinct advantage, see Fig. 13(2) (f).

Outdrive engines (sometimes referred to as sterndrives) consist of a power unit mounted on the forward side of a boat's transom, through which a short horizontal shaft transmits the drive to an external lifting leg similar to that of an outboard, with bevel gears at top and bottom Fig. 13(2) (c). The gears incorporate ahead/neutral/astern operation, and whatever reduction ratio is required. In order to steer the boat the leg swivels

like an outboard, to direct the thrust of the propeller. Outdrives are commonly fitted in smaller transom-hulled boats, and have several attractions. The engine is mounted inside the boat, where it is protected and secure. Installation is simple, and there is no shaft alignment to consider. The drive leg can be raised out of the water if the boat has to take the ground, or for access to the propeller, and more powerful units are fitted with power tilt, so that the trim of the boat can be adjusted under way. There are, however, some disadvantages. Some power is lost with the two sets of gearing, each changing the direction of the drive through 90°. The propeller is not very deeply immersed, which can be dangerous with a following sea. Handling is more difficult at lower speeds, since when the propeller is not driving there is no directional effect.

Sailboat drives are a more recent innovation, rather similar in concept to an outdrive, but with the engine mounted in the bottom of the boat - Fig. 13(2) (d). Originally intended for smaller sailing yachts, they are also suitable for small motor cruisers. Like an outdrive, they are easy to install, and can be located where most convenient on the fore and aft line of the boat.

Outboard motors are familiar to many yachtsmen as the power units for tenders, whether solid or inflatable. But they are also extensively used for the propulsion of small cruisers, both power and sail. Outboards are self-contained units with a good power/weight ratio. easily portable (at least in the lower powers), and simple to install or to move from boat to boat. Being secured to the very stern of the boat, the engine does not occupy useful space, and the complete unit can be tilted in shallow water. Nearly all outboards are 2-strokes, which are heavy on fuel and also consume a special lubricant mixed with it.

13.1.4 Power and performance

In discussing the performance of an engine, or in comparing different makes or types, the word power is frequently used.

Power is the rate of doing work. The SI unit of power is the watt (W), which is 1 joule per second, but for practical use with engines power is expressed in kilowatts (kW).

The basic imperial unit of power is the foot-poundal per second (ft pdl/s). But in practical engineering the technical term horsepower (hp) is used, and equals 550ft lb/s, or 17 695ft pdl/s.

1 hp = 0.7457kW   1kW = 1.3410hp

The technical unit of metric horsepower is a cheval-vapeur (CV) in France, a Pferdestarke (PS) in Germany, and a hastkraft (HK) in Scandinavia, and it equals 75kgf m/s, or 7.355kW.

1hp (Imp) = 1.014hp (metric)

1hp PS, CV or HK = 0.986hp (imp)

The actual power developed is measured with the engine on a test bed, using a brake or dynamometer. In practice the torque produced is measured, and the brake horsepower is calculated from the formula:

$$bhp = \frac{Torque\ (lbf\ ft) \times rpm}{5252}$$

If all the various ancillary equipment such as alternator, water pump, gearbox and exhaust system are fitted to the engine, an indication is given of what power will be transmitted to the propeller in service, and this is termed the shaft horsepower (shp). But engine tests are usually conducted without all the above impedimenta, and the resulting figures for brake horsepower (bhp) as taken at the engine flywheel can be 15-20 per cent greater than shp.

The power an engine develops may be quoted, for example, as 'continuous' or 'intermittent'. The former is the power that the engine will develop hour after hour. The intermittent rating is a higher output that can be used for a short period, usually one hour in 12, without mechanical damage or overheating.

Technical information about an engine should include power curves - intermittent and continuous outputs plotted against rpm. The torque curve may also be plotted on the same graphs, and also a typical propeller law curve, showing the power the propeller absorbs at different rpm. Where the propeller law curve meets the power curve represents the conditions at which the engine will develop maximum

continuous power. At lower rpm the engine is only under partial load, the vertical distance between the power curve and the propeller curve showing the reserve of power available at that speed.

Factors that are of interest when comparing two engines of similar power include (apart from the price!) the power/weight ratios, piston speeds, and specific fuel consumptions. Engine weight can be important in a high performance boat, but one way of getting extra power from an engine is to run it faster, and piston speed is a useful measure of the likely life of an engine.

$$Piston\ speed\ (ft/min) = \frac{Stroke\ (ins) \times rpm}{6}$$

Long lasting marine diesels usually have piston speeds of about 1500ft/min. Faster running diesels (almost certainly with better power/weight ratios) have figures of 2000-2500ft/min. Petrol engines may have figures of 3000ft/min or higher.

Specific fuel consumption, the quantity of fuel used per horsepower per hour, is obviously a measure of an engine's economy - or otherwise. There are striking differences between types of engine, with medium-speed diesels returning figures that are nearly twice as good as some 2-stroke outboards. Sadly the internal combustion engine is not a remarkably efficient machine and only about one-third of the available energy in the fuel is transferred into useful thrust from the propeller of a boat.

13.1.5 Basic engine construction

All 4-stroke engines, whether petrol or diesel, have similar structural and internal parts. The internal details of 2-stroke engines differ somewhat - see 13.4.2.

The main structural items are the cylinder block and the cylinder head, shown in Fig. 13(4). The former contains the bores of the cylinders, usually arranged in line, together with passages for cooling water and oilways for the lubrication system. The block also normally incorporates the crankcase, housing the crankshaft which rotates in the main bearings, and to the cranks of which connecting rods deliver the thrust of the pistons.

The piston has to transmit the force of the burning and expanding gases in the cylinder to the connecting rod, form a good seal within the cylinder, take away the heat to which its crown is subjected, be strong enough to carry the bearing for the small (upper) end of the connecting rod, and be able to suffer continual reversals of movement - about 80 or 90 times a second. Pistons are therefore made of a light alloy which combines strength at high temperatures with a low coefficient expansion, to permit small clearances to be used. Typically two compression (or gas) rings are fitted, and below them an oil control (or scraper) ring which removes excess oil from the cylinder walls. Some pistons are oil-cooled, to prevent the piston rings sticking, or gumming up.

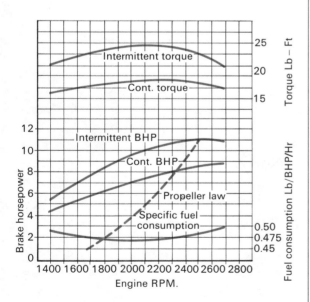

Fig. 13(3) Curves of torque, power and specific fuel consumption, plotted against engine rpm, for a small twin-cylinder diesel. Also shown (dotted) is a propeller law curve — for a propeller which is matched to the engine at 2500rpm, when it will absorb the full 11bhp that the engine can deliver. At lower (cruising) speeds (say 2000rpm, where the specific fuel consumption is least) the propeller can only absorb about half the power that the engine could theoretically deliver.

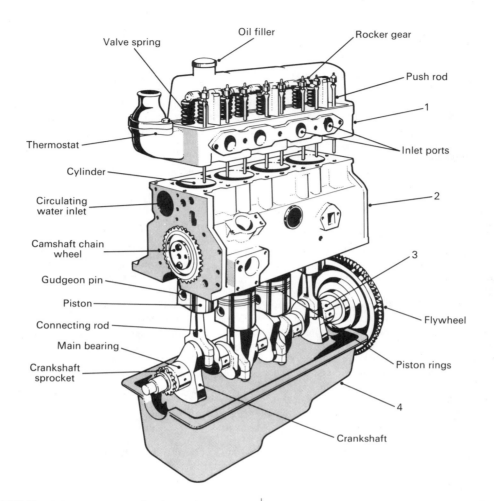

Fig. 13(4) The main components of an internal combustion engine. 1 — cylinder head, with inlet and exhaust valves and the rocker gear to operate them, inlet and exhaust ports, and combustion chambers.
2 — cylinder block, with bores for the pistons, cooling passages for water, and oilways for the lubrication system.
3 — crankshaft assembly, with pistons linked to the crankshaft by connecting rods, and engine flywheel.
4 — sump, enclosing the bottom of the engine, and forming a reservoir for lubricating oil.

The bottom of the connecting rod (usually a steel forging) is split, and is bolted round the crankpin of the crankshaft. This bearing is known as the crank head bearing or big end bearing, and it is lubricated through holes drilled in the crankshaft, pressure fed from the main bearings.

The function of a bearing is to reduce friction where one part rotates within another. Main and big end bearings have steel shells lined with a suitable bearing metal - an alloy such as copper-lead or tin-aluminium. White metal may be used for lightly loaded bearings. Apart from the correct design and precise manufacture of bearings (and the journals, or shafts, which rotate within them), it is essential that they are given adequate quantities of clean, cool oil. This enters the bearing under pressure at a point of low bearing

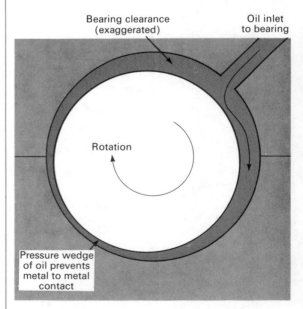

Fig. 13(5) As the journal (shaft) rotates inside the bearing, oil is carried round with it, and builds up into a wedge at the point of maximum loading, preventing metal to metal contact.

load - where there is maximum clearance between the journal and the bearing. As the journal (shaft) rotates inside the bearing it builds up a wedge of oil which is thinnest along the line of maximum bearing load, but which builds up sufficient internal pressure to prevent metal to metal contact. The oil also removes heat from the bearing.

Oil from the main bearings passes through holes drilled in the crankshaft to feed the big end bearings of the connecting rods, which may also be drilled to supply oil for the gudgeon pins (which hold the top end of the connecting rods in the pistons) and for piston cooling. Often however the gudgeon pins are lubricated, like the cylinder walls, by the oil escaping from the bearings of the rotating crankshaft, surplus oil being removed by the oil scraper rings on the pistons. Details of the general lubrication system of an engine are discussed in 13.2.6.

Above the cylinder block, and bolted to it with a joint called a gasket in between (to prevent the escape of cylinder gases or cooling water) is the cylinder head. This contains on the underside the combustion chambers of the cylinders, at the sides the inlet and exhaust ports which connect with the inlet and exhaust manifolds respectively, and on top the valve operating mechanism (rocker gear) for the inlet and exhaust valves of each cylinder. Through the cylinder head run cooling water passages, particularly round the combustion chambers and the exhaust ports where very high temperatures are reached.

The valves are held on their seats by valve springs, and are opened at the correct moment by rocker arms: these may be operated directly by a camshaft running along the top of the cylinder head (overhead camshaft engines), or via push rods from a camshaft along the side of the cylinders, as in Fig. 13(6). In either case there is a cam for each inlet valve and for each exhaust valve, and the camshaft is driven at half engine speed by chain, belt or gears. At the correct moment in the engine timing cycle, the cam for an individual valve depresses the valve stem, opening the valve against the pressure of the spring. Further movement of the cam releases the pressure

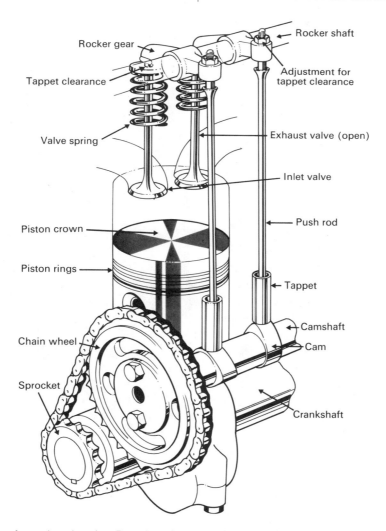

Fig. 13(6) Valve gear for push-rod engine. For a 4-stroke engine the camshaft rotates at half engine speed.

on the valve stem at the right moment, and the spring closes the valve. A gap is provided between the top of the valve stem and the rocker arm to allow of expansion, and this tappet clearance must be kept correctly adjusted according to the maintenance instructions for the particular engine.

13.1.6 Engine configurations

The simplest 4-stroke engine consists of a single cylinder, mounted vertically over a crankshaft with a single throw (crank), and there are a few low-powered boat engines of this type which are available for small boats. They are fitted with a relatively heavy flywheel to help improve the uneven torque which results from one power stroke for every two revolutions, but the out-of-balance revolving and reciprocating forces within the engine inevitably cause vibration. Even a second cylinder greatly improves the balance of the moving parts, and reduces vibration.

Although there are a few power units with three cylinders in line, most marine engines of between 30 and 80hp have four cylinders in line. Above 80hp, six cylinders in line is the most usual arrangement, and such engines can develop powers of 200hp or more, with the emphasis on turbo-charged diesels at the top end of the range.

A four-cylinder in-line engine, with two power strokes for each revolution, gives smoother running and better mechanical balance than one, two or three cylinders. A six-cylinder in-line engine is even better in these respects, and also allows more main bearings for better support of the crankshaft. Fig. 13(7) shows a cut-away drawing of a six-cylinder Perkins diesel engine.

There are however other possible layouts, and one which is found in boat engines is with the pistons horizontally opposed. This arrangement gives a shorter crankshaft for the same number of cylinders, and also better balance of the moving parts than with an in-line engine, since the movement of a piston in one direction is offset by the movement of its opposite number in the other direction.

Engines with the cylinders arranged in V formation are not common afloat, except in powerful V-6 and V-8 petrol engines, as are fitted to larger outdrive units. V-4 engines, although compact and with torque as even as a four-cylinder in-line, suffer from inherent vibration problems. V-6 engines (with a V of 60°) are slightly worse balanced than their in-line equivalents. V-8 engines (with a V of 90°) are very well balanced, and extremely smooth running.

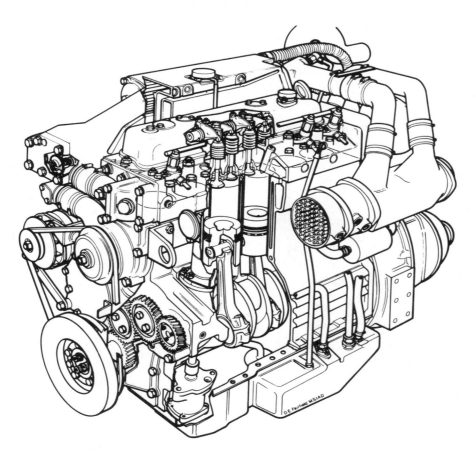

Fig. 13(7) Cut-away drawing of Perkins T6.3544 marine diesel engine.

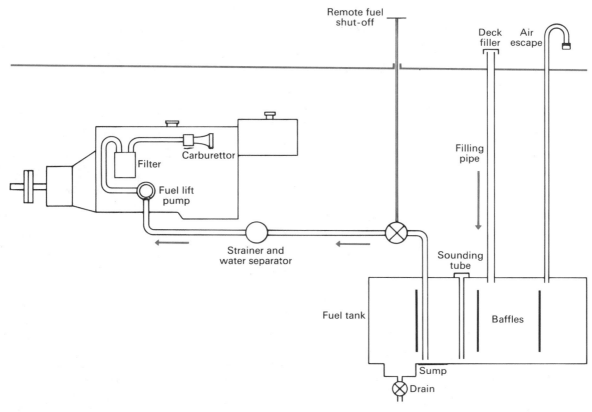

Fig. 13(8) Fuel system — petrol engine.

13.2 Marine engine systems

13.2.1 Fuel system (petrol engine)

To save space and to keep weight low, fuel tanks are usually sited in the bottom of the boat, and need to be firmly secured. Petrol tanks should be made of galvanised steel, lead-coated steel, brass, or copper (tinned on the inside).The filling position should be on deck, so that any overflow does not get inside the boat, Fig. 13(8). With a car the vapour from a petrol leak is easily dispersed, with a boat any leak in the fuel system can cause a dangerous concentration of petrol vapour in the bilges. Filling positions for fuel and fresh water must be clearly tallied, so that no confusion can result. If a flexible hose is used for the filling pipe, the deck connection and the tank must be electrically bonded, in order to avoid the possibility of any build up of static electricity causing an explosion.

The tank needs an air escape, leading to a position on deck which is sheltered and fitted with a gauze, or spark arrestor. Unless it is very small, the tank should have internal baffles. There must be a fuel gauge or dipstick. Ideally there should be a sump at the bottom of the tank, with a drain cock to remove any sediment or water, but with tanks in bilges this is obviously difficult to arrange. There must a shut-off cock where the fuel pipe leaves the tank, and this must be operable from a remote position - on deck or in the cockpit.

Fuel pipes should be made of seamless copper, copper-nickel or stainless steel tube with the minimum of joins, and properly clipped at regular intervals. The final length before the engine should be an approved type of flexible tubing. Somewhere, in a convenient place for examination and cleaning, there must be an efficient fuel filter. In most marine petrol engines the pump which draws petrol from the tank to the carburettor is driven off the engine, and often fitted with a hand priming lever.

A petrol engine relies on the carburettor to provide the correct mixture of air and petrol for efficient combustion, and in the right quantity for the power to be developed. All carburettors work on the principle that air which is being drawn into the cylinder by the induction (down) stroke of the piston passes through a venturi, or choke tube, where the speed of the airstream increases and its pressure drops. The low air pressure sucks petrol from the float chamber, where it is maintained at a certain level by a float controlled needle valve working on the same principle as a lavatory cistern. A throttle valve controls the quantity of air flowing through the venturi to the engine. At high speeds, with the throttle valve open, more air flows through the venturi, resulting in a greater drop in pressure and hence more petrol being sucked out of the float chamber. When the throttle valve is partly closed, to reduce engine speed, less air flows - so that there is not such a big pressure drop in the venturi, and hence less petrol is drawn into the airstream. A choke, or strangler, is fitted so that the air supply can be restricted to give a richer mixture for starting. There should also be an air filter, with a flame trap.

Because air and petrol have different flow characteristics, and because an engine needs different mixture strengths depending on operating conditions (e.g. starting, idling, cruising and full power), a carburettor needs to incorporate various refinements in the form of variable jets or multiple jets for maximum efficiency and economy to be obtained. Naturally, these jets need to be clean and properly adjusted.

Good design of the inlet manifold (between the carburettor and the inlet valves) is necessary to ensure vaporisation of the air/petrol mixture and its even distribution to the cylinders. High performance engines may be fitted with more than one carburettor, in which case correct tuning is needed to ensure that they deliver equal quantities of fuel at all throttle settings.

In any petrol engine it is important to use the specified grade of petrol, technically defined by the octane number but more commonly identified in Britain by the star rating. Two-star petrol corresponds to a minimum octane number of 90; three-star to 94; four-star to 97 and five-star to 100 octane. In a 4-stroke engine there is no objection to using a higher-grade (more expensive) petrol than is specified, but neither is there any advantage in doing so. Use of a lower grade than specified, or overheating of the engine, will cause uncontrolled burning of the fuel in the combustion chamber. This is called detonation, and is accompanied by a noticeable knocking sound; it will soon cause damage to pistons if allowed to continue. Note that some engines run on unleaded petrol.

Petrol tanks should be kept as full as possible to reduce the amount of moisture from the atmosphere condensing on internal surfaces and entering the fuel, but at the same time petrol does not improve if stored for long periods.

13.2.2 Ignition system (petrol engine)

The petrol engine is dependent on the spark from very high voltage at the spark-plug to ignite the air/fuel mixture in the combustion chamber of each cylinder in turn, at precisely the right moment. The spark may be provided by a magneto or a high-tension coil. The latter is more common, and gives a better spark at (low) starting speeds, but the former has the advantage that an engine can be started by hand even with a flat battery. In the conventional coil ignition system, as shown in Fig. 13(9), a primary coil is energised

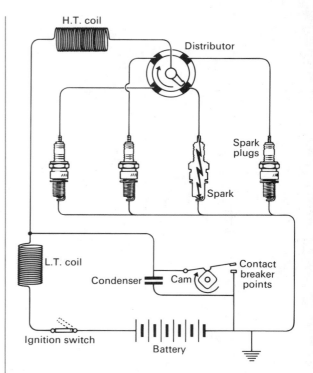

Fig. 13(9) Coil ignition system — petrol engine.

with current from the battery, and generates a magnetic field in the iron core. The secondary winding consists of very many more turns of wire, and is connected via the distributor to the spark-plugs. When the primary circuit is broken by the contact breaker, the magnetic field around the secondary coil collapses, and this generates a very high voltage in the secondary coil which creates the spark across the gap of the appropriate spark-plug. The ignition switch, in the primary circuit, supplies current from the battery to the primary coil when it is turned on; when it is turned off the supply ceases and the engine stops. The contact breaker and the distributor are combined into one unit, gear driven off the engine. The 'gap' of the contact breaker is opened by a number of cams, depending on the number of cylinders, and it is important that this gap (or maximum opening) is kept to the right dimension (usually about 0.4mm or 0.015in) to avoid alteration of ignition timing. To give a quick break in the primary circuit and to prevent sparking across the contact breaker, a condenser is fitted across the contacts. The distributor consists of a rotating arm, which engages in turn with segments which are connected to the plug leads for each of the cylinders.

On many engines the distributor incorporates an automatic timing device, which optimises the timing of the ignition depending on the engine speed. This may be a centrifugal advance, which depends on the speed of the engine, or a vacuum advance operated from the inlet manifold to the carburettor.

A magneto works on much the same principle as coil ignition, except that it generates its own primary current internally so that no battery is needed for ignition purposes. This is obviously an advantage for small petrol engines which can be started by hand, and so this system is particularly applied to outboards, where the magneto is housed in the flywheel on top of the engine.

An increasing number of petrol engines, particularly outboards, are now fitted with capacitor discharge (CD) ignition systems, which eliminate contact breakers, distributors and other moving parts and give greater reliability. Each spark-plug has a separate coil; rotating magnets in the flywheel generate a voltage stored in the capacitor; at the correct moment a sensor magnet in the flywheel triggers the discharge of this voltage to the appropriate coil, where it is stepped up to give a very high voltage at the spark-plug. The higher voltages achieved by CD ignition give better spark, and allows the use of surface-gap spark-plugs where the spark can jump radially from a central electrode in any direction; this reduces plug fouling and routine maintenance.

Spark-plugs are vital components of the ignition system, but can be maintained by any competent boat owner who knows how they function. A plug consists of a metal body, with a hexagon portion whereby it is screwed into the cylinder head, with a copper sealing ring between. Inside the body is a ceramic insulator, down the centre of which passes the central electrode, connected at the top to the plug lead from the distributor or magneto. Since the body of the plug is earthed in the cylinder head, a high voltage spark will pass across the gap between the bottom of the electrode and the plug body.

Different engines require different types of plugs, and it is most important to use the specified type. A boat should carry a complete spare set. Apart from physical dimensions which alter the reach of the plugs into the combustion chamber, the length of the insulator inside the plug can vary so that heat from the plug is dissipated into the cylinder head at a controlled rate - keeping it hot to burn off deposits which would prevent a spark, but cool enough to avoid pre-ignition (of the air/fuel mixture before the spark occurs).

The gap between the central electrode and plug body must be kept clean, and the right dimension - usually about 0.75mm (0.030in). When adjusting the gap never try to move the central electrode. For further notes on spark-plug maintenance see 13.5.13.

13.2.3 Fuel system (diesel engine)

So far as tanks and filling arrangements are concerned, diesel engines need similar arrangements to petrol engines (see 13.2.1) but, due to the chemical composition of diesel fuel, tanks must not be copper or galvanised steel. Plain steel or lead-coated steel are the preferred

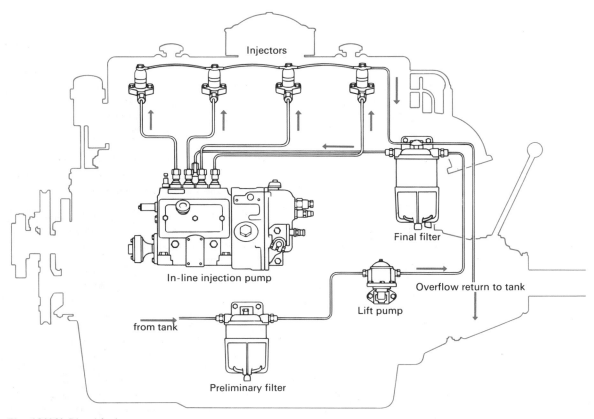

Fig. 13(10) Diesel fuel system.

materials, but glassfibre tanks built into the boat are satisfactory if proper provision is made for access for cleaning purposes: such tanks should not be adjacent to fresh water tanks.

A potential problem in diesel fuel tanks is the presence of microbiological organisms which can live and breed on the interface between the fuel and any water present at the bottom of the tank. If water can be eliminated - by regularly draining off and by only embarking 'clean' fuel - the situation should not occur. But in many boats there are no proper facilities for draining off tanks, and fuel from larger storage tanks ashore may well be suspect. If these organisms are allowed to develop, they can soon start blocking fuel filters. Biocides can be used to kill them, and prevent further growth, but this does not remove any sediment created.

Serious infestation can only be tackled by emptying the tank and steaming it out. Fuel lines must be blown through, filters changed, and the whole system treated with a suitable biocide for a day or two in order to kill off any lingering spores. The tank can then be dried out and refilled with clean fuel, suitably dosed with biocide to inhibit further growth. The tank should be kept as full as possible at all times in order to minimize condensation and possible airborne infection by organisms.

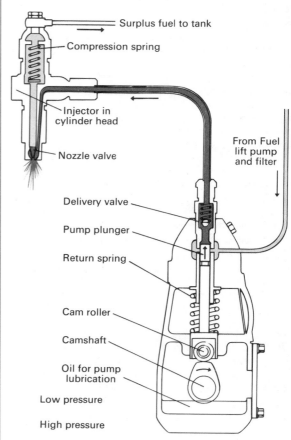

Fig. 13(12) A simplified diagram, showing a cross-section of a fuel injection pump, connected to one fuel injector. The pump plunger is cam operated, against a spring, by the camshaft which is driven off the engine. As the plunger rises, fuel is forced at very high pressure through the delivery valve to the injector, and thence to the combustion chamber. The delivery valve acts as a non-return valve while the pump plunger is descending, gives a rapid build-up of pressure in the pipe to the injector, and provides a quick cut-off of fuel injection at the end of the pump stroke.

Magnetic devices are available which are inserted into fuel lines and break the organisms down into single cells small enough to pass through fuel filters.

For diesel fuel mild steel piping is acceptable, apart from the materials already suggested for petrol engines. There is also the possibility of using nylon tubing (but only of an approved, flameproof specification) which facilitates tracing any air which may get into the system (see 13.5.6).

In other respects the fuel system of a diesel engine is totally different from that of a petrol engine, and deserves detailed explanation. A typical diesel fuel system is illustrated in Fig. 13(10). Fuel is sucked from the tank by a lift pump mounted on the engine, via a preliminary filter which should include means of separating any sediment or water in the fuel. The lift pump then passes the fuel through a very fine, final filter to the fuel injection pump, which delivers it at

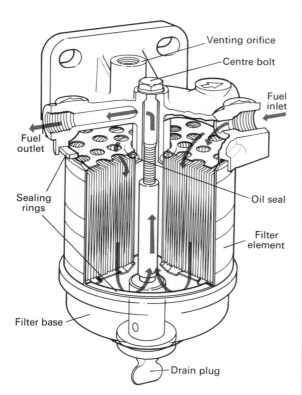

Fig. 13(11) A typical fuel filter of the CAV range, with three main parts — the filter head, the element and the base. Note the positions of the sealing rings, and of the drain plug at the bottom for drawing off water and sediment.

extremely high pressure to the injectors (or atomisers) mounted near the top of each cylinder. Fuel which is surplus to the requirements of the engine is returned to the tank through a separate pipe.

Both the injection pump and the injectors have very fine clearances inside, and these closely machined parts can soon be damaged by any dirt or water present in the fuel: hence the great importance of good filtration. The preliminary filter, as its name implies, is intended to remove the worst of any impurities, and in particular it should separate any sediment and water.

The lift (or feed) pump must include arrangements for hand operation, which is needed when venting (or bleeding) the system to remove any air - after routine maintenance work, for example (see 13.5.6).

The final filter is intended to remove the smallest particles of dirt, and any small water droplets which have become emulsified with the fuel in the lift pump. Such a filter, as shown in Fig. 13(11), has a renewable element, usually made of many layers of very fine filter paper. Although it should pass about 7000 litres (1500 gallons) of fuel before choking, it is a sensible precaution to change the filter in a boat engine at the start of every season. The procedure is explained in 13.5.5. If the filter bowl is fitted with a drain plug, this should be removed every month or so, to draw off any water or sediment that may have collected.

The fuel injection pump is the most important unit in a diesel fuel system: it has to deliver very small, accurately metered quantities of fuel, at extremely high pressure, to each cylinder in turn, and at exactly the correct moment. Fig. 13(12) is a simplified cross-section of an in-line fuel pump connected to one injector. Each cylinder has its individual pumping element, consisting of a plunger in a barrel. A camshaft driven off the engine operates the plungers of each pumping element, which are mounted in a line. The length of stroke of each plunger is constant, but the working part of the stroke, during which pressure is applied, can be varied by rotating the plunger so that a helical groove cut in it uncovers a spill port, and releases the pressure in the barrel - see Fig. 13(13). The rotation of the plungers, and hence the amount of fuel delivered to the injectors, is done by the throttle control and the engine governor, via a rack which is incorporated within the fuel pump.

Some engines are fitted with a distributor type of pump, which operates on a different principle. It has only one pumping element, from which fuel is fed through a distributor to each injector in turn.

Maintenance or repair of fuel injection pumps must not be attempted except by authorised service agents, who have the necessary equipment and data. But the yachtsman owner can play his part by keeping the pump clean and free from

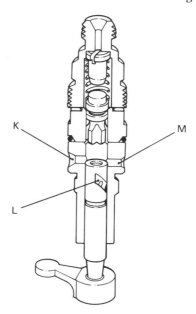

Fig. 13(13) Diesel fuel injection pump — details of one pumping element. K — inlet port; M — spill port; L — helical spill groove in plunger. The plunger is shown at the bottom of its stroke. When it rises, and covers the inlet port, pumping starts. Pumping continues until the upper edge of the spill groove uncovers the spill port, allowing high pressure oil above the plunger to pass down the central hole in the plunger and out through the spill port. The effective stroke of the plunger is determined by rotating the plunger in the barrel.

leaks. With in-line pumps the lubricating oil for the internal camshaft should be drained off and replenished at intervals of 100 running hours. Above all, make sure that the injection pump is always supplied with good, clean fuel - free of any water and impurities.

The fuel injectors (or atomisers) provide the fuel to each cylinder in a form most suitable for good combustion - in a very fine spray. Injector nozzles come in different types, specially designed for individual engines, and it is essential to use the right one. An injector is a spring-loaded valve, operated by the pressure of fuel from the injection pump. When the pressure rises suddenly to a peak, the nozzle opens, and when the fuel pressure suddenly drops it closes.

Injectors need professional servicing. The maintenance period varies, from as little as 100 running hours in some high-powered engines to nearly 1000 hours in lower rated engines. It is however within the capacity of the average owner to replace a defective injector with a spare one. Loss of power, overheating, black smoke from the exhaust, difficult starting, cylinder knock and increased fuel consumption are all possible signs of injector faults.

A defective injector can be identified by running the engine at a fast idling speed, and slacking back on the union of the pressure pipe to each injector in turn. Little or no change in engine revolutions indicates a faulty injector. Disconnect both ends of the pressure pipe (do not bend it), and remove the defective injector by slacking back the two securing nuts each side. Store the faulty injector carefully until it can be sent away for reconditioning.

It is important to fit the replacement injector properly in the cylinder head: it must be seated squarely, with the clamp or securing nuts tightened evenly, and with the correct washer or insert in place. Do not overtighten the fuel pipe unions.

13.2.4 Air supply

For every pound of fuel supplied to it an engine needs about 6.8kg (15lb) of air in order to achieve proper combustion. There should be an air filter to remove harmful impurities, and this will require servicing at the intervals given in the engine handbook. Some air is also required to help keep the space round the engine reasonably cool, and a forced draught fan may be used for this purpose. Petrol engined boats should have an exhaust fan, sucking from the bottom of the engine compartment; this fan should be run for five minutes before the engine is started, to remove any dangerous petrol vapour which might be present.

13.2.5 Cooling system

Any engine must have some form of cooling system to remove surplus heat, which represents about one-third of the total energy available from the fuel. The cooling system of a marine engine is quite different from that of an automotive unit of similar power. Instead of an air-cooled radiator, boat engines mostly use the water in which the boat is floating as the cooling medium, although a small number of low-powered boat engines are air cooled.

A typical, simple cooling system is shown in Fig. 13(14). Raw (e.g. sea or river) water is sucked in through a seacock and a strainer by a pump, driven off the engine. The water passes through an oil cooler (for the engine lubricating oil) and then round the cylinder block and exhaust manifold before it is discharged overboard. Engine temperature is controlled by a thermostat, as in a car.

Direct (raw water) cooling does however have some disadvantages. First, corrosive seawater is circulating round inside the engine. Second, unless the engine is run at an unduly low temperature (which is inefficient), salt deposits can and will build up on internal surfaces. So a better arrangement is for the engine to be cooled by fresh water, pumped round it in a closed circuit, and the fresh water then to be cooled by sea (raw) water. An illustration of a fresh water (or indirect) cooled engine is shown in Fig. 13(15). It should be noted that raw water is used for the gearbox oil cooler and engine oil cooler before it is pumped through the heat exchanger, and then overboard via the exhaust pipe.

A variation of fresh water cooling is keel cooling. Here the engine coolant (fresh water) is passed through external pipes which run along the bottom of the boat and are thus cooled by the surrounding water.

Maintenance of the cooling system involves making sure that inlet strainers are kept clean, that there are no leaks in the system (hoses and hose clips being kept in good order), and that in fresh water (indirect) cooled engines the fresh water header tank is kept topped up, just like a car's radiator. Pump impellers are liable to wear if operated in sandy or muddy water, or if run dry. A spare should always be carried. Thermostats can also give trouble: in emergency the thermostat can be removed, if a spare is not available. Whenever the engine is started, check that cooling water is flowing correctly, and while the engine is running keep a watch on the temperature gauge.

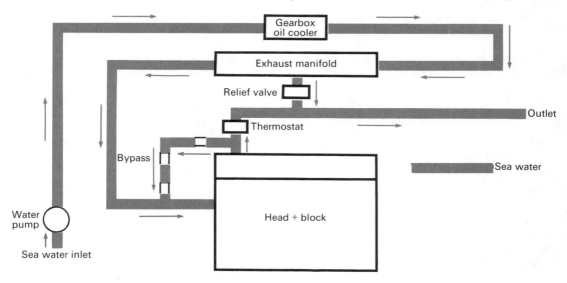

Fig. 13(14) Direct cooling system — Perkins 4.108(M) Lowline diesel.

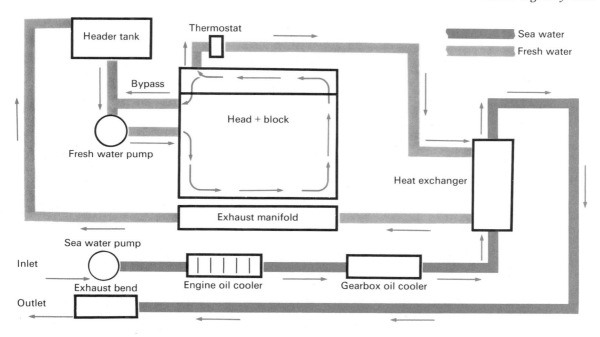

Fig. 13(15) Indirect cooling system — Perkins 4.108(M) Lowline diesel.

13.2.6 Lubricating system

Mention of bearings and their lubrication has been made in 13.1.5. The lubricating systems of all 4-stroke engines, whether petrol or diesel, are basically similar. Most 2-stroke petrol engines have a different method of lubrication, described in 13.3.4.

Fig. 13(16) shows a typical system for a 4-stroke engine. The sump forms a reservoir for the oil, which is pumped through a cooler and a filter to the various working parts. A relief valve controls the pressure, indicated by a gauge or warning light. The oil drains to the sump under gravity.

Modern oil filters have a renewable element made of impregnated paper which should be changed every season, and whenever the oil is changed. Filters can be either full flow, where all the oil passes through the filter as it circulates, or of the by-pass type where only a proportion of the oil goes through the filter each time.

From the filter the oil passes to the main oil gallery, running the length of the engine and feeding the main crankshaft bearings, and thence to other moving parts, as already described in 13.1.5.

In some marine units the gearbox is lubricated from the engine system, but a modern hydraulic gearbox has its own lubricating system complete with oil cooler.

Looking after engine lubrication presents few problems if some simple rules are followed. Always check the level of oil in the sump (and in the gearbox, where applicable) before starting the engine: with some engines and gearboxes a specific method of checking oil level may be given in the handbook. Only top up the system with clean oil of the recommended grade (see below). Cleanliness

is essential, and oil must never be stored in opened cans which can easily become contaminated with dirt or moisture. While the engine is running keep a careful watch on the oil pressure, and investigate any low reading which could be due to a blocked filter, overheating, insufficient oil in the sump, the wrong grade of oil, or (more ominously) worn bearings. Change the oil and renew filter elements as recommended in the engine handbook.

The correct type and grade of oil must be used, since modern oils are complex substances which include various oil-soluble chemicals to improve their performance and to increase their life. Viscosity is an indication of how an oil flows: a thin oil has a low (numerical) viscosity, and thick oil has a high viscosity. Viscosity is measured by the time a certain quantity of oil flows through a standard orifice at the specified temperature (because viscosity drops with increase of temperature). The viscosity of oil affects the oil film thickness, and the load which a bearing can carry; its correct choice is a compromise to give good starting from cold, rapid oil film formation on starting, satisfactory load carrying at high temperatures, and low oil consumption. Additives reduce the amount the viscosity drops with rise of temperature and also lower the temperature at which the oil remains fluid.

The Society of Automotive Engineers (SAE) system is used for classifying lubricating oils for engines and gearboxes, the lower the SAE number the thinner the oil. SAE 5W, SAE 10W, SAE 15W and SAE 20W are oils with viscosities falling within certain limits at $-18°$ ($0°F$), the W signifying that they are suitable for winter use. Viscosity ranges of SAE 20, 30, 40 or 50 however indicate that the oil falls within certain limits at

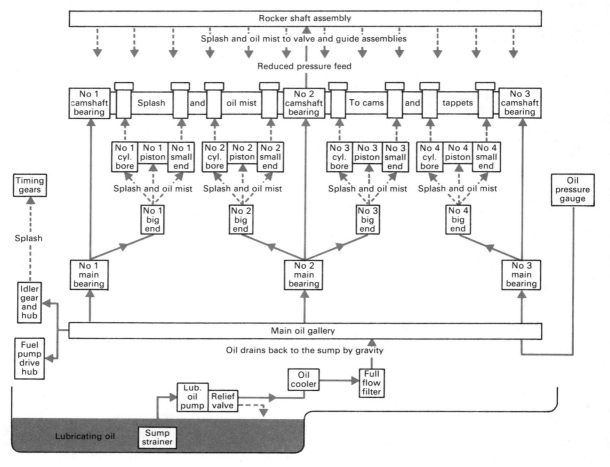

Fig. 13(16) Lubrication system diagram — Perkins four-cylinder diesel engine.

99°C (210°F) which is a typical engine operating temperature. Multigrade oils are designated (for example) as SAE 20W-50, indicating that the oil has the viscosity of a 20W oil at −18°C (0°F), and of a SAE 50 oil at 99°C (210°F). Multigrade oils give easier starting in cold conditions but retain their lubricating properties at high temperatures.

Other additives are put into oils to improve detergency, oxidation resistance and dispersancy. Detergent qualities are needed to keep internal surfaces clean - particularly pistons and rings. Oxidation inhibitors reduce the chemical reaction between oil and air at high temperatures in the crankcase, and the tendency to form lacquer and gummy substances. Dispersant additives keep combustion products of the fuel and lubricant in suspension in the oil, so that they do not form harmful sludge which might otherwise block filters or oilways; instead such products are held in the oil, and drained away from the engine when the oil is changed. Darkening of the oil in service shows that it is doing its job. But the additives in an oil gradually get used up, and cannot continue to fulfil their important functions. Diesel engines are particularly dependent on lubricating oils which have the necessary additives included, and

this applies especially to turbocharged engines which operate at higher temperatures.

A great deal can be learned about the mechanical condition of an engine from regular chemical analysis of samples of the lubricating oil.

13.2.7 Exhaust system

Any internal combustion engine needs an efficient exhaust system to remove the hot, waste gases as freely as possible while at the same time keeping exhaust noise to the minimum. Carbon monoxide in exhaust gases is very poisonous, so that very great care is necessary where exhaust systems pass through living spaces or cabins.

Most boat engines have wet (water injected) exhausts, which do not need bulky or expensive jacketing. The (raw) cooling water from the engine is injected into the silencer, where it quietens and cools the exhaust gases. It is important that the layout ensures that water cannot get back into the engine through the exhaust system; where the engine is fitted on or below the waterline a swan neck should be fitted high enough for all possible sea conditions, angles of heel, or boat loading. In some installations which do not provide much of a gradient or fall in the exhaust pipe, it is sensible to fit a shut-off valve which can be closed when the engine is not in use.

Exhaust pipes may be iron or galvanised steel: copper or brass are acceptable for petrol engines, but not diesels. Suitable synthetic hose can be used for the wet part of the system, from the point where water is injected. A flexible length of pipe is needed between the engine and the silencer if the engine is flexibly mounted.

13.2.8 Gearbox

All but the very simplest type of boat engine needs a gearbox, or some equivalent means of controlling its operation, whereby ahead/neutral/astern can be selected. Usually the gearbox also incorporates reduction gearing, so that the propeller revolves at about half engine speed which gives more efficient propulsion. Some small sailing cruisers fitted with auxiliary engines have a sailing clutch, which automatically engages by centrifugal force when the engine speed is raised above idling. An alternative to the conventional marine gearbox is a controllable pitch propeller, which provides ahead/neutral/astern power by altering the angle of the propeller blades, with the engine rotating steadily in one direction.

There are two main types of marine gearbox - layshaft and epicyclic. Layshaft gearboxes have two sets of clutch plates, one being engaged for ahead and the other for astern. In neutral both are disengaged. The principle of operation is shown in Fig. 13(17). The clutches may be engaged mechanically in small gearboxes, but with larger units this is done hydraulically, the oil pressure also being used to lubricate the bearings and the gear teeth.

With epicyclic gearing, astern operation is obtained by a brake band which locks the gear assembly, making the intermediate (planetary) gears rotate in the opposite direction and drive the output shaft astern. Most such gearboxes are hydraulically operated.

It is most important that the correct lubricant is used in a gearbox, and this is usually different from the engine oil. Hydraulic gearboxes often use automatic transmission fluid. Oil level should normally be checked at the same time as the engine oil level - before the engine is started. But with some gearboxes the correct level is taken after the engine has been stopped. Certain marine gearboxes cannot be trailed in neutral for any length of time without risk of damage from lack of lubrication. If applicable, this should be stated in the engine handbook. Hydraulic gearboxes have an oil cooler, which must be supplied with cooling water from the engine cooling system, and may be fitted with temperature and pressure gauges. In some cases the gearbox can be locked in 'ahead' operation, to permit the boat to get back to harbour in the event of any hydraulic failure.

Never shift the gearbox control from ahead to astern, or vice versa, with the engine turning at more than a fast idling speed, or damage may result.

13.2.9 Propeller shafting

The drive from the gearbox to the propeller is transmitted by the propeller shaft, which is supported by bearings in the stern tube of the boat - and in the case of many motor boats also by a 'P' bracket at the outboard end, immediately forward of the propeller - see Fig. 13(18).

Preferred materials for shafting are monel metal, stainless steel or manganese bronze. There must be proper provision to take the axial thrust of the propeller: this is normally arranged at the output shaft in the gearbox. One or two flexible couplings

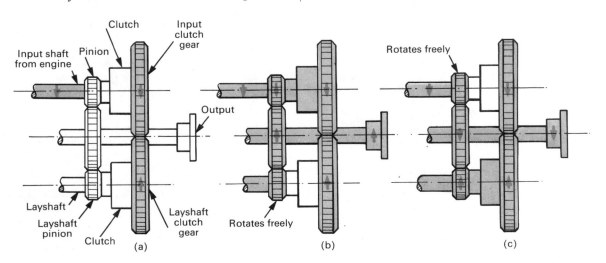

Fig. 13(17) How a layshaft gearbox works. The arrows up and down the page indicate the directions of rotation of the revolving parts, viewed from above. (a) Neutral — both clutches disengaged. Power from the input shaft only revolves the input clutch gear — nothing else revolves. (b) Ahead — input clutch gear engaged, so that power returns through that clutch and its pinion to drive the output shaft. (c) Astern — layshaft clutch gear engaged, so that power passes through the layshaft, to rotate the output shaft astern.

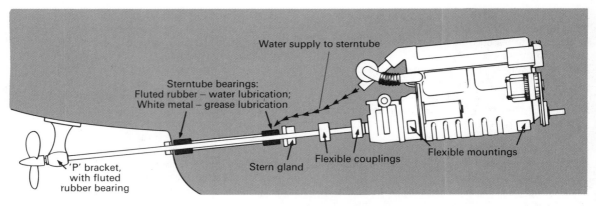

Fig. 13(18) Sterngear arrangement, with rigid stern gland and bearing at each end of sterntube. If there is sufficient length of shaft between the gearbox and the sterntube, a single flexible coupling may be fitted.

may be fitted between the gearbox and the shaft. Correct alignment between engine and shaft is essential. When connecting a coupling, the clearance between the two faces should be checked with a feeler gauge at 90° intervals, rotating each shaft in turn.

The arrangement of shaft bearings varies in different installations. The bearings themselves may be white metal or cutless rubber: the former are grease lubricated – normally from a remote greaser which should be replenished as required and given a turn before using the engine, and about every four hours while the engine is running. Cutless (fluted rubber) bearings rely on water lubrication, and if fitted at the forward end of the stern tube such a bearing will be supplied from the engine cooling water system.

The stern gland, at the forward end of the stern tube, prevents water getting into the boat, and may need tightening occasionally to prevent undue leakage. This should be done very carefully: a small drip of water is perfectly acceptable, and helps keep the gland cool.

13.2.10 Propeller

However efficient or powerful an engine may be, it is the thrust from the propeller which drives the boat through the water. It is most important that the correct propeller is fitted to match the characteristics of the hull concerned, and the power/rpm available from the engine and its gearbox.

The main factors which determine the shape of a propeller are its diameter, pitch, blade area, number of blades, and direction of rotation; other details such as the precise shape and sections of the blades need not concern us here. Diameter, blade area and number of blades are self-explanatory. Pitch is the theoretical distance that the propeller would move ahead through the water in one complete revolution, if there was no slip - as, for example, when a screw is driven into wood - see Fig. 13(19). Direction of rotation is defined as right-hand for a propeller which, when driving ahead, turns clockwise when viewed from astern.

The function of the propeller is to convert the torque in the propeller shaft into thrust which will drive the boat. This is achieved by changing the momentum of the water which passes through the propeller, which is done more efficiently when the quantity of water is large and the change of velocity is relatively small. This implies that, for maximum efficiency, a propeller should be as large as possible – which obviously presents problems in trying to fit it into the available space under the stern of a boat.

So propeller design is a compromise. Diameter obviously governs the total blade area that can be achieved, and is related to the shaft horsepower and shaft rpm. The choice of pitch is governed by the designed (required) speed of the boat, shaft rpm and slip – the difference between the actual speed of the propeller through the water and what would be calculated from propeller pitch multiplied by rpm. Different types of propeller are illustrated in Fig. 13(20).

A fairly recent development has been the Brunton-Weil Autoprop. This has hinged blades so that under sail they adopt the least line of resistance to reduce drag. Under power the pitch alters according to rpm and boat speed, claimed to give more efficient performance, while going astern the blades automatically swing through 180° to give better stopping power.

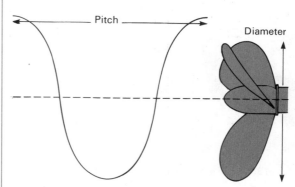

Fig. 13(19) Propeller pitch is the distance the propeller would move ahead in one revolution, if it did not slip in the water.

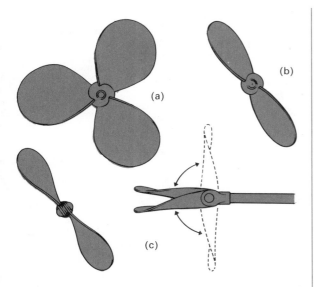

Fig. 13(20) Types of propeller. (a) High-speed. (b) Two-bladed propeller for auxiliary powered yacht. (c) Folding propeller.

The correct choice of gearbox reduction ratio is important. As a rough rule, preliminary calculations of reduction ratio can be based on a propeller speed of 100rpm for each knot of boat speed. Diameter and pitch are chosen so that at full throttle the engine runs at its maximum rpm and is developing its maximum power. If the diameter of the propeller is too big, or if the propeller has too much pitch, the engine will not reach its proper rpm. If the diameter of the propeller is too small, or if the propeller has too little pitch, the engine will tend to overspeed without producing the required power. In practice there is a certain amount of trial and error in selecting the correct design of propeller for a new boat.

Propellers are accurately machined and balanced. Any damage, such as may occur to the tip of the blade, will not only detract from performance but cause unbalance and consequent vibration and wear of bearings. Propellers are also liable to corrosion from galvanic action unless the proper precautions are taken (see 10.5.7), and also to erosion which can be aggravated by cavitation. Cavitation is not normally a problem in low-powered craft, but is common in more powerful motor boats. It occurs when the water flow breaks down, and cavities are formed on the forward sides of the blades where there are low pressure areas; when these cavities collapse the water impinges suddenly on the blade surface, causing pitting.

A Stripper propeller protector can avoid the trouble of a rope fouling the screw, and prevent damage to propeller brackets, shaft or gearbox. The original 'Spurs' cutter for propeller protection is marketed by Harold Hayles Limited, Yarmouth, Isle of Wight PO41 0RS. Tel: 01983 760373. Fax: 01983 760666. The stainless steel cutters function

in ahead and astern, and will fit shafts from $\frac{3}{4}$in to 7in diameter, plus metric sizes.

Where it is desired to lock the shaft when under sail, it is preferable to fit a shaft brake rather than engage the engine in gear. There should however be some form of inter-lock to prevent the engine being started with the brake applied.

13.2.11 Controls and instruments
The controls for engine throttle and for the gearbox must be positioned where they can be easily reached from the steering position; for simplicity their movements should be in the correct sense - that is the gearbox lever should be pushed forward for ahead, and the opposite way for astern. Similarly it is helpful if the throttle is pushed forward to increase the rpm. If 'single-lever' control is fitted (operating both throttle and gearbox) it is important that both are correctly adjusted, so that the moment of engaging ahead or astern can be felt, and so that it is quite evident when neutral has been selected. Most engine controls are of the cable type, and need very little maintenance other than an occasional smear of grease over the end connections.

The minimum instrumentation for any boat engine should consist at least of oil pressure gauge, thermometer for circulating water, tachometer for rpm, ammeter, and a contents gauge for the fuel tank. More complex installations need a greater variety of instruments - for boost pressure and gearbox oil pressure, for example. Some form of instrument lighting is needed for use at night.

13.3 Electrics

13.3.1 Electrical systems - general
Most boat engines rely on electric starting (see 13.3.5), although a few small units can be started by hand. With the proliferation of navigational aids, radiotelephones, autopilots, electric winches, water pumps, refrigerators and the like that are now available, electrical systems have become increasingly complex, and the total requirement for electric current more and more demanding. Since, as will be seen below, it is strongly recommended that a dedicated battery be reserved for engine starting, the rest of the electrical system can to a large extent be considered as a separate and important service, but one where the balance between power consumed and the available battery capacity plus charging ability is often unsatisfactory.

In many boats it is necessary to run the engine for lengthy periods each day to keep batteries charged. To add to this, unsuitable automotive-type batteries have a limited life when required to deliver a steady current repeatedly over long periods, while outmoded regulators fail to charge batteries to their full capacity.

First it is essential to carry out an audit of the likely electrical consumption, say over a period of 24 hours, balanced against a battery capacity and the frequency at which it is necessary to run the engine (or other generating device) for recharging. This requires a list of all the electrical equipment on board (e.g. lighting, autopilot, radio etc.) with the likely usage of each per 24 hours, and the current which each consumes. This last information should be available from manufacturers' handbooks if not marked on the item. Engine starting can be omitted, on the assumption that this will be covered by a separate battery, as can for example an electric anchor windlass which takes a heavy current and should only be used when the engine is charging.

Items such as refrigerators and navigation lights are very demanding in power, as indeed are electrically powered autopilots if used instead of the wind vane variety. Motor cruisers should have no difficulty in generating the required current when they are under way, but once in harbour they have the same problems as sailing craft. So for both power and sailing craft it is advisable to do the exercise both for sea and harbour, because different conditions will prevail. When one has calculated the total number of ampere hours required, one can assess the battery capacity needed and how often it will be necessary to recharge.

Luckily the modern alternator can generate a high current even when driven at moderate rpm, as discussed in 13.3.3. But other sources of power are available which may avoid the need to run the engine at sea, or in some cases in harbour. They are wind generators, (towed) water-driven generators, shaft-driven generators and solar cells as discussed in 13.3.4. Larger yachts can be expected to have auxiliary generator sets, diesel driven which can be run independently of the main machinery.

In harbour increasing use is made of shore power to keep batteries topped up while the boat is lying idle, or to run essential services when lying idle alongside. For continuous operation it is important to use a proper marine charger, such as a Constavolt or Lucas Marinapower, which will convert AC shore power to DC for battery charging, while at the same time float any DC load on board. Such charges will automatically shut down when batteries reach gassing level, at about 80 per cent of full charge. The shore power lead must be heavy enough to take the anticipated load, and be fitted with waterproof plugs each end. 220 volt AC can be lethal in a marine environment and such circuits must be professionally installed and well protected.

In a boat which otherwise has no source of alternating current an inverter can be used to provide 220/240V AC for equipment such as microwave oven, computer, power tools and general domestic items from a 12V or 24V battery supply. The consequent battery drain has of course to be made good by whatever generating capacity is available. Inverters are quiet, need no maintenance, and have a long service life. They should incorporate protection devices against overload, high temperature, short-circuits and abnormal input voltages. Units are available which combine the functions of an inverter and battery charger.

13.3.2. Batteries

Lead/acid batteries are most commonly fitted in boats, and systems in small yachts are usually 12 volt – although there are advantages in using 24 volts, as commonly fitted in larger craft. The capacity of a battery is measured in ampere-hours, and it is important that a battery with adequate capacity is fitted to allow for reduced performance with age, plus the probable addition of new electrical equipment to the boat. The charge to discharge ratio of most batteries is about 1.4, which means that for every 100 ampere-hours of discharge, 140 ampere-hours of charging are needed to restore full capacity.

The capacity of a battery is normally expressed in terms of a 10-hour rating, when for example a 150 ampere-hour battery will give 15 amperes for 10 hours. At higher rates of discharge the capacity is reduced quite considerably.

Lead/acid batteries are in two main categories. The more common automotive type is constructed internally to give a high current over a short period for engine starting, and then to be promptly recharged once the engine is running. This type does not respond well to repeated cycles of deep discharge over several hours, followed by recharging, for which a traction battery (as might be fitted in a milk float for example) is more suitable due to its heavier internal construction with fewer but thicker plates. In recent years there has been the growing use of batteries with a gelled electrolyte because they need no maintenance, can be recharged at a higher rate, and can be left standing for longer. But they cost more and may not last so long.

A battery should normally be charged at the 10-hour rate, but a higher rate of charge may be used if the battery is in good condition, provided that its temperature is kept below 43°C (110°F). The charging rate is automatically controlled in a properly fitted marine installation, allowing a higher rate of initial charge, then falling off as the battery voltage rises. It is possible to damage a battery if it is left connected to an ordinary car battery charger for too long.

Lead/acid batteries must be charged regularly to keep them in good condition and available for use, particularly in warm weather, and must not be left standing idle for more than a month or two. The state of charge of a lead/acid battery is determined from the specific gravity of the electrolyte, as measured by a hydrometer. Typical readings at 16°C (60°F) are: 1,280 – fully charged; 1,200 – half discharged; 1.115 – fully discharged.

The level of the electrolyte should be checked weekly, and distilled water added as necessary to keep the tops of the plates just covered. Some modern batteries are sealed and do not need this attention. With most of these the electrolyte is liquid. They need accurate recharging, and a heavy discharge can mean a long recharging time. In more recent maintenance-free batteries the electrolyte is stored in a gel (jelly). These are more expensive but can tolerate a deeper discharge. If they are overcharged they can boil dry, so some form of temperature sensor should be fitted.

Alkaline (nickel-cadmium) batteries are more expensive but have the advantage of retaining their charge for long periods, and therefore do not require special attention during winter lay-ups. They come in two basic types: one is high-performance, for heavy discharge currents and hence particularly suited for engine starting; the other is more for general service purposes. Discharge capacities of the former (high-performance) batteries are quoted at a 2-hour rate, while those of the latter (normal resistance cells, for general use) are given at a 5-hour rate. The specific gravity of the electrolyte in an alkaline battery does not vary with the state of charge, and is usually 1.200 at 20°C (68°F). This figure falls as the electrolyte deteriorates, indicating that it should be renewed.

Whatever type of battery is fitted, it must be securely mounted in a tray which will collect any possible spillage. The compartment must be well ventilated, to remove explosive gases generated during charging and discharging, and the battery must be readily accessible for maintenance. There must be a main isolating switch which will disconnect both poles of the battery when it is not in use. This switch must never be opened when the alternator is running, or damage will be caused to the rectifying diodes (see 13.3.3).

When two batteries are fitted, blocking diodes are used to allow both to be charged from one alternator, and to prevent mutual discharge between them.

13.3.3. Generating equipment

Alternators are fitted to the engines of most modern boats. The alternating current (AC) generated is converted into direct current (DC) for battery charging by silicon diodes which function like non-return valves – allowing a free flow of current in one direction but giving a high resistance in the other. A regulator is fitted to control voltage, and also to control current if the alternator is not self-limiting in this respect. Great care is needed in handling and testing these items, since they contain semi-conductors which can be damaged either by excess voltages or by reverse polarity. Do not open the battery switch while the alternator is running, since this may damage the rectifying diodes and the regulator.

On smaller or older engines, dynamos or dynastarts (combined dynamos and starters) may be found. Whatever type of generating equipment is used, it must have sufficient capacity to recharge the battery and to sustain the total electrical load, during its expected running time. Here an alternator is an advantage, because it can generate a high current even when driven at modest speed. The correct pulley ratio must however be selected for a particular application, care being taken that the alternator does not exceed its designed speed at full engine rpm.

Apart from ensuring that the drive belt is kept at the right tension, a modern alternator needs little maintenance. When depressed by moderate finger pressure in the middle of its longest run, the belt should only give about 12mm ($\frac{1}{2}$in). It is advisable to carry a spare belt.

The conventional automotive-style voltage controlled regulator is satisfactory for a battery which is used primarily for engine starting and is then promptly recharged. But for a battery subject to deep discharge over several hours – supplying lights, refrigerator, water pump, radio and so on – this conventional regulator fails to return the battery to full capacity when charging eventually takes place.

The charging process requires the alternator to overcome the battery's own internal resistance, which rises with the battery voltage so that the charging current is reduced to a minimum well before a full discharge is given. This is due to the irregular distribution of electrically charged ions within the electrolyte. Those near the battery plates are affected more readily, both when charging and discharging, than those in the body of the electrolyte. With a sudden discharge, as when starting the engine, only the ions in the electrolyte nearer the plates are affected in the short term, and these are soon restored when recharging commences. But with a slow discharge the whole of the electrolyte becomes affected, and when recharging occurs the acid nearer the plates is more quickly restored, giving the regulator the false impression that the battery is recharged. The conventional fixed-voltage regulator is unable to resolve this problem, which leads to undercharging and sulphation of the battery plates.

To over this problem, 'smart' regulators are now available which continually monitor battery voltage and temperature to evolve a sophisticated programme controlling the charging voltage. One such device is the TMC regulator marked by Aqua Marine Mfg (UK) Ltd, 215 Fair Oak Road, Bishopstoke, Eastleigh SO5 6NJ. This produces a succession of alternate periods at high and low voltages, the latter being best described as rest periods to allow the battery counter-voltage to level off. This high/low charging sequence takes a couple of hours, after which there is a longer rest period to prevent gassing and overcharging. The cycle is then repeated as necessary. A timer takes care of such eventualities as the engine being stopped or being slowed down so that the alternator voltage falls below a certain level. Indicator lights show when the boat is drawing more current than the alternator can supply, or if a fault develops. The regulator will function with one, two, three or four battery banks, and with one or two alternators. It is not suitable for outboard motors or for dynamos.

Although a smart regulator will much improve battery performance, it should be noted that it will place extra demand on the alternator and associated wiring.

13.3.4 Alternative power sources

For the serious cruising boat it makes sense to use whatever satisfactory options present themselves for generating 'free' electricity and to back up an engine driven generator. These are wind generators, towed water generators, shaft generators and solar cells. Each has its advantages and limitations. Portable generators also have some applications and these will be considered first.

Portable generators
Portable is a relative term since even the smallest, single-cylinder four-stroke petrol generator has a dry weight of 20kg (44lb) or more. These typically have outputs of about 500 watts at 240V DC, or a DC output of about 8 amps at 12V. They have two main uses. In a small yacht a portable generator can recharge the main battery, should this be discharged so that it is impossible to start the main engine. Or it can be useful to feed power tools, TV, video, personal computer, or various other domestic items requiring 240V AC in boats which otherwise do not have alternating current when not hooked into a marina supply.

The disadvantages are noise, the stowage space required, and the necessity to carry petrol on board – although some can be adapted to run on liquefied petroleum gas. Larger and more powerful diesel-driven generators are available, but these are not really portable in the strict sense of the word and are better described as free-standing.

All these units need to be run on deck, for safety reasons not only in connection with the fuel but the exhaust. They are not marinised, and great care is needed when operating with 240V AC even in a slightly damp environment. It should therefore be evident that in general they are only suitable for harbour use.

Towed water generator
A water generator is applicable to a sailing yacht or a motor sailer. It can supply a useful charging current of about 5 amps with sufficient boat speed, and is well suited to trade wind sailing, for example, when it can provide all reasonable electrical demands in a small yacht. However, a towed generator is vulnerable to weed, debris and large fish and is not a good companion for a towed log.

Shaft generator
A shaft generator comprises an alternator, belt-driven off the propeller shaft, and can typically deliver 10 amps when the shaft is under power, but rather less when trailing under sail. With a cutting-in speed of (say) 600 rpm the boat needs to be sailing at four or five knots for a worthwhile charge to be delivered.

Wind generator
Wind generators are available in a range of sizes (capacities) from small units which produce less than 1 amp of current at best to larger and more powerful ones developing up to 5 amps of current in strong winds. In general, a relative wind speed of at least 12-15 knots (force 4) is required to produce any worthwhile current. Most wind generators have a voltage regulator incorporated or as an optional extra. Except for the small units which only give a modest trickle charge, wind generators should not be left running unattended.

The larger generators, such as the Ampair 100 have large propellers up to 0.9m (3ft) in diameter, which rotate at high speeds and are potentially lethal. They are also quite noisy. The best site is probably on a pole mounting above the stern of the boat, with the blades just above head height.

Dual purpose generators are available which can be wind-driven (in harbour) or towed (at sea).

Solar cells
Modern solar cells are cheaper, more efficient and more durable than those which were originally available to yachtsmen. They have no moving parts and, like wind generators, they have the advantage that they can be used at sea and in harbour. A major problem, however, is where best to mount them, particularly in a sailing boat, and they obviously perform better in parts of the world where sunlight is more reliable. They need to be pointed to the sun, and best secured with clamp-on brackets that can be fixed to guardrails, shrouds or wherever they can be best positioned. This allows them to be removed when required – for seagoing or for security in harbour. Some solar cells are flexible, allowing them to be mounted on the curved surfaces of a boat such as the coachroof.

The efficiency of different cells varies, but a panel measuring 700mm x 400mm (28in x 16in) can give a peak output of 0.70 amperes at 15.6 volts. This might typically give a charge of 25 ampere hours in the course of a week. There should be a blocking diode to prevent discharge from the battery when the sun is not shining. In general, when the peak charge from the solar cell is less than 1.5 per cent of the battery capacity in ampere hours, a charging regulator is not necessary. Larger panels require a regulator to prevent possible overcharging of the battery.

13.3.5 Electrical circuits

The electrical installation of a boat must be carefully designed to avoid long cable runs, and to site components such as switchgear in convenient places. Stranded copper cable, with an insulation of approved marine specification, must be used, and all items such as switches, fuses and junction boxes must be non-corroding and waterproof. Special arrangements may be necessary where electrical equipment is subject to high ambient temperatures.

Cables should be installed so that they are accessible for subsequent inspection and maintenance, high up in the boat and clipped at regular intervals. Insulated return (two wire) systems should always be used for boat electrics: any insulation failure on earth return circuits (as used in cars) can cause dangerous electrolytic action. Different circuits (such as navigation lights, radio, or general lighting) should be individually fused or fitted with their own circuit breakers.

Attention should be given to the bonding on all the metal parts of the boat to the keel (if not encapsulated) or preferably to an earthing (grounding) plate on the wetted surface of a GRP or wooden hull, as a protection against electrolytic damage and lightning strike. Items to be so connected include engine, tanks, shroud chain plates, stays, the chassis of navigational instruments and radio, keel bolts, skin fittings and stern gear.

In order to avoid unwanted interference on radio circuits, it is important that the whole electrical system is properly suppressed. The most likely causes of interference are engine-driven generators and their control systems, but other sources can be fluorescent lighting, electric motors (as in water pumps, bilge pumps or windscreen wipers), or ignition systems in petrol engines. Although local reduction of unwanted radio energy can be achieved by the proper use of capacitors and inductors, serious problems of radio interference need professional advice.

Of even more importance can be the corrosion of underwater fittings due to leakage currents from faulty insulation or badly installed electrical components. Even if the boat is fitted with cathodic protection (see 10.5.7) this can be overcome by leakage currents, which render former cathodic areas anodic and thereby cause serious damage. Apart from ensuring that electrical circuits are properly wired (particularly where extra equipment is added) and well maintained, make certain that the main battery switch is always broken when the boat is not in use, and that water is excluded from all sockets, switches, junction boxes etc.

For technical details of boat electrics reference is suggested to the booklet *Marine Electrical Systems* published by Lucas Marine.

13.3.6 Electric starting

Apart from those small engines which can be started by hand, the great majority of boat engines rely on electric starting. The function of the starter motor is to turn the engine at sufficient speed for ignition of the fuel to be achieved, and then be sustained so that the engine will continue to run.

Usually the pinion of the starter motor shaft engages with teeth on the engine flywheel through a Bendix drive, which connects the starter to the flywheel when the starter begins to rotate, and disengages it once the engine fires. A possible fault is for the pinion not to disengage properly from the flywheel, in which case the starter can be freed by applying a spanner to a square on the other end of the armature shaft, and turning it clockwise. This trouble is usually caused by dirt on the Bendix drive. First disconnect the battery leads to the starter, and then remove the starter motor. Carefully clean the drive (only) with WD40 or petrol, until it operates freely by hand.

A lot of current is needed from the battery to get the engine turning over quickly enough, particularly in cold weather if the engine oil is thick (see 13.2.6). If the engine fails to start, continual cranking will soon discharge the battery or damage the starter. Attempting to start an engine with a partly discharged battery, where the terminal voltage is low, only gives too low a cranking speed and the likelihood of putting too high a current through the starter motor. Hence the importance of reserving one battery for engine starting, and ensuring that it is kept well charged at all times.

To avoid an unacceptable voltage drop, the cables which carry the high current from the battery to the starter motor must be heavy, and they must be kept as short as possible.

Consequently the switch in this circuit is remotely controlled by a solenoid, which is operated by a smaller switch at the helmsman's position. It is important that all cable connections, such as battery terminals, are kept clean so that they ensure a good electrical contact.

Diesel engines, with their high compression ratios, make a very heavy demand on their starter motors. Many diesel engines are fitted with starting aids for use in cold weather. Usually these consist of heater plugs, fitted in the cylinder head, which are actuated for a short period before using the starter motor. A decompressor may also be fitted, whereby a higher cranking speed can be achieved before the mechanism is released – so that normal compression is restored to enable the engine to start.

Another way to help cold starting is where an electrically heated element ignites a small quantity of fuel, as in the Lucas Thermostart unit mounted in the inlet manifold. Some engines use an ether starting aid, whereby a strictly metered quantity of ether is admitted to the air intake. Do not, however, use an aerosol spray with a diesel engine since this is liable to cause pre-ignition with possible damage to pistons and connecting rods.

13.4 Outboard engines

13.4.1 Outboard engines – general
Outboards are the natural choice for propelling small tenders and dinghies, and for auxiliary propulsion in small sailing craft; they are also extensively used in small motor cruisers up to about 6m (25ft) in length. Very powerful outboards are available for high-speed powerboats.

Outboards are ideal for dinghies of all types. They are light and easily portable; they come as a complete installation, with no need for propeller shafting or steering gear; they do not take up useful space within the boat; and the engine and propeller can be tilted up in shallow water – as for example when coming to a beach.

But outboards also have some disadvantages. Most of them work on petrol/oil mixture and are expensive on fuel; being outside the boat they are exposed to the elements and to theft; since steering is done by swivelling the entire engine, and thus altering the direction of the propeller thrust, there is no steering effect when the propeller is not rotating; installation is not easy on a boat which does not have a flat transom of suitable height; and spares tend to be rather expensive.

In choosing an outboard it is important to buy one of suitable power for the particular application. If in doubt, get advice because too small an engine will not give the required performance, while too large a one will incur penalties not only of cost but also of weight and portability.

Powers of outboard engines are rated according to tests that are specified by the American Boating Industry Association (BIA). These give the power at the crankshaft and are a 'sprint' rating, so they tend to exaggerate the power available at the propeller.

13.4.2 Two-stroke outboards
Nearly all outboards have two-stroke engines, and run on petrol/oil mixture (typically 30:1 or 50:1). Fig. 13(21) shows a two-stroke engine with a reed valve controlling the air/fuel mixture entering the crankcase from the carburettor. In (a) of Fig. 13(21) the piston is moving up the cylinder, drawing in behind it a fresh charge of air/fuel into the crankcase: above the piston the previous charge is being compressed, and will be ignited by the spark-plug when the piston nears the top of its stroke. In (b) the piston is on its working (power) stroke: the reed valve is shut, and the next charge in the crankcase is being compressed as the piston descends. In (c) the piston is more than half-way down its working stroke, and has started to open the exhaust port, through which the burnt gases are starting to flow: the transfer port is about to open, to allow the next charge of air/fuel mixture to be transferred from the crankcase to the cylinder. In (d) the piston is at the bottom of its stroke, the transfer of fuel is almost complete, and the cycle recommences.

Remembering that the engine may be running at 5000rpm, it will be appreciated that the expulsion of the exhaust gases and their replacement by a fresh charge of air/fuel mixture has to be achieved very quickly. Efficiency suffers if exhaust gases are not properly scavenged, or if part of the incoming charge is lost through the exhaust port. This problem is tackled two ways – some engines are 'loop charged', and other are 'cross flow'. With the former the ports are arranged so that the incoming gases are given a swirling action: in cross flow engines the inlet and exhaust ports are on opposite sides of the cylinder, while the piston has a hump on it to direct the incoming charge towards the top of the cylinder.

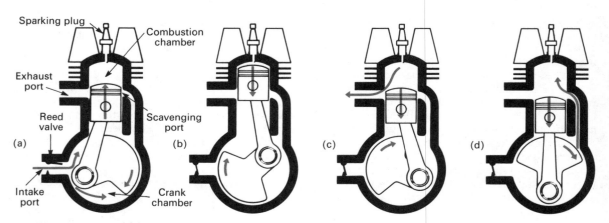

Fig. 13(21) Combustion cycle — two stroke engine. (a) Up stroke, drawing fresh charge into crankcase, and compressing charge already in cylinder. (b) Down (working) stroke. (c) Near end of down stroke the exhaust port is opened. (d) New charge being transferred from crankcase into cylinder.

It may be dangerous to predict the success or significance of a new type of two-stroke engine not yet (1992) in quantity production. But considerable promise is shown by the application of the Orbital Combustion Process (OCP) to two-stroke outboards.

The first Orbital engine ran more than 20 years ago, and the concept has been in development ever since. A fundamental factor is the air blast fuel injection system, whereby very finely atomised fuel is directed into the combustion chamber in a form where the mixture will burn more readily. This is the key to the unit's ability to deliver high powers with low exhaust emission levels, and with better fuel consumption than existing types. The air comes from a small engine-drive compressor at about 5.5 bar, with the fuel pressure slightly higher. Electronics control injection timing, the exhaust port scavenge flow valve, and the amount of lubricating oil dispensed – according to engine load and speed.

The new technology adapts itself well to the general layout of existing two-stroke outboards, some of which have already been converted for trials. If development proceeds according to plan there should be a new breed of outboard which for a given power output will be lighter, smaller, cheaper and more efficient, and which will have emission levels that more than meet future requirements.

13.4.3 Lubrication of two-stroke petrol engines

Since they fire twice as often, two-strokes run hotter than four-stroke engines, making them more liable to sticking piston rings and whiskering on spark-plugs. As in other engines, the function of the oil is to lubricate all the moving parts, including the cylinder walls. But instead of being pumped around, the oil is added to the fuel in a certain ratio as dictated by the maker. The amount of oil entering the engine therefore depends upon the throttle opening. Modern engines however are increasingly fitted with oil injection, separate tanks being provided for petrol and oil. Having done its job, the oil is burnt with the fuel, and must not leave excessive deposits of carbon at exhaust ports or in the combustion chamber.

For these reasons it is most important that the correct oil is used, and that it is mixed in the proper proportions. Some manufacturers specify slightly more oil during the running-in period. Never use ordinary multi-grade engine oil in a two-stroke. Outboards even need slightly different oil from that used in two-strokes ashore, because they are water cooled and operate at somewhat lower temperatures. They also tend to run for longer periods at fixed throttle settings.

Two-stroke engines consume a great deal more lubricating oil than four-strokes, which is one reason that their operating costs are considerably higher.

13.4.4 Outboards – installation

The transoms of most boats intended for outboard propulsion have a height of 380-500mm (15-20in) above the bottom of the boat. A 20in transom needs a long shaft engine, and a 15in transom needs a short (standard length) shaft. The exact measurements differ from make to make, and some models are available with extra-long shafts for special applications.

When the engine is fitted to the boat the cavitation plate above the propeller should be about level with the boat's bottom, or slightly below it. Make sure that the circulating water inlet is well immersed. The tilt of the engine should be adjusted so that it is vertical when the boat is running. Small engines are secured by two clamps, which should be well tightened, and checked periodically. An anti-theft device of some kind is essential, and the engine should also have a strop which should be secured to some fixed point in order to prevent accidental loss overboard. Larger engines are bolted in place.

It may be found that the tilt of the engine needs to be altered slightly so that the trim of the boat is correct when she is under way; this is because the direction of thrust of the propeller – slightly above or slightly below the horizontal – can have a significant effect on pushing the bow up or down. In higher powered sportsboats and ski-boats the tilt of the engine can be adjusted under way, in order to get the best trim depending on load, speed and sea conditions.

13.4.5 Outboards – propellers

General notes on propellers, including mention of the choice of diameter and pitch, are given in 13.2.10. Most outboards are supplied with a propeller which has a standard diameter and pitch, suitable for the most usual applications of an engine of that power. But propellers of different diameter and pitch are generally available if required for special purposes. This can be very useful, because it is such a simple matter to swap the propeller of an outboard. For example, it is quite feasible to operate one engine on two boats with quite different hull characteristics – having widely varying speeds and weights. In such cases it may well prove that different propellers for the two jobs will greatly increase performance or economy.

13.5 Maintenance

13.5.1 Maintenance – inboard engines

If an engine is supplied with clean fuel and lubricating oil, air for combustion, and plentiful quantities of cooling water (or air in the case of air cooled engines), very little should ever go wrong. There are other details which require periodical attention, as should be stated in the engine handbook, but if all these matters are attended to methodically (preferably with the aid of some kind of check list), any yachtsman should be able to ensure reliable service from his engine, and not have to incur heavy repair bills. Keep a careful check on engine running hours, so that maintenance is undertaken at the correct intervals: the easiest way to do this is to fit an hour meter, if not already provided.

Proper maintenance of an engine cannot be undertaken without the relevant handbook or workshop manual, nor without a good set of tools and appropriate items of spare gear.

13.5.2 Tools

Sufficient tools must be carried not only for routine maintenance, but for coping with any breakdowns at sea. Most engine manufacturers will give advice on the outfit needed for any particular engine – for example, whether any special socket spanners are required – but a basic tool kit should include: sets of open ended and ring spanners, screwdrivers, including Phillips; a pair of mole grips; pliers; hammer; mallet; files, rough and smooth; Allen keys; small hacksaw; plug spanner (petrol engine); hydrometer (for battery). The competent mechanic will know how this list should be extended.

13.5.3 Spares

The quantity of spares carried depends partly on the usage of the boat. Obviously more items are needed in a boat which makes extended cruises than in one which seldom moves far from her home port. A suggested list should include: a set of drive belts (alternator, circulating pump etc as appropriate); a set of hoses and spare hose clips; a set of gaskets; fuel and lubricating oil filter elements; circulating water pump impeller and gasket; thermostat; spark-plugs (petrol engine) or injectors (diesel engine); points and plug leads (petrol engine); lubricating oil for a complete refill of engine and gearbox; general purpose grease; penetrating oil; distilled water for battery; fuses of all capacities on board; spare bulbs for navigation lights etc.

13.5.4 Fuel system – general

Be sure to have enough fuel on board for any intended passage, and preferably a reserve supply: if this is petrol it must be stowed in a proper metal can on deck, never down below. You should have a calibrated dipstick or an accurate fuel gauge.

Use the correct grade of fuel and keep it clean. Fuel can easily be contaminated by dirty containers or filling funnels, or by water entering deck filling connections – always replace the cap tightly as soon as fuelling is complete. Filters must be serviced at the stipulated intervals.

If there is a drain cock on the bottom on the fuel tank, this should be opened periodically to drain off any sediment or water which may have collected.

13.5.5. Diesel fuel system

Cleanliness is half the battle. The injection pump and the injectors must be professionally serviced at the stated intervals. Keep the pump clean, and

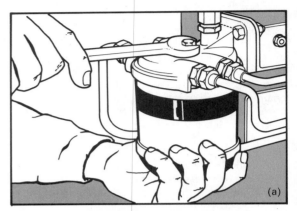

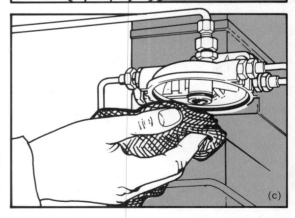

Fig. 13(22) (a) Servicing a diesel fuel filter. First remove all external dirt, turn off the fuel supply if by gravity, and drain the base if the filter has a drain plug. Unscrew the centre bolt, while holding the filter base to prevent rotation. (b) Release the element and base by pulling downwards with a twisting action, to free from the internal 'O' ring. Discard the element, but retain lower sealing ring. Clean filter base, and rinse with clean fuel oil. Renew sealing ring, if necessary. Refit and tighten drain plug (where fitted). (c) Clean the filter head with a clean brush or a non-fluffy cloth, particularly the groove housing the sealing ring. Fit new sealing ring and 'O' ring where necessary. When replacing new element, turn it slightly so that it slides over the 'O' ring. Do not overtighten the central bolt. Turn on the fuel system, and vent it in accordance with the engine handbook.

connections tight. With some injection pumps the cambox should be drained and replenished every 100 running hours. It is perfectly within the capacity of the average owner to change a faulty injector, as described in 13.2.3, but care is needed when working on diesel fuel systems. It is easy to damage fuel pipe nipples by overtightening, or to bend pipes by faulty assembly. Injectors must be correctly installed, on clean seatings, squarely mounted, and with any seating washer or insert properly in place.

Fuel filters must be cleaned and serviced at the interval given in the handbook. In the average yacht it is appropriate to do this at the start of the season. Cleanliness is essential, and it is first necessary to clean off all external dirt around the filter assembly. It is good practice to keep all parts of an engine clean, since this reduces corrosion and permits any leakage to be identified at an early stage. If there is a drain plug on the filter bowl, open it and drain out the contents into a suitable can. Dispose of all dirty oil ashore – not over the side. Hold the base of the filter and unscrew the central bolt at the top Fig. 13(22a). Twist and pull the base downwards. At this point observe exactly how the element and sealing rings are positioned, so that the filter is reassembled correctly Fig. 13(22b). Discard the used element, but keep the sealing rings if they are in good condition – otherwise renew them. Clean out the base and rinse with diesel fuel. Clean, refit and replace the drain plug, if present. Using a clean cloth (not a fluffy one) or a brush, wipe out the underside of the filter head including the groove for the sealing ring Fig. 13(22c). Reassemble the filter with a new element, carefully rotating it slightly so that is slides easily over the small 'O' ring at the top. Do not overtighten the bolt.

13.5.6 Diesel fuel system – venting

Running out of fuel, or any work on the fuel system such as servicing filters, will allow air to get into the system and will prevent proper operation of the fuel injection pump. It is then necessary to vent or bleed the system before the engine will start. The exact procedure varies slightly from engine to engine, and should be described in the engine handbook. It is important to know the correct drill, since it may have to be done at sea or in the dark. Basically the procedure is to slacken vents on the final fuel filter and on the injection pump in turn, while operating the hand priming level of the fuel lift pump until all the air has been expelled. Finally the connections at the injector end of two high pressure fuel pipes are slacked back, and the engine turned over on the starter until fuel free from air emerges. Then re-tighten the connections.

Before venting the system, make certain that vent screws and connections which are to be slackened are completely clean externally, in order to prevent any dirt entering the system. It is a good idea for such vent screws to be painted a distinctive colour to assist identification. With some installations, during the final stages of venting, the governor may not function correctly, so be prepared to stop the engine in event of any overspeed.

13.5.7 Lubrication system

Be careful to use an approved type and grade of oil, both for the engine and for the gearbox. Always check the levels in the engine and gearbox before starting up. On a long passage under power, oil levels should be checked at intervals of 4-6 hours. Oil must be clean, which means that it must only be stowed in a closed container, which should be clearly marked as to the contents.

Do not overfill. Investigate any departure from the correct level, whether it is too low or too high. The latter may be caused by fuel or water getting into the sump, and both are serious matters.

13.5.8 Cooling system

In the case of air cooled engines, there is little to attend to provided that air intakes and exhausts are kept clear and are not obstructed.

With water cooling the most likely cause of trouble is blockage of the circulating water inlet strainer. If the engine temperature rises, check the water discharge overboard if this is readily visible: steam from it will indicate that the strainer is probably blocked, but this can soon be rectified by shutting the inlet seacock and examining the strainer. If this proves to be clean, the trouble may lie with the pump or thermostat. If the engine is fresh water cooled, then the fresh water system may need replenishing – rather like a car radiator.

Before starting the engine make certain that the circulating water inlet seacock is open. If the engine is fresh water cooled, check the level in the header tank.

13.5.9 Electrical system

As already described in 13.3.2, it is most important that lead/acid batteries are kept charged, and not left idle for more than a month or so. The level of the electrolyte should be checked weekly. The tension of the alternator drive belt should also be checked regularly.

On starting the engine, the alternator will initially charge at quite a high rate, gradually reducing as the battery becomes fully charged.

When the boat is left unattended, the main battery switch should be broken.

13.5.10 Engine checks

Before getting under way, check:
    FUEL TANK CONTENTS AND FUEL RESERVE
    ENGINE AND GEARBOX OIL LEVELS
    SPARE LUBRICATING OIL LEVELS
    HEADER TANK LEVEL (fresh water cooling)
    CIRCULATING WATER SEACOCK OPEN
    BATTERY SWITCHES ON
    ENGINE COMPARTMENT FAN (Run for 5
        minutes, if fitted)

ENGINE BILGES CLEAR
FUEL FILTER BOWL CLEAR
BATTERY ELECTROLYTE LEVEL CORRECT
ENGINE IN NEUTRAL
NO ROPES NEAR SCREW

After starting engine check,
    LUBRICATING OIL PRESSURE
    CIRCULATING WATER FLOW
    GENERATOR CHARGING
    AHEAD/NEUTRAL/ASTERN
      OPERATION OF GEARBOX
    ENGINE IDLING RPM

When engine running, check:
    ENGINE RPM
    LUBRICATING OIL PRESSURE
    GEARBOX OIL PRESSURE (if separate system)
    COOLANT TEMPERATURE
    TURBOCHARGER OIL PRESSURE (if fitted)
    TURBOCHARGER BOOST PRESSURE (if fitted)
    AMMETER, OR CHARGING LIGHT
    FUEL TANK CONTENTS

On return to harbour, check:
    ENGINE COMPARTMENT FOR LEAKS ETC
    PETROL COCKS SHUT (leave diesel systems
      open)
    CIRCULATING WATER INLET SEACOCKS
      SHUT
    MAIN BATTERY SWITCHES OPEN
    FUEL REMAINING
    LUBRICATING OIL LEVELS
    ENGINE RUNNING HOURS (enter in log)
    BILGE CLEAR

13.5.11 Laying up – care of engine

Any engine which is left idle for more than two or three weeks at a time will start to deteriorate. So during the winter months it is most important that machinery is either run regularly or is properly inhibited; much more damage can be caused by one winter of neglect than by many summers of normal use.

The protection needed during the winter falls into two categories. First all the internal working surfaces such as crankshaft journals, cylinder walls (and particularly, with a diesel engine, the insides of fuel injection pump and fuel injectors) must be suitably treated to prevent corrosion. Second, with a water cooled engine, the cooling system must be treated not only to eliminate corrosion but also the possibility of frost damage. So attention is needed to the lubricating system, the fuel system, and the cooling system. In addition the battery must be removed from the boat, and stored where it is safe from frost and can be charged about once a month.

In order to achieve the desired result, it is necessary that the various jobs are undertaken in the correct sequence, and in some cases concurrently, briefly as follows. First run the engine to warm it up. Stop it and pump out all the lubricating oil into a suitable drum for disposal

ashore; also drain the gearbox. Fit a new oil filter element. If an oil bath air filter is fitted, this should be cleaned and filled with fresh oil. Replenish the engine with rust-proofing oil such as Duckhams Adfilm 730, and the gearbox with its normal transmission oil. Run the engine for about 15 minutes at a fast idling speed, with the gearbox in neutral.

Next, the fuel system. With a diesel engine, drain the fuel filter, disconnect the suction pipe from the fuel lift pump and insert it in a can with a mixture of 2/3 diesel fuel and 1/3 rust-proofing oil. Bleed the system, start the engine, and run it at idling speed for five or ten minutes so that the preserving oil reaches the injection pump and the injectors. With a petrol engine, drain out and clean the carburettor, fuel pump and fuel filter. Preferably empty and clean the petrol tank. During this work remember the danger when working on petrol systems in a confined area – no smoking and no naked lights.

Concurrently with the above, tackle the cooling system. If the boat is to be left afloat during the winter, treat the fresh water system with anti-freeze. Shut (and lash) the circulating water inlet seacock, and drain down the salt (raw) water side of the system through whatever drain plugs are provided. Remove the cover from the circulating pump, take out the impeller and store it carefully. However, if the boat is out of the water or if circumstances permit (perhaps alongside with fresh water readily available) the following additional flushing procedure is recommended. Drain all the raw water from the cooling system, including the gearbox oil cooler, through the drain plugs, and then close these again. Shut the inlet seacock, disconnect the pipe from it, and insert the end in a bucket which can be kept topped up with a supply of fresh water. Run the engine at a fast idling speed for ten minutes to flush through the system with fresh water. (It is not advisable to connect the mains water supply direct to the engine, since the pressure may be too high). Then flush through with water to which some soluble rust-proofing oil has been added. During these operations do not allow the pump to run dry, or damage may be caused to the impeller. Finally, drain out all the water from the system as before, and reassemble the pump suction to the inlet seacock.

Remove the injectors (or spark-plugs) and pour a little preserving oil into each cylinder, rotating the engine with the starter so that the oil is distributed on the cylinder walls. Fit old injectors/spark-plugs (or suitable blanks) to the engine for the winter. Injectors should be sent away for servicing.

Using polythene and sticky tape, seal off all the openings to the engine (e.g. air filter, exhaust). Wash off the exterior of the engine, and touch up any damaged paintwork. Any bare metal parts should be sprayed with WD-40 or equivalent. Grease all control mechanisms or similar fittings.

If the boat has an outdrive, rather than conventional shafting and propeller, drain off some oil from the gear case through the drain plug at the bottom of the leg to make sure that it is clean and with no sign of water. Then fill the drive fully with oil for the winter, and remember to restore it to the normal working level in the spring.

13.5.12 Engine – preparation for summer

Preparing the engine for the coming season involves putting into reverse the preservation that should have been done in the autumn. It is necessary to pump or drain out inhibiting oil, and replace it with oil of the correct type and grade. Blanks that have been fitted must be removed, and hoses reconnected; at the same time check the condition of all hoses and their clips. Replace the water pump impeller, having made sure it is in good condition, and shut all drain cocks on the water system. Renew filter elements, if this was not done before the winter.

Check that the battery is fully charged, and that the level of the electrolyte is correct, and fit it in the boat. Remove temporary blanks fitted in place of injectors or spark-plugs, and turn the engine over on the starter to remove most of the oil that was put into the cylinder, but place some rags over the holes to avoid oil splashing about. With a diesel engine, replace the injectors, which should have been serviced during the winter. Before starting the engine it will be necessary to bleed the fuel system. With a petrol engine it is wise to fit new spark-plugs at the start of the season. Check drive belts for wear, and make sure they are correctly tensioned.

When the boat is afloat, run the engine and check all control and instruments. Look around all systems for leaks. Remember to replace all spares that may have been used since the previous season, and make sure that any tools or gear that may have been taken ashore are brought back on board.

13.5.13 Maintenance – outboard engines

The general arrangement and features of outboards have already been discussed in 13.4. Where applicable the previous comments about the maintenance of inboard engines apply equally to outboards, but these engines have certain characteristics which demand special attention.

Outboard engines are particularly exposed to the elements so it is important to keep them in good condition externally, to inspect regularly for damage which can lead to corrosion, and to grease the various lubrication points indicated in the engine handbook at the intervals stated.

Internal lubrication has been discussed in 13.4.3, but it is worth repeating the importance of using the correct outboard motor oil, and of mixing it with petrol of the correct grade and in the proper proportions. Before filling the tank give the can a good shake to make sure that the petrol and oil are well mixed.

The lower unit (the bottom part of the leg, near the propeller) requires special attention. Most engines have a zinc anode here to give protection against galvanic action. This must not be painted and should be inspected periodically, and replaced when it is about half wasted.

Check the oil level in the lower unit regularly by means of the plug(s) fitted in the gear housing, and change the oil as recommended in the engine handbook. A special gear oil must be used. Drain a little oil off from time to time to check for any sign of water, since there is always the possibility of leakage at the seal between the propeller shaft and the housing. This danger can be minimized if the engine is always tilted up after use, so as to raise the propeller and gear housing out of the water.

All outboards have some means of protecting the gearing, should the propeller hit anything solid. In small engines this takes the form of a shear pin, passing through the propeller boss and the shaft, which breaks if too large a force is suddenly applied. A new shear pin must then be fitted by removing the fairing cone at the aft end of the boss. Larger engines have a slipping clutch on the final drive to the propeller. Do not run the engine at high speed if a propeller blade is damaged.

As already explained, most outboards have two-stroke engines, which are sensitive to spark-plug fouling at low rpm. So particular attention should be given to plug maintenance. Always keep a spare set of plugs on board. Ideally a plug removed from the engine should be fairly clean, with only slight deposits light brown or light grey in colour. The electrodes should be intact, and there should be no deposits of oil or carbon. Before removing a spark-plug make sure that the surrounding area is clean, so that no dirt will enter the cylinder. Use a proper plug spanner, and take care not to damage the insulator. The spark can be tested by placing the plug body against the cylinder head and turning the engine over so that the spark can be observed visually. Plugs can be cleaned with a stiff brush in a bath of petrol or white spirit. Reset the gap only by bending the earthed (outer) electrode: do not exert any pressure on the central electrode, or the insulation will be damaged.

Before using a new engine read the instruction book carefully and make yourself familiar with the controls and with the various parts of the motor. Open the fuel cock (usually on the side of the engine) and the air vent on the filler cap. If the engine has a separate, remote tank see that there are no kinks in the fuel line, and prime the system with the hand bulb.

If the engine does not start, first ensure that there is enough fuel in the tank and that it is getting to the carburettor. Then check the spark-plug(s), which should be clean and dry; if they are wet with unburnt fuel, pull the engine over several times to expel the excess, before cleaning and replacing the plug(s). If the engine still will not start, check the spark as described above. Care is needed, since modern engines generate a high voltage in the secondary circuit of the ignition system Possible causes of ignition failure with a magneto system, could be breaker points pitted or wrongly set, cam follower worn or cracked, defective condenser, or faulty plug lead. With multi-cylinder engines check that the plug leads have not been crossed. Capacitor discharge systems are in general more reliable, since they do not have so many moving parts. If the engine is still obstinate, even if the spark is satisfactory, it is necessary to turn again to the fuel system, and check for dirt in the filter or in the carburettor. Also check the float and needle valve assembly, so that it gives the correct level in the float chamber.

After any trip, shut off the fuel cock and close the air vent. Tilt the engine to raise the lower unit out of the water. When carrying an outboard, or laying it down on the jetty, do not allow the propeller end to rise above the engine, or water may run into the engine and cause serious damage.

13.5.14 Rescuing a drowned outboard
If the engine should ever get immersed, it should be given professional attention as quickly as possible. But in the meantime, speedy action will help to minimize any internal damage. Flush the whole engine liberally with fresh water, to remove as much salt and dirt as possible. Flush out the interior by removing the spark-plug(s), turning the engine upside down, and turning it over by hand. If the motor does not rotate easily, do not use excessive force because it may have suffered internal damage (e.g. a bent connecting rod) if it was running when it entered the water. Repeat the process using methylated spirit or any other suitable fluid available, and then several times with lubricating oil – pouring it through the plug hole(s) and the carburettor in turn, and turning the engine end for end so that the oil is thoroughly distributed inside. Replace the plug(s) and get the engine to the nearest dealer or workshop as quickly as possible.

13.5.15 Laying up an outboard
Before the winter an outboard engine needs similar inhibiting to that required by an inboard unit. First carefully clean the whole exterior. Flush out the cooling system with fresh water: this can be done most conveniently by running the boat in fresh water, but if this is not possible the engine should be mounted so that the lower unit is well immersed in fresh water in a suitable container such as a dustbin. Empty and refill the container, this time adding a corrosion inhibitor such as Esso Kutwell 40 – an emulsifying oil to preserve the internal parts of the cooling system – and run the engine for about five minutes. Towards the end of

this period, before cutting off the fuel supply and stopping the engine, inject a suitable preservative such as Duckhams Adfilm 730 or Esso Rust-Ban 623 into the air inlet, to protect the moving parts during the winter. It should be noted that this is a different type of oil from that used in the cooling system. Remove the spark-plug(s) and insert a teaspoonful of oil into the cylinder(s), turning the engine by hand so that it is well distributed. Replace the plug(s).

The carburettor should now be empty, but check this, and give it a good clean out. Clean the fuel filter. Empty the fuel tank, or gummy deposits may form during the time the engine is left idle. Examine the contact breaker points (where fitted), clean them up as necessary and adjust the gap; if the points are pitted a new set should be fitted before the engine is re-commissioned. Check all wiring and connections.

Drain the lower unit, examining the oil for any signs of water, which would require replacement of the propeller shaft seal. Refill the lower unit with an inhibiting oil for the winter (remembering to replace it with gear oil in the spring). Remove the propeller, clean off the propeller shaft and grease it. If necessary, get the propeller faired up during the winter, or order a replacement if it is badly damaged.

Check that all fastenings are secure to the correct torque, as in the engine handbook, using a torque wrench. Clean and grease all cables, linkages, mounting brackets, swivel and tilt mechanism etc. Blank off the air inlet and the exhaust. Touch up any damaged paintwork, and store the engine in a dry place, hanging on its normal support and not standing on the skeg.

13.5.16 Preparing an outboard for the summer
Assuming that the motor was properly inhibited (as described in 13.5.15) for the winter, getting it ready for the following season is mostly a matter of reversing the process. Clean off the exterior from any winter grime. Drain and refill the lower unit with the approved type of gear oil. Remove and clean the spark-plugs, and turn the engine over to expel the worst of the lubricant inserted into the cylinders in the autumn. Replace the plugs and connect the ignition leads. Fill and prime the fuel system. Choke the engine and start it. As the inhibiting oil is burnt away there will be quantities of blue smoke, and the spark-plugs may become so fouled that they will require cleaning. Check the cooling water system – most engines have a visible discharge. All this should be done with the engine either installed on the boat, or mounted in the same tank as was used to inhibit it in the autumn. Never run the engine dry. When the engine is running satisfactorily, fit new spark plugs for the coming season.

13.5.17 Fault finding
When a fault develops in an engine there are

DIESEL ENGINE FAILS TO START

Engine does not turn	Engine only turns slowly	Engine rotates normally
In a few cases a switch prevents starting unless neutral gear is engaged – if so check accordingly.	A low cranking speed is a major cause of poor starting in diesel engines.	Check fuel tank contents, and sedimenter clear.
A repeated clicking sound accompanied by a drop in voltmeter reading indicates a discharged battery.	Check battery state and electrical connections.	Check fuel tank valve open.
	With twin engines, operate battery paralleling switch, if fitted.	Check throttle setting.
Total silence is likely indication of a defective solenoid, or a fault in the starter switch circuit. In the latter case, try jumping out the smaller cables leading from the switch to solenoid in order to operate solenoid.	Check gearbox in neutral.	Check stop control reset.
	Check air filter/air supply clear.	Check decompression lever (if fitted).
	Check correct grade of lubricating oil.	Check solenoid-operated fuel shut-off (if fitted).
If a click is heard from starter, check battery state and see connections are clean and tight. If these are satisfactory, and still no rotation, starter is probably defective. Pinion may be jammed in engaged position.	Apart from recharging battery, anything that will help warm up the engine will assist. A low cranking speed is particularly harmful in cold weather.	Check cold start aid operated correctly.
		If above are all found correct:
		Slack high pressure fuel pipes at injectors, put fuel setting to maximum and crank engine.

	(*Note:* The above is also applicable to petrol engines. But do not use any form of naked flame in attempting to warm a petrol engine.)	If fuel, free of air, is delivered, there is indication of mechanical problems:
		    Poor compression (see Note 1, below).
		    Faulty injectors (see Note 2, below).
		    Fuel pump timing (see Note 3, below).

If a click and a whirring sound is heard, starter pinion is failing to engage. Tap starter motor, or remove to clean Bendix gear.		

	———	If no fuel is delivered, or there is air in the system, it is necessary to check back through fuel system to identify trouble:
		    Open vent screw(s) on fuel pump, operate lift pump and check flow. If this is satisfactory, fuel injection pump is suspect.
		    If no flow, or air in system, go back to final fuel filter (renewing element if necessary) and so on through the system to lift pump (diaphragm and strainer), and preliminary filter or sedimenter.

(*Note:* The above symptoms and actions refer equally to petrol engines.)	*Notes:*	
	(1) Poor compression may be sometimes overcome by injecting a small quantity of oil into air filter while cranking engine. This assists seal between rings and cylinder wall.	Having located blockage (or air leak or water) bleed the system thoroughly.
	(2) Fit spare injectors.	Check for fuel leaks when engine running.
	(3) See engine handbook.	

Fig. 13(23) Diesel engine starting. Fault-finding chart.

certain logical steps that should be taken to find the reason, depending on the particular circumstances. Usually the cause is fairly obvious. The most likely reasons for an engine which has been running normally to stop are shortage of fuel (an empty tank or a blockage in the fuel system) or overheating (with water-cooled engines due to a choked strainer in the circulating water system). The latter ought to be detected at an early stage from the instruments and from the rough running of the engine. Of course there are other possibilities, including a rope round the screw.

Modern engines are very reliable in the mechanical sense, but they cannot (yet) replenish their own fuel or lubricating oil, or clean their own circulating water strainer. It is in such human failure that nearly all trouble originates.

Regular observation of the engine instruments and of the exhaust smoke should forestall most engine failures, but if the engine does stop try to use all your senses when looking for trouble.

Is there a hot smell somewhere? If so, locate it: did you notice any unusual noise or vibration before the engine stopped? Are any parts unduly warm?

In what follows only the more common reasons for failure appear, but they are the ones where the remedy is obvious and usually within the capability of the average yachtsman to rectify – even at sea, given the engine handbook, proper tools and a sensible outfit of spares. Other more sinister defects, usually including mechanical failure of some part of the engine, are less likely and have not been included because in general it would be impossible to rectify them without outside help.

Trouble with marine engines is often manifested by reluctance to start, particularly with diesel machinery in cold weather. Under these conditions the oil is thicker and the engine is more difficult to turn. A low turning speed allows more time for compression to be lost past the piston rings, and more time for the heat generated by compression to be lost to the (cold) cylinder walls, while at the same time the cold air needs more heat to reach ignition temperature – a vicious circle.

A summary of the symptoms and possible procedures when a diesel engine fails to start is indicated in Fig. 13(23). Other modes of failure are discussed below:

(1) *Petrol engine fails to start*. The two left-hand columns in Fig. 13(23) are equally applicable to petrol engines. Due to the lower compression ratios petrol engines are easier to crank over at a satisfactory speed for starting. Assuming this can be achieved, there are two probable causes of failure to start – either the fuel system or the ignition system. Since the former is more liable to human error it deserves consideration first. See whether none or too much fuel is being delivered by the carburettor, possibly by visual examination of the carburettor mouth having removed the air filter. If the engine is 'flooded' (due to being over-choked and repeated cranking) let it stand for a few minutes with the throttle open to allow surplus petrol to evaporate. Otherwise remove and dry the plugs, turn the engine over to displace surplus petrol, and replace the plugs.

If on the other hand there appears to be a shortage of fuel, check the supply to the carburettor from the lift pump. *Remember that whenever working on a petrol engine there must be no smoking or naked lights in the vicinity.* Check fuel tank contents, fuel shut-off cock, and fuel filter.

If the engine still will not start, turn attention to the ignition system. Disconnect one spark-plug lead and hold it with a pair of insulated pliers close to the cylinder block. Turn the engine over and a healthy spark should appear, proving that the ignition system is functioning (apart from the remote possibility of fouled plugs or faulty timing). If, however, there is no spark it is necessary to identify the fault. This is not too difficult with the old-style coil ignition system but a different matter with modern capacitor discharge ignition. Check, and if necessary replace, plugs and plug leads. With coil ignition check the contact breaker points and the rotor arm. Check the high tension lead from coil to distributor. Work round the system with a test lamp to find any break in the circuit.

Having eliminated any defect in the ignition system it is necessary to revert to the fuel system if the engine still fails to start. Check the fuel pump diaphragm for possible failure, if the pump is not delivering fuel. If it is, it is necessary to consider the carburettor itself, after referring to the engine handbook. It should be possible to check that the piston is not stuck in a variable-jet carburettor, or to clean the jets of other types. Check the float chamber and the float-controlled needle valve that regulates the petrol level.

(2) *Engine stops while running*. Apart from running out of fuel, a rope round the prop, or some sudden ignition system failure in a petrol unit, an engine seldom ceases to run without some indication of pending trouble – either from the instruments, a change of beat, fluctuations in speed, ominous noises or a suspicious smell. The most likely cause is fuel shortage, which needs to be investigated accordingly; with a diesel engine there may be air in the system which in any case will require venting after checking filters etc.

Sudden failure of a petrol engine may be due to ignition problems. Fuel shortage is more likely to cause gradual stopping, with spluttering noises from the carburettor.

(3) *Engine overheats*. This should be detected from the instruments, or by steam from the exhaust, before it causes serious trouble. It is most commonly due to blockage of the strainer in the raw water cooling system, which is simple to clear. If the trouble occurs soon after starting, make sure the seacock is open. Other possible causes are: defective raw water cooling pump, defective thermostat, loss of coolant from fresh water system (indirect cooling), broken belt (where pump is belt-driven), or a blocked air channel with an air-cooled engine. Should none of the above resolve the problem, it could be due to a low oil level in the sump, faulty injection with a diesel engine, a dirty air cleaner, wrong valve timing (unlikely unless the engine has just been overhauled), some restriction in the exhaust, partially choked cooling passages inside the engine – or the need of an overhaul.

(4) *Engine will not develop full power*. The likely

cause depends very much on the circumstances. If it is an elderly engine where the performance has gradually dropped, the most probable reason is general mechanical deterioration – poor compression due to worn rings or cylinder bores, or pitted valves or seats, comes high on the list and can be assessed by a compression test; or with a diesel engine the fuel pump and injectors may need servicing. But if the engine had been running well and suddenly loses power there are a number of less drastic items to investigate. These include some restriction in the fuel system, dirt in the fuel, or blocked air vent on the fuel tank; defective throttle mechanism; wrong engine timing; boat overloaded or with a dirty bottom; fouled propeller; defective tachometer; dirty air cleaner; restriction in exhaust pipe; incorrect operating temperature; or, with a turbocharged engine, fouling of the turbocharger. In a diesel engine the governor may require attention. In a petrol engine the carburettor may need cleaning or adjustment, or there is a problem with the ignition system – make a start by checking the plugs, and then work back from there.

(5) *Misfiring*. It is possible to identify whether this is restricted to a particular cylinder by earthing each plug cap in turn with a petrol engine, or by slackening the high pressure fuel pipe at each injector in turn in the case of a diesel engine. If it is shown that one cylinder is missing, then pay attention to the items that affect that one only – for example, plug and plug lead in a petrol engine or the injector in a diesel. Other causes may be wrong valve (tappet) clearances or perhaps a sticking valve. The latter may be corrected, at least for the time being, with a squirt of penetrating oil.

Misfiring on more than one cylinder points to more general problems with the engine, such as have already been described under (4) above.

(6) *Low oil pressure*. The most serious possibility is a low level in the sump, which needs to be rectified before total failure occurs. Low pressure may also be due to the oil overheating, which may be caused by a failure in the flow of water to the oil cooler or by a low level in the sump (the smaller quantity of oil circulating becoming hotter). Other possibilities are: a choked oil filter, wrong grade of oil being used, defective oil pump, pressure relief valve sticking, or a defective pressure gauge. A gradual drop in oil pressure over a period indicates worn bearings.

(7) *Exhaust smoke* (or the lack of it) is a good indication of problems (or health) in the case of a diesel engine, and also in some respects of a petrol engine. In either case blue smoke comes from burning lubricating oil which has reached the combustion chamber past worn piston rings/ cylinder bores or valve guides (signs that the engine needs overhaul), or possibly past worn turbocharger seals.

White smoke from a diesel engine is often seen when first starting up, and is due to the engine running cold. It is a fog of partly burned or unburned droplets of fuel, which may have a grey/ blue tinge, and may be caused by low grade fuel. If it persists it can indicate a number of problems such as water in the fuel, defective injector(s), or perhaps a coolant leak into a cylinder.

Black smoke is carbon from partially unburned fuel, and is usually an indication of an overloaded diesel engine, with more fuel being delivered than can be burned properly. This can be caused by the boat being physically overladen, by fitting the wrong propeller(s), by the boat having a dirty bottom, or when towing another craft. Otherwise it is likely to be caused by fuel injection problems or a dirty air cleaner. If it still persists when these possible causes have been eliminated, the engine is due for servicing.

13.6 Bibliography

Trouble Shooting and Maintenance of Boat Engines by Peter Bowyer (Adlard Coles Nautical).

The Care and Repair of Marine Petrol Engines by Loris Goring (Adlard Coles Nautical).

The Care and Repair of Small Marine Diesels by Chris Thompson (Adlard Coles Nautical).

Marine Conversions by Nigel Warren (Adlard Coles Nautical).

Outboard Motor Handbook by Nigel Warren (Stanford Maritime).

Power for Yachts by Tom Cox (Stanford Maritime).

Boat Electrics by John Watney (David & Charles).

Motor Boat and Yachting Manual by Dick Hewitt (Stanford Maritime).

Clymer Outboard Manuals – for various engines (Clymer US)

Boat Owner's Mechanical and Electrical Manual by Nigel Calder (Adlard Coles Nautical).

Repairs at Sea by Nigel Calder (Adlard Coles Nautical).

Marine Inboard Engines – Petrol and Diesel by Loris Goring (Adlard Coles Nautical).

Boat Engines by Dick Hewitt (Fernhurst).

Propeller Handbook by Dave Gerr (Adlard Coles Nautical).

Marine Diesel Engines by Nigel Calder (Ashford, Buchan & Enright).

Diesel Boat Engines by Peter Bowyer (Haynes).

The Outboard Motor Manual by Keith Henderson (Adlard Coles Nautical).

The Marine Electrics Book by Geoffrey O'Connell (Ashford, Buchan & Enright).

Boat Electrical Systems by Dag Pike (Adlard Coles Nautical).

The 12 Volt Bible for Boats by Miner Brotherton (International Marine).

Living on 12 Volts with Ample Power by David Smead and Ruth Ishihara (Rides Publishing Co).

Chapter 14

Below Decks

Contents

14.1 Accommodation layout

14.1.1 Human dimensions

Though human beings come in all shapes and sizes the sketches of Fig 14(1) represent the space occupied by the average male, who is assumed to be about 1.8m (6ft) tall. From these, various deductions can be made as, for instance, to the proper height of a table or working surface; how much space needs to be left between obstructing items for a reasonable passage between; the amount of foot room needed in front of a toilet and so on. They may also demonstrate why a settee wide enough to form a berth is much too wide for comfortable sitting unless special provision is made to reduce the width when required.

14.1.2 Cabin entry

The majority of small and medium size sailing craft use hatch boards rather than doors to close the entry between the cabin and the cockpit. These boards, which drop individually down channels each side of the entrance, are complemented by a sliding hatch to give headroom where it is required. The argument for hatch boards rather than doors is that in bad weather only the lower boards need be dropped in place, leaving a gap at the top for ventilation and through which there is some line of communication between the helmsman and those below. If the entrance is above a bridgedeck at the same height as the cockpit seats, or the entrance is cut at this height, it means that the cockpit can be flooded to that depth before water starts to find its way below. Hatch boards are not in themselves watertight, of course, though they will prevent anything more than a minor stream getting past them. After the 1979 Fastnet Race, in which several yachts foundered, the RORC recommended that hatch boards be permanently fastened to the parent vessel (with simple lanyards being the easiest method of achieving this) and that the hatch over the entrance should be lockable from both sides. In other words, the hatch should be arranged such that it is impossible to lock from one side without it equally being possible to unlock it from the other side.

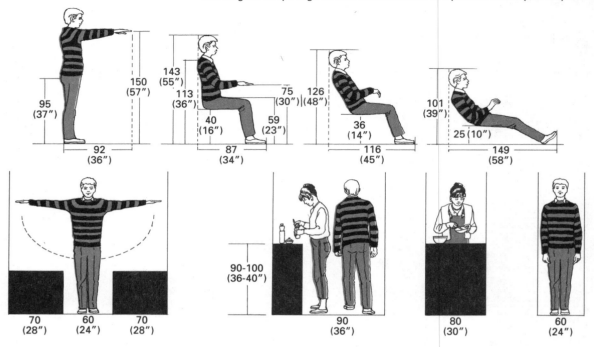

Recommended standing (1), sitting (2), and reclining (3–4) heights and lengths. They are given here in centimetres. The person is 1.8m (5ft11in) tall.

Fig. 14(1) Man needs a certain minimum space to move about comfortably on board. These are some typical limiting dimensions.

The argument against hatch boards is that they are not very quick to operate. That is, it takes time to take out or drop in the individual boards, and though it is normally possible simply to slide back the hatch and climb over the boards in an emergency, this may not be a sensible course in bad weather. An open hatch is an invitation to disaster. A door can be operated and shut in a trice, and if properly and stoutly made is just as waterproof as hatch boards. If a stable door arrangement is employed, with a door opening in two halves, the bottom half can be left closed in bad weather to give ventilation and communication through the open top half. On some sailing vessels the angle through which the door swings as it hinges back may well get in the way.

Motor boats are generally not planned with bad weather in mind. Their cockpits are not intended to be watertight, and large doors for easy access are the order of the day.

14.1.3 Wet lockers

Fig. 14(2) shows the layout of a 8.5m (28ft) centreboard cutter. The boat is a 'one off' but will serve as a discussion vehicle for the various aspects of a below-decks layout.

Few production yachts have proper wet lockers in which to house soaking oilskins or even wet clothing when going below, but such a locker is essential if the interior is to be kept reasonably dry in bad weather. It should be tall enough to stow a full-length oilskin coat and should have a grating at the bottom draining into the bilges. Clothing will dry more quickly if draped over a

plastic clothes hanger than if merely suspended from a hook, and so there should be a short rail in the locker. The door should have a louvred section to admit air. Alternatively hit or miss ventilators, Fig. 14(3) should be fitted top and bottom. The locker should be immediately inside the cabin door for best results.

14.1.4 Chart tables

Somewhere reasonably close to the cabin door should be the chart table. The navigator may need to talk to the helmsman, and if the skipper and the navigator are the same person quick access to the charts is important. On sailing craft the table should be sited for the navigator to sit fore and aft, but on motor boats the table can be arranged in any way to suit the layout. In both cases, though, the minimum size of the table is 0.76m × 0.55m (2ft 6in × 1ft 9in) which will take a folded Admiralty chart. Spread out, the chart occupies a space of about 1m × 0.76m (3ft 6in × 2ft 6in). The table should have a full-size but quite shallow drawer to hold spare charts, but if this is not possible for some reason a large net on a bulkhead is a reasonable substitute. Spare charts are often also stowed under bunk mattresses where at least they stay flat.

Convenient to the navigator should be a bookshelf and a rack where he can stow the pencils, rubbers, pencil sharpeners, parallel rules etc. Ideally there should be a red light for night work and a spot light for more detailed work when the rest of the crew are asleep. This can have a dimmer with advantage. Additionally, good

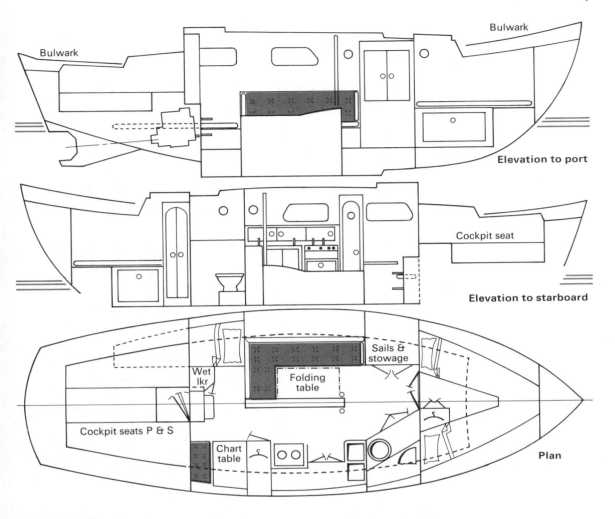

Fig. 14(2) The layout of a 8.5m (28ft) centreboard cutter. Stable doors give entrance from the cockpit above a bridgedeck formed by the engine box. A wet locker is sited close by the cabin steps and the back of the settee is removable to make it wide enough to double up as a berth when required.

natural lighting through a port or window is always helpful. To the basic chart table set-up can be added as many instruments or their repeaters as the owner wants or can afford. Whatever is fitted should be visible and controllable by the navigator without his having to stretch or twist about too much.

14.1.5 Berths
Yacht berths should be at least 1.9m (6ft 3in) and preferably 2m (6ft 6in) in length. They should not

Fig. 14(3) Hit or miss ventilators fitted to lockers in the accommodation allow a circulation of air.

be too wide, 0.8m (2ft 6in) being a reasonable figure, but berths as narrow as 0.6m (2ft) are still perfectly useable. From that width at the shoulders they can taper down to about 0.5m (1ft 6in) at the foot if required. Bunk cushions or mattresses ought to be at least 100mm (4in) thick and preferably, if of a foam material, covered in cotton or some other fabric that does not sweat. Vinyl, for instance, is not very satisfactory. The bunk base on which the mattress lies should have holes drilled in it to allow air to get at the underside of the mattress or it will become damp.

Double bunks, which were once derided as being hopelessly non-seagoing, are increasingly used on yachts. They are perfectly satisfactory provided there are two mattresses and it is possible to erect a division between them for use in rough weather. The division may be of canvas or solid wood and is, in effect, a bunk board.

Bunk boards themselves are the subject of argument. Traditionally, they are of wood which is permanently fixed at the head and foot of the

451

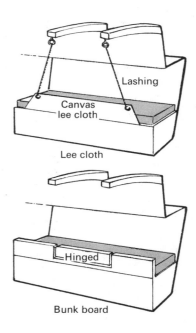

Fig. 14(4) Both permanent bunk boards and leecloth are designed to keep a sleeper in his berth.

berth with a hinged section between. Their height should be some 300mm (12in) above the top of the mattress. The object is to prevent the occupant of the berth from having to cling on in order to stay in and, in the last extremity, to prevent him being pitched on to the cabin sole. A typical bunk board is shown in Fig. 14(4), as is a leecloth. The latter has the same objective, that is to contain the berth occupant, but here it is done by stretching a cloth, which is held down under the mattress, up towards the deckhead with lanyards. A leecloth is lighter and cheaper. It is also more comfortable to lean against than a bunk board (though the latter can be upholstered) but it tends to create rather a hot berth in warm weather. If used, a leecloth ought to extend at least 300mm (12in) above the top of the mattress and the lanyards should be capable of being tightened or slacked off by the person in the bunk.

Quarter berths

When a bunk extends under some permanent part of the boat's structure, usually the cockpit seats, it is called a quarter berth. Such a berth is shown on the port side, aft on Fig. 14(2). These berths are usually snug and comfortable since it is impossible to roll out, but they demand the use of sleeping bags since there is no way the bunk can be made up in the normal manner.

Pilot berths

Another snug and comfortable bunk is the pilot berth which is built in outboard of and above a

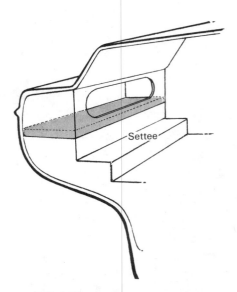

Fig. 14(5) A pilot berth fitted outboard of and above a settee makes a comfortable and secure bunk.

settee, usually in the saloon. It is entered through an oval cut in the bulkhead which otherwise shields it, Fig. 14(5). Usually a curtain is arranged to draw across the entrance hole to give the occupant privacy and dark. There needs to be at the very least 0.55m of height (1ft 9in) above the top of the mattress to allow turning-over, but even that makes for a potentially very hot berth in warm weather. On boats fitted with them, the pilot berth is generally the most popular of all the sleeping spaces.

Fo'c'sle berths

Up in the bows of the boat V-berths are usually found. These join at their feet and can be seen on Fig. 14(2). An alternative, where there is plenty of height, is to use two berths one above the other on different sides of the boat, Fig. 14(6). Their feet

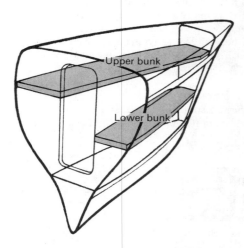

Fig. 14(6) In some craft it may be possible to install fo'c'sle berths one above the other with the feet crossing towards the bow.

cross and the two berths at this point should have about 300mm (12in) difference in height. This is a practical solution in many cases and is preferred where strangers may be called on to share the fo'c'sle. It is difficult to be dogmatic about the height between sole and deckhead required to achieve this arrangement, since the shape of the boat will govern how low the lower bunk may be sited, but as a guide it is worth considering where headroom is 1.7m (5ft 6in) or more.

Pullman berths

This type of bunk forms the backrest of a settee during the day but is hinged up to form a berth at night. It is important that the angle to the horizontal the berth makes when up can be adjusted, especially on sailing craft. The space behind the berth when it is lowered forms an excellent stowage for bedding.

Pipe cots

These are made up with tubular steel or aluminium alloy surrounds with tightly stretched Terylene or similar material between forming the base of the berth. Normally their outboard edges sit in U-shaped brackets fastened to the vessel's sides, while the inboard faces have lanyards lashed to them which make fast to eyes on deck beams. Therefore their angle can be adjusted. Pipe cots are most often found in fo'c'sles. They are perfectly satisfactory and light in weight but need some sort of mattress to make them comfortable. The one trouble with berths like the pipe cot and pullman berth mentioned earlier is that on sailing craft it is usually necessary to adjust their angle on each tack. This is a confounded nuisance for the occupant. Leecloths can be fitted but cannot be set up tight without the whole weight of the

berth coming on their lashings which may be more than they can stand.

14.1.6 Settees

Whereas it is possible to sit for quite a few hours on a seat in an airliner without too much discomfort, the same cannot be said for the average yacht settee. The trouble is that the settee, being used at different times for sitting, lounging and sleeping, cannot be designed to be really satisfactory in any of these roles. If simple sitting comfort can be catered for, Fig. 14(7) shows the cross section through a suitable shape. The cushions should be about 75mm (3in) thick and of firm foam. The 100mm (4in) thickness recommended for bunks is too much for seats.

14.1.7 Cabin tables

At one time cabin tables were quite often gimballed so that they remained level whatever the heel of the yacht. On a narrow table this is still a good idea, though the table needs to be ballasted with weights in a box well below the table top and its pivoting point. In addition it may be necessary to dampen the swing of the table. On high-class work this used to be done with a brake on the pivot but shock cord can be substituted. With a wide table gimballing is not recommended since the table top will be up around the ears of the occupant on one side and hitting the ankles of the person on the other side, Fig. 14(8).

Most yachts these days make do with a fixed table bounded by fiddles. The shape of a proper fiddle is shown on Fig. 14(9). It should stop short of the corners of the table or work-top or wherever it is fitted so that crumbs and other debris can be swept clear. Alternatively it can be removable. This is achieved with pegs in the bottom of the fiddle dropping into holes in the surface it is bounding.

Someone plying a knife and fork occupies a space at least 0.6m (2ft) wide and preferably could do with a little more than that. This dimension

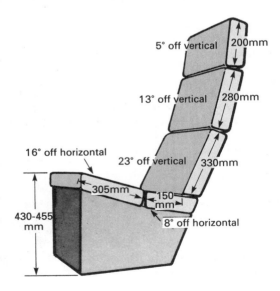

Fig. 14(7) If room is available for a comfortable seat that does not have to double up as a berth, this gives a suitable shape and is akin to airline seating.

Fig. 14(8) A wide gimballed table is not much use at big angles of heel.

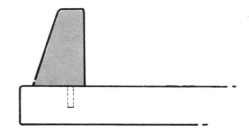

Fig. 14(9) A fiddle should have a vertical inner face and be some 65–75mm (2½–3in) high. If pegs in its bottom drop into holes in the surface it bounds, the fiddle can be made removable.

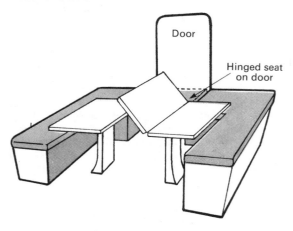

Fig. 14(10) Sometimes it may be possible to arrange a passageway through a table with a hinged flap filling the gap as required.

governs how many people can sit round a table. If there are problems in arranging enough seating it is sometimes possible to have a passageway through a pair of tables which is closed with a hinged section at mealtimes, Fig. 14(10). The table on the cutter of Fig. 14(2) is hinged on the centreboard case so that it can be dropped out of the way as required. A permanently wide table is always a nuisance on board a small yacht.

14.1.8 Dinettes
On motor boats in particular, use is often made of dinettes where a table set between athwartships seats can be lowered to be flush with those seats. The overall length of the structure is then sufficient for it to form a berth, Fig. 14(11). The result may be a single or double berth but the arrangement is not really suitable for sailing craft, where seating should run fore and aft to cater for the fact that under sail a craft may be well heeled over.

Dinettes are space-savers since they combine the functions of eating, sitting and sleeping. The backs of the settees are normally removed to fit over the table when it is used as part of a berth. This multiplicity of rather inadequate berth cushions means that a dinette is not really very comfortable as a bunk. Nor is it ideal as a spot for lounging, since seats narrow enough to allow comfortable eating are too narrow for sprawling on.

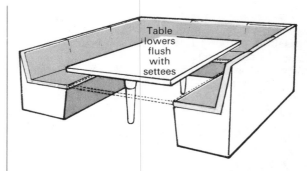

Fig. 14(11) A dinette is most often found in motor boats. With the table lowered a berth is formed.

14.1.9 Toilet compartments
Fig. 14(1) showed the space needed for comfortable sitting with the implication that the distance between the back of the toilet itself and a bulkhead or other obstruction in front of it should be around 0.9m (3ft). This is a practical minimum and one to be exceeded wherever possible, but equally important is shoulder room. People have to be able to turn around, pull their trousers up and generally stretch in a minor manner. This means that the width of the compartment should not be less than 0.76m (2ft 6in). Ideally the toilet should be situated so that the user is sitting athwartships but this is not always possible, and since a toilet is used for only a few minutes a day some departures from the ideal can be accepted.

Washbasins are too often set under side decks where they are impossible to use effectively. Even if mounted clear of such obstructions but close to, say a bulkhead or cabin side they can be difficult unless at a good height above the sole. That reduces the need for the user to lean forward when washing. Such a height can be as much as 1m (3ft 4in) with advantage and at that even quite short people would have no problems. Otherwise 0.8m (3ft) is normally right.

There should be a fiddle at the basin surround and somewhere to stow the paraphernalia of washing; preferably each crew member should have an individual space. Since there may be a fair amount of water splashing around, the sole should have a non-slippery surface and by the same token the door sill should be reasonably high, especially if there is a shower installed in the compartment. A 150mm (6in) sill is not excessive.

14.1.10 Sail lockers
Small cruising yachts commonly store sails in the cockpit lockers but there is a good case for having them in the accommodation. Here they will stay drier and can be sorted out under more favourable conditions. If fitted, the sail locker should be convenient to the forehatch. It may take the form of a simple bin, but if a proper full-height locker is used the top half may be employed for general stowage. There is generally a shortage of good stowage on board and one more will not come amiss.

14.1.11 The galley area

Though most small yachts have the galley arranged at the aft end of the accommodation there is really no best place for it, and each position has its advantages. The motion is generally worse forward than somewhere nearer midships, but the cook is less bothered by the passage of people wanting to get by and go on deck or into the cockpit if the galley is forward. The draught through a boat is generally from aft forward, so that with the forehatch open a crack the sometimes hideous smells from the galley have less far to travel before they escape overboard. The odour of cooking will not appeal to potentially seasick members of the crew. On the other hand, the draught close by the companionway (but to one side of it) will be less fierce than that forward, so that there is less danger of the gas blowing out with an aft galley. In the end the galley will be found where it is convenient for the designer to put it, and very good reasons will then be concocted for its position.

In any case since only one person at a time is usually occupying the galley, the floor space can be small and, indeed, it is an advantage if the cook has everything within easy reach. Since, especially on sailing boats, the motion may be wild and the vessel well heeled, it is useful if the galley is so shaped that the cook can wedge his or herself in position aided by a strap to lean back against and a bar to reduce the risk of falling forward on to the stove. This means that the most practical galley configuration is either an L or a U shape. In Fig. 14(2) the galley is U-shaped and there is only 0.6m (2ft) between the arms.

Cooking at sea is not quite like doing the job at home and the layout needs to be rather different. Sandwiches of one sort or another are frequently the principal source of sustenance in bad weather, and there should be an adequate working surface to prepare them. On the one hand a draining board is not a requirement since everything would fall off it. Its place can be taken either by a rack above the sink or by a second sink in which dirty dishes and pots and pans can be deposited until they can be attended to. If space is really tight, the sink (which should be at least 200mm (8in) deep) can be closed off with a portable cover which is used as an additional working surface.

Within these limitations the galley has to be arranged to suit its equipment. A gimballed stove needs to have its axis fore and aft so that it can swing as the boat rolls. Since gas piping (if gas is used) should be as short as possible, the stove will be sited as close to the gas cylinder and locker as can be arranged. Refrigerator doors must open into the centre of the vessel if they are to take advantage of the fact that many can accept quite fierce rolling without harm. The outlet pipe from the sink should be as short as possible so that its downward path is steep to get rid of the water quickly.

Working surfaces must be bounded by non-continuous fiddle rails to allow the mess to be swept off without difficulty and all potentially harmful corners should be rounded. All locker shelves, even those behind doors, should have fiddles or some form of retaining bar to prevent the contents from raining out. If gas is used the tap to turn off the supply (which should be used every time the stove is not wanted and be quite separate from the main supply shut-off which is on the gas bottle itself) must be visible and easy to reach. Good natural lighting through a port or window is a desirable feature, as is the provision of proper artificial lighting. The cook does not want to operate constantly in his own shadow. A ventilator in the galley is a good thing but it should be able to be closed. There can be quite fierce draughts through a vent which may blow out the gas. That is inconvenient at best and dangerous at worst.

The galleys of motor boats are not often arranged with seagoing cooking as a priority. The implication is that food will be prepared beforehand if a passage is to be made and proper cooking only undertaken in a sheltered berth. If that is the intention, then the normal motor boat galley will suffice but otherwise the same rules apply as to sailing craft. It is, though, worth mentioning that pre-cooking some sort of meal and storing it in a large vacuum flask is a sensible way of going about things even under sail if only a short passage is to be made. The same thing applies to hot drinks or soup but there must be a good stowage for the flasks.

Stowage

It is sensible to use unbreakable crockery and glasses on a boat but even so their stowage should be secure. They should not simply be piled up in a locker from which they can avalanche if the door is opened on the wrong tack. There are many ways of achieving neat stowages, the most basic being to drop the plates, for instance, between vertical dowels. These hold them in position but allow them to be extricated without difficulty. Cutlery is probably best stowed in a box with an open top.

In the absence of a refrigerator or other cooling unit it should be remembered that the hull will be cooler below the waterline than some way up the topsides, so that vegetables and other perishables are best stowed low down and even in a suitable container in the bilges if this is feasible. If these perishables have to be kept in lockers around the galley, the doors should be louvred or have some similar way of ensuring a flow of air in the locker itself. Airtight containers should be used for items like salt, sugar, flour and biscuits. There must be some form of rubbish or gash bucket convenient to the cook but preferably stowed out of sight. There are household containers made which hold disposable plastic bags and can be fastened to a locker door. These are handy and, with a bag clipped at the top, taking the rubbish ashore is not the messy task it might otherwise be.

A dustpan and brush and damp cloth will find frequent employment in the galley area and should be stowed somewhere handy. On this score it is worth mentioning that cutting bread on board seems to spread the crumbs over unimaginable distances. Sliced bread, despite its rather poor image, is preferable.

14.1.12 Galley stoves

Cooking may be done by solid fuel, electricity, paraffin, alcohol (methylated spirits) or bottled gas. On large yachts the Aga, Esse or Rayburn type of solid fuel burning stove is appropriate, especially where the constant heat given off is appreciated. However such stoves really need to be backed up by something more speedy, such as a couple of gas rings, for times when nearly instant meals are called for. Electric cooking where microwave ovens can be used to back up the main cooker for really speedy work is popular in bigger craft, too, but having to run the generator even to boil a kettle is a nuisance for those on board as well as to other boats nearby. If for any reason the electric supply fails, then the crew will go hungry unless some form of emergency cooking has been catered for.

Paraffin pressure stoves in the form of the much revered Primuses were once just about the sole form of cooking aboard smallish cruising boats and there is still much to recommend the method. Paraffin is relatively easy to procure in any part of the world, though it has recently become rather expensive. Though paraffin burns of course, it does not present the explosion hazard of gas, and the stove is quick in operation. Its main drawback is that it is not quite as clean, or as swift to start as a gas stove. The paraffin has to be pre-heated either by using methylated spirits in a cup below the burner or, on the latest models, pumping up the pressure and lighting an auxiliary jet directed towards the main burner. In the fullness of time (something like one minute), either pre-heating method will allow the main burner to light properly. Failure to pre-heat properly can lead to spectacular jets of burning paraffin climbing towards the deckhead. Although, if the stove is turned off immediately, this is more alarming than dangerous it does tend to deposit oily soot about the place. It is not easy to get a really satisfactory oven for a paraffin pressure stove nor to turn the heat down sufficiently for gentle simmering (although an asbestos mat can be used), but it adds a properly nautical air to the galley.

Overseas, methylated spirit stoves are popular but they, too, need pre-heating and the smell of the meths is not pleasant for those with squeamish stomachs. The fuel in this country is expensive and not easily procurable in any but small quantities. Alcohol is safe and a fire can be put out with water, but the great majority of boat-owners here choose bottle gas for cooking since it is convenient, readily available, clean and quick. It is also dangerous if leaks occur. As mentioned

further in 14.2.2 the piping should be as short as possible and it should be professionally installed. Gas cookers should have a flame-failure shut-off device.

Cookers in sailing yachts need to be gimballed and on all types of craft should have adjustable fiddle rails such that individual pots and pans can be clamped in position. Two burners and a grill are about the minimum requirements; an oven will be much appreciated at times.

14.1.13 Calor gas

Calor Gas Ltd (Calor) is the leading UK supplier of butane and propane, in a variety of cylinder sizes which are hired to the user. Strictly speaking, these cylinders may only be refilled by Calor dealers, but Calor recognizes that cruising yachtsmen will, where possible, get them refilled abroad. In that only a hire charge is made, Calor hopes that a yachtsman's cylinders will eventually be returned to the UK market.

Both propane and butane are heavier than air and present a fire/explosive danger unless properly handled. The safety aspects have already been discussed in Chapter 8 (8.3.5). Butane ceases to vapourise at about freezing point while propane can withstand temperatures of $-42°C$ ($-44°F$) before this happens, so that in a boat used all the year round propane may be preferable. On the other hand butane has a higher calorific value and is less highly pressurised in its container: 2.1kg/sq cm (30lb/sq in), compared with propane at about 7kg/sq cm (100lb/sq in). Thus butane is slightly safer should a fire break out. If the intention is to use butane in the summer and propane in the winter, then the 14.5kg (32lb) and 4.5kg (10lb) butane cylinders are the same size as the 13kg (29lb) and 3.9kg ($8\frac{1}{2}$lb) propane cylinders and will thus stow in the same lockers.

The following sizes of calor cylinders are available in the UK. Butane (blue cylinders): 4.5kg, 7kg and 15kg. Propane (red cylinders): 3.9kg, 13kg, 19kg and 47kg. Cylinders may be connected singly, in pairs, or manifolded together. An automatic changeover valve is available for propane cylinders. Propane must never be filled into a butane cylinder because the setting of the pressure relief valve is unsuitable for propane's higher pressure.

All Calor propane cylinder valves have a female 'POL' connection with a $\frac{5}{8}$in BSP female left hand thread. Calor 4.5kg butane cylinder valves have a $\frac{5}{8}$in BSP male left hand thread on to which a hexagonal union nut screws. Calor 7kg and 15kg butane valves are quite different and are designed to take the 21mm 'Kosan Teknova Compact' system of connectors or regulators.

Liquified petroleum gas (LPG) used in the UK, France, the Mediterranean and tropical countries, is predominantly butane. On a world-wide basis propane is more readily available and is the predominant form of LPG in Scandinavia, USA, Australia and New Zealand, and most countries south of 30°S.

Calor 4.5kg refills are available in Northern Ireland, but the larger butane cylinders have a Kosan 'click-on' valve which is not compatible with Calor GB regulators. Propane 3.9kg and 13kg cylinders with standard (GB compatible) 'POL' connections are available. In the Republic of Ireland none of the cylinders (butane or propane) is compatible with Calor GB regulators. Ways of overcoming these problems with different cylinders and connections are described below.

Note that for safety reasons a LPG cylinder should never be filled to 100% capacity. In tropical or semi-tropical regions 70% capacity should not be exceeded, and in temperate regions 80%. Many small cylinders do not have relief valves, and if heated when overfilled could burst with disastrous results.

Cylinders generally have the 'tare weight' (the weight of the cylinder empty) stamped on an aluminium tare disc attached. If you intend to have Calor cylinders refilled abroad, leave the UK with ones that will not require testing before your return. Calor cylinders are tested and revalved every 15 years, and the next test date is stamped on the tare disc by the last two digits of the year. Also select cylinders with the smartest paintwork, to avoid problems with depots that will not handle cylinders that are 'scruffy' or near their test date.

As noted above, butane and propane cylinders have different connections, and the regulators are not interchangeable. However, the gases may be interchanged with safety if certain precautions are taken. For appliances approved for butane use only, the butane regulator (28m bar) may be exchanged for a propane regulator (37m bar), as described below. The resulting performance may not be perfect, but it will be satisfactory and safe. Similarly, if butane appliances and a butane regulator are supplied with propane, they will work safely but the performance will be reduced, since the calorific content of propane by volume is less than that of butane.

Advice for extended cruising

Check each appliance in the boat to see if it is intended to use butane or propane. This can be determined from data on the appliance, from handbooks etc., from Calor dealers, or from the manufacturer. Ideally gas appliances should be approved for both butane and propane operation. Most boats built in the UK have a butane installation, but since propane is more universally available it is wise to convert to propane before an extended cruise.

To overcome the problem of butane and propane connections not being interchangeable, and different cylinders in different countries having different connections, the regulator should be fixed to a bulkhead with a 'wall-block manifold' (obtainable like all other Calor fittings from Peter Spreadborough, Southampton Calor Gas Centre, Third Avenue, Millbrook Trading Estate, Southampton SO1 0JX. Tel: (01703) 788155. Fax:

(01703) 774768, and not fitted directly to the cylinder. If the primary intention is to use propane, fit the appropriate propane regulator (such as Calor Gas 766P) to the wall-block manifold and take an equivalent butane regulator.

The regulator on the bulkhead should be connected by high pressure LPG tubing to a suitable male connector for a propane cylinder, or female connector for butane. It is most important to use 'Calor Gas Approved' tube to British Standards or equivalent, to avoid attack by propane or butane. The tube must be secured at each end by a stainless steel hose clip.

For American waters note that UK and US 'POL' connections on propane cylinders are different, the US versions being slightly smaller in overall diameter, and usually with a smaller AF nut form. While it is usually possible (but bad practice) to get a tight seal with US 'POL' regulator into a UK 'POL' cylinder, it is physically impossible to get a UK 'POL' regulator into a US 'POL' cylinder.

As Camping Gaz International markets its range of small butane cylinders in over 100 countries, it may be good sense to take its largest cylinder (2.72kg) and a Camping Gaz/Calor adaptor (available from Calor dealers), thus allowing a Camping Gaz cylinder to be connected to a Calor butane installation. It should be noted however that the amount of gas contained in a Camping Gaz cylinder is fairly limited.

Camping Gaz is universally obtainable in Spain, where it is also possible to get Calor cylinders recharged with butane at certain major ports – Alicante, Barcelona, Bilbao, Cadiz, Giron, Huelva, Ibiza, Alcudia (Mallorca), Ciudadela (Menorca), La Coruna, Malaga, Pontevedra, San Sebastian, Santander, Tarragona, Valencia. Be warned, however, that the Butano factory is often well outside the town.

In the Republic of Ireland LPG is provided by Kosan, a sister company of Calor Gas Ltd, in both butane and propane form. Calor cylinders can be exchanged for Kosan, but the latter are bigger and may not fit in a boat's gas locker.

In Norway, Calor cylinders can be refilled by Progas Co. at Oslo, Kristiansand, Stavanger and Bergen. This can also be done at a few places in Denmark, and at Holtenau at the E end of the Kiel Canal.

For a lengthy cruise in Scandinavian waters it is best to use the Primus propane cylinders, available in the UK from Calor Gas, although they are small (1.9kg) and have a unique connection.

Mention should also be made of BP Caravangas, which comes in a 7kg aluminium cylinder, and is fairly generally available in Europe except in France and Italy. The cylinder does however have rather a large shroud, and as the name implies it is intended primarily for caravans.

For a lengthy cruise to foreign countries it is advisable to take about three metres of Calor LPG tubing and half-a-dozen hose clips, for connecting local butane or propane cylinders to the boat's system. The ends of the tubing so used must be kept in good condition, and cut back as necessary, while it is important to tighten hose clips by just the right amount. Always check for possible gas leaks after installation with a little soapy water, and turn the gas off at the cylinder after use.

Any gas appliance must have adequate ventilation in order to avoid the generation of carbon monoxide – invisible, tasteless and deadly poisonous.

Further information on LPG can be obtained from Calor Gas Ltd, Appleton Park, Riding Court Road, Datchet, Slough SL3 9LG so far as the United Kingdom is concerned, and from the European Liquefied Petroleum Gas Association (AEGPL), 4 Avenue Hosche, 75008 Paris, in respect of European countries.

For further notes on LPG, see 8.3.5 and 14.2.2.

14.1.14 Accomodation in general

Though it is tempting to take into account the fact that going up a few inches from the cabin sole probably increases the available sole width quite dramatically, and some builders succumb to that temptation by elevating dinettes or making the floor height in a sleeping cabin higher than elsewhere, all the accommodation should lie on the same level. Steps up or down are dangerous at sea and it is all too easy to trip over them in bad weather. Keeping one's feet below is aided by handholds. These may take the form of handrails under the deckhead or vertical pillars at strategic points. There are for instance, a pair of pillars bounding the forward end of the centreboard case in Fig. 14(2). These double up as supports for the deck-stepped mast. All corners should be rounded as in the case of the two ends of the galley in the 8.5m (28ft) cutter.

There are many neat catches on the market which can be used on lockers and doors but the old-fashioned barrel bolts and cabin hooks should not be forgotten. They may not look quite as

smart, but they are completely reliable and their operation is obvious to any newcomer on board. Drawers should be of the lift-out type, Fig. 14(12), and not rely on catches. Hinging locker fronts should hinge along their bottom edges as a general rule.

The sole should have inspection hatches in it and not be a single sheet of material. There may be an urgent need to have a look at the inside of the hull bottom at some time. The sole itself can be of timber in some form but it might be considered a luxury for a family cruising boat to have carpet. As long as a wet locker is provided, and used, this is not as impractical as it may sound. The actual area of the sole to be covered will probably be quite small and a meagre offcut from the carpet shop will often suffice and leave enough over for a spare. So when the original becomes too stained, chuck it out and, after using it as a pattern, replace it with the spare. Provided the carpet was a good fit to begin with it will probably not need fastening down, but the edges will need binding.

14.1.15 Condensation

In the days when wooden boats were the norm, condensation was not a serious problem though the generally damp conditions on board might have led people to believe otherwise. The comparatively thin skins of modern craft, built of materials such as GRP and steel, with far poorer insulating properties than timber, have led to the need to take active steps to reduce condensation. This is achieved in some cases by the use of an inner skin in the cabin area of GRP craft and, though the object of that skin is as much to give a smooth surface to the inside of the accommodation as it is to cut down condensation, it is quite effective.

The first defence against damp is good ventilation. A flow of air works wonders. After this some form of insulating layer against the skin is valuable. On steel craft, for example, the plating between frames can be sprayed with a polyurethane foam up to the level of the frames, and then lined. This is excellent but rather expensive. A cheaper method is to use slabs of foam tailored to fit between those frames. The latter have timber battens fastened to them into which can be screwed the ply lining. Not quite as effective but good enough for most purposes is to stick a foam-backed vinyl direct to the steel, alloy or GRP shell. The thicker the foam, the better. Overheads can have battens glued, bonded or in some other way fastened in position; slabs of thin foam wedged between; and then tongue and groove planking screwed up to cover everything. This looks nice, and the combination of timber and foam has good insulating properties. This sort of approach is difficult on cabin sides where there are probably window or port cut-outs to contend with.

In areas where a lining might be inappropriate, such as in wheelhouses, forepeaks and the like, a

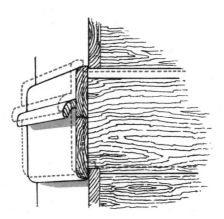

Fig. 14(12) If a drawer is arranged such that it has to be lifted to slide out, it will remain secure under almost any angle of heel.

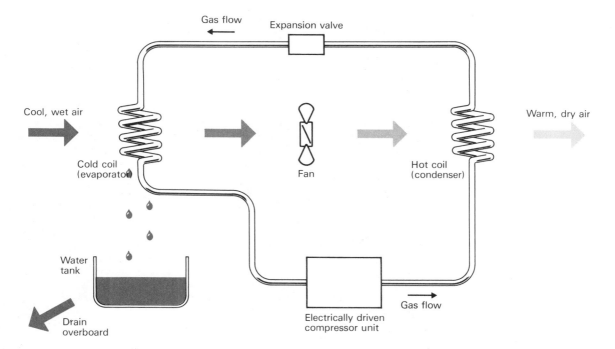

Fig. 14(13) A dehumidifier has a similar gas circuit to a domestic compressor-type refrigerator. Air from the space concerned is blown by a fan first across the cold coil of the evaporator where moisture condenses out, and then across the hot coil of the condenser, before passing back into the space, drier and warmer.

paint containing cork chippings, such as Korkon, made by International Paints, is surprisingly good.

Dehumidifiers

Any boat which is occupied, and therefore heated, during the winter months is certain to suffer problems with condensation which the steps described above are unlikely to overcome completely. The warmer the air inside the boat, the more water vapour it can hold — until the temperature falls, say at night, when condensation streams down windows and other cool surfaces. Gas heaters make the problem worse, because they actually produce water vapour.

The modern approach to reducing condensation afloat is to fit a dehumidifier. This type of machine, which works on a principle similar to that of a domestic refrigerator, has been in use ashore for some time, and similar machinery on a larger scale has been used to preserve the interiors of warships when laid-up in reserve for extended periods. But it is only in recent years that suitably 'marinised' units have been available for yachts. Although they cost £400 or more, they are not particularly expensive to run, and can soon pay for themselves by reducing the deterioration of fittings, fabrics, furnishings, clothes, books etc which will otherwise occur, as well as providing healthier and more pleasant living conditions on board.

A dehumidifier, as illustrated in Fig. 14(13), has a larger cold coil (evaporator) than an ordinary refrigerator. Moisture-laden air from the accommodation is blown across this coil by a fan, so that the moisture condenses on the cold surface and is collected in a tank which can either be emptied manually or piped overboard. If ice should form in the machine an automatic defrost sequence comes into operation. The air, now cooler and drier, then passes over the hot coil (condenser) of the machine, extracting heat from it and allowing the refrigeration cycle to continue.

The air, now both drier and warmer than it was originally, then passes back into the accommodation and the cycle is repeated. Gradually the humidity is reduced throughout the vessel. An automatic control can be set to maintain the relative humidity (the percentage of water vapour contained in the air compared with the maximum amount that it could contain at a given temperature) at the required level — typically 55 to 60 per cent.

Depending upon the temperature and relative humidity maintained, it would be quite possible for a dehumidifier to extract 2 litres ($3\frac{1}{2}$ pints) of water in the course of 24 hours — a good indication of just how much moisture can be present in a boat. In order to obtain maximum efficiency from the unit, all ventilators and openings should be shut while the vessel is unoccupied, and used sensibly while people are on board.

The water which is collected can be used for washing or for topping up batteries, but should only be drunk in emergency.

Machines are available which work on 12 volts DC, as well as models for 230 volts AC mains operation.

14.2 Cabin heating

14.2.1 Solid fuel

Though infrequently seen these days, except on such rather specialised craft as canal boats, a solid fuel or bogie stove is a very good and quite convenient source of cabin heat. It circulates and dries air better than any other type and, on models where the fire can be seen through the doors, gives a cheerful glow guaranteed to lift the spirits after a cold watch on deck. It is quiet, undemanding and not in the least technical. It takes no power to operate and the amount of heat given off is simply controlled.

There are several stoves made for yachts but it is important when choosing one to ensure that there are draught controls both at the firebox and flue. It must be capable of being bolted down, and if it is fed through opening doors these must have a secure fastening. The flue pipe will get very hot on occasions. Thus is should either have an expanded metal or some other form of guard round it; or the flue should be a double one, with inner and outer pipes. With the latter arrangement the outer pipe is continued up through the level of the deckhead to obviate the danger of burning the structure. Where a guard only is used a water well should be fitted. Fig. 14(14). This projects down through the deckhead and is filled with water to keep the surrounding area cool. The flue pipe fits over the lower projection of the water well and the chimney, or smoke head, over the upper.

The Liverpool head type of chimney is normally quite effective under yacht conditions and is unobtrusive. If space is not a premium in the deck area around the smoke head, the twin head type is excellent especially if it can be swivelled to suit wind direction. Both are shown in Fig. 14(14). Fuel for a solid fuel stove can be anything from the gleanings of a beach to coal packed in standard 10kg (22lb) plastic bags. Using the latter a stove should be able to burn for at least eight hours without attention.

A typical stove is the Tor-Gem which is 550mm (21in) high by 340mm (13½in) deep by 280 mm

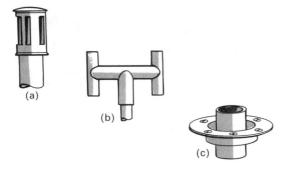

Fig. 14(14) The chimney of a solid fuel stove may have a Liverpool head (a) or a twin head (b). If the stove pipe passes through the deckhead without any form of outer casing, a water well (c) should be fitted.

(11in) wide. The flue has a diameter of 100mm (4in). Bulkheads and similar structures in way of a stove should be lined with a heat resistant and fireproof material while the cabin sole in the immediate vicinity should be similarly treated.

14.2.2 Gas heating

The liquefied petroleum gas (LPG) used on board yachts may be either butane or propane. Both are heavier than air and thus an escape will collect in the bilges where it is a potential source of explosion. See 8.3.5. Good installation and care in use minimises the risk, but pipes should be as few in number and as short as possible, which is a reason why a gas fire is not often seen on board. The appliance itself, though, is generally safe enough since modern types are fitted with flame failure cut-offs and atmospheric sensors. This means that if the flame is extinguished for any reason the gas supply is automatically cut off. The same thing happens if the CO_2 in the atmosphere rises above a certain limit. The latter device is not quite as important if the appliance has a flue. There must always be some permanently open ventilator in any area heated by gas.

Gas bottles should preferably be stored in a locker on deck with an overside drain at the bottom. Failing this, the locker must be gas tight, but again with an overboard drain which emerges above the waterline. Bottles may be coupled together so that when one is empty the other can be turned on to operate through the same regulator and supply pipe. If this means too big a locker it is hardly much trouble to bring in a spare and link up after taking away the empty. Gas should always be turned off at the cylinder when it is not required, and this means after every cooking or heating session – not just at the end of the day.

For the safety aspects of gas installations see Chapter 6 (8.3.5), and for other details of LPG see 14.1.13.

14.2.3 Hot air heating

Most hot air heating sets work in the same way. They comprise a glow plug which lights an atomised paraffin or diesel supply, the latter being generally drawn from the engine fuel tank. In the case of a boat without an engine or one with a petrol motor, a separate jerry-can type of container may be installed with a suitable connection. The heat from this burning warms outside air passing through a heat exchanger which is then blown into the cabin, or is trunked to different parts of the boat. Normally safety devices are fitted such that if the heater does not ignite or goes out unintentionally it is switched off. Similarly, if it becomes overheated it will switch off, and most models have a thermostat control fitted to allow the cabin temperature to be selected. When this has been reached the unit will cut out. It will start again automatically once the temperature has dropped below the desired level.

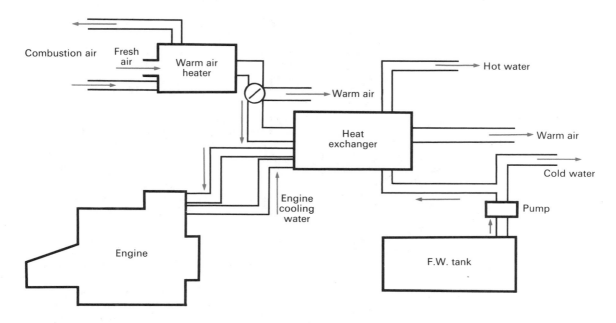

Fig. 14(15) A hot air blower can be used to heat water in a heat exchanger, and also used as a calorifier to extract waste heat from the engine cooling system.

Some models require the main body to be installed in or around the cockpit where there is plenty of fresh air; others can be installed below decks where fresh air is trunked to them. There are various sizes available from about 1.5 to 3 kilowatts and fuel consumption is modest, from about 0.2 to 0.4 litres (0.05 to 0.09 gallons) per hour. Models of 12 and 24v are available. The 3000W Volvo Penta Ardic Minimax, for example, on 12v operation has a current consumption of about 3 amps during combustion but, due to thermostat control, the average consumption is about 1 amp.

14.2.4 Heating by hot water
A development of the Ardic heater mentioned in 14.2.3 uses the unit to heat up water by trunking the hot air through a calorifier or heat exchanger. Alternatively the water may be heated by using the cooling water from an indirectly cooled engine (see also 14.3.3). A third method is to plug into the mains and employ the immersion heater built into the heat exchanger. The hot water so produced can heat radiators in various parts of the boat, and, of course, be used for washing as well. If required, the hot air heater could be used on its own – diverted from the calorifier – or part of its output could heat the water and the other part still be employed in producing hot air. Fig. 14(15) shows the whole layout in diagrammatic form.

A more conventional approach and one suitable for bigger vessels is to fit what amounts to a miniature central heating boiler, such as the types made by Perkins Boilers. Models may be selected producing 60,000, 100,000 or 150,000 BTUs/hr and operate off the engine diesel fuel. Hot water

circulates through small bore piping to radiators or panel heaters. It may also be used, in a heat exchanger, to heat air. Heat exchangers also allow this circulating water to be used for domestic hot water supply . A 60,000 BTU type would weigh about 96kg (212lb) and would be about 720mm (28in) high; 560mm (22in) deep; and 360mm (14in) wide.

In such a system it is important to bear in mind the need for protection against frost while the boat is lying unattended during the winter months. If the boat is lying alongside, the simplest solution is to install one or more electric heaters of the simple tubular type, run off shore power. These will protect the entire contents of the boat against both damp and frost. If this is not possible, all water systems must be drained down, but it is difficult to avoid small pockets of water remaining. A small bore central heating system can be protected by adding anti-freeze (ethylene glycol). A 25 per cent solution by volume will give protection down to −12°C (+10°F). Anti-freeze must not of course be added to water systems which form part of the domestic supply.

14.3 Fresh water systems

14.3.1 Galley pumps
There is a wide range of manual and foot-operated galley pumps available, ranging from those where the actual pump is mounted at sole level and is worked by the foot (useful if the galley slave has his or her hands fully occupied); to those where the pump is a little lever that is flipped backwards

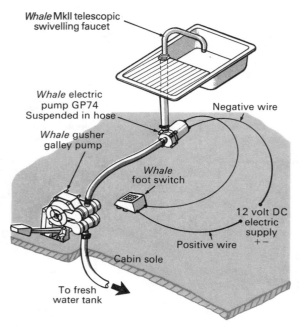

Fig. 14(16) The simplest type of electric water pump is incorporated into an existing system with a foot-operated pump.

and forwards and mounted integrally with the tap; and others where the pump is a more conventional up-and-down affair. There are also pedal operated

diaphragm pumps on the market. All these have quite a modest output of somewhere between about 4.5 to 9 litres (1 to 2 gallons) per minute. This is quite adequate for galley use and serves also to keep water consumption down. It is astonishing how dramatically the demand for water increases once it is freely available through an electric pump, and how inadequate once ample water tanks then become. However sophisticated a water pumping system is fitted, there should always be a hand pump at the galley sink for emergency use.

On craft intended for long cruises a pump drawing on sea water is also useful. Washing up can be done in salt water, potatoes can be washed in sea water, and a dash of salt water in fresh is suitable when cooking many vegetables.

14.3.2 **Electric systems**
The simplest form of electric water pumping is to install a pump in an existing hand-operated system. Whale make such a suitable model and it is light enough (220g or $\frac{1}{2}$lb) to be suspended from the water hoses, which eliminates mechanical vibration. This particular pump is not self-priming and in the absence of a gravity fed system has to be primed through the manual pump. Fig. 14(16) shows a typical layout. In the event of it failing the hand pump will still operate, which is a considerable advantage. As will be seen the electric pump has to be switched on each time it is needed.

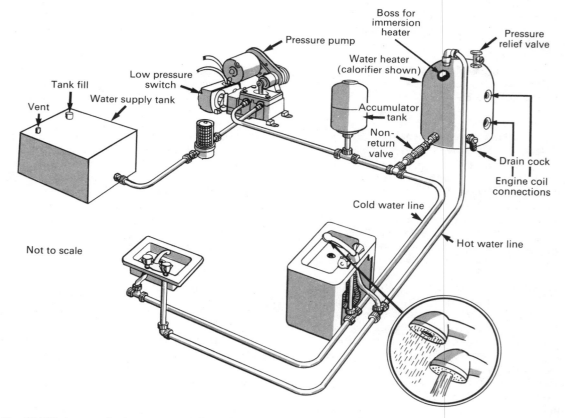

Fig. 14(17) A pressurised water system. Some form of manual water pump should be added.

This is in contrast to the more sophisticated pressure sets where the whole system is kept under pressure by a pump with automatic operation. When a tap is turned to allow water to flow out, the pressure is reduced and the pump cuts in to keep the water flowing, and to keep the pressure up to the required level. An accumulator tank in the system is an advantage since it holds a pressure reservoir of trapped air. This makes for a smooth flow of water and also means that the pump does not have to start every time an outlet is opened. This lengthens its life and reduces battery drain. These electric systems tend to be rather noisy but they do mean that showers and running hot water are available. Fig. 14(17) shows a typical layout which includes a calorifier to produce the hot water.

14.3.3 Water heating
The three principal methods of heating water on board (apart from putting a kettle on a stove) are to use an electric immersion heater in a tank; put a gas heater (like a geyser) in the system; or employ the engine cooling water from an indirectly cooled engine to give up its heat in a calorifier or heat exchanger. The first and last of these methods are usually combined in that an immersion heater is sited in the calorifier. Since operating an immersion heater would lead to an impossible load on the battery, it is normally only linked to a main voltage connection. On bigger yachts with ample generating capacity an immersion heater can be run without relying on shore facilities.

Like all gas appliances, gas water heaters are treated with some reserve and are probably best used on craft whose lives are spent mainly on tranquil waters. The heater should have a flame-failure shut-off device and an atmospheric sensor (see 14.2.2). Such a heater can, of course, supply hot water at any time in any quantity. A calorifier can only produce hot water in relation to the length of time the engine has been run. Typically, if the engine cooling water is at 82°C (180°F), 15 minutes running will give a modest-sized tankful of water at 60°C (140°F). If the tank is well lagged and the engine is run some time during the evening, the water next morning will still be hot enough for washing and washing up. Standard calorifiers are available with capacities from about 22 litres (5 gallons) to 70 litres (15 gallons).

14.3.4 Desalination plant
Fresh water can be a limiting factor on the endurance of a cruising yacht, particularly in parts of the world where supplies of drinking water are hard to come by. The problem can be alleviated by fitting a desalination plant, operated by waste heat from the cooling system of the main engine or of an auxiliary generator.

The heat is employed to boil sea water in a vacuum, whereby the boiling point is considerably lowered and the amount of heat required is reduced. The resulting vapour is condensed in a distiller, cooled by sea water, and is then pumped away to a storage tank. The brine in the evaporator shell is discharged overboard by another pump. The purity of the made water is continually monitored by a salinometer, which will automatically divert any suspect water overboard.

It is possible to produce up to 13 litres (3 gallons) of fresh water per hour from the waste heat of a 11kW (15hp) propulsion engine or of a generator set developing 7.5kW.

Such plant should only be used in the open sea where there is no pollution, because the low boiling point of the sea water under vacuum is not enough to sterilise it from any bacteria which may be present.

Reverse osmosis plants
In recent years a new desalination method, by reverse osmosis, has come into prominence. The normal process of osmosis is defined as the property of a fluid of a given density, separated by a semi-permeable membrane from a fluid of lower density, to draw the less dense fluid through this membrane, in order to equalise the densities – increasing the volume of the higher density fluid and generating a pressure if there is no escape behind the membrane. If pure water is separated by a semi-permeable membrane from salty water, then pure water will pass through the membrane into the salty side.

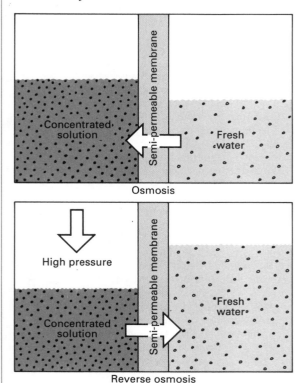

Fig. 14(18) The principle of a reverse osmosis desalinisation plant.

However, if sufficient pressure, about 55–62 bar (800–900lb/sq in), is exerted on the salty water, and if a suitable membrane can physically resist such pressure, then pure water can be made to pass out of the salty water, through the membrane, and into the pure water side. This is the principle of reverse osmosis, as illustrated in Fig. 14(18). The process became a reality in the 1970s with the development of a suitable synthetic membrane.

In practical installations a reverse osmosis plant consists of a primer pump which delivers sea water to one or more filters which remove all silt and suspended matter. The (filtered) sea water then passes to a positive displacement pump which delivers it to a vessel containing the semi-permeable membrane, through which some fresh water passes. This is then led through a salinity sensor to a solenoid (dump) valve. Any impure water is dumped overboard, depending on the set value of the monitoring equipment, while pure water is filtered and sterilised before going to the storage tank.

The main advantage of a reverse osmosis plant is that it requires about 70 per cent less energy than the evaporator type of unit. Also the materials used do not have to withstand high temperatures, which permits the use of plastics, glass fibre etc. to reduce weight and cost. It is also claimed that reverse osmosis plants are easier to maintain, and are more reliable.

A reverse osmosis plant for a yacht, producing 600 litres (130 gallons) of fresh water per day, can weigh less than 50kg (110lb) and will consume about 2kW of electricity when running, although the start-up load will be considerably higher. Alternatively the plant can be engine driven, using an electromagnetic clutch and pulley arrangement.

Solent Yacht Services at Shamrock Quay, William Street, Northam, Southampton SO1 1QL (Tel: (01703) 335294) markets the range of Horizon desalinators, with outputs from 30 to 400 litres (6.5 to 90 gallons) per hour. The smaller units, up to 80 litres (17.5 gallons) per hour, are either direct drive with magnetic clutches or AC powered.

An attractive package for the larger cruising yacht is a combined generator and reverse osmosis plant such as the Water-Gen provided by Sea-Fresh Watermaker Systems, Premier Centre, Abbey Park, Romsey, Hants SO51 9AQ (Tel: (01794) 830363). This consists of a single-cylinder, four-stroke diesel which drives a marine alternator for AC services and battery charging and also the high pressure pump for a reverse osmosis Watermaker, giving 15.7 litres ($3\frac{1}{2}$ gallons) of fresh water per hour. With overall dimensions of about 760mm × 460mm × 530mm (30in × 18in × 21in) it is very compact, and the total weight is about 80kg (176lb). The firm also markets the Water-Gen-Plus which delivers 6kW 240v AC, and also provides fresh water, hot water, battery charging, compressor drive for refrigerator or freezer, hydraulic drive for bow thruster or windlass, plus a fire and bilge pump.

On a much smaller scale there are available hand operated watermakers which could be vital for survival in a liferaft. The Survivor 06 and the Survivor 35 are distributed in the UK by CT Electronics (DES) Ltd, Riverview House, Weyside Park, Catteshall Lane, Godalming, Surrey GU7 1XE (Tel: (01483) 861717). They are made feasible by a clever energy recovery system whereby the brine from the high pressure side of the membrane is directed to the reverse side of the piston, so that the force required to pressurise the incoming sea water is considerably reduced.

The Survivor 06 produces 1.1 litres (1.9 pints) per hour, weighs only 1.1kg (2.4lb) and is very compact. For optimum performance it needs a pump rate of 40 strokes per minute. The Survivor 35 is slightly larger and delivers 4.6 litres (8 pints) per hour, and there is also a power operated version taking 4 amps at 12v DC. Also produced is a larger DC model, the PowerSurvivor 80 which produces 12.5 litres (22 pints) per hour at 8 amps.

14.3.5 Water storage

Depending on the number of persons on board, the average cruising boat needs storage for at least 450 litres (100 gallons), and more often larger quantities, in at least two separate tanks. If they are kept properly clean, fresh water tanks made of GRP or stainless steel are quite satisfactory, but it has been established that even short lengths of some types of clear plastic tubing, as commonly used in boats, can produce an unpleasant taste in the water. This is probably due to the chemical reaction of added chlorine in the water with the material of the tubing, producing excessive levels of phenol. Black polythene tubing does not have this effect, and there are also advantages in using an opaque material which discourages the internal growth of mould and algae.

As a palliative, it is possible to fit one of the types of water filter, such as the Fresh-Ness, which are charged with activated carbon. These will eliminate unpleasant tastes, but they will not completely remove bacteria, for which purpose water purification tablets are available.

Boats which cruise extensively should have arrangements for collecting rainwater from awnings.

14.4 Bilge pumping

14.4.1 Hand pumps

It is not so long ago that semi-rotary pumps were the standard bilge pump. In their way these were good because the back and forth motion of the handle was not tiring and a big type could pass 180 litres (40 gallons) per minute at 52 double strokes a minute. However such a model was big and heavy – weighing some 40kg (90lb) – and once semi rotaries became a bit worn they were no longer self-priming. In other words, water had to

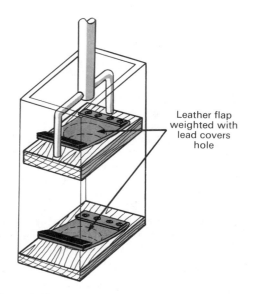

Leather flap weighted with lead covers hole

Fig. 14(19) This is the traditional wooden deck pump made up, basically, from four planks. It is effective and usually has a standard and lever mounted on deck to ease the pumping process.

be introduced to the top of the pump before it would suck. The innumerable bolts holding the face plate to the main body of the pump made it impractical to pour water in there before starting since it would all drain away before the plate could be re-assembled. Thus a special priming spigot, with a shut-off valve and water container, was often threaded into the face. This worked well but since the pumps also did not really like passing even the smallest bits of rubbish their popularity diminished. Other pumps such as the traditional wooden deck pump, Fig. 14(19), which could be home-made and worked moderately well even when quite badly worn have also passed from the scene, though deck pumps made of modern materials are still available. These days diaphragm types dominate the market. They are robust, reliable and easily taken apart to clear blockages though, in fact, they will pass surprisingly large bits of debris. They range in capacity from about 22 litres (5 gallons) per minute to about 112 litres (25 gallons) per minute but at the top end of the scale these are capacities at maximum pumping rates which cannot be sustained for very long.

Diaphragm pumps are made easier to work if over-length handles are used, and all pumps must be sited where the user is reasonably sheltered and comfortable at his work. Strum boxes or strainers should be fitted at the inlets, and the whole of the boat should be capable of being pumped dry. Thus, if the yacht has a watertight bulkhead in its length, there should be a diverter valve close to the pump itself, such that either length can be pumped. Equally, if a sailing vessel has a wide, shallow bilge it may very well be that when she is heeled, an inlet on the centreline will not pick up bilge water. That means there should be two suctions, again with a diverter valve. A

combination of a shallow bilge and watertight bulkheads may very well mean that two pumps are required. If so, so be it, for every boat, regardless of whether she also has electric or mechanical bilge pumps, should be capable of being cleared by hand. On some form of marine toilets, such as the Lavac (14.5.2), the toilet pump, again with the aid of a diverter or change-over valve, can be used as a bilge pump. It can suitably be employed for the accommodation space bilges. The most likely area of leaks is around an engine where there are usually several holes in the hull to take such things as the propeller shaft, sea water cooling inlet, exhaust outlet and so forth.

Bilge pumps outlets should run directly overboard and not pump into a self-draining cockpit, for instance, for bilge water is often oily and a smear of oil left on the cockpit sole will make the going hazardous. There should be a sea cock fitted at the outlet, unless it is well above the waterline and a swan neck curve can be made in the pipe before if reaches the outlet. This curve will have its highest point well above the skin fitting and so will reduce the chance of water flooding inboard, as could happen if the craft were heeled over and the outlet submerged. All curves in the piping should be gentle and smooth or there will be back pressure which will reduce the pump's capacity, and the inlet suction hose, in particular, should be of the reinforced type.

14.4.2 Electric pumps

Electric bilge pumps can be had in a wide range of capacities and can either be mounted high up, clear of likely bilge water, or be a submersible type which will operate under water if required. The pumps may be switched on manually or may be fitted with a switch which automatically operates when the bilge water reaches a certain height. There are three types of automatic operation available. One has a float mounted in the pump casing which is then installed at the required height. With another, the pump is mounted remotely with a hose and air bell reaching into the bilge. The air bell transmits air pressure through a tube to a diaphragm switch, turning the motor on or off. Clearly, as the bilge water rises in the air bell, air pressure will increase.

A recent innovation is the Bilge Eye pump switch which is optically triggered, with no moving parts. It is manufactured by Index Marine, Clump Farm Industrial Estate, Blandford, Dorset DT11 7TE. Tel: (01258) 452398.

Generally speaking, belt driven electric pumps are to be recommended on non-submersible types since this form of drive allows the motor to turn more slowly than a direct drive type and the pump will be quieter and have a longer life. As a guide, the current draw on a small bilge pump with a capacity of around 20 litres ($4\frac{1}{2}$ gallons) per minute will be about 7 amps on 12v operation and 5 amps on 24v, while at 85 litres (19 gallons) per minute on a bigger pump the draw will be 9.5 amps on 12v and 7 amps on 24v. An electrical bilge pump is a valuable tool on board but just to emphasise the need for hand pumps as well, it will only function when the electrics are working and the battery has not been flooded.

14.4.3 Mechanical bilge pumps

These are the giants of the bilge pumping brigade, and big versions will shift tremendous volumes of water. The dual pump is an interesting variation on the theme of bilge pumps since it combines the operations of the engine cooling water impeller with that of a bilge pump. It is shaft driven off the engine and continuously pumps the bilges. When they are dry the bilge pump impeller is automatically lubricated by a bleed from the cooling pump chamber. A typical Jabsco dual pump, for example, can handle a flow rate of 210 litres (46 gallons) per minute on the cooling side with a bilge pumping rate of 90 litres (20 gallons) per minute. Smaller versions are available.

More conventionally, mechanical bilge pumps are belt-driven off the main engine or generator, and incorporate either a remotely controlled electro-magnetic clutch or a manual clutch. At 1500rpm and absorbing 1kW (or about $1\frac{1}{2}$hp) such a pump will discharge about 200 litres (44 gallons) per minute which will cope with most leaks. By use of change-over cocks and a sea water inlet, pumps like this can double up as deck wash and fire pumps. They will continue to pump down to about 100rpm. Types capable of discharging nearly 320 litres (70 gallons) per minute are available.

14.5 Marine toilets

14.5.1 Chemical toilets

Though much derided, chemical toilets are really not at all bad, especially if they can be installed in a compartment where their rather odd smell can be isolated. Most models come in two parts. The top section holds the flushing water, while the bottom half is the waste holder: a chemical is added to one or the other, depending on make. The two separate once a sliding clamp arrangement has been operated, and the bottom can then be carried away for emptying. The jointing clamp is secure and a very basic, though quite effective, hooked catch keeps the whole toilet in place on board. In civilised surroundings the waste is emptied ashore. At sea it can be dumped overboard. These chemical affairs are much preferable to the traditional bucket since they can be carried without fear of spillage and need not be emptied after every use. A full upper tank will give about 40 flushes, but the waste container in practice only lasts two people two or three days with normal use. A chemical toilet is cheap and needs no pipework or through-hull inlets and outlets. There are superior types available where

the chemically treated flushing water is stored in a separate tank, and electrically recirculated. These models can usually also be had as a permanent installation with pump-out connections.

14.5.2 Conventional marine toilets

These come in a bewildering array of types and arrangements. All have inlets and outlets leading to the sea, but after that the situation changes. Some, like the SL400 and Lavac, require a single pump operation only. There are no levers to throw or wheels to turn or valves to open (apart from seacocks.) Others have a single pump with a lever to operate or a valve to open, and yet others have two pumps, one inlet and one discharge. Many can be converted to electric operation (that is, the pumping is done electrically rather than manually). All toilets from reputable manufacturers are reliable and if serviced according to their instructions will have a long life. Choice will ultimately depend on cost, size, weight and comfort. Some are really rather small for easy sitting.

These days as the authorities become increasingly concerned over the discharge of raw sewage into the oceans of the world and especially into confined harbours and rivers, pumping out directly is often forbidden. Thus holding tanks have to be incorporated into the toilet systems. Such tanks can be bought commercially in small sizes with something like 22 litres (5 gallons) to 45 litres (10 gallons) capacity but most are fabricated by the boatbuilder. Fig. 14(20) shows a typical arrangement allowing the toilet to discharge direct into the sea or into the holding tank from which it can be pumped either by the boat's own toilet pump or by an onshore facility. The system illustrated is based on the Lavac toilet since that has a separate pump which is normally sited above the toilet bowl, but something similar can often be arranged with other types.

The holding tank may also be used to collect the waste from basins, sinks and showers. If so its size will have to reflect this use. A shower, for instance, will need about 14 litres (3 gallons) of water for each operation. If the tank is connected to the toilet only, a guide to its minimum size is given by multiplying the number of berths by the number of days anticipated between pump-outs and then multiplying this figure by $1\frac{1}{2}$. That gives the answer in gallons capacity. Thus a five-berth yacht with an anticipated 14 days between pump-outs would ideally need a holding tank of $5 \times 14 \times 1.5 = 105$ gallons or 470 litres capacity. This is a hefty affair which, when full, would weight 450kg (1000lb) excluding the weight of the tank itself. Clearly on many small five-berthers this is simply not on, and pump-outs would have to be undertaken much more frequently.

The tank itself is usually of GRP but aluminium alloy and stainless steel are very satisfactory, if more expensive. A large inspection hatch must be arranged in the top surface.

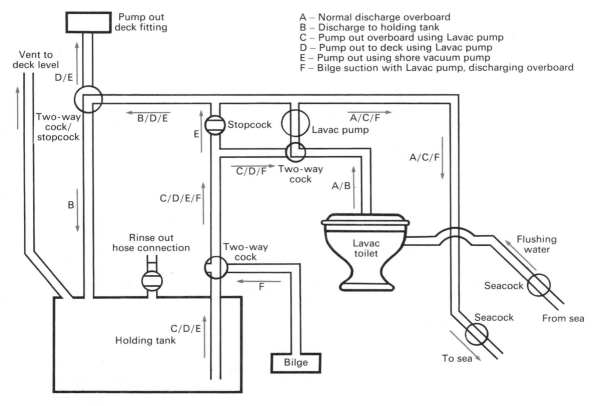

A – Normal discharge overboard
B – Discharge to holding tank
C – Pump out overboard using Lavac pump
D – Pump out to deck using Lavac pump
E – Pump out using shore vacuum pump
F – Bilge suction with Lavac pump, discharging overboard

Fig. 14(20) A Lavac toilet pump can be used to pump the toilet to an overboard discharge or to a pump-out connection on deck. It is also used to flush the toilet, and can be arranged to pump the bilge in emergency. This diagram shows a versatile layout.

14.5.3 **Toilet maintenance**

Marine toilets require and deserve routine maintenance since this is the best way to avoid possible trouble, which can be inconvenient in the middle of a family cruise. Most of them have some perishable parts such as rubber seals, glands, washers, etc. which, together with items like hose clips, need checking periodically and probably require renewal about every five years. Most manufacturers provide kits of these parts, and it is advisable to carry these on board.

When the time comes to lay up, make sure that the whole system is well washed through, rinsed with disinfectant, and then drained out. If any water is liable to be lingering somewhere, add a little anti-freeze. Chemical toilets must be emptied out and cleaned. Some of these units are sensitive to chemicals, so that use of the wrong materials can cause damage; it is best to stick to the maker's instructions.

At the start of the season, or whenever the boat is out of the water, check the strainer on the sea water inlet and make sure that the seacocks are free and in good condition. The tapered plug type of seacock is best, but make certain that the plug is seating correctly, and that the gland is tight but not so tight as to make the seacock hard to operate. It is a good rule to turn off all seacocks when the boat is unattended. Soil pipes can become restricted with a hard deposit. If they are

plastic pipes it may be simplest just to replace them, or alternatively they can be removed and flexed or tapped with a wooden mallet to loosen the deposit. Another method is to treat such pipes with vinegar. Pump glands should be tight, and may need repacking. Recirculating toilets have a filter, which should be cleaned.

If properly used, a marine toilet should be relatively trouble-free. Keep it clean at all times, and only use the recommended cleaning fluids and disinfectants. Above all, make sure that everybody who comes on board understands that no solid items of any kind must be put down the toilet – nothing in fact that has not been eaten.

14.6 **Refrigerators**

Refrigerators aboard yachts have become increasingly popular over the years as manufacturers have coped with the difficult environment in which they operate. On a sailing vessel, for instance, they are expected to function happily almost regardless of the angle of heel, while few small craft can allow really sufficient moving air space round the cooling coils. Nevertheless they work well enough on most occasions, though their drain on the batteries is serious – especially on yachts which are used principally at weekends and even then run their engines only occasionally. In these cases a well-insulated ice box or even a cooling cabinet is probably preferable. The latter have been in existence for many years and have a porous lining which is kept moist by pouring water on it. The water evaporates and in doing so cools the interior of the cabinet. This is not a refrigerator and will not freeze or cool anything put in it, but if milk, for example, is taken from a proper fridge and placed in the cabinet it will be kept cold far longer than if stowed in a locker. These coolers come in sizes up to about 0.03cu m (1cu ft); Easicool is one make. They should be installed such that air can circulate round, and so that water can be tipped into the recess at the top. This is a complete, insulated unit but an ice box is generally fabricated especially for the boat.

Going back to refrigerators, since cold air is heavier than warm air it tend to fall out of the usual front opening door. Naturally this happens in the home too but there the fact that the refrigerator has to work hard to cool the new warm air passes unnoticed. Hence a top opening is the better bet, though it may not be easy to site where this can be accomplished. On absorption refrigerators (see 14.6.1) which have a front-opening door, the door should face the centreline of the boat and not be installed for and aft.

14.6.1 Absorption refrigerators

These operate by causing a liquid, usually ammonia, to vapourise in a coil inside the unit. In vapourising it absorbs heat. The vapourised refrigerant is then condensed outside the cold chamber where it gives off the heat absorbed. It is then recirculated and vapourised again. The initial heat source may be electricity, or a gas or paraffin burner. As there are no moving parts there is little to go wrong or maintain, but operated electrically they draw some 5 amps at 12v for a 0.04cu m (1.5cu ft) model, for example, and that is about as small a fridge as is useful on board. With gas or paraffin burning away as a naked flame, the crew may not be too happy, even though it doesn't matter if a paraffin burner goes out, apart from the smell and the mess. Gas types ought to have flame-failure devices that shut off the supply should the flame be extinguished, but even so a flame burning constantly on a boat fitted with other gas appliances may not inspire confidence. Nor may the fact that the gas supply must be constantly on.

Electrolux make a model which will run on either electricity or gas, and can be switched from one to the other. If installed as described above, it will handle angles of heel of up to 10–15° and pitching up to $7\frac{1}{2}°$. The gas combustion chamber is completely sealed from the interior of the boat, and draws fresh air and expels burnt gases through separate pipes and a deck-mounted ventilator. In addition there is an air pump to change the air in the combustion chamber before lighting, and an automatic ignition button. There is the usual flame-failure device. These features appear to answer most of the safety queries that are posed by absorbent refrigerators.

14.6.2 Thermo-electric refrigerators

In the early 1800s the Frenchman, Jean Peltier, noted that when a voltage is applied across the junction between two dissimilar metals, heat is removed from one of the metals and transferred to the other. This Peltier effect is the basis of thermo-electric refrigeration. In practice aluminium alloy fins inside a cold chest absorb heat and transfer it through thermo-electric modules to heat-dissipating fins outside. A fan helps disperse the heat into the surrounding air. The fan, and a shroud on the cold fins, circulate the air in the cabinet. This fan is the only moving part and these units are quite efficient in operation, though really good insulation is required if the demand for electricity is to be kept down. On the other hand they are unaffected by heel or pitching and are quiet in operation. This type of refrigerator, the Coolaspace being an example, is normally sold as a module which can be fitted very easily to an insulated cabinet. The unit draws about 4 amps at 12v when running, but only comes into operation when needed and is controlled by a thermostat. Thus its normal current drain is around 3 amps when operating with a well-insulated 0.08cu m (3cu ft) cabinet. If a yacht has a shore supply, an automatic 10-amp or higher battery charger could be fitted connected to the mains to keep the unit running.

14.6.3 Electro-mechanical refrigerators

These are electrically driven compressor types. An electric motor compresses a refrigerant such as Freon, which then expands in coils inside the cooling cabinet, extracting heat as it does so. This heat is released when the gas is cooled in an outside condenser, whether by air or sea water. The latter is necessary if the refrigerator is to work in a high ambient temperature.

The compressor normally used is a rotary type but better results are obtained with a 'swing motor' or linear compressor which has the compressor piston connected to a vibrating mechanism which, apart from eliminating surge currents, is quieter. It can be arranged to function on either AC or DC. Electrolux and Engel make refrigerators of this type and, typically, current consumption is about 2.5 amps when the unit is running on a 60 litre (2.1cu ft) model. Being able to switch from 12v DC to mains voltage AC means that for yachts berthed convenient to a mains supply the refrigerator can be allowed to operate without draining the batteries. The swing compressor unit will work up to 45° of heel, and is available in modules that can be installed in well-insulated cabinets.

The length of time a refrigerator needs to run to maintain the selected temperature can be considerably reduced by the use of holdover plates

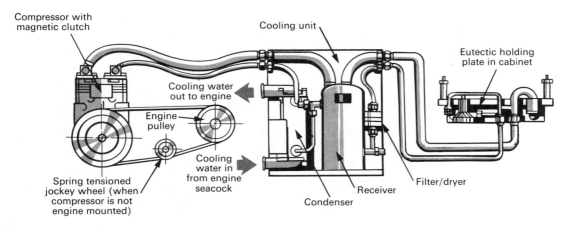

Fig. 14(21) An engine-driven refrigerator unit for larger yachts.

in the cabinet. These plates contain a eutectic solution which freezes at a low temperature and, by virtue of its latent heat, stores coldness within the cabinet for several hours. Using such eutectic plates the refrigerator's cooling unit need only run for an hour or so, twice a day. This is a considerable advantage. The plates themselves need to be installed vertically or horizontally near the top of the cabinet, but with at least 15mm ($\frac{3}{4}$in) clearance from the body of the cabinet to allow for proper air circulation.

An average refrigerator that may be reasonably satisfactory in home waters, will soon have its limitations exposed when used in tropical or even semi-tropical conditions. Any unit with an air-cooled condenser will start to give problems once the ambient temperature between decks climbs to 30°C (90°F) or more, with the compressor running almost continuously and causing a very big drain on battery capacity. For such heavy duty a water-cooled condenser is essential, and a very high standard of cabinet insulation is required. To avoid the inconvenience of running the engine very regularly just to recharge the batteries it is desirable to install larger battery capacity and some alternative charging arrangements such as a wind generator and/or solar cells (see 13.3.4).

On bigger yachts a deep freeze compartment is quite common in addition to the normal refrigerator. Fig. 14(21) shows the Simpson Marine Refrigeration system. A twin-cylinder compressor is driven via a magnetic clutch from a vee belt from the main engine. The sea water supply to the condenser is incorporated with the engine cooling system; the cooling water passing through the condenser on its way to the engine. Holdover plates are designed to maintain the desired temperature for up to 12 hours. Standard kits provide for refrigerators/deep freezers with capacities from 110 litres (4cu ft) to 450 litres (16cu ft). With this system the cooling unit and main engine should be reasonably close together to reduce the length of cooling water and refrigerant pipes.

14.6.4 Ice boxes and cooling cabinets

Such things are quite easily built as a DIY job. Fig. 14(22) shows the professional approach utilising the hull side as one part of the structure, but it may be easier for the amateur to achieve well fitting joints if he first makes a rectangular box to fit into the available space. This can be of 6mm ($\frac{1}{4}$in) ply and to it is glued the required thickness of polyurethane (closed cell) foam. For a cabinet of 0.06cu m (2 cu ft) at least 50mm (2in) thick foam should be used and as cabinet capacity rises, so must the thickness of the foam at the rate of 12mm ($\frac{1}{2}$in) per 0.03cu m (cu ft) capacity. Thus a 0.17cu m (6 cu ft) box would need at least 100mm (4in) of foam insulation. The foam panels installed must be a tight fit on the ply shell. Next Formica (or something similar) is glued to more $\frac{1}{4}$in ply to form a bottom panel with the Formica forming the inner face of the cabinet. The process is repeated with the fore and aft and athwartships panels, glueing each panel to the foam and making sure it is a tight fit. A drain with either a valve or a U-shaped water trap should be provided at the bottom, and

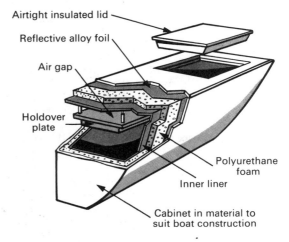

Fig. 14(22) Ice box or refrigerator construction using the hull side as one face of the box.

finally all joints can be sealed with a silicone bath sealer. A close fitting lid is made the same way. The object of having the ply behind the Formica is to give something to screw into if shelves or racks are to be installed. A refinement that improves insulation is to place a sheet of reflective aluminium foil inside the outer casing of ply, as shown in Fig. 14(22).

There is some skill in using an ice box in a way that gets the best results from it. A little care will greatly prolong the effective cooling obtained from a given load of ice—a precious commodity in some cruising areas. Some form of subdivision, so that different items cannot get mixed with (or possibly contaminate) others is a great help. Plastic bags and boxes are the easiest to store while making the most economical use of the available space, and make sure that they are very clearly marked so that the contents can be quickly identified. To help, plastic containers are available in different colours, so some simple colour code will speed the search for specific items. This reduces the time that the lid is opened on any occasion, but it is also necessary to reduce the frequency of opening. One solution is to have a small portable container of the insulated 'picnic' variety, which can be employed for ready-use items and stocked with things like milk, butter and cold drinks each morning.

Before loading an ice box make sure that it is scrupulously clean, with no unpleasant debris left from a previous cruise. If necessary, wash it out thoroughly with fresh water and a mild cleaner, rinse it down and leave it open for several hours to get rid of any smell. It helps if the temperature of the whole ice box can then be reduced by inserting a block or two of ice before loading proper begins.

Ice cubes, such as are dispensed by machines at marinas, are of little or no use for ice boxes. What are needed are large blocks, which melt relatively slowly. These should first be inserted, shaped with an icepick if necessary, so that they completely cover the bottom of the ice box, and then built up to form walls around the sides. The food goes into whatever space is left in the middle.

It is possible to make ice blocks in a deep freeze ashore, in suitable sized plastic containers. If salted water is used a lower temperature can be achieved. Naturally such blocks need to be transported to the boat in an insulated container of some kind, and this is only feasible if the distance is short.

The life of the ice will be extended if the food put into the ice box comes from a refrigerator or freezer ashore.

If a cooling unit such as the Coolaspace (14.6.2) is to be installed it should face into the cabin or some other reasonably large area to allow adequate movement of air. To this end, if a locker is to enclose the unit (the locker must have a volume of at least three to four times that of the ice box and should not be too full of gear) there must be louvres or vents top and bottom.

14.6.5 Air conditioning

The need for air conditioning is seldom felt aboard yachts in British waters, where more commonly there is need for warmth, as already described in 14.2. But in some yachting areas conditions can considerably exceed those in which human beings are reasonably comfortable – temperatures of around 18–21°C (65–70°F) and relative humidities of 40–65 per cent.

Air conditioning is theoretically quite possible even in a small boat, but there are practical difficulties with the space occupied by the unit and, more notably, with the large amount of electric power consumed. The latter disadvantage can of course be overcome if the yacht is alongside and shore power is available.

Full air conditioning implies the delivery of air which can be cooled or warmed, and have its humidity either lowered or raised, to maintain a desirable internal atmosphere regardless of outside conditions. It should also include means of removing dust, smells and bacteria from the air, and even the injection of beneficial elements. Enough oxygen must be provided, in the form of fresh air, for the crew to breathe. So the detailed design and control of the amounts of fresh and recirculated air inlets and exhausts, are all very important factors. The design involves a detailed calculation of heat gained from outside the yacht (which depends on the efficiency of such insulation as may be fitted), from the fresh air admitted, from the occupants, and from internal sources of heat such as the galley, electrical appliances and machinery. Such a plant would only be found in the largest and most luxurious yachts. Units fitted in smaller craft normally only aim to reduce temperature and humidity to more acceptable levels, combined with some form of air circulation and perhaps a dust filter.

Air conditioning sets found in yachts are of the compressor type. In larger yachts a central refrigeration unit, probably sited in the engine room, distributes chilled water to air treatment units situated in the various spaces. Smaller yachts normally have individual air conditioning units in each cabin or space to be cooled, but since each unit has its own compressor and fan, they are more noisy.

An approximation to the cooling capacity per hour required is 14BTU per cu ft for cabins and spaces below deck level, and 17 BTU per cu ft above. Hence a cabin of 450 cu ft (13 cu m) might require a unite of about 6500 BTU/hr. (For conversion to metric units 1 BTU=1055 Joules.) Such a unit would take about 1kW to run, but on first starting up the compressor might take a surge load of 3kW. These sorts of loads require an auxiliary generator, unless the yacht is connected to shore power.

Good heat insulation of superstructure, deck and topsides reduces the demands on air conditioning units (and makes any yacht not air conditioned more comfortable in hot or cold weather). Teak decks have good insulating properties, but even a wooden-hulled boat can be improved with an insulating lining. As already stated in 14.1.15, foam plastic is widely employed, although it should be noted that such materials are flammable and may give off toxic fumes in the event of fire. Large windows in the superstructure can make the interior very hot, and in warm climates it is sensible to have external screens which can be rigged in harbour, plus awnings to keep the decks cool.

Chapter 15

Boat handling and passage making

Contents

15.1 Boat handling – general

15.1.1 Handling under sail

Many yachts habitually start their engines and lower their sails before the simplest manoeuvre – even just anchoring – and thereby miss the satisfaction of doing such evolutions under sail. What is more, their owners are foregoing experience in handling their boats under sail against the day when they need to do so.

It may be unwise to enter a marina or a crowded anchorage under sail, but a good skipper should be able to cope if the situation requires. There are few problems that cannot be resolved under sail – albeit perhaps with the help of a warp or two, or even the anchor or the dinghy.

For manoeuvring under sail it is essential to have an understanding of hull and sail balance, as described in Chapter 10 (10.1.14). Boat handling is something of an art, but an art which does need practice, especially in a strange craft. Every boat has different characteristics, which need to be learned. Find out how your boat handles under just the mainsail – how difficult is it to get her to bear away? Coming up head to wind, how much way does she carry, in different wind strengths? Find out how well she will sail to windward under jib alone. Try heaving-to, with the jib backed, mainsheet well eased, and the helm down. At what angle to the wind will she lie a-hull, with no sail set?

When it comes to executing some special manoeuvre under sail, plan ahead against every eventuality. Navigational details and tidal problems should be sorted out well in advance. Explain to the crew exactly what has to be done, and have all gear likely to be needed ready at hand. If it is in the nature of a training exercise, by all means have the engine ticking over in neutral in case it should be needed.

Never be in a hurry – proceed as slowly as possible (while still retaining full control) so that there is time to make any manoeuvre within the limited space that may be available. It takes as much skill to sail a boat as slowly as possible as it does to achieve maximum speed on a spinnaker reach, maybe more, but there are plenty of opportunities to experiment with this in open water and to allow each member of the crew to share the experience. Find out how the boat handles under different combinations of sail, and in different wind strengths. Obviously more sail is needed in light airs, and at the other end of the scale it is necessary to know how the boat behaves under bare poles.

Apart from making the best use of tidal streams for coastal passages, they can be a great help when manoeuvring in confined waters. For example, with wind against tide, careful sail trimming should allow progress over the ground to be reduced to a fraction of a knot, greatly facilitating evolutions such as coming alongside or picking up a mooring. In other circumstances, when approaching a berth roughly against wind and tide, the latter may be used to ease the boat almost sideways into a small space. In these situations it is important to be able to lower whatever sail is set at a moment's notice, and also to observe any local eddies in the tidal stream that can be used to advantage.

Important attributes which the successful boat handler must acquire are a sense of location and an awareness of what is (and what will be) affecting the boat. Learn to assess the boat's movements in two dimensions by lining up different objects. In any harbour there are plenty of masts, boats, buildings, beacons and so on which can form transits to tell you which way the boat is moving relative to the land, and how quickly.

There are different factors to assess: the boat's progress through the water by the propulsion of sails and/or engine, the effect of the wind also moving her through the water, and the influence of tidal stream or river current. The effect of sails or engine can be controlled by the skipper, the others cannot and they need to be assessed on a continuing basis because they are continually changing. The wind may funnel round the corner of a building, or disappear completely under its shadow. Tidal stream or river current vary in strength and direction from place to place, and from time to time. One moment the wind may be the dominant factor, the next the tide may take control.

While absorbed in the two-dimensional problem do not forget that there is a third dimension to consider – the depth of the water. Particularly in a strange harbour always have the echo sounder functioning, and if available set the alarm to give early indication of approaching shallows.

15.1.2 Handling under power

The basic principles expressed in 15.1.1 apply equally to handling under power, when it is necessary to recognise certain factors:

(1) A conventional rudder has no steering effect unless water is flowing past it in one direction or the other; similarly, for an outboard or outdrive installation, there is no steering effect unless the propeller is driving either ahead or astern.

(2) When a boat is under helm she swings around her pivoting point, the position of which varies. When she is at rest the pivoting point is amidships, but when she is going ahead it moves forward – so that as she turns the stern describes a bigger circle than the bow. See Fig. 15(1). Conversely, when going astern the pivoting point moves well aft, so that when the boat is under helm the bow describes a larger circle. When running astern in any weight of wind the boat will tend to 'weather cock', with the stern 'seeking the wind' as in Fig. 15(2). Steering may be very difficult in such conditions with a single-screw boat.

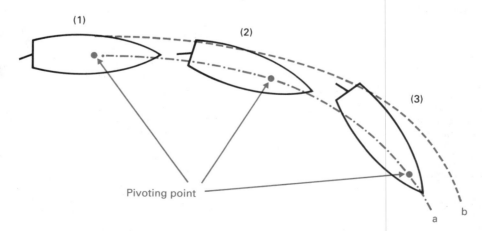

Pivoting point

Fig. 15(1) Starboard helm, going ahead. (1) Helm over. (2) Boat sliding sideways, hydrodynamic forces start to initiate the turn proper. (3) Turning. Curves *a* and *b* show the lines taken respectively by the pivoting point (which has moved forward in the boat) and the stern (which has swung out). The turning circle of a single-screw boat is different to port and to starboard, depending on the direction of rotation of the propeller.

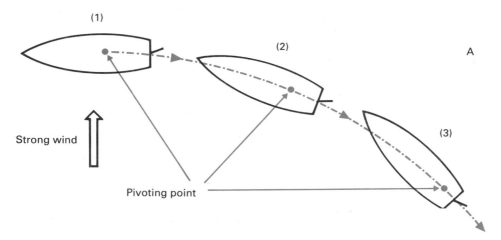

Fig. 15(2) In position (1) the boat is going astern, intending to proceed towards A. Due to the pivoting point moving aft, and the windage of the boat forward of that point, the stern tends to 'seek the wind', and the boat proceeds as in positions (2) and (3). It may be impossible to prevent this in a single-screw boat, but it can be controlled with twin-screws.

(3) A rotating propeller generates sideways thrust, as well as propelling the boat ahead or astern. Most single-screw boats have right-handed propellers – revolving clockwise when viewed from aft, with the engine going ahead. When starting from rest, a right-handed propeller kicks the stern to starboard. When starting off astern, or going from ahead to astern, it kicks the stern to port, and the effect can be very significant see Fig. 15(3). With a left-handed propeller the effect is opposite. Provided its action is understood and anticipated, propeller effect (or paddlewheel effect, as it is sometimes called) can be put to good use when handling a single-screw boat.

Before manoeuvring any boat at close quarters, it is wise to test her reaction to helm and to engine movements in open water. See how she lies to the wind, and how she steers at different speeds, and when going astern.

Propeller effect can be used to advantage when handling a single-screw boat, as for example when turning round in a restricted space as shown in Fig. 15(4). Similarly when coming alongside port

Right-handed propeller, viewed from aft

Propeller effect pushes stern in this direction

Going ahead   Going astern

As boat starts to move ahead (left)
or
astern (right)
she swings as indicated by the dotted lines

Fig. 15(3) Propeller (or paddlewheel) effect for a right-handed propeller, viewed from aft, pushing the stern of the boat in the direction indicated by the arrows. The effect is opposite for a left-handed propeller.

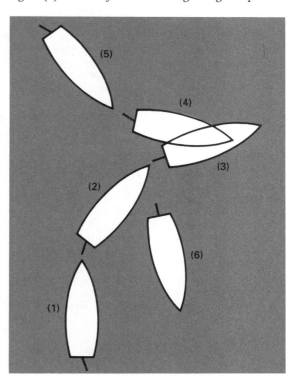

Fig. 15(4) Turning a boat with a single, right-handed propeller in a restricted space. (1) Go ahead slowly, full starboard helm. (2) Stop engine. (3) Full astern – propeller effect swings stern to port. (4) As boat gathers sternway, reverse helm. Stop engine. (5) Full ahead, starboard helm. (6) Reduce engine rpm, helm amidships.

side to with a right-handed screw, the final kick astern to bring the boat to rest can be used to place her nicely parallel to the jetty.

Special factors apply in restricted waters. Keep speed as low as will provide good steerage. Most boats will steer provided that the propeller is creating some slipstream for the rudder so, when coming to a berth or an obstruction, reduce engine rpm well beforehand so that the engine can be kept ticking over ahead as long as possible, and hence retain steerage way.

Shallow water greatly modifies the normal flow pattern round the hull of a boat. Larger waves build up at bow and stern, increasing resistance. If excessive speed is maintained the boat becomes directionally unstable. It is also more difficult to turn a boat in shallow water.

In channels that are both shallow and narrow, such as a canal, steering can be made difficult by what is known as canal effect. Due to the restricted flow of water past the hull, waves build up ahead and astern of the boat. In between these two areas of higher pressure is a trough of low pressure amidships. A stream of water flows down each side of the boat, and in at each quarter: if this stream is disturbed, due to the boat getting close to the bank, the boat may take a sudden, violent sheer. The moral is to keep speed low.

A similar phenomenon is the difficulty of avoiding collision between two craft which are proceeding too close to each other on parallel courses. While this more frequently occurs between power vessels it can also happen with sailing yachts, at crowded starts, for example, or when one boat luffs another during a race. It is caused by the speeding up of the water flow as it enters the restricted space between the two hulls, which results in a drop in pressure and consequently an attraction between the two craft. The effect increases with higher speeds, so before going alongside another craft under way both should slow down.

Boats with outboard or outdrive propulsion need special handling techniques. They have no rudders as such, but are steered by pointing the propeller in the required direction. This gives very positive handling provided that the propeller is rotating either ahead or astern – but none if the gear shift is in neutral. At close quarters it is therefore nececssary to give short bursts of low or moderate power, making sure each time that the helm is first applied in the required direction before engaging ahead or astern. In these circumstances a helm indicator can be useful. Steering astern is very positive and the pivoting point of the boat is brought well aft which means that the bow can swing out widely.

15.1.3 Twin-screw boats

With practice a twin-screw boat is easier to handle because with one shaft going ahead and the other astern she can be turned at rest in her own length. For manoeuvrability a twin-screw boat should have out-turning propellers – right-handed on the starboard side, and left-handed on the port side. Then their propeller effect cancels out when both are running ahead or astern, and when turning at rest the joint effect of both propellers assists the swing.

Fast motor boats have very small rudders, in order to reduce drag at high speeds. But at low speeds such rudders are ineffeective for manoeuvring, and it is best to put the helm amidships and steer only on the engines.

15.1.4 Fouling a propeller

A real danger, particularly to motor boats, is the possibility of fouling a propeller on moorings, or on lobster pots or other fishing marks. Even in daylight fishing marks are sometimes very difficult to see, possibly with the floats almost submerged in a strong tidal stream.

Several turns of rope are likely to be bound tightly round the shaft before it is brought to rest and it may be necessary to cut them strand by strand. But if it is possible to get hold of the end of the rope, and if the shaft can be rotated by *hand* in the astern direction, the worst of the tangle may be unwrapped. Make certain, however, that the engine cannot possibly start while attempting this.

A face mask is better than nothing for this sort of work, but some motor yachtsmen very sensibly carry sub-aqua gear for this purpose, and for other underwater work and examinations.

15.1.5 Running aground

Depending on the boat, the state of the sea and the type of bottom, running aground can be a serious matter or a trivial occurence. The deep keel of a sailing boat is the first thing to make contact, whereas with a motor boat the stern gear and rudder may be very vulnerable to damage. Therefore in a motor boat the first action should be to put the engine into neutral and take stock of the situation. On a rising tide, perhaps uncertain of the boat's true position, it is wise to anchor while the boat floats off and her position is established. On a falling tide more urgent action is needed, particularly on a lee shore.

It is seldom wrong to turn the boat through 180°, if possible, and steer a reciprocal course until deeper water is regained. The draught of a keel boat can be reduced by heeling her over, by any available means, and the spinnaker pole can be used to swing her round or propel her. A shallow-draught boat can be manhandled into deeper water, but it is important to be able to get people in the water back on board again and the engine must not be used if anybody is near the stern of the boat. A more seamanlike, but slower, operation is to lay out a kedge from the dinghy, using the longest warp that is available. Alternatively, it may be possible to tow the boat off, either with her own tender or with the help of some other craft with less draught, when the dinghy may be useful to pass a line across.

If a yacht is truly stranded on a falling tide, all that can be done is to safeguard her as far as possible. If she is on the edge of a bank it is most important to ensure that she heels over in an 'uphill' direction, not towards deep water. This can be done by transferring weights to the 'uphill' side, and by taking a masthead line inshore to pull her over in that direction.

Should the hull be going to settle on rocks or stones, it must be padded with whatever is to hand – bunk cushions, sail bags etc.

15.1.6 Picking up a mooring buoy

Picking up a buoy is a good way to start boat handling, since it teaches the skipper to take charge of the boat, and if the buoy is small and in reasonably open water there is no risk of any damage – apart from the possibility of getting the buoy rope round the propeller.

Under sail the aim must be to bring the boat to rest with the buoy nicely positioned close under one bow or the other. First check the directions and strengths of wind and tide, and in particular their relative effects on other moored boats nearby: how they are lying will determine the proper approach. If there is little or no tide it is usually best to lower the headsail early, and steer for a point to leeward of the buoy on a close reach; then come into the wind when to leeward of the buoy, so that the boat stops at the buoy. This is a matter of judgement, depending on the characteristics and displacement of the boat as well as the prevailing conditions. Do not lower the mainsail until the buoy is inboard, and if it becomes obvious that the manoeuvre has been misjudged do not hesitate to abandon that approach – bear away while still retaining steerage way, and go round again for another attempt.

The same tactics are employed if the tide is running strongly with the wind, except that of course the boat will not travel so far over the ground once she is brought head to wind.

When there is significant strength of tide, and it is against the wind, a different approach is needed – downwind, against the tide. Then it is best to come to the buoy under headsail only, so trimmed that the boat is just stemming the tide. Just before the boat reaches the buoy, spill the wind completely from the headsail, and be ready to lower it as soon as the buoy rope has been secured.

When the wind is across the tide, which is often the case, the above tactics must be modified according to the conditions. It may be possible to approach under headsail, stemming the tide – as for the downwind approach just described above. Or it may be best to come to rest head to wind just uptide of the buoy, and then drift down to it.

Care is needed when coming to a large mooring buoy, contact with which could damage the boat. Particularly if short-handed, one of the patent boathooks which snaps a picking up rope to the eye of a buoy can be most useful.

Some of the considerations above apply equally when coming to a buoy under power. In a single-screw boat remember that if it is necessary to go astern at the last moment to check the boat's way, propeller effect (see 15.1.2) will throw the bow to starboard with a right-handed screw. In this case keep the buoy fine on the starboard bow during the final approach. On all occasions it is helpful if the person on the foredeck continually points in the direction of the buoy, because the helmsman inevitably loses sight of it at the critical moment. Other signs, such as 'come ahead' or 'go astern' can be mutually agreed.

When leaving a buoy under power it is best to drop astern initially, until the buoy is well clear ahead, so that there is no danger of fouling the mooring with the propeller. Tactics under sail depend on the relative directions of wind and tide. If the wind is against tide, and the boat is riding to the tide, it is preferable to slip from the buoy under headsail – rounding up in open water to hoist the mainsail. If the boat is lying head to wind, hoist the mainsail and throw the boat off on the required tack by walking the buoy aft down whichever will be the windward side. The same effect is obtained by rigging a slip rope down whichever side of the boat is required (depending on which tack is decided on) to a position near the cockpit. Then let go the buoy rope and heave in on the slip rope to throw the bow off on the required tack.

In some harbours, to save space, boats moor to buoys fore and aft instead of swinging to a single mooring. The techniques for picking up and leaving head and stern buoys are similar to those employed for pile moorings as discussed in 15.4. The two buoys may be connected by a light line with a small buoy centred between them. This helps the picking up process but take care that the line does not foul the boat's propeller.

15.2 Anchor work

15.2.1 Anchor gear

Anchoring is a useful facility in various circumstances – perhaps for a sailing craft when progress against the tide is impossible in a falling wind and with no auxiliary power. But there are many other occasions when it is convenient to drop the hook: waiting for the tide to rise for entering harbour, in fog when keeping clear of a shipping channel, or in a motor boat suffering engine failure. The anchor can also be used when maneouvring in restricted space, or to regain deeper water when aground. And in a cruising boat anchoring is certainly the cheapest and often the most pleasant way to pass a night compared to the doubtful pleasure (and cost) of a marina berth. But for anchoring to be enjoyable and safe it is first necessary to have the right gear, which is discussed in detail in Chapter 12.

For a cruising yacht there is no substitute for chain cable: its weight helps to keep the pull on the anchor horizontal and the catenary which it forms absorbs the jerks on the cable as the yacht pitches; cable also resists chafe, on the bottom and at the stemhead. The minimum amount of cable to be veered should not be less than three times the depth of water at high water, and a lot more in heavy weather. In really bad conditions an anchor weight (or something equivalent) can be lowered part way down the cable to maintain the catenary and reduce snubbing.

Boats up to about 10m (33ft) in length may often be able to use a nylon anchor warp – in moderate conditions, or where the boat is not to be left unattended for any length of time. There should be about 5m (3 fathoms) of cable between the anchor and the warp. This gives a little bit of weight where it is most needed, and takes the chafe on the bottom. Where an anchor warp is used, veer a minimum of five times the depth at high water. Particular care is needed to prevent chafe where the warp passes over the stemhead roller; a piece of canvas, stout rag, or split polythene hose firmly seized to the warp at this point should do the trick.

Whatever the cable or anchor warp is secured to on the foredeck – bitts, bollards or anchor windlass – must be extremely strong, and well connected to the vessel's structure. Many modern boats have inadequate cleats for this purpose. The inboard end of the chain or warp should be secured in the chain locker, but in a way so that it can be slipped quickly if necessary. The cable or warp should be marked at intervals, so that it is easy to tell how much has been veered.

15.2.2 Choosing an anchor berth

When approaching an anchorage study the chart carefully and decide where best to anchor – considering the depth (at high and low water), the holding ground, the present and forecast direction of the wind, any obstructions in the area, and the position of any landing place. Any boat which anchors must keep clear of craft already at anchor or on moorings nearby, so it is important to visualise how the boat will swing and where she will lie if the wind shifts or at the turn of the tide. It is important to estimate how other nearby yachts will swing, and where their anchors are. A boat riding on chain cable will not range through such a large circle as one lying on a warp. Never anchor amongst, or too close to, moorings because there is every likelihood of your anchor becoming foul of the ground chains. It is also necessary to anchor clear of channels or fairways.

Unless the sea is rough, it is wise to fake out on deck sufficient cable for three times the depth of water – ranged so that it will run out clearly when the anchor is let go.

Before finally deciding on the place to anchor, motor (or sail) around the immediate vicinity to check the actual depths from the echo sounder or lead line. Knowing the height of tide at the time, these soundings can be compared against the chart and serve as a useful check against anchoring where there well be insufficient depth at low water or where it is unnecessarily deep.

See which way any boats already at anchor are lying, because this will indicate the direction of your final approach to the chosen position for dropping the hook. Don't forget that after the anchor has been let go the yacht will drop back several lengths before she is riding to the cable – depending of course on such factors as the depth of water and how much cable is veered, and how quickly the anchor gets a hold.

It is important to know the range of the tide at the place that day, and the times of high and low water – so that the present height of tide can be calculated. Then it is possible to work out the depth in which the yacht can be safely anchored, and still remain afloat at low water: also what the depth will be at high water, which will govern the amount of cable to be veered.

15.2.3 Anchoring

Normal practice is to come up head to wind (or head to tide, if this is stronger), let go the anchor as the boat comes to rest at the chosen spot, and then allow her to drop astern as the cable is veered. Initially don't let go much more cable than is needed to allow the anchor to reach the bottom – or there is a danger that it will pile up on top of the anchor and foul it. As the boat falls astern the cable (or warp) can be snubbed to help set the anchor; this effect can be increased by running the engine astern for a short burst.

In a sailing yacht it is easiest to come up head to wind, dropping any headsail previously and lowering the mainsail once the anchor has set. But there may be times, in a very strong tide for example, when it is necessary to anchor downwind. In such cases lower the mainsail first, to windward of the chosen position, and blow down to it under jib alone. The speed of approach can be adjusted with the jib sheet, or by partly lowering the sail if necessary. The jib should be fully lowered when the anchor is let go as the chosen position is reached.

If no engine is available, it is important to be able to set sail again quickly – should the anchor drag, or should there be danger of fouling another vessel.

When the boat has 'got her cable', that is to say is riding to her anchor, take anchor bearings of three prominent objects and write them in the log, so that later it is possible to tell if the anchor has dragged. Or line up any prominent objects ashore. Also note the depth of water shown by the echo sounder, or lead line.

If the bottom is foul it may be wise to buoy the anchor by securing a tripping line (longer than the depth at high water) to the crown of the anchor and the other end to a small buoy. If the anchor becomes foul, hauling on the tripping line may help to clear it. Do not use a floating line, and put a weight a couple of metres below the buoy to keep the line clear of propellers etc.

In some harbours, more particularly abroad, it is usual for boats to moor stern to the quay with an anchor out ahead. In this case it is important to drop the anchor in the right place – opposite the berth, and the right distance from the quay. Just a little weight on the cable helps keep the boat straight when going astern into the berth, but good communication between the helmsman and the foredeck is necessary.

It is sometimes useful to drop an anchor when coming alongside in a tideway under bad conditions – both to control the approach to the berth (in the case of a strong onshore wind, for example) and to help haul the boat off when leaving.

The anchor can also be used when turning the boat in a narrow channel with the tide under her, by dropping the anchor under the forefoot and allowing the boat to swing on it.

15.2.4 Mooring with two anchors

A boat lying to a single anchor swings through quite a big circle as wind or tide changes, and in restricted waters it may be helpful to moor with two anchors. Two anchors also give greater security, if properly laid, in the event of bad weather.

In a tideway two anchors would normally be laid in line with the tidal stream, so that the boat lies to one on the flood and the other on the ebb, the heavier anchor being arranged to take the heavier load. This is best done by dropping the first anchor as normal – the upstream one on the ebb, or the downstream one on the flood. The

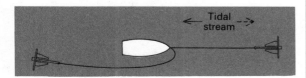

Fig. 15(5) Lying to two anchors in a tideway.

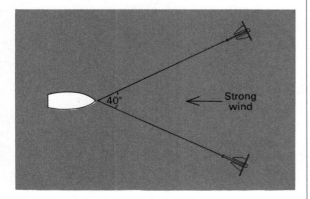

Fig. 15(6) Boat lying to two anchors, open hawse.

boat is then allowed to drop back by veering twice as much cable as normal, when the second anchor is let go. The boat is then middled between the two as in Fig. 15(5). Alternatively the second anchor can be laid by taking it away in the dinghy.

In the event of bad or threatening weather it is always best to lie to two anchors if possible – both set ahead of the boat, one on either bow, with their cables or warps making an angle of not more that 40°, as in Fig. 15(6).If the anchors are properly set, and their cables or warps adjusted correctly, they will share much of the load – although there will be times when all the weight is on one. However two anchors do reduce the amount that the boat sheers about. In a boat with an engine mooring with open hawse, as this is called, can be conveniently done when first anchoring. First let go one anchor in the normal way, preferably buoyed so that its position is known and so that the cable can be slipped if later it should prove difficult to recover both anchors. Once that anchor is set, veer a little more cable and motor forward at the required angle to drop the second anchor. Having set this, middle the vessel between the two, as in Fig. 15(6). Or in favourable weather the second anchor can be laid out later from the dinghy. When doing this it is important to decide on which bow to set the second anchor, and this, in the event of impending had weather, will depend upon the forecast wind direction. See 15.2.7.

When lying to two anchors in a tideway, to avoid the likelihood of the chain and warp getting foul at the stemhead and damage to paintwork on the topsides, it is a good idea to lash the warp securely to the cable at deck level, and then veer them both well below the waterline. The warp should be parcelled (wrapped) where it is in contact with the chain, to prevent chafe.

15.2.5 Weighing anchor

Before weighing anchor it is essential to have made all necessary preparations for getting under way and leaving harbour. If leaving under sail it is important to decide which tack to be on, once the anchor is aweigh. Normally only the mainsail should be set, to keep the foredeck clear. But with wind against tide it may be necessary to get under way with jib alone and set the mainsail later. Before setting sail much of the cable can be hauled in until the anchor is at short stay; it helps to go slow ahead on the engine while heaving in.

If lying head to wind and tide, and with no engine available, hoist the mainsail only and recover the anchor with a succession of short tacks to windward. On each occasion there will come a time when the cable leads astern, and the bight lying on the bottom can be brought in quite easily. Before it grows tight again, secure the cable and form another bight before tacking and repeating the process. When unmooring with two anchors, first weigh the one which has less weight on it.

This may be done from the dinghy, in which case it is useful to have rigged a tripping line.

If a tripping line has been used for the main anchor, recover the anchor buoy and bring it inboard. Once the cable is up and down (when the boat is directly over the anchor) it should be possible to break the anchor out, using the tripping line if necessary, and heave it in as quickly as possible. If the boat is reluctant to pay off on the required tack, back the headsail, and remember to reverse the helm if the boat gathers sternway. If necessary be prepared to re-anchor. Be ready to clean the anchor of mud etc. as soon as it is brought inboard, and preferably beforehand.

15.2.6 Foul anchor

By misfortune the anchor may get foul on the bottom, usually on an old cable or a mooring chain. Or another boat may have dropped her anchor across your cable. This is where a tripping line may help. Otherwise try pulling on the cable from different directions, using the engine, to free it from the obstruction.

If the anchor is foul of a chain or cable it may be possible to bring it near enough to the surface to pass a warp under the obstruction, and the anchor then dropped clear. Otherwise try lowering a loop of chain on a warp down the cable, in the hope that it can be manoeuvred near the crown of the anchor, and then pulled from the opposite direction to free it.

15.2.7 Laying out a kedge, or a second anchor

There are four distinct methods, involving different preparations, and as in many aspects of seamanship good preparation is a recipe for success.

The anchor can be taken away in the dinghy together with the entire length of warp (plus chain where desirable). Make sure that what will be the inboard end of the warp is well secured to the stern of the dinghy, and then coil down the warp with the anchor on top. Having reached the chosen spot, lower the anchor to the bottom and row back to the yacht with the end of the warp. Care is needed in transferring it inboard to the yacht. This has the advantage of being able fairly easily to select where to drop the anchor but be careful that this is not too far from the boat so that there is insufficient line for the return trip. To avoid this it is better to secure the end of the warp to the yacht, and then row away paying out the warp as you go. This means putting the anchor in the dinghy first, and then coiling down the warp on top of it.

Alternatively, only put the anchor in the dinghy and have somebody on deck to pay out the warp as the dinghy is rowed away. A prearranged signal can tell the person in the dinghy when the extremity of the warp is reached. But the simplest method is to lay the second anchor from the yacht, using the engine. First arrange the cable or warp to

be used on deck, with a length equal to the scope to which the boat is lying. Go slow ahead, steering in the required direction, keeping the rode that is in the water fairly tight and clear of the boat's propeller. If necessary veer a little more cable so that the boat arrives at a position slightly ahead of the anchor already on the bottom. Let go the second anchor and allow the boat to drop back between the two.

15.3 Mooring alongside

15.3.1 Coming alongside

When arriving in a strange harbour always check the depth of water alongside any quay or jetty, the rise and fall of the tide, and the state of the tide at the time. Also check from the chart or sailing directions whether there are likely to be any underwater obstructions. If it is intended to dry out alongside it is important to know the kind of bottom, and also what the wall is like to rest against. Should there be piles along the face of the wall it will be necessary to have a couple of short planks, each placed across two fenders next to the hull and to bear against convenient piles. It will also be necessary to find somewhere to lead a mast line to hold the boat against the wall.

When coming alongside a quay where there are mooring bollards, it may be useful to put bowlines in the ends of the mooring warps in advance, particularly if short handed.

If there are already one or more warps looped over a bollard, the eye of a fresh warp should be passed up through the eyes(s) of existing warp(s) before slipping it over the bollard. In this way any individual warp can be let go without interfering with the others, as is shown in Fig. 15(7).

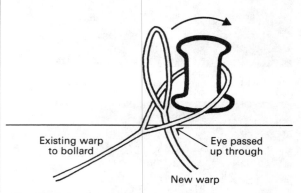

Fig. 15(7) Passing the loop of a warp up through the loop of a warp already on a bollard.

When coming alongside, always approach at as slow speed as possible consistent with maintaining steerage way, and heading into wind or tide – whichever is the stronger. Have warps led ready for taking ashore, and fenders in position.

Four ropes are normally necessary to secure a boat alongside a jetty, quay or pontoon – a head

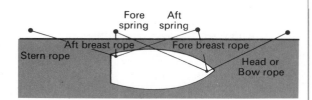

Fig. 15(8) Boat moored alongside, port side to, with head and stern ropes, springs, and breast ropes fore and aft. The latter should be dispensed with if there is any rise or fall of tide since they will need continual adjustment, but they are useful when mooring alongside another vessel.

rope led well forward and a stern rope led well aft, and springs led from bow aft (fore spring) and from stern forward (after spring). These are shown in Fig. 15(8). In non-tidal waters, or when lying alongside another vessel, breast ropes can be added at right angles to the jetty. When lying on another vessel, whether alongside or at piles or buoys, always take out your own lines forward and aft, and secure them to shore/piles/buoys as appropriate, and adjust them so that they are taking their share of the weight.

Under power in a boat with a right-handed screw, it is easier to berth port side to, because when going astern to check the boat's way the stern swings to port and helps to bring the boat parallel to the quay.

When lying alongside a jetty or wall on a lee shore, a heavy anchor can be used to hold the boat away from the shore and prevent her bumping alongside. The anchor can either be dropped from the yacht on arriving and before securing alongside, which is the simpler and preferred method, or taken away in the dinghy subsequently as described in 15.2.7. Such an anchor is also a great help when leaving the berth in these circumstances.

15.3.2 The use of warps and springs

Apart from securing a yacht alongside, warps can also be used to manoeuvre a boat – as for example by the proper use of a spring when entering or leaving a difficult berth.

The effect of a warp secured to a boat depends upon its point of attachment and the direction of pull. For a simple example, as in Fig. 15(9), if it is desired to haul a boat ahead along a quay, or a canal bank, a warp secured at the chainplates (at the deck edge, abreast the mast) will pull the boat ahead, clear of the wall, with little or no rudder

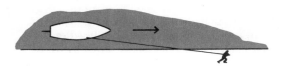

Fig. 15(9) Hauling a boat with warp attached to the chainplates.

needed. Should the warp be secured right forward, it continually pulls the bow towards the wall. By motoring ahead against a fore spring, with a suitably placed fender, the stern of the boat will swing out when the other lines are let go. Similarly, going astern against an aft spring will swing the bow out – see Fig. 15(10) and Fig. 15(11).

A boat can be held temporarily alongside with just a spring, as illustrated in Fig. 15(13). This can be very convenient because if the spring is led aft beforehand a single-handed person can do everything with little need to leave the cockpit, and without having to go on to the foredeck and leave the helm unattended. Similarly on departing, all that it needed is to let go the spring and recover the fender.

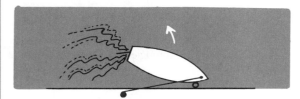

Fig. 15(10) Swinging the stern out by going ahead against fore spring.

Fig. 15(11) Swinging the bow out by going astern against aft spring.

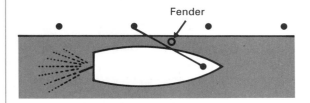

Fig. 15(12) Using a spring while lying temporarily alongside, with the engine running slow ahead and helm adjusted to keep the boat parallel to the jetty.

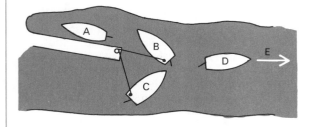

Fig. 15(13) Use of spring for leaving a difficult berth.

A spring can be most useful when a boat has to turn a significant corner, perhaps when leaving a difficult berth. For example in Fig. 15(13) the boat at A has to proceed in the direction E, involving a turn through 180° in a confined space. A spring is rove from the port quarter round a bollard at the end of the jetty, and brought back inboard. The boat then proceeds slow astern out of the berth. At B the spring is snubbed, and the boat starts to swing as shown, still going slow astern, until she reaches C – when the spring can be recovered, and the boat can go ahead with starboard helm as in D. During the evolution the boat is in complete control.

15.3.3 Leaving an alongside berth
Before getting under way from an alongside berth, consider carefully the effects of wind and tide, and decide in which order the various warps should be let go.

If the boat is heading into the stream, or a strong wind in still water, let go the lines in turn until the boat is lying just on the after spring, which should have been arranged previously as a slip rope (taken round a convenient object ashore, and the end brought back inboard). Push the bow out, or go slow astern on the engine, and tide or wind will then complete the process so that the spring can be recovered and the boat allowed to proceed ahead out of the berth. Watch the stern against the quay or other craft and make sure the stern rope is kept clear of the screw. Once clear, get the fenders inboard and coil down all the warps.

When wind or tide is from astern, or if there is a wind blowing the boat on to the jetty, it is best to proceed astern out of the berth. In this case the fore spring is rigged as a slip rope and is the last to be let go. One of the crew is stationed with a fender near the bow, and the engine is put slow ahead to swing the stern out from the jetty. When the boat has reached the required angle, let go the spring and go astern – but not before being sure that no other craft is approaching.

15.3.4 Rafting up
It is quite common for several boats to be rafted up alongside each other in harbour. So far as possible the larger yachts should be inboard, and the smaller ones outboard. Masts of sailing boats should be staggered to prevent rigging and crosstrees fouling. Plenty of springs and fenders are needed, and each boat should be connected to shore by her own head and stern lines.

Harbours often limit the number of boats that can raft up alongside each other, but in any case always ask permission before going alongside another boat. The inner boats of a raft have to endure a lot of traffic across their decks and consideration should be shown in this respect.

When an inside boat wishes to leave it is advisable to seek the co-operation of those outboard of her, since with their help the manoeuvre is relatively straightforward. In order

to control the outboard boats it is important that the one leaving departs in the direction of wind or tide, whichever is stronger. Then the semi-detached part of the raft is more easily reformed alongside. In some circumstances it is helpful if one of the outer yachts uses her engine for this purpose.

The departing boat must let go her shore lines, and then in succession the springs and other lines connecting her to the boats each side. Meanwhile – see Fig. 15(14) – the bow line(s) of the boat(s) outboard of her must be brought round her stern, ready to be made tight once the leaving boat is clear of the gap thus created.

In the event that the outboard boats are not manned, then it is necessary for one or two crews from the departing yacht to stay in the raft and resecure them – being picked up from the outboard boat on completion.

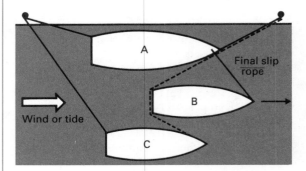

Fig. 15(14) When B leaves from the middle of a raft she should depart with wind or tide, whichever is stronger; this helps to bring C alongside A when B has left. Here B is about to let go her bow line, rigged as a slip rope, while the bow line of C has been passed round the stern of B ready to be made up once B has moved clear.

15.3.5 Mooring stern-to
In Mediterranean harbours it is common practice to moor stern-to the quay or harbour wall, with an anchor out ahead. In a twin-screw motor boat the manoeuvre should present no problem, but it can be a different matter in a single-screw vessel that does not handle well astern, or in a strong cross wind. Before entering harbour have everything ready – warps aft, fenders each side and one over the stern, and the anchor cleared away on the foredeck; the boathook may also be useful.

Unless you are directed to a specific berth, spend a little time deciding where best to go. The obvious vacant spot may have drawbacks such as underwater obstructions or the town sewer. In general it is best to lie among other yachts, who are more likely to help with taking your lines than fishing boats or commercial craft.

It is important to drop the anchor in the right place. If, as is likely, there are already other boats moored up, see how their cables are lying so as to avoid dropping your anchor on top of them. Should it be unavoidable to cross another boat's cable or anchor line, drop your anchor well beyond. The anchor should be placed opposite the intended berth and a sufficient distance from the quay to veer at least three boats' lengths of cable – but not so far that you cannot reach the quay. With a strong cross wind it is necessary to anchor slightly upwind of the berth, so that some tension in the cable will stop the bow being blown off as you go astern into the berth.

Even in good conditions a little tension in the cable helps to keep the boat straight as the boat goes astern. Good communication (perhaps by hand signals) is needed between the helmsman and the foredeck so that the cable is veered the required amount, and in a larger boat it is also needed with the stern as the boat gets nearer the quay.

It is helpful to be able to lie temporarily alongside another boat, one side or other of the berth, while your stern lines are taken ashore. But if there is nobody to take your lines you have to get close enough to the quay for one of the crew to jump ashore.

Stern lines need to be led out in each direction so as to locate the boat sideways in the berth, as well as to hold her the required distance from the quay. In Mediterranean harbours with no

significant rise and fall they should not need adjusting.

On the principle that it is easier to manoeuvre out of a narrow space rather than into it, a different approach can be made in a boat that does not handle well or in bad conditions. Proceed ahead into the berth and pass a long line ashore. Then go astern into open water to anchor. The line to shore can then be passed aft so that the boat is hauled into the berth as the cable is veered.

Leaving a stern-to berth presents no difficulty unless your anchor proves to be foul of another boat's. This situation can sometimes be anticipated, and often remedied with the helpful co-operation of the other vessel (see also 15.2.6). But it can be a tedious business and it is best to avoid the possibility in the first instance.

15.3.6 **Drying out alongside**
Apart from the occasional need to dry out alongside for a scrub, there are many attractive harbours which can only be visited by yachts prepared to take the ground.

The operation depends on several factors – the details of the wall or jetty, the nature of the bottom alongside it, the hull form of the boat, and

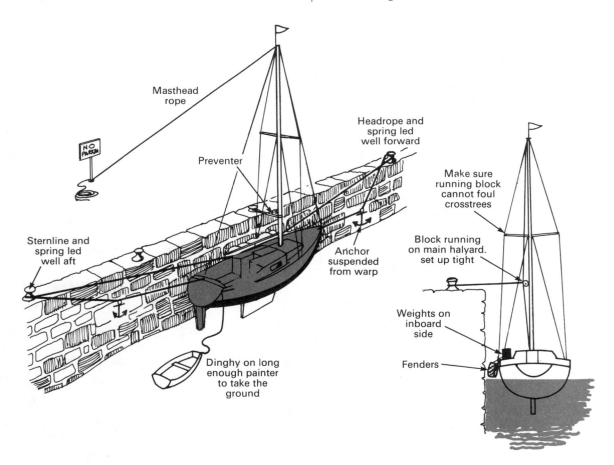

Fig. 15(15) Drying out alongside. In conjunction with Fig. 15(16), this diagram shows the basic precautions to be taken.

Fig. 15(16) As an alternative to a masthead rope, a running block can be attached to a halyard, set up tight down the mast.

the rise and fall of tide. If the boat is to take the ground soon after high water, make sure the next tide is big enough to float her off again.

Not all harbour walls are smooth or vertical: there may be protrusions below the water. The bottom may be uneven, perhaps rocky, or it may slope downwards from the foot of the wall at a dangerous angle. So seek advice in a strange harbour, and whenever possible survey the site beforehand.

Some boats take the ground better than others. Catamarans or boats with twin bilge keels present no problem, unless the ground slopes significantly away from the quay. Cruising yachts with long, straight keels should dry out comfortably, but steps must be taken to ensure that they lean towards the wall. Boats with shorter keels, and particularly the extreme fin and skeg type of hull, can give difficulty.

Much depends on what part of the keel touches first, and starts to take the weight. This in turn depends upon the shape of the keel and the slope of the bottom (not outwards from the wall, but along the length of the boat). If one end of the keel takes the ground first, the boat can pivot laterally about this point as the water falls, so that either the bow or the stern may tend to swing towards the wall. Consequently the boat must be firmly secured, with warps taken well out ahead and astern if there is any appreciable rise and fall: and she needs to be very well fendered at points about one-third and two-thirds along her length, where she will rest against the wall. To avoid continual adjustment of the headrope and sternline, heavy weights can be attached to the bight of each.

Weights, such as chain cable, should be transferred to the inboard side of the yacht so that she has a slight list towards the wall. If the boat is going to be alongside for just one tide a masthead rope can be rigged to some object ashore, possibly backed up by a preventer round the mast to a convenient bollard on the quay as in Fig. 15(15). But this type of masthead rope needs constant adjustment, and for a longer stay it is more convenient to rig a mastline to a block running on a halyard close to the mast, as in Fig. 15(16).

Some of the above points apply to motor boats, but their main consideration is often the protection of sterngear and rudders. Many fast motor cruisers are not suited to taking the ground without risk of damage to these items.

15.4 Pile moorings

15.4.1 Pile moorings – general

Pile moorings are a way of accommodating more boats in a harbour, often with two or more boats secured between a pair of piles. In tidal waters the piles have sliding rings each side, to which warps can be secured. A line is made fast to each ring so that it can be retrieved from below the water

when necessary. Even when sharing the space between piles with some other boat(s) always take out your own lines fore and aft.

On arrival you must first decide which way the boat should face, and generally it is best to have the bow into the stronger tidal stream or river current (the ebb). In bad weather it may be preferable to face any strong wind that is forecast, while in other circumstances it may be easier to depart with the boat facing to seaward. However, all these considerations may be overridden by the mechanics of getting into the berth in the first instance – particularly under sail with no auxiliary power available. In all cases it is important to plan well ahead, to brief the crew as to what is intended, and to have lines prepared fore and aft. Possibly the dinghy may be needed to take out the stern line. The boathook and fenders should also be at the ready. It is often quicker and easier when initially securing to a ring on a pile to pass the line through the ring (or round the bar on which the ring travels) as a slip rope, bringing the end back inboard, and then make it fast properly later.

15.4.2 Arrival under power

If there is already another boat in the berth it is a straightforward manoeuvre to go alongside her and then take out lines fore and aft, using the dinghy if necessary. But if the berth is vacant the method will depend on the relative strengths and directions of wind and tide. Pile moorings are invariably laid in line with the stream, and if necessary the boat can always be turned through 180° subsequently.

With wind and tide together, it is easy to approach into them, secure to the upstream pile, and then ease the bow line to drift slowly back to allow the stern line to be made fast. An even neater manoeuvre, as shown in Fig. 15(17), is to take the stern line well forward along the deck, outboard of everything, and secure it to the downstream pile as the boat passes slowly by. Keep the stern line slack but clear of the propeller while proceeding ahead to the upstream pile. Then middle the boat between the piles. This method is called a running moor.

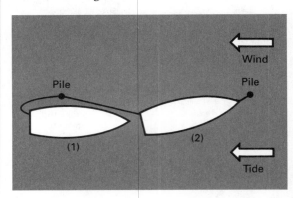

Fig. 15(17) With a running moor the stern line is secured to the aft pile as the boat passes close by, before securing the bow line. The boat is then middled between the piles.

With wind against tide, approach into whichever is the stronger. Under these conditions it is less easy to maintain directional control, and the running moor may be preferred. Alternatively, secure to the forward pile and take out the stern line by dinghy.

By the nature of things the wind is most likely to be blowing across the berth to make matters more difficult, and the method used will depend on its strength and direction relative to the tide. With twin screws there should be no difficulty but in a low-powered sailing cruiser it may be useful to make a trial run to see how the boat behaves and how she drifts under wind and tide.

With the wind roughly at right angles to the line of piles, approach close to leeward of the first (stern) pile and secure the stern line for a running moor. Then motor slowly ahead so that the combined action of wind and tide carries the boat slightly broadside to the further pile so as to secure the bow line, as in Fig. 15(18). Should however the boat be difficult to control, with the bow being blown off by the wind, it is safer to secure to the further pile and take out the stern line by dinghy, as in Fig. 15(19). With a large crew on board, so that a couple of hands can be spared from deck, it is a good idea to have the dinghy already manned and in the water, perhaps with a line already made fast to the stern pile so that it can be passed quickly and easily.

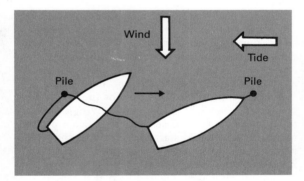

Fig. 15(18) With wind across the tide a variation of the running moor can still be used.

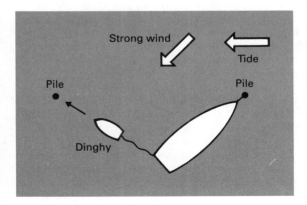

Fig. 15(19) With a strong wind across the berth it is likely that the stern line will need to be passed by dinghy.

15.4.3 **Arrival under sail.**

As in the case of arrival under power, the line of approach will be determined by the directions and relative strengths of wind and tide. Except in a very strong wind it is usually best to head into the tide. The final approach must be very slow and well controlled, with the boat coming to rest in the required place.

With the wind forward of the beam, approach on a close reach under mainsail only, with the mainsheet eased as necessary to reduce speed; and then round up alongside the forward pile to secure the bow line. If the wind is blowing across the berth it will probably be necessary to take out the stern line by dinghy. See Fig. 15(20).

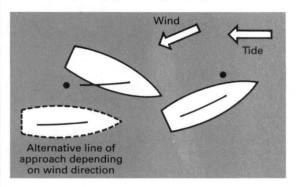

Fig. 15(20) With the wind ahead, approach the berth under mainsail only, trimming the mainsheet as necessary to control speed. Lower the mainsail as soon as the bow line is secured.

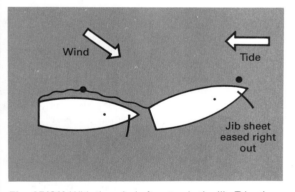

Fig. 15(21) With the wind aft, set only the jib. Trim the jib sheet, and if necessary partly lower the sail, in order to control speed. Be ready to lower the sail as soon as the bow line is secured.

If the wind is aft of the beam, blow down into the berth under jib alone, adjusting speed by easing the jib sheet or by half lowering the sail if there is much wind. It should be possible to pass close to the downstream (aft) pile and execute a running moor as already described in 15.4.2. See Fig. 15(21).

15.4.4 **Departure under power.**

If lying alongside another vessel between piles the procedure is similar to that used when leaving any alongside berth. Rig temporary slip lines to the other boat and let go the head and stern lines to the piles. If to leeward of the other vessel the wind will blow the boat off, but if to windward it may be more difficult to get away. In a strong tidal stream, depending on its direction it should be possible to go ahead or astern on a spring to swing out the stern or the bow.

When she is the only one between piles, and lying head to wind and current, pull the boat ahead to rig the bow line as a slip rope, and then let her drop astern to release the stern line. If necessary the bow line can be led aft down one side of the boat or the other to give her a sheer in the required direction.

Lying stern to wind or tide, whichever is stronger, the above procedure is reversed. The stern line is rigged as a slip rope before the bow line is let go. Having given the boat a sheer by means of the helm, or by taking the stern line forward down the required side of the boat, proceed astern out of the berth. If the boat is underpowered, or does not handle well astern, turn her through 180° in the berth by warps – a procedure known as 'winding ship'.

With a beam wind, rig bow and stern lines as slip ropes, and allow the boat to be blown to leeward before letting go fore and aft and proceeding.

15.4.5 Departure under sail

Since a sailing boat needs to leave the berth proceeding ahead (not astern), better control is given if this is done head to tide. If necessary, wind ship to achieve this. Rig head and/or stern line(s) as slip rope(s) on the same principle as in 15.4.4. If the wind is ahead, depart under mainsail but with the jib ready for hoisting. If the wind is aft leave under jib until it is convenient to round up and hoist the main.

When lying alongside another boat on piles the procedure is the same as for leaving any alongside berth; this is not too difficult when the wind is blowing the boat off, but more of a problem when it is in the opposite direction so that you may have to take a line to some object upwind to haul the boat off.

Unless the wind is aft, and in the same direction as the tidal stream, it is unwise to attempt to leave the middle of a raft under sail alone.

15.5 Towing

15.5.1 Towing – procedure

Every seagoing yacht should have at least one really long warp – say 50m or 30 fathoms in length, and perhaps 16mm nylon or 18mm polyester of three-strand construction. Such a rope can be useful for kedging, or when an extra long mooring warp is needed – or for towing, at sea. In smooth water a boat can be towed at short stay, or alongside in a congested harbour.

Even in good weather, towing requires co-operation between the two boats concerned and amongst the crew of each. In calm water the towing craft can usually manoeuvre with her stern close to the other's bows, so that the tow can be passed. In any wind or sea it may be necessary to establish contact by heaving line, by which the tow rope can then be hauled across. In severe conditions a line can be floated down to the other craft. In all these cases it is usually more sensible for the towing craft to supply the tow line, since she will probably be to windward of the other, but see 15.5.4 in respect of salvage situations. It is essential for both boats to be almost stationary, or moving at the same speed through the water, while the tow is being passed.

Only tugs are designed for towing, and the average yacht is poorly equipped in this respect, since it is impossible to get the point of tow far enough forward. Normally the tow rope has to be made fast to a cleat near the stern, and this prevents the towing boat manoeuvering freely. In a tug the tow hook is almost amidships, and certainly well forward of the propeller, but in a yacht things like backstays and guardrails normally prevent any such arrangement. If possible however, avoid having to tow from one quarter because this will make steering even more difficult; some form of bridle between bollards or cleats on each quarter should overcome this difficulty.

When a boat is stopped in the water it takes quite a weight on the towline to get her moving, so the tow must be taken up very gently or it will part. The towing craft must not go ahead until the other signifies that she is ready. If a tow parts, anybody standing near is likely to be injured.

While lying stopped, waiting for the tow to be connected, the yacht is likely to be lying beam-on to any swell or sea. When the tow is taken up, the towing vessel should start towing across the swell before gradually entering course into it, if this is necessary.

The tow should be secured so that it can be released under load, which may be necessary if the tow has to be slipped in an emergency. In a large boat it is advisable to have an axe handy. When towing a small boat like a dinghy or runabout, the line should be turned up on a cleat and tended by hand – so that it can be slipped immediately, if the boat being towed takes a sudden sheer or is about to collide with something for example.

It is a great help if the boat being towed can steer, so that she does not yaw from side to side. This may not always be possible, but in any event the boat being towed should be trimmed somewhat by the stern, and not by the bow.

When towing, avoid any sudden alterations of course, particularly if the tow is unable to steer; and try to give advance warning of your intentions. When reducing speed, do so gradually – most important when towing a heavy vessel which carries a lot of way. Always be careful not to tow too fast – a common fault when yachts are taken in tow by larger ships. When towing a small boat which has been swamped proceed very slowly, or either the boat will be damaged or the tow will part.

When there is any sea or swell to contend with, it is important to adjust the length of the tow so that the two craft are 'in step' in relation to the waves. Avoid the situation, for example, where the towing boat is going down a wave when the boat in tow is climbing the face of a wave astern.

In calm water it is easier to tow alongside if any manoeuvering is involved. The tow boat should be positioned well aft, on the other's quarter. The choice of side may be dictated by the job in hand – where the other boat is to be berthed for example. When going ahead the weight is taken by a spring led aft from the bow of the towing boat: similarly when going astern the pull is by a spring led forward to the boat being towed. Proper positioning of the towing craft and correct adjustment of the warps give surprising freedom of manoeuvre. Good fendering is of course necessary.

If towing more than one boat the biggest should be next astern, and the lightest at the end of the tow. If towing a large number of dinghies it is better to form two lines, one from each quarter.

Towing at sea can put tremendous strains not only on the tow rope but on the samson post, bollard, bitts or cleat to which it is secured. In many boats the bottom of the mast, at deck level, may be the strongest point of attachment – although it will be necessary to constrain the towline at the stemhead in order to avoid damage to the forestay. Special precautions must be taken about chafe at this point. One method of towing at sea is to attach the towing vessel's hawser to the anchor of the casualty, who then veers her cable as shown in Fig. 15(22). The weight of the anchor and cable gives some spring to the tow, apart from being stronger than the average warp.

In many modern yachts there is no fitting on the foredeck sufficiently strong for towing in a seaway, and even the foot of a mast stepped on deck may not be designed for this. In such cases it may be possible to rig some kind of towing bridle from strong warps taken round the superstructure and cockpit at deck level, and attached to strong points such as sheet winches. Depending on the

details of the boat, this is not likely to be easy, and will certainly take time if a proper job is to be made of it – anything hastily contrived will soon come adrift once the tow is taken up.

Most tows are taken or given as a matter of convenience, and on an informal basis between the parties concerned. If commercial bargaining is necessary it is advisable to agree on a reasonable sum for a pluck into harbour. But what may start as a simple towing operation can develop into salvage, if for example the weather deteriorates or the tow gets into danger through no fault of the towing boat.

15.5.2 Signals when towing

Under the *International Regulations for Preventing Collisions at Sea*, vessels towing or being towed are required to show certain signals, and these are given in section 2.1. Yachts or other craft not normally used for towing are excused from showing the special towing signals required by Rule 24(a) and (c), but are required to take measures to indicate the relationship between the towing vessel and the vessel being towed, as for example by illuminating the towline.

A vessel being towed should show sidelights and sternlight, but not a masthead light. In poor visibility a vessel towing sounds one long blast followed by two short blasts ('D'), at intervals of not more than two minutes. The vessel being towed sounds one long blast followed by three short blasts ('B'), when practicable immediately after the signal sounded by the towing vessel.

15.5.3 Communication between vessels

Communication between the two vessels is important, and often difficult in bad weather without VHF. A few signals are likely to be universally understood, such as 'thumbs up'. Arms extended at waist height with the palms of the hands paddling downwards may be taken to mean 'slow down'. Arms extended slightly higher with palms upwards conveys 'increase speed'. Arms waved criss-cross in front of and above the head should be interpreted as 'no good' (the opposite of 'thumbs up') or 'stop'.

There are a number of appropriate groups in the *International Code of Signals*, and a selection is given below:

Z   I require a tug
KK   Towing is impossible under present weather conditions
KL   I am obliged to stop towing temporarily
KM   I can take you in tow
KN   I cannot take you in tow
KP   You should tow me to nearest port or anchorage
KQ   Prepare to be taken in tow
KR   All is ready for towing
KS   You should send a line over
KT   You should send me a towing hawser
KU   I cannot send towing hawser
KV   I intend to use my towing hawser/cable

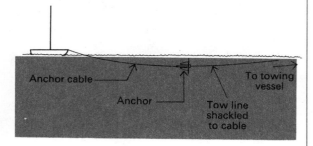

Fig. 15(22) Towing at sea, using the boat's anchor cable.

KW	You should have towing hawser/cable ready
KX	You should be ready to receive the towing hawser
KY	Length of tow is . . . (numbered) fathoms
KZ	You should shorten in the towing hawser
LA	Towing hawser/cable has parted
LB	You should make towing hawser fast to your chain cable
LD	You should veer your hawser/cable
LE	I am about to veer my hawser/cable
LF	You should stop veering your hawser/cable
LG	You should prepare to cast off towing hawser
QD	I am going ahead
QE	I have headway
QF	I cannot go ahead
QG	You should go ahead
QH	You should not go ahead any more
QI	I am going astern
QJ	I have sternway
QK	I cannot go astern
QL	You should go astern
QM	You should not go astern any more
RL	You should stop your engines immediately
RM	My engines are stopped
LI	I am increasing speed
LJ	I am reducing speed

15.5.4 **Salvage**

A successful claim for salvage may be made if the person concerned can show that he voluntarily saved, or helped save, a vessel and perhaps her crew, which was in danger on tidal waters, while he was not performing any legal or official duty. Danger must have existed, and another basic principle of salvage is 'no cure, no pay'.

Some acts of salvage are self-evident – where a boat is towed off a lee shore or off rocks in a rising wind, for example – but other instances may not be so obvious. A claim might be upheld because a vessel answered a distress signal, even if that had been made hastily and prematurely (and hence also illegally). The moral here is that if you require assistance, but are not actually in distress, you should use the appropriate signal such as 'V' (Victor) in the *International Code of Signals,* meaning 'I require assistance'. Again, a vessel might claim salvage just because she stood by and gave advice; or if she assisted in pilotage to avoid a local danger; or if she provided equipment such as pumps, fire extinguishers, or even a towing warp to a boat in danger. For the last reason it is better (when possible) for a boat to use her own warp when being taken in tow in emergency, or at least to show that she has a suitable rope for the purpose.

Other factors which might support a claim for salvage could be the physical condition, ignorance or lack of skill of the crew of a boat in danger. Even their unguarded remarks might be construed as evidence that the boat was in real trouble.

Unless the boat is really in danger, do not accept help from a stranger without politely making it quite clear that you have the situation well in hand, and that you are only availing yourself of his kind offer of assistance as a matter of convenience.

The normal yacht insurance policy covers salvage, but not a convenient tow if the boat is becalmed or the engine has broken down. In such cases it is always important to agree beforehand a price for a pluck into harbour. Although yachtsmen can be expected to provide such a service free to their fellows, the same cannot be said of commercial craft to whom time is money.

If the situation is such that a claim for salvage may arise, there are two suggested courses of action. First, it may be possible to agree a reasonable sum in advance – either verbally or better (if feasible in the circumstances) by a written agreement in the form shown. In emergency this could be torn out of the Handbook and used for the purpose. If a verbal agreement is made, be sure that your crew witness what is discussed and the price quoted, and write down the conversation promptly. In practice it may be impossible to agree a figure, or even to establish proper communication, and then it is necessary to adopt the second course of action – to turn the whole business over to your insurers as soon as possible on reaching harbour, for them to negotiate a settlement. They will need to know the full facts, including the degree of risk to your own vessel and also to the salvor. In this connection it is important to be able to produce the boat's log, the chart with previous course and position correctly plotted, and relevant information on the present and forecast weather.

If and when a salvage claim comes to court for adjudication the court will examine all the circumstances of the case, not only the value of the vessels concerned and the time and danger involved, but also the degree of skill shown in the salvage and whether the salvor's vessel was specifically engaged as a salvage vessel or whether the salvage was simply opportune.

Do not disclose the value of your boat to the claimant. Also be warned that although your policy includes salvage claims it might not cover the full sum if the boat is under-insured.

It should be noted that the RNLI never claims salvage or makes any charge for rescuing persons or property. Yachtsmen who benefit accordingly should at least make a healthy contribution to RNLI funds, while some personal appreciation to the crew would not be amiss. Very occasionally a lifeboat crew may claim salvage, but if they do they have to bear the cost of the rescue and of any damage to the lifeboat, regardless of the outcome of the claim.

In salvage cases, in the unusual event of the claim not being settled out of court, awards tend to be very much lower than feared by the owner. In the highest cases an award of more than 50 per cent of the salved value is unusual, and that would presuppose a skilful operation in circumstances of great danger, where the loss of

SIMPLE FORM OF SALVAGE AGREEMENT
NO CURE NO PAY

On board the yacht ....

Date ....

IT IS HEREBY AGREED BETWEEN ....

....

(afterwards called 'The Master') and ....

....

(afterwards called the 'Contractor') as follows:-

1. The Contractor agrees to use his best endeavours to salve the yacht ....and take her into...or other place to be hereafter agreed with the Master providing at his own risk all proper assistance and labour. The services shall be rendered and accepted as salvage services upon the principle of 'no cure no pay' and the Contractor's remuneration in the event of success shall be £   – or if no sum be herein named such sum as may be decided by subsequent arbitration in accordance with the terms of Clause 3 herein.

2. The Contractor may make reasonable use of the vessel's gear anchors chains and other appurtenances during and for the purpose of the operations but shall not unnecessarily damage abandon or sacrifice the same or any other of the property.

3. Any question or difference at any time arising out of this agreement whether as to construction or otherwise or the operations thereunder shall be referred to arbitration by a sole arbitrator to be nominated by agreement between the parties hereto or in default of agreement by an arbitrator to be appointed by the secretary of Lloyd's.

    Any award by arbitration shall be final and binding on the parties hereto and the arbitrator shall have power to obtain call for receive and act upon any such oral or documentary evidence or information (whether the same is strictly admissible as evidence or not) as he shall think fit. Save as aforesaid the statutory provisions as to arbitration for the time being in force in England shall apply.

4. All costs of and incidental to any arbitration shall be paid by such of the parties hereto as the arbitration shall direct.

Signatures of Master and Contractor

....

....

Fig. 15(23) Simple form of salvage agreement.

the salved vessel was virtually certain and where the operation took a great deal of time and effort involving an expensive salvage vessel. In other cases the award will be proportionally less, and an award of a few per cent may be all that is merited.

Once the salvage has been effected, the salvor has a maritime lien on the property salved. This is a right to arrest the vessel at any time, even if she has subsequently been sold to a third party, and to sell her to meet the claim. Since this lien gives good legal protection to the salvor, he is not permitted to detain the vessel after she has been brought to port unless he found her abandoned and derelict, or can prove that there is a substantial risk that his claim may not be met (e.g. if the owner lives overseas and has no resources or property in the jurisdiction of the British courts). Apart from having a claim against the vessel herself, the salvor also has a claim against the other personal assets of the owner if he is unable to satisfy his claim from the sale proceeds.

15.6 Practical passage making

15.6.1 Navigational records

Any seagoing yacht should keep a form of log. Some owners like to write up a fair record of their various cruises: while this is a nice idea and often useful for subsequent reference, it is not essential. What is essential however is a ruled notebook of some kind in which the following information can be recorded periodically and on specific occasions, such as when course is altered or when a fix is obtained.

(1) Course ordered
(2) Course actually steered
(3) Log reading
(4) Distance run
(5) Wind speed and direction
(6) Barometer reading

There should also be a wide column for general remarks such as the bearings of shore objects (and time taken), and the times at which lights appear or disappear etc.

When under power engine readings should be taken and recorded regularly, so that it is possible to detect any change in cooling water temperature or oil pressure. Details will depend on the installation, but other readings which should be noted include engine rpm, ammeter, fuel gauge, and turbocharger boost pressure (where applicable). It is sensible to make provision for these to be recorded in the log too, perhaps on the opposite page to navigational entries.

While all the above figures are often only of passing interest, they can be invaluable when something goes wrong. If for example the visibility starts to deteriorate it can become vital to know what the log reading was when passing a buoy an hour or so previously, and what course has been maintained meanwhile.

If the cooling water temperature appears to be higher than normal it is useful to be able to check what it was half-an-hour ago, and whether the rate of increase is significant. At least if the skipper insists that the necessary readings are entered in the log regularly it is more likely that any problem will be detected before it becomes really serious.

Times of starting/stopping the engine(s) should be noted, so that a record can be kept of engine running hours. In motor yachts it may be preferred to keep a separate record of engine maintenance, but otherwise it is useful to record in the log the dates (and engine hours) at which routine maintenance is carried out. This should include such items as cleaning fuel filters and injectors, renewing oil filter elements and changing lubricating oil, checking drive belts and flexible hoses, and other similar routines in the engine handbook. The log may also be a useful place to keep a record of such things as fuel and oil consumption, and when batteries are topped up.

15.6.2 Passage planning

Before embarking on any seagoing passage in a boat it is necessary to do some preliminary planning. The amount of work involved depends upon the scope of the passage, and to some extent upon the experience of the skipper and crew, but there are some matters which should always be examined beforehand. They include the seaworthiness of the boat and the strength of the crew, in relation to the waters concerned and the likely weather conditions; preliminary chart work to establish the best route in the light of principal dangers, tidal streams, reliable navigational landmarks and other pilotage details – together with the distances involved and hence the likely time required; and an examination of possible harbours of refuge which will give good or acceptable shelter in the event of bad weather, with a study of any restrictions on entering them due to tidal or gale conditions.

For motor yachts it is also necessary to relate the cruising range of the boat with the distance to be covered, and to investigate the fuelling facilities at the port of arrival or along the way.

All this can mean quite a lot of reading when planning a passage or cruise to a strange place or coast, but it is work which will be amply repaid, particularly if events do not go entirely as planned.

For a start it is essential to have the necessary charts and other publications for the area concerned: make sure that charts are also held of adjacent areas, in case of any diversion due to bad weather. Charts must be corrected, up to date. Large scale charts are needed of ports and harbour approaches.

Where it is necessary to navigate through an area of sandbanks or narrow channels – such as the Thames estuary – select the preferred route taking account of the lack of obstructions, the available navigational marks, depth of water and tidal streams, but be prepared to accept other routes in the event (for example) of a head wind. It is obviously preferable to choose channels which are wide enough to permit some margin of error should the visibility be bad, even if they add to the distance to be sailed. Often it is possible to plan alternative routes, leaving the final decision until the time comes.

In selecting a route take account of the height of tide at the time you expect to be there. It may be possible to plan on taking a short cut with perfect safety if the tide permits, but always have a fall-back plan if things don't go as expected.

Particularly in a sailing yacht the time for starting a passage is likely to be dictated by the time the tide turns in your favour – not necessarily at your moorings, but out in the main channel. It is often worthwhile plugging for a while against the last of a foul tide in order to be in the best position to take full advantage of the next six hours of favourable stream

Special consideration may have to be given to rounding certain headlands, or passing through narrow channels where the tide runs strongly. Information on these points is contained in the various sailing directions and should not be disregarded.

Sort out all your charts, put them in the order in which they are going to be used, and rub out all previous pencil markings. Most skippers like to mark up the tidal atlas with the time of each tidal stream for ease of reference. Times and heights of HW and LW can also be extracted from the tide tables for the ports of departure and arrival, and for any other Standard Port along the route. All this information can be written in a navigator's notebook, which should be small enough to go into an oilskin pocket so that it can be referred to in the cockpit if necessary. The characteristics of the principal lights, the frequencies and call signs of appropriate radio-beacons, and the times of various weather forecasts can also be included.

The more such work that can be done beforehand, the less worry there will be when the boat is at sea. Preliminary chart work is particularly important in fast planing motor cruisers. In these boats it is often impossible to write or draw a line on the chart when under way, so all courses and distances should be worked out and listed in advance. In such craft it is also necessary to keep an accurate record of the fuel state, and it is important to know the likely speed through the water and fuel consumption at various engine rpm. Here allowance must be made for factors such as a strong head wind, dirty bottom, or an exceptional load on board.

Other matters which need planning are food (including fresh provisions), water and galley fuel. Warn the crew what gear to bring and when to be on board.

If the boat is bound foreign, passports will be required, and should any of the crew be of another nationality it is necessary to conform to the immigration rules. Any Customs formalities must be completed in accordance with current regulations. The Certificate of Registry (or, where acceptable, the International Certificate for Pleasure Navigation) should be on board, and in any case it is important to make sure that the insurance policy covers the intended cruising area. The Ship Radio Licence, together with the operator's Certificate of Competence must also be carried.

If the boat participates in the HM Coastguard Yacht and Boat Safety Scheme (Form CG66) make sure that your shore contact is kept informed of the boat's movements and knows what to do should you fail to report.

15.6.3 Passage planning checksheets

Every sea passage has three distinct aspects – departure, the sea passage in open water, and arrival at the destination. Each needs careful consideration. The checksheets on the following pages provide ways of organising the relevant information into a form that can be used at sea.

As already discussed in 15.6.2, most of the information can be entered in advance, and until this is done it may not be possible to decide the best times for departure and arrival.

Traditionally small craft sail towards a destination, since there may be good reasons that make the prime objective dangerous or impossible to achieve.

Passage planning checksheet (1)
Information from the almanac about the port of departure can be extracted and entered in that section (e.g. the times that the lock gates open, port exit signals, working VHF channels, and the earliest/latest times for crossing the bar). The port of arrival box can be completed in the same way. Items of special importance can be written in a different colour for emphasis.

Listing the required charts ensures that none are forgotten, and that they are corrected and put in sequence. The details of radiobeacons and other aids can be extracted and listed.

Tidal information can be documented so that the navigator can make the best use of tidal streams, and minimise their adverse effects. The times of sunset, moonrise etc can be worked out at comparative leisure and are often useful to know.

An approximate and conservative speed of advance needs to be assumed, so that a rough time can be worked out for each leg of the passage – sufficient for basic planning. A more detailed plan will be needed for the navigator's notebook.

Passage planning checksheet (2)
If it becomes necessary to seek a harbour of refuge, it will probably be at a time when, for one reason or another, the passage is not going

Passage planning check sheet (1)						
Date:	From:	ETD:	Towards:	Distance:	ETA:	

Port of departure – Information

Charts required (in order)

Customs formalities (as appropriate) _____

Form CG 66   _____

Port of arrival – Information

Waypoints etc.

Tidal information   Springs/Neaps/between   Sunset _____   Sunrise _____   Moon _____

Standard port:		Other ports:		HW	LW
Times/heights of HW Times/heights of LW					
Streams favourable:					
Streams critical:					

Sea passage   Traffic schemes/prohibited areas

From	Towards	Distance (nm)	Time for leg at _____ kts	Remarks

according to plan. To have details of available harbours easily accessible allows the skipper to concentrate on other aspects of making what may be a strange harbour.

It is easy to overlook dangers when using small scale charts for passage planning. They need to be searched out and noted, so that they are not forgotten. Visual aids and fog signals can conveniently be listed in advance. Details of all sources of weather information can be extracted from the almanac.

Some kind of watch system is essential on any passage lasting more than about four hours. Having considered the strengths and abilities of the crew, a plan can be made and noted so that the vessel is always well served. Finally come some important checks on fuel, water and similar items.

Passage planning checksheet (3)
This makes provision for setting out the relevant tidal stream data from whatever source, such as tidal diamonds on the chart, hour by hour for the duration of the passage.

Passage planning checksheet (4)
This provides for setting out the basic passage plan in terms of tracks, distances and notes of special features along the route.

Not every passage will require all sheets or all sections to be completed, but if not there for consideration it could be that the one aspect which is forgotten turns out, on that occasion, to be the vital one.

15.6.4 Planning with electronic aids
Despite the improved performance and reliability of modern position fixing systems, these are still only aids to navigation, and traditional methods are not obsolete. Electronic systems can give quick and accurate solutions to navigational problems, but only if they are fed with the correct data. And they cannot reveal the presence of a rock or sandbank on the track which the navigator has chosen. For this reason, and to expose any blunders, it is still necessary to maintain some form of plot on the chart, as hitherto.

Waypoints need to be entered carefully and methodically, which requires some sort of tabular passage plan as already suggested in Chapter 4 – see 4.3.1 and Fig. 4(5).

15.6.5 Sailing directions
When cruising in strange waters it is important to be able to refer to sailing directions which supplement the navigational details shown on even the largest scale chart. In some areas where pilotage is particularly difficult such information is almost indispensable – unless many attractive places and secure anchorages are not visited.

Like any other navigational information, sailing directions and pilot guides become dated, unless they can be corrected periodically, so older copies of these books should be used with caution. Some

of the publications listed are out of print but have been included because they may be available from clubs, libraries and other yachtsmen.

Inclusion of any publication in the list which follows is not necessarily a recommendation. Pilot guides for yachtsmen vary considerably in their accuracy and usefulness. The information they give should be regarded as additional to, and not a replacement for, a good up-to-date chart of the area concerned.

General
Cruising Association Handbook (Cruising Association) – British Isles and Europe, Elbe to Gibraltar.
Atlantic Crossing Guide revised by Anne Hammick (Adlard Coles Nautical).
Ocean Passages for the World (NP 136), (Hydrographer of the Navy).
Atlantic Pilot Atlas by James Clarke (Adlard Coles Nautical).
World Cruising Handbook by Jimmy and Doina Cornell (Adlard Coles Nautical).

England – South Coast
Channel Harbours and Anchorages – by K. Adlard Coles (Adlard Coles Nautical).
Creeks and Harbours of the Solent by K. Adlard Coles (Adlard Coles Nautical).
Solent Hazards and *Wight Hazards* by Peter Bruce (Boldre Marine).
South England Pilot Vols. I–V by Robin Brandon (Imray).
The Shell Pilot to the English Channel (1) by K. Adlard Coles Nautical, revised by J. O. Coote (Faber).
The Solent by Derek Bowskill (Imray).
West Country Cruising by Mark Fishwick (Yachting Monthly).
Yachtsman's Guide to the Scillies by Norm (Armorel Studio, St. Mary's).
The Channel Handbook, Vols. I–III by Bowker (Bowker and Bertram).
Sail West by Shaw (West of England Press).

England – East Coast
East Coast Rivers by Jack Coote (Yachting Monthly).
North Sea Passage Pilot by Brian Navin (Imray).
Tidal Havens of the Wash and Humber by Henry Irving (Imray).
Sailing Directions, Humber Estuary to Rattray Head (Royal Northumberland Yacht Club).
The East Coast – The Wash to Ramsgate by Derek Bowskill (Imray).

Scotland
Clyde Cruising Club Sailing Directions. (1) Firth of Clyde. (2) Kintyre to Ardnamurchan. (3) Ardnamurchan to Cape Wrath. (4) Outer Hebrides. (5) Shetlands. (6) Orkneys and N & NE Coasts.
Clyde to Colonsay by Martin Lawrence (Imray).
Crinan to Canna by Martin Lawrence (Imray).

Passage planning check sheet (2)				
Harbours of refuge available				
Port				
Pilot book				
Access				
Tides				
Dangers				
Shelter				
Local regs.				
VHF watch				

Dangers on route		
Danger	Marked by	Clearing lines

Visual aids on route

Forecast	On sailing	Forecast	Outlook period
Wind			
Weather			
Visibility			
Barometer			
Sea state			

Watches

Checks			
Engine:	Fuel:	Water:	Electrics:
Customs:	CG advise:	Radio:	

Passage planning check sheet (3) — Tidal data

Date:		HW:	Springs/Neaps	Chart(s)

Time	Hours before/ after HW	Information

Passage planning check sheet (4) — Sea passage

From	Towards	Track	Distance	Remarks

Castle Bay to Cape Wrath by Martin Lawrence (Imray).

West Highland Shores by Maldwin Drummond (Adlard Coles Nautical).

Forth Yacht Clubs' Association Pilot Handbook (Forth Yacht Clubs' Association).

The West – A sailing companion to the West Coast of Scotland by Ronald Faux (Bartholomew).

Scottish West Coast Pilot by Mark Brackenbury (Stanford Maritime).

Solway Sailing Directions and Anchorages (South West Scotland Sailing Association).

Ireland/Irish Sea

Lundy, Fastnet and Irish Sea Pilot – The Bristol Channel by David Taylor (Imray).

Bristol Channel and Severn Pilot by Peter Cumberlidge (Adlard Coles Nautical).

Irish Sea and Bristol Channel Pilot by Robert Kemp (Adlard Coles Nautical).

Cruising Guide to Anglesey and Menai Strait by Dr. Kemp (J. Laver Printing).

Cruising Guide to the Isle of Man by Robert Kemp (J. Laver Printing).

Ireland, East and North Coasts (Irish Cruising Club).

South and West Coasts of Ireland (Irish Cruising Club).

Bristol Channel Yachting Conference Handbook (Bristol Channel Yachting Conference).

Isle of Man Sailing Directions (Manx Sailing and Cruising Club).

Morecambe Bay Sailing Directions (Blackpool and Fleetwood Yacht Clubs).

Rivers and Inland Waterways

Port of London Authority Guide for Pleasure Craft Users (Port of London Authority).

London's Waterway Guide by Chris Cove-Smith (Imray).

Visiting Yachtsman's Guide to the tidal Thames (Cruising Association).

Inland Waterways of Great Britain by Lewis Edwards (Imray).

Nicholson's Guide to the Waterways (Five regional volumes – British Waterways Board).

Inland Waterways Guide (Haymarket Publishing).

The Thames Book, The Broads Book and *The Canals Book* (Link House).

Inland Cruising Map of England (Stanford Maritime).

North West Europe – General

Cruising Association Handbook (Cruising Association).

Channel Crossings around Britain by Peter Cumberlidge (Adlard Coles Nautical).

Planning a Foreign Cruise – Vol. 1 (Royal Yachting Association/Cruising Association).

European Harbour Pilot (Hans Gades).

Waterways in Europe by Roger Pilkington (John Murray).

The Guinness Guide to Waterways of Western Europe by Hugh McKnight (Guinness Superlatives).

Through the German Waterways by Philip Bristow (Adlard Coles Nautical).

France and Channel Islands

Channel Harbours and Anchorages by K. Adlard Coles (Adlard Coles Nautical).

North Brittany Pilot by RCC Pilotage Foundation (Adlard Coles Nautical).

Channel Islands Pilot by Malcolm Robson (Adlard Coles Nautical).

French Pilots – Volumes 1–4 by Malcolm Robson (Adlard Coles Nautical).

Normandy and Channel Islands Pilot Mark Brackenbury (Adlard Coles Nautical).

Brittany and Channel Islands Cruising Guide by David Jefferson (Adlard Coles Nautical).

Through the French Canals by Philip Bristow (Adlard Coles Nautical).

Inland Waterways of France by David Edwards-May (Imray).

Notes on French Inland Waterways (Cruising Association).

The Shell Pilot to the English Channel (2) by J. O. Coote (Faber).

North Biscay Pilot by N. E. Heath and RCC Pilotage Foundation (Adlard Coles Nautical).

South Biscay Pilot (Gironde to La Coruna) by Robin Brandon (Adlard Coles Nautical).

Yachting in French Waters (French Government Tourist Office).

A Cruising Guide to the Lower Seine by E. L. Howells (Imray).

Cruising Guide to the Channel Islands (Capra Press).

Cruising French Waterways by Hugh McKnight (Adlard Coles Nautical).

Through France to the Med by Mike Harper (Cadogan Books).

North Brittany and Channel Islands Cruising by Peter Cumberlidge (Yachting Monthly).

North Brittany by Nick Heath/RCC Pilotage Foundation (Imray).

Belgium

The Yachtsman's Pilot, Antwerp to Boulogne by W. T. Wilson (Imray).

North Sea Harbours and Pilotage, Calais to Den Helder by E. Delmar-Morgan and Jack Coote (Adlard Coles Ltd).

Through the Dutch and Belgian Canals by Philip Bristow (Adlard Coles Nautical).

Netherlands

North Sea Harbours and Pilotage, Calais to Den Helder By E. Delmar-Morgan and Jack Coote (Adlard Coles Nautical).

Inland Waterways of the Netherlands by E. E. Benest (Imray).

Through the Dutch and Belgian Canals by Philip Bristow (Adlard Coles Nautical).

Almanak Voor Watertoerisme (Vols. I and II, in Dutch) from Royal Netherlands Touring Club.

Small Boat Through Holland by Roger Pilkington (Macmillan).

Dutch Inland Sailing Pilot by Henry Levison (Adlard Coles Nautical).

Germany
Frisian Pilot – Den Helder to Brunsbuttel and the Kiel Canal by Mark Brackenbury (Stanford Maritime).

Scandinavia
Baltic Southwest Pilot by Mark Brackenbury (Adlard Coles Nautical).
British Kiel Yacht Club Guide (British Kiel YC).
Norwegian Cruising Guide by Mark Brackenbury (Stanford Maritime).
Norwegian West Coast (Volumes 3a and 3b) (Norwegian Hydrographic Service).
The Baltic Sea by Barry Sheffield/RCC Pilotage Foundation (Imray).

Spain, Portugal, Mediterranean
Atlantic Spain and Portugal by RCC Pilotage Foundation (Imray).
East Spain Pilot (Chapters I–VII) by Robin Brandon (Imray).
Down the Spanish Coast by Philip Bristow (Nautical).
South France Pilot by Robin Brandon (Chapters I–IV) (Imray).
Tyrrhenian Sea by H. M. Denham (John Murray).
Italian Waters Pilot by Rod Heikell (Imray).
Greek Waters Pilot by Rod Heikell (Imray).
The Adriatic by H. M. Denham (John Murray).
The Aegean by H. M. Denham (John Murray).
The Ionian Islands to the Anatolian Coast by H. M. Denham (John Murray).
Mediterranean Cruising Handbook by Rod Heikell (Imray).
Planning a Foreign Cruise – Vol. 2 (Royal Yachting Association/Cruising Association).
The Adriatic Pilot by T. and D. Thompson (Imray).
Pocket Guide to South East Aegean by Rod Heikell and Mike Harper (Imray).
North Africa by Hans van Rijn (Imray).
Votre Livre de Bord – Méditerranée (Bloc).
Turkey and Dodecanese Cruising Pilot by Robin Petherbridge (Adlard Coles Nautical).
Turkish Waters Pilot by Rod Heikell (Imray).
North Africa: Gibraltar to Morocco, Algeria, Tunisia and Malta by Hans van Rijn (Imray).
South France Pilot: La Corse by Robin Brandon (Imray).
Mediterranean France and Corsica – A Sea Guide by Rod Heikell (Imray).
Yachtsman's Handbook and Cruising Guide to Malta (S. & D. Yachts).
A Guide to the French Mediterranean Ports by Derek Bowskill (Adlard Coles Nautical).
Canary Islands Cruising Guide by Doina Cornell (World Cruising Publications).
South France Pilot – West by Robin Branden (Imray).
The Ionian by Rod Heikell (Imray).

Caribbean
The Lesser Antilles, Barbados and Grenada to the Virgin Islands by Oz Robinson (Imray).
A Cruising Guide to the Caribbean by Michael Marshall (Adlard Coles Nautical).

Cruising Guide to the Eastern Caribbean, Vols 1–3 by Don Street (Norton).
Yachtsman's Guide to the Greater Antilles by Harry Kline (Tropic Isle Publishers).
Yachtsman's Guide to the Windward Isles by J. M. Wilensky (Westcott Cove).
Cruising Guide to the Caribbean and Bahamas by Messrs Hart & Stone (Dodd Mead & Co).

Admiralty Sailing Directions
In all these consist of 74 volumes, covering the entire world. They are corrected by supplements which are usually issued every two years, and by periodical new editions. Those which cover North-West Europe are listed below:

NP 22   *Bay of Biscay Pilot*.
NP 27   *Channel Pilot* (South coast of England west of Selsey Bill, and north coast of France west of Cap d'Antifer, Scilly and Channel Islands).
NP 28   *Dover Strait Pilot*. (South coast of England from Selsey Bill to Orford Ness, and coast of Europe from Cap d'Antifer to Scheveningen).
NP 37   *West Coast of England and Wales Pilot* (Lands End to Mull of Galloway, including Isle of Man).
NP 40   *Irish Coast Pilot* (Coast of Ireland).
NP 52   *North Coast of Scotland Pilot* (Faeroes, Shetlands and Orkneys).
NP 54   *North Sea (West) Pilot*.
NP 55   *North Sea (East) Pilot*.
NP 66   *West Coast of Scotland Pilot* (Mull of Galloway to Cape Wrath, including Hebrides).

15.6.6 Preparations for sea

Before any trip to sea, and particularly before a lengthy passage, it is necessary to make a thorough examination of the boat's material state and to check a number of things. The details depend a good deal on the size and complexity of the boat, but here are summarised the more common items which need attention. For convenience they are given under different headings.

On deck
—All deck gear, dinghy etc stowed and secured for sea
—All hatches and openings closed
—Anchor secured, but available for letting go if required
—Standing rigging checked. All bottlescrews and shackles moused
—Sails to be used bent on, sheets led correctly, battens in
—Ensign and burgee hoisted
—Radar reflector in place

Engine
—Check battery state indicator (if fitted)
—Fuel tank contents
—Lubricating oil in engine and gearbox

—Header tank contents
—Battery level correct
—Grease for stern tube etc
—Circulating water seacock open
—Circulating water strainer clear
—Spares, tools, engine handbook on board
—Spare lubricating oil, grease, distilled water on
  board
—Visual inspection of drive belts and hoses
—Bilges vented and clear of water
—Check no ropes over side, propeller clear
—Check gearbox in neutral
—After starting check oil pressure, circulating
  water flow and charging rate
—Check ahead/astern operation of controls
—Read engine hour meter

Navigation
—All required charts and publications on board
—Tidal details extracted from tide table
—Functional checks of echo sounder, radio, radio-
  telephone (as fitted)
—Compare ship's head by steering compass and
  handbearer
—Navigation and compass lights
—Horn
—Log reading
—Barometer reading
—Clock checked and wound
—Obtain and record weather forecast
—Determine pilotage details and course to be
  steered on leaving harbour

Safety equipment
—Gas detector – switch on and check
—Lifejackets
—Safety harnesses
—Flares
—Fire extinguishers
—Liferaft
—Bilge pump – test operation
—Emergency steering arrangements
—First aid box
(All crew should know the positions of the above,
and how to use.)

Other items
—Fuel for outboard and galley
—Steering gear examined and tested
—Provisions, water and fresh food embarked
—All moveable gear down below secured for sea.

15.6.7 Night passages
There is often much to be gained by making a
night passage. Apart from increasing cruising
range within a given period, it may also allow full
advantage to be taken of favourable wind or tide.

There is nothing difficult about being at sea by
night, and sometimes navigation is easier because
lights can be positively identified by their
characteristics. Experienced cruising yachtsmen
often arrange to make their landfall just before
dawn, when lights are still available, and then

make the final approach into a strange harbour in
daylight.

At sea by night it is important to retain one's
night vision, by using the minimum amount of
illumination possible for the compass, engine
instruments, chart table etc. In a sailing yacht the
crew should be able to perform all normal sail drill
in the dark, knowing the position of ropes and
cleats by feel. Bright spreader lights may help on
the foredeck but they leave the helmsman and
navigator almost blind for the next few minutes.

It is of course essential to carry the correct
navigation lights, and to be able to recognise the
lights of other craft. These are described in section
2.1.

A good radar reflector, combined with powerful
navigation lights, is the best safeguard against
being run down. A powerful torch and white
flares to attract attention should be stowed close at
hand.

With nothing else to steer by (no distant point
of land, or cloud on the horizon) the compass is
even more important by night than it is by day.
Proper illumination, with a dimmer so that it can
be adjusted to the minimum level depending on
the conditions, is essential. Preferably there should
be stand-by compass lighting for emergency use.

D/F bearings taken at night of beacons more
than 40km (25 miles) away may prove unreliable,
particularly near sunset and sunrise, so they
should be used with caution.

Sufficiently warm clothing and oilskins should
be worn by those on watch: even summer nights
can be cold. Personal safety requires even greater
attention on deck in the dark: when conditions
warrant the crew should wear safety harnesses and
be clipped on.

Before it gets dark make a complete check of the
boat. See that everything is secured on deck, and
that any items which may be required during the
night are to hand; check the navigation lights and
compass light; pump the bilges; inspect the engine
compartment; read the barometer; if bad weather
threatens, consider the advisability of reefing or
shortening sail before darkness falls. The cook
may well prepare some snacks or sandwiches
which can be eaten at the change of the watch.

The skipper must leave clear, written
instructions to the man on watch so that there is
no doubt about navigation or other matters.

A book which covers the subject in more detail
is *Night Sailing* by J. F. Whitaker (Stanford
Maritime).

15.6.8 At sea in bad visibility
Many of the remarks under 'Night passages' (15.6.7)
apply equally to bad visibility, but the fundamental
requirements when at sea in fog are to sound the
required fog signal, to slow down (or even stop if
necessary), and to double the efforts of lookouts in
detecting other shipping by eyes or ears.

The main danger is the risk of being run down
by a larger ship, but this can often be avoided by

keeping in relatively shallow water – just out of the main channel for example, rather than in it. A really efficient radar reflector is another safeguard. There remain however the possibilities of collision with small craft, or of going aground due to the inability to locate buoys or shore objects.

Fog is the time when radar in a small boat is a real bonus – both for collision avoidance and for navigation. But it will only be an advantage if the set is working efficiently and adjusted correctly, and if the operator has sufficient experience in interpreting what is on the screen.

It is usually possible to see that visibility is deteriorating, and the following action should be taken:

(1) Slow down.
(2) If possible get a fix, and note the time, log reading, speed. Review the course to steer in the changed circumstances.
(3) Hoist radar reflector (if not permanently fitted).
(4) Sound the prescribed fog signal. A sailing vessel sounds one long followed by two short blasts ('D') at intervals of not more than two minutes. A power-driven vessel making way through the water sounds one long blast (and if stopped two long blasts) at least every two minutes.
(5) Switch on navigation lights.
(6) If near land, or where soundings may help navigation, switch on the echo sounder and record depths at regular intervals.
(7) Keep a very good look-out. If possible post one person in the bow. If he should see or hear anything, tell him to point in the direction concerned.
(8) Lifejackets to be worn and inflated if conditions and traffic warrant.
(9) Check liferaft or dinghy ready for launching.
(10) In inshore waters prepare the anchor for letting go.
(11) At night have flares and a powerful torch or signalling lamp ready.
(12) In a sailing yacht run the engine, or have it available for instant starting.

In fog a small yacht without radar must rely on accurate plotting to determine her estimated position, although this can be supplemented by soundings and by bearings of radio beacons. It is therefore important that the helmsman maintains the course ordered, and that changes in course are properly recorded with times and log readings.

Tactics depend on the situation. If offshore the only danger is from other shipping. If a large ship is seen directly approaching, only a radical alteration of course (preferably to starboard) plus the use of the engine may take the boat clear. In a fast motor boat the best initial action may be to turn sharply through 180° and increase speed, while deciding which way to avoid her without crossing her bows.

Always try to keep clear of shipping lanes. If possible get into shallow water inshore, where no

larger craft can be, and anchor until the visibility improves.

If coasting it may be possible to make slow progress in comparative safety well inshore, by maintaining a certain depth on the echo sounder, but this depends on the coastline.

The best advice in respect of fog is to try to avoid it. If the forecast hints that visibility will be poor, stay in harbour – particularly if your passage involves crossing shipping lanes.

15.6.9 Preparing for bad weather

With modern radio forecasts available a yacht should never have to face heavy weather without some warning. Even if her radio is out of action, or a vital forecast has been missed, the tell-tale signs of the sky and a falling barometer should give sufficient notice of bad weather in the offing (see Chapter 7).

The onset of what may be called bad weather varies from boat to boat and from crew to crew, but for our purposes we can define it as the point where the conditions of wind and sea dictate the handling of the boat rather than the skipper's original passage plan. For a small sailing cruiser with a family crew this will probably be less than real gale force winds – perhaps even force 6 or the top end of force 5 in some cases. Most modern yachts, properly handled, are perfectly seaworthy and it is often the ability and the physical strength of the crew which are the limiting factors in rough weather.

Given due notice that strong winds are on the way, certain action should be taken in advance of their arrival. First the general strategy must be decided. If there is a suitable port or other shelter within a convenient distance, then it is sensible to head for it – always provided that it can be reached before conditions in the approaches could be dangerous, and without hazarding the boat on a lee shore. If possible aim for a harbour to windward, so that you will be sailing into sheltered water.

There are comparatively few harbours round the coasts of Britain which can be entered in safety in bad weather and at any state of tide. Seas get shorter and steeper, and are more likely to break in shallow water. Wind against tide can greatly aggravate sea conditions, and this is more commonly experienced off headlands and in the approaches to harbours. Such factors as the tidal state at the likely time of arrival, and whether the harbour marks or buoys will be visible all need to be carefully considered.

Larger commercial ports, even if they lack the normal facilities sought by yachtsmen, are usually safer to enter in bad weather. They are deeper and wider, with better marks and buoyage, and with lights which are more likely to be seen in poor visibility.

Motor boats which have a limited fuel endurance should consider seeking shelter at an earlier stage than sailing boats, but having taken that decision they are better equipped to get into harbour without undue delay.

If no suitable shelter is available within a safe distance the only alternative is to stay at sea, and then the prime consideration is to ensure that the boat has plenty of sea room. Having once decided not to close the land, the main aim should be to keep as far away from it as possible, but also choosing a course which will keep you clear of tide races, shipping routes and shallow water.

If however the direction of the approaching storm is reasonably certain it may be possible to progress slowly towards a lee – provided by a stretch of coast for example – but only if an unexpected shift of wind is not going to put the boat on a lee shore.

In a sailing boat it is important to take early action to shorten sail, before conditions get too bad. The skipper should insist that safety harnesses are put on at an early stage, and that they are always secured to a suitable strongpoint on deck. All the crew should be dressed in warm clothing, with lifebelts worn, even if uninflated.

Since poor visibility will prevent any fix being obtained once the bad weather arrives, every effort must be made to determine the boat's position, and then to keep an accurate plot of DR and EP. Remember that in strong winds leeway will be more pronounced.

Check that all gear on deck such as the tails of halyards and the ends of sheets are well secured. Any rope which may be swept over the side may foul the propeller if the engine has to be started. All hatches, ventilators and other openings must be closed; if necessary ventilators should be blanked off by stuffing in towels or tea cloths. The bilge should be pumped dry and then examined at regular intervals. All moveable gear down below should be stowed away so that the decks are cleared for action. Shut all seacocks, and have buckets available in case pumps get clogged. If washboards are available for the companionway leading from the cockpit, they should be fitted. Cockpit drains should be checked clear.

Items such as storm canvas, foghorn, torches, flares, reefing gear, warps and sea anchor (if carried) must be readily accessible – not buried under other gear.

Take every opportunity to get weather forecasts, from whatever radio stations are available, so as to build up the best possible picture of the developing weather situation. The barometer should be read and recorded every half-hour. A record of the estimated wind speed and direction, sea state, and type of cloud cover should be made at similar intervals. In fact keeping a check on the weather situation is almost a full time job in bad weather, but few small yachts have the resources for this.

Meanwhile it is advisable for the cook to take the opportunity to prepare some sandwiches or similar food, and to put some soup or coffee into a thermos flask for consumption later on, when it may not be possible to use the stove.

15.6.10 Handling in bad weather

As wind and sea increase, and sail area is progressively reduced, there will come a time when it is imprudent to try to make any real progress in a particular direction and it is necessary to heave-to. This is something which can and should be practised under less demanding conditions. When cruising, and time is no object, it is often sensible to heave-to for an hour or so in order to eat in comfort.

Most yachts will heave-to satisfactorily under reefed main and storm jib but it all depends on balance, and boats with longer keels behave best in this respect, so it pays to experiment. The jib should be backed, that is the weather sheet should be hauled in, and the reefed main sheeted well in, with the helm lashed down. A boat may also be hove-to under trysail, or well reefed main, with no headsail, either being steered or with the helm lashed up – but this will depend upon the type and can be determined by trial and error.

In even more severe conditions it will be necessary to lie a-hull – with all sail lowered, allowing the boat to drift as she pleases. This is probably the best tactic to adopt in a multi-hull in really bad weather. It may help prevent the boat gathering way if the helm is lashed down, and this also reduces leeway. Seas will break on board (so the crew should keep below) and they may knock the boat on her beam ends or even capsize her completely in extreme conditions. Then her survival will depend largely upon how well she was designed and built.

Most authorities, but not all, consider that a sea anchor is of doubtful benefit when streamed over the bow of a modern yacht, although it may be useful in a yawl or a ketch with the mizzen set to keep the boat head to wind – if indeed the sail remains intact when flogging in gale force winds. But very large strains are put upon the gear, and there is danger to the rudder when the yacht gathers sternway.

Under survival conditions the traditional alternative, but only if there is ample sea room to leeward, is to run before the wind and sea, streaming long warps over the stern to hold the boat steady and reduce her speed. Nowadays a specially designed drogue is better than warps. To be effective a drogue needs to be large, with a mouth diameter of at least 10 per cent of the boat's waterline length. The shrouds need to have anti-tangle lines to prevent the drogue capsizing into its own shrouds. A weight should be fitted to keep the drogue well submerged at all times. A long line is required, of terylene (dacron) – not nylon, which is too elastic – adjusted in length depending on the length of the seas, and secured to the strongest point available, such as sheet winches. Chafe will be a problem and it is necessary to freshen the nip from time to time. Otherwise the stern of the boat should be vacated, with the helm lashed securely amidships, because seas will break aboard over the stern. All openings such as cockpit lockers must be well secured.

The other school of thought is exemplified in recent years by numerous yachts which have successfully kept sailing (often racing) downwind in extremely bad weather. This suggests that speed is needed to maintain control, and that the greatest danger is to reduce speed to the extent that steerage is lost in the troughs of the waves, just when good control is most needed to counter the next crest looming up astern. In these circumstances, when excessive speed is maintained the greatest danger is that the yacht surfs down a sea into an exceptional trough, and into the face of the wave ahead, and is consequently pitch-poled.

It is possible to reach some general conclusions about the onset of surfing conditions and the risk of broaching. A wave length about 1.25 times the waterline length of the hull is that most likely to cause loss of steering and broaching. The maximum longitudinal force exerted by a wave occurs when its crest is just forward of the stern, and this peak force varies approximately with wave height. A reduction in boat speed, whether by lower rpm or particularly by towing a drogue, lessens the tendency to surf, with the consequent risk of broaching. A speed reduction is especially helpful when the boat is near the crest of a wave, in order to reduce the time spent in this potentially unstable position and with the rudder possibly half out of the water. When the boat is in a trough a boost of power can be given if necessary to assist steering and bring the boat back on course, rpm then being reduced as the next crest begins to overtake.

Motor boats are usually best able to cope with heavy seas by being kept almost bow on to them, speed being adjusted to give little more than steerage way. Under less severe conditions it may be possible to make progress to windward by careful manipulation of the throttle(s) to help the boat over the waves, the techniques being to accelerate when the bow begins to fall and to ease back as the bow lifts to a wave. If it is necessary to run off before the sea, warps or a drogue towed astern will help to keep the boat running straight but care is obviously needed to prevent them fouling the propeller(s).

Bad weather can be very frightening for those who have not previously experienced it, but if the boat is well equipped and maintained, and if the correct preparations are made in advance, it can be faced with confidence provided the right decisions are taken in sufficient time. Remember that everything will take much longer to do, and that you can't afford to make mistakes.

For those who sensibly would like to study the subject in greater detail, the following books are recommended: *This is Rough Weather Cruising* by Erroll Bruce (Adlard Coles Nautical), *Heavy Weather Sailing* by K. Adlard Coles, revised by Peter Bruce, and *Fast Boats and Rough Seas* by Dag Pike (Adlard Coles Nautical).

Chapter 16

Running a boat

Contents

16.1 Where to keep a boat

16.1.1 Moorings – general

Moorings are a problem in most popular yachting centres, and if it is desired to keep a boat in one of these the only counsel that can be given is to explore every possible source (harbour master, boatyards, marinas, clubs) and to get your name on any waiting list(s) that may be open. Contrary to common opinion, moorings do become available from time to time, but to hunt them down often requires both patience and perseverance. Every season a number of yachtsmen give up the sport for some reason or other – age, finance, change of family circumstances, or even moving house to a different area - so there is in fact a steady turnover. However it must be admitted that in a number of harbours the waiting time for a berth is unduly long, in which case it is best to look elsewhere in the short term.

Deep water moorings are somewhat naturally more difficult to come by than those in shallower water, but the latter are perfectly acceptable for some boats which are able to take the ground for an hour or two near low water. Multihulls, bilge keelers and motor boats which have outdrive units can all use such moorings if the minor inconvenience of drying out is accepted. In fact this is not always a great disadvantage because it is a good chance to scrub or antifoul the hull, if the harbour bottom is hard enough to walk on.

Details of individual moorings vary, depending on the weight of boat they are intended to take, but basically a mooring consists of a heavy sinker of some kind, a heavy chain called the riser, plus a buoy rope and a buoy to take the weight of the mooring when it is unoccupied. Sometimes a number (or trot) of moorings are all secured to a ground chain lying along the sea bed with an anchor or a sinker at each end of it. Heavier moorings often have a separate picking-up buoy; where the rope for this is attached to the top of the riser, there is usually a strong rope strop which can be taken inboard and secured to the boat's mooring bollard or bitts, with the large mooring buoy remaining in the water.

16.1.2 Laying a mooring

In some remote places it is possible to lay your own mooring. While this is a cheap approach to the problem, it also involves a lot of work – not just in originally laying the mooring, but in lifting it each year for examination which requires special gear.

The two distinct types of mooring – for deep water and drying out – have different requirements. For a deep water mooring there is more upward pull. For a drying mooring in normal tidal areas the pull is more horizontal, but the boat must not sit on the anchor(s) or whatever else is used on the bottom, which demands the sort of arrangement shown in Fig. 16(1).

Bear in mind the type of bottom. Mud or firm sand provide good holding, while at the other extreme rock must be avoided. Shingle, pebbles,

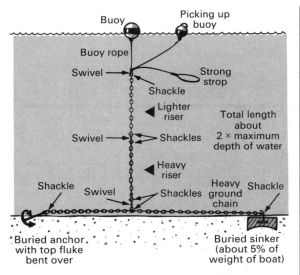

Fig. 16(1) A typical yacht mooring. The riser chain, some of which is going to drag around on the bottom, should be considerably heavier than the yacht's anchor cable. The ground chain should be about four times the length of the boat.

shell or soft mud give only poor holding. This needs to be considered in deciding the type and weight of whatever is going on the bottom, together with whether the site is sheltered or exposed, or subject to strong tidal streams. Heavy and efficient anchors with large flukes and heavy chain give the best holding power, but are costly. Cheaper but less efficient are concrete clumps or old truck engines. Remember that a concrete clump will lose about a quarter of its weight when sunk in water. For general guidance a concrete clump needs to be at least five per cent of the weight of the boat, and much more for exposed locations or where the holding is suspect.

Ideally a permanent mooring should have two special mooring anchors (or two heavy sinkers) which are laid in line with the tidal stream, and are connected together by a heavy ground chain, which should be about four times the length of the boat. A swivel is shackled to the centre of the ground chain, and above this is shackled the riser. Except in very shallow water, the riser should be divided into two lengths of chain, separated by another swivel. The lower riser is made up from heavier chain, because the bottom end of it will be in regular contact with the bottom. The upper riser can be one size larger than the yacht's normal anchor chain. A sketch of the general arrangement is shown in Fig. 16(1). The total length of the two risers should be about twice the depth of water at HW springs. All shackles must be securely moused.

16.1.3 Marinas

Although some yachtsmen positively dislike marinas, preferring a quiet berth up some secluded creek, it must said that the majority of people who have savoured the convenience of a marina would not willingly return to a swinging mooring.

It depends what you like, and what you can afford, and also on the way that you use the boat.

Most marinas operate under the terms of business agreed by the Yacht Harbour Association, and it is as well to read the small print of the agreement, which is likely to include various restrictions that might not have been expected.

The agreement may provide that vessels are moored entirely at the owner's risk, although it is doubtful that the marina could get away with denying liability for damage actually caused by their own employees. Except by written permission a boat in a marina cannot be used for a commercial purpose of any kind, and any owner chartering his yacht out will therefore need the consent of the marina.

In some cases the agreement will provide for a commission of one per cent to be paid if the vessel is sold during the licence period (i.e. at any time the boat is permitted to be at the marina even if not there at the moment of sale), and this will be enforceable if framed clearly and unambiguously. The contract will visually provide for the marina brokerage to have equal selling rights if the vessel is placed with another broker.

Most conditions prohibit work by outside contractors without the consent of the marina, but such consent should not be withheld for warranty work or for work which the marina cannot undertake from its own resources or within a necessary time. It is also usually the case that a general lien is attached to a vessel and her gear while on the premises, in respect of outstanding work or storage charges, but this lien is broken when the yacht is taken away, which leaves the marina with only a personal claim against the owner for unpaid fees.

In most cases the agreement will provide that the marina has the right to move the yacht from one berth to another at their discretion. It is quite unusual for a customer to have more than a simple licence to occupy a marina space, marina companies being at pains not to create any relationship which could be construed as giving the owner the right of a leaseholder to hold over after the expiry of the contractual period.

Upon expiry of the licence period most marinas will be ready to offer a fresh term, but in areas of high demand some marinas will only offer renewal terms to owners who have provided a reasonable amount of maintenance and repair work to their yard in the course of the season. Distasteful as this may appear, it is quite lawful, and owners intending to change to a new marina would be well advised to check whether such a policy is followed at the intended new base.

A further difficulty that can arise is where work is carried out at the marina yard, and a dispute arises as to the standard of workmanship or the costs involved. In such cases the marina has very much the upper hand as they are liable to expel the owner at the end of the licence period irrespective of the merits of the case under dispute. Where a considerable amount of work has to be carried out it is well worthwhile obtaining alternative quotations from other yards to avoid such a difficulty arising, unless the marina operates the closed shop policy described above.

16.1.4 Security

Wherever a boat is moored, it is necessary to think about security. Although most yachtsmen are familiar with the Police slogan 'Watch out! There's a thief about', many boat owners take no serious precautions regarding the security of their craft. In creeks and harbours all round the coast there are rich pickings for sneak thieves – items such as outboard motors and liferafts worth several hundred pounds apiece, and even entire boats.

An elementary precaution is to record the serial numbers of all items of equipment that are remotely portable-radios and other navigational instruments, portable generators, outboards, binoculars and the like. This at least may help recover any stolen property, but it is better to stop it disappearing in the first place.

If the boat is being left for any length of time, even items such as the liferaft should be taken below. It is important that the cabin door should be fitted with a really stout lock – something of a rarity in the average boat. Hatches must be firmly secured from inside, with some form of strongback if necessary. Windows in yachts are seldom large enough to gain access, but they must be securely fastened too.

It is useful to have one really good stowage down below – a strong locker which can be fastened securely, and in which all valuables can be placed.

If an outboard engine cannot be locked away, it must be locked in place so that it cannot be unshipped, even by a determined thief with spanners and screwdrivers. Securing nuts can be fitted which need to be key operated to release them.

The smaller the boat, the more difficult it is to guard against her removal. Unless they can be stored in a locked shed (or firmly chained to some solid object) tenders, dinghies and runabouts are all very simple to remove. Any boat which is kept on a trailer is simply asking to be stolen, unless the trailer is immobilised in some way. One possibility is a fixed point, strong and securely set in concrete or into a wall, to which the trailer hitch can be secured and very firmly locked. Or the trailer can be jacked up and the wheels removed, or the wheels fitted with some form of clamp.

Larger boats can be fitted with anti-burglar devices, which safeguard equipment as well as the boat herself. Boat windows can be etched with the owner's postcode, in the same way as car windows are marked with the vehicle's registration number. As another form of deterrent, consideration should be given to ways of immobilising the engine. A lock on the stop control of a diesel engine is one

suggestion, and there are various simple ways of rendering a petrol engine inactive.

Advice about the security of your boat can be obtained from the local Crime Prevention Officer.

16.2 Trailers and trailing

16.2.1 Advantages of trailing

Small cruising boats, whether sail or power, can be conveniently moved from place to place on a road trailer. Apart from saving mooring fees, trailing allows the boat to be kept at home where it is conveniently placed for maintenance work, and of course it greatly extends the possible range of operation. It is, for example, perfectly feasible to trail a boat from Britain to the Mediterranean.

There are however practical difficulties in trailing a boat which is over about 6m (20ft) in length, notably the problem of getting the boat into the water and back on the trailer, which depends very much on the type of boat and the configuration of her keel. Fairly obviously, a heavy boat with a deep keel is much more difficult to handle than one with a centreboard or retracting keel – or a motor cruiser with a relatively flat bottom and outdrive engines which tilt out of the way.

The other main problem is that the laws which govern road trailers are very complicated and forever changing. Note that trailers imported from (say) America may not comply with UK or European regulations. What follows is a digest of the regulations applying in 1992, but if intending to purchase a boat with a trailer it is advisable to consult the latest regulations on the subject – available from HM Stationery Office or from motoring organisations. Much useful advice is given in the Indespension Trailer Manual, obtainable for a small fee (currently £4.50 including postage) from Mechanical Services Ltd, Belmont Road, Bolton BL1 7AQ. The RYA also issues an Information Sheet on the subject.

The law differentiates between trailers with and without brakes, and in some respects it varies with the date of manufacture of a trailer.

16.2.2 Trailers without brakes

A trailer does not need to be fitted with brakes if its gross weight (its weight plus the weight of the load carried) is less than 750kg (1650lb). Such a trailer must be marked with the maximum gross weight, the capacity of a given trailer depending on its suspension, wheels and tyres. It is an offence to exceed the stated gross weight. It is illegal to tow an unbraked trailer unless the towing vehicle is at least twice the weight of the trailer and its load.

An unbraked trailer should be fitted with a safety chain, short enough to stop the front of the trailer meeting the ground if the trailer becomes detached.

16.2.3. **Trailers with brakes**

Braking systems on new trailers must comply with EEC directive 71/320, which requires a coupling and correctly matched brakes and linkage, giving a minimum braking efficiency of 45%g, as tested on a special instrument. A parking brake must be fitted.

Braked trailers first used from 1 April 1989 must have auto-reversing brakes, whereby the trailer can be reversed without the driver having to leave the vehicle to operate an override. A braked trailer should be fitted with a breakaway cable, attached to the handbrake operating mechanism of the trailer and to the towing vehicle, so that in the unlikely event of the trailer becoming detached the brakes are applied. (This does not apply to a single-axle trailer up to 1500kg (3300lb) gross weight fitted with a chain or cable to prevent the tow bar touching the road if it becomes uncoupled.)

16.2.4 **General regulations – all trailers**

(1) Two red triangular reflectors must be fitted at the rear. A trailer over 5m in length (excluding the drawbar) must be fitted with orange side-facing reflectors. Trailers made since 1 October 1990 need white, non-triangular forward facing reflectors.

(2) Two red rear lights and two red brake lights (operated with the brakes of the towing vehicle) must be fitted.

(3) Trailers manufactured since 1 October 1979, and first used since 1 April 1980, must have one or two rear fog lights.

(4) Amber direction indicators, flashing in unison with those of the towing vehicle must be fitted, unless the trailer was built before September 1965.

(5) The trailer's number plate must correspond with that of the towing vehicle, and must be illuminated at night. The number plate must be yellow and reflective, with black letters/numbers (unless the towing vehicle was registered before 1 June 1973).

(6) The speed limit for a vehicle towing a trailer on unrestricted roads is 50mph on single carriageways, and 60mph on dual carriageways and motorways. A vehicle drawing a trailer must not use the right-hand (offside) lane of a three-lane carriageway unless passing another vehicle drawing a load of such exceptional width that it can only be passed in that lane. Where the gross weight of towing vehicle and trailer exceeds 7.5 tonnes, speed limits are 40mph on single carriageways, 50mph on dual carriageways, and 60mph on motorways.

(7) Trailers made before October 1985 do not need sidelights when towed by a car or dual-purpose vehicle. Otherwise trailers need two sidelights (one each side) if the overall length of the trailer exceeds 2.3m (7ft 6in). All trailers built since 1 October 1985 need two sidelights if they are more than 1.6m (3ft 5in) in width.

(8) There must be no dangerous projections. Hence items such as outboard motors should be well covered and padded.

(9) Tyres and tyre pressures must conform to legal requirements as with cars.

(10) Mudguards must be fitted.

(11) The length of a trailer and its load (excluding drawbar and coupling) must not exceed 7m (23ft), unless special conditions are fulfilled. The width of the trailer must not exceed 2.3m (7ft 6in), and the width of the load must not exceed 2.9m (9ft 6in)

16.2.5 **Trailing - general**

Most vehicle insurance policies cover the towing of a trailer, but this should be confirmed - if necessary with the insurance company. It should be noted however that such insurance only covers the trailer, not the boat loaded on it.

It is important to have a trailer which is suitable for the shape and weight of the boat concerned. It should support the weight of the boat, along the length of the keel, on rollers which also run the boat on and off the trailer. Side rollers support the boat athwarships, and should be adjusted to hold her steady with the minimum of transverse movement. When loaded, the trailer weight at the coupling should be about 23kg (50lb), and the boat must be securely fastened.

Break-back trailers, which have a hinged backbone, can be used to facilitate loading and unloading. They may also eliminate the need to immerse the trailer's vulnerable wheel bearings in water. Where this is necessary, consideration should be given to fitting Bearing Buddy seals or Bearing Savers. These replace the dust caps in the wheel hubs, and a spring-loaded piston maintains a slight pressure inside the hub, which is filled with grease, and keeps the water out. Otherwise it is necessary to clean and repack the bearings after every launching, or risk inconvenient and expensive failures. Against this possibility it is a wise precaution to carry a spare bearing kit in the car.

Even though it may not be used very often, a trailer needs regular maintenance. The tow hitch should be checked, cleaned and greased every three months, making sure that the jaws which grip the ball on the tow hitch are operating correctly. The ball itself should be cleaned and greased, and protected by the normal plastic cover, while the attachment of the bracket to the car needs checking occasionally.

Wheels and tyres require attention, as for a car. Check wheel nuts for security, and jack up the trailer once or twice a year to check the wheel bearing – which should be greased, but not too liberally. This is also the time to check the brakes and grease the linkages.

The jockey wheel needs examining from time to time, when the trailer is unloaded. Unwind the handle to remove the inner spindle, so as to clean and grease the assembly, together with the clamp.

Check that it is securely bolted to the backbone.

Any rollers fitted need to be lubricated. If there is a winch, unwind the wire to make sure it is sound, and clean and grease the moving parts. If the trailer is not galvanised its paintwork it likely to need attention.

Finally check the electric cable, connect it up to the car and make sure the lights function properly. In the event of a problem a squirt of WD40 in the plug can work wonders, but it pays to keep both the plug and socket protected from the weather.

16.2.6 Trailing in Europe

Each member of the party must hold or be named on a valid passport. In most European countries, particularly on inland waters, it is necessary to have a Helmsman's (Overseas) Certificate of Competence, or the new International Certificate of Competence, available from the Royal Yachting Association after a test, or as described in Chapter 1, 1.5.4. If you have some other formal qualification or licence, it should accompany you.

It is important to ensure that both boat and trailer are included in insurance documents, or on the Green Card required in most European countries. Some countries require separate cover for a trailer.

In most cases it is wise to have Small Ships Register documentation (see 1.5.2) as evidence of your ownership of the craft. Evidence that VAT has been paid on the craft should be carried. This will normally permit tax-free importation, subject to the condition that the boat should not be sold or used for any commercial purpose while in the host country.

In the Netherlands owners of motor boats capable of 20 kph (12.4 mph or 10.75 knots) must obtain a *Vaarbewijs* (motoring certificate) before taking their craft on any inland water.

In Switzerland there is compulsory registration and licensing in some cantons, and you may be required to undergo a test before using your boat on some lakes despite holding a Helmsman's Certificate. Generally the minimum age for driving is 16 years.

In Germany drivers of speedboats must obtain a *Sportbootführerschein* (driver's licence) available from the Deutscher Motoryacht Verband, 2 Hamburg 76, Stormsweg 3, Germany.

16.3 Organisation

16.3.1 Boat Management

Back in Chapter 1, we briefly mentioned the importance of an organised approach to running a boat. In the intervening chapters we have discussed some of the detailed considerations involved – not just in handling and navigating a boat, but also details of her equipment with some indication of the care and maintenance which it derserves. So by now readers may have a better idea of the many points which need regular attention if skipper and crew are to enjoy safe and trouble-free cruising.

Do not underestimate the number of items which need systematic attention in a boat of any size. Only a small proportion require any degree of technical skill, but the important thing is that they should all be looked at. This implies some kind of documentation, even if this only comprises simple check lists, in order to be sure that nothing vital is overlooked.

The more that an owner can do himself, the more he will learn about his boat, and the less will be the cost. But it is appreciated that many owners are busy people, and if it is not possible to carry out routine inspections in person, then some system is needed to ensure that the work is satisfactorily completed by somebody else. In either case it is a matter of organisation. The question of maintenance has been mentioned in several places throughout this book, when dealing with specific parts of the boat or different items of equipment. Some of this work can be progressed on a week to week basis, but there comes a time when proper provision must be made for the more major items to be undertaken. This involves making the boat available for whatever period is needed for the work to be done, making arrangements for somebody to do it, and making financial provision to pay for it! In other words, the more significant items of the maintenance bill do not just happen, they have to be planned and arranged, or important things will get overlooked, probably affecting the boat's safety.

Traditionally yacht maintenance has been conditioned by the fact that nearly all yachts had wooden hulls which needed extensive re-painting at the start of each season (both to preserve them and make them presentable), and this period was a convenient time to undertake the other essential work. Also in those days the sailing season was short for most yachts, probably only from May to September, when they were hauled out of the water or put in a mud berth for the winter.

Now things have changed. For many owners the sailing season relates more closely to the duration of British Summer Time. The great majority of yachts are constructed in GRP, requiring only to be hauled out for a coat of antifouling, and otherwise they are kept in the water throughout the year. It makes good sense to visit and live in the boat during the winter, because items such as engines and electrical equipment which are used regularly are not so likely to deteriorate, and do not need the same degree of preparation to withstand the rigours of the winter.

So work can now be spread more conveniently over the year, rather than concentrated into what were well defined periods for fitting out and laying up. It is however necessary to evolve a sensible plan. Jobs undertaken in the spring should include all those important checks, without which the season might come to an early end. Similarly work that is done in the late autumn must include whatever is necessary to safeguard the boat during the winter. Otherwise, within reason, maintenance work can be undertaken whenever it is convenient – or perhaps least inconvenient – but always remembering that certain jobs go hand in hand. For example, while the boat is out of the water for antifouling is the logical time to do all other underwater work; if the mast has to be unstepped for any reason, there is an opportunity to survey all the rigging and the mast fittings; if the engine should have to be removed, seize the chance to clean and examine everything in that area and do any repainting.

16.3.2 Dealing with boatyards
Many owners rely on a yard for doing at least part (and some most) of the annual maintenance work on their boats. This means facing up to a fairly hefty bill, but may be necessary because the owner does not have the necessary time, skill, or inclination to tackle the work himself. In order to get the right result it is essential to give the yard precise instructions about what is to be done, which means compiling a defects list. This is best divided into two parts, one for matters affecting seaworthiness and safety, and one for items which are no more than desirable for reasons of comfort or appearance.

Some of the items on the list will be routine jobs which need to be done every year – things like antifouling, examining underwater fittings , changing oil filters and lubricating oil, overhauling winches and checking all rigging fittings. Other important items may be defects which have arisen during the past season but which have not received immediate attention.

Then there are a number of items which do not need annual attention but which should be examined say, every three or four years. These might include withdrawing the propeller shaft(s), examination of keel bolts and other important fastenings, looking at rudder bearings, and more major items of engine maintenance. It is best to plan these ahead, and to budget accordingly for the work involved and for the probable replacement of expensive items such as batteries. .

Items of lower priority include cabin furnishings, interior paintwork or varnishing, joinery, and other matters of a more domestic nature which do not affect the boat's seagoing capability.

Having produced the list of work, inspect each job with the yard manager, and request an estimate for each one (not the total bill). The quotations should be broken down into costs for labour and material, which enables individual items to be queried if the estimate seems to be unduly high. It is then also possible to assess the priority of work in order to keep within a budgeted figure, and perhaps make other arrangements for certain items. Some you may

decide to tackle yourself, or to defer to a later date.

Then it is necessary to decide a programme for the work to be done. The earlier that agreement can be reached on all these matters, the more likelihood there is of the boat being ready when required. Remember that boatyards are always very busy in the spring, when all their customers want to have their boats refitted and put back into the water.

If often happens that, when the yard is carrying out work on some item of equipment or some part of the boat, it is discovered that certain additional work, not originally foreseen, should be undertaken. It is advisable to get a quotation for this, just as for the bulk of the work, even if this involves a little delay. This is another reason for making an early start. Boatyards are notoriously bad at meeting dates, but you can help by trying to anticipate your requirements and by allowing a reasonable time for the work to be completed.

It is important to know the exact terms upon which the boatyard is carrying out the work. So long as they are members of the British Marine Industries Federation and use the standard BMIF/ RYA terms and conditions of business, you will have a degree of protection.

The standard form agreement provides that delivery dates will not be guaranteed (unless there is an express agreement to the contrary), that the owner uses the premises at his own risk, that the owner will be responsible for any charges involved in moving other vessels to enable his to be launched or taken ashore for lay-up, that quotations are subject to inflation and subject to acceptance within seven days, and that the yard will have a lien on vessels and gear against unpaid bills.

The agreement also provides that no work may be done on the vessel by outsiders, other than work under warranty or which the yard or its subcontractors cannot undertake, or minor work being carried out by the owner or his crew.

Although the standard form gives some protection, owners will be well advised to satisfy themselves on the following points:
(1) In the event of liquidation, any new equipment paid for in whole or in part by the owner for the benefit of his yacht will be deemed to be the property of the customer and not that of the receiver or other creditors. It would be as well to have a specific agreement from the yard to this effect.
(2) That the yard has the facilities and manpower available to tackle the job in question. In many cases work has gone weeks or months beyond the target date as a result of a yard taking on work beyond its capability or capacity. There is no reason why a yard should not be prepared to include a penalty clause in a substantial repair or conversion contract.
(3) That the company has adequate boatyard insurance. Circumstances may arise where a

substantial claim could be beyond the capacity of the company to settle, and the yacht's own policy may not cover certain causes of damage.

(4) That there will be an adequate opportunity to inspect and test the work done before payment of the final instalment of the fees. In the case of a new yacht a 5 or 10 per cent retention is normally allowed until the satisfactory completion of sea trials, and there is no reason why a yard should not agree to a similar proportion in respect of major repair or conversion work. If after taking delivery of the yacht after repair or conversion it is found that some aspect of the work is unsatisfactory, the yard is in the same legal position as if it had sold unsatisfactory goods. The Supply of Goods and Services Act 1982 provides very much the same sort of legal remedies as the Sale of Goods Act (see 1.3.2) does for new yachts. In the event of a dispute it is important to understand your legal rights, though it is always preferable to attempt a negotiated settlement rather than going straight to the lawyers.

In order to keep a proper record of the general state of the boat, it is important to get full details of what has been done by the yard at the end of a refit. For example, if the anchor windlass has been overhauled and put in working order, the owner really wants to know exactly what was wrong with it in the first instance and what has been done to rectify matters. If spare parts have been used, have these been replaced? Has a proper trial been carried out to ensure that the windlass is now working to its proper specification – if there is an overload trip does it function at the right loading? What caused the original problem, and what has been done to avoid a repetition? As the person paying the bill, you have a right to know the answers to all these questions, and often it is advisable to record them in some form of notebook for future reference – in case something similar occurs at a later date.

And, talking about bills, it is not a bad idea to file receipted invoices because these can be a help when budgeting for future refits.

16.3.3 Budgeting
It used to be said of yachting that if you were worried about what it cost, you could not afford it. If that was true in an era when a young man could often afford to run a ten-tonner and have a paid hand to look after her, it is certainly true today. Sadly, the costs of owning any kind of boat have soared in recent years, and it is therefore essential to have some kind of financial plan to meet recurring expenses. If the thought depresses you, it is best to skip the next paragraph, but no attempt has been made to insert actual figures because these can vary so greatly, depending on the type and size of boat, where she is kept, and how she is run and used.

Marine mortgage payments, insurance premium, mooring fee, hauling out and antifouling, fuel, sail repairs and replacement, club subscription, charts and publications, and travelling to and from the boat are likely to be the main items of expenditure. Most of these can be anticipated on certain dates. It is also sensible to make some provision for contingencies – miscellaneous costs for maintenance and repair, chandlery etc.

16.4 Clubs and associations

16.4.1 Clubs
Most owners find it of benefit to belong to one or more clubs or associations. Quite apart from the social contacts derived, clubs provide a wonderful opportunity for the interchange of information between members. A very good example is the Cruising Association, which was founded in 1908. At its new purpose-built headquarters at the side of Limehouse Basin alongside the River Thames, the Cruise Planning Section comprises material which has been collected by members for members. Here is a wealth of information for anybody planning a cruise to North-West Europe, the Baltic, the Mediterranean, or the eastern seaboard of North America. Apart from all the necessary publications (such as pilots and light lists) there are files which are compiled from information sent in by members who have cruised the different areas. There is also an excellent library. There is a marina, with access to the Thames and to the Inland Waterways. For further information contact The Cruising Association, CA House, 1 Northey Street, Limehouse Basin, London, E14 8BT. Tel: 0171 537 2828.

The Little Ship Club has a rather different emphasis and runs a whole series of courses on navigation, seamanship and related subjects during the winter months. These are followed up by practical training afloat during the summer, organised from the club's centre at Yarmouth, Isle of Wight. The address is The Little Ship Club, Bell Wharf Lane, Upper Thames Street, London EC4R 3TB. Tel: 0171-236 7729.

The Royal Cruising Club now has its headquarters at the Royal Thames Yacht Club, 60 Knightsbridge, London SW1X 7FF, and is the elite of the cruising organisations. For over a century it has encouraged good seamanship, and its membership of genuine cruising yachtsmen is respected world-wide. It too provides port information, largely compiled by members, and in recent years the club has been active in producing pilot guides for yachtsmen.

In the context of clubs which have a national interest, mention should be made of the Royal Ocean Racing Club, founded in 1925 when ocean racing on this side of the Atlantic was in its infancy. It is no exaggeration to say that the RORC has greatly influenced the sport in Europe as a whole, while it still continues to administer British ocean racing activities from its pleasant clubhouse at 20 St James's Place, London SW1A 1NN. Tel: 0171-493 2248.

Yachting affairs in Britain are co-ordinated by the Royal Yachting Association (RYA), notes on which appear in 2.7.1. The names and addresses of affiliated organisations are published each year in the RYA booklet, G25. This indicates which clubs operate in the different regions.

16.4.2 Visiting clubs

Many yacht clubs are preoccupied by racing, or by domestic matters, but there are a few which do encourage cruising in an active way and welcome visiting yachtsmen to their premises. Some can even offer useful facilities such as moorings or a club launch, and in other parts of the world major clubs often have attached to them a small boatyard where yachts can be repaired or hauled out – the like of which is sadly lacking in Britain.

The fact that a club welcomes visitors does not mean that a yachtsman can just arrive and make himself at home without further ado. The owner or skipper should call on the secretary, or in his absence see the club steward or boatman. Most probably an invitation will be extended to use the club's facilities, and it is tactful to enquire about temporary membership (which in any case is likely to be needed to comply with licensing regulations), at the same time indicating the probable length of stay.

Visitors should be punctilious about observing club rules – in the matter of dress for example – and also about the appearance of the yacht, particularly if she is lying on a club mooring. Flag etiquette should be followed (see section 6.8), and this is very important in foreign harbours in the matter of flying the correct courtesy flag (6.8.3.).

Club servants should never be tipped, but contributions to the club and staff funds are appropriate ways of expressing appreciation for services received. Hospitality ashore can sensibly be repaid by entertaining a few of the club's officers or members on board. Another way, which can be pursued separately, is to ensure that visitors get the same treatment at your own club.

16.5 Crews

16.5.1 Advice to crews

Much of this book contains information or advice which is equally applicable to skippers and their crews, but it seems appropriate to direct just a few words to crews – particularly the less experienced ones or those who are embarking in a strange boat for the first time. Some well organised skippers have available a checklist which covers the points mentioned below, even with spaces in which can be inserted the time and place to join the yacht.

But for any cruise or passage a crew member needs to have certain information, and it is the responsibility of the skipper to provide it.

(1) What sort of clothing, shoes, equipment etc should be brought? (For advice on sea-going clothing see Chapter 18.) Will there be shore-going functions to attend which may require a certain standard of dress? All gear must be stowed in a soft, collapsible bag. For a short passage you may have to live out of that bag so care in packing it will reap dividends.

(2) Are lifejackets and safety harnesses provided on board? If not, take your own. Be sure that they are of the right standard.

(3) Take and use your own brand of anti-seasickness pills, which suit you and do not have undesirable side effects.

(4) Take your own waterproof torch, and a yachtsman's knife on a lanyard.

(5) Take off your shore-going shoes before stepping on board (always).

(6) Find out where to stow your gear, together with oilskins which are likely to have a special stowage. Many boats have individual spaces for toilet gear in the heads. Keep the immediate area of your allocated bunk clean and tidy at all times. Do not leave gear, books, papers etc lying around.

(7) Find out how the heads work. Many yachts sensibly have clear instructions posted inside the compartment, but if in doubt, ask. Remember that apart from toilet paper only food and liquids taken by mouth should be put down the heads. Many toilet compartments have some necessary form of ventilation – learn how to use it. Find out how to work the shower and the shower tray pump. Remember that fresh water is always in short supply afloat.

(8) Find out how to work the galley stove. Most British yachts use Calor gas (see 8.3.5 and 14.1.13). Any galley fuel is dangerous if not properly used.

(9) As soon as possible find out the stowages (and where necessary the method of operation) for all the safety and emergency equipment. This includes fire extinguishers, lifejackets and safety harnesses (if provided on board), liferaft, man overboard gear, flares, first aid kit, bilge pump and distress radio.

(10) Remember that many yachting accidents occur in dinghies or tenders.

(11) Be able to tie and use correctly the following basic knots: reef knot, clove hitch, bowline, round turn and two half-hitches.

(12) Always return any items of equipment to their correct stowage, e.g. winch handles, pencils from the chart table.

(13) Do whatever the skipper tells you. Should you have queries, ask tactfully afterwards.

(14) Dress sensibly and warmly. In rough weather or when so directed, wear a safety harness and keep it clipped on.

(15) Alcohol is splendid for a party in harbour, but should be taken in strict moderation when at sea.

(16) Do your fair share of domestic chores. The good crew should not need to be asked to help in these respects.

(17) When in harbour always ask permission before crossing the deck of another craft, certainly on the first occasion. Cross the deck forward, not by the cockpit, Remove shore-going shoes.

(18) Do not make unnecessary noise.

(19) Do not throw any gash over the side.

(20) If you are a smoker, find out what the rules are on board.

(21) In a sailing yacht find your way round all the gear – for example, where the different halyards run and are made fast. How does the reefing gear work?

(22) As a crew member you may well be called upon to work the anchor gear. If a windlass is fitted, learn how to operate it.

(23) When in doubt – ask.

16.5.2 Consider the crew

Most owners (and certainly those of racing yachts) rely on crews to help them sail their boats. Crews, whether they are friends or family, are presumably on holiday too, and they deserve full consideration when individual passages are being planned or when other arrangements are being made. In this context let us discount the contrived discomforts of modern ocean racing, and just consider the average cruising yacht.

For enjoyment, as well as ultimately for safety, it must be possible to break down the crew into two watches, either of which can handle the boat under normal conditions without continual supervision by the skipper. There are obvious occasions, as for example when in soundings or making a landfall, that the skipper will want to be around. There may also be times, such as when shortening sail, which require all hands on deck. But otherwise the watch on deck should be able to cope, and those below should be allowed to feed and rest in peace. On any passage which lasts more than about 12 hours this is essential, or the entire crew will become exhausted. Offshore sailing makes big demands on stamina, and people who come straight from an office desk at the end of a tiring week can soon succumb to the effect of hard work and lack of sleep – to say nothing of being cold and wet, and possibly seasick.

A proper watchkeeping system should be put into effect soon after leaving harbour, and the skipper ought to ensure that those off watch go below and get some rest. The watchkeeping system is a matter of personal choice, but the traditional four hours on and four hours off has withstood the test of time.

Sadly it must be said that very few family cruising yachts match the requirements above. Many are very undermanned, with the skipper having to do the lion's share of all the work. While this may be reasonably satisfactory on a short passage in fair weather, it allows no margin for contingencies such as deteriorating weather or trouble with the boat – nor of course for anything untoward happening to the skipper.

If it is necessary to go to sea short-handed, the skipper should arrange the passage very carefully – making optimum use of tidal stream, for example. The watch bill should be made out so that the skipper is most likely to be on watch at 'key' times, but he should be careful not to overwork himself. The less experienced members should do the bulk of the watchkeeping, and if the skipper can do a short spell with each of these in turn, he can give them guidance and confidence in the prevailing conditions, see Fig. 16(2).

Time	Skipper	Wife	Son	Daughter	Notes
1400	■			■	Sail Mudport
1500	■			■	
1600			■		
1700			■		
1800			■		
1900			■		
2000		■			2040 Sunset
2100		■		■	
2200		■			
2300		■			
2400	■				
0100	■				
0200	■				
0300	■				
0400	■				
0500		■			0530 Sunrise
0600		■			
0700			■		
0800			■		
0900	■				Arrive Belle-Havre?
1000	■				
1100	■				
1200					

Fig. 16(2) In a family crew the watchkeeping routine must be planned to make the best use of the available persons. In this example the son is assumed to be capable of standing watch by day, but the daughter is learning the ropes and does not keep watch alone.

By the same token, the overall plan for a family cruise needs to be most carefully considered – how far to go, adequate rest days in harbour, and a flexible programme which allows ample time for the passage home in the event of bad weather.

16.5.3 Ship husbandry

Cleanliness on board is good not only for health

and aesthetic reasons, but because dirt harbours moisture and encourages deterioration. There is truth in the old saying that if the corners are kept clean, the rest will look after itself, and the crew have a part to play in this.

Cleaning has become something of a science both in the home and in industrial applications, but once afloat these principles tend to get overlooked. Always use the right materials, not only to get the best results, but to avoid damage to the surfaces being cleaned. Use clean materials, cloths, brushes etc. and change the water frequently. When washing down, do not use more water than necessary.

Proper care of a boat reduces the amount of cleaning that is needed, and minimises the number of minor repairs that have to be carried out. Remember that guests may not be familiar with practices afloat, so tactful instruction about not blocking the heads or the galley sink may not come amiss. Some owners may seem obsessed with tidiness, but in a small yacht gear which is left lying about soon collects damp and dirt, or gets damaged. Galley spillages are not only dirty but dangerous, by causing slippery conditions on the cabin sole.

Crew members can make a more positive contribution to the cleanliness of a boat if their efforts are properly directed. Painted surfaces or Formica should be wiped down with warm water, to which a small quantity of soap or detergent has been added, and then be lightly rinsed off. Glass (such as doghouse windows) should be washed with soap and fresh water, and then be polished with newspaper – unless a proprietary window-cleaning fluid is available. Perspex needs care to avoid scratches, and should be cleaned with a soft cloth. Dirty leather cloth should be washed with soap and warm water, although normally it is sufficient to wipe it over daily with a damp cloth, not using too much water. Shower curtains need to be washed down with liquid soap and water, with the addition of a mild antiseptic to prevent mould or mildew and the possibility of permanent staining.

16.5.4 Etiquette afloat

Too many yachts have to share the same stretch of water. Sadly, in many places what were once peaceful and deserted anchorages have disappeared with the development of marinas and the pressing demand for moorings. So the congestion in many harbours becomes increasingly unpleasant each year. In these circumstances only consideration for the interests of other boat owners can make matters tolerable for all concerned. The following are some items where a good standard of behaviour and conduct will contribute to the well-being of your fellow yachtsmen – and what they may rightly expect from you.

(1) Many harbours have by-laws or other regulations which control activities afloat. It is up to you to find out what these are, and to obey them. They may include:
  (a) A speed limit, at least in certain areas, and the requirement to proceed in such a manner as will not cause excessive wash or inconvenience.
  (b) The requirement for craft to obey the Collision Regulations, and (for example) to keep clear of larger vessels navigating in the fairway.
  (c) Traffic signals controlling entry to or departure from the harbour.
  (d) Prohibited areas for anchoring, fishing, water skiing or board sailing.
  (e) The payment of harbour dues.
  (f) No mooring to navigational buoys, beacons etc.
  (g) No underwater diving activity.
  (h) The required channel(s) to be used for VHF communication with the harbour authority.
  (i) The location of visitors' berths.
(2) In an anchorage take care to anchor clear of other vessels already lying there, and clear of vacant moorings, oyster beds etc. Having anchored make sure that you are not too close to any other boat, and that the anchor is not dragging. Take anchor bearings if necessary.
(3) Never leave the boat unattended on somebody else's mooring, except with permission. Do not overload a mooring.
(4) Avoid shouted orders or enquiries, which should be unnecessary in a small vessel.
(5) Before going alongside have plenty of warps and fenders available, and see that they are clean.
(6) Seek permission before going alongside another boat.
(7) Always take your own lines to shore or to a buoy or piles, even when lying alongside a larger vessel – which may need to move.
(8) Do not run the engine or an auxiliary generator at times when it will be a nuisance to others nearby.
(9) Keep halyards frapped so that they do not flap against the mast.
(10) Keep the boat clean and tidy (for example sails properly furled, mainsail cover on, gear squared off). It is unpleasant to have to lie alongside a neglected boat.
(11) Give attention to flag etiquette (see Chapter 6). Dirty or frayed bunting, slack halyards, ensigns left flying overnight all show lack of attention to the proper running of the boat.
(12) If, when leaving harbour, your movement is going to affect some other boat(s) outboard of you, give them due notice of your intentions. If, for example, you are leaving early in the morning it may be feasible to move to the outer berth the previous evening, so that you can slip without disturbing others.

Some of the matters already discussed in 16.5.1 are also relevant.

16.6 Bibliography

Ready for Sea by Basil Mosenthal & Dick Hewitt (International Log Book).

Care and Repair Below Decks by Percy Blandford (Adlard Coles Ltd).

The Sailing Lifestyle by John Rousmaniere (Adlard Coles Nautical).

Comfort in the Cruising Yacht by Ian Nicolson (Adlard Coles Nautical).

Yacht Crewing by Malcolm McKeag (Fernhurst).

Psychology of Sailing by Michael Stadler (Adlard Coles Nautical).

Trailers and Towing (Indespension Ltd).

Chapter 17

Feeding afloat

Contents

17.1 Food and its preparation

17.1.1 Choice of food

Recipes and cooking techniques are not within the scope of this chapter. Most of us are well aware that there are innumerable ways in which basic ingredients can be prepared, cooked and served to delight our palates. Equally there are many more ways that food can be spoiled or our digestive systems ruined. If your knowledge of cooking is strictly limited there are better places to acquire the art than the galley of a small boat at sea. It is more sensible to experiment at home, where bad results can if necessary be rectified by a visit to the nearest take-away.

We will therefore assume that at least one member of the crew is a reasonably skilled cook. In a large crew or on an extended voyage it is a good thing to have at least two persons, so that the work can be shared – more on this subject anon.

The choice of food to be provided afloat depends on several factors:

(1) It needs to be sustaining, with sufficient calories, remembering that the physical effort in sailing a boat is often greater than might be imagined. Greasy meals should be avoided, because they make people more prone to seasickness.

(2) Meals should not take too long to prepare, particularly when at sea, since the time involved must come out of the few hours that are available for sleep or relaxation between watches, unless the yacht boasts the services of a full-time cook.

(3) Quite apart from the likely unavailability (and cost) of more exotic ingredients, recipes afloat should take account of the facilities available for the preparation and cooking of food on board. The average boat's stove is not likely to have more than two burners and a small oven, with only limited working space around it. So it is necessary to use as few saucepans as possible, and to limit the number of mixing bowls required. Incidentally this also reduces the subsequent washing up.

(4) What food can be prepared under way will depend at least to some extent on the sea conditions and the point of sailing. It may sometimes be sensible to postpone a meal a short while, if the boat is just approaching shelter for example. But, in general, food at sea should be served punctually so that it fits in with the watchkeeping schedule and does not dictate it. Meals at sea must be easy to eat, preferably with only a spoon in bad weather so that the other hand can steady the bowl.

(5) In deciding menus, consider the season of the year. In midsummer a cold lunch with a cool drink should satisfy most people. But in spring or autumn, and always in bad weather, the crew will welcome something hot, even if it is only a warming mug of soup.

(6) The fluid intake must be sufficient particularly in warm weather or in the event of seasickness. Since water from a boat's tank is not always very pleasant to drink, other liquids need to be provided according to individual taste, but the consumption of alcohol afloat should be controlled.

(7) On longer voyages a properly balanced diet should be ensured, as discussed in more detail below (17.2.4).

One thing is certain, with the wide range of convenience foods now available, catering afloat has never been easier. Deep-frozen foods may only be suitable for larger yachts with the necessary storage, but tinned foods come in all varieties, either as complete meals or as ingredients with which to embellish some basic dish. Packet foods however are lighter to stow, where weight is a problem. The ultimate in convenience are self-heating foods, but be warned that they are not only expensive but very heavy since each tin weighs about twice as much as the food it contains.

17.1.2 Methods of cooking

There are various basic ways of cooking food, both ashore and afloat, but some are more suitable than others in a small boat.

(1) *Boiling* Boiling in one form or another is the most common and simplest method of cooking food, particularly vegetables. Stews and casseroles should be gently simmered on a low heat, for which purpose an asbestos mat may be convenient to use. Also stews can be simmered more safely in the oven than on top of the stove. A pressure cooker provides a simple, safe and economical way of boiling food when afloat.

(2) *Frying* Most foods can be fried successfully providing that the right fat or oil is used, and the process is quick and easy, although smelly in a boat. Health considerations demand that the amount of fried food eaten should be limited (see 17.2.4). For safety reasons deep fat frying should be avoided when afloat, and even normal frying is dangerous when under way.

(3) *Grilling* Although grilling is a useful way of cooking meats and fish, few yachts have an efficient grill. It is important that the temperature can be correctly adjusted for the food being cooked, and for the stage of cooking reached. It is also necessary to have adequate clearance between the heating surfaces and the grill pan.

(4) *Roasting* With a reasonable oven small joints of meat and poultry, for example, can be roasted on board. But most vegetables cannot be roasted, so other pans will be needed for them. Being a protracted process roasting consumes a lot of fuel for the galley stove.

(5) *Baking* Baking is the process of cooking food in a hot, dry oven. It is normally confined to bread, cakes, biscuits, pies and tarts, and like roasting it is expensive in fuel. But any genuine sea cook will need to bake bread on longer passages. Although it is possible to make bread of sorts in a saucepan, or even under the grill, the genuine variety using yeast and baked in the oven is more satisfying. Yeast can be obtained in little packets, each enough for one loaf. Remember that yeast is a living agent and requires the correct amount of heat to function: too little heat and the bread will be soggy; too much and the yeast will be destroyed.

17.1.3 Galley equipment

Galleys, together with items such as galley stoves, water systems and refrigerators have already been discussed in Chapter 14, to which reference should be made. Here we can however elaborate on subjects such as cooking utensils and stowages. Even if the seagoing cook may not have quite the range of appliances that one might expect ashore, there are certain basic necessities and the following list is a suggested minimum for the average yacht. Larger craft may have the need and space for a somewhat increased outfit.

3 saucepans, with lids. Non-stick pans have obvious advantages in saving not only labour but water when washing up. In small boats, where space is at a premium, it is possible to obtain saucepans with a shared, detachable handle so that they nest one inside the other, together with a small frying pan and poacher.

1 pressure cooker. This has the obvious advantage of restraining the contents at sea, and the less obvious benefits of saving time and gas (or whatever other fuel is used). Some pressure cookers have internal divisions so that two or more items can be cooked simultaneously.

1 frying pan. Again, a non-stick pan has an advantage.

1 kettle, with whistle

1 egg poacher set

1 grill pan/toaster

2 heatproof oven dishes

1 roasting/baking tin, with cover

1 flameproof casserole

2 insulating mats, for simmering

1 slice

1 wooden spoon

1 draining spoon

1 ladle

1 spatula

1 pair of tongs

1 pair of scissors

4 skewers of different lengths

3 sharp knives (large, medium, small)

1 knife sharpener

1 set of spoon measures

1 potato peeler

1 egg whisk

1 grater

2 tin openers

2 corkscrews

1 chopping board

1 colander

1 strainer

1 sugar bowl

1 milk jug

1 salt cellar

1 pepper mill

1 butter dish (insulated)

1 bread bin

1 mug per crew member

1 bowl per crew member

1 large plate per crew member

1 small plate per crew member
1 egg cup per crew member
1 set of cutlery per crew member
2 kitchen plates
1 gas lighter

1 pair oven gloves
6 drying-up cloths
1 plastic pan scourer
1 brush for washing dishes
6 plastic, screw-top containers for provisions

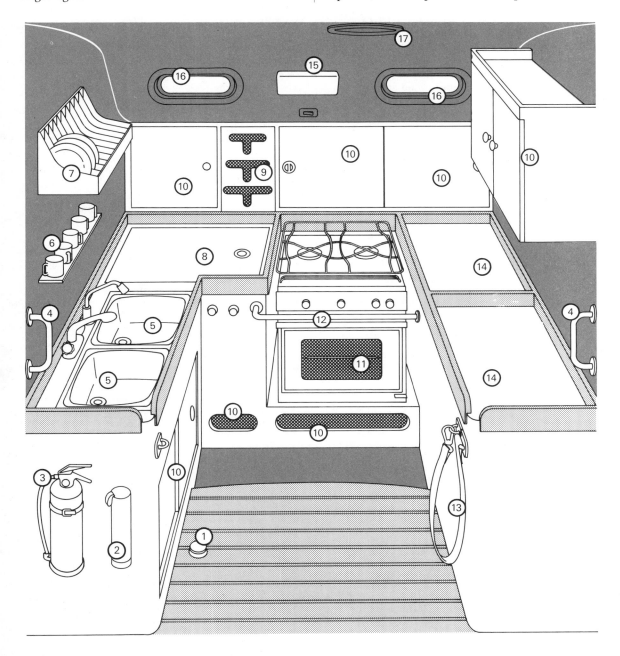

Fig. 17(1) Some features of a good galley:
(1) Foot-operated water pump
(2) Fire blanket
(3) Fire extinguisher
(4) Handholds
(5) Twin sinks with fresh and salt water
(6) Mug stowage
(7) Plate rack, draining into sinks
(8) Refrigerator or ice box
(9) Plate stowages
(10) Ready-use lockers and stowages
(11) Gimballed stove, with movable fiddles

(12) Safety bar
(13) Belt/harness
(14) Working tops, with deep fiddles
(15) Electric light over stove and sink
(16) Natural light
(17) Ventilation

With respect to items specifically mentioned in the text, the lockers under the sink can conveniently house the gash bucket; teacloths can be hung to the left of the stove beside the sink, and the kitchen-roll dispenser can be fitted under the lockers top right of the sketch.

Consumable items such as detergent, kitchen rolls and scouring powder for washing pans are dealt with under 17.2.2.

All these items need individual stowages, so that they are easily accessible and yet securely stowed at sea and can neither break loose nor rattle. A fitted drawer is ideal for cutlery, with a space for each knife, spoon and fork. Plates, bowls and mugs should be of the nesting variety, so that they stack neatly and securely on top of each other.

Details that are sometimes overlooked by designers and builders include a good stowage for the refuse bin or sack (where it can be reached conveniently, but is not obtrusive), a place for hanging tea-cloths, and a handy dispenser for the kitchen roll.

17.2 Provisioning

17.2.1 Planning what to take

The aim should be to embark enough of the various foodstuffs and ingredients to cater for the needs of a hungry crew over whatever period is required – but not to stow away too much. There should of course be a small margin of food which can be conveniently carried in tins or packets, to allow for delays or contingencies. But stowage space in a small boat is always limited, and weight can be an important consideration particularly in a racing yacht. Modern ocean racing crews mostly seem to survive on packets of sandwiches and the occasional Mars bar while sitting on the weather rail, but whether this is sensible or very much fun is a matter of question. So we will confine this subject to the more discerning needs of the crews of average cruising boats. People who are cruising are enjoying a well-earned holiday, and should be able to enjoy the food – as well as the sailing.

Provisioning requires good planning from the outset. It is necessary to work out that breakfasts will be required by x people on y mornings, and so on through the day.

The sort of feeding routine which usually works well in a boat, whether at sea or in harbour, is to enjoy a good breakfast, and to plan the sort of lunch that can be conveniently eaten in the cockpit, followed by tea and then a more substantial meal in the evening. Much depends on whether or not it will be possible to top up with basic food, and perhaps the occasional luxury, at various ports of call. In this respect a cruise along the coast of, say, Brittany will present less of a problem than a fortnight in the Western Isles of Scotland where shops are scarce. But half the fun

---

Checklist – Non-perishable foods and drinks

☐ Barley sugar	☐ Dried fruits	☐ Milk powder	☐ Soda water, tins
☐ Beer, tins	☐ Fish, tins	☐ Mustard	☐ Soups, tins
☐ Biscuits, chocolate	☐ Flavouring essences	☐ Nuts	☐ Spaghetti
☐ Biscuits, plain	☐ Flour	☐ Oil, cooking	☐ Spices
☐ Bovril	☐ Foil	☐ Oil, salad	☐ Stock cubes
☐ Brandy	☐ Garlic	☐ Orangeade	☐ Sugar
☐ Butter, tinned	☐ Gin	☐ Pepper	☐ Tea bags
☐ Cake, tinned	☐ Ginger ale, tins	☐ Pickles	☐ Toilet paper
☐ Cereals	☐ Herbs, mixed	☐ Plastic bags	☐ Tomato purée
☐ Chocolate, bars	☐ Honey	☐ Porridge oats	☐ Tonic water, tins
☐ Chocolate, drinking	☐ Jam	☐ Rice	☐ Vegetables, tins
☐ Chutney	☐ Juices, fruit, tins	☐ Ryvita	☐ Vinegar
☐ Coffee	☐ Kitchen rolls	☐ Salt	☐ Whisky
☐ Cornflour	☐ Lemonade	☐ Sauces	☐ Worcester sauce
☐ Custard powder	☐ Lime juice	☐ Scouring powder	☐ Wine, white
☐ Dehydrated soups	☐ Marmalade	☐ Sherry	☐ Wine, red
☐ Dehydrated vegetables	☐ Mars bars	☐ Snacks, assorted	
☐ Detergent	☐ Meat, tinned	☐ Soap	

Fig. 17(2) A checklist for stores to be kept on board during the season. This may be duplicated and put to practical use.

of cruising is to be independent of the shore, and if it is intended to go shopping regularly it is necessary to carry the cash that will be required.

17.2.2 Non-perishable items

Certain stores live on board throughout the season, and it may be necessary to replenish them from time to time. Some items need to be provided pretty regularly. Experience shows that when leaving the boat to go ashore there is often some haste, and that this is not the best time to do any stock-taking. It is therefore wise to have a checklist of all the items normally kept on board (that is all stores except perishable ones such as butter, milk, eggs and bread). This list can be duplicated, and one copy used during a weekend or a longer cruise in order to tick off the items which will need to be replenished next time the boat is used.

Fig. 17(2) shows a suggested list which is not necessarily comprehensive, but which can be amended or augmented depending on the circumstances. At the very least, if this stock of basic provisions is maintained the crew will not go hungry, or thirsty. There are a few things more annoying than to discover the first morning on board that there is no marmalade for breakfast, or paper for the heads. Non-perishable items need to be supplemented by fresh foods, for which a separate list can be prepared.

17.2.3 Stowing and keeping food

Provisioning for a lengthy cruise is a much more demanding business than collecting together the stores that are likely to be needed for a long weekend or for a cruise lasting a week or two. For a start, the sheer quantity of provisions that are needed will almost certainly pose a stowage problem. Single-handers come off best in this respect, with only one mouth to feed and lots of surplus space in and under unoccupied bunks. Small boats with large crews present the greatest challenge in selecting and stowing away everything that is likely to be required for more than about a week.

For a lengthy cruise it is well worth finding out the likes and dislikes of the intended crew beforehand, and also whether individuals may be allergic to any particular food. Some people will only drink decaffeinated coffee, anybody suffering from gout should avoid offal, while others are allergic to shellfish in almost any form.

Then some sort of weekly menus should be planned, if only to determine the likely quantities of different goods that will need to be embarked. It is not necessary always to have a particular dish (say) on Monday evenings, and the actual choice of meals each day will be governed by other factors – whether the boat is at sea or in harbour, the prevailing weather, and so on. But if one has a reasonable idea of the quantities needed per person per week (best of all from recorded experience on a previous cruise) there is a fair

chance that the crew will not go hungry, although it is always wise to overstock a little to allow for emergencies. Surplus tinned food can always be left on board for future occasions, or taken home towards the end of the season.

Much thought needs to be given to the question of how and where to stow food and drink on board a boat. Modern materials such as plastic boxes, plastic bags, plastic bottles, aluminium foil and cling film all help to overcome the difficulties of sealing up perishable or semi-perishable foods – that is to say those which prefer such attention. Certainly it is good policy to avoid all glass containers in a boat – not only because of the risk of breakages but also because they are heavy and can clink together at sea. Most drinks are now obtainable in plastic bottles, or can at least be decanted into such a container.

Many modern boats have small domestic refrigerators, but the capacity of such units is usually very limited. Although they can store dairy products and a few other items for a long weekend, they become of diminishing importance after a few days at sea. Refrigerators and iceboxes are discussed in Chapter 14 (14.6).

Iceboxes, being independent of a source of power, are reliable and can often have a larger capacity than a refrigerator, but they do need stocks of ice at regular intervals – say every three or four days, depending on the ambient temperature.

There is some skill in stocking up an icebox. First it needs to be cleaned out very thoroughly (how well depends upon the last user), and then the interior surfaces need to be dried. The bottom and the sides should be lined with large blocks of ice, shaped as necessary with an ice pick. Keep the blocks as large as possible, since then they melt more slowly. The chippings can be put into plastic bags and used for drinks – assuming that the ice is clean in the first place. Stow the contents methodically, so that they can be reached quickly in order to reduce the time that the lid is open. Keep the drain from the icebox clear, so that melted water can flow away quite freely.

No one locker in the average boat is large enough to stow the provisions needed for more than two or three days, so the bulk of the stores must be distributed in whatever space is available around the accommodation. This needs some organisation, in order to know just what is where. One sensible approach is to keep the bulk supplies of any one item in the same place, and to have a ready-use locker which is topped up as necessary every couple of days or so. If the main stores list is then amended on each occasion, there is a record of what is left in the bilges or in other remote parts of the boat.

Stowing food is largely common sense. Dry foods, even in plastic bags, should be stowed in the higher lockers. Heavy, tinned foods must go in the bilges and as near amidships as possible. Tins should have their labels removed, and be marked

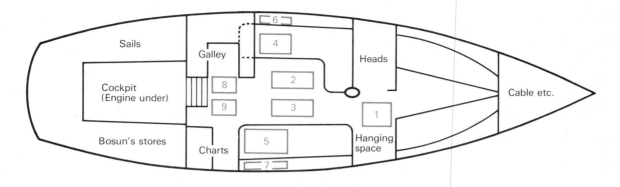

Fig. 17(3) Stowage plan for provisions. Much depends upon the layout of an individual boat, and useful space in the bilges is limited by water and fuel tanks. Sufficient locker space must be retained for the use of the crew, and for the multitude of other gear carried in a boat. It is traditional at sea to number items from forward to aft, odd on the starboard side and even on the port side.
(1)   Bilge, starboard abreast the mast. Tinned goods.

(2)   Bilge, port, saloon. Tinned goods.
(3)   Bilge, starboard, saloon. Tinned goods.
(4)   Locker under settee, port, saloon.
(5)   Locker under settee, starboard, saloon.
(6)   Locker, ship's side, port, saloon.
(7)   Locker, ship's side, starboard, saloon.
(8)   Bilge, port, galley.
(9)   Bilge, starboard, chart space.

with indelible ink; if they are likely to be in the bilges for long they can be stowed in plastic bags or varnished to reduce rusting.

Some foods obviously need special treatment, as described below. It is useful to have a plan of the boat, showing where the various stowages are, and what each contains, along the lines of that shown in Fig. 17(3).

Keeping food

(1) *Biscuits* Biscuits are a great stand-by at sea, because in airtight containers they will keep for several months. Once opened they soon go soft in a marine environment, so it is better to have several small tins rather than one or two big ones.

(2) *Bread* Bread keeps best (up to ten days) in a dry but airy place, if such a spot exists in a small boat, rather than sealed in a plastic bag which encourages mildew. Sliced bread does not keep quite so well, nor does bread which has previously been frozen. On ocean passages various recipes are available for home-baked bread, using dried yeast which, if properly packed, has a life of six months.

(3) *Butter* Where a refrigerator is available the storage of butter presents no problem, at least in small quantities. Otherwise fresh butter soon goes rancid in a warm climate unless sensible precautions are taken. It can, for example, be wrapped in foil, sealed in plastic bags and placed in the bilges, which are the coolest part of the boat. Tinned butter will keep at least six months and probably longer, provided it is freshly tinned on purchase. As an alternative it is possible to salt down fresh butter in a plastic container.

(4) *Cheese* Fresh, hard cheese keeps well in large portions, while the vacuum-packed variety will stay fresh for months if unopened.

(5) *Eggs* Eggs that are really newly laid will keep for at least three weeks, or longer if they are lightly smeared with Vaseline. It helps if the boxes holding them are turned once a week, so that the yolks do not settle at one end. Avoid buying eggs which have been stored in chilled counters, since they do not last. Keep old egg boxes for future use, since in most countries eggs are sold loose.

(6) *Fruit* If bought when not quite ripe, citrus fruits (oranges, lemons, limes) will keep for several weeks. Hard apples keep well. Green bananas on the stem should be stowed in the dark and where they will not get bruised. Dried fruits such as raisins and sultanas last well. Soft fruits quickly deteriorate. In hot climates any fruit (or vegetable) which may be eaten uncooked or unpeeled should be washed in dilute potassium permanganate.

(7) *Meat* Vacuum-packed jars of meat keep better than tins. Salt beef, salt pork and smoked hams all last for months.

(8) *Milk* Fresh milk will keep for several days in a refrigerator, but the longer-distance sailor must acquire a taste for powdered milk or the condensed or evaporated variety. The former of course takes up less space, but tins of evaporated milk can be reconstituted to give normal milk by diluting with water.

(9) *Poultry* Fresh chicken should be cooked and eaten within a couple of days, but can be kept a day or two longer in a refrigerator. Frozen chicken that is brought on board must be thoroughly thawed out before it is cooked.

(10) *Vegetables* Depending on the season, potatoes will keep for several months if they are stored in a dark, dry and airy place. Onions require similar treatment. Hard white cabbage will last at least a month. Green tomatoes will last two or three weeks.

Fresh water

Fresh water is a vital ingredient to support life, even more important than food, so a good supply must be ensured. Notes about water systems and water storage will be found in section 14.3 (Fresh water systems). Wherever possible it is advisable for the stock of water on board to be divided between at least two tanks – to minimise the effect of any leakage or pollution. It is also wise to have a separate emergency supply of at least 9 litres (2 gallons) available in portable containers, which could be placed in a liferaft.

The requirement for more than average fluid intake will be evident in warmer weather, or where the face or body is exposed to wind or spray for long periods, or in the event of seasickness or diarrhoea.

One advantage of the proliferation of marinas is that they have increased the number of places round the coast where potable water can be safely and conveniently embarked, albeit it for a price. Should there be the slightest doubt about the quality of any water which is embarked, it is best to err on the safe side and to treat it with one of the purifying tablets that are marketed for this purpose, or with the recommended dose of a liquid such as Milton 2.

17.2.4 Diet for longer voyages

Food at sea fulfils several roles. It is not only a source of nutrients to sustain normal body maintenance, but it also satisfies the 'inner man' by creating a feeling of contentment and well-being, which sustains happiness and morale. By satisfying nutritional and social needs, correctly constituted food allows maximum body performance under all conditions. Whereas this may not be so important in day sailing, whilst undertaking longer passages a correct diet becomes vital as deficiencies of nutrients in the body may otherwise occur. The problems of feeding at sea in order to maintain health have paved the way for many nutritional discoveries, ever since Dr James Lind proved by the first controlled experiments in diet that oranges and lemons were an effective cure for scurvy in the middle of the eighteenth century.

Food should be varied, appetising, attractive and nutritious within currently accepted nutritional guidelines. It must possess good keeping properties and should pose few problems for stowage. Fresh provisions are ideal because they provide the most essential nutrients, but where preservation techniques must be employed it is essential that they have either preserved the original nutrients or that the food has been fortified with added nutrients, which can be determined from the label.

To perform well the body must have the correct amount of fuel or energy, which varies from person to person and with the activity performed. In harbour energy expenditure is low, and should be reflected in lighter meals. At sea energy expenditure rises with activity, and appetite increases disproportionately with the changed environment. Care must therefore be taken to satisfy the energy demand without eating too many calories to satisfy the increased appetite. In heavy weather the energy requirement increases considerably through the extra activity – not only when working on deck or to keep warm, but just to keep still, even when sleeping.

Modern thinking for the average British diet is that we should eat 25 per cent less fat, 50 per cent less sugar, 25 per cent less salt, 50 per cent more dietary fibre, and 10 per cent more starch.

(1) *Fat* Fat is a rich source of energy (9 calories per gram) which readily contributes to obesity. Saturated fat in animal products increases the level of cholestrol in the blood and clogs up the cardiovascular system. Therefore choose leaner meats and remove excess fat, eat more poultry and fish in place of red meat, and avoid full fat milks. Semi-skimmed or skimmed milks are readily obtainable dried; they keep well and are fortified with vitamins. To reduce the amount of fat consumed avoid frying, which in any case can be dangerous in the confines of a yacht. Use margarines and cooking oils high in polyunsaturates (based on sunflower, safflower or corn oils). These oils have other advantages in that their keeping qualities are superior to the 'hard fats' (butter and lard).

(2) *Sugar* Sugar provides no vitamins, minerals or other nutrients – just calories. It is the major source of tooth decay, often encouraged by infrequent cleaning. Dental problems at sea are almost invariably related to teeth that are decayed, so a reduction in sugar will result in less likelihood of toothache on passage. It is a fallacy that sugar is a major source of energy (3.75 calories per gram) – most foods supply energy. So avoid or reduce the addition of sugar in food preparation and in hot drinks. Select tinned products that are low in sugar, fruits that are tinned in fruit juice, and fizzy drinks that are diet or low calorie. Biscuits and cakes are not only high sugar foods but they contain much fat, therefore choose fruit in their place for snacks between meals.

(3) *Salt* Salt not only helps to raise blood pressure but also increases thirst. If that thirst is quenched with carbonated drinks it will contribute markedly to sugar intake (some fizzy drinks contain over eight teaspoonfuls of sugar). The imaginative use of spices and seasonings readily replaces the role of salt as a flavouring. There is no need to add salt to food even in the Tropics. All the salt we need (and a lot more) is to be found in the food we eat, most of it as a result of food processing. More than 75 per cent of the food eaten in Britain has been processed at least once, and food processors are renowned for adding liberal amounts of both salt and sugar to our food.

(4) *Fibre* Fibre is the indigestible part of our diet and is found in cereal products, vegetables and fruit. It speeds the passage of food through the gut, helping to avoid constipation, piles, and (in longer term) gut disorders such as colon cancer and diverticulitis. Constipation at sea is indicative of a diet which is deficient in fibre. Rather than ameliorating the problem with proprietary laxatives, an increase in fibre element of the diet will prove much more beneficial. Potatoes in their skins, either baked, boiled or mashed, are not only a rich source of fibre but most of their vitamin C lies just under the skin. Pulses and pastas are not only easy to store and to prepare, but are high in fibre and add variety. Tinned pulses are very convenient in that they only require heating rather than soaking and long cooking. At least one piece of fresh fruit a day should be planned in all but the longest passages. Wholewheat and multigrain breads are high in fibre and in nutrients, and are also more filling than their white counterparts, so that fewer are needed and less stowage space is required.

(5) *Starch* The reduction in fat and sugar brings about a lower energy diet which requires some compensation. This should be in the form of starches (complex carbohydrates). They tend to add bulk to the diet, and are digested very readily to provide a steady source of energy. Starches are found in bread, potatoes, rice and pasta.

In a varied diet based on the above principles there is little need to worry about vitamins. However, when fresh produce is restricted in supply, a supplement of vitamin C is a wise precaution. This is widely available in all chemists and health food shops. Some individuals may consider taking a multinutrient preparation which supplies all the essential vitamins and micronutrients. If in doubt on this matter, consult a physician who will have access to the advice of a nutritionist if need be.

Fig. 17(4) shows the food required by one moderately active person for one week, but note that the requirement increases in bad weather.

17.3 The work of the cook

17.3.1 Galley duties
In most boats one individual is designated as cook or galley slave. From the start it is important to establish the exact role of such a person. Does he or she prepare, cook and serve each meal (and then clear it away and do the washing up) or do some other people help with one or more of these functions? How is this help allocated fairly among the rest of the crew, as it should be in a well-run vessel?

In a largish yacht a full-time cook is both desirable and feasible, particularly if he or she has the necessary culinary skills and a strong stomach. But even then, with a large crew to feed, the cook will welcome help with such chores as peeling the potatoes and doing the washing up.

Another routine, which is more suitable for smaller boats, is for duty in the galley to be rotated, either a day at a time or perhaps a week at a time on a longer voyage. Whatever method is adopted, it must suit the routine for working the boat at sea. If only one of the crew is a competent navigator, then navigational duties must take priority over scrambling the eggs for breakfast, although in most circumstances it should be possible to combine these functions.

At this point it should be emphasised that the punctuality of meals is essential at sea if a proper watchkeeping system is to be maintained.

Even when galley duties are shared in some way, it is still necessary for one individual to be in overall charge of the commissariat – generally planning menus, keeping an eye on the stocks of different items, and ensuring that the requisite standards of cleanliness and hygiene are maintained. In a small yacht this duty inevitably falls, like everything else, on the skipper, unless he very sensibly makes somebody else responsible.

17.3.2 Safety in the galley
All too often accidents occur due to careless use of the galley stove. In British yachts Calor gas is the most usual fuel; other fuels that may be met are paraffin and alcohol. The characteristics and use of these are discussed in Chapter 14 (14.1.12 and 14.1.13). It is most important that the cook, and anybody else who lights the galley stove, is thoroughly familiar with the correct sequence of events. Equally important is to shut down the stove properly when cooking is finished – always turn off a gas system at the bottle as well as at the stove. It is a sensible precaution to turn off the bottle first, so that gas is drained from the line leading to the stove.

Any newcomer to a boat should be carefully instructed in handling the stove (like using the heads), and should understand the use of the gas detector, fire extinguisher and fire blanket. When it is lit the stove should not be left unattended.

Just as dangerous to the cook, or anybody else in the vicinity, is the possible spillage of boiling liquid in a seaway. Even with a gimballed stove a cooking pot may be caught, so to speak, off balance. The risk can be minimised if the stove is fitted with fiddles to stop pans sliding about, but only if these are properly used.

Another possible danger is that the cook may lose balance or slip. There should a bar in front of the stove to prevent a person falling over the burners, and a belt or harness which will restrain the cook in the normal working stance. The galley floor must be kept clean and dry, free from oil or grease. As a further safeguard it is wise for the cook to wear oilskin trousers and sea boots in bad weather.

Food	Amounts	Remarks
Meat and meat products	1.5kg	At least ¼ to be poultry
Fish	640g	May be increased at the expense of meat
Vegetables	4.25kg	1.6kg potatoes, 500g rice or pasta. Remainder fresh or tinned
Bread and flour	2.5kg	At least half to be wholemeal
Cereals	200g	High fibre, low sugar
Dairy produce: Milk Margarine Cheese Eggs	2 litres 175g 120g Three	Skimmed or semi-skimmed Polyunsaturated Size 3
Fruit	1.25kg	Mainly fresh, but can also be dried or tinned
Biscuits	200g	
Sugar and preserves	350g	
Oxo Cubes	35g	

Fig. 17(4) Foods sufficient for one moderately active person for one week, providing 3100 calories daily. The amounts are for guidance only, but the proportions are balanced within current nutritional guidelines to provide adequate amounts of all nutrients for a moderately active adult. Any alcohol taken will increase the energy content and proportionately reduce the percentage energy contributed by other nutrients. Note that energy requirements may increase by up to 50 per cent in adverse weather. See also Fig. 17(5).

Meat and meat products
Chicken – roast	500g
Beef – topside	250g
Lamb – chop	300g
Sausages – grilled	250g
Bacon – grilled	200g
Total	1500g

Fish
Cod – fillet	180g
Plaice – fillet	180g
Mackerel – whole	180g
Sardines/pilchards – (tinned in tomato sauce)	100g
Total	640g

Vegetables
Potatoes	1600g
Rice/pasta	650g
Peas – tinned	500g
Carrots – tinned	500g
Cabbage – fresh	400g
Beans in tomato sauce	300g
Tomatoes – tinned	300g
Total	4250g

Bread and flour
Flour – wholemeal	250g
– white	250g
Bread – wholemeal	1000g
– white	1000g
Shredded wheat	200g
Total	2700g

Dairy produce
Milk – skimmed	1000ml
– semi-skimmed	1000ml
Margarine – sunflower	175g
Cheese	120g
Eggs – fresh, size 3	165g

Fruit
Apples	375g
Oranges	375g
Tinned fruit	500g
Total	1250g

Sugar and preserves
Sugar	200g
Preserves	150g
Total	350g

Fig. 17(5) List of individual foods contributing to the groups given in Fig. 17(4).

17.3.3 Cleanliness and hygiene

Cleanliness is only an extension of good yacht husbandry. Surfaces on which dirt and dampness are allowed to accumulate soon deteriorate. Mildew can form on any material, and wooden structures are soon attacked by rot given dampness and inadequate ventilation. Even small particles of food, left in some corner, can cause an unpleasant smell within the confines of a boat and its somewhat limited circulation of air.

The stove, sink and working surfaces should be cleaned down after each and every meal, and the whole area given a special buff-up say every forenoon. It is important that the galley is kept tidy, and that utensils are returned to their proper stowages after use. Attention to these matters becomes increasingly necessary when the weather deteriorates. At the end of a cruise, and certainly at the end of the season, the entire galley, including the interiors of all lockers, needs to be thoroughly washed down with fresh water and a mild detergent.

Gash

There must be strict routine for dealing with gash. Ideally there should be two gash bins – one for waste food, vegetable matter etc which will rot away and which can therefore be put overboard when sufficiently far from the coast (see 19.6.3), and a second for plastic wrappings and empty containers which must be disposed of ashore at the next port of call. When about three-quarters full a gash bag should be securely tied around the neck, and stowed out of the way until it can be got rid of in the most appropriate way.

Special care must be taken with respect to glass bottles, which must never be thrown over the side unless first filled with water so that they will definitely sink, and then only in deep water. Beer cans must be punctured in two or three separate places for the same reason.

Cockroaches

Given half a chance, cockroaches will establish themselves in the galley area of a boat – where there are many dark, dank and attractive places for them to live and breed – and quickly infest the whole accommodation. Not only are they an unpleasant nuisance, but they can taint food and spread bacteria. They thrive on any dirt or food left lying around, so the first precaution is to keep the boat spotlessly clean and to store even scraps of food in plastic containers.

An even better plan is to try to prevent them getting on board in the first place, by taking sensible care. Try to avoid shopping where any cockroaches are evident. Even if the insects themselves are not taken on board you may unwittingly embark their eggs, which will hatch out in due course – perhaps several weeks later. When embarking provisions, examine them and any packaging carefully for any sign of insects. Cockroaches often lurk in cardboard boxes and even if it is inconvenient it is wise to unpack these on the jetty, and not take them on board. Laundry brought on board is another way that cockroaches can intrude. An even simpler way for cockroaches, and of course rats, to get on board a boat is over any gangway to shore, so this should be raised off the dockside at night. Spray warps and fenders with an insecticide.

As soon as there is any sign of cockroaches on board, take immediate steps to eliminate them. Various proprietary sprays and powders are available for the purpose, and a stock should be carried. They need to be used thoroughly and systematically, penetrating every corner and crevice. Remove the contents of each locker in turn, and gain access behind fittings such as sink and galley stove in order to treat the likely runs.

If the determined use of insecticides does not succeed, consideration must be given to fumigating the entire boat. This means sealing every opening, and the crew moving out for a day or more.

17.4 Weights and measures

Recipes are expressed in various terms - in metric or Imperial units and sometimes in practical measures such as tablespoons. For conversion factors and other details of units see 2.5.1, 2.5.2

and 2.5.3, but here are some useful equivalents for immediate reference.

1oz	= 28g
4oz	= 113g (just over $\frac{1}{10}$kg)
8oz	= 227g (just under $\frac{1}{4}$kg)
16oz (1lb)	= 454g (just under $\frac{1}{2}$kg)
100g	= $3\frac{1}{2}$oz
250g ($\frac{1}{4}$kg)	= 9oz
500g ($\frac{1}{2}$kg)	= 18oz (1lb 2oz)
1000g (1kg)	= 35oz (2lb 3oz)

1fl oz	= 28ml
$\frac{1}{4}$ pint	= 142ml (about $\frac{3}{20}$ litre)
$\frac{1}{2}$ pint	= 285ml (about $\frac{3}{10}$ litre)
1 pint	= 568ml (about $\frac{3}{5}$ litre)
$\frac{1}{10}$ litre (100ml)	= $3\frac{1}{2}$fl oz
$\frac{1}{4}$ litre (250ml)	= 9fl oz
$\frac{1}{2}$ litre (500ml)	= $17\frac{1}{2}$fl oz (about $\frac{7}{8}$ pint)

For practical units of measurement:

2 teaspoons	= 1 dessertspoon
4 teaspoons (or	
2 dessertspoons)	= 1 tablespoon

(level spoonfuls in each case). It takes 12 tablespoons of 24ml (rather less than 1fl oz) to fill an average-sized breakfast cup holding 285ml ($\frac{1}{2}$ pint).

Since scales are not likely to be on the inventory of the average yacht, the following very approximate measures may be useful. They refer to level spoonfuls.

1oz (28g) breadcrumbs, porridge oats	= 4 tablespoons
1oz (28g) cocoa, custard powder, cornflour, dried fruit, flour, grated cheese, lentils, sugar	= 2 tablespoons
1oz (28g) rice, jam, syrup, honey	= $1\frac{1}{2}$ tablespoons
1lb non-fat dry milk solids	= 4 cups
32 tablespoons	= 4 cups
8 tablespooons	= 1 cup
1lb butter/margarine	= 2 cups
1lb (dried) rice	= 2 cups
1lb macaroni	= 4 cups
1lb spaghetti	= 5 cups
1lb noodles	= 6 cups

17.5 Bibliography

The Sailing Cook by Kitty Hampton (Willow Books).

Seacook – A Guide to Good Living Afloat by Bob Heppel (Adlard Coles Nautical).

Care and Feeding of the Offshore Crew by Lin & Larry Pardey (Norton).

Reluctant Cook by Jane Gibb (Adlard Coles Nautical).

Good Food Afloat: Every Sailor's Guide to Eating Right by John Betterley (Ashford Press).

The Gourmet Galley by Terence Janericco (Ashford Press).

Chapter 18

The Sailor's Wardrobe

Contents

18.1 Sailing clothes

18.1.1 Sailing clothes - general

In recent years sailing clothing has made great advances in design, materials and construction. Outwardly, it is more fashion conscious, often utilising bright colours in smart combinations, but the developments are more than skin-deep. Now materials are better than ever, tailoring is much improved, and the detailed features built into modern foul-weather suits make them very effective garments.

Modern yachtsmen should be grateful for the fact that they do not have to endure bad weather clad in the traditional oilskin coat and sou'wester, made of fine canvas which was treated with an oil-based preparation (hence the name) to produce a material which was initially glossy and waterproof. But the garments were stiff and uncomfortable to wear, and exposure to sun and sea soon made them crack and become sticky, and far from waterproof. Even the first breed of unlined PVC garments were not much better. The openings at the neck, wrists and ankles were so large that it was accepted that water would penetrate through them, even if the material or its seams did not leak. But now, with the modern materials available (discussed in more detail below), we can worry about such luxuries as reducing condensation inside suits because they are so good at keeping other forms of water out.

The prices of modern sailing clothes may alarm some people, but there is a strong case to say that they are very good value for money. Shore-going and more fashion orientated clothes attract high prices while offering little inherent value, but the same cannot be said of the best sailing gear. Look closely at the work that goes into a suit of foul-weather clothing, gauge the price of the accessories, feel the quality of the material, and they appear excellent value when compared with (say) tennis or ski clothing.

The real point about sailing clothes is that they must provide protection from wind, sun, salt, water and the cold. In temperate climates, even such as prevail in Europe, cold is the biggest enemy and it can be a killer. Less dramatically, it can speed the onset of seasickness, and it can put newcomers off the sport simply because they feel cold and wet.

It is comparatively recently that cold has been recognised as a killer in its own right. Previously deaths at sea were often attributed to drowning, but the real cause in many cases was hypothermia – the body's inability to produce heat at a faster rate than it is being lost. Keeping the body core temperature at about $37.6°$ ($98.4°F$) is vital for the correct working of the various organs. Conversely, being overheated (hyperpyrexia) can be just as dangerous.

You do not have to fall overboard to become prone to hypothermia, since the air can draw out body heat just as effectively as the sea unless there is sufficient protection. Most sailors know the sensation of 'feeling the cold in their bones' when on watch in miserable conditions. Along with low morale, an empty stomach and tiredness it is an early sign of the onset of hypothermia. The condition worsens through listlessness and weak, cumbersome movement – symptoms which most sailors will have experienced. In extreme cases, when life is endangered, sufferers can experience cramp, numbness, nausea, slurred speech, hazy vision and even unconsciousness. Urgent and correct treatment is required, as described in

Chapter 8 (8.6.17). So the correct clothing goes beyond questions of fashion. The right clothes are vital to safer sailing.

18.1.2 Layers for warmth

Many people still wear what are conventional shore-going clothes under their foul-weather gear, but nowadays there are better alternatives available based on the layer system of specially designed garments. Whether materials are natural or man-made, the most important factor in terms of insulation is air, and how it is trapped determines the thermal properties.

The choice between man-made and natural fibres is not clear and most sailors happily mix the two, preferring the material in which they feel most comfortable. Natural materials such as cotton and wool still have many friends in respect of comfort, but they have their disadvantages. Eiderdown, for example, may give the best heat insulation but it is very expensive and loses much of its efficiency when wet. Similarly, wool has long been a favourite for sailing sweaters in Guernsey and Norwegian style, but woollen garments are smelly when wet and slow to dry. Artificial materials known as fibre pile (fur fabric) or the more expensive variations such as fleece (bunting in American terms) will dry relatively quickly provided that there is some circulation of air.

Artificial fibres such as polypropylene are more thermally efficient for underclothes, but their main advantage is their ability to transport, or wick, moisture away from the skin to prevent the feeling of clamminess experienced with most cotton garments.

Specially designed sailing clothes using man-made fibres are much more practicable and convenient than ordinary shore-going garments. Take jeans for example: at first they may seem like ideal sailing trousers, but they absorb moisture, are slow to dry, and their close-fitting style makes them uncomfortable to bend and kneel in.

Whether artificial or natural fibres are preferred, keeping warm relies on the common principle that several thin layers are better than one thick one. A typical layer system might run like this: thermal T-shirt, normal thick shirt with collar, pullover or pile jacket, topped by oilskins. For summer sailing this should be enough, but experience will tell you if more is needed – for example an extra pullover or jacket might be necessary for night watches. Personal needs vary widely. Lean, thin people feel the cold quicker than thicker-set persons, who find that for once a layer of fat has a real benefit. Also the more you go boating either throughout the season or during an extended cruise, the lower the threshold of coldness becomes. Passage-makers will tell you that they feel much less cold on the third day at sea than on the first.

For sailing outside the summer season more substantial clothing will be needed. Here the layer system will be more like: thermal T-shirt and long johns, a one-piece pile or quilted garment of long-john style (or thermal pile/quilted trousers with pile jacket), an additional bodywarmer waistcoat, and apart from oilskins special provision for hands, feet and head.

Thermal vests and trousers are now particularly soft and warm, often with a knitted inside surface

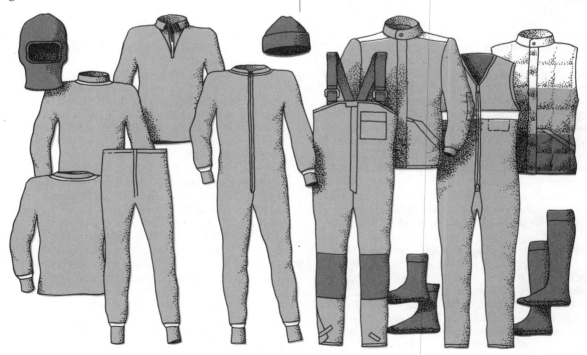

Fig. 18(1) There is a variety of bodywarmer garments which can be worn on the layering principle beneath a suit of oilskins to keep you warm at sea.

to make them pleasant to wear next to the skin. Apart from high street clothing stores, leading manufacturers of sailing clothing such as Musto, Equinox and Helly-Hansen offer a good choice. Indeed Helly-Hansen has been a leader in thermal wear and one of the recent ideas is to combine their Lifa polypropylene fabric with wool. The Lifa is used on the inside where its easy stretch characteristics provide a pleasant feel to the skin, as well as wicking away perspiration to the wool which is then able to absorb the moisture.

With regard to thermal trousers, or indeed to any one-piece garment, it is important to have an opening fly. Some garments have a two-way zip.

Over these can be worn thicker thermal garments, probably either fibre pile or with polyester quilted linings. A gauge of quality with fibre pile items is how well the pile is anchored, preferably double-loop stitched and bonded to a backing. The better the pile is attached, the longer the garment will last and the more it will resist pilling tendencies. Another check for quality is to hold the garment up to the light. The denser the pile, the less light (and therefore wind) will pass through. Some of these garments have a smooth, outer, spray-resisting shell which is a worthwhile addition.

Makers of pile clothing have produced another fabric described as fleece, which resembles very light but dense blanket material. Fleece clothing can be styled better than pile fabrics, so permitting more shapely garments. Brighter colours help to make fleece jackets very smart, while their tight weave makes them warm and wind resistant. Like most artificial fibres, fleece jackets can still be tolerably warm even when they are wet. This is less true with quilted clothing, made from wads of fibres similar to those used in domestic duvets. While the fibres are dry they are well lofted and able to trap air. Once they become wet they mat down, greatly reducing the thermal properties.

When the weather turns foul it is the outer layer that matters, for thermal clothing is only really efficient if it is itself protected from wind, spray and rain. Simply hardening up on to the wind after a leisurely sail downwind with the sun on your back can transform conditions by increasing the apparent wind speed and causing a bit of spray to fly around.

18.2 Foul-weather gear

18.2.1 Materials

More than anything, oilskins exemplify the adage that you get what you pay for. A basic suit can be obtained for a quarter of the price of the best available. If you go to sea once or twice a year and only in fine weather, then such suits will suffice. But if you intend to get the most from your boating then more substantial oilskins are necessary.

Heat is lost more quickly from the body through wet clothing than through dry. Hence the importance of wearing good foul-weather gear which will protect the inner layers of clothing from sea, spray and rain.

Modern waterproof materials, when properly used to construct a foul-weather suit, can more or less guarantee to resist the passage of water from outside to inside. Apart from attention to the actual details of construction (for example, seams that are sensibly located and which are double-stitched and taped) this also requires very good design of the various openings for neck, wrists and ankles, with Velcro closures over zips on both jacket and trouser fly. Even then it is necessary to wear a neck towel to absorb moisture which is likely to penetrate the large hood and collar opening, and in bad weather it is almost impossible to prevent some dampness around the cuffs of the sleeves. But for the most part the body can be kept dry enough.

There is however another equally important factor to consider in the material – its breathability. There is not much sense in having clothing which will resist water penetration from the outside if the interior is soon wet from the wearer's perspiration, which even with moderate activity can amount to 0.85 litres ($1\frac{1}{2}$ pints) per day. Another complication is that, particularly in cooler climates, the material needs to be non-air permeable in order to avoid a serious loss of body heat in bad conditions.

Hence the ideal requirement is for a material which prevents the flow of water and of air vapour, but which encourages the transference of water vapour from inside to outside. Such materials with a special molecular structure do in fact exist today, and are used in some more sophisticated foul-weather garments. At the other end of the scale are water-repellent nylon materials which are cheap and which will resist light rain or spray for a while. They are comfortable and weigh very little, and are easily packed, but they are not a serious proposition for real seagoing.

Most foul-weather gear is made from materials which are either nylon or cotton, and with a waterproof coating of either polyvinyl chloride (PVC), neoprene or urethane. If it has a shiny outside and a textured fabric interior, then the waterproof surface is on the outside and is probably PVC or urethane. If the outside of the garment is textured, then the waterproof coating is on the inside and is likely to be neoprene or urethane.

PVC proofing

Polyvinyl chloride (PVC) is the traditional material for foul-weather gear, and when it first appeared it was a significant advance on the old-style oilskins which older yachtsmen will remember. It has a distinctive glossy appearance and is rather heavy,

Fig. 18(2) A good suit of foul-weather clothing should incorporate the following features: peaked hood with drawstring; deep collar and adjustable throat tab; two-way, heavy duty zip with double storm flap; waterproof inside pocket; external cargo and hand-warmer pockets; tabs for lifejacket and harness; crotch or thigh straps; pockets for whistle and light stick; waterproof closures at wrists and ankles; reinforced seat and knees; reflective tape on hood and shoulders; chest-high trousers with strong elastic braces; strong loops for hanging up.

but it is relatively cheap and its seams can be welded after they have been sewn to make them completely watertight. Although PVC garments have many proponents, fewer manufacturers offer them today. One reason is colour, since there is little choice outside the standard range of yellow, blue, red or orange. In reality this is not such a disadvantage, because yellow or orange are the only sensible colours to wear at sea and to give good visibility in a man-overboard situation. More important, as foul-weather gear has become more sophisticated in design and detailing, so the limits of PVC have been reached. This is because with welded seams complicated tailoring is easy. Other disadvantages are that the garments tend to be heavy and not very flexible, especially in cold conditions, while in warmer climates they are very hot and lack the breathability referred to above. PVC advocates maintain that they afford good value for money, that the welded seams are genuinely watertight and that the material has good resistance to abrasion.

Neoprene proofing
Neoprene is used as an interior coating on garments made by some well-known British firms including Musto and Henri-Lloyd. Neoprene is much more expensive than PVC, and while it can be tailored in complicated ways, making the seams watertight is a much more involved process. Some companies dope the thread, but this is not enough since any load will open the stitching. The better suits have seams that are stitched not once but twice, and are then taped over on the inside. An inspection inside a jacket will show if this has been done.

Urethane proofing
Urethane can be applied to nylon fabric as a liquid, or as a film glued to the shell. Either method provides a good, lightweight, waterproof material, but seams need careful attention when making up garments just as for neoprene above, and some remarks on this subject are appropriate, as in 18.2.2

Clearly, the fewer seams that are included the better, and it is well worth looking at the styling of jackets and trousers to see where the seams are.

18.2.2 Style and construction
The knees and seats of trousers, and the elbows of jackets are all high-wear areas, where manufacturers try to avoid seams and sometimes fit reinforcing patches. Jacket seams across the top of the shoulder will also often be under load and Musto, in particular, take great care to move the seam away from the yoke of their jackets which is the part most exposed to the weather.

This gives rise to different cuts. Lower cost jackets use a simple inset seam to join an arm on to the body of the jacket. A tougher form of construction is the raglan style familiar from raincoats. Most complicated is the magyar seam, which takes the seam from the arm into the neck of the jacket at the top, and across the chest on the lower side.

There is a large choice of jackets. Few people now wear the smock style, preferring the convenience of an opening front. The zip closure must be well protected with a single, or better still a double, storm flap. Simple, unlined models come at lower prices. When linings are added a draining facility is needed. With more and more pockets and tags being added to jackets a waterproof inner lining is valuable to preserve water resistance.

Pockets are useful for carrying knives, keys, handkerchiefs and so on. They should drain and be well protected by storm flaps. Hand-warmer pockets are a welcome addition too. Careful attention to detail is essential at the openings for wrists and neck. No matter how good the material of the jacket is, water is always liable to find its way in at these points. Inner cuffs at the wrists together with external straps, both perhaps with Velcro adjusters, help to seam the arms. At the neck a good high zip helps, and careful shaping of the neck and hood ought to permit the collar to fit inside the hood to give protection up to the height of the cheeks. A peak on the hood boosts protection enormously, and some hoods fold back to allow the wearer to look up – to check sail trim for example. A big advance in convenience has been the fitting of small toggles to the hood drawstring, allowing the hood to be drawn really tightly round the head without the need for fiddly knots underneath the chin. The best toggles can be worked easily with numb hands or when wearing gloves, and can be released quickly to permit conversation.

Other features found on jackets are less for comfort and convenience but more for safety. Pockets can have loops inside to secure whistles, knives and hand-bearing compasses. External pouches can be used to house mini-flares, torches and personal man-overboard lights or radio beacons. Hoods, shoulders, cuffs and jacket front can be fitted with retro-reflective patches which help identify a person overboard at night.

With trousers there is a basic choice between those which are waist-high and those which are supported by braces up around the chest. For anything other than very occasional fair weather boating, waist-high trousers fail to provide sufficient protection. It pays to consider the worst conditions that you have experienced or can envisage – changing sails on a pitching foredeck, clearing sheets down to leeward with water coursing past at ankle height, or sitting on the weather rail with waves landing in your lap. Even sitting huddled in the cockpit in driving rain and spray will expose any weakness in design.

When choosing chest-high trousers the choice of features rises with cost. Top of the range trousers will have inner linings with drains at the bottoms where they can be tightened round the ankles, reinforced seat and knees, an opening front or fly

with both internal and external storm flaps, pockets, and adjustable braces. Both trousers and jackets require very strong loops for hanging up with other suits in an oilskin locker.

If the cost of the best clothing is too high for your budget, try to buy the best that you can possibly afford. Underspending is rarely a long term economy when durability, comfort and indeed personal safety are taken into account.

18.2.3 Personal buoyancy and safety harness

As this edition prepares for press the situation regarding 'Personal Protective Equipment' or PPE (lifejackets, buoyancy aids, safety harnesses and immersion suits) is in transition between previous national standards and what is or will be required by European law. Hence references below to British Standards (BS) which are being overtaken

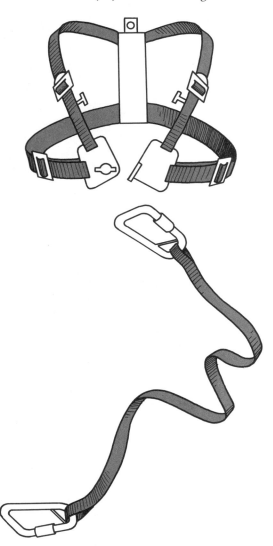

Fig. 18(3) Multifit safety harness with loop and toggle attachments. Any harness and its safety line (or tether) must be very strong, and should conform to BS 4224 or equivalent European Standard.

by new European Standards, which are often equivalent but in some cases less or more demanding. See for example new European Standards for lifejackets and buoyancy aids in 8.3.6.

The basic requirements for lifejackets and harnesses have been discussed in Chapter 8 (see 8.3.6 and 8.3.7), but no longer need they be considered as separate entities from foul-weather clothing. Today the problems of trying to make a lifejacket and harness fit over oilskins without compromising either the wearer's movements or the operation of either safety aid can be avoided.

Harnesses have been built into jackets for some time, but they have continued to improve. Remember that being pulled through the water at even five knots exerts tremendous pressure, so an integral harness needs to be adjusted to the wearer's frame just as carefully as a harness worn externally. Improperly donned safety gear can only fulfil a small proportion of its potential capacity, and can endanger life in certain circumstances.

Some built-in harnesses form a simple loop around the chest. The better designed coats have shoulder and crotch straps too, preferably with some means of keeping them from slipping. Jackets with harnesses should have external 'cargo' pockets which are large enough to allow the safety tether to be carried. After all, the whole point of a built-in harness is that it is instantly available, so when there is the slightest suggestion that conditions warrant a harness being worn there is no excuse for not clipping on. It is a good idea to be able to tuck away the D-rings of the harness since if left exposed they can prove painful to knuckles when winding a winch. Experiment too with a hand-bearing compass because some buckles can cause deviation.

Personal buoyancy can be worn either inside or outside the jacket. Many leading makes, such as Musto, Henri-Lloyd, Imhoff and Splash Down, provide loops on the outside of jackets to permit a Multifit lifejacket to be worn. This fits like a collar round the neck and is held to the jacket by toggles mating with the loops, and with a substantial strap around the chest. It has no permanent buoyancy but uses gas bottle or oral inflation when needed. Careful shaping means that harness D-rings are unobstructed and that the lifejacket can be kept on the jacket if it is taken off when going below, ready for wear next time.

Buoyancy inside jackets takes more varied forms. It can be either a waistcoat-style buoyancy aid which coordinates with the makers jacket, or it can be an integral part of the jacket itself. The latter uses either closed-cell foam (which may or may not be removed from the jacket by means of a zip) or an inflating lung. Now that Multifit lifejackets have proved popular, integral buoyancy is increasingly provided by foam jacket linings which both are convenient and afford extra insulation.

But remember that compromises may have been made. Some, but not all, Multifit lifejackets conform to the standards described in 8.3.6. The situation is less satisfactory with closed-cell foam linings. The British Marine Industry Federation recommends an 18lb minimum for adult buoyancy aids, but several jackets with built-in buoyancy have as little as 7lb, which would require an adult to tread water to stay afloat. It should however be stated that some of these jackets with minimal internal buoyancy are fitted with tabs for external Multifit lifejackets.

One final feature is essential to make all harnesses and personal buoyancy work properly. This is a strap underneath the crotch or around the thighs to prevent them riding up when pulled up by the tether or the buoyancy aid.

Fig. 18(4) Dry suit top and trousers, which are joined at the waist by a special seal. The top incorporates rubber seals around the neck and the wrists. The trousers end in waterproof socks.

18.2.4 Specialist clothing

Besides the conventional jacket/trouser suits of foul-weather gear, there is a wide variety of alternative sailing garments. One of these is the deck coat, often styled in navy blue proofed nylon, and popular among cruising sailors. Most major manufacturers produce such garments because they are useful as shore-going gear, and they are also favoured by owners and crews of motor boats and motor sailers who enjoy much more protection from the elements. Some deck coats have a measure of built-in buoyancy but few have a harness. As with oilskins, look for good detailing at the pockets, wrists, neck and front opening.

Some manufacturers provide overall-type, one-piece suits which combine the functions of jacket and trousers in one garment. These provide good protection since they have no opening at the waist, but they lack the flexibility which a jacket/trouser combination provides, being a case of all or nothing at all. They have another disadvantage in that one serious tear may mean scrapping the entire garment. For these reasons they are not very popular in Britain.

Wet suits provide thermal insulation by retaining a thin layer of water next to the body. While extensively used for subaqua work, they are difficult to put on and take off. They are available in a number of styles – long johns, two-piece, short-sleeved and with different lengths of leg.

A dry suit is a more practical proposition for small boat sailors. Mostly they are one-piece suits, rather difficult to get into, with waterproof seals at neck and wrist. They may have integral socks or seals at the ankles. Some have separate tops and bottoms, joined together by a special seal at waist level, and these are easier to put on and take off. This type of suit appeals to racing sailors who have to stay on deck with only the minimum of time off watch down below. Such garments are pretty uncomfortable, and racing crews pack talcum powder in their kit bags if they use a dry suit, because the body cannot breathe inside them. There are also obvious difficulties in going to the heads. Cruising sailors who can afford the luxury of bearing away or heaving to will not need a dry suit, while the racing crewman changing headsails as the bow buries in the waves most certainly will.

Survival suits are the ultimate in seagoing wear, but they are not really intended for working around the deck of a yacht. While they provide good protection even against arctic conditions they are heavy and awkward to wear, and also very expensive.

18.2.5 Footwear

There is no real need to buy special sailing shoes provided you have a pair which give good grip when dry and when wet, and which do not mark the deck. Unfortunately these criteria are seldom met by ordinary shore-going shoes, and most people in any case prefer to look the part in proper boating gear. Deck shoes can be nylon athletic-style or leather. Both are more durable than canvas.

Whatever the uppers are made of, the soles must grip the deck, but not pick up dirt which is then walked aboard. Many owners, quite sensibly,

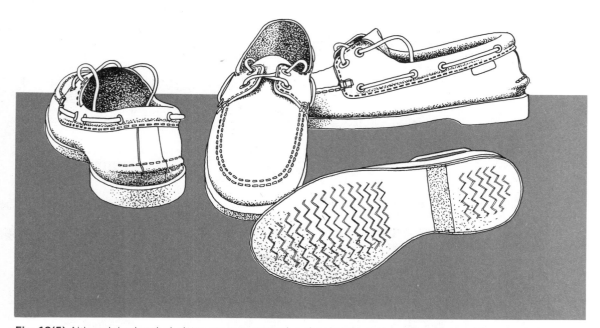

Fig. 18(5) Although leather deck shoes are more expensive, they last much longer than those with canvas/nylon uppers. Non-slip soles have a very large number of small corrugations to squeeze away the water, like a modern car tyre. The best varieties are hand-stitched with rot-proof thread.

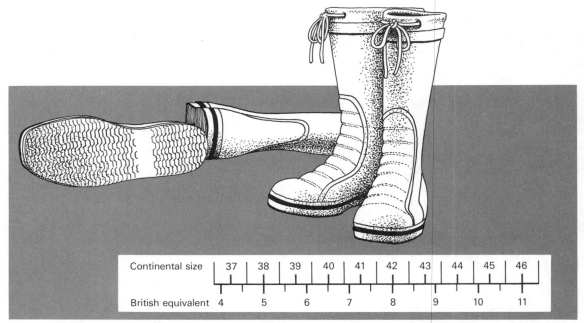

Continental size	37	38	39	40	41	42	43	44	45	46
British equivalent	4	5	6	7	8	9	10	11		

Fig. 18(6) Features of a good pair of sea boots include: hardwearing, non-slip sole; reinforcements at toe, heel and instep; arch support; quick-drying lining; broad fitting for warmth and comfort; and lightweight, flexible construction. Also shown are British/Continental size equivalents for footwear. For American sizes, add $\frac{1}{2}$ to the British figure.

expect visitors to take off shore-going shoes before coming on board, and this should invariably be done when wearing leather-soled shoes.

The conflicting requirements of giving a good grip and not picking up dirt are best met by one of the varieties of razor-cut soles that are on the market. All eyelets and heel reinforcements should be non-rusting and non-magnetic.

The leather, moccasin-style shoe can be worn comfortably without socks but these are advisable for warmth in cooler weather and to absorb perspiration (which may damage stitching) in hot climates. These purpose-styled shoes also have the advantage that they can be pulled on and off without having to untie the leather thongs, provided these are correctly adjusted.

While deck shoes are fine for fair weather sailing or for use in harbour, when it comes to seagoing it is essential to wear a good pair of sea boots. Almost nothing is more demoralising than wet feet while on watch, and this is a state of affairs which should be preventable at least most of the time. Sea boots need just the same good grip on the soles as a pair of shoes, and although there was once a fashion for boots which were only calf-height, most sailors now recognise that they need to come to as near the knee as is compatible with comfort. Then, provided there is a really good seal between the oilskin trouser and the boot, it should be possible to prevent water surging up inside and into the boot. Drawstrings round the top of the boots add to the protection.

Lined boots are more comfortable, and the ultimate must be those with linings which are leather or specially fitted fleece. Separate boot liners are also available, and these can be removed

to speed up drying – an important consideration. Some firms also provide special rubber ankle seals for the gap between boot and trouser bottom.

Donning and removing boots with oilskin trousers can be an awkward operation. A useful tip when taking them off is to roll down the trousers to the ankles and step out of the boots. Next time that they have to be worn it is a simple matter to step into the boots again and roll up the trousers.

18.2.6 Head, hands and feet
Keeping the extremities warm is fundamental to keeping the body trunk warm. The head for instance can lose as much heat as the body can produce, so some form of headwear is essential in bad weather. A sou'wester or a hood incorporated in the jacket are the two alternatives for keeping water at bay and stopping it running down the neck, but both are inclined to restrict vision and communication.

Many people find that a woolly hat is adequate most of the time. It is warm and provides some protection against knocks and bumps. In colder conditions a Balaclava-type hat can make a miserable watch more bearable – if necessary under a sou'wester or hood.

If hands are allowed to become cold, dexterity is lost. Leather sailing gloves are good in fine weather for protecting soft hands, but their fingerless style and cut-out backs mean that they are of little use during periods of inactivity in the cold. So two pairs of gloves makes sense – leather ones for warp and anchor handling, and fleecy mits for inclement conditions. A solution is to provide a couple of ship's pairs of gloves for whoever is on watch.

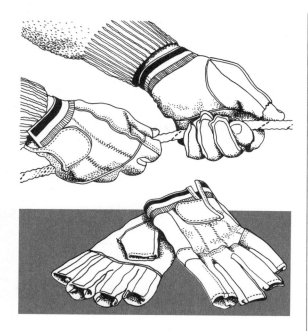

Fig. 18(7) These days not all sailors have tough hands, so a pair of sailing gloves can be useful to protect soft skin.

Wet feet have already been mentioned, but cold feet are almost as bad. Thick, fleecy, thermal socks can help, but they are not the whole answer. This is because the body cuts down the circulation of blood to the extremities when it is cold, in order to keep the vital organs in the core warm. You can warm up feet by movement to stimulate the flow of blood, and also by having boots which are not too tight.

18.3 Care of clothes, and what to take

18.3.1 Care of clothing
Washing codes now have to be shown on garments by law, and it certainly pays to take heed of them for sailing clothing, which does need special treatment. Failure to follow instructions can damage a garment and render it useless.

Take thermal wear for example. Some polypropylene clothes cannot be hot washed without risk of shrinkage. Similarly, hot air tumble drying may cause such garments to shrink to almost half their normal size. Cool washes and gentle spinning should not harm most thermal fabrics.

For oilskins, regular washing is highly recommended. Even a cold fresh water rinse when returning ashore will help remove the salt, and reduce the risk of black mildew staining. As a general rule detergents should be avoided on proofed garments. Use mild soap instead. Although oil, grease and petrol should not damage the proofing, it pays to remove such spillages with a gentle wash in warm soapy water. Some manufacturers allow machine washing, but hand washing is kinder. Spin drying should be avoided on proofed garments as the centrifugal action tries to force water out through the weave of the garment.

Regular cleaning keeps garments supple and prevents them holding salt, which attracts moisture and makes clothing feel damp even if no actual moisture passes through.

Proofed garments eventually lose some of their coating, though water-repellent silicone sprays can help to put some of this back and assist water to run off the fabric. Most manufacturers offer repair and reproofing services which can extend the life of expensive oilskins.

18.3.2 What to take
This is a question which is asked as many times as people go boating. Experience whittles the list down to what is necessary to suit the type of sailing being done – not forgetting shore-going occasions. Boats today are dryer down below and have more stowage space than ever before, so do not worry about taking too much gear just so long as it is in a soft holdall or kit bag. Hard suitcases and framed rucksacks are definitely unwelcome on board.

In the days when ocean racing yachts had long bowsprits it was recommended that the crew should take a change of clothes for every hundred miles to be sailed! But now bowsprits are largely things of the past, and foul-weather clothing is much more effective. Even so it pays to think through a trip in advance. If you can answer the questions below you will know what to take from the suggested packing list. If there is doubt about an item, take it, especially if it is an item of personal safety gear. Here are the questions.
(1) Is this a day trip, or will I spend a night or more on board?
(2) Will casual clothes be sufficient, or will we be dining ashore, or attending a prize-giving function or something similar?
(3) What is the forecast? Do I need more sun clothing or thermal wear?
(4) Do I have enough to change into if I get soaked to the skin?
(5) Will a lifejacket, safety harness, oilskins, sleeping bag and towel be provided on board?
Having decided the likely answers to these questions, you can decide what needs to be taken from the following list:
Shore-going clothes – casual/smart
Change(s) of sailing clothes
Extra layers – body warmer waistcoat and/or jacket
Trousers/shirts for deck wear
Cold protection – socks, hat, gloves, thermal wear
Sun protection – light shirt, sun hat, sunglasses, visor, lipsalve, sun cream
Oilskins

Personal buoyancy
Safety harness
Knife
Waterproof torch and/or man overboard light
Reefer jacket/tie
Toilet gear
Towel
Sleeping bag, pyjamas
Shoes and seaboots
Money, credit card, passport

Smart clothes can be stowed in suit-hangers, while other gear is best kept in a soft kit bag. Shirts and similar items are best rolled up. Remember to wrap everything up in plastic bags that are well sealed. It only has to rain, or for there to be water in the bottom of the tender, for kit to get wet through even at the outset of a passage. Some holdalls for sailing gear have internal divisions to separate dry clothing from that which is wet or damp.

Chapter 19

Legal advice

Contents

Previous legal references
Throughout this Handbook there are various references to legal matters in other chapters, in the discussions on different problems which are of interest to boat owners. These are summarised below:

In the pages which follow there are a number of other legal subjects which concern yachtsmen. Should legal advice be required, it is best to consult a solicitor who is versed in maritime law. A list of such firms is available from the Royal Yachting Association.

19.1 Public right of navigation

19.1.1 Right of navigation on tidal waters

For the purposes of most cruising and racing yachtsmen it is a safe generalisation that a public right of navigation exists over all tidal waters, and that this can only be interrupted with the express consent of Parliament. It is subject to some limitations. The fact that tidal water might, on a spring high water, reach an otherwise dry ditch, does not necessarily mean that the right extends to that ditch. By the same token, while a large ship might under the most favourable circumstances negotiate a narrow crowded river, the automatic right that extends to smaller craft would not necessarily be enjoyed by that ship. It is a question of fact and degree in each case for each vessel as to whether the right exists.

The bed of all navigable rivers up to high water mark is almost invariably the property of the Crown, but in many cases has been vested or leased to a harbour authority or conservancy, or to a local authority. The right of navigation is similar in many ways to a right of way on land. Just as on a public highway the right is enjoyed to pass and repass, and to stop for a reasonable length of time, so on tidal waters a vessel may navigate and anchor, but may not permanently occupy an area of water by laying a fixed mooring without consent.

The right to navigate does not include the right to ground or rest on the seabed for repairing or cleaning the hull, although this is a common and accepted practice.

There are a number of authorities who may purport to have a power to prevent navigation on tidal waters, but where such a power exists it may well be for limited purposes only.

19.1.2 Ministry of Defence

Many coastal areas are occupied by the Ministry of Defence as gunnery or bombing ranges, or as proving ranges. During firing times these ranges, which are normally marked clearly, are patrolled by MOD Police who are entitled to request yachts to keep clear of certain limits. While it obviously makes sense to cooperate with reasonable requests where possible, all gunnery range by-laws maintain a specific exemption for vessels, in the ordinary course of navigation, crossing the sea area and taking no longer than is required for that purpose. The range by-laws on all such ranges controlling the right to navigate are carefully worded so as not to exclude the bona fida right to transit the range at any time whether firing is scheduled or not. The effect of this exemption is to entitle cruising and racing yachts to cross the area or part of it, but not to enter only in order to round a mark and then leave it again.

19.1.3 Harbour authorities

Harbour authorities of every harbour in the country are, quite necessarily, given wide powers to control traffic leaving and entering a harbour. What a Harbour Master may not do is exclude craft for any reason (except under the Dangerous Cargoes Act or other specific legislation), or to prevent craft from moving except for the day-to-day control of traffic. In the leading case of *Pearn v. Sargeant* (1973) the Harbour Master at Looe gave instructions that the harbour should be closed for a substantial part of the day to allow a regatta to take place. The owner of a craft within the harbour was prosecuted for failing to comply with the Harbour Master's directions even though the movement of his vessel could not conceivably have interfered with the craft competing in the regatta. In the course of his successful appeal against his conviction in the local Magistrates Court, the Lord Chief Justice said

> 'The function of the Harbour Master under the act is to regulate the traffic; after all it is a public harbour where the public have a right to be and it is not the Harbour Master's function, as such, to keep them out. His function is to control and regulate them rather like a traffic policeman regulating traffic. Of course there will be cases where he has to go beyond these simple functions; of course there may be cases where necessity arises and he has to impose wider prohibitions for a particular time, but when that happens it is for consideration whether the directions he has given are reasonable for the emergency or circumstances which prompted them.'

As with all public authorities, harbour administrators are under a duty implied by law to exercise their powers reasonably and only for purposes associated with their undertaking.

19.1.4 Queen's Harbour Master

The powers of the Queen's Harbour Masters in Naval Ports and Dockyards are very much wider than those applying to civil/commercial harbours. In Portsmouth Harbour for example the Queen's Harbour Master has introduced regulations prohibiting the use of sailboards (which otherwise have all the rights and responsibilities attaching to other vessels through UK tidal waters) in clear conflict with the general principles governing the public right of navigation. The wide powers of the Queen's Harbour Master make this a lawful exercise, as indeed would all regulations affecting the navigation of craft unless a complainant was able to show that the imposition of such regulations was entirely unreasonable. These powers derive from the Royal Prerogative without the need for any specific parliamentary authority.

19.1.5 English Nature

A further amendment to the general public right of navigation on tidal waters appears in the Wildlife and Countryside Act 1981, which includes a provision for English Nature to make by-laws excluding pleasure craft from certain parts of marine nature reserves at certain times of the year. At present there are only two marine nature reserves in the country, at Skomer and Lundy, where very limited areas are subject to restrictions on navigating and anchoring. A proposal to make a very much more extensive area in the Menai Strait subject to by-laws has been the subject of discussion for some years.

19.1.6 Public right of navigation on non-tidal waters

Public rights of navigation over non-tidal waters can be established by dedication (i.e. gift by the owner), by statute, by custom (being used since time immemorial) or by prescription (uninterrupted use as of right over a period in excess of 20 years). It was originally believed that the right to navigate on non-tidal waters extended to waters only where there was commercial traffic, but a recent High Court case shows that recreational traffic (in this case canoeing) can keep the right alive. Whether recreational use can 'create' a new public right of navigation is debatable, being a question that has never been settled in court. A recent appeal to the House of Lords regarding the Yorkshire Derwent resulted in a ruling that the general law governing rights of way over land does not apply to rivers or watercourses. Where there is no right to navigate, any attempt to do so will constitute a trespass and in the 1972 case of *Rawson v Peters* an incursion by a canoeist into a valuable angling beat, even though it was not being fished on the day in question, was held to be an actionable trespass

giving rise to damages and an injunction restraining further trespass.

A public right of navigation also exists on a number of lakes in the Lake District but, as is the case on most major rivers and canals, the right is subject to the payment of licence fees to the controlling authority.

19.2 Collision, injury and damages

19.2.1 Collision between yachts

The most common cause of liability arising on behalf of the yacht owner will be that of collision. Although all owners and skippers are presumed by law to have a knowledge of the International Regulations for Preventing Collisions at Sea (including the rules for navigation lights and sound signals) errors of judgement can occur and, where an injured party is able to show negligence on the part of the person who caused the damage, there will be a liability to compensate the plaintiff to the full extent of his loss as described below.

Although any legal action will be dealt with by a Court of Admiralty jurisdiction, the principles of liability follow those that apply in any action for negligence. In all cases, the plaintiff must show to the satisfaction of the court, on the balance of probabilities, that the defendant was in breach of his duty of care. The court will need to hear evidence on all the circumstances of the collision (not simply that there was a breach of the IRPCS) and the defendant will be entitled, where appropriate, to raise the accepted defences of contributory negligence, inevitable accident and *volenti non fit injuria*. (This Latin tag conveys the concept that a willing participant in an activity cannot generally be heard to complain of injury or damage resulting from that activity.)

Where a collision occurs between racing yachts, a common misconception is that retirement or acceptance of an alternative penalty following an infringement of the International Yacht Racing Rules can prejudice a civil claim for negligence, or amount to the sort of admission of liability that entitles an insurer to repudiate a claim. It is important to remember that an act or error of judgement that may amount to an infringement of the racing rules will not necessarily amount to negligence for the purposes of civil law. The RYA prescription to IYR Rule 76.1 specifically provides that the findings of fact of a protest committee can only be brought into evidence in a civil court with the written consent of both parties. In other words, such findings are irrelevant to the question of liability for damage.

It would also be quite wrong for an insurer to avoid a claim by reference to an insured's acknowledgement of infringement by retiring from a race after a collision. If a yacht is covered for racing risks, then that cover itself provides an acceptance by the underwriter of the precise terms and requirements of the rules. Rule 33.1 requires a yacht which realises that she has infringed a rule to retire from the race or take an alternative penalty. Thus the duty to retire prevails over the requirement of certain underwriters that no action should be taken which could be construed as an admission of liability.

19.2.2 Measure of property damage

The successful plaintiff will be entitled to full compensation for all his losses arising from an incident. If there is a total loss the owner will be compensated to the full market value. Where repairable damage has been caused, the cost of repair is recoverable, also any towage, salvage. harbour dues, survey fees or delivery costs.

In addition any expenses suffered by the crew, and the cost to the owner of the loss of use of his yacht (which may even be measured by the cost of chartering an alternative vessel for the time that the owner would have been using his yacht had she not been out of commission) will also be recoverable.

19.2.3 Personal injury and death

Clearly the skipper of a yacht has a liability to those on board to take reasonable care in all the circumstances of the case, and not to expose the crew and passengers to any unnecessary danger. So far as the third party liability is concerned, it is worth remembering that this is a contract of indemnity for the insured alone, and does not automatically entitle any third party to compensation unless it can be proved that the damage was the result of the skipper/owner's fault and that none of the defences or partial defences to negligence (see below) applied at the time.

19.2.4 Defences to negligence

The types of defence to an action for negligence are numerous, and indeed the use of the term 'defence' is open to different interpretations. In this context we shall treat it as any ground for claiming non-liability or reduced liability, or a claim for damages made by a party claiming damages for some injury.

Non-liability

As in most civil law situations, the burden of proving a claim rests on the plaintiff, the standard of proof being that of the balance of probabilities. To show that a defendant is liable for damages, the plaintiff in an action for negligence has to satisfy the court as to the three elements of any claim – namely that a duty of care exists between the plaintiff and the defendant; that the defendant has been in breach of that duty of care; and that the plaintiff has suffered damage from that breach.

(1) *No duty of care.* The question as to whether a person owes a duty of care to another is not always immediately obvious but has been defined in the following terms. 'You must take reasonable care to avoid acts or omissions which you can reasonably foresee would be likely to injure your neighbour' and a neighbour is defined as 'any person as I ought to have in contemplation as being so affected when I am directing my mind to the acts or omissions which are called into question'. The situation often arises where a person may be injured by the result of an act of another who owes him no duty of care. Thus a trespasser on private property, or a person wrongfully interfering with a boat in a dangerous state, cannot complain of injury since the owner of the property or boat owes no duty of care except to those who are expressly or impliedly authorised by him.

(2) *No breach of duty.* The duty to take reasonable care to avoid damaging another's person or property is not an absolute duty. Many instances will come to mind where an accident may occur in a harbour, or in the course of a race, where it may be possible for an observer to apportion 'blame' in the sense of causation, but where a court would not find blame since the error of judgement, or chain of circumstances resulting in the incident, does not amount to negligence.

A relatively common cause of danger in mooring areas is a yacht breaking adrift and striking another as she drifts on the wind or tide. To the layman it may often seem that the facts of the matter speak for themselves, and that the owner of the yacht or whoever was responsible for the broken mooring must be liable. That is however not always the case. It is possible for a latent defect in a chain, or a storm of exceptional severity, to cause a yacht to break free in circumstances where if the owner can show that he took reasonable care (e.g. by having his mooring examined each year or having tackle of sufficient strength to cope normally with exceptional weather conditions) he will escape liability.

In a County Court case a motor yacht manoeuvring slowly in a marina struck a moored yacht when the engine control stuck in the 'ahead' position. The defendant was able to show that he took reasonable care to service his installation on a regular basis. The defendant's expert surveyor investigating the incident was unable to recreate the fault without first removing the gear box cover and 'helping' the cable to jump its guide. The court took the view that this was a one-in-a-million chance from which no liability arose.

Circumstances will often arise in the course of a yacht race where helmsmen will have to make snap decisions, and where a wrong decision or momentary inattention may have serious consequences. It will not always follow that an error of judgement or loss of concentration will be considered 'negligent' by a court. In an unreported County Court case involving a collision between two Laser dinghies, where the leading dinghy capsized, and the helmsman of the following Laser took insufficient avoiding action and damaged the capsized craft, it was held that this error of judgement did not amount to negligence (even though he was clearly in the wrong under the IYR Rules, and very properly retired immediately). Accordingly the owner of the damaged boat was not entitled to damages.

(3) *No damage.* It goes without saying that the plaintiff must show that he has suffered damage of some sort. While the damage need not necessarily be material, it must be such that monetary value can be put on it. The loss of use of a yacht can be valued by reference to the cost of chartering a replacement, but the loss of opportunity to gain personal satisfaction by winning an important race or series is probably too remote and ill-defined to be evaluated. It is also essential to liability that the defendant's wrongdoing should have demonstrably caused the plaintiff's damage. The case of *The Douglas* (1882) illustrates this concept. The ship sank in the Thames solely as a result of the negligence of those in charge of her, and became a wreck obstructing the river. Without any further fault on the part of the defendant, the wreck was struck by the plaintiff's ship which was damaged. It was held that this damage was not the consequence of the original negligence, which had ceased to be relevant after the sinking. The defendant's negligence had 'exhausted' itself at the time of the original incident and the wreck thereafter had been properly marked.

19.2.5 *Volenti non fit injuria*

Like most Latin maxims employed by lawyers this is an over-simplification. Loosely translated it means that one who consents to an injury or to circumstances resulting in injury cannot complain of it thereafter.

Thus an experienced yachtsman, who appreciates and accepts the intrinsic risks of yacht racing, can reasonably be expected to foresee that damage or loss may be occasioned as a result of starting a race or sailing a particular course in bad weather, and may even be deemed negligent himself in so doing. On the other hand, a competitor known to be inexperienced will not foresee the possible harm, nor could he reasonably be expected to, and would not necessarily be negligent in undertaking the risks. In such a case the skipper of a boat and the organising club may owe a duty of care to a crew member, and the defence of *volenti* will fail.

Although consent is normally implied by the courts in all properly conducted sports, no one is deemed to consent to a deliberate foul. While one has to accept the risk of damage or injury arising from an honest mistake, carelessness, or error of judgement, a deliberate act outside the rules resulting in injury or damage will usually be actionable.

Where children are involved, the courts will take a practical view as to whether the child, in all the circumstances, and having regard as to the nature of the risk, can sensibly be held to have consented to the risk. Below the age of 13 or 14 the onus of proof will be very much on the defendant to show that a child, particularly if inexperienced in the sport, knew the risks.

19.2.6 Contributory negligence

The Law Reform (Contributory Negligence) Act 1945 provides that where any person suffers damage as a result partly of his own fault and partly the fault of another, he is entitled to recover damages with such reduction as the court thinks just and equitable having regard to his share in the responsibility for the damage.

In practice the concept of the contributory negligence is not a defence, but it can be pleaded where the defendant feels the plaintiff has to accept some of the blame for an occurrence, or has by his own behaviour aggravated the damage caused.

19.2.7 Act of God

Act of God can be defined as an operation of natural forces which is so unexpected that any consequence arising from it must be regarded as too remote to be the foundation for legal liability. It need not be spectacular such as lightning or flooding; even a rat gnawing through a wire can be held to be an Act of God.

19.2.8 Inevitable accident

This is defined as an accident not avoidable by any such precaution as a reasonable man, doing such an act, there and then, could be expected to take. In the context of an action for negligence, it really amounts to a more specific means of denying a breach of the duty of care. In truth all accidents can be avoided, so long as adequate precautions are taken, but the law will never impose a higher standard of care than could be expected of a reasonable man under the circumstances.

19.2.9 Limitation of liability

Under the terms of the Merchant Shipping Act 1894 (Section 583) as amended by more recent legislation (in particular the Merchant Shipping Act 1976), the owner of a ship (including a yacht) is entitled to limit his liability or damage caused by his negligence. For many years (until December 1986) these limits were unrealistically low, entitling the owner of a yacht, in cases of property damage, to limit his liability to no more than £40 per ton of his own yacht's registered tonnage. Since December 1986 new legislation, following international convention, sets the notional minimum tonnage at a very much higher level linked to International Units of Account (equivalent to approximately 80p per unit). For property damage an owner/skipper is not entitled to limit below 83,033 Units of Account, while for loss of life or personal injury the platform is 166,677 Units of Account.

It must be remembered that limitation will only be available in cases where the owner has not been negligent in his capacity as owner (but may have caused the damage while acting as skipper, helmsman, deckhand or engineer). Thus if a collision occurs through bad seamanship, poor helmsmanship, or faulty servicing of equipment, the owner is entitled to limit even if it was his own personal fault. If damage results from an act of ownership, no such entitlement occurs. In a recent case the owner of a fishing vessel decided to move the steering position to the aft cockpit so that he could work his nets without leaving the wheel, thus obscuring his view ahead. When a collision occurred as a result of his inability to see where he was going, it was held that the cause of the accident was not his negligence as a helmsman, but rather his lack of judgement as an owner, and thus he was not entitled to limit his liability.

19.3 Harbour Law

19.3.1 Public harbours
As we have seen most public harbours are under the jurisdiction of Harbour Authorities or Conservancies, or of the Harbour Committee of the relevant local authority.

By the terms of the Harbours Act 1964, 'harbour' is defined as 'any harbour whether natural or artificial, any port, haven, estuary, tidal or other river or inland waterway navigated by seagoing ships, and includes a dock, wharf and in Scotland a ferry or boatslip being used for marine work'.

The Harbours Act also defines a Harbour Authority for the purpose of the Act as 'any persons in whom are vested under this Act, by another Act or by any Order or instrument, powers or duties for improving, maintaining or managing a Harbour'.

Nearly all harbours with a significant degree of commercial or recreational use are managed under statutory powers. One reason for this is that the taking of harbour dues and tolls is part of the Royal Prerogative and can only be assigned to a subject as a franchise by the Crown or by an Act of Parliament. Harbour Authorities which rely on grant or prescription from the Crown are now very rare and do not include any major Harbour authorities (with the exception of Naval Dockyards). Another reason why statutory powers are necessary to manage a harbour is that the construction and maintenance of harbour works below high water mark may be open to challenge

in the courts unless such construction and maintenance is authorised by statute, on the grounds that the works interfere with the public right of navigation. Moreover harbour authorities for large harbours need to have powers to regulate activities of persons using the harbour, and in particular the movement and berthing of vessels within the area. Adequate powers for these purposes can only be obtained by statute.

Local circumstances of the many harbour authorities in Britain are very varied. This is perhaps one reason why harbour authorities still operate to a large extent under local statutory powers. The nature and function of harbour authorities vary from one place to another as does the size of the area under jurisdiction.

Charges made by harbour authorities are of two kinds. There are dues, which pay for the enjoyment of the basic or essential harbour or port, and there are further charges paying for the enjoyment, usually optional, of ancillary services such as slipways, moorings and the use of other facilities. Dues are, to some extent, in the nature of tax, the amount payable by a user not necessarily being directly related to the service received by the user. However, the distinction between dues and other charges is now often blurred by the levying of combined charges which include both dues and charges. The practice of levying combined charges is expressly authorised under the Transport Act 1981. The Harbours Act 1964 made a number of important changes in the law relating to harbour charges so that as regards the imposition of harbour dues the harbour authority can impose such charges as they think fit, subject only to a right of appeal by users to the Secretary of State if harbour dues are thought to be unreasonable.

Although there are no recorded cases involving the Secretary of State on ship, passenger, or goods dues, an enquiry ordered by the Secretary of State into a charge by the Weymouth Harbour Commissioners for vessels requiring lifting of the bridge for navigation, resulted in an order that the bridge should be raised upon reasonable notice, as required, free of charge. This indicates that the Secretary of State for Transport, to whom in effect all harbour authorities are answerable, will not hesitate to intervene in harbour affairs where a case for so doing has been made.

19.3.2 Mooring responsibilities
In most harbour legislation, the authority or conservancy will normally have a specific right to control and regulate moorings, and to make reasonable charges for that purpose. As we have seen, the fundus (i.e. seabed for all navigable tidal waters) is vested in the Crown (or in some person or corporation granted title by the Crown) and accordingly a person wishing to lay a mooring within the area controlled by a harbour authority will need to obtain the consent not only of the authority under its statutory jurisdiction, but also

of the Crown Estate Commissioners (or other landowner) in recognition of their ownership.

The Crown Estate Commissioners will grant individual licences to boat owners wishing to lay moorings on their ground and leases to harbour authorities, local authorities, fairways committees and yacht clubs as appropriate. The Crown Estate Commissioners are under a statutory duty to obtain the 'best consideration' from their leases. In former times it was accepted by the Commissioners that, in view of the Crown's virtual monopoly over tidal fundus, mooring rents should be kept down to a reasonable level, and not allowed to rise in line with market forces. In recent years however the growing excess of demand over a fixed supply of mooring areas has enabled the Commissioners to increase rents by far in excess of inflation. Individuals, clubs or even small harbour authorities negotiating Crown leases should seek advice from the Royal Yachting Association which maintains a current database of all new leases and rent reviews of mooring areas. Many harbour authorities of course provide mooring tackle in accordance with statutory powers to make facilities available for harbour users, and in such cases the cost of providing the tackle plus maintenance and replacement costs are properly charged to the mooring holder. Where the Crown Estate Commissioners lease the area of fundus to a marina operator for development, a very much higher rent is charged by the Crown in recognition of the profit element expected by the developer.

Where a club or harbour authority has taken a regulating lease, it is always subject to the condition that they should not 'uplift' the ground rent charged to individual boat owners by more than 25 per cent, to cover administration and other charges.

Until 1984 it was the policy of a number of local authorities to levy rates on moorings. The 1984 Rates Act specifically provides that moorings of a kind designed to be raised from time to time for inspection shall not be subject to rates. This means in effect that only fixed-pile moorings or marina-type pontoons attached to poles or fixed to the shore should be rateable.

19.3.3 Other controls on moorings

So far as the laying of moorings is concerned, local authorities have a general planning jurisdiction down to the low water mark, or to the mid point of any narrow creek or river (which is defined by ancient case law as being a river not so wide that one cannot see what a man on the other side is doing). Under the terms of the Coast Protection Act 1949, consent for the construction of any works or deposit of any article (and this is interpreted to include mooring tackle) requires the consent of the Secretary of State for Transport. This consent will not be given where the proposal would cause an interference with, or danger to, navigation. The Department of Transport normally consults widely with all interested parties when proposals for development or new moorings are made, and conditions such as the size and type of vessels using the moorings, together with a specification for ground tackle and mooring buoys, are often imposed.

19.3.4 Anchoring and the use of moorings

With the very much restricted space that is available for boats in most harbours and estuaries around our coasts, problems often arise with cruising yachts trying to find a place to anchor or moor – even overnight. The right to navigate in tidal water implies a right to anchor at least for a reasonable time, or for purposes connected with navigation, as already mentioned in 19.1.1. But local by-laws often prohibit anchoring in certain areas, and sometimes throughout the entire harbour as applies in the Hamble River.

A vessel which anchors (where anchoring is permitted) must do so clear of other vessels already at anchor or on moorings. Consideration needs to be given to what will happen with the change of tide, or with a shift of wind to another quarter. Except in extreme conditions, dragging an anchor and causing damage to some other craft implies negligence, either due to not using the right ground tackle, failing to let go a second anchor when conditions so require, or leaving the boat unattended.

Moorings allocated to an individual by a harbour authority are private, for the use of that individual. In practice most yachtsmen do not object to some other craft using their mooring in their absence, always provided that the vessel is not too heavy for the mooring and that sufficient crew are left on board to shift berth should the absent owner of the mooring return.

A problem may arise however when an owner finds an unattended yacht on his mooring. As a last resort there may be a temptation to cast the stranger adrift, but this could amount to a criminal offence and would almost certainly entitle the owner to damages if the yacht suffered some injury. The only correct procedure is for the owner of the mooring himself to find an alternative mooring, or to move the stranger to some other safe berth – in either case recovering the expense involved from the stranger, by legal action if necessary.

19.4 Law for yachts, boats and club launches

19.4.1 Passengers and crew

Although for the most part privately owned pleasure craft are exempt from any statutory interference, when such craft are put to certain uses (e.g. chartering) they may, under certain circumstances, be subject to statutory controls.

When examining the Merchant Shipping Acts and Regulations it is important to remember that the primary purpose of the regulations is to promote the safety of passengers. Passengers are defined as 'any person not employed or engaged in any capacity on board on the business of the vessel (or travelling by reason of circumstances which could not have been prevented, e.g. a shipwreck) and not being children under one year of age'. In a recent High Court case it was held that the term 'engaged' implied the need for a binding contractual agreement. Thus, although the person engaged may be unpaid, or may even have paid the shipowner for the voyage or have come aboard a sail training yacht as a trainee, he will be deemed to be a member of her crew if he has signed some contractual document relating to the voyage.

19.4.2 Compulsory requirements for pleasure yachts used entirely for private purposes

The following is a summary of the legal requirements for pleasure craft used entirely for private purposes:

(1) Although the former requirement for all yachts over 13.7m (45ft) in length to be registered has been repealed by the Merchant Shipping Act 1988, the International Convention on the High Seas (to which the United Kingdom is a signatory) requires all craft going into foreign territorial waters to fly the flag of their state and to carry documents as evidence of the right to fly that flag. Thus registration, in effect, remains compulsory under international law for craft going foreign.

(2) With the advent of the Single European Market, customs formalities between EU member states have been reduced, as described in Chapter 2. It is still a requirement to complete documentation (now Form C1331) and to report departure/arrival when sailing to or coming from countries outside the EU. Customs Notice 8B refers, and the laws covered by this notice are the Pleasure Craft (Arrival and Report) Regulations, 1990, made under 35(4) and 42(1) of the Customs and Excise Management Act 1979 as amended, and the Commissioners' Directions made under sections 35(1) and 64(2) of that Act.

(3) Owners or masters of pleasure craft over 80 gross registered tonnes may be subject to the Merchant Shipping (Certification of deck officers and/or marine engineer officers) Regulations unless eligible for exemption. (Merchant Shipping Act 1970, Sections 43/44.)

(4) Pleasure Yachts in Class XII, over 45ft (13.7m) in length, are subject to lifesaving and fire appliances rules (see 8.2.1).

19.4.3 Pleasure yachts let on charter

Under the Public Health Act 1907 (Section 94) pleasure yachts let on charter may require to be licensed. The licence would be issued by the appropriate local authority (for yachts on charter see 1.7.2. above). It is arguable whether a yacht taking people to sea will be taking them as 'passengers' rather than crew, and each case will depend on the particular facts. See also 1.7.1

19.4.4 Club launches

It is clear from existing cases that club launches cannot be said to be carrying a crew. Most of those on board must be described as 'passengers' for they are in no way working the ship.

(1) Launches carrying more than 12 passengers will have to be surveyed by a representative of the local Department of Transport Marine Division survey office. Launches carrying more than 12 passengers are subject to this requirement whether or not they are let on hire, and whether or not the passengers have paid any money.

(2) Launches carrying 12 or fewer passengers will not require a Department of Transport licence, but may require a local authority licence if they are 'let on hire to the public' or are 'used for carrying passengers for hire'. If the service is provided free or is merely reflected in club membership fees then the vessel will not be subject to the statute, for there is no element of 'hire to the public' involved.

(3) Merchant Shipping Notice M856 to owners and persons in charge of small passenger vessels is issued by the Department of Transport and applies equally to club launches. Generally it states that to ensure the safe handling of such vessels which carry a limited number of passengers and which ply in smooth or partially smooth waters, the Department of Transport will issue Boatman's Licences to all persons suitably qualified to take charge of such vessels. So far as club launches are concerned, the notice applies to Classes IV and V vessels carrying not more than 250 passengers. In brief, to obtain a Boatman's Licence, a candidate must be aged 18 or over, not be suffering from any disease or disability which could make it unsafe for him to be in charge of a passenger vessel, pass an eyesight test, and pass an oral test as to his practical seamanship and local pilotage knowledge. The test will include manoeuvring, rule of the road, use of lifesaving precautions and firefighting appliances, knowledge of fire precautions and weather reporting systems, and also test his knowledge of the coastline, buoys, tides etc.

Exemptions are available for holders of 2nd Mates Certificates, and of RYA Coastal Skipper Certificates and above. The area of validity of the licence will be restricted to the area in which the holder has passed a test of local pilotage or has produced evidence to show that he has had adequate experience. It should also be noted that possession of a local Department of Transport Boatman's Licence will not necessarily relieve the holder from complying with any legal requirements of local harbour authorities which similarly have jurisdiction to issue a Boatman's Licence.

19.4.5 British Waterways Board and other inland navigation authorities

Most navigation authorities controlling these rivers or canals have statutory jurisdiction to license all craft using their navigations and to attach conditions and requirements to such licences. The National Rivers Authority, which exercises jurisdiction over the Thames, the Fen rivers, and the Upper Medway, maintains design, construction and equipment standards over the Thames alone. There is a proposal that these requirements will be extended to the other rivers under the NRA's control, to the Norfolk and Suffolk Broads, and the canals and rivers under the jurisdiction of the British Waterways Board by 1994.

19.4.6 Merchant Shipping (Load Lines) Act 1967

This Act applies to all ships except warships, fishing craft and pleasure yachts. Clearly therefore, if a vessel can be described as a pleasure yacht, she does not fall within the load line rules. There is some doubt that the owners of such vessels which are used for commercial or semi-commercial purposes (e.g. sail training or charter) will need to comply with the Act. Following the *Marques* incident, the Department of Transport applied a more restrictive interpretation on the expression 'pleasure yacht', but in the case of the *Chalice* (1991), the High Court held that the Department was wrong to try to apply Merchant Shipping Acts and Regulations to a pleasure yacht simply because the yacht was being used for a commercial purpose. The court held that a pleasure yacht remains entitled to all the exemptions allowed by the Acts and Regulations whatever use it was being put to at the time. The Department of Transport proposes to introduce new regulations with effect from 1993 to require all pleasure yachts used commercially (whether for training, passenger carrying or charter) to comply with a Code of Practice governing design, construction and equipment standards.

19.4.7 Merchant Shipping Act 1970 (official log books)

This Act gives a number of powers to create regulations with respect to registered ships on specific items. Almost invariably pleasure yachts are exempt from the requirements of the Act, but yachts such as sail training yachts are required to complete crew muster lists and complete official log books. Statutory Instrument 1972 No. 1874 specifically provides that official log books shall be kept in every ship registered in the United Kingdom, but that requirement shall not apply to ships of less than 25 tonnes and pleasure yachts. Other requirements that do apply to pleasure yachts under this Act are the keeping of a safe navigational watch and the use of automatic pilots. The regulations recognise that yachts may not always carry sufficient crew to allow regulations to be met in full, and it is for this reason that the regulations carry the words 'where practicable' and specifically state that they do not, for example, debar the single-handed yachtsman from using an automatic pilot.

19.5 Clubs and sailing schools

19.5.1 Potential liabilities of yacht club officers and sailing school instructors

Every yacht club and sailing school will organise or engage in activities in the normal course of its business which, by their very nature will involve some element of risk.

As we have seen (19.2.4) a person will owe a duty to all others to take care that they are not injured by his carelessness or negligence, and this duty applies particularly to yacht club officers and to sailing school instructors, or to others in positions of responsibility.

When confronted with a claim from a competitor or trainee injured in the course of sailing activities, the court examining the problem will look at the following criteria:

(1) What was the relationship of the injured person to the club or school?
(2) What would a reasonable yacht club or school have done in similar circumstances?
(3) What may be the normal accepted activities of a club or school in that context, and in particular exactly what responsibilities are assumed in the organisation of a race or of a sailing course?
(4) What standards do the club or school, or other comparable clubs or schools, maintain?

In recent years it has become clear that the courts are increasingly willing to find that a duty of care exists in particular circumstances. While the basic rule remains that an injured party, to recover compensation, must prove that the injury was the result of some other person's negligence, if a basic case is made out against that person then he must be able to show that one of the defences referred to above in 19.2.4 applies to the case in question.

Where a club is involved in litigation, it can of course only be sued by a person who is a non-member since the members themselves form the club as a body. If however, the injury was due to an officer or agent of the club exceeding his authority, he may be made a defendant but he could not be sued merely because he was a member of the committee of the club. Nowadays an increasing number of clubs are incorporated as a limited company. Where that is the case, then a member will be able to sue the club, which constitutes a separate entity in law.

19.5.2 Clubs and school premises

Most yacht clubs and schools own or lease premises, and are subject to the legal requirement to exercise care to avoid injury to visitors who come on those premises. If a visitor is harmed in some way and can prove negligence on the part of the club he will be entitled to receive damages.

This duty extends to the club house, bar and any other building; also jetties, slipways, piers and even the adjacent seabed if this is relevant. There have, for instance, been a number of claims made recently against proprietors of windsurfing schools who have allegedly failed to warn novice students of rocky outcrops or other potentially dangerous obstructions on an otherwise smooth and sandy bottom. The same would apply to a club that invites yachts to use its moorings or slipway if there is a particular and unusual hazard in the area.

19.5.3 Club organising yacht races

Persons likely to be affected by a yacht club's activities will be the competitors (i.e. owners or skippers of competing yachts), crew members and third parties. As against competitors and crew members the club must adopt a reasonable standard of care, having regard to the age and experience of the competitors, in such things as laying the course, determining the classes of entrants, starting and finishing the race, and making arrangements for safety boat cover and for scrutineering of yachts for safety equipment. Although it is a fundamental principle of the yacht racing rules that competitors enter races at their own risk, this rule cannot be enforced against competitors below the age of 18, nor against competitors who are too young or inexperienced to understand the risks they are facing. So far as the position of safety regulations is concerned, it is for each club to decide whether, in the light of the experience and competence of its race officers, and available manpower, a code of safety regulations and planned inspection should be imposed, or whether competitors should be left to carry their own responsibility for these matters. Whatever the policy the club follows, it is important that it be followed consistently and a reasonable attempt be made to ensure compliance with any safety rules that are imposed.

When faced with a claim for damages, a club or school may seek to rely on one of the defences referred to above in 19.2.4, and in particular the defence of *volenti* in that competitors and crew cannot be heard to complain of injury or damage if they voluntarily accepted the risk of such damage.

Thus a competitor in a race may reasonably be assumed to accept the following risks:

(1) The risk of racing without proper lifesaving equipment
(2) The risk of the perils of the sea including adverse weather.
(3) The risk that other competitors will not be as competent as he himself is.
(4) The risk of racing in an unseaworthy yacht owned by another.
(5) The risk of using an inexperienced crew.
(6) The risk of sailing in an area which he knows may be unsafe.

19.5.4 Other sources of liability

The launching of vessels and their subsequent recovery are activities in which a club or school will from time to time engage and which, if not carried out in a proper manner, could cause damage for which club or school could be liable, if for example it manages the launching in a negligent manner or the physical condition of the slipway is not of a reasonable standard.

19.5.5 Organising escorts, rescue boats etc.

Any escorts or rescue vessels must be managed in a proper manner, although in cases of emergency the standard required at law will not necessarily be as high. Where the operator owns the vessel he stands in the same position as any other boat owner. If some other person's boat is being borrowed, then the club or school will be responsible for the safe navigation of the boat. Where an officer or employee is in charge, even though the vessel remains under the control of her owner, the club or school may very well find itself liable under the law of vicarious liability for the negligence of the owner. It is emphasised therefore that the vessels and personnel appointed for escort/rescue operations should be suitable and capable, and insurance arrangements confirmed.

Where the owner of the vessel 'volunteers' himself and his vessel rather than being requested, the club or school is not likely to be liable for the vessel owner's negligence unless it can be said that he acts as an agent on behalf of the club.

19.5.6 Exclusion and exemption clauses

Such clauses are now all subject to the provisions of the Unfair Contract Terms Act 1977. This Act applies to clauses in a contract or in a notice given to persons generally (e.g. entry forms or sailing instructions). Restrictions are placed on the use of such clauses and notices where they seek to exclude liability for breach of obligations or duties arising:

(1) From things done in the course of a business, or
(2) From the occupation of premises used for the business purposes of the occupier.

In the case of a school or a large yacht club habitually used and visited by non-members, their activities will almost invariably be classified as 'business' and therefore will fall within the scope of the Act.

A competitor or pupil entering into a contract with a club or school should be referred to any exclusion clauses by the document which he signs, especially if not contained in the same document.

In the event of a race entry, the exclusion clauses are of course contained in the rules governing the race, and the competitor will be assumed to have knowledge of such rules.

Where an activity is deemed to be a business, the Act provides that liability for death or personal injury caused by the negligence of the race organisers or school proprietors cannot be excluded by reference to an exclusion clause. In the case of other loss or damage (e.g. damage to a competitor's or pupil's property) liability cannot be excluded unless the clause or notice satisfies the test of reasonableness – matters such as the bargaining strength of the parties, or whether the clause was drawn to their attention, are to be used as guidelines in assessing reasonableness.

In the case of occupiers' liability, the Unfair Contract Terms Act applies when the premises are occupied for the purpose of a business and will have a similar effect.

Rules such as the IYR rules do not appear to offend the Act. The parts in the rules about laying marks, provision of information about tides and weather, choosing courses etc. could give rise to liability where such tasks were performed negligently, but it is not really desirable to seek to exclude such liability since the club or school can always protect itself by insurance. On the other hand, exclusion of liability is usually desirable to protect a club from liability arising from matters beyond its control – such as seaworthiness of vessels and the provision of lifesaving equipment. The IYR rules, as they stand at present, adequately serve this purpose.

19.6 Pollution

19.6.1 Pollution – general
The International Maritime Organization (IMO) Convention of Marine Pollution (MARPOL) has now been extended to cover small pleasure craft for the first time. It is an offence to throw anything overboard within 12 miles of land – even food waste, paper packets or wrappers, let alone plastic, glass or tins. Fines of up to £2000 can be imposed on offenders. Further details are given below.

19.6.2 Sewage pollution
So far as sewage pollution is concerned, only craft 'certified' to carry more than 10 people are affected. In practice this is interpreted to cover craft with 11 or more permanent berths, which are prohibited from discharging sewage less than 12 miles from the nearest land. The effect of this is to require all such vessels to be fitted with holding tanks. The regulations also provide that holding tanks should not be discharged instantaneously, but at a moderate rate with the vessel proceeding at a speed of 4 knots or more. As an alternative, vessels may be fitted with approved sewage treatment plants. Vessels subject to the regulations also require a standard shore connection for sewage discharge. A certificate of compliance must be obtained from the Department of Transport when the vessel is first commissioned, and be renewed at five-year intervals thereafter.

19.6.3 Garbage pollution
Annex V of the IMO convention defines garbage as 'all virtual, domestic and operational waste, excluding fresh fish and parts thereof'. The controls established by Annex V, which covers pleasure craft, are strict, and vary according to the type of garbage and the area in which the yacht is operating, as follows:
(1) The disposal into the sea of all plastics including synthetic ropes and fishing nets, and plastic garbage bags is prohibited absolutely.
(2) Floating dunnage, lining or packing materials may not be disposed of into the sea less than 25 miles from land.
(3) Food waste, and all other garbage including paper products, rags, glass, metals, bottles, crockery and similar refuse may not be disposed of less than 12 miles from land.
(4) Garbage specified under (3) above, if ground to particles less than 25mm across, may be disposed of at sea not less than three miles from the nearest land.

Special rules are in force for the Mediterranean Sea, Black Sea, Baltic Sea, Red Sea and Persian Gulf, prohibiting all disposals, except for food wastes which may be disposed of at least 12 miles from land.

Chapter 20

Multihulls

Contents

20.1 Multihulls – general

20.1.1 History and advantages of multihulls

Multihulls – the term which covers catamarans, trimarans and proas – go back a long way in history. On one of his voyages, Captain Cook noticed their presence in Polynesia long before any interest was shown in them by Europeans or Americans. He was evidently impressed by their speed which is still a feature, but nowhere did he indicate that the Polynesians and Melanesians emigrated long distances across the Pacific with whole villages carried on huge catamarans. They transported not only people but livestock, plants, food and water, and they navigated by systems that have only just been rediscovered by such eminent multihull sailors as Dr David Lewis and Robin Knox-Johnston.

The name catamaran describes a vessel with two hulls of equal size. A proa means one with two unequal-sized hulls which are symmetrical fore-and-aft, and rigged so that it can be sailed in either direction. The term trimaran is of more recent origin and refers to a vessel with three hulls, where the central hull is larger than the two outrigger hulls, or amas.

In the 1660s the English eccentric, Sir William Petty, caused a catamaran to be built which resembled nothing so much as a conventional boat sawn in half lengthways and planked up the middle both sides, with a bridgedeck joining the two halves. A more serious attempt was by the famous American yacht designer Nathaniel Herreshof. In the 1870s he designed, built and raced *Amaryllis* which was 7.6m (25ft) long and an unbelievable 5.5.m (18ft) wide. She was fast but not very stable, because he had omitted to take in a basic fact, well known to any modern Tornado sailor, that fine slim bows do not offer much buoyancy, so unless the crew is very fast on the trapeze getting his weight aft, she can easily trip over her own lee bow. Herreshof found out the hard way.

The advantages that the multihull employed so successfully in the Pacific are still with us today. Their huge internal volume gives vastly superior accommodation compared to a monohull of equivalent length. Or in racing boats a considerable power/weight advantage makes them the fastest sailing boats afloat. You can either have accommodation equivalent to the finest TSDY or speed greater than the largest maxi, but not both. Catamaran hulls are now common in racing powerboats, where their slim hulls combined with the lifting effect of the connecting bridge deck give them a speed advantage over monohulls in smooth water. Twin hulled vessels of various forms are also increasingly found in high speed passenger ferries for short sea crossings.

The designers of multihull sailing craft found another way of counteracting the overturning moment of the rig, other than by fitting a heavy lead keel. The extreme width of the hull prevents her overturning, so that there is a huge saving in weight (see also 10.2.11).

All designers are familiar with the upward spiral that more weight means more sail area, which necessitates a taller mast, which in turn requires heavier rigging and scantlings, and a bigger engine. This spiral is an inevitable movement towards a much bigger, heavier, slower and more expensive boat than was ever envisaged. On the other hand, if at a stroke you can halve the weight of the boat by removing ballast, the spiral goes the other way. Sail area can be smaller, masts shorter, rigging perhaps a little lighter, hull scantlings reduced, and the engine smaller in terms of size, weight, price and fuel consumption.

For example, a well known 9m (30ft) catamaran, fully rigged and engined, only weighs $2\frac{1}{2}$ tons, and is regularly powered with a 9.9 hp four-stroke outboard and pushed along very fast by a working sail area of under 50sq m (500sq ft). Another 11.3m (37ft) cruising cat quite often fits a 17hp diesel, with the 27hp option being the largest recommended, to give a very respectable 8 knots.

20.1.2 Development of British multihulls

The multihull story began in Britain with such pioneers as Bill O'Brien, James Wharram and the Prout brothers. Their beginnings have the air of legend about them and have been rehearsed endlessly – O'Brien's experiments in Ireland with a pig trough in a duck pond; Francis and Roland Prout lashing two kayak canoes together to make a catamaran; the young James Wharram dreaming of reinventing the Polynesian catamaran, capable of cruising long distances yet made out of simple materials with primitive tools by dreamers with only a basic knowledge of carpentry.

From these crude beginnings blossomed the huge international industry that we know today. Unfortunately, or fortunately, our multihull pioneers were almost too enthusiastic about their early efforts. Arthur Piver, in America, perhaps typified this fervour. He had discovered the ideal sailing boat and anyone who was not instantly converted to multihulls in general, and his rather boxy plywood trimarans in particular, was dense or insensitive, or crass – or all three. To a lesser extent Bill O'Brien's first effort, the Saro catamaran, the Prouts' early Shearwater and Wharram's first boat *Tangaroa* were not beautiful to monohull sailors' eyes. Some of them, if loaded down too much, would not sail very well, had the reputation of not pointing, and would not go about without backing the headsail and going astern before setting off on the new tack. Even worse, it was discovered that some of these new creations could capsize, which set multihull development back a long way.

The critics were smug, confident that their prejudices had been confirmed and that these upstart multihulls were nothing to fear and no competition to worry about. But the seed had been sown. Piver started what became a flourishing trimaran industry nurtured by Norman Cross, Jim Brown and Dick Newick, all of whom in the early days mainly produced roomy cruising trimarans.

In England Bill O'Brien developed his designs into the greatly loved Bobcat range, all built in ply, sheathed with GRP, and all hard chine. These were built mostly by Pikes, a caravan builder in Totton, and with pronounced rocker so that they would tack. Thanks to the efforts of ace salesman Tom Lack, ably assisted by his sailor wife Mary, this somewhat tubby marque introduced more people to safe cruising catamarans than any other. The design range developed into the 10 metre Bobcat, where perhaps for the first time the huge internal volume of the cruising cat was properly exploited, with a very large cockpit, four private cabins, and a saloon with seating for twelve.

Bill O'Brien's greatest triumph came when he designed the 9m (30ft) Oceanic, which immediately found a niche in the long-distance cruising market. She was of GRP construction with twin Volvo diesels, giving excellent performance under power and good electrical generating capacity. There was a big doghouse over the bridgedeck saloon giving full standing headroom, an excellent galley, and two good double berth cabins forward. This allowed serious cruising people to live aboard in some comfort, yet without the attendant expense of great overall length and excessive beam. Colin and Rosie Swale sailed to New Zealand and back via Cape Horn in *Anne Liese* and the success of the Oceanic was assured.

James Wharram's early Polynesian cats were not easy on the eye, but they have developed into things of beauty, epitomised by the delightful little Tiki 26 which is a joy to behold and marvellous to sail. (See also Fig. 10(29) in 10.2.11).

If you venture into the upper and less expensive reaches of almost any river creek in the world, you will find, under a polythene tunnel and behind a pile of sheets of ply, a Wharram enthusiast building one of his V-hulled catamarans – with dreams of ocean cruising on a shoestring on his mind. Forget the hours of carpentry, the sacks of nails, the gallons of sticky resin and the yards of glass mat that will be required, it is off to the blue waters with cat and babies and guitar. Many have done it, and Wharram has now constructed his ultimate 18m (60ft) catamaran for world cruising and ecological research.

Meanwhile, back in Canvey Island the Prout brothers were developing a cruising range of catamarans. The early Rangers came in 8.5m (28ft), 9.5m (31ft) and 13.7m (45ft) lengths, moulded in fibreglass. They proved to be sound cruising boats with few pretensions to speed, though some were raced and none more enthusiastically than an Ocean Ranger called *Ocean Highlander*, built for Sandy Munro, which competed in the 1968 OSTAR.

Then, in a stroke of genius, the Prouts invented two features which have remained crucial to their designs ever since. One was the Prout nacelle which has two very useful attributes first, by providing a convenient mount for the centreline engine with a Sonic outdrive retractable leg attached to the aft end, and second, by breaking up the otherwise flat surface under the bridgedeck so that less slamming occurs. The other feature was the idea of mounting the mast right over the cockpit bulkhead, giving a huge foretriangle and a mainsail more like a mizzen. The advantages are

that the main saloon is not cluttered with a mast support, and that the rig (with the advent of headsail roller furling) can be easily and quickly reduced. Also, with the mast stepped at the forward end of the cockpit, all halyards and reefing lines and so on are easily to hand without having to leave the shelter of the cockpit. Over the years the sizes have covered almost every length from 8m (27ft) to 15m (50ft), the most popular being the Quest 31, the Snowgoose 35 and 37 (see Fig. 20(1), and at the top of the range the Quasar 50.

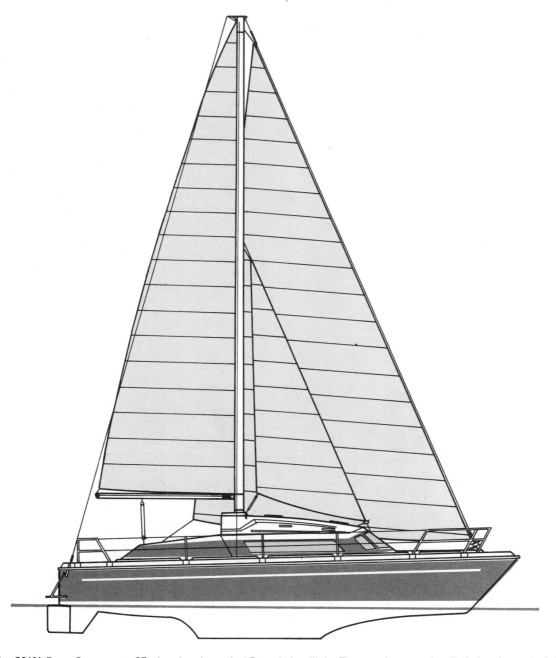

Fig. 20(1) Prout Snowgoose 37, showing the typical Prout 'minsail' rig. The mast is stepped well aft, just forward of the cockpit bulkhead, with halyards ready to hand. The large genoa is roller furling. The boat has shallow draught, with low aspect ratio keels and rudders.

These three designs typify the early development of British multihulls though, as we shall see. many other companies and individuals made important contributions to the development of these craft.

A Scotsman named Roderick Macalpine-Downie, who had a charming if reserved approach to life and no formal training in naval architecture, believed that if a boat was beautiful and looked right, she probably was right. Like most other designers he started with a small dinghy, which was reflected in his later work. With Reg White of Sail Craft, he calculated that a semi-circular bottom gave the least wetted area, and to give the lie to the critics who decried the catamaran's windward ability he fitted twin leeboards, mounted inside the hulls in boxes. Starting with the 9m (30ft) Iroquois he went on to give us the 9.75m (32ft) Comanche, the 10.7m (35ft) Cherokee, the 12.8m (42ft) Apache and the 14m (46ft) Navajho. These were all similar in shape and concept, though the higher and wider Cherokee proved to be more designed for the American market.

These designs are elegant and practical, and in the cases of the Iroquois and Apache quite fast — cruiser racers rather than racer cruisers. With their mast set centrally and with a large foredeck area often filled with webbing trampolines, they gave us the very best of both worlds in the 1970s. Regrettably Rod died at a very young age and Reg White, an Olympic gold medallist in one of his own Tornado catamarans, decided to concentrate on racing boats. The moulds, suitably modified became different models under new names from other manufacturers.

20.2 Accommodation

20.2.1 Catamaran layouts

Perhaps the second most popular reason for buying a multihull, next to reduction of motion sickness, is the great internal volume offered by all types. The average catamaran will have at least three bunks situated in the ends of the hulls. In the smaller sizes, Striders and Tikis for instance, these bulks are singles but as length increases they become progressively wider so that at 13.7m (45ft) plus they can be 'Queen sized' doubles. The fourth corner is often taken up by the heads/shower compartment as in the Prout range, see Fig 20(2). It will be noticed that on most catamarans the saloon is rarely used for sleeping, although often there is the facility of dropping the table down to form a double bunk. To many people a big advantage of a cat is no longer having to sleep on the dining room table.

With this accommodation layout a catamaran gives great privacy, even in the smallest sizes. There is, however, still some argument among designers as to whether berths are better placed on the bridgedeck (as in Fig. 20(3) for the Solaris 42 for example) or in the hulls (as in the Prout range). With bunks on the bridgedeck access can be something of a problem.

Typically, midships in one hull will be the navigation areas with full sized chart table and repeater instruments, and midships in the other hull will be a galley which would not shame a small apartment, with plenty of room for food, stowage, refrigerator, work tops and sinks. The

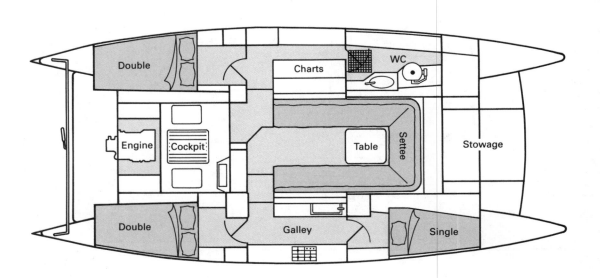

Fig. 20(2) Prout Snowgoose standard accommodation layout. There is a double bunk aft in each hull, and a single berth starboard side forward. The settee at the forward end of the saloon converts into a double bunk. The heads compartment is port side, forward. The galley and chart table are amidships in the starboard and port hulls respectively.

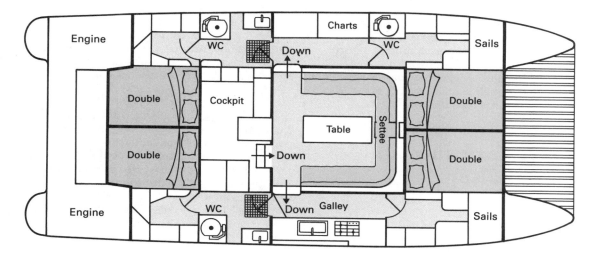

Fig. 20(3) A different approach to catamaran layout, with berths on the bridgedeck in the Solaris 42.

main drawback is that often the cook is blocking the way to one bunk and the navigator is obstructing access to the heads.

Several designers have gone for the bridgedeck galley option which is fine if the cook does not mind operating under the scrutiny of passengers and crew. This arrangement is very convenient when on passage with a short-handed crew, as communication with the cockpit is much easier.

20.2.2 Trimaran layouts

In boats under 9m (30ft) the accommodation is virtually as for a monohull with the usual fo'c'sle berth, heads compartment, saloon with dinette/double berth, galley opposite the chart table, companionway up to cockpit, and possibly an aft cabin. In larger boats, berths are found in the

wings, connecting the main hull to the amas or outriggers. This is a little like sleeping on a windowsill, with little overhead space to rotate or to engage in any other activity. The amas themselves will probably only be used for light stowage – fenders, warps, sails, deflated inflatables etc. It is really only in the bigger trimarans with lengths of 12m (40ft) or more that accommodation really comes into its own; each ama is used as a corridor with the wing bunks reached from there and the bow providing an ensuite heads, so that each ama is a private ensuite double cabin, as in Fig. 20(4). In this size there will almost certainly be a grand cabin aft in the main hull and another large double right forward, leaving the centre part of the main hull for the saloon, galley and chart table, and maybe an inside steering position.

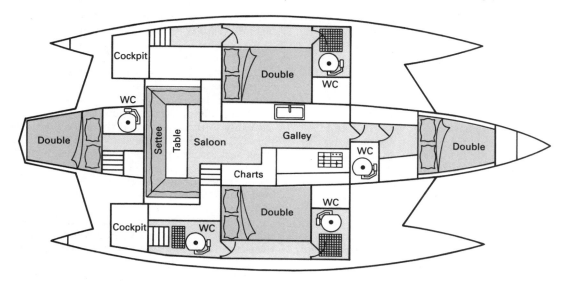

Fig. 20(4) In larger trimarans it is common to find double bunks in the wings, reached from the amas, and double bunks forward and aft in the main hull.

These larger trimarans make ideal charter boats, with the bigger ones providing guest accommodation for eight as well as a private suite for the crew. The main problem is that there is almost too much room, and where there is space something will be found to fill it. When going racing even the most weight-conscious skipper will find it easy to fill a large shooting brake with surplus gear that has found its way aboard.

20.3 Performance and handling

20.3.1 Performance
The relative speed advantage of multihulls over monohulls of comparable size has already been noted, and high speed is a feature that attracts many people to multihulls. When it comes to racing most organisers recognise this and give them separate classes.

For sheer speed around the buoys, or even Transatlantic or Transpacific, no one can beat the big multihulls. The French dominate this area, as these monsters appeal to the French craving for style, speed and macho image, and this has attracted huge television, radio and newspaper coverage which in turn has produced extensive sponsorship money. Thus large fleets of exciting multihulls take part in regattas all round the coast of France, while from St Malo and La Rochelle they speed across the ocean to Martinique on the Route du Rhum, or to Newport, Rhode Island, in the singlehanded and doublehanded Transatlantic races, as well as the Dakar and Round Britain.

Recent outstanding performances have included Laurent Bourgnon's 538 miles in 24 hours during his 1994 single-handed west-east Atlantic crossing in *Primagaz*, and (at a second attempt) the 75 day circumnavigation by *ENZA New Zealand*. *ENZA* was originally designed by Nigel Irens with a length of 22m (72ft) and built in Canada as long ago as 1982, one of the first high-tech composite yachts. She was later modified and lengthened to 28m (92ft) to designs by David Alan-Williams, who was one of the crew, jointly skippered by Peter Blake and Robin Knox-Johnston.

In Britain there has been little of the media coverage necessary for substantial sponsorship, and apart from the British input to *ENZA* little in the way of serious multihull sailing.

20.3.2 Micro-multihulls
The micro-multihull world however is still alive and well, having been started in England by Richard Wood and his Strider range and then picked up by the Multihull Offshore Cruising and Racing Association (MOCRA). It organises a series of highly competitive races for young people who do not have to spend too much on their sport. A Strider can be raced competitively for an outlay no greater than £15,000. The beauty of these boats is that by definition they must be transportable by trailer, which in itself limits size, weight and thus expense. With Dragonflys coming over from Denmark and a respectable number of the elegant little Firebirds, this class looks all set for success. For trailer multihulls see also 20.4.5.

20.3.3 Cruiser/racers
Cruising boats still do a limited amount of racing, mainly in local regattas, and probably the most popular event is the annual Round the Island Race where the multihull classes are sent off first to get them out of the way. They used to start last and have the fun of sailing through the monohull fleet to compete on unequal terms with the larger monohulls. This was considered vulgar showing off by the lead swingers, and hence the change. But it did show that a flat-out racing multihull was a match for anything, and even the cruising boats would show a couple of transoms to monohulls that were 3m (10ft) longer.

There was once a little competition between a 9m (30ft) Iroquois cruiser/racer and a Class 3 9.75m (32ft) monohull, both with highly competent crews. On the windward leg the monohull pointed much higher and did many fewer tacks, but the catamaran footed faster. At the windward mark the monohull rounded first by about a minute and up went the spinnakers on both boats. The catamaran took off at 15 knots, surfing past the monohull and leaving her standing. Whereas one boat was three-quarters above the water and a quarter below and weighed only $2\frac{1}{2}$ tons, the other was three-quarters below the water and only a quarter above and weighed six tons.

Most cruising sailors are not interested in achieving 500 miles a day across an ocean or planing up-Channel at 25 knots. The question most asked is how much faster will the cruising multihull go, and realistically this only amounts to about a two-knot difference. However, the difference between six knots and eight knots is the equivalent of a passage taking eight hours instead of ten, so the difference becomes quite significant. Even if the speed were the same the comfort of the ride and particularly the absence of heeling sells the boat convincingly to many yachtsmen – and certainly to their families. If there are children on board the large flat bridgedeck is an ideal play area, and the cockpit is normally big enough to be flooded as a paddling pool.

The other invaluable feature is beach ability, and multihulls often dry out deliberately. If the tide is suitable the cat will sit right on the beach, so that toddlers can slide down the transom to play, while their elders can stop worrying about whether the anchor will drag and whether, when the tide returns, the boat will be foul of a neighbour. The only problem is the heads.

With a shallow draught exploration of the upper reaches of rivers and creeks is a possibility.

It is not necessary to wait outside the entrance for the tide to rise so high over the bar – simply jump over the bow with a line and walk in, towing your cruising multihull.

20.3.4 The capsize bogey

On the debit side there are horror stories about capsizing, and indeed dinghy cats often fly their windward hulls. Cruising cats prefer to keep their hulls in the water. For one thing a lee hull digging deeply is inefficient, causing a lot of lee helm, while an inverted catamaran is a devil to right. Some older cats carry a masthead float which was very effective in preventing total inversion, but the practice has been largely discontinued. With sophisticated computer aided design it is now believed that increasing beam to something like half the overall length will create enough stability. Having said that, in the ultimate storm a lead keel is a comforting thing to have.

The capsize bogey was very real in the early days, when the sportier catamarans were being raced to the limit (with relatively narrow beam by today's standards) and were crewed by men who were still learning. Prevention is the best cure, and experience has shown that reducing sail early is one precaution and the other is to keep the boat sailing fast and free. The situation to avoid is

arriving at the top of a large wave in gale force conditions head to wind and stalled. The wind will push the boat sideways into the trough, where she will gently tip over.

For most classes of catamaran a table is available that indicates how much sail can safely be carried in different wind speeds. It is important to establish whether the wind speeds quoted are for the true or apparent wind. Since catamarans sail so fast there can be a significant difference (see 11.5.8). Note also that the figures apply to smooth water. In a beam or confused sea the boat must be sailed more carefully and with less sail. In a strong wind it is safer to sail (where so fitted) with the leeward board raised and the windward one down. Remember to change them round when tacking.

Certain basic rules should be remembered. Reef early, and never let the windward hull lift. In gusts, if capsizing seems a possibility, when close hauled or reaching, luff up to spill wind from the sails; when broad reaching, bear away to flatten the boat down. Do not sail with sheets cleated in strong winds.

At over a certain wind speed the boat may be reduced to storm jib only. This will not give much progress to windward in a seaway, for which it is helpful to run the leeward engine at modest rpm.

A theoretical assessment of the safe wind speed for different sail areas can be made from formulae for static and dynamic stability, as explained below. Fig. 20(5) shows the forces acting on a catamaran under sail, around a point (P) of rotation taken as the foot of the leeward hull. If a is half the distance between the centrelines of the hulls, and b is the height of the centre of effort of the sail plan above P, the boat will capsize if:

Wind pressure × b is greater than Displacement × a

a can be measured, or found from the boat's drawings, while b can be calculated geometrically or may be given by the builder – remembering that it varies with the amount of sail actually set. Wind pressure (F) on the sails in lb/sq ft can be taken as:

$0.0051 \times$ Wind Speed^2
(Where wind speed is in knots)

From the above, at the moment when the boat is about to capsize:

$0.0051 \times$ Wind Speed$^2 \times$ Sail Area × b
$=$ Displacement × a

From this can be expressed the formula:

$$\text{Wind Speed (knots)} = 14 \times \sqrt{\frac{\text{Displacement} \times a}{\text{Sail Area} \times b}}$$

(Displacement in pounds, sail area in square feet and dimensions a and b in feet).

The formula above refers to what is termed 'static stability'. Because for any wind force there are gusts which often greatly exceed the average

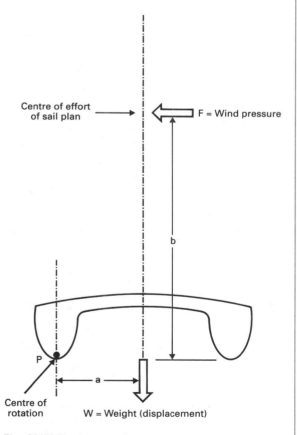

Fig. 20(5) The forces acting on a catamaran under sail. Taking moments about the bottom of the leeward hull (P), for the boat to capsize F × b must be greater than W × a.

Centre of effort of sail plan → F = Wind pressure

b

P

a

Centre of rotation   W = Weight (displacement)

wind speed it has become customary to adopt a safety factor of 60 per cent in calculating 'dynamic stability' of practical sailing. Thus:

$$\text{Dynamic stability} = 0.6 \times \text{Static stability, or}$$

$$= 8.4 \times \sqrt{\frac{\text{Displacement} \times a}{\text{Sail Area} \times b}}$$

This can be used for working out in advance, for a known displacement, in what wind speeds different combinations of sail can be carried.

Another type of capsize that must be recognised is the classic lee bow trip, when the boat is being driven fast down wind and the lee hull digs into a sea, tripping the boat and causing a capsize. Hobie Cats often do it, but in a cruising boat it is not amusing. Some way must be found to keep the bows up and the stern down. The Ellison brothers found it necessary to flood the stern compartment on the Iroquois when racing round Britain. Others have found that trailing something like a heavy warp or a parachute drogue does the trick. But quite often the easiest thing to do is to heave to if you are not racing, although it is amazing how rarely this old fashioned remedy is used. Most multihulls are well enough balanced to lie quite comfortably under a backed spitfire jib and triple reefed main. If things get worse most of these boats will lie a-hull. The noise is the most frightening thing, with breakers coming normally from just forward of the beam and, as the windward hull lifts, crashing on to the windward side of the lee hull. This is very trying for the nerves of the crew, but the boats themselves are designed to stand it – as described in 20.4.4.

20.3.5 Handling

A multihull is a lightweight yacht, floating on top of the water rather than in it. In practice this means that she will never point as high as a monohull and should not be asked to do so. Bear away and the speed will rise, the weight will be more evenly distributed between the hulls, and the speedometer will show the result. Off the wind it is often preferable to tack down wind when the genoa is blanketed by the main and it is either not possible to run 'wing and wing' or for some reason to hoist a cruising chute. Safety lies in keeping the boat moving fast and easily. The boat will tell you by her speed and general ease of motion whether she is giving her best possible performance for the prevailing conditions. It is worthwhile reducing speed early so that the boat is not too hard pressed; the speed will not be reduced, it may even increase.

Going about or picking up a mooring needs careful judgement because the boat will stop dead in the water surprisingly quickly, and gather sternway. Reversing the helm will bring the bow round but the technique is undoubtedly to shoot round, cutting the headsail a second or two after it backwinds to give the bow a final push. In this way, when picking up a mooring under sail, you can get much closer to it before rounding up. This will certainly cause panic and consternation on the foredeck if your crew is used to sailing monohulls. However, having secured the mooring he will realise that the cat, being light, is not so difficult to hold. Having a lot of windage a multihull stops quickly and is more likely to be affected by the wind direction than by the tidal stream. This can be embarrassing in a tight anchorage, with the multihulls lying to the wind and the monohulls to the tide. However, as the multihull can often squeeze into some shallow corner unavailable to the deep keelers it is not too often a problem.

When a catamaran is fitted with centreboards these can be partly lowered where it is desirable that the boat lies to the tide. But if the boat is going to take the ground be sure that the boards (and rudders) are fully raised. This is very important in boats where the centreboard casings are angled out of the vertical, since in these circumstances taking the ground with the boards lowered places considerable strains on the cases and fittings.

The excessive beam of a multihull can present difficulties, particularly for yachtsmen who want to use the French canal system where the maximum beam is 5m or sometimes less. With a modern catamaran this virtually restricts buyers to a boat of about 9.75m (32ft). When using conventional marinas where you are charged on beam it is expensive, and you find yourself moored between much longer monohulls. But it is the same beam which provides stability, internal volume and privacy. The beam also makes it possible to tack down the spinnaker to the bows without a pole. Set flying in this way the sail can more easily be handled, without all the attendant problems and dangers of a pole and its rigging.

In gale force conditions, it is normally possible to continue under reduced rig – snugging down to storm jib or rolled up genoa balanced by a suitably reefed main. Roller reefing headsails have made this job much easier, particularly on the Prouts where the headsail area is about twice as big as the main. Sporting catamarans are following the racers' trend of fully battened mainsails dropping into lazyjacks. If the backstays do not get in the way a large roach will give an extra bit of sail area.

Various types of mainsail reefing have been tried – in mast, behind mast, into or on top of boom, as well as round boom and slab. For racing the general consensus seems to favour the accepted slab method, although it takes more time and effort; the better set of sail makes it preferred. For the short-handed, many sailors like the behind the mast roller furlers on the premise that it is much easier to sort out any problem. There have been several instances of jams inside masts which are almost impossible to disentangle in a gale at sea. Some other boom arrangements are too new to be able to judge their merits. Certainly they keep the rig and weight lower, but that is also true of slab reefing. Maybe the KISS motto (Keep It Simple Stupid!) is the one to follow.

20.4 Multihull developments

20.4.1 Internal improvements

In the past 25 years multihulls have developed dramatically. Previously the interiors were 'bachelor pads', lino floored, with bare GRP deckheads, thin mattresses and cushions, and narrow bunks. This has all changed and we are now seeing yachts, even small ones, with interiors that are professionally designed, artistically attractive and ergonomically correct.

This inevitably means more weight, with the addition of a refrigerator and deep freeze, more battery capacity to feed the extra electronics, a bigger generator, Satnav, weatherfax and computer aided yacht management. Air conditioning is not yet obligatory in Britain, but abroad it is creeping into even small yachts. Happily we still have the Wharram owners to keep us in perspective. Sextants still have a place, as do Walker logs: an ordinary grid compass backed up by a handbearer will still take them around the world.

20.4.2 Changing shapes

Wharrams are mostly built out of sheathed marine ply, and are V-sectioned to give useful resistance to leeway: this results in narrow footroom compared to wide deckspace. The slatted bridgedeck allows water to flow through and makes them ideal for the tropics where a large plastic sheet over the boom converts the space into a marine patio – open to the breezes but shady.

The Prouts opted for a canoe stern which gives a very quiet wake but also made them a shade prone to hobby horsing until they introduced bow bulbs, which dampen down the motion considerably. Prouts, in common with almost all other designers, have gone for a stub keel which is small enough to make them shoal draught but deep enough to grip the water without the use of centreboards. They have also incorporated 'planning extensions' which on the Snowgoose Elite provide extra beam in the stern cabins to give much wider berths.

The classic 7.9m (26ft) design Heavenly Twins from Pat Patterson has developed out of all recognition. From being a splendid little centre cockpit family cruiser, with an outboard mounted on the centreline and two tiny double cabins aft (no ocean greyhound, but very seaworthy), she is now 8.25m (27ft) long with twin diesels, higher freeboard, and a stoop-through corridor under the side deck so that one of the aft doubles can be reached without going on deck. She is inevitably heavier and more expensive than her predecessor, but much better built.

20.4.3 The French connection

With the tremendous interest stirred up by the media about high performance multihulls in France, designers and builders turned to cruising boats, headed by Benetau who, however, after one effort with the Blue II, pulled out of the race due to an osmosis problem. Fountaine Pajot now leads the way with a cruising range that has a distinctive profile. They have vertical slim bows, heavily cambered deck and an ultra-modern plastic finish internally. Right for their size and appealing to the *avant-garde*, they sail very well and the largest models make wonderful charter boats. The Marquises has accommodation for eight charter passengers plus two crew, all with their own ensuite double cabins in a 16m (53ft) boat.

The Caribbean is full of French catamarans and other French yachts as it is very tax efficient to buy a charter boat, place her in a French Caribbean Island and have the whole purchase price and any operating loss all tax deductible. This gives the French boatbuilding industry a terrific boost, help that, sadly, is unavailable to British manufacturers.

Two other French multihulls are worth mentioning. The Jeantot Privilege is the Rolls-Royce of the large cruising catamarans, designed for top quality long distance cruising in considerable comfort – or inevitably for charter. They are built in two sizes, 14.6m (48ft) and 11.9m (39ft), and both show the input of Philippe Jeantot who is known as a tough, uncompromising sailor. His boats reflect this, for they sail well, are traditionally elegant, and are well built out of first class materials.

The Catana Company builds high performance cruising boats more on the lines of the latter day Iroquois. Designed by Australian Lock Crowther, they have covered long distances at high speed. With not too many compromises they are rather masculine in orientation, practical rather than luxurious.

20.4.4 Construction

In bad weather crucial parts of a multihull get thoroughly tested. These are the joins where the crossbeams meet the amas on trimarans, together with those where the beams cross the main hull. These joints are critical and particularly in racing boats they have to be strengthened with the most sophisticated carbon fibre strapping. Similarly, on catamarans the joint between the hull and the bridgedeck requires careful inspection. The impact strains at these points are enormous.

The other area where stress is evident is at the points where the bulkheads are attached to the hulls and deckhead. So often manufacturers get these joints wrong. If the joint is too soft and the bulkhead is a sloppy fit all round, then in storm conditions the bulkheads will pop their joints. On many catamarans a good push on the transverse bulkheads, which are not normally load carrying, will produce longitudinal movement. If on the other hand the bulkhead is a load carrier under the mast, it is time for drastic action. Hard joints between hull and bulkhead can cause vertical hair cracks at that point, where impact from waves cause the hull sides to flex except where prevented by the bulkhead.

On most catamarans (except the Prouts) the mast is supported by a massive steel A-frame which stretches across the bridgedeck to spread the load to the hulls. In the middle the mast support holds up the deck, on top of which is the mast tabernacle. At each end of the A-frame uprights extend vertically through the deck, forming chain plates for the inner shrouds. The exceptions to this system are the Prouts, who mount their masts right over the cockpit bulkhead, and the Heavenly Twins whose centre cockpit arrangement gives the same effect.

All the early multihulls in the USA and Europe were constructed in marine plywood, either forced into the conventional shape or, more often, if they were designed to be amateur built, V-shaped like the Wharrams or hard chined like the Pivers or early O'Briens. Generally speaking they were set up on wooden frames upside down on a strong back, which provided a light but reasonably strong structure. The boats were fairly easy to build though too many people were seduced into taking on much too large a model for their strength and time available.

In the early days paint was all that protected the ply from water, and the integrity of the hull depended very much on the quality of the ply. Top quality Bruynzeel, though heavy, seems to last for ever but some of the other, cheaper imports should never have been given the BS1088 grading. It soon became general practice to sheathe the ply with GRP. If economy was the prime factor, chopped strand mat was used (see 10.4.3), or otherwise woven cloth. The Cascover system came into its own, and even now it is hard to find a stronger and easier way to build than with Glasply. Bill O'Brien has developed this a stage further in his recent Oceanics. Only the hull moulds remain, so the bridgedeck and all the upperworks must be in wood or sandwich, and he decided that the ideal core for the sandwich is plywood. This certainly makes an extremely strong material, which O'Brien demonstrates by hitting a panel of it with a sledgehammer, being careful to avoid the rebound.

Sandwich construction, though not invented by Derek Kelsall, has been brilliantly developed by him. He devised the system of GRP panels using a glass table. He casts huge flat panels of GRP/foam/GRP sandwich on tables 9m (30ft) long and 1.5m (5ft) wide, and then uses these panels exactly like plywood sheets. He also devised clever curved sections to give soft chine and keel angles. Kelsall and his men had spent thousands of hours building conventional foam sandwich boats on male slatted moulds, with all the attendant work of sanding and filling. With his new system the sanding and filling is reduced to a minimum, only being necessary where the panels join.

Sail Craft used balsa sandwich in its range of catamarans, not normally in the hulls but extensively in the bridgedeck and cabin top. Sandwich construction can be a very satisfactory and quick form of construction, providing the boat is large enough to have skins of sufficient strength and thickness to resist impact damage.

Naturally, as with monohullls, the most common constructional material is still GRP. With all its faults it remains the most trouble-free material, needing relatively little maintenance and infrequent painting. With modern resins osmosis seems to be increasingly rare, and manufacturers are even offering guarantees.

The racing fraternity is continually pushing back the boundaries in the search for lighter, stronger and faster boats, and the latest advanced material is a form of wood epoxy construction – layers of epoxy-saturated cedar (or similar lightweight wood) vacuumed together and suitably strengthened at stress points with Kevlar. This is incredibly expensive, and only for sponsored racing boats. Probably the Gougeon brothers' WEST system (see 10.4.9) is the one most commonly used internationally, though there are similar systems being used in Europe.

As multihulls often dry out it is essential that the rudders are either integral with the hull (as on the Prouts with their canoe hulls and streamlined shapes), or transom-hung with swinging or retractable blades (such as the Hirondelle, Catalac 9m or Iroquois). Alternatively they should be normal spade rudders where there are stub keels giving the rudders sufficient clearance to be well short of the ground when dried out.

Problems can arise with noise and vibration caused by ill-fitting blades of wood or galvanised steel that rattle around in the rudder stocks. Some boats, like the Iroquois, have balanced blades which have to be lowered to a certain point to give neutral helm. If they are lowered too far or not far enough the helm becomes too heavy to handle. In the retracted position the blades can be vulnerable to passing craft. Where possible the tiller bar should be taken off the tillers and the blades lifted and left facing inwards to each other. The Hirondelle and Telstar have a good arrangement whereby the dagger board blades retract vertically with adjustable rake.

For the most part centreboards are things of the past, deemed unnecessary for the sailor and expensive in space and production costs for the builder. However, if performance is important the extra grip that centreboards or daggerboards provide is certainly most valuable. Two new 9m (30ft) catamarans by Richard Woods illustrate this perfectly. The Sagitta is a sporting boat with taller rig and daggerboards, while the Symphony, using the same hull moulds, has low aspect ratio keels and a cruising rig.

20.4.5 Trailer multihulls

As marina charges became more and more excessive in line with the increasing value of property, the attraction of a boat that you can tow home each weekend became apparent. Tony Smith started the trend when he worked at Sandwich, making the Telstar 26. This was a small trimaran with fairly basic accommodation for a conventional family of four. A fo'c'sle berth doubled as a head, with a double berth to port in the saloon and a single quarter berth to starboard. The boat had a deep cockpit right aft and was tiller steered. She sailed very well, helped by a deep quadrant centreboard, on top of which the saloon table was mounted. Normally outboard powered, she provided – and continues to provide since there are many still afloat – cheap, quick and not too uncomfortable sailing for a young couple. The clever part was the folding geometry which enabled the amas to hinge down under the main hull on immensely strong hinges, so that the boat can easily be trailed behind a two-litre car. Unfortunately Tony Smith emigrated to the USA where some disaffected workers burnt the moulds.

The void left by the demise of Telstar has been elegantly, if expensively, filled by the F27, designed by Ian Farrier, built by Corsair Marine in the USA and imported into Britain by gold medal Olympic sailor Rodney Pattison. The F27 is an extremely sophisticated development of the Telstar with a clever cantilever system of raising and lowering the folding amas, which can easily be done singlehanded. So she combines ingenious design with very fast performance in the water. From the accommodation point of view she scores in having a neat little aft cabin for that essential requirement for family sailing – privacy.

For speed and elegance it would be difficult to beat the Quorning designed Dragonfly. This tiny jewel of a boat sails like a fast dinghy yet has quite adequate accommodation – and if you want to stand up you can always go on deck. This is a boat which boys of all ages itch to get their hands on. The original design was a pain to disassemble, taking a lot of time and causing loss of knuckle because the amas had to be totally disconnected and stowed upside down on the trailer under the main hull, but the latest version has solved most of these problems, making it into a true weekender.

All the mirco-multihulls will by definition dismantle, and they are suitable for far more than round-the-buoys racing; witness Richard and Lilian Woods and Stuart Fisher, who cruised three Striders to Russia in 1990, proving that with grit and determination quite long cruises can be undertaken at a unit cost approximating to the price of a new Kevlar mainsail for a Banshee.

In 1992 designer David Alan-Williams produced a very neat trailer sailer, provisionally titled Project 8. This has a unique James Labouchere folding system, and a folded width of only 2.3m (7ft 7in). The low profile road trailer carries the yacht with the mast on top. After launching (still folded) the boat can be motored to a mooring. Then one line is taken to a winch, and this extends the hulls while at the same time raising the mast. A full width trampoline tightens up as the hulls move apart. Connect the boom, which has the mainsail stowed on it, to the gooseneck, hank on and raise the jib, and away you go. Recovery is quite simple. The prototype has undergone sailing trials and achieved speeds of more than 22 knots.

The beauty of all these trailer sailers is not only the added security and cost saving of having your boat parked in the garden, but also the facility of being able to avoid long and tedious passages, and to be able to arrive at a distant cruising ground without wasting precious holiday time. Moreover, you never have to worry about getting home at the end of the holiday if the weather is bad.

20.4.6 Engines

Trimarans are almost always powered by a single engine. They either have an outboard, operating on a sliding bracket as on the Telstar, or else a more conventional petrol or diesel engine under the cockpit driving through normal shafting.

On sailing catamarans up to 9m (30ft) outboards are still favoured, the most popular being the remarkably quiet Yamaha 9.9hp four-stroke. It gives good torque at quite low rpm and can push even a 30-footer along at an acceptable six knots without providing unacceptable drag when not required. The bigger sizes of boat (where weight is less critical) have twin-engined installations, often mounted right aft in separate little engine rooms as in the Catalac and Oceanic classes, separated from the accommodation by a watertight bulkhead and driving a conventional shaft. If the buoyancy aft is sufficient, as in the Solaris Sunstream, the engines are mounted quite far aft, under the double berths and driving through outdrives. This installation is less noisy than might be imagined.

In larger boats of about 15m (50ft) in length, like the Prout Quasar, the engines are moved right forward, somewhat amidships in each hull – providing a step down as you turn right or left into the accommodation. This arrangement is better for the sleeping cabins but a little less attractive with respect to noise and exhaust fumes in the saloon. The Quasar is the only Prout design that has a twin-engined installation. The rest have a centrally mounted single engine in a compartment at the after end of the cockpit, operating through a Sonic outdrive leg which can be locked up out of the water to avoid drag under sail.

The other option is to have a cockpit-mounted engine, as on the Catfisher 28, operating two hydraulic motors, one in each hull. This works well, but with a big power loss. For instance, the Catfisher 28, which resembles a small Scottish fishing boat, needs a 42hp Mercedes engine to give her 7–8 knots.

20.4.7 Other applications

Quite distinct from the role of multihulls as boats for cruising or racing under sail, the catamaran in particular has lent itself to many other applications. Multihulls make very stable platforms on which new rigs have been developed including foils, wing sails, air propellers driving water screws and modern dipping lugsails. Jacques Cousteau even used a 32m catamaran for experiments with a Flettner rotor.

Mention has already been made of catamarans for powerboat racing. Basically such craft consist of a wing between two hulls, forming a 'tunnel'. The wing provides lift in proportion to its size and the speed of the boat, thereby reducing the amount that the hulls are immersed – to the extent that the drive units are virtually all that is in the water at speed. This original type of racing catamaran is credited to Angelo and Renato Molinari, father and son, with the wing extending roughly the length of the hulls. Later the chord of the wing was shortened to bring its leading edge further aft, and move the centre of lift to a point which reduced the likelihood of the bows rising to flip the boat. This formed what became known as the 'picklefork' configuration, when looked at in plan view.

While catamarans initially made their impact on the racing scene in the smaller classes where they soon became dominant in smooth water, it took some while for the same thing to happen in offshore racing. But in 1977 *Yellowdrama III*, designed by James Beard and built by Cougar Marine, won the Cowes/Torquay/Cowes race at an average speed of 65 knots and became the world's first class I catamaran to get the better of the long, sleek monohulls that had previously prevailed. By the time of the 1991 Cowes/Torquay race 30 of the 35 entries were catamarans.

Encouraged by the success of *Yellowdrama III*, Cougar Marine launched a high speed cruiser in 1979. The Cougar Cat 900 was a weekender with fairly basic accommodation and a large cockpit, and was intended for warmer latitudes. She had a length of 9.1m (30ft) and an overall beam of 2.97m (9ft 9in). The tunnel width was only 0.6m (2ft) between the two sponsons, each of which had six spray rails, four outboard and two inboard. Two 330hp petrol outdrives gave a speed of 45 knots.

It must be said, however, that multihulls have as yet made little impact on the motor cruiser scene. This could be because two (or three) hulls are inevitably more expensive to build than one, and in a power craft this cost is not offset by a smaller rig or the elimination of a ballast keel. While athwartships, stability is excellent, the substantial topweight of accommodation at deck level can produce an unpleasant pitching moment in some multihulls, accompanied by the slamming of water in the tunnel under the bridgedeck.

In 1987 Prout, the successful builder of sailing catamarans, produced its Panther 44 Royale, a fairly isolated example of a motor cruiser in catamaran form. The two hulls are asymmetric, with a vertically sided tunnel which has a central nacelle similar to the Prout sailing cats. Each hull has a 320hp turbocharged diesel, giving a top speed of 24 knots.

More recently the Australian firm of Kevlacat has been importing a range of power catamarans into Britain. These consist of 20 models in sizes from 3.3m (11ft) to 12.6m (41ft) in length.

If powered catamarans have made little progress as pleasure craft, this is far from true so far as commercial applications are concerned. Their large and stable area of deck suits them for many roles such as diving, fishing and survey work, and of course for passenger carrying.

Catamaran ferries are becoming increasingly common. For example, holidaymakers and yachtsmen in the Solent will be familiar with the 30m cats on the Ryde/Portsmouth route. One of these made the 13,000 mile voyage from her builders in Tasmania under her own power. Fitted with extra fuel tanks to give a 3000 mile range, she averaged 20 knots on passage. More recently catamarans have replaced hydrofoils on the Red Funnel route from Southampton to Cowes. On the Thames three 25m (82ft) catamarans are included in the RiverBus service through the capital. Powered by waterjets, and with small beam/length ratios, for their slim hulls, they create very little wash at their cruising speed of 23 knots. Elsewhere, large and fast catamarans have been introduced on many short sea routes all around the world.

20.5 The present multihull scene

The greatest development over the past few years has been the opening of Multihull centres. The largest of these was Multihull World at Port Solent, near Portsmouth. Apart from selling a wide range of British and French multihulls, activities included a multihull sea school, brokerage and chartering. Unfortunately this important focal point of multihull activity went into liquidation in October 1992.

Pat and Pip Patterson have been established for years at Millbrook near Plymouth, where Pat builds his own designs to order. Best known is the delightful Heavenly Twins, which has two adequate double cabins aft, a centre cockpit (often completely covered in with a pram hood), a small but very comfortable saloon, a galley and heads. He built a few Ocean Twins which were virtually big sisters with a length of 10m (33ft), and sailed one of them round the world. As a serious blue water sailor he knows what is essential in an ocean cruising yacht and what is not. He has now added to the range the Summer Twins, at 7.6m (25ft), which seems expensive at around £40,000. But she is so wide and cleverly designed inside that you feel you are in a bigger boat. This Multihull Centre is a splendid place for multihulls – a quiet creek with huge facilities for them to dry out, together with haul-out facilities and a modern building shed.

Round the corner live Richard and Lilian Wood. Until recently the Palamos factory built the whole range of Wood's boats. Opening out into Plymouth Sound it is perhaps the more homely end of the multihull scene.

For many years the old wartime yard known as Willments at Southampton has been home to Bill O'Brien and more recently Solaris Catamarans. As well as being a designer, O'Brien is no mean hand with chisel and plane, but now devotes his time to the drawing board. His factory was taken over by Malcolm and Glenda Taylor, proprietors of Solaris. Their business was originally based on the famous Compton Solaris 42, a venerable and greatly loved design with four identical double cabins, a huge saloon, twin 42hp Mercedes engines and a modest rig. This boat became home to many couples in comfortable circumstances who wanted a motor sailer as a floating apartment. Since then Solaris has expanded into a full range of modern designs, of which the Sunbeam and the Sunstar are the latest. The Sunstar 32, introduced in 1991, is of French extraction and looks it. The vertical bow, curved sloping transoms with steps, and the semi-circular trampoline are all features of the most modern Continental tradition. The Sunbeam, at 7.3m (24ft), is a Kelsall design, typically English with two double berths right aft like a cross between a Hirondelle and an 8m Catalac. She sails very well and in common with every boat turned out by Solaris is beautifully built and immaculately finished. Solaris is, in a word, the Saville Row of multihull manufacturers. Malcolm Taylor is a trained woodwork instructor and it shows.

In a book, now out of print, called *Catamarans in Close-up*, the author praised the lines and performance of the 7m (23ft) Hirondelle. Remembering this, a young computer expert called David Trotter bought the moulds, updated the boat to 1992 standards and she is now being offered for sale once again at a very competitive price.

The little Cracksman, an old design by Mike Henderson, has also been revived by Bob and Brenda Carraco at Modular Mouldings at Gweek in Cornwall. In most clinical conditions, they build the delightful, elegant, but exciting little Firebird, and the much larger Freebird. Such meticulous moulding is rare to find, and it is a sin to put the finished product into our dirty and polluted English Channel. Two Freebirds were at the Southampton Boat Show in 1991. One, built for an expatriate Englishman for the Miami/Bermuda charter trade, was completed by Camper & Nicholson to the highest standard and most elaborate specification of any catamaran ever built – a floating memorial to what is best in British manufacture. On the other hand, the little Cracksman is being offered as a fast motor boat. So in short, whatever the size and performance you are looking for, the British multihull designer can give you what you want, from the most modern to the most comfortable, while the builders can work to any specification from the cheap and cheerful to the needs of a millionaire. And boat for boat multihulls work out very economical indeed.

The leading organisation to sponsor multihulls in this country is the Multihull Offshore Cruising and Racing Association (MOCRA). MOCRA was formed in 1969 to encourage and foster the sailing of multihull cruisers and to help improve their seaworthiness; to protect the interests of owners and to offer help when required; to encourage cruising and racing in UK waters, and to disseminate information on multihulls. MOCRA is affiliated to the RYA and is recognised to be the National Authority for British cruising multihull sailors.

Secretary: Heather Millner, 28 Keynshambury Road, Cheltenham GL52 6HB. Tel: 01242 511982.

Membership Secretary: Mike Butterfield, Old Thatched House, Fairmile Avenue, Cobham, Surrey KT11 2JB. Tel: 01932 862190.

20.6 Bibliography

Multihulls for Cruising and Racing by Derek Harvey (Adlard Coles Nautical).

The Cruising Multihull by Chris White (Waterline).

Multihulls Offshore by Rob James (Adlard Coles Nautical).

This is Catamaran Sailing by Ernst Barth and Klaus Enzmann (Adlard Coles Nautical).

Multihull Seamanship by Michael McMullen (Nautical Books).

Cruising Catamarans (Amateur Yacht Society).

Design for Fast Sailing by Edmund Bruce and Henry Morss (Amateur Yacht Research Society).

Two Girls Two Catamarans by James Wharram (Abelard Schuman).

The Catamaran Book by Brian Phipps (Fernhurst)

Chapter 21

Starting to race

Contents

21.1 Yacht racing – an introduction

21.1.1 The attractions

Most yachtsmen like to make their boat sail faster on occasions – maybe on passage in order to catch the tide at some critical spot, or to get into harbour in time for a meal or before the pubs shut. Eventually this quest for speed can be translated into the idea of competing in races. Sadly many people find this difficult to achieve because the sport of yacht racing is surrounded by countless rules and regulations which are rife with terms that are incomprehensible to the ordinary sailor.

But take heart. The aim of this chapter is to explain some of these mysteries, at least to a level sufficient for the average sailor to compete in club events without causing disruption or damage. If you wish to race more seriously (as may well happen once you have tried it) you will need to make a detailed study of the rules so that you are able to take advantage of various tactical situations which present themselves. There are many good books available for this purpose, and a selection is given in the bibliography at the end of the chapter.

Races are organised by individual clubs, whose standards and methods can vary considerably. Some are large, well-run concerns which cater primarily for the more expert sailors and which hold regattas that attract large fleets of yachts in different classes, possibly including competitors from overseas. Other clubs are smaller and less formal, perhaps giving races for a few local boats, and without the cut and thrust of national or international competition.

The local geography largely dictates the type of racing that will be found in any one place. Small stretches of inland waters such as lakes and reservoirs are necessarily only suitable for dinghy racing or perhaps the smallest sizes of keelboats. These small craft may also flourish in estuaries and other sheltered waters around the coast, but here too will be larger yachts which are suitable and equipped for racing from port to port and even offshore. Yet these different categories of racing all have certain things in common. For a start they all compete under the same basic rules, as will be discussed below. With no spectators to cheer them on their way they will all take part for the satisfaction of defeating the elements as well as their rivals, whether they are near the front of the fleet or bringing up the rear. With no umpires afloat to oversee proceedings, they all share a sense of trust in adhering to the rules. And within each class there is likely to be a wide spread of ages, with the experience of older men and women compensating for the physical agility of their more youthful opponents.

21.1.2 The organisation of yacht racing

As described below, those who sail in bona fide competitive events must belong to a sailing club or yacht club that is recognised by the national authority, which in the case of the United Kingdom is the Royal Yachting Association (RYA). In return the RYA is represented, like the national authorities of all principal countries which control yacht racing, on the International Yacht Racing Union (IYRU). The IYRU frames and administers the racing rules, which are revised every four years following the Olympic Games, while various sub-committees deal with technical, measurement and other related matters.

So every individual who races, even in a modest handicap event at a local club, is racing under the same rules as people all round the world. In the (unlikely) event of some major protest about the interpretation of a rule, an owner has recourse through his club to the RYA, and ultimately to the IYRU.

The IYRU recognises and administers a limited number of 'International' classes. These include those classes of boats that compete in the Olympic Games every four years, but also some other classes which have either been used in past Olympics or which have special international appeal.

In a similar way the RYA recognises various 'National' classes, which are mostly dinghies but include for example the National Squib, a 5.8m (19ft) one-design keelboat of which more than 750 have been built.

21.1.3 Obligations of owners

Racing imposes obligations as well as offering enjoyment and competition. When entering a race an owner undertakes to be bound by the racing rules, to conform to the written sailing instructions which spell out such details as the course to be sailed, and where appropriate to obey whatever regulations may be imposed by the class to which the boat belongs. These may specify various details such as safety equipment to be carried and the number of persons on board.

When a yacht has been measured for handicapping purposes, or if she belongs to a one-design class, the owner must not make any changes that will invalidate the boat's rating (measurement).

A yacht may only compete in a race if she is owned by, or chartered to, a member of a recognised club, and there must be such a member on board as the owner or the owner's representative. So you must join a suitable club, which so far as the racing rules are concerned may or may not be the club providing the racing. However, many clubs rather naturally require an owner to be a member in order to compete in the regular club races, probably run on a weekly basis during the season, even if they stage less frequent open meetings to which outsiders are very welcome.

For identification purposes a yacht must carry numbers, of a specified size, on her mainsail and spinnaker. Larger boats may also be required to have numbers on their headsails. These numbers may be allocated by the national authority (the Royal Yachting Association in the United Kingdom), or by an organisation such as the Royal Ocean Racing Club or the boat's class association.

There are strict regulations about advertising that may be displayed on racing yachts. For all normal club events and for most regattas this is restricted to the small marks such as are placed by sailmakers near the tack of a sail, or by other manufacturers on spars and clothing. The full details are given in Appendix A3 of the rules of the International Yacht Racing Union (IYRU).

As has already been mentioned, sailing races are self-policing. There is no umpire afloat (apart from special match races) to call foul. It depends on each individual skipper to make sure that the rules are obeyed from start to finish – a situation which prevails in few other competitive sports.

If you touch a mark (an infringement) you may be the only person to know. But it is up to you to take whatever alternative penalty is available, or retire from the race. Similarly if you accidentally foul another competitor.

The modern racing rules permit alternative penalties – for example making two 360° turns with two tacks and two gybes – in situations which previously required immediate retirement or subsequent disqualification. Whether such dispensation is a good idea is arguable, because it can lead to a casual regard for the rules. In any case the responsibility lies with the offender to do the right thing without prompting from any other competitor.

Of course there are occasions between two boats when both helmsmen feel that they are in the right, and if a collision occurs this must be dealt with fairly under the protest procedure described below, not by verbal abuse across the water. If you make a mistake and baulk another boat, regardless of what penalty you may accept, apologise as soon as possible, either during the race, at the finish, or on getting ashore.

Finally, if you are not satisfied with the course or with some other arrangements regarding a race do not complain too much to the Race Officer. He is almost certainly a volunteer, who is taking his turn at a thankless task. Where you have constructive ideas about running the race they are best passed to the Sailing Secretary for consideration at the next meeting of the Sailing Committee.

21.2 The racing yachts

21.2.1 A wide range available
There are a bewildering number of different types of boat that race, even just around the shores and inland waters of Britain. They vary in size from tiny dinghies like the Optimist, intended for children, to large (and very expensive) seagoing craft which are quite capable of racing across the oceans as well as participating in coastal regattas. Between these two extremes lie a variety of 'classes' which in general belong to one of the following headings.

21.2.2 One-design classes
As the name implies, boats of a one-design class are as near as possible identical in all important respects. With modern GRP construction it is likely that all hulls have been produced from one mould, thus ensuring the same external shape even if the distribution of the building materials (resin and glass) within the hull may not be very precise. However, most one-design classes are governed by a minimum weight.

The dimensions and weights of spars and sails are also closely controlled within fairly small tolerances. Some classes require spars and sails to come only from nominated firms. There will certainly be regulations about the equipment that may or may not be carried, together with a minimum outfit of safety gear. Some classes have limitations on the maximum and minimum number of crew to be carried,

Before competing in races a one-design boat must have whatever certification is required by the club or class association concerned. This is likely to mean inspection and measurement by an approved measurer, and quite possibly a requirement to weigh the boat. Naturally the owner is not at liberty to alter any item without a repeat measurement.

Most one-design classes are of commercial origin, where a designer or builder has set out to provide a specific boat for racing purposes as well as for cruising or day sailing. In such cases it is in the builder's interests to try to ensure that all boats are as similar as possible, and to avoid any changes in building procedures that may deviate from the original standards. The success of such a class depends greatly on how carefully the class rules are drafted initially, and on how closely they are controlled by the class association which administers them.

One-design classes provide the purest and closest racing, boat against boat and with no handicapping. Success depends on how well a boat is tuned and sailed. A one-design boat should hold her value well, because she is not outdated by subsequent developments in hull or rig.

21.2.3 Restricted classes
Restricted classes have rules similar to those for one-designs, but the tolerances stipulated are a good deal wider, and there is much more choice in materials, spars, sails and general equipment. Hence there is greater scope for development, which may appeal to the racing enthusiast or amateur boat builder. Against this the older boats become less competitive and do not hold their value. In general costs are higher.

21.2.4 Formula (or rating) classes
A quite different approach is where, instead of certain measurements being stipulated with defined tolerances, actual measurements of the completed boats are fed into a formula which must not result in more than a certain figure (of length). If that figure is exceeded the boat is not 'in class'.

The formulae that have been used over the years are varied and often very complicated, embracing certain prime measurements such as length, beam, draught and sail area plus various allowances (or penalties) for factors considered desirable (or undesirable) as the case might be. Even the measured length may only be arrived at after a calculation to establish exactly where and how it is measured. In essence, those factors such as length, sail area and low freeboard which improve speed are pluses or multipliers in the formula, while those which decrease speed like abnormal beam or draught are minuses or dividers.

These attempts to relate mathematical formulae to actual speed on the water have inevitably caused designers to search for combinations of measurements that will produce a shape of hull to give a little more speed. This has often introduced unwelcome characteristics such as poor stability or difficult steering – as well as some very unattractive looking yachts.

A rating formula can be used in two different ways. One is to produce a number of yachts that have the same rating, and hence the same potential speed. This gives yachts of 'level rating', which race against each other boat for boat with no time allowances. They have the same theoretical speeds, but they are not identical. For example, one boat might have slightly more length at the expense of a little sail area.

Alternatively a measurement formula may be used to produce numerical ratings of boats of different sizes and with different characteristics. Each individual rating can be then transferred into a time allowance, based on elapsed time or on course distance, to provide a handicapping system.

21.2.5 Handicapping

The history of how successive handicapping formulae have been developed over the last 150 years, and how each in turn has been abandoned, makes interesting reading – albeit of a rather mathematical nature. But here we are more concerned with what is with us today, or with rules of the recent past that have influenced the shape of countless yachts which will still be afloat well into the next century.

In 21.3 below are described the types of handicapping systems most likely to be encountered today.

21.3 Handicapping methods

21.3.1 International Offshore Rule (IOR)

From the early 1930s until the 1970, yachts that took part in offshore races or raced in the coastal waters of Western Europe, the Mediterranean and Australasia were measured and rated under the then Royal Ocean Racing Club (RORC) rule. It should be emphasised that the RORC rule originally came into being as a means of handicapping as fairly as possible, yachts of diverse types and sizes, few of which had been specifically designed for racing.

Any measurement rules become 'type forming' as designers learn how best to exploit the formulae involved, but in general the RORC rule produced good seaworthy yachts many of which are still actively sailed and raced. Across the Atlantic the Cruising Club of America (CCA) rule produced seaworthy boats from different formulae.

From a yacht's linear rating must be calculated a factor for handicapping purposes. In Britain a 'time correction factor' (TCF) – the equivalent of the modern 'time multiplying factor' (TMF) – was calculated from a formula based on the square root of the rating. TCF multiplied by elapsed time gave corrected time, and this 'time on time' method is still used today. Yachts racing under the CCA rule traditionally used 'time on distance', expressed in so many seconds per mile and calculated from special tables. Both systems have their disadvantages with boats of disparate size that may be sailing under very different conditions of wind and tide during a long race.

There were obvious disadvantages, particularly in respect of international competition, in having two different measurement rules each side of the Atlantic, and in 1970 there came into being the new International Offshore Rule (IOR). This incorporates some features from both the previous RORC and CCA rules. The calculations are complex and are intended to be done by computer. Hull measurements are taken at fixed points or stations much as before. An innovation was an inclining experiment in which the yacht is heeled a small amount by known weights in order to determine a 'centre of gravity factor' (CGF) which is a multiplier in the basic formula.

In its early years many boats around the world had IOR certificates, up to 10,000 in 1977, but numbers have now dropped dramatically. In 1994 only 200 boats in the UK and Ireland held current certificates. IOR continues for a few major events but has steadily been replaced elsewhere by other systems described below.

The assistance of the RORC Rating Office and of Sir Peter Johnson, author of several publications on rating rules, is gratefully acknowledged.

21.3.2 International Measurement System (IMS)

In 1975 in the USA, the Massachusetts Institute of Technology developed Velocity Performance Predictions (VPPs) for a range of wind speeds and directions, and this subsequently became the Measurement Handicap System (MHS). In 1985 it was adopted as IMS for international use. Its main advantage is the ability to apply VPPs to assess handicaps. Thus the previous state of affairs where certain boats would perform well on corrected time in heavy weather while others might prevail in light conditions, is taken into account. In theory a boat does not win 'in her own weather'.

An advantage is that by machine-measuring the computer program draws a full lines plan of the hull – eliminating problems caused in the IOR by taking measurements only at selected points and thus allowing designers to exploit the rule with artificial bumps in what would otherwise be a fair surface. Wetted surface is also measured and, like IOR, there are measurements afloat, for freeboard and inclining.

From the available data the IMS program produces a boat's certificate, giving a table of some 35 time allowances for different wind conditions and courses, from which a race officer can work a computer program. A refinement is to have each boat's data stored in the race computer. The race officer then inputs the course type and length, starting times and finishing times. The computer works out the average speeds to assess the wind, and then produces the required handicaps.

Measurement under IMS (or IOR) is not cheap. Full measurement (based on overall length) cost £58.00 per metre in 1994, plus the measurer's expenses. However, it works out less for most production boats where hull measurement costs can be shared by a number of boats. A two tier system is planned, less for the cruiser racer and more for the grand prix type of yacht.

IMS has become established in several countries such as the United States, Italy, Australia, Holland, Sweden and Finland, but has made poor progress in the UK and Ireland where only 330 yachts held current certificates in 1994.

IMS was intended not to be type forming, and to encourage genuine cruiser/racers. To this end IMS calls for minimum accommodation requirements which score points, and a certain number of points are need to qualify for IMS certification. But the steady demise of IOR has concentrated the energy of designers, keen owners and some leading builders, especially in the USA, on IMS and it has already become a very competitive arena, mostly confined to grand prix events.

An owner wishing to have a yacht measured either for IMS or IOR must apply to the RORC Rating Office, Seahorse Building, Bath Road, Lymington, Hants SO41 9SE. Tel: (01590) 677030. Fax: (01590) 679478. A certificate will be issued after measurement. Any change to a yacht must be reported promptly to the Rating Office, which will arrange remeasurement as necessary. Once measured and rated under IMS or IOR a yacht's rating can be revalidated cheaply and easily if a copy of her last valid certificate exists.

21.3.3 International Level Class (ILC)

More recently introduced are International Level Class yachts designed to the relevant ILC Rule. In 1994 there were only two sizes, the ILC 40 (between 11.5m and 12.5m in length overall) and the ILC 46 (between 13.4m and 14.5m in length overall). It is however planned to introduce ILC 30s and ILC 70s, and possibly others in the future. As the name implies, these various classes will each race level (without handicapping) and are seen primarily as a replacement for the old ton cup classes.

21.3.4 Channel Handicap System (CHS)

For the average cruising yachtsman who intends to enter the occasional race, the Channel Handicap System (CHS) is the likely starting point. It is a time on time rating system for all types of monohull cruising yachts to be handicapped for coastal or offshore racing at club level.

Each yacht is given a time correction factor (TCF) depending on her key hull measurements,

hull and keel type, principal sail measurements and sail materials, and so on. An owner should be able to take all the required dimensions, and many of them can be extracted from a valid IOR or IMS certificate if held, but where preferred a measurer can be arranged. In some races and regions measurement is compulsory. The RORC rating office, which administers the scheme in the United Kingdom has a vast amount of data on boats of all types and sizes, and will check measurements submitted. Increasingly race organisers are requiring official weights of hulls, obtained with an authorised load cell. For some events an endorsed certificate — CHS(E) — is required, which may need official check measurements.

To discourage design optimisation, TCF formulae are not published. They are revised annually to refine handicapping and to allow for new design trends. So a certificate has to be revalidated each year at a cost of £40.00 (1994).

From the outset CHS was intended for cruising yachts with proper accommodation, and while yachts designed for racing are not excluded they are at some disadvantage compared to genuine cruiser/racers. Light displacement boats and day boats may be rated CHS, but should be classified as such so that they race in special divisions.

Handicaps are influenced by the boat's sail wardrobe, with sail cloth classified into three grades. Low-tech sails must be woven, soft-finish polyester (or nylon or cotton). By accepting a rating penalty a boat may use mid-tech cloth which includes a wide range of materials from highly resinated woven dacron to dacron/mylar laminates. For an increased penalty hi-tech cloths may be used — for example, Kevlar and Spectra laminates. Only sails declared for rating purposes can be carried on board.

TCFs for CHS are calculated to three decimal places, whereas for IOR TMFs are shown to four places and are normally slightly lower in value. No attempt should be made to compare the two systems with each other, nor with IMS time on distance allowances.

Normally under CHS the corrected time is obtained by multiplying the actual elapsed time by the TCF. If preferred, time on distance may be used from the following formulae if the course distance is known:

Time allowance $= 5513/((TCF \times 10) - 0.88)$
Corrected time $=$ Elapsed time $-$ (Time allowance $\times$ course distance)

	World	UK	USA	France	Italy	Spain	Australia
CHS	4505	2375	10	999	315	464	265
IMS	4964	323	873	79	960	463	349
IOR	1555	286	200	28	118	115	140

Fig. 21(1) Numbers of certificates for CHS, IMS and IOR at the end of 1993, world wide and in sample countries. Some boats have dual (i.e. IMS/IOR or CHS/IMS) or even triple certificates, so the figures cannot be added arithmetically. These figures are reproduced by kind permission from 'Channel Handicap', an annual publication edited by Peter Johnson.

CHS was originated jointly by the Royal Ocean Racing Club (RORC) in this country and the Union National pour la Course au Large (UNCL) in France. In 1993 nearly 4505 valid CHS certificates were issued, half of them to boats in the United Kingdom. 203 yachts competed in the 1993 Fastnet Race under CHS.

In terms of application, measurement and computation, CHS is considerably cheaper than IOR or IMS. The minimum charge for a new application is (1994) £40.00 for yachts up to 8.0m overall. For yachts over 8.0m it is £5.00 per metre (i.e. £50.00 for a 10m boat). As stated above, there is annual revalidation fee of £40.00 (1994).

To apply for a CHS rating, send an application for the rules, explanation and measurement form to the Royal Ocean Racing Club, Rating Office, Seahorse Building, Bath Road, Lymington, Hants SO41 9SE. Tel: (01590) 677030. Fax: (01590) 679478.

European regional representatives are:

For France, Italy, Spain: UNCL Centre Nautique, Quai A le Gallo, 92100 Boulogne-sue-Seine, Paris.

For Ireland: Irish Yachting Association, 3 Park Road, Dun Laoghaire, Co. Dublin. Peter Murray, Ferry House, Curabinny Avenue, Carrigaline, Cork.

21.3.5 RYA Portsmouth Yardstick Scheme

The Portsmouth Yardstick is a measure of performance, originally conceived for dinghy racing and later extended to keelboats, cruising yachts and multihulls. The scheme is administered by the Royal Yachting Association (RYA) and has gained international recognition. Full details are contained in the RYA booklet YR2, *Portsmouth Yardstick Scheme*, published annually. To understand a little about how the scheme works it is necessary to state some definitions.

(1) Portsmouth Numbers (PN). These are measures of performance, stated as times over a common but unspecified distance. For example, the distance that a yacht rated at 95 covers in 95 minutes should be the same as a yacht rated at 110 covers in 110 minutes in the same race. On another occasion the yachts might both sail faster, and then the distance that they would sail in 95 minutes and 110 minutes respectively would be greater. Portsmouth Numbers are allocated to different classes as whole numbers from 60 (which would be an extremely fast boat if any existed) to 130, and as even numbers above 130.

(2) Primary Yardsticks (PY). These are Portsmouth Numbers which are published by the RYA and which have become well established by the experience of many clubs over several years. For example, for cruisers (in 1991) they included: Contessa 32 (104), Hunter Impala (100), Sadler 25 (113), Sigma 33 (98), Sonata (110), Westerly Centaur (126), Westerly GK 24 (107).

(3) Secondary Yardsticks (SY). These are Portsmouth Numbers also published by the RYA, but which are not so well established.
(4) Recorded Numbers (RN). These are Portsmouth Numbers published by the RYA but on the basis of limited information.
(5) Club Numbers (CN). These are Portsmouth Numbers which are allocated by a club. They may be derived from Trial Numbers (see below) or adjusted by a club from RYA lists.
(6) Trial Numbers. These are numbers that are allocated by a club on a trial basis until a Club Number can be determined.

Within any (non-one-design) class of cruising yacht there may be significant variations in matters such as rig. Some boats may have only small headsails, or carry no spinnaker. These variations from what is defined as 'Base Trim' are allowed for by small additions to the Portsmouth Number – for example, plus 4 for a yacht with no spinnaker. A similar scale of allowances is laid down for different engine/propeller configurations and for different keel configurations. A Portsmouth Certificate may be issued to a yacht when she is allowed a Club Number, and should specify what allowances have been made for variations from Base Trim.

Every year clubs which use the scheme are invited to render a 'Yardstick Return' to the RYA, to assess how the system has worked and to make recommendations for any changes in Portsmouth Numbers.

The results of individual races are obtained most conveniently from 'Langstone Tables', which give corrected times direct from elapsed times and Portsmouth Numbers. Alternatively the following formula may be used.

$$\text{Corrected Time} = (\text{Elapsed Time}/\text{Portsmouth Number}) \times 100$$

21.3.6 Other handicapping system

There are in existence a large number of regional or local handicapping systems. These include for example ECHO in Ireland, NECRA in the North Sea, Clyde Handicap Nationale (HN) in France, Scandicap Mk II and Danish Handicap (DH). There are about a dozen systems in the United States. For their annual 'Round the Island' race the Island Sailing Club uses the West Solent Handicap Formula but adjusted in some cases after comparison with the Portsmouth Yardstick.

Many clubs run their own handicapping systems for local club events. In some ways these are the most satisfactory of all with a fixed fleet of boats – until some stranger appears and sweeps the board.

21.3.7 Special Regulations

For many years the Royal Ocean Racing Club (RORC) issued its own Special Regulations governing the minimum equipment and accommodation standards for yachts racing offshore. These were replaced by the similar regulations of the Offshore Racing Council (ORC), the international body which now governs the sport.

Apart from specifying that a boat must be strongly built, properly rigged and fully seaworthy, the regulations cover a large number of details which include: engine installations, security of hatches, sizes and watertight integrity of cockpits, seacocks on hull openings, lifelines, stanchions, pulpits, fire extinguishers, bilge pumps, anchors and cable, first aid kit, foghorn, radar reflectors, compasses and navigational equipment, navigation lights, storm sails, emergency tiller, tools and spares, radio receiver, lifejackets, whistles, safety harnesses, liferaft and flares. The ORC also lays down minimum standards for safety harnesses and liferafts.

Various degrees of compliance to the regulations are arranged by defined categories of races, briefly as follows :-

0 – Long, transocean races with yachts completely self-sufficient for very extended periods, and with no outside assistance.
1 – Long distances races, well offshore.
2 – Extended races along or not far from shore, with likely help available in case of serious emergency.
3 – Races across open water, relatively protected or close to shore.
4 – Short races, normally in daylight, close to shore.

For example, most RORC races are now Category 3 (plus liferaft), with yachts recommended to equip to Category 2 – which applies to the Fastnet Race.

Most clubs which run races, even inshore, for handicap classes specify the standard of equipment by reference to the ORC Special Regulations as above. For example, yachts racing in the Solent might be required to comply with Category 4.

The Special Regulations are published in the annual programmes of the RORC and the Junior Offshore Group (JOG), and are also obtainable from ORC, telephone 0171-629 8701.

21.3.8 RORC Stability and Safety Screening (SSS)

The SSS or 'triple S' numeral scheme was developed by the RORC for race organisers to assess the suitability of yachts for offshore races. It is also available for inshore and dayboat racing. The SSS numeral comes partly from the yacht's dimensions and partly from her compliance with the Special Regulations (see 21.3.7) and her constructional features.

Certificates issued by the RORC and (for CHS) by UNCL show the SSS numerals in the following form as an example:

SSS Base Value	27
(plus) Adjustment Value	6
SSS Numeral	33

The base value is derived from safety-related features as determined from principal dimensions

– length, beam, displacement – and rig. Also taken into account are factors such as displacement/length, beam/displacement, sail area/displacement and beam/length. Light displacement, large beam, big sail area and flimsy rigs are factors that give a low SSS base value.

Adjustment value is a bonus for a yacht with certain equipment or good seagoing features. For example, in 1991 the following adjustment values applied for yachts conforming to ORC Special Regulations in the five race categories.

Category	Adjustment figure
0	+8
1	+7
2	+6
3	+5
4	+3

There is a maximum limit for the adjustment value (whether from category compliance or from specified features) depending on the boat's base value, as follows:

Base value	Maximum adjustment value
less than 8	0
8–14	3
15–23	5
24–32	6
33–41	7
more than 41	8

The following table shows the suggested minimum SSS numerals for a yacht to compete in the five ORC race categories:

Race category	Minimum SSS numeral
0	50
1	40
2	30
3	20
4	10

For most of their races the RORC requires a minimum SSS figure of 20, but this is increased for certain races – for example, it is 30 in the case of the Fastnet Race.

Most yachts over 12m in overall length can achieve a figure of 30 fairly easily, but this may not apply with smaller boats, particularly those of very light displacement or with flimsy rigs. In such cases the SSS figure will alert a race committee to an entry which may be disallowed, while at the same time encouraging an owner to make whatever improvements are possible.

21.4 The conduct of yacht races

21.4.1 Race organisation

Before taking part in a race it is necessary to understand the general procedure. Races are run by individual clubs, who are bound to follow in all important respects the rules prescribed by the International Yacht Racing Union (IYRU).

A club gives the outline arrangements for a forthcoming event in 'a Notice of Race', which among other details such as time and date should prescribe the method of entry. For a major regatta the Notice of Race is a lengthy document. The entry form will require an owner to declare that the boat has the necessary measurement certificate and that he or she will conform to the rules and belongs to a recognised club.

The owner then obtains the 'Sailing Instructions' – an important document which deserves very careful study because it includes such details as the starting signals and arrangements, the course to be sailed, and finishing line, the time limit, the method of shortening the course and many other matters as appropriate. Do not forget to take it afloat with you, and for major events it is best to take a photocopy.

21.4.2 Race committee

To organise even a single race properly takes some effort, and for a major regatta where there are several classes and many entries a large number of helpers are needed. In some clubs competitors are expected, or even required, to assist on the race committee on a regular basis and this can be interesting and instructive. A newcomer to racing could do worse than help on the race committee before actually competing, because this will soon give an insight to the general procedure and from quite a different viewpoint.

21.4.3 Course to be sailed

One of the first duties of the race committee is to decide and signal the course to be sailed. The method of doing this will be described in the sailing instructions, but it is helpful to know the location of the possible marks in advance, rather than have to locate them on the chart in the hectic minutes before the start.

The marks will be stated in order, and in each case it will be indicated whether the mark is to be rounded or passed, and whether it is to be left to port or to starboard. Note that there is a distinction between rounding and passing. If a string represents the wake of the yacht from start to finish, it must when drawn taut lie on the required side of each mark, and be touching each rounding mark.

It is an infringement to touch a mark while rounding or passing. However, a yacht may exonerate herself from this offence by making one complete 360° turn, which must include one tack and one gybe. This 'alternative penalty' as it is called must be taken as soon as the yacht can sail clear of other competitors.

When possible the course should be set in order to give a good test of sailing to windward, and of reaching and running. When circumstances permit the opening leg will normally be a beat.

21.4.4 Starting

There are two basic types of starting line. If in open water it will be an imaginary line between two objects – usually between a buoy and the mast of the committee vessel which is running the race. For races conducted from a shoreside club the starting line is usually defined as the transit of two poles or flagstaffs ashore, with probably a buoy to mark the outer limit of the line. This buoy, called the distance mark, will not necessarily be exactly on the starting line, but probably a boat's length or so on the course side of the line. This has lulled many beginners (and also experienced sailors) into making a premature start.

For most races there is a standard starting procedure. Ten minutes before the start the 'Warning Signal' (class flag) is broken out, with a sound signal (gun or hooter). Five minutes before the start the 'Preparatory Signal' (Flag P of the International Code) is broken out, with another sound signal. From this moment the yachts are subject to the racing rules. A yacht must be away from her mooring (although she may be anchored), and she must not be propelled other than by sail (no engine, no paddling). Also note that a yacht does not wear an ensign while racing, so if an ensign has been worn (quite correctly) while sailing out to the starting area, it must be removed at or before the Preparatory Signal.

Five minutes later again, both the Warning Signal and the Preparatory Signal are lowered, with another sound signal, and the race has started. Note that on each occasion it is the flag which is the actual signal from which the time is taken. The sound signal is only to call attention. However, in a well run race the two should be synchronised.

If a boat is a premature starter, or 'across the line before the gun' a further sound signal is made and Flag X of the International Code is hoisted. The offender must then return – keeping clear of the other boats which have started correctly – and start properly (when Flag X will be lowered).

If a large number of boats are over the line, and if they cannot be identified, the race committee will signal a 'General Recall'. This is done by hoisting the First Substitute and making two sound signals. Then the whole fleet (including any boats which started correctly) must return for a fresh start, with the Preparatory Signal hoisted one minute after the First Substitute is lowered.

Other flags are used in connection with starting races. The most common are the Answering Pendant which is the postponement signal, and Flag N which indicates that the race is abandoned.

Often one end of the starting line or the other will be favoured by the line not being precisely square – to the wind direction if the first leg is a beat, or to the direction of the first mark if the opening leg is either a reach or a run. It is therefore important to decide the best place to start, and in open water this can best be done with the boat's compass, by comparing the bearing

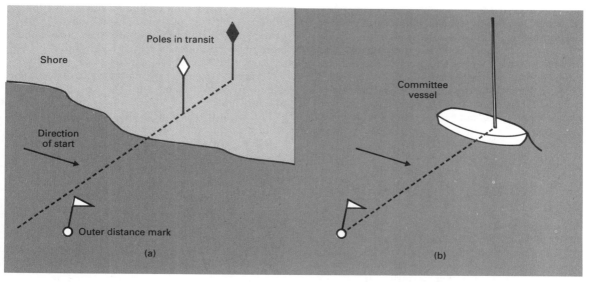

Fig. 21(2) Two types of starting line. With (a) the line is formed by the transit of two poles or flagstaffs ashore, and the outer limit is defined by a buoy called the outer distance mark (ODM). In open water the starting line may be formed as in (b), between the mainmast of the Committee Vessel (CV) and a buoy moored a certain distance away. This type of starting line has the advantage that it can be orientated at right angles to the wind direction to give a windward start.

of the starting line with the wind direction or the direction of the first mark. Remember that both of these can change in the minutes before the Preparatory Signal. The effect of any tidal stream across the course also needs to be considered.

It is also important to decide whether it is likely to be better to work one side of the course or the other, due to predictable wind shifts or tidal stream, or maybe to tack up the middle of the course on wind shifts which are sometimes quite pronounced in coastal waters.

Having decided where to start the next problem is to be there when the starting gun fires, and with plenty of boat speed. Here experience counts, and a good knowledge of the rules, because other boats will be aiming to be at the same point at the same time.

21.4.5 Some general racing rules
Certain fundamental rules must always be obeyed:
A. A yacht must give whatever help she can to any vessel or person in peril.
B. It is the sole responsibility of each yacht to decide whether or not to start or to continue to race.
C. A yacht must compete only by fair sailing, and in compliance with the rules.
D. A yacht which infringes a rule must either retire promptly or accept an alternative penalty (when available).

The right-of-way rules between two boats when racing are summarised in section 21.5 below, where different circumstances are dealt with in turn. Here it is convenient to state some general rules which apply throughout a race. The relevant IYRU rule number is given in brackets.

A boat under way must keep clear of a boat at anchor. If two boats are anchored, the one which anchored last must keep clear. (Rule 46.)

If a collision results in serious damage, the right-of-way yacht shall be penalised if she would have been able to avoid collision but failed to do so. (Rule 32.)

A right-of-way yacht should hail before making an alteration of course that may not be foreseen by another yacht. (This does not apply in the case of a leeward yacht luffing a rival overtaking her to windward.) (Rule 43.)In general a right-of-way yacht must not alter course so as to baulk another yacht which is in the act of keeping clear. However, there are exceptions to this, as students of the rules will discover, when a leeward yacht is permitted to luff a yacht overtaking her to windward and when a yacht is assuming a proper course at the start or rounding a mark. (Rule 35.)

A yacht may anchor during a race, but must not secure to a buoy or alongside a jetty etc. (Rule 53.1.)

An ensign must not be worn while racing, but should be displayed when a yacht retires or has finished the race. (RYA prescription to Rule 66.)

If two yachts collide, both shall be penalised unless one of them retires or accepts an alternative penalty or one or both of them lodges a protest. Minor and unavoidable collisions, such as may occur in a flat calm, however, are exonerated. (Rule 33.)

To signify her intention of lodging a protest a yacht is required to display a protest flag (normally the red flag 'B', International Code) as soon as possible. The sailing instructions will detail the procedure to be followed, but she must notify the other boat of her intention to protest and will probably be required to inform the race committee as soon as possible. A written protest must be submitted within a prescribed time, and cannot then be withdrawn.

21.4.6 **Finishing**

The finishing line will be described in the sailing instructions in a similar way to the starting line, and may be the same. Note that the finishing line must be crossed from the direction of the last mark. A boat remains subject to the racing rules until she has cleared the finishing line. In some races a competitor may be required to record her own finishing time, and this is often a wise precaution in case of subsequent dispute.

21.5 **Racing right-of-way**

21.5.1 **Definitions**

These notes on the racing right-of-way rules (Part IV of the IYRU rules) are not intended to be comprehensive or to cater for the expert sailor. They should however be sufficient to keep a beginner out of trouble, and to allow him or her to race without causing disruption or damage. If at any moment you are unsure of your rights, play it safe and keep well clear of other boats.

Certain definitions appear repeatedly in the IYRU rules, and will need to be used in what follows, so it is important that they are understood. Many of them are self-evident or in general sailing use, but notes on some of the other more important ones are given below and explained in Figs. 21(3) – 21(7).

Tacking. A yacht is tacking from the moment she is beyond head to wind until she has borne away to close-hauled.

Bearing away. Altering course away from the wind until the yacht begins to gybe.

Gybing. A yacht is gybing from the moment that the boom crosses her centreline until the mainsail has filled on the new gybe.

On a tack. A yacht is on a tack when she is not tacking or gybing.

Close-hauled. A yacht is close-hauled when sailing as close to the wind as she can with advantage when going to windward.

Clear astern, clear ahead; overlap. A yacht is clear astern when she is abaft a line drawn abeam from the stern of another yacht. In this situation the other yacht is clear ahead. Two yachts overlap when neither is clear astern or when an intervening yacht overlaps both of them.

The definitions of clear astern, clear ahead and overlap above only apply to yachts on opposite tacks when rounding or passing marks or obstructions (Rule 42).

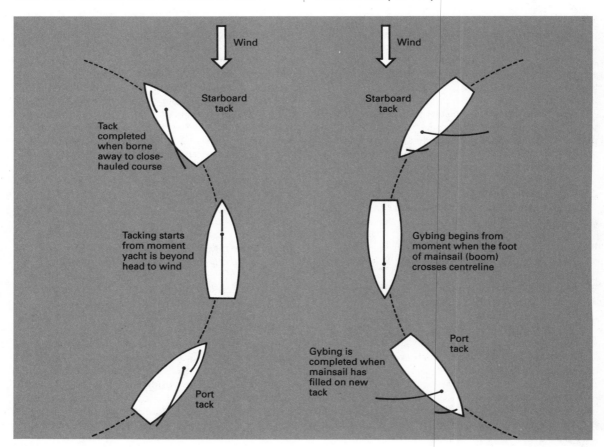

Fig. 21(3) Definitions – tacking (left) and gybing (right).

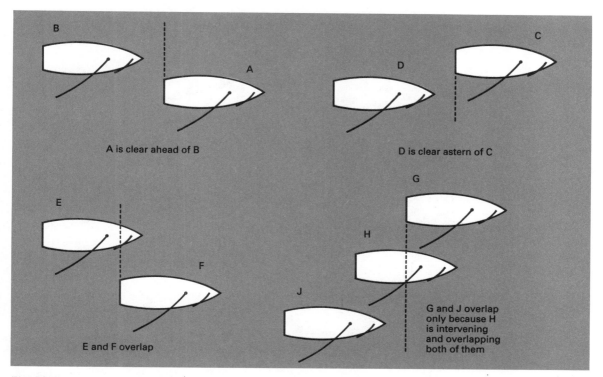

Fig. 21(4) Definitions – clear ahead, clear astern and overlapping. A yacht is clear astern of another when her hull is abaft a line projected abeam from the aftermost part of the other yacht. The other yacht is clear ahead. Two yachts overlap when neither is clear astern; or when, although one of them is clear astern, an intervening yacht is overlapping both of them.

Leeward, windward. The leeward side is the one on which a yacht carries her mainsail. The other is the windward side. When yachts on the same tack overlap, the one to leeward of the other is defined as the leeward yacht, and the other is the windward yacht.

Mast abeam. A windward yacht sailing no higher than a leeward yacht, is mast abeam when her helmsman's line of sight abeam is forward of the leeward yacht's mainmast. See Fig. 21(11).

Proper course. This is the course a yacht might sail, in the absence of other competition, to finish as quickly as possible. It is not necessarily the direct course from mark to mark. There is no proper course before the starting signal.

Obstruction. This is any object, including another vessel under way, which requires a substantial alteration of course for a yacht to pass, or any object (such as the shore) that can be passed on one side only.

Room. The space needed by a yacht to manoeuvre in a seamanlike manner in the prevailing conditions.

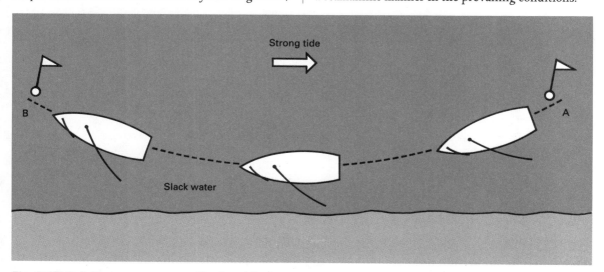

Fig. 21(5) Definition – proper course. The dotted line is a proper course for the yacht sailing from A to B, if for example there is less tidal stream or more wind inshore.

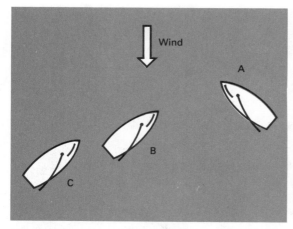

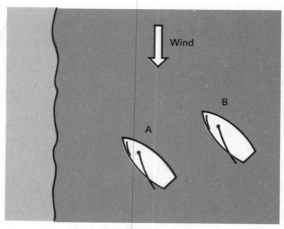

Fig. 21(6) Boat A on the starboard tack has right of way and is an obstruction to B. B may require C to tack so that B may keep clear of A. (Rule 43).

Fig. 21(7) The shore is an obstruction, and A may call upon B to keep clear so that she may tack to avoid it. B must either tack when hailed or reply 'You tack', and give B room to tack and keep clear of her. (Rule 43).

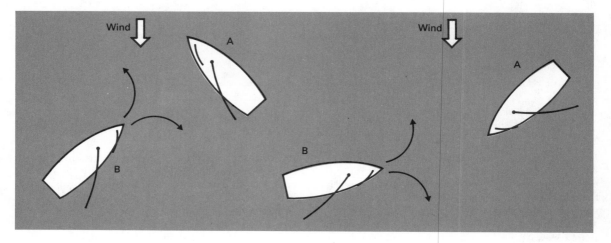

Fig. 21(8) Basic rule – opposite tacks. In each case B on port tack must keep clear of A on starboard tack. (Rule 36).

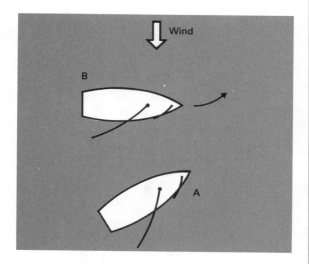

Fig. 21(9) Basic rule – same tack, overlapped. B, the windward yacht, must keep clear of A to leeward.

21.5.2 **Right-of-way in open water**

In open water the basic rules which govern the right-of-way between two or more boats are similar to the 'Collision Regulations' for ordinary vessels:

On opposite tacks – port tack keeps clear of starboard tack (Rule 36).

On the same tack, when overlapped – windward yacht keeps clear of leeward yacht (Rule 37.1).

On the same tack, when not overlapped – yacht astern keeps clear of yacht ahead (Rule 37.2).

When a yacht which has been clear astern establishes an overlap to leeward of a yacht on the same tack, she must initially allow her room and an opportunity to keep clear (Rule 37.3). This requires and deserves some explanation. Originally the yacht clear astern must keep clear, but the moment she establishes an overlap the responsibility passes to the windward yacht, under Rule 37.1. In the extreme case it would be unfair if the leeward yacht could establish her overlap just a few inches from the windward yacht's stern, since the latter would then be physically incapable of luffing to keep clear. Given

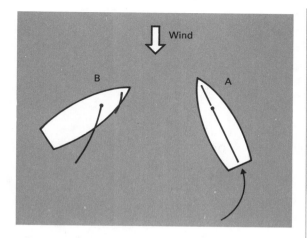

Fig. 21(10) Basic rule – changing tacks, tacking and gybing. Here A has tacked too close to B. A must tack far enough from B to allow the latter to keep clear without having to alter course before A completes her tack (or gybe). (Rule 41).

the initial opportunity, which is not a continuing one, the windward yacht must respond and keep clear. Under the luffing rule (see 21.5.4) the leeward yacht may not in these circumstances sail above her proper course.

21.5.3 Tacking and gybing

A yacht which is tacking or gybing must keep clear of a yacht on a tack (not tacking or gybing) under Rule 41.1. A yacht must not tack or gybe into a position giving her right-of-way unless she does so far enough from a yacht on a tack to allow the latter to keep clear without starting to alter course before the tack or gybe is completed (Rule 41.2). This is illustrated in Fig. 21(10) where A has tacked too close to B to allow the latter to keep clear. It is a situation which is difficult to judge, so when in doubt do not tack.

21.5.4 Luffing

The racing rules depart significantly from the Collision Regulations in allowing a leeward yacht to luff in order to try to stop an opponent overtaking to windward. However, there are restrictions. A leeward yacht may only luff above her proper course unless the helmsman of the windward yacht, sighting abeam, is abaft the mainmast of the leeward yacht (Rule 39.2). This is explained in Fig. 21(11).

For the purposes of this rule, an overlap only exists if the yachts are within two lengths of each other. An overlap that exists when the leading yacht starts, or when one or both of them

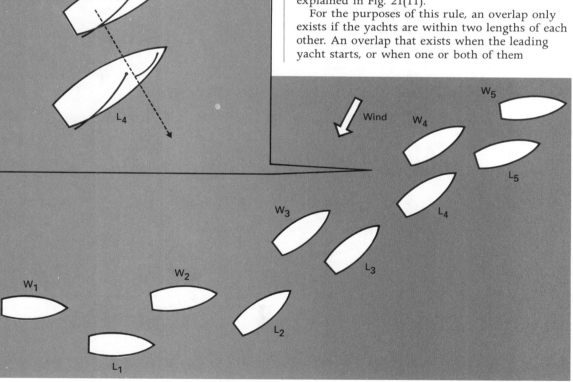

Fig. 21(11) Luffing after starting.
(1) W_1 is sailing faster, and overtaking L_1 to windward.
(2) L_2 is within her rights to luff (suddenly and head to wind if she pleases) to try to stop W_2 passing.
(3) L_3 continues her luff, but W_3 is overtaking her.
(4) At position 4 (see inset) W_4 reaches the position where her helmsman, sighting abeam, is abreast the mast of L_4, and may hail 'mast abeam'.
(5) L must then bear away (as at L_5) and may not sail above her proper course – close-hauled. (Rule 39).

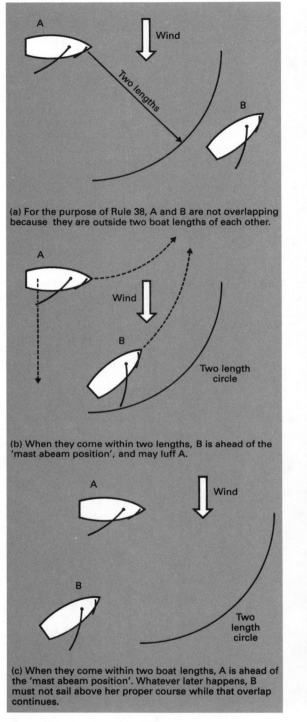

(a) For the purpose of Rule 38, A and B are not overlapping because they are outside two boat lengths of each other.

(b) When they come within two lengths, B is ahead of the 'mast abeam position', and may luff A.

(c) When they come within two boat lengths, A is ahead of the 'mast abeam position'. Whatever later happens, B must not sail above her proper course while that overlap continues.

Fig. 21(12) With respect to the luffing rule (39) only, an overlap does not exist unless the boats are within two overall lengths of the longer one.

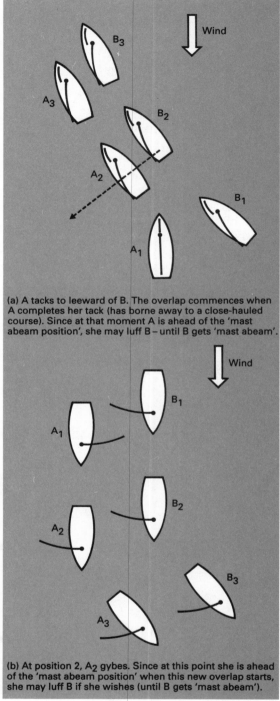

(a) A tacks to leeward of B. The overlap commences when A completes her tack (has borne away to a close-hauled course). Since at that moment A is ahead of the 'mast abeam position', she may luff B – until B gets 'mast abeam'.

(b) At position 2, A₂ gybes. Since at this point she is ahead of the 'mast abeam position' when this new overlap starts, she may luff B if she wishes (until B gets 'mast abeam').

Fig. 21(13) An overlap that exists when one or both yachts completes a tack as in (a) above, or a gybe as in (b), is a new overlap beginning at that time.

completes a tack or gybe, is regarded as a new overlap beginning at that time. The implications are shown in the diagrams (Fig. 21(12) and (13)).

Where there is doubt, the leeward yacht may luff or sail above her proper course until the windward yacht hails 'mast abeam' or 'obstruction' as may be appropriate.

A yacht may not luff unless she has the right to luff all yachts to windward of her that may be affected, in which case they must all respond even

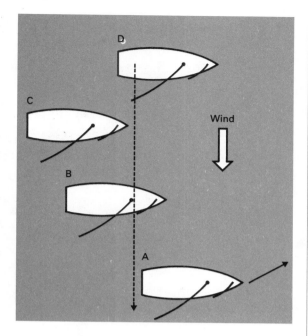

in the case where an intervening yacht does not have the right to luff a yacht to windward of her. See Fig. 21(14).
It is difficult to establish the relative positions of the various yachts if a protest should arise, and A should take care in this situation.

21.5.5 Bearing away

When two yachts are on a free leg of the course (not beating to windward), a yacht must not sail below her proper course when she is within three lengths of a leeward yacht or of a yacht astern which is steering a course to leeward of her own (Rule 39). Note that this only applies on a free leg of the course. A yacht ahead may bear away if she can justify this as her proper course, or she may bear away and gybe onto another proper course provided she does not interfere with the other yacht.

21.5.6 Rules at the start

This is an exciting and hectic phase of any race, and special rules apply until a yacht has cleared the starting line. Also there is no proper course before the starting signal.

Before crossing the line a yacht clear ahead or to leeward may luff only slowly and in such a way as to allow a windward yacht to keep clear. Also she must not sail above close-hauled unless the helmsman of the windward yacht, sighting abeam, is aft of the mast of the leeward yacht (Rule 38).

Fig. 21(14) Luffing rights over two or more yachts. A has luffing rights over B, C and D. If A luffs all must respond (so long as A remains ahead of 'mast abeam'). Although C does not have luffing rights over D, D must respond when C luffs in response to A. (Rule 40.3).

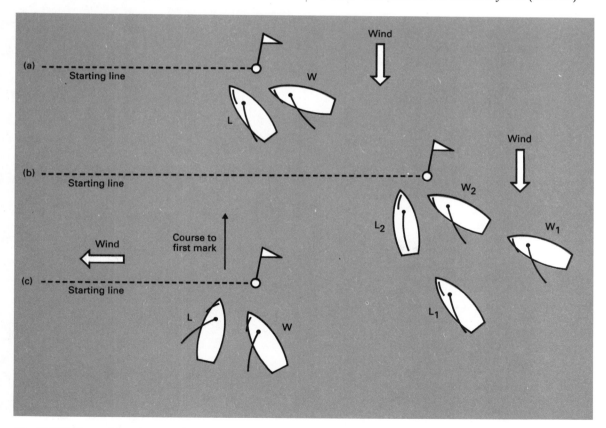

Fig. 21(15) The anti-barging rule. Approaching the starting line, a leeward yacht need not give a windward yacht room to pass to leeward of a starting mark (either end of the line) that is surrounded by navigable water. In (a) above L does not have to give room to W. But after the starting signal L must not deprive W of room either by sailing above close-hauled as in (b) above, or by sailing above the direction of the first mark of the course as in (c). (Rule 42(a)).

In the period after the Preparatory Signal yachts will be sailing in all different directions, and a very sharp lookout is needed to prevent collision. In the final minute or so they will be jockeying for the best position at the start, and until a helmsman is really familiar with the rules it is best not to get too involved.

There is one special rule that is often broken, concerning a buoy marking the end of the starting line. When coming to the start, a leeward yacht need not give a windward yacht room at such a mark if it is surrounded by navigable water – see Fig. 21(15). But after the starting signal she must not deny room by sailing above the course for the next mark (when the first leg is for example a reach), or above close-hauled (when the first leg is a beat). (Rule 42(a).)

When a yacht is returning after a premature start, she must keep clear of all other yachts which have started correctly (Rule 44).

21.5.7 Approaching the shore, or other obstructions

With two yachts on the same tack approaching the shore, or some other obstruction, it would obviously be dangerous if the yacht to leeward or close ahead was unable to escape sailing up the beach. In these circumstances she may hail for room to tack – 'Water'. The other yacht must then tack (followed by the hailing yacht), or she may reply 'You tack', in which case the hailing yacht must tack immediately and be given room by the other. (Rules 43.1 and 43.2.) See Fig. 21(7).

21.5.8 Rounding marks

A whole section of the IYRU rules (Section C) is devoted to special rules that apply when yachts are 'about to round' a mark or an obstruction. The rules are complicated and deserve careful study. Here we will only discuss the basic principles.

There is no definition of 'about to round'. It certainly applies when a yacht is within two lengths of a mark, but it could be a greater distance when yachts are sailing fast and perhaps down tide.

In essence the rule says that if an inside yacht establishes an overlap before the outside one is within two lengths of the mark, the outside yacht must give the inside yacht room to round inside her (Rule 42.1). Room is defined as the space she needs to round safely in a seamanlike manner in the prevailing conditions (See Fig 21(16)).

The written rule is long and complicated, because it has to cater for different situations, but for our purposes simply remember that if you have established an overlap on an outside boat on the same tack in ample time, you may call for water and expect to get it. Remember, however, that there may be a yacht or yachts ahead who are already almost at the mark, and on whom you may not have established an overlap in sufficient time. Also, having rounded the mark the situation may change. Having been the windward but inside boat

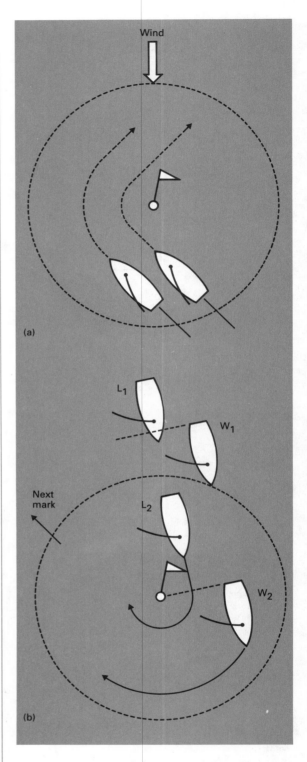

Fig. 21(16) An inside, overlapping yacht must be given room to round or pass a mark or obstruction. She must establish her overlap at least before the outside yacht is within two lengths of the mark or obstruction. Room means enough space for the inside yacht to round in a seamanlike way, and either to tack or gybe when this is part of the manoeuvre. In (b) above L_1 has established an overlap on W_1 before the latter is within two lengths of the mark. Even if the overlap is subsequently broken, W_2 must still give room to L_2. (Rule 42).

with right-of-way actually rounding the mark, you suddenly may become the windward yacht and responsible for keeping clear of the boat to leeward of you.

Never try to establish an overlap at the very last moment. If you fail you will probably be forced the wrong side of the mark, because it will be too late to go under the stern(s) of the boat(s) ahead – which is where you should have gone in the first place.

21.6 Faster sailing

21.6.1 The quest for speed

The search for boat speed is of course vital when racing, but can also be put to good use when cruising. Certain important factors must be dealt with in advance. The boat's bottom must be clean, something often neglected in the boat which races only occasionally. The best fore and aft trim must be determined, and it is best to keep weight out of the ends of the boat to reduce pitching which upsets the flow of air over the sails. Rigging must be set up so that the mast is straight, and remains straight when the boat heels under pressure of sail, and the mast needs to have the correct fore and aft rake to give a nicely balanced helm. Some homework has to be done before going afloat – a detailed weather forecast will help tactical decisions and the selection of sails to be used, while characteristics of tidal streams (more readily predictable) need to be worked out and recorded.

Keeping a boat sailing at or near her optimum speed demands constant attention. Conditions are steadily changing with small shifts in wind direction, variations in wind speed and different sea states – all factors which a racing helmsman should be continually assessing, and to which the crew must react correctly in terms of sail trim.

Whether beating to windward or sailing off the wind, it is the correct angle of the sails to the apparent wind which results in good performance; that, and the actual shape (curvature) of each individual sail and its trim in relation to other sails. Sails must be set so that they generate the greatest lift or drive, together with the minimum drag and heeling effect.

21.6.2 Sail shape

Given that fore and aft sails are of triangular shape in elevation – with a luff, leech and foot – there are subtle differences that can be built into the third dimension, that is to say how full or flat the sail is cut, and where the maximum draught (depth, or fullness) occurs. As will be seen, the shape of a given sail can be greatly influenced by the different sail controls available. First it is necessary to understand the terms described in Fig. 21(17).

The amount of draught is an important factor, and it is expressed as a percentage of the chord, usually at about half height. So d/c in the diagram can vary from about $10 - 12\%$ for a flat cut sail to $15 - 20\%$ for a full one. The upper parts of a sail have rather more draught than at half height, and the lower parts have rather less. The position of maximum draught along the chord of the sail is another important factor, and typically a/c is about 45% but, like the maximum draught itself, this will depend upon the conditions.

So a sail can be set with an infinite number of shapes in terms of entry angle (that is, how close it will set to the wind), maximum draught, and the point of maximum draught. The aim is to get the right combination for jib and mainsail.

However, there is yet another complication – twist. Wind velocity increases with height above the water due to the reduction of friction. Thus the apparent wind moves aft in proportion to the height up the sail. To maintain a constant angle of

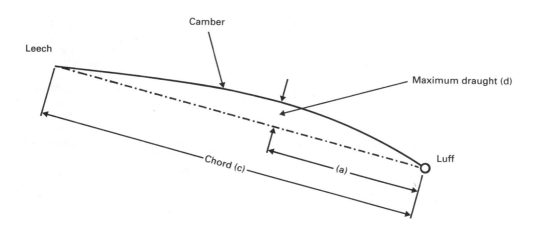

Fig. 21(17) Terms used to describe the shape of a sail.

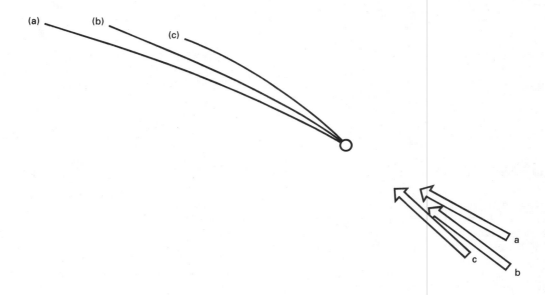

Fig. 21(18) How a sail has to twist to allow for the change in direction of the apparent wind with increasing height above the water. (a) indicates the shape near the foot, (b) at half height, and (c) near the head of the sail. a, b and c show the corresponding directions of the apparent wind.

incidence the sail must be allowed to twist. This is illustrated in Fig. 21(18), but exaggerated to show the point.

When beating to windward it must be understood that the correct trim of the jib in relation to the mainsail is of considerable importance. The gap between the two sails forms a narrowing slot, and when the wind passes through this it is speeded up, causing a drop in pressure along the lee side of the mainsail. This 'negative pressure' is the major force that drives the boat ahead through the water, and therefore needs to be encouraged.

21.6.3 Jib shape
Jib shape is controlled by the luff tension, sheeting position, sheet tension and barber hauler (where fitted). Luff tension is set by the halyard and possibly also by a jib Cunningham at the tack. It affects the position of maximum draught in the sail. When fairly slack the draught will be further aft, and the angle of entry at the luff gives good pointing ability. As tension is increased for stronger winds the draught is pulled forward, giving more power to the sail for going through waves but at the expense of pointing ability.

The fore and aft sheeting position, normally governed by a car on a track at or near the deck edge, affects not only the draught in the sail but also the twist. Moving the sheet lead forward reduces the twist (closes the leech). Bringing the lead aft increases the twist (opens the leech).

Where fitted, barber haulers adjust the position of the clew of the jib athwartships, so that in conjunction with the sheet tension and sheeting position the clew can be placed in any chosen position.

21.6.4 Mainsail shape
There are even more factors controlling mainsail shape: fore and aft mast bend, athwartships mast bend, luff tension, clew outhaul tension, mainsheet tension, mainsheet traveller position, kicking strap (vang) tension, clew Cunningham adjustments (where fitted), and leech line (where fitted).

In boats which have relatively flexible masts, increasing the fore and aft bend flattens the mainsail and opens the leech, so depowering the sail. Athwartships bend, depending on its position, alters the flow in the mainsail and the position of maximum draught. If for example the lower part of the mast is allowed to fall slightly to leeward, that part of the mainsail becomes fuller and power increases. When the head of the mast falls off to leeward (a relatively common occurrence with increasing wind strength) the mainsail flattens, the draught moves forward, the leech opens and power is reduced – a desirable state of affairs.

Luff tension can be applied in various ways depending on the boat. Commonly it is by a sliding gooseneck, supplemented by a Cunningham hole a short distance above the tack. Increased luff tension pulls the draught forward and opens the leech.

The mainsail clew outhaul also needs regular adjustment. Increased tension flattens the lower mainsail area, opens the lower leech, and moves the draught forward. Incidentally, it should always be slackened off on return to harbour.

Mainsheet tension and the position of the traveller need to be considered together. Between them they control not only the sheeting angle of the mainsail but the important amount of twist in the sail. A key to mainsail trim when on the wind is that the top batten should be parallel to the boom, and that the upper leech telltale (described below) should be flying clear. To achieve this in light winds it may be necessary to haul the traveller up to windward of the centreline with less tension in the mainsheet, so that the leech is open. Conversely in strong winds the traveller is progressively let down to leeward, and sheet tension is increased to give a flat sail and a hard leech. For intermediate wind strengths a wide range of combinations is available, but only one setting will be just right!

The kicking strap (or vang) plays an important part in controlling leech tension and mainsail twist once the boat comes off the wind. More tension is needed with increasing wind strength.

Where fitted, a clew (or leech) Cunningham is an additional flattening device for strong winds, while a leech line can prevent flutter of the leech when sailing to windward, or stop battens falling to leeward in light airs.

All these sail controls must be easy to adjust, which means that they must be sufficiently powerful — using winches or muscle boxes for example. Those most frequently used should be operable from either side of the boat in order to keep crew weight properly disposed.

21.6.5 Telltales

Telltales are essential for efficient sailing and good sail trimming and yet many cruising yachts do not have them. There should be about four telltales, equally spaced, along the luff of the jib, and just a short distance aft of the tabling for the luff wire, or of the foil, or of the roller furling gear. In a small yacht they should be about 250mm (10in) back, and slightly further in larger vessels. A number of materials can be used, but tufts of wool put through the cloth with a needle and knotted in place each side serve the purpose. They should be about 200mm (8in) long in the average boat. In wet weather they can be coated with candlegrease which reduces the chance of them sticking to the sail.

When sailing to windward with the sail trimmed correctly and the boat on a close-hauled course, the smooth air flow over both windward and leeward sides of the luff keeps both sets of telltales streaming steadily. If the boat is allowed to sail too close to the wind (or similarly if the jib sheet is eased) the windward telltales will flutter as the air flow round that side of the sail becomes turbulent. If the boat bears away from a close-hauled course the leeward telltales will flutter. Hence the helmsman's aim is to keep both sets at rest, although in practice a slight upward flutter by the windward set gives the best results. Off the wind the helmsman steers the required course while the sail trimmer takes over the job of keeping the telltales quiet and maintaining the correct air flow over the jib.

Jib telltales are useful for another purpose — to determine the proper fore and aft sheeting position for the jib. When this is correct and the boat is slowly luffed above a close-hauled course, all the windward telltales should flutter at the same time. If, however, the top telltale flutters first, the sail has too much twist and the sheet lead needs to be moved forward. Conversely if the bottom telltale flutters first, the lead should be moved aft.

Mainsail telltales are usually of ribbon, equally spaced along the leech, and between the batten pockets. When they all stream smoothly aft most of the time, and the top batten is parallel to the boom, all is well and the mainsail twist is satisfactory. But if they flutter round the leeward side of the sail then it is not correctly sheeted. Often the top telltale gives the first such indication.

21.6.6 Spinnakers

Once the wind is on the beam, or further aft, a spinnaker is essential for racing, while even in a cruising yacht it provides a welcome boost to speed on what can otherwise be a rather dull point of sailing. With the proper gear a spinnaker is easy to handle provided that a certain routine is followed. Hoisting and lowering (handing) need to be done carefully and methodically, and until the crew know the drill the evolution should not be hurried.

Admittedly a spinnaker is less easy to handle than a fore and aft sail because it is only attached at the three corners — by the halyard at the head, the sheet at the clew, and the guy (led through the end fitting of the spinnaker pole) at the tack. Most spinnakers are symmetrical and what is the tack on one gybe becomes the clew on the other. Similarly the luff becomes the leech, and vice versa; they are usually coloured red and green to avoid confusion when sorting out the sail.

Once hoisted the sail is controlled only by the sheet and the guy, but in respect of the latter the position of the spinnaker pole is important. The heel of the pole should be adjustable for height up the mast, while its outboard end has a lift to take its weight and a downhaul (or foreguy) to resist the upward pull of the sail. The pole needs to be roughly at right angles to the apparent wind, and also at right angles to the mast so that the sail is spread as much as possible. It also needs to be the right height up the mast.

Before hoisting a spinnaker should be packed into a 'turtle' — a special bag — rather like packing a parachute. The two edges of the sail are sorted out so that there are no twists, and the two clews need to be left protruding each side, ready for sheet and guy, with the head at the top to take the halyard.

The turtle is secured on the lee side, on deck somewhere forward of the shrouds. Sheet and guy are attached, each being run from their respective leading blocks outboard of everything. The guy has to be led forward, through the end fitting of the pole, round the forestay, and back aft to the spinnaker. Then the halyard is attached, making sure that it is clear aloft, and not say wrapped round the forestay.

The pole is then attached to the mast, and raised with the lift so that it is at the right height, and square to the mast. When ordered by the skipper, the sail is hoisted smartly (under the lee of mainsail and jib), and the guy is then trimmed aft so that the tack of the sail is brought to the end of the pole and the spinnaker catches the wind. At this moment the sheet is trimmed and the sail is set. Once it is pulling it may be necessary to make adjustments to the various settings of the pole, guy and sheet. The latter needs constant attention. Ease it out until the leech just begins to curl, and then trim it in slightly. If the upper part of the leech starts to curl first the pole is too low: if the lower part curls first the pole is too high.

In most yachts the headsail is lowered on deck as soon as the spinnaker is hoisted, although in a few cases it may be possible to persuade them both to set together.

When racing there are two distinct methods of gybing the spinnaker. In smaller yachts the helmsman brings the yacht's stern into the wind, the old guy is released from the pole end and the other end of the pole is taken off the mast. The pole is then transferred across the boat. The pole end that was on the mast is clipped over the new guy, and the other end is then attached to the mast. This is not too difficult if the helmsman can hold the boat directly downwind. But if for example he has to luff on the new gybe (perhaps because of another competitor) it may be very difficult to get the pole on to the mast.

Therefore in larger yachts a dip pole gybe is better, even though this means a separate guy and sheet for each clew of the spinnaker with all the extra rope that this entails. The end of the pole is never detached from the mast, but is pushed as far as necessary up its track so that, when the old guy has been released from the outer end of the pole, the lift can be lowered to allow the pole to swing forward and dip under the forestay. At this point the lazy guy on the other side of the boat is snatched into the end of the pole and is winched aft to take the weight from the old sheet. With good co-ordination between all concerned it should be possible to keep the spinnaker full throughout the gybe which helps the procedure and eliminates the chance of a wrap around the forestay.

Handing (dropping) the spinnaker on a run need not be too difficult because once the jib is rehoisted, it and the mainsail provide a useful lee under which the sail can be lowered. The procedure is that the guy is eased forward until the pole is against the forestay, while at the same time the sheet is trimmed in as much as possible and one or more of the crew prepare to get hold of the foot of the sail on the lee side aft of the shrouds. The guy is either released from the sail or

it is allowed to run through the pole end, and at the same time the halyard is gradually eased away as the crew gather in the sail. The same basic procedure is used when lowering the spinnaker on a reach, but this can be more difficult because the jib and mainsail do not provide such an effective lee.

21.7 Race preparation

21.7.1 Preparing the boat

If a yacht has not previously been used for racing there are several items which will need to be examined and possibly improved. The underwater hull needs to be as clean and smooth as you can reasonably get it, not forgetting the keel and especially the rudder where good preparation can really help the boat's performance. Clean off the propeller and if, as is common, it has two blades, mark the shaft inboard so that they can be arranged vertically behind the keel with the engine in gear. Remove all superfluous cruising gear from the boat, except any safety equipment which commonsense or class rules require to be retained on board. Concentrate all heavier items amidships, and as low down as possible.

It should not be assumed that the way a mast is rigged in a cruising yacht is necessarily ideal for racing. It may not be possible to move the heel of the mast without major surgery, but mast rake and shroud tensions should be easily adjustable. The basic procedure for setting up the rigging is described in Chapter 11 (11.2.4).

Where a boat is fractionally rigged (i.e. not masthead) there is scope for altering the degree and distribution of the mast bend, depending on the flexibility of the spar. Mast bend affects the amount and position of draught (fullness) in the mainsail, as well as forestay tension and the tightness of the mainsail leech. The most obvious method of controlling fore and aft mast bend is with backstay tension, and there needs to be a simple way of adjusting this. A small amount of pre-bend can be exerted on a mast that is stepped on the keel by moving the heel and adjusting the chocks at deck level.

When racing speed in setting and changing sails is vital, so it is important that all the gear functions correctly and smoothly, with the minimum effort for the crew. Check over all the items such as snap shackles and halyard stoppers or clutches. In order to minimise the risk of somebody pulling the wrong rope, all sheets, halyards and other control lines should be colour coded. All halyards should be marked, say at the exit point from the mast or at their cleat, at the point where the sail is fully hoisted.

The various sail controls already described in 21.6 need to be provided, and it is important that they can be operated easily and positively. Wherever possible there should be some form of graduated scale so that optimum settings can be determined, recorded, and repeated as necessary. This is particularly important for items such as the positions of genoa sheet cars.

21.7.2 Preparing the crew
Even quite large yachts can be handled by two or three people when cruising. But for racing the number needs to be increased significantly. Speed in tacking and in sail handling demands several pairs of hands, and it is a sad fact that most modern yachts when going to windward require human ballast on the weather rail for best performance in any breeze.

Certain key positions need to be filled by people who are familiar with the boat and who are sufficiently competent and experienced to fulfil their particular role without too much supervision. The key personnel are:
(1) Helmsman, who steers the boat and who is probably, but not necessarily, in overall charge.
(2) Tactician, who thinks the boat around the course – deciding the best route and tactics with regard to other competitors, tidal conditions, predicted weather and actual wind shifts, and navigational features of the area. In a small yacht this person may also be in charge of the deck – planning and supervising sail changes, gybing, reefing and so on – but in a larger boat this needs to be a separate person.
(3) Bowman, who works the foredeck when shifting headsails, gybing the spinnaker etc.
(4) Headsail and spinnaker trimmers (two), who operate and trim the sheets and guys to obtain optimum boat speed.
(5) Mainsail trimmer, who handles the mainsheet and traveller. May also assist with other jobs around the cockpit, such as tailing genoa sheets.

The six people nominated above can be augmented or assisted by other hands depending on the size of the boat. Obtaining (and retaining) the necessary number of persons of the required calibre can be a daunting task, particularly for a boat with a very heavy racing schedule where a 'crew secretary' may well take over the job from the owner.

Good crewing depends not just on skill but also on teamwork, and this can only be achieved by practice. Early in the season dedicate a full day to going through all the stock evolutions –changing headsails, hoisting and lowering the spinnaker, gybing the spinnaker and reefing the mainsail. It is often possible to practise some of these evolutions by getting out early to the start of a race.

21.7.3 Pre-race preparations
Before any race a number of very necessary preparations must be made. Below are listed the more basic requirements, but these will be multiplied when entering an important regatta, perhaps remote from the boat's home port.
(1) Make the necessary entry for the race, obtain and study the sailing instructions. Ensure that the boat conforms to requirements for insurance, measurement certificates etc.
(2) Check such details as time of start, how far to sail from mooring to race area.
(3) Arrange crew and notify them when and where to join the boat.
(4) See that all outstanding repairs (e.g. to sails) are completed, and all items returned on board.
(5) Study tidal conditions for the day of race, and work out predictions for tidal streams. When racing in shoal waters it is also useful to work out tide heights hour by hour over the period of the race, so that instant decisions can be taken about crossing sandbanks etc.
(6) Complete all material preparations of the boat – bottom clean, surplus gear removed, fuel and water tanks in race condition, all necessary safety equipment on board, chart(s) and tide tables etc. available, navigational instruments all functioning.
(7) As day of race approaches, study the weather pattern in outlook period.
(8) On day of race, final check that all necessary items such as sailing instructions are on board. Ensure no amendments to sailing instructions. Obtain weather forecast as late as possible. Embark food and drink. Check bilge dry. Have correct sails on board. Check watch/stopwatch and compass.

21.7.4 After the race
A race does not end for skipper or crew when the finishing line is crossed. There needs to be a wash-up to discuss what went right and what went wrong, and this is best conducted while events are fresh in the memory – perhaps while sailing into harbour. No race is ever sailed without a few mistakes being made, and the boat with the fewest errors is usually the winner. In order to make sure that everything is covered it is helpful to make a list of the different points which may be relevant.
(1) *Material preparation.* Were there any gear or equipment failures, and what can be done to avoid any repetition? Can the performance of any items be improved, and how? Sails are very important to a racing boat – were any shortcomings exposed? Were the correct sails on board?
(2) *Rig and sail adjustments.* Are fundamental items like mast position, mast rake and rig tension correct? Was proper use made of the various sail controls – sheeting positions, Cunningham, kicking strap, mainsheet traveller, main clew outhaul etc?
(3) *Crew.* Was the crew strong enough for the conditions? Were there errors in sail handling, and were these due to the wrong drill or poor execution? Were fundamental evolutions such as tacking and gybing performed as well as possible?
(4) *Conditions and tactics.* Was sufficient information available to helmsman and

tactician about wind and weather forecasts, tidal stream predictions over the course area? Was such information acted on correctly, or were opportunities missed – in detecting major wind shifts, for example?

(5) *The start.* Did the boat start at the right end of the line, on the gun, and in clear wind? Was the boat on the right tack after the start, to choose the right side of the beat?

(6) *The rules.* Were the crew in doubt at any time about the interpretation of any of the racing rules?

This is also a useful occasion to brief crew about the next race or future programme.

Any defect, however small, needs to be properly recorded for action to be taken. Experience shows that it is much better to note such items in a proper defect book rather than on odd scraps of paper. Before leaving the boat make sure that everything is stowed away, clean the boat up and take any rubbish ashore.

In some events it is necessary to sign a declaration that the rules have been obeyed, on getting ashore. Do not forget this!

21.8 Bibliography

This is Racing by Richard Creagh-Osborne (Adlard Coles Nautical).

This is Boat Tuning for Speed by F. Imhoff and L. Pranger (Adlard Coles Nautical).

Racing – A Beginner's Manual by John Caig and Tim Davison (Fernhurst).

Tactics by Rodney Pattison (Fernhurst).

RYA Race Training Manual by Jim Saltonstall (Macmillan).

The Yacht Racing Rules: A Complete Guide by Mary Pera (Adlard Coles Nautical).

Paul Elvstrom Explains the Yacht Racing Rules by Paul Elvstrom (Adlard Coles Nautical).

Race Winner by Ian and Richard Nicholson (Adlard Coles Nautical).

Race Navigation by Stuart Quarrie (Adlard Coles Nautical).

The Rules Book by Eric Twiname (Adlard Coles Nautical).

Index

A